W9-CQI-712

Student Quick Tips

Use this Student Quick Tips guide for a quick and easy start with McGraw-Hill Connect. You'll get valuable tips on registering, doing assignments, and accessing resources, as well as information about the support center hours.

Getting Started

TIP: To get started in Connect, you will need the following:

- Your instructor's Connect Web Address

    Sample of Connect Web Address:

    http://www.mcgrawhillconnect.com/class/instructorname_section_name

- Connect Access Code

TIP: If you do not have an access code or have not yet secured your tuition funds, you can click "Free Trial" during registration. This trial will provide temporary Connect access (typically three weeks) and will remind you to purchase online access before the end of your trial.

Registration and Sign In

1. Go to the Connect Web Address provided by your instructor
2. Click on **Register Now**
3. Enter your email address

TIP: If you already have a McGraw-Hill account, you will be asked for your password and will not be required to create a new account.

4. Enter a registration code or choose **Buy Online** to purchase access online

(Continued: **Registration and Sign In**)

5. Follow the on-screen directions

TIP: Please choose your Security Question and Answer carefully. We will ask you for this information if you forget your password.

6. When registration is complete, click on **Go to Connect Now**

7. You are now ready to use **Connect**

Trouble Logging In?

- Ensure you are using the same email address you used during registration

- If you have forgotten your password, click on the "Forgot Password?" link at your Instructor's Connect Course Web Address

- When logged into Connect, you can update your account information (e.g. email address, password, and security question/answer) by clicking on the *"My Account"* link located at the top-right corner

Home (Assignments)

TIP: If you are unable to begin an assignment, verify the following:

- The assignment is available (start and due dates)

- That you have not exceeded the maximum number of attempts

- That you have not achieved a score of 100%

- If your assignment contains questions that require manual grading, you will not be able to begin your next attempt until your instructor has graded those questions

TIP: Based on the assignment policy settings established by your Instructor, you may encounter the following limitations when working on your assignment(s):

* Ability to Print Assignment

* Timed assignments – once you begin a *"timed assignment,"* the timer will not stop by design

TIP: *"Save & Exit"* vs. *"Submit"* button

* If you are unable to complete your assignment in one sitting, utilize the *"Save & Exit"* button to save your work and complete it at a later time

* Once you have completed your assignment, utilize the *"Submit"* button in order for your assignment to be graded

Library

TIP: The *Library* section of your Connect account provides shortcuts to various resources.

* If you purchased ConnectPlus, you will see an *eBook* link, which can also be accessed from the section information widget of the *Home* tab

* *Recorded Lectures* can be accessed if your instructor is using *Tegrity Campus* to capture lectures. You may also access recorded lectures when taking an assignment by clicking on the projector icon in the navigation bar

* Many McGraw-Hill textbooks offer additional resources such as narrated slides and additional problems, which are accessible through the *Student Resources* link

Reports

TIP: Once you submit your assignment, you can view your available results in the *Reports* tab.

- If you see a dash (-) as your score, your instructor has either delayed or restricted your ability to see the assignment feedback

- Your instructor has the ability to limit the amount of information (e.g. questions, answers, scores) you can view for each submitted assignment

Need More Help?

CONTACT US ONLINE

Visit us at:

www.mcgrawhillconnect.com/support

Browse our support materials including tutorial videos and our searchable Connect knowledge base. If you cannot find an answer to your question, click on "Contact Us" button to send us an email.

GIVE US A CALL

Call us at:

1-800-331-5094

Our live support is available:

Mon-Thurs: 8 am – 11 pm CT
Friday: 8 am – 6 pm CT
Sunday: 6 pm – 11 pm CT

Introduction to
ANIMAL SCIENCE

Sylvia S. Mader

Michael Windelspecht
Appalachian State University

With contributions by

April Cognato
Michigan State University

David Cox
Lincoln Land Community College

Jeffrey Isaacson
Nebraska Wesleyan University

Ian Quitadamo
Central Washington University

ASCI 112 | CALIFORNIA POLYTECHNIC STATE UNIVERSITY

Boston   Burr Ridge, IL   Dubuque, IA   New York   San Francisco   St. Louis
Bangkok   Bogotá   Caracas   Lisbon   London   Madrid
Mexico City   Milan   New Delhi   Seoul   Singapore   Sydney   Taipei   Toronto

INTRODUCTION TO ANIMAL SCIENCE
ASCI 112 | CALIFORNIA POLYTECHNIC STATE UNIVERSITY

This book is a McGraw-Hill Learning Solutions textbook and contains select material from *Biology*, Eleventh Edition by Sylvia S. Mader and Michael Windelspecht, with contributions by April Cognato, David Cox, Jeffrey Isaacson and Ian Quitadamo. Copyright © 2013, 2010, 2007, 2004 by The McGraw-Hill Companies, Inc. Reprinted with permission of the publisher. Many custom published texts are modified versions or adaptations of our best-selling textbooks. Some adaptations are printed in black and white to keep prices at a minimum, while others are in color.

1 2 3 4 5 6 7 8 9 0 DIG DIG 15 14 13

ISBN-13: 978-0-07-781975-0
ISBN-10: 0-07-781975-6

Learning Solutions Representative: Jennifer Beecher
Project Manager: Lynn Nagel
Printer/Binder: Digital Impressions

Brief Contents

A Brief History of Biology

Year	Name	Contribution
1628	William Harvey	Demonstrates that the blood circulates and the heart is a pump.
1665	Robert Hooke	Uses the word cell to describe compartments he sees in cork under the microscope.
1668	Francesco Redi	Shows that decaying meat protected from flies does not spontaneously produce maggots.
1673	Antonie van Leeuwenhoek	Uses microscope to view living microorganisms.
1735	Carolus Linnaeus	Initiates the binomial system of naming organisms.
1809	Jean B. Lamarck	Supports the idea of evolution by the inheritance of acquired characteristics.
1825	Georges Cuvier	Founds the science of paleontology and shows that fossils are related to living forms.
1828	Karl E. von Baer	Establishes the germ layer theory of development.
1838	Matthias Schleiden	States that plants are multicellular organisms.
1839	Theodor Schwann	States that animals are multicellular organisms.
1851	Claude Bernard	Concludes that a relatively constant internal environment allows organisms to survive under varying conditions.
1858	Rudolf Virchow	States that cells come only from preexisting cells.
1858	Charles Darwin, Alfred Wallace	Independently present evidence that natural selection guides the evolutionary process.
1865	Louis Pasteur	Disproves the theory of spontaneous generation for bacteria; shows that infections are caused by bacteria.
1866	Gregor Mendel	Proposes basic laws of genetics based on his experiments with garden peas.
1882	Robert Koch	Establishes the germ theory of disease and develops many techniques used in bacteriology.
1902	Walter S. Sutton, Theodor Boveri	Suggest that genes are on the chromosomes, after noting the similar behavior of genes and chromosomes.
1904	Ivan Pavlov	Shows that conditioned reflexes affect behavior, based on experiments with dogs.
1910	Thomas H. Morgan	States that each gene has a locus on a particular chromosome, based on experiments with Drosophila.
1924	Hans Spemann, Hilde Mangold	Show that induction occurs during development, based on experiments with frog embryos.
1929	Sir Alexander Fleming	Discovers the toxic effect of a mold product he called penicillin on certain bacteria.
1937	Konrad Z. Lorenz	Founds the study of ethology and shows the importance of imprinting in learning.
1937	Sir Hans A. Krebs	Discovers the reactions of a cycle that produces carbon dioxide during cellular respiration.
1940	George Beadle, Edward Tatum	Develop the one gene—one enzyme theory, based on red bread mold studies.
1944	O. T. Avery, Colin MacLeod, Maclyn McCarty	Demonstrate that DNA alone from virulent bacteria can transform nonvirulent bacteria.
1945	Melvin Calvin, Andrew A. Benson	Discover the individual reactions of a cycle that reduces carbon dioxide during photosynthesis.
1950	Barbara McClintock	Discovers transposons (jumping genes) while doing experiments with corn.
1952	Alfred D. Hershey, Martha Chase	Find that only DNA from viruses enters cells and directs the reproduction of new viruses.
1953	James Watson, Francis Crick, Rosalind Franklin	Establish that the molecular structure for DNA is a double helix.
1953	Harold Urey, Stanley Miller	Demonstrate that the first organic molecules may have arisen from the gases of the primitive atmosphere.
1954	Linus Pauling	States that disease-causing abnormal hemoglobins are due to mutations.
1954	Jonas Salk	Develops a vaccine that protects against polio.
1958	Matthew S. Meselson, Franklin W. Stahl	Demonstrate that DNA replication is semiconservative.
1961	Francois Jacob, Jacques Monod	Discover that genetic expression is controlled by regulatory genes.
1964	Marshall W. Nirenberg, Philip Leder	Produce synthetic RNA, enabling them to break the DNA code.
1973	Stanley Cohen	Uses recombinant DNA technique (genetic engineering) to place plant and animal genes in Escherichia coli.
1977	Carl Woese	Based on differences in ribosomal RNA sequences, proposes the three domain system of classifications.
1978	Peter Mitchell	Determines chemiosmotic mechanism by which ATP is produced in chloroplasts and mitochondria.
1989	Sidney Altman, Thomas R. Check	Independently discover that some RNA molecules can act as enzymes.
1990	R. Michael Blaese, W. French Anderson, Kenneth W. Culver	Develop procedure to infuse genetically engineered blood cells for treatment of immune system disorder—first gene therapy used in a human.
1997	Ian Wilmut	Clones an adult mammal for the first time.
2003	Human Genome Project	Complete human genome sequenced, creating push to discover genomic links to health and disease.
2010	Craig Venter	Leads team that develops the first synthetic life form.

Metric System

Unit and Abbreviation	Metric Equivalent	Approximate English-to-Metric Equivalents
Length		
nanometer (nm)	$= 10^{-9}$ m (10^{-3} µm)	
micrometer (µm)	$= 10^{-6}$ m (10^{-3} mm)	
millimeter (mm)	$= 0.001$ (10^{-3}) m	
centimeter (cm)	$= 0.01$ (10^{-2}) m	1 inch = 2.54 cm
		1 foot = 30.5 cm
meter (m)	$= 100$ (10^{2}) cm	1 foot = 0.30 m
	$= 1,000$ mm	1 yard = 0.91 m
kilometer (km)	$= 1,000$ (10^{3}) m	1 mi = 1.6 km
Weight (mass)		
nanogram (ng)	$= 10^{-9}$ g	
microgram (µg)	$= 10^{-6}$ g	
milligram (mg)	$= 10^{-3}$ g	
gram (g)	$= 1,000$ mg	1 ounce = 28.3 g
		1 pound = 454 g
kilogram (kg)	$= 1,000$ (10^{3}) g	= 0.45 kg
metric ton (t)	$= 1,000$ kg	1 ton = 0.91 t
Volume		
microliter (µl)	$= 10^{-6}$ l (10^{-3} ml)	
milliliter (ml)	$= 10^{-3}$ liter	1 tsp = 5 ml
	$= 1$ cm³ (cc)	1 fl oz = 30 ml
	$= 1,000$ mm³	
liter (l)	$= 1,000$ ml	1 pint = 0.47 liter
		1 quart = 0.95 liter
		1 gallon = 3.79 liter
kiloliter (kl)	$= 1,000$ liter	

Units of Temperature

Temperature scale showing °F and °C with reference points:
212° , 160° , 134° , 131° , 105.8° , 98.6° , 56.66° , 32° on °F scale and
100° , 71° , 57° , 41° , 37° , 13.7° , 0° on °C scale.

°C	°F	
100	212	Water boils at standard temperature and pressure.
71	160	Flash pasteurization of milk
57	134	Highest recorded temperature in the United States, Death Valley, July 10, 1913
41	105.8	Average body temperature of a marathon runner in hot weather
37	98.6	Human body temperature
13.7	56.66	Human survival is still possible at this temperature.
0	32.0	Water freezes at standard temperature and pressure.

To convert temperature scales:

$$°C = \frac{(°F - 32)}{1.8}$$

$$°F = 1.8\,(°C) + 32$$

Periodic Table of Elements

Group Ia																	**VIIIa**
1 ¹ **H** hydrogen	**IIa**																**2** ⁴ **He** helium
3 ⁷ **Li** lithium	**4** ⁹ **Be** beryllium										**IIIa**	**IVa**	**Va**	**VIa**	**VIIa**		
											5 ¹¹ **B** boron	**6** ¹² **C** carbon	**7** ¹⁴ **N** nitrogen	**8** ¹⁶ **O** oxygen	**9** ¹⁹ **F** fluorine		**10** ²⁰ **Ne** neon
11 ²³ **Na** sodium	**12** ²⁴ **Mg** magnesium	**IIIb**	**IVb**	**Vb**	**VIb**	**VIIb**		VIIIb		**Ib**	**IIb**	**13** ²⁷ **Al** aluminum	**14** ²⁸ **Si** silicon	**15** ³¹ **P** phosphorus	**16** ³² **S** sulfur	**17** ³⁵ **Cl** chlorine	**18** ⁴⁰ **Ar** argon
19 ³⁹ **K** potassium	**20** ⁴⁰ **Ca** calcium	**21** ⁴⁵ **Sc** scandium	**22** ⁴⁸ **Ti** titanium	**23** ⁵¹ **V** vanadium	**24** ⁵² **Cr** chromium	**25** ⁵⁵ **Mn** manganese	**26** ⁵⁶ **Fe** iron	**27** ⁵⁹ **Co** cobalt	**28** ⁵⁹ **Ni** nickel	**29** ⁶⁴ **Cu** copper	**30** ⁶⁵ **Zn** zinc	**31** ⁷⁰ **Ga** gallium	**32** ⁷³ **Ge** germanium	**33** ⁷⁵ **As** arsenic	**34** ⁷⁹ **Se** selenium	**35** ⁸⁰ **Br** bromine	**36** ⁸⁴ **Kr** krypton
37 ⁸⁵ **Rb** rubidium	**38** ⁸⁸ **Sr** strontium	**39** ⁸⁹ **Y** yttrium	**40** ⁹¹ **Zr** zirconium	**41** ⁹³ **Nb** niobium	**42** ⁹⁶ **Mo** molybdium	**43** ⁹⁸ **Tc** technetium	**44** ¹⁰¹ **Ru** ruthenium	**45** ¹⁰¹ **Rh** rhodium	**46** ¹⁰⁶ **Pd** palladium	**47** ¹⁰⁸ **Ag** silver	**48** ¹¹² **Cd** cadmium	**49** ¹¹⁵ **In** indium	**50** ¹¹⁹ **Sn** tin	**51** ¹²² **Sb** antimony	**52** ¹²⁸ **Te** tellurium	**53** ¹²⁷ **I** iodine	**54** ¹³¹ **Xe** xenon
55 ¹³³ **Cs** cesium	**56** ¹³⁷ **Ba** barium	**57** ¹³⁹ **La** lanthanum	**72** ¹⁷⁸ **Hf** hafnium	**73** ¹⁸¹ **Ta** tantalum	**74** ¹⁸⁴ **W** tungsten	**75** ¹⁸⁶ **Re** rhenium	**76** ¹⁹⁰ **Os** osmium	**77** ¹⁹² **Ir** iridium	**78** ¹⁹⁵ **Pt** platinum	**79** ¹⁹⁷ **Au** gold	**80** ²⁰¹ **Hg** mercury	**81** ²⁰⁴ **Tl** thalium	**82** ²⁰⁷ **Pb** lead	**83** ²⁰⁹ **Bi** bismuth	**84** ²¹⁰ **Po** polonium	**85** ²¹⁰ **At** astatine	**86** ²²² **Rn** radon
87 ²²³ **Fr** francium	**88** ²²⁶ **Ra** radium	**89** ²²⁷ **Ac** actinium	**104** ²⁶¹ **Rf** rutherfordium	**105** ²⁶⁰ **Db** dubnium	**106** ²⁶³ **Sg** seaborgium	**107** ²⁶¹ **Bh** bohrium	**108** ²⁶⁵ **Hs** hassium	**109** ²⁶⁶ **Mt** meitnerium	**110** ²⁸¹ **Ds** darmstadtium	**111** ²⁷² **Rg** Roentgenium	**112** ²⁸⁵ **Cn** Copernicum	**113** ²⁸⁴ **Uut** Ununtrium	**114** ²⁸⁹ **Uuq** Ununquadium	**115** ²⁸⁸ **Uup** Ununpentium	**116** ²⁹³ **Uuh** Ununhexium	**117** ²⁹⁴ **Uus** Ununseptum	**118** ²⁹⁴ **Uuo** Ununoctium

58 ¹⁴⁰ **Ce** cerium	**59** ¹⁴¹ **Pr** praseodymium	**60** ¹⁴⁴ **Nd** neodymium	**61** ¹⁴⁷ **Pm** promethium	**62** ¹⁵⁰ **Sm** samarium	**63** ¹⁵² **Eu** europium	**64** ¹⁵⁷ **Gd** gadolinium	**65** ¹⁵⁹ **Tb** terbium	**66** ¹⁶³ **Dy** dysprosium	**67** ¹⁶⁵ **Ho** holmium	**68** ¹⁶⁷ **Er** erbium	**69** ¹⁶⁹ **Tm** thulium	**70** ¹⁷³ **Yb** ytterbium	**71** ¹⁷⁵ **Lu** lutetium
90 ²³² **Th** thorium	**91** ²³¹ **Pa** protactinium	**92** ²³⁸ **U** uranium	**93** ²³⁷ **Np** neptunium	**94** ²⁴² **Pu** plutonium	**95** ²⁴³ **Am** americium	**96** ²⁴⁷ **Cm** curium	**97** ²⁴⁷ **Bk** berkelium	**98** ²⁴⁹ **Cf** californium	**99** ²⁵⁴ **Es** einsteinium	**100** ²⁵³ **Fm** fermium	**101** ²⁵⁶ **Md** mendelevium	**102** ²⁵⁴ **No** nobelium	**103** ²⁵⁷ **Lr** lawrencium

About the Authors

Sylvia S. Mader   Sylvia S. Mader has authored several nationally recognized biology texts published by McGraw-Hill. Educated at Bryn Mawr College, Harvard University, Tufts University, and Nova Southeastern University, she holds degrees in both Biology and Education. Over the years she has taught at University of Massachusetts, Lowell; Massachusetts Bay Community College; Suffolk University; and Nathan Mayhew Seminars. Her ability to reach out to science-shy students led to the writing of her first text, *Inquiry into Life*, that is now in its thirteenth edition. Highly acclaimed for her crisp and entertaining writing style, her books have become models for others who write in the field of biology.

Although her writing schedule is always quite demanding, Dr. Mader enjoys taking time to visit and explore the various ecosystems of the biosphere. Her several trips to the Florida Everglades and Caribbean coral reefs resulted in talks she has given to various groups around the country. She has visited the tundra in Alaska, the taiga in the Canadian Rockies, the Sonoran Desert in Arizona, and tropical rain forests in South America and Australia. A photo safari to the Serengeti in Kenya resulted in a number of photographs for her texts. She was thrilled to think of walking in Darwin's steps when she journeyed to the Galápagos Islands with a group of biology educators. Dr. Mader was also a member of a group of biology educators who traveled to China to meet with their Chinese counterparts and exchange ideas about the teaching of modern-day biology.

Michael Windelspecht   As an educator, Dr. Windelspecht has taught introductory biology, genetics, and human genetics in the online, traditional, and hybrid environments at community colleges, comprehensive universities, and military institutions. For over a decade he served as the Introductory Biology Coordinator at Appalachian State University, where he directed a program that enrolled over 4,500 students annually. He was educated at Michigan State University and the University of South Florida. Dr. Windelspecht is also active in promoting the scientific literacy of secondary school educators. He has led multiple workshops on integrating water quality research into the science curriculum, and has spent several summers teaching Pakistani middle school teachers.

As an author, Dr. Windelspecht has published five reference textbooks and multiple print and online lab manuals. He served as the series editor for a ten-volume work on the human body. For years Dr. Windelspecht has been active in the development of multimedia resources for online and hybrid science classrooms. Along with his wife, Sandra, he owns a multimedia production company that actively develops and assesses the use of new technologies in the classroom.

Contributors

April Cognato serves as an Assistant Professor in the Department of Zoology at Michigan State University. She was educated at University of California–Davis, and at Texas A&M University where she earned a master's degree and Ph.D. in evolutionary biology. Dr. Cognato is an accomplished research biologist and educator. As an educator, Dr. Cognato designs and teaches introductory non-majors biology, majors biology, and genetics. In addition to her teaching assignments, Dr. Cognato has expertise in the integration of digital resources into education, and she authors fully online courses in genetics and evolution.

Dave Cox serves as Associate Professor of Biology at Lincoln Land Community College, in Springfield, Illinois. He was educated at Illinois College and Western Illinois University. As an educator, Professor Cox teaches introductory biology for non-majors in the traditional classroom format as well as in a hybrid format. He also teaches biology for majors, and marine biology and biological field studies as study-abroad courses in Belize. He serves as the Educational Director for the Sibun Education and Adventure Lodge, located in Belmopan, Belize.

Jeffrey Isaacson is an Associate Professor of Biology at Nebraska Wesleyan University, where he teaches courses in microbiology, immunology, and cell biology. He currently serves as Chair of the Undergraduate Curriculum Committee and Co-Chair of the General Education Revision Team at NWU. Dr. Isaacson was educated at Nebraska Wesleyan, Kansas State College of Veterinary Medicine, and Iowa State University. Previously, he worked as a small-animal veterinarian, and completed a post-doctoral fellowship in the Department of Immunology at the Mayo Clinic. As an author, Dr. Isaacson has served as a significant contributor and coauthor for the twelfth and thirteenth editions of Mader's *Inquiry Into Life*.

Ian Quitadamo has a dual appointment in Biological Sciences and Science Education at Central Washington University where he teaches courses in cell biology, genetics, biotechnology, and non-majors biology. In addition, he facilitates courses in teaching methodology for future science teachers and interdisciplinary content courses focused on alternative energy and sustainability. Dr. Quitadamo was educated at Washington State University where he earned an interdisciplinary Ph.D. in science, education, and technology. Dr. Quitadamo is a recipient of the Crystal Apple award for teaching excellence. He is a fourth-degree black belt in Kyokushin Karate and owns an academic consulting company.

Preface

Goals of the Eleventh Edition

The mission of Dr. Sylvia Mader's text, *Biology*, has always been to give students an understanding of biological concepts and a working knowledge of the scientific process. The concepts of biology and the methodology of science can be used to understand the particulars of new ideas or of a system, on any scale, from the cell to the biosphere.

In the twenty-first century, students are being exposed, almost on a daily basis, to exciting new discoveries and insights that, in many cases, were beyond our predictions even a few short years ago. It is our task, as instructors, not only to make these findings available to our students, but to enlighten students as to why these discoveries are important to their lives and society. At the same time, we must provide students with a firm foundation in those core principles on which biology is founded, and in doing so, provide them with the background to keep up with the many discoveries still to come. In this text, we integrate a tested, traditional learning system with modern digital and pedagogical approaches designed to stimulate and engage today's student.

The authors of the text identified several goals that guided them through the revision of *Biology*, Eleventh Edition:

1. build upon the strengths of the previous editions of the text,
2. introduce themes that connect the content of the text across multiple chapters,
3. deploy new pedagogical elements, including multimedia assets, to increase student interaction with the text,
4. develop a new series of digital assets designed to engage the modern student and provide assessment of learning outcomes.

Unit Themes

We recognize that scientific literacy is not based upon the memorization of a series of facts. Instead, learning is based on establishing associations and links between what, at first glance, appear to be diverse topics. The main themes we have chosen to emphasize include

- Evolution
- Nature of Science
- Biological Systems

The cover of this textbook, a gray wolf over a caribou skeleton with the Colorado mountain range in the background, was selected to reflect the importance of these three themes to the life sciences. By studying the historical evolutionary relationship of these species in their natural environment, biologists have been able to better understand the interdependence of the occupants of this ecosystem.

These themes are integrated into all aspects of the textbook, from the unit learning outcomes to the theme-based feature readings in the text. At the start of each chapter, "Following the Themes" introduces the relationship of the chapter's content to each of the themes. At the end of each chapter, "Connecting the Concepts with the Themes" not only reminds the student of the relationships between chapter content and the three core themes, but also acts as a prelude to topics in the next few chapters of the text. In essence, the themes act as the threads that unite the concepts throughout the text, enabling the student to see relationships from the molecular to ecosystem levels of biology.

UNIT LEARNING OUTCOMES

The learning outcomes for this unit focus on three major themes in the life sciences.

Evolution	Support, with examples, the statement that "Darwin's theory of evolution by natural selection is a unifying theory of biology."
Nature of Science	Examine the methods by which scientists obtain evidence in support of evolutionary change.
Biological Systems	Analyze how evolution occurs at the molecular, organismal, and population levels of biology.

FOLLOWING the THEMES

UNIT 3 EVOLUTION — CHAPTER 15 DARWIN AND EVOLUTION

Evolution	Darwin's theory of natural selection proposes that all life on Earth descends from a common ancestor.
Nature of Science	A scientific theory, such as Darwin's theory of evolution by natural selection, is supported by abundant evidence.
Biological Systems	Evolution by natural selection comes about from interaction between the organism and its environment.

CONNECTING the CONCEPTS with the THEMES

Evolution

- All life on Earth has the same building blocks of inheritance, namely DNA, and shares in common many proteins essential to life.
- Vertebrate embryos develop the same set of features early in development, even though these features develop into very different structures in the adult.
- All animals have genes in common that control the development of the body plan. *Hox* genes orchestrate the development of the body plan in all animals.
- The Tree of Life project has collected information on hundreds of organisms. Anatomy, DNA, and behavior are used to trace all of life back to a single common ancestor.

Nature of Science

- Fossils provide us with a glimpse of life in the past. Transitional fossils have been discovered that support the theory of evolution via gradual changes to preexisting forms, such as alteration of hindlimbs in whale ancestors.
- At the level of the gene, small changes in the DNA sequence of switches that turn genes "on" and "off" can produce new features, such as the black spot on the wings of *Drosophila biarmipes* males that play a role in mating rituals.
- Evolution does not always occur over millions of years; it can be witnessed over a short period of time. On the Galápagos Islands, a shift in the average beak depth of ground finches can be observed as the weather changes.

Biological Systems

- Darwin proposed that natural selection is, in essence, a struggle for existence.
- Organisms tend to produce more offspring than can be supported by the environment.
- All living things require resources such as food, water, and mates in order to survive and reproduce—the intensity of competition is determined by the availability of resources in the environment.
- Natural selection operates on variation in populations. Change in the environment, both long and short term, can cause populations to evolve.

Evolution Theme

Evolutionary change, along with the mechanism of natural selection, represents the unifying concept of the biological sciences. In essence, biological evolution is the thread that links all life together. Throughout this textbook, feature readings on this theme both demonstrate the process of evolution and illustrate how scientists study and measure evolutionary change. By following this theme through the book, students develop a better understanding of why evolution is a dynamic process, and one that has shaped, and will continue to influence, life on this planet.

Nature of Science Theme

Through the processes of observation, the application of the scientific method, and the use of both inductive and deductive reasoning, scientists study life. To develop a deeper understanding of the biological sciences, students must appreciate that the study of life is a process, and that this process has application in their everyday lives. This theme focuses not only on how biologists do science, but also on the influences scientific inquiry has on our understanding of our world.

Biological Systems Theme

From cells to ecosystems, all life is interconnected. Increasingly, scientists are becoming aware that small changes in the chemical composition of an ecosystem can have a tremendous influence on the life in that ecosystem. This theme was chosen to provide a holistic approach to the study of the life sciences, by demonstrating not only that all life is interconnected, but also that the principles regulating life at the cellular level play a role in physiology and ecosystem biology as well.

Guided Chapter Tour

Pedagogy

Chapter Opener Each chapter opener now includes two to three questions designed to integrate the subject matter into the chapter and stimulate class discussions.

Chapter Outline The major sections that will be discussed in the chapter are listed for easy reference.

Before You Begin The content of each chapter is linked with material from earlier in the text. The questions designate important topics that students should understand before proceeding into the chapter.

Following the Themes The three themes are introduced at the beginning of each chapter, providing a summary of how the chapter content is linked to each of the themes.

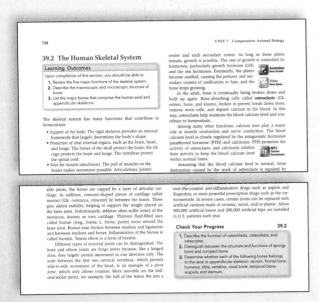

Learning Outcomes The major goals of each section of the chapter are provided for the student. All learning outcomes may be fully assessed using McGraw-Hill Connect® Biology activities.

Media Integration Media enhances the study of biology. Go to Connect or **www.mhhe.com/maderbiology11** to access the animations, videos, and MP3 files referenced throughout this book. Related quizzes are available through Connect® Biology for instructors to assign.

Check Your Progress Each of the statements in this section is designed to help the student assess or apply their understanding of the material in the section.

Thematic Feature Readings

The author team has prepared feature readings to engage students in the three major themes of the textbook—evolution, nature of science, and biological systems. Each feature reading contains a series of "Questions to Consider" that may be used to stimulate classroom discussions.

Connecting the Concepts with the Themes   At the end of each chapter, the authors have provided a brief synopsis of how each theme was integrated into the chapter. This further develops the themes as a series of learning threads, allowing the instructors and students to link related concepts more easily and facilitate the interconnectedness of the topics in the text.

Media Study Tools   This feature provides a link to the *Biology* website, which contains practice tests and other assets to assist the student in comprehending the topics of the chapter. Also present on this site are animations, videos, and multimedia assets that can help the student succeed in their study of biology. In many chapters, icons in this section direct the instructor to the presence of 3D animations that may be used in the classroom, or placed on course management systems, to further student comprehension of difficult topics.

The McGraw-Hill ConnectPlus® platform provides a media-rich eBook, interactive learning tools, and access to the LearnSmart system and Tegrity lecture-capture materials.

Summary   A concise overview of the chapter is provided in an easy-to-read paragraph style.

Key Terms   The glossary of this edition has been completely reworked, with a focus on reducing the key terms to those that are essential for student comprehension of the topic. All key terms in this section are linked to an updated glossary at the back of the text.

Reviewing This Chapter and Testing Yourself   Questions help students review material and prepare for tests. (See Appendix A for Testing Yourself answers.)

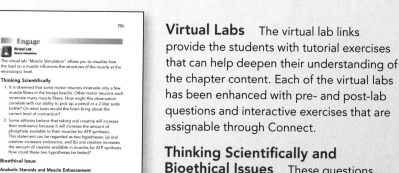

Virtual Labs   The virtual lab links provide the students with tutorial exercises that can help deepen their understanding of the chapter content. Each of the virtual labs has been enhanced with pre- and post-lab questions and interactive exercises that are assignable through Connect.

Thinking Scientifically and Bioethical Issues   These questions provide students with an opportunity to explore additional aspects of the chapter content, including bioethical issues and the design of experiments. These questions are ideal for classroom discussions.

Guided Chapter Tour

Art

Multi-Level Perspective
Illustrations depicting complex structures show macroscopic and microscopic views to help students see the relationships between increasingly detailed drawings.

Combination Art Drawings of structures are paired with micrographs to provide the best of both perspectives: the realism of photos and the explanatory clarity of line drawings.

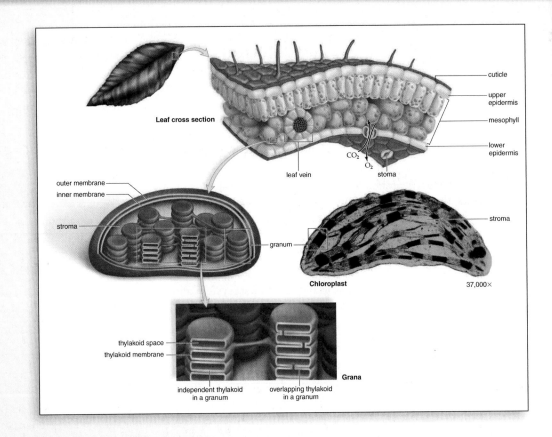

Process Figures Complex processes are broken down into a series of smaller steps that are easy to follow. Numbers guide readers through the process.

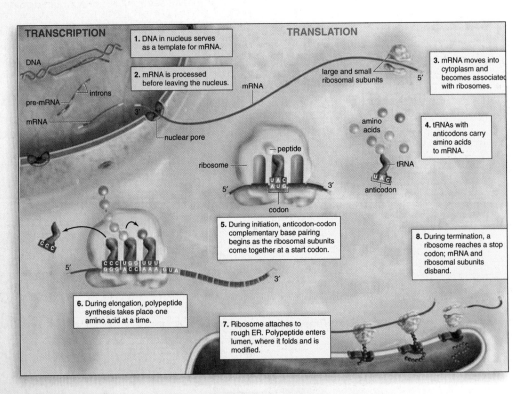

A Student's Guide to Media

Students can improve the effectiveness of their learning by integrating the digital assets of today's courses into their study habits. To facilitate this integration, the authors have prepared a video tutorial that not only outlines the role of each asset, but also explains to the student how to best utilize these materials for the comprehension of the course content. Included are descriptions on how both LearnSmart™ and Connect®, McGraw-Hill's flagship digital tools, can increase student preparedness for class as well as increase retention of difficult topics.

These assets may easily be uploaded into any course management system to provide your students with useful study tutorials.

Media Integration

As educators, the authors recognize that today's students are digital learners. Therefore, a significant new feature of this edition is the integration of media assets into the chapter content. Virtually every section of the textbook is now linked to MP3 files, animations of biological processes, and National Geographic and ScienCentral videos. In addition, McGraw-Hill's new 3D animations are integrated into the more difficult chapters of the text.

MP3 Files

These three- to five-minute audio files serve as a review of the material in the chapter, and they also assist the student in the pronunciation of scientific terms.

Animations

Drawing on McGraw-Hill's vast library of animations, the authors have selected animations that will enhance the student's understanding of complex biological processes.

3D Animations

For topics such as photosynthesis and cellular respiration, McGraw-Hill has produced a series of dynamic 3D animations that may be used both as presentation tools in the classroom, and as mini-tutorials that can be assigned within Connect or your course management system.

Videos

Two different types of movies are integrated into this edition of the text. The ScienCentral videos are short news clips on advances in the sciences. The National Geographic videos provide students with a glimpse of the complexity of life that normally would not be possible in the classroom.

Virtual Labs

These simulated experiments serve as excellent tutorials, allowing students to explore the topics covered in select chapters of the text.

McGraw-Hill Higher Education and Blackboard Have Teamed Up

The Best of Both Worlds

Blackboard®, the Web-based course-management system, has partnered with McGraw-Hill to better allow students and faculty to use online materials and activities to complement face-to-face teaching. Blackboard features exciting social learning and teaching tools that foster more logical, visually impactful, and active learning opportunities for students. You'll transform your closed-door classrooms into communities where students remain connected to their educational experience 24 hours a day.

This partnership allows you and your students access to McGraw-Hill's Connect® and McGraw-Hill Create™ right from within your Blackboard course—all with one single sign-on.

Not only do you get single sign-on with Connect and Create, you also get deep integration of McGraw-Hill content and content engines right in Blackboard. Whether you're choosing a book for your course or building Connect assignments, all the tools you need are right where you want them—inside of Blackboard.

Gradebooks are now seamless. When a student completes an integrated Connect assignment, the grade for that assignment automatically (and instantly) feeds your Blackboard grade center.

McGraw-Hill and Blackboard can now offer you easy access to industry leading technology and content, whether your campus hosts it or we do. Be sure to ask your local McGraw-Hill representative for details.

McGraw-Hill LearnSmart™

McGraw-Hill LearnSmart™ is available as an integrated feature of McGraw-Hill Connect® Biology and provides students with a GPS (Guided Path to Success) for your course. Using artificial intelligence, LearnSmart intelligently assesses a student's knowledge of course content through a series of adaptive questions. It pinpoints concepts the student does not understand and maps out a personalized study plan for success. This innovative study tool also has features that allow instructors to see exactly what students have accomplished and a built-in assessment tool for graded assignments. Visit the following site for a demonstration.

www.mhlearnsmart.com

McGraw-Hill Connect® Biology

McGraw-Hill Connect® Biology provides online presentation, assignment, and assessment solutions. It connects your students with the tools and resources they'll need to achieve success.

With Connect Biology, you can deliver assignments, quizzes, and tests online. A robust set of questions and activities are presented and aligned with the textbook's learning outcomes. As an instructor, you can edit existing questions and author entirely new problems. Track individual student performance—by question, assignment, or in relation to the class overall—with detailed grade reports. Integrate grade reports easily with Learning Management Systems (LMS), such as WebCT and Blackboard—and much more.

ConnectPlus Biology provides students with all the advantages of Connect Biology, plus 24/7 online access to an eBook. This media-rich version of the book is available through the McGraw-Hill Connect platform and allows seamless integration of text, media, and assessments.

To learn more, visit
www.mcgrawhillconnect.com

My Lectures—Tegrity®

McGraw-Hill Tegrity® records and distributes your class lecture with just a click of a button. Students can view anytime/anywhere via computer, iPod, or mobile device. It indexes as it records your PowerPoint® presentations and anything shown on your computer so students can use keywords to find exactly what they want to study. Tegrity is available as an integrated feature of McGraw-Hill Connect Biology and as a standalone.

Animations for a New Generation

Dynamic, 3D animations of key biological processes bring an unprecedented level of control to the classroom. Innovative features keep the emphasis on teaching rather than entertaining.

An options menu lets you control the animation's level of detail, speed, length, and appearance, so you can create the experience you want.

Draw on the animation using the whiteboard pen to highlight important areas.

The scroll bar lets you fast forward and rewind while seeing what happens in the animation, so you can start at the exact moment you want.

A scene menu lets you instantly jump to a specific point in the animation.

Pop-ups add detail at important points and help students relate the animation back to concepts from lecture and the textbook.

A complete visual summary at the end of the animation reminds students of the big picture.

Animation topics include: Cellular Respiration, Photosynthesis, Molecular Biology of the Gene, DNA Replication, Cell Cycle and Mitosis, Membrane Transport, and Plant Transport.

McGraw-Hill Create™

With **McGraw-Hill Create™**, you can easily rearrange chapters, combine material from other content sources, and quickly upload content you have written, like your course syllabus or teaching notes. Find the content you need in Create by searching through thousands of leading McGraw-Hill textbooks. Arrange your book to fit your teaching style. Create even allows you to personalize your book's appearance by selecting the cover and adding your name, school, and course information. Order a Create book and you'll receive a complimentary print review copy in 3–5 business days or a complimentary electronic review copy (eComp) via e-mail in minutes. Go to www.mcgrawhillcreate.com today and register to experience how McGraw-Hill Create empowers you to teach *your* students *your* way.

www.mcgrawhillcreate.com

Presentation Tools

Everything you need for outstanding presentations in one place.

www.mhhe.com/maderbiology11

FlexArt Image Powerpoints—including every piece of art that has been sized and cropped specifically for superior presentations, as well as labels that can be edited and flexible art that can be picked up and moved on key figures. Also included are tables, photographs, and unlabeled art pieces.

Lecture PowerPoints with Animations—animations illustrating important processes are embedded in the lecture material.

Animation PowerPoints—animations only are provided in PowerPoint.

Labeled JPEG Images—full-color digital files of all illustrations that can be readily incorporated into presentations, exams, or custom-made classroom materials.

Base Art Image Files—unlabeled digital files of all illustrations.

Presentation Center

In addition to the images from your book, this online digital library contains photos, artwork, animations, and other media from an array of McGraw-Hill textbooks.

Computerized Test Bank

A comprehensive bank of test questions is provided within a computerized test bank powered by McGraw-Hill's flexible electronic testing program, **EZ Test Online.** A new tagging scheme allows you to sort questions by Bloom's difficulty level, learning outcome, topic, and section. With EZ Test Online, instructors can select questions from multiple McGraw-Hill test banks or author their own, and then either print the test for paper distribution or give it online.

Instructor's Manual

The instructor's manual contains chapter outlines, lecture enrichment ideas, and discussion questions.

Laboratory Manual

The *Biology Laboratory Manual* is written by Dr. Sylvia Mader. Every laboratory has been written to help students learn the fundamental concepts of biology and the specific content of the chapter to which the lab relates, as well as gain a better understanding of the scientific method.

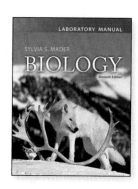

Companion Website

www.mhhe.com/maderbiology11

The Mader *Biology* companion website allows students to access a variety of free digital learning tools that include

- Chapter-level quizzing
- Animations and videos
- Vocabulary flashcards
- Virtual labs

Overview of Content Changes to *Biology,* Eleventh Edition

Chapter 1: A View of Life. This chapter introduces the three themes, Evolution, the Nature of Science, and Biological Systems, that will act as the focal points for the text. The virtual lab "Dependent and Independent Variables" has been added to the end of the chapter.

Unit 1: The Cell

Chapter 2: Basic Chemistry. The pH scale (Fig. 2.13) has been revised to provide students with a better understanding of acid/base relationships. The Biological Systems feature has been enhanced to include graphs of U.S. acid rain–causing emissions. **Chapter 3: The Chemistry of Organic Molecules** contains a new Nature of Science feature on fats in the diet. **Chapter 4: Cell Structure and Function.** The graphic on the endosymbiotic theory has been enhanced to include a more detailed explanation of the evolutionary significance of each stage of the process. **Chapter 5: Membrane Structure and Function** now contains links to the 3D animation "Membrane Transport." **Chapter 6: Metabolism: Energy and Enzymes** has been linked to the virtual lab "Enzyme Controlled Reactions." The 3D animation "Photosynthesis" has been integrated into **Chapter 7: Photosynthesis**. **Chapter 8: Cellular Respiration** includes links to the 3D animation "Cellular Respiration" and contains updated explanations on theoretical versus actual ATP yields.

Unit 2: Genetic Basis of Life

Chapter 9: The Cell Cycle and Cellular Reproduction has been enhanced by links to the 3D animation "Cell Cycle and Mitosis" and the virtual lab "Cell Reproduction." **Chapter 10: Meiosis and Sexual Reproduction** has been revised to include a more detailed explanation of chromosomes, including bivalent and tetrad combinations. In **Chapter 11: Mendelian Patterns of Inheritance,** an additional figure (Fig. 11.5) has been added to enhance an understanding of how the 3:1 ratio was developed using Mendel's data. The Science Focus box on Mendel's Laws and Meiosis is now integrated directly into the discussion of Mendel's laws. Two virtual labs, "Punnett Squares" and "Sex-Linked Traits," are now linked to this chapter as tutorials. Figure 12.5 of **Chapter 12: Molecular Biology of the Gene** has been revised to better indicate the directionality of the DNA molecule. In addition, Figure 12.6 has been modified to illustrate the role of RNA polymerase in DNA replication. Two 3D animations, "DNA replication" and "Molecular Biology of the Gene," have been added to the chapter. **Chapter 13: Regulation of Gene Expression** now contains a revised discussion of how sRNA molecules influence gene expression and new illustrations on the role of sRNAs in the cell (Fig. 13.9) and the action of proteasomes (Fig. 13.10). **Chapter 14: Biotechnology and Genomics** now starts with a new chapter opener on biotechnology-produced fuels. Also included is a more detailed explanation of intergenic sequences. The virtual labs "Knocking out Genes," "Gene Splicing," and "Classifying Using Biotechnology" have been linked to the chapter.

Unit 3: Evolution

Chapter 15: Darwin and Evolution has been substantially revised to better present the historical basis behind the theory of evolution to students. The chapter begins with a new article on *Tiktaalik*. New figures include Lamarck's inheritance of acquired characteristics (Fig. 15.2), the role of wingspots in *Drosophila* species (Fig. 15.11), and transitional fossils (Figs. 15.12 and 15.13). The material on Alfred Wallace is now integrated into the main text, and the evolution theme is enforced by an evolution feature reading on the "Tree of Life Project." The chapter also includes material on the criticisms of evolution. **Chapter 16: How Populations Evolve** begins with a new article on HIV. The discussion of microevolution now focuses on the peppered moth and a discussion of allele frequencies, and it includes new figures (Figs. 16.1, 16.2, 16.4, and 16.7) and a summary table (Table 16.1) to enforce these concepts. New figures on directional (Fig. 16.10) and disruptive (Fig. 16.11) selection have been added. A new Nature of Science feature reading on achromatopsia and the Pingelapese population reinforces the fact that microevolution occurs in humans. **Chapter 17: Speciation and Macroevolution** starts with a new article on micro-frogs. The chapter has been revised to include more detailed discussions on the various concepts of species, including new figures (Figs. 17.1 and 17.3). The cichlids of Africa are the focus of a new figure (Fig. 17.12) on convergent evolution. Two new feature readings are included: one of how to interpret phylogenetic trees, and a second on the genetic basis of beak shape in Galápagos finches. **Chapter 18: Origin and History of Life** has been reorganized to make a clear connection between chemical and biological evolution (Fig. 18.1). This includes more detailed discussions of the various hypotheses involved in these processes (Figs. 18.4 and 18.5). **Chapter 19: Taxonomy, Systematics, and Phylogeny** has been reorganized so that the material on the three-domain system (Section 19.2) occurs prior to the discussion of phylogeny (Section 19.3). The chapter starts with a new article on how systematics may be used in crime investigations. Figure 19.3 provides an enhanced visual explanation of classification categories, and Figure 19.5 illustrates the relationship between phylogeny, classification, and traits. A new Nature of Science feature reading examines the concept of DNA barcoding.

Unit 4: Microbiology and Evolution

Chapter 20: Viruses, Bacteria, and Archaea now begins with an article on the H1N1 virus. The structure of the influenza virus has been updated in Figure 20.1. New figures on emerging diseases (Fig. 20.5) and the features of prokaryotic cells (Fig. 20.7) have been provided. **Chapter 21: Protist Evolution and Diversity** now contains a focus on neglected tropical diseases and contains an opening article and Biological Systems feature reading on this topic. The chapter format reflects the current concept of protist "supergroups" (Table 21.1, Fig. 21.1). **Chapter 22: Fungi Evolution and Diversity** begins with an article on the use of fungal products as a form of green packaging material. Figure 22.1 now relates the fungi to the other eukaryotic supergroups. Table 22.1 has been enhanced to provide the key features of the fungal phyla.

Unit 5: Plant Evolution and Biology

Chapter 23: Plant Evolution and Diversity starts with a new article on plant diversity. A new Evolution feature on the evolutionary history of maize has been added, and the chapter includes a link to the virtual lab "Classifying Using Biotechnology." In **Chapter 24: Flowering Plants: Structure and Organization,** a new Evolution feature examines the survival mechanisms of plants. A second Nature of Science feature reading explores the many uses of bamboo in society. **Chapter 25: Flowering Plants: Nutrition and Transport** begins with a new article on artificially colored flowers. The 3D animation "Plant Transport" is integrated throughout the chapter. The chapter is linked to the virtual lab "Plant Transpiration." **Chapter 26: Flowering Plants: Control of Growth Responses** contains a new table (26.1) summarizing the major plant hormones. In **Chapter 27: Flowering Plants: Reproduction,** the Evolution feature reading has been enhanced to provide a more evolutionary perspective.

Unit 6: Animal Evolution and Diversity

For **Chapter 28: Invertebrate Evolution,** a new opener examines the fad of tapeworm diets. A new Evolution feature reading examines the genetic basis of the animal body plan. The phylogenetic tree of animals (Fig. 28.4) has been upgraded. Two virtual labs, "Earthworm Dissection" and "Classifying Arthropods," have been linked to the chapter. **Chapter 29: Vertebrate Evolution** includes a revised phylogenetic tree for the chordates (Fig. 29.4). The material on amphibian evolution (Section 29.4) has been updated to reflect recent advances in the field. The evolution of mammals (Section 29.6) now includes a timeline of important events (Fig. 29.19) and a summary table of important characteristics (Table 29.1). A new table (29.2) summarizes the major orders of placental mammals. **Chapter 30: Human Evolution** begins with a new article on the evolutionary relationship of Neandertals and *Homo sapiens*. The chapter and figures (30.4) have been upgraded to reflect changes in classification terminology. The chapter now includes a Nature of Science reading on how scientists are using comparative genomics to study similarities between the chimp and human genomes. The material on the ardipithecines and Cro-magnon *Homo sapiens* has been enhanced to focus on the significance of these groups.

Unit 7: Comparative Animal Biology

Chapter 31: Animal Organization and Homeostasis contains a new Nature of Science feature on regenerative medicine. The chapter is now linked to the virtual lab "Virtual Frog Dissection." **Chapter 32: Circulation and Cardiovascular Systems** now starts with an article on the consequences of aortic dissection. A new Nature of Science feature on the use of horseshoe crabs in cardiovascular medicine is included in the chapter. Two virtual labs, "Earthworm Dissection" and "Virtual Frog Dissection," are now linked to this chapter. **Chapter 33: The Lymphatic and Immune Systems** now begins with an article on severe combined immunodeficiency syndrome. The chapter also features a new section (33.1) on the evolution of immune systems. In addition, a new Nature of Science feature on cancer vaccines has been added to the chapter. **Chapter 34: Digestive Systems and Nutrition** begins with a new article on ruminant mammals. The chapter also includes a new Nature of Science feature on treating obesity and is linked to three virtual labs, "Earthworm Dissection," "Virtual Frog Dissection," and "Nutrition." **Chapter 35: Respiratory Systems** begins with a new article on the evolution of the diving response. The chapter also includes a new Nature of Science feature on artificial lung technology. **Chapter 36: Body Fluid Regulation and Excretory Systems** includes a new Nature of Science feature reading on the misuse of erythropoietin in sports and links to two virtual labs, "Earthworm Dissection" and "Virtual Frog Dissection." **Chapter 37: Neurons and Nervous Systems** includes a new opening article and Nature of Science feature on Parkinson disease. **Chapter 38: Sense Organs** begins with a new article on sensory perception in pit vipers. The chapter has been reorganized to include more details on sensory receptors (Section 38.1) and the somatic senses (Section 38.5). A new Nature of Science feature examines the development of artificial retinas. **Chapter 39: Locomotion and Support Systems** contains a new Nature of Science feature on diluted botulinum toxin and links to the "Muscle Stimulation" virtual lab. **Chapter 40: Hormones and Endocrine Systems** contains new images on Cushing syndrome (Fig. 40.14). **Chapter 41: Reproductive Systems** has been updated to include recent statistics on the prevalence of sexually transmitted diseases. The chapter is linked to the virtual lab "Virtual Frog Dissection." **Chapter 42: Animal Development and Aging** has been revised to include a focus on the aging process (Section 32.4).

Unit 8: Behavior and Ecology

The virtual lab "Mealworm Behavior" has been linked to **Chapter 43: Behavioral Ecology.** In **Chapter 44: Population Ecology,** a new chapter opener has been introduced that focuses on the impact of introduced species. Figure 44.7 has been modified to improve the explanation of the process of exponential growth. The comparison of the environmental impact of developed versus undeveloped countries has been enhanced by changes to Figure 44.17. The chapter is linked to the virtual lab "Population Biology." **Chapter 45: Community and Ecosystem Ecology** now opens with an article on wolves in the Yellowstone National Park, thus providing a link to the cover of the textbook. The chapter includes a new Nature of Science feature reading on global climate change and a link to the "Model Ecosystems" virtual lab. **Chapter 46: Major Ecosystems of the Biosphere** starts with a new article on the migration patterns of Canada geese. The Biological Systems feature "Biomagnification of Mercury" is new to this chapter. **Chapter 47: Conservation of Biodiversity** contains a new Nature of Science feature on floodplain restoration in the Illinois River system.

Acknowledgments

Dr. Sylvia Mader represents one of the icons of science education. Her dedication to her students, coupled to her clear, concise writing style, has benefited the education of thousands of students over the past three decades. It is an honor to continue her legacy, and to bring her message to the next generation of students. I have been privileged to work with the ultimate team of science educators—April Cognato, Dave Cox, Jeff Isaacson, and Ian Quitadamo. These dedicated and talented individuals have made a significant contribution to this text, and my abilities as a science educator have been enhanced by our teamwork. Together, we have striven to ensure that the material was written and illustrated in the familiar Mader style.

Many dedicated and talented individuals assisted in the development of *Biology*. I am very grateful for the help of so many professionals at McGraw-Hill who were involved in bringing this book to fruition. In particular, let me thank Rose Koos, the developmental editor who lent her exemplary talents, project management skills, advice, and most of all, patience, to all those who worked on this text. The biology publisher is Michael Hackett, who steadfastly encouraged and supported all aspects of this project. The desire of my editor, Eric Weber, to impact the lives of our students, is evident throughout this text. The project manager, Jayne Klein, faithfully and carefully steered the book through the publication process. Tamara Maury, the marketing manager, tirelessly promoted the text and educated the sales reps on its message.

The design of the book is the result of the creative talents of Laurie Janssen and many others who assisted in deciding the appearance of each element in the text. I was very lucky to have Jody Larson as my copyeditor, and Lauren Timmer and Dawnelle Krouse as proofreaders. Lachina Publishing Services produced this textbook, in the process emphasizing pedagogy and beauty to arrive at the best presentation on the page. Lori Hancock and Evelyn Jo Johnson did a superb job of finding just the right photographs and micrographs.

Who I am, as an educator and an author, is a direct reflection of what I have learned from my students. Education is a two-way street, and it is my honest opinion that both my professional and personal life have been enriched by my interactions with my students. They have encouraged me to learn more, teach better, and never stop questioning the world around me. I would also like to acknowledge my wife, Sandra. She has never wavered in her patience and support of my endeavors.

Michael Windelspecht, Ph.D.
Blowing Rock, NC

The eleventh edition of *Biology* would not have the same excellent quality without the input of these contributors and those of the many contributors and reviewers listed below.

McGraw-Hill's 360° Development Process is an ongoing, never-ending, market-oriented approach to building accurate and innovative print and digital products. It is dedicated to continual large-scale and incremental improvement driven by multiple customer feedback loops and checkpoints. This is initiated during the early planning stages of our new products, and intensifies during the development and production stages, then begins again upon publication in anticipation of the next edition.

This process is designed to provide a broad, comprehensive spectrum of feedback for refinement and innovation of our learning tools, for both student and instructor. The 360° Development Process includes market research, content reviews, course- and product-specific symposia, accuracy checks, and art reviews. We appreciate the expertise of the many individuals involved in this process.

Ancillary Authors

Connect Question Bank: Krissy Johnson, Alex James, and Betsy Harris, *Appalachian State University;* Sandy Windelspecht, *Ricochet Creative Productions;* **Test Bank:** Dave Cox, *Lincoln Land Community College;* **Lecture Outlines:** Felicia Scott, *Macomb Community College;* **Instructor's Manual:** Andrea Thomason, *Roxbury Community College;* **Practice Tests:** Deborah Dardis, *Southeastern Louisiana University;* **eBook Quizzes:** Eric Rabitoy, *Citrus College;* **LearnSmart Authors:** Patrick Galliart, *North Iowa Area Community College;* Sylvester Allred, *Northern Arizona University;* Tammy Atchison, *Pitt Community College;* Dena Berg, *Tarrant County College;* Joy Brookshire, *Kennesaw State University;* Jeffrey Isaacson, *Nebraska Wesleyan University;* **LearnSmart Reviewers:** Jill Nugent, *University of North Texas;* Murad Odeh, *South Texas College*

Eleventh Edition Reviewers

Nina Abubakari, *Wayne County Community College District*
LaQuetta B. Anderson, *Grambling State University*
Rachele Arrigoni-Restrepo, *New York City College of Technology*
Dennis Bakewicz, *New York City College of Technology*
Sarah Bales, *Moraine Valley Community College*
Marilyn Banta, *Texas State University–San Marcos*
Isaac Barjis, *New York City College of Technology*
Morgan Benowitz-Fredericks, *Bucknell University*

Gretchen Bernard, *Moraine Valley Community College*
Karen Bledsoe, *Western Oregon University*
Lois Borek, *Georgia State University*
Anthony Botyrius, *York College of Pennsylvania*
Denise Chung, *Long Island University–Brooklyn*
Pamela Anderson Cole, *Shelton State Community College*
David Cox, *Lincoln Land Community College*
Deborah Dardis, *Southeastern Louisiana University*
Diane Day, *Georgia State University*
Lewis Deaton, *University of Louisiana at Lafayette*
Helen Donis-Keller, *Franklin W. Olin College of Engineering*
C. Craig Farquhar, *University of Texas–Austin*
Jennifer Foulk, *Montgomery County Community College*
Cynthia M. Galloway, *Texas A&M University–Kingsville*
Raul Galvan, *South Texas College*
Kristine Garner, *University of Arkansas–Fort Smith*
Michele B. Garrett, *Guilford Technical Community College–Jamestown*
Sandra Gibbons, *Moraine Valley Community College*
Melanie Glasscock, *Wallace State Community College*
Andrew Goliszek, *North Carolina A&T State University*
Lula (Gwen) Gordon, *Wayne County Community College–Downtown*
Susan Michele Green, *Texas State University–San Marcos*
Robert Greene, *Cranbrook Kingswood School*
Bradley L. Griggs, *Piedmont Technical College*
Tray Hamil, *University of South Alabama*
Jerrie Hanible, *Southeastern Louisiana University*
Chris Haynes, *Shelton State Community College*
Jennifer (Wearly) Hooks, *Winthrop University*
Brenda Hunzinger, *Lake Land College*
Felix Ifeanyi, *Grambling State University*
David Jarrell, *Armstrong Atlantic State University*

Ragupathy Kannan, *University of Arkansas–Fort Smith*
Carolyn Lebsack, *Linn-Benton Community College*
Stephen G. Lebsack, *Linn-Benton Community College*
Julian Lee, *University of Miami*
Tammy J. Liles, *Bluegrass Community and Technical College*
Lynne Lohmeier, *Mississippi Gulf Coast Community College*
Chintamani S. Manish, *Midland Lutheran College*
Jessica Mayfield, *Southeastern Louisiana University*
Mark Meade, *Jacksonville State University*
Sandra L. Millward, *The Christ College of Nursing and Health Sciences*
Scott Murdoch, *Moraine Valley Community College*
Joseph Murray, *Blue Ridge Community College*
Necia M. Nicholas, *Calhoun Community College*
Therese Poole, *Georgia State University*
Michelle Priest, *Los Angeles Valley College*
Kirstin Purcell, *Saint Paul College*
Jason Raymond, *University of California–Merced*
Pamela Riddell, *Macomb Community College–Center Campus*
Abraham Saraya, *New York City College of Technology*
Dale Smoak, *Piedmont Technical College*
Phillip Snider, *Gadsden State Community College*
Lisa Strain, *Northeast Lakeview College*
Diane Teter, *South Texas College*
Mark X. VanCura, *Cape Fear Community College*
Van Wheat, *South Texas College*
Leslie Whiteman-Richardson, *Virginia State University*
Ann R. Witham, *University of Cincinnati, Raymond Walters College*
Frank Wray, *University of Cincinnati, Raymond Walters College*

Contents

Readings

The tuatara (*Sphenodon punctatus*).

1

A View of Life

At first glance, the tuatara of New Zealand appears to be just another lizard. However, recently, scientists have realized that this reptile, which may live as long as 80 years, is something very special. The tuatara represents a living fossil, a remnant of the type of reptiles that lived before the age of the dinosaurs hundreds of millions of years ago. Yet, despite being very old, the tuatara continues to mystify scientists. Some studies suggest that some traits in tuataras are evolving at rates faster than any other vertebrate animal, allowing scientists to use this organism as a test case for how species evolve over long periods of time.

The Earth hosts a wide variety of ecosystems, from which spring a mind-boggling diversity of life, including the tuataras. Even so, all Earth's organisms, regardless of form, are united by a number of common characteristics, such as the need to acquire nutrients, the ability to respond to a changing environment, and to reproduce their own kind. Incredibly, even organisms as diverse as the tuatara and a human being share similar characteristics, including a common chemistry and genetic code. As you read this chapter, reflect on the staggering diversity of life on Earth and on the many ties that bind even the most diverse organisms, from bacteria to the titan arum to humans. It is through these ties that our fates are linked together in the web of life.

As you read through this chapter, think about the following questions

1. What are the general characteristics shared by all living organisms?
2. What is the relationship between evolutionary change and the study of biology?
3. How do scientists use the scientific method to study living organisms?

FOLLOWING *the* THEMES

CHAPTER 1 A VIEW OF LIFE	
Evolution	The study of biology is based on the principles of evolutionary change and the adaptations of species to their environments.
Nature of Science	Scientists make observations, form hypotheses, and conduct experiments in an attempt to understand the principles of life.
Biological Systems	From communities of organisms to individual cells, all life is based on atoms and molecules.

1.1 How to Define Life

Biology is the scientific study of life. Life on Earth takes on a staggering variety of forms, often functioning and behaving in ways strange to humans. For example, gastric-brooding frogs swallow their embryos and give birth to them later by throwing them up! Some species of puffballs, a type of fungus, are capable of producing trillions of spores when they reproduce. Fetal sand sharks kill and eat their siblings while still inside their mother. Some *Ophrys* orchids look so much like female bees that male bees try to mate with them. Octopuses and squid have remarkable problem-solving abilities despite a small brain. Some bacteria live their entire life in 15 minutes, while bristlecone pine trees outlive ten generations of humans. Simply put, from the deepest oceanic trenches to the upper reaches of the atmosphere, life is plentiful and diverse.

Figure 1.1 illustrates the major groups of living organisms. From left to right, bacteria are widely distributed, tiny, microscopic organisms with a very simple structure. A *Paramecium* is an example of a microscopic protist. Protists are larger in size and more complex than bacteria. The other organisms in Figure 1.1 are easily seen with the naked eye. They can be distinguished by how they get their food. A morel is a fungus that digests its food externally. A sunflower is a photosynthetic plant that makes its own food, and an octopus is an aquatic animal that ingests its food.

Although life is tremendously diverse, it may be defined by several basic characteristics that are shared by all organisms. Like nonliving things, organisms are composed of chemical elements. Also, organisms obey the same laws of chemistry and physics that govern everything within the universe. The characteristics of life, however, will provide great insight into the unique nature of organisms and will help us distinguish living things from nonliving things.

MP3 Life Characteristics

Living Things Are Organized

The levels of organization depicted in Figure 1.2 begin with atoms, which are the basic units of matter. Atoms combine with other atoms of the same or different elements to form molecules. The **cell,** which is composed of a variety of molecules working together, is the basic unit of structure and function of all living things. Some cells, such as **unicellular** paramecia, live independently. Other cells, for example, the colonial alga *Volvox,* cluster together in microscopic colonies.

Many living things are **multicellular,** meaning they contain more than one cell. In multicellular organisms, similar cells combine to form a tissue; nerve tissue is a common tissue in animals. Tissues make up organs, as when various tissues combine to form the brain. Organs work together in systems; for example, the brain works with the spinal cord and a network of nerves to form the nervous system. Organ systems are joined together to form a complete living thing, or organism, such as an elephant.

The levels of biological organization extend beyond the individual organism. All the members of one species in a particular area belong to a population. A nearby forest may have a population of gray squirrels and a population of white oaks, for example. The populations of various animals and plants in the forest make up a community. The community of populations interacts with the physical environment (water, land, climate) to form an ecosystem. Collectively, all the Earth's ecosystems make up the biosphere.

Emergent Properties

Each level of biological organization builds upon the previous level and is more complex. Moving up the hierarchy, each level acquires new **emergent properties** that are determined by the interactions between the individual parts. When cells are broken down into bits of membrane and liquids, these parts themselves cannot carry out the business of living. For example, you can take apart a lump of coal, rearrange the pieces in any order, and still have a lump of coal with the same function as the original one. But, if you slice apart a living plant and rearrange the pieces, the plant is no longer functional as a complete plant, because it depends on the exact order of those pieces.

Bacteria   *Paramecium*   Morel   Sunflower   Octopus

Figure 1.1 Diversity of life.   Biology is the scientific study of life. Many diverse forms of life are found on planet Earth.

Biosphere
Regions of the Earth's crust, waters, and atmosphere inhabited by living things

Ecosystem
A community plus the physical environment

Community
Interacting populations in a particular area

Population
Organisms of the same species in a particular area

Organism
An individual; complex individuals contain organ systems

elephant   tree

Organ System
Composed of several organs working together

nervous system   shoot system

Organ
Composed of tissues functioning together for a specific task

the brain   leaves

Tissue
A group of cells with a common structure and function

nervous tissue   epidermal tissue

Cell
The structural and functional unit of all living things

nerve cell   plant cell

Molecule
Union of two or more atoms of the same or different elements

methane

Atom
Smallest unit of an element composed of electrons, protons, and neutrons

oxygen

Figure 1.2 Levels of biological organization.

In the living world, the whole is indeed more than the sum of its parts. The emergent properties created by the interactions between levels of biological organization are new, unique characteristics. These properties are governed by the laws of chemistry and physics.

Living Things Acquire Materials and Energy

Living things cannot maintain their organization or carry on life's activities without an outside source of nutrients and energy (Fig. 1.3). Food provides nutrients, which are used as building blocks or for energy. **Energy** is the capacity to do work, and it takes work to maintain the organization of the cell and the organism. When cells use nutrient molecules to make their parts and products, they carry out a sequence of chemical reactions. The term **metabolism** [Gk. *meta*, change] encompasses all the chemical reactions that occur in a cell.

The ultimate source of energy for nearly all life on Earth is the Sun. Plants and certain other organisms are able to capture solar energy and carry on **photosynthesis,** a process that transforms solar energy into the chemical energy of organic nutrient molecules. All life on Earth acquires energy by metabolizing nutrient molecules made by photosynthesizers. This applies even to plants themselves.

Living Things Maintain Homeostasis

To survive, it is imperative that an organism maintain a state of biological balance, or **homeostasis** [Gk. *homoios*, like, and *stasis*, the same]. For life to continue, temperature, moisture level, acidity, and other physiological factors must remain within the tolerance range of the organism. Homeostasis is maintained by systems that monitor internal conditions and make routine and necessary adjustments.

Organisms have intricate feedback and control mechanisms that do not require any conscious activity. These mechanisms may be controlled by one or more tissues themselves, or by the nervous system. When you are studying and forget to eat lunch, your liver releases stored sugar to keep blood sugar levels within normal limits. Many organisms depend on behavior to regulate their internal environment. In animals, these behaviors are controlled by the nervous system, and are usually not consciously controlled. For example, a lizard may raise its internal temperature by basking in the sun, or cool down by moving into the shade.

Living Things Respond

Living things interact with the environment as well as with other living things. Even unicellular organisms can respond to

Figure 1.3   Acquiring nutrients and energy.   a. An eagle ingesting fish. **b.** A human eating an apple. **c.** A cypress tree capturing sunlight. **d.** An amoeba engulfing food. **e.** A fungus feeding on a tree. **f.** A bison eating grass.

their environment. In some, the beating of microscopic hairs or, in others, the snapping of whiplike tails moves them toward or away from light or chemicals. Multicellular organisms can manage more complex responses. A vulture can detect a carcass a kilometer away and soar toward dinner. A monarch butterfly can sense the approach of Fall and begin its flight south where resources are still abundant.

The ability to respond often results in movement: the leaves of a land plant turn toward the Sun, and animals dart toward safety. Appropriate responses help ensure survival of the organism and allow it to carry on its daily activities. All together, these activities are termed the behavior of the organism. Organisms display a variety of behaviors as they maintain homeostasis and search and compete for energy, nutrients, shelter, and mates. Many organisms display complex communication, hunting, and defense behaviors.

Living Things Reproduce and Develop

Life comes only from life. Every type of living thing can **reproduce,** or make another organism like itself. Bacteria, protists, and other unicellular organisms simply split in two. In most multicellular organisms, the reproductive process begins with the pairing of a sperm from one partner and an egg from the other partner. The union of sperm and egg, followed by many cell divisions, results in an immature stage, which grows and develops through various stages to become the adult.

An embryo develops into a humpback whale or a purple iris because of a blueprint inherited from its parents. The instructions, or blueprint, for an organism's metabolism and organization are encoded in genes. The **genes,** which contain specific information for how the organism is to be ordered, are made of long molecules of DNA (deoxyribonucleic acid). DNA has a shape resembling a spiral staircase with millions of steps. Housed within this spiral staircase is the genetic code that is shared by all living things.

When living things reproduce, their genes are passed on to the next generation. Random combinations of sperm and egg, each of which contains a unique collection of genes, ensure that the new individual has new and different characteristics. The DNA of organisms, over time, also undergoes mutations (changes) that may be passed on to the next generation. These events help to create a staggering diversity of life, even within a group of otherwise identical organisms. Sometimes, organisms inherit characteristics that allow them to be more suited to their way of life.

Living Things Have Adaptations

Adaptations [L. *ad*, toward, and *aptus*, suitable] are modifications that make organisms better able to function in a particular environment. For example, penguins are adapted to an aquatic existence in the Antarctic. An extra layer of downy feathers is covered by short, thick feathers that form a waterproof coat. Layers of blubber also keep the birds warm in cold water. Most birds have forelimbs proportioned for

Figure 1.4 Living Things Have Adaptations.   Penguins have evolved complex behaviors, such as sliding across ice to conserve energy, to adapt to their environment.

flying, but penguins have stubby, flattened wings suitable for swimming. Their feet and tails serve as rudders in the water, but the flat feet also allow them to walk on land. Penguins also have many behavioral adaptations to living in the Antarctic. Penguins often slide on their bellies across the snow in order to conserve energy when moving quickly (Fig. 1.4). Their eggs—one or at most two—are carried on the feet, where they are protected by a pouch of skin. This also allows the birds to huddle together for warmth while standing erect and incubating eggs.

From penguins to fire ants, life on Earth is very diverse because over long periods of time, organisms respond to ever-changing environments by developing new adaptations. These adaptations are unintentional, but they provide the framework for evolutionary change. **Evolution** [L. *evolutio*, an unrolling] includes the way in which populations of organisms change over the course of many generations to become more suited to their environments. All living things have the capacity to evolve, and the process of evolution constantly reshapes every species on the planet, potentially providing a way for organisms to persist, despite a changing environment.

Check Your Progress   1.1

1. Distinguish between an ecosystem and a population in the levels of biological organization.
2. List the common characteristics of all living organisms.
3. Explain how adaptations relate to evolutionary change.

1.2 Evolution, the Unifying Concept of Biology

Learning Outcomes

Upon completion of this section you should be able to

1. Distinguish between the three domains of life.
2. Explain the relationship between the process of natural selection and evolutionary change.

Despite diversity in form, function, and lifestyle, organisms share the same basic characteristics. As mentioned, they are all composed of cells organized in a similar manner. Their genes are composed of DNA, and they carry out the same metabolic reactions to acquire energy and maintain their organization. The unity of living things suggests that they are descended from a common ancestor—the first cell or cells.

An evolutionary tree is like a family tree (Fig. 1.5). Just as a family tree shows how a group of people have descended from one couple, an evolutionary tree traces the ancestry of life on Earth to a common ancestor. One couple can have diverse children, and likewise a population can be a common ancestor to several other groups, each adapted to a particular set of environmental conditions. In this way, over time, diverse life-forms have arisen. Evolution may be considered the unifying concept of biology because it explains so many aspects of biology, including how living organisms arose from a single ancestor.

Table 1.1 Levels of Classification

Category	Human	Corn
Domain	Eukarya	Eukarya
Kingdom	Animalia	Plantae
Phylum	Chordata	Anthophyta
Class	Mammalia	Monocotyledones
Order	Primates	Commelinales
Family	Hominidae	Poaceae
Genus	*Homo*	*Zea*
Species*	*H. sapiens*	*Z. mays*

*To specify an organism, you must use the full binomial name, such as Homo sapiens.

by systematists to revise current information and to discover previously unknown relationships between organisms.

Several of the basic classification categories, or *taxa*, going from least inclusive to most inclusive, are **species, genus, family, order, class, phylum, kingdom,** and **domain** (Table 1.1). The least inclusive category, species [L. *species*, model, kind], is defined as a group of interbreeding individuals. Each successive classification category above species contains more types of organisms than the preceding one. Species placed within one genus share many specific characteristics and are the most closely related, while species placed in the same kingdom share only general characteristics with one another. For example, all species in the genus *Pisum* look

Organizing Diversity

Because life is so diverse, it is helpful to group organisms into categories. **Taxonomy** [Gk. *tasso*, arrange, and *nomos*, usage] is the discipline of identifying and grouping organisms according to certain rules. Taxonomy makes sense out of the bewildering variety of life on Earth and is meant to provide valuable insight into evolution. **Systematics** is the study of the evolutionary relationships between organisms. As systematists learn more about living things, the taxonomy often changes. DNA technology is now widely used

Figure 1.5 Evolutionary tree of life. As existing organisms change over time, they give rise to new species. Evolutionary studies show that all living organisms arose from a common ancestor about 4 billion years ago. Domain Archaea and domain Bacteria include the prokaryotes. Domain Eukarya includes both unicellular and multicellular organisms that possess a membrane-bounded nucleus.

pretty much the same—that is, like pea plants—but species in the plant kingdom can be quite varied, as is evident when we compare grasses to trees. Species placed in different domains are the most distantly related.

Domains

Biochemical evidence suggests that there are only three domains: **domain Bacteria, domain Archaea,** and **domain Eukarya.** Figure 1.5 shows how the domains are believed to be related. Both domain Bacteria and domain Archaea may have evolved from the first common ancestor soon after life began. These two domains contain the **prokaryotes,** which lack the membrane-bounded nucleus found in the **eukaryotes** of domain Eukarya. However, archaea organize their DNA differently than bacteria, and their cell walls and membranes are chemically more similar to eukaryotes than to bacteria. So, the conclusion is that eukarya split off from the archaeal line of descent.

Animation
Three Domains

Prokaryotes are structurally simple but metabolically complex. Archaea (Fig. 1.6) can live in aquatic environments that lack oxygen or are too salty, too hot, or too acidic for most other organisms. Perhaps these environments are similar to those of the primitive Earth, and archaea (Gk. *archae,* ancient) are the least evolved forms of life, as their name implies. Bacteria (Fig. 1.7) are variously adapted to living almost anywhere—in the water, soil, and atmosphere, as well as on our skin and in our mouths and large intestines.

Taxonomists are in the process of deciding how to categorize archaea and bacteria into kingdoms. Domain Eukarya, on the other hand, contains four major groups of organisms (Fig. 1.8). **Protists,** which now comprise a number of kingdoms, range from unicellular forms to a few multicellular ones. Some are photosynthesizers, and some must acquire their food. Common protists include algae, the protozoans, and the water molds. Figure 1.5 shows that plants, fungi, and animals most likely evolved from

Domain Eukarya: Protists

- Algae, protozoans, slime molds, and water molds
- Complex single cell (sometimes filaments, colonies, or even multicellular)
- Absorb, photosynthesize, or ingest food

1 μm

Paramecium, a unicellular protozoan

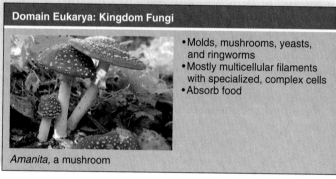

Domain Eukarya: Kingdom Fungi

- Molds, mushrooms, yeasts, and ringworms
- Mostly multicellular filaments with specialized, complex cells
- Absorb food

Amanita, a mushroom

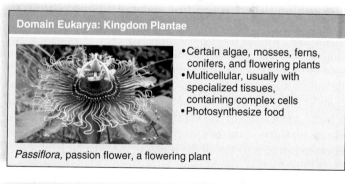

Domain Eukarya: Kingdom Plantae

- Certain algae, mosses, ferns, conifers, and flowering plants
- Multicellular, usually with specialized tissues, containing complex cells
- Photosynthesize food

Passiflora, passion flower, a flowering plant

Domain Archaea

- Prokaryotic cells of various shapes
- Adaptations to extreme environments
- Absorb or chemosynthesize food
- Unique chemical characteristics

1.6 μm

Methanosarcina mazei, an archaean

Figure 1.6 Domain Archaea.

Domain Bacteria

- Prokaryotic cells of various shapes
- Adaptations to all environments
- Absorb, photosynthesize, or chemosynthesize food
- Unique chemical characteristics

1.5 μm

Escherichia coli, a bacterium

Figure 1.7 Domain Bacteria.

Domain Eukarya: Kingdom Animalia

- Sponges, worms, insects, fishes, frogs, turtles, birds, and mammals
- Multicellular with specialized tissues containing complex cells
- Ingest food

Vulpes, a red fox

Figure 1.8 Domain Eukarya.

protists. **Plants** (kingdom Plantae) are multicellular photosyn-thetic organisms. Example plants include azaleas, zinnias, and pines. Among the **fungi** (kingdom Fungi) are the familiar molds and mushrooms that, along with bacteria, help decompose dead organisms. **Animals** (kingdom Animalia) are multicellular organisms that must ingest and process their food. Aardvarks, jellyfish, and zebras are representative animals.

Scientific Name

Biologists use **binomial nomenclature** [L. *bi,* two, and *nomen,* name] to assign each living thing a two-part name called a scientific name. For example, the scientific name for mistletoe is *Phoradendron tomentosum.* The first word is the genus, and the second word is the species designation (or *specific epithet*) of each species within a genus. The genus may be abbreviated (e.g., *P. tomentosum*) and if the species has not been deter-mined, it may simply be indicated with a generic abbreviation (e.g., *Phoradendron* sp.). Scientific names are universally used by biologists to avoid confusion. Common names tend to over-lap and often differ depending on locality and the language of a particular country. But scientific names are based on Latin, a universally used language that not too long ago was well known by most scholars.

Evolution Is Common Descent with Modification

The phrase "common descent with modification" sums up the process of evolution because it means that as descent occurs from common ancestors, so do modifications that cause organ-isms to be adapted to their environment. Through many observa-tions and experiments, Charles Darwin came to the conclusion that **natural selection** was the process that made modification—that is, adaptation—possible.

Natural Selection

During the process of natural selection, some aspect of the envi-ronment selects which traits are more apt to be passed on to the next generation. The selective agent can be an abiotic agent (part of the physical environment, such as altitude) or it can be a biotic agent (part of the living environment, such as a deer). Figure 1.9 shows how the dietary habits of deer might eventually affect the characteristics of the leaves of a particular land plant.

Mutations fuel natural selection because mutation introduces variations among the members of a population. In Figure 1.9, a plant species generally produces smooth leaves, but a mutation occurs that causes one plant to have leaves that are covered with small extensions or "hairs." The plant with hairy leaves has an advantage because the deer (the selective agent) prefer to eat smooth leaves and not hairy leaves. Therefore, the plant with hairy leaves survives best and produces more seeds than most of its neighbors. As a result, generations later most plants of this species produce hairy leaves.

As with this example, Darwin realized that although all indi-viduals within a population have the potential to reproduce, not all do so with the same success. Prevention of reproduction can run the gamut from an inability to capture resources, as when

Some plants within a population exhibit variation in leaf structure.

Deer prefer a diet of smooth leaves over hairy leaves. Plants with hairy leaves reproduce more than other plants in the population.

Generations later, most plants within the population have hairy leaves, as smooth leaves are selected against.

Figure 1.9 Natural selection.   Natural selection selects for or against new traits introduced into a population by mutations. Over many generations, selective forces such as competition, predation, and the physical environment alter the makeup of a population, favoring those more suited to the environment and lifestyle.

long-necked, but not short-necked, giraffes can reach their food source, to an inability to escape being eaten because long legs, but not short legs, can carry an animal to safety.

Whatever the example, it can be seen that living things with advantageous traits can produce more offspring than those that lack them. In this way, living things change over time, and these changes are passed on from one generation to the next. Over long periods of time, the introduction of newer, more advantageous traits into a population may drastically reshape a species. Natu-ral selection tends to sculpt a species to fit its environment and lifestyle and can create new species from existing ones. The end result is the diversity of life classified into the three domains of life (see Fig. 1.5).

Video
Finches—Natural Selection

Check Your Progress   1.2

1. List the levels of taxonomic classification from most inclusive to least inclusive.
2. Describe the differences that might be used to distinguish the various kingdoms of domain Eukarya.
3. Explain how natural selection results in new adaptations within a species.

1.3 How the Biosphere Is Organized

Learning Outcomes

Upon completion of this section you should be able to

1. Distinguish among populations, communities, ecosystems, and the biosphere.
2. Recognize the importance of maintaining biodiversity.

The organization of life extends beyond the individual organism to the **biosphere**, the zone of air, land, and water at the surface of the Earth where organisms exist (see Fig. 1.2). Individual organisms belong to a **population**, which is all the members of a species within a particular area. The populations of a **community** interact among themselves and with the physical environment (e.g., soil, atmosphere, and chemicals), thereby forming an **ecosystem.**

Figure 1.10 depicts a grassland inhabited by populations of rabbits, mice, snakes, hawks, and various types of land plants. These populations exchange gases with and give off heat to the atmosphere. They also take in water from and give off water to the physical environment. In addition, populations interact by forming food chains in which one population feeds on another. Mice feed on plants and seeds, snakes feed on mice, and hawks feed on rabbits and snakes, for example. Interactions between the various food chains make up a food web.

Ecosystems are characterized by chemical cycling and energy flow, both of which begin when photosynthetic plants, aquatic algae, and some bacteria take in solar energy and inorganic nutrients to produce food in the form of organic nutrients. The gray arrows in Figure 1.10 represent chemical cycling—chemicals move from one population to another in a food chain, until with death and decomposition, inorganic nutrients are returned to living plants once again. The yellow to red arrows represent energy flow. Energy flows from the Sun through plants and other members of the food chain as one population feeds on another. With each transfer some energy is lost as heat. Eventually, all the energy taken in by photosynthesizers has dissipated into the atmosphere. Because energy flows and does not cycle, ecosystems could not stay in existence without a constant input of solar energy and the ability of photosynthesizers to absorb it.

Video
Tallgrass Prairie Ecology

The Human Population

Humans possess the unique ability to modify existing ecosystems, which can greatly upset their natural nutrient cycles. When an ecosystem's natural energy flow has been disrupted by eliminating food sources for other animal populations even the human population can eventually suffer harm. Humans clear forests or grasslands to grow crops; later, they build houses on what was once farmland; and finally, they convert small towns into cities. Coastal ecosystems are most vulnerable. As

Figure 1.10 Grassland, a terrestrial ecosystem.   In an ecosystem, chemical cycling (gray arrows) and energy flow (yellow to red arrows) begin when plants use solar energy and inorganic nutrients to produce food for themselves and directly or indirectly for all other populations in the ecosystem. As one population feeds on another, chemicals and energy are passed along a food chain. With each transfer, some energy is lost as heat. Eventually, all the energy dissipates. With the death and decomposition of organisms, inorganic nutrients are returned to the environment and eventually may be used by plants.

heat

solar energy

heat

heat

heat

heat

heat

WASTE MATERIAL, DEATH, AND DECOMPOSITION

Chemical cycling
Energy flow

they are developed, humans send sediments, sewage, and other pollutants into the sea. Human activities destroy valuable coastal wetlands, which serve as protection against storms and as nurseries for a myriad of invertebrates and vertebrates.

Biodiversity

The two most biologically diverse ecosystems—tropical rain forests and coral reefs—are home to many organisms. These ecosystems are also threatened by human activities. The canopy of the tropical rain forest alone supports a variety of organisms including orchids, insects, and monkeys. Coral reefs, which are found just offshore of the continents and islands of the Southern Hemisphere, are built up from calcium carbonate skeletons of sea animals called corals. Reefs provide a habitat for many animals, including jellyfish, sponges, snails, crabs, lobsters, sea turtles, moray eels, and some of the world's most colorful fishes (Fig. 1.11a). Like tropical rain forests, coral reefs are severely threatened as the human population increases in size. Some reefs are 50 million years old, and yet in just a few decades, human activities have destroyed an estimated 25% of all coral reefs and seriously degraded another 30% (Fig. 1.11b). At this rate, nearly three-quarters could be destroyed within 40 years. Similar statistics are available for tropical rain forests.

Video Coral Reef Ecosystems

Destruction of healthy ecosystems has many unintended effects. For example, we depend on them for food, medicines, and various raw materials. Draining the natural wetlands of the Mississippi and Ohio rivers and the construction of levees has worsened flooding problems, making once fertile farmland undesirable. The destruction of South American rain forests has killed many species that may have yielded the next miracle drug and has also decreased the availability of many types of lumber.

We are only now beginning to realize that we depend on ecosystems even more for the services they provide. Just as chemical cycling occurs within a single ecosystem, so all ecosystems keep chemicals cycling throughout the entire biosphere. The workings of ecosystems ensure that the environmental conditions of the biosphere are suitable for the continued existence of humans. And several studies show that ecosystems cannot function properly unless they remain biologically diverse.

Biodiversity is the total number and relative abundance of species, the variability of their genes, and the different ecosystems in which they live. The present biodiversity of our planet has been estimated to be as high as 15 million species, and so far, less than 2 million have been identified and named. **Extinction** is the death of a species or larger classification category. It is estimated that presently we are losing as many as 400 species per day due to human activities and that as much as 38% of all species, including most primates, birds, and amphibians, may be in danger of extinction before the end of the century. Many biologists are alarmed about the present rate of extinction and hypothesize it may eventually rival the rates of the five mass extinctions that have occurred during our planet's history. The last mass extinction, about 65 million years ago, caused many plant and animal species, including the dinosaurs, to become extinct.

It would seem that the primary bioethical issue of our time is preservation of ecosystems. Just as a native fisherman who assists in overfishing a reef is doing away with his own food source, so are we as a society contributing to the destruction of our home, the biosphere. If instead we adopt a conservation ethic that preserves the biosphere, we would help ensure the continued existence of our own species.

Check Your Progress   1.3

1. Explain the relationship between a population, a community, and an ecosystem.
2. Describe some unintentional ways in which human activities affect ecosystems.
3. Discuss why ecosystems with high biodiversity might be more vulnerable to destruction by human activities.

a. Healthy coral reef

Figure 1.11 Coral reef, a marine ecosystem. **a.** Coral reefs, a type of ecosystem found in tropical seas, contain many diverse forms of life, a few of which are shown here. **b.** Various human activities have caused catastrophic damage to this coral reef off the coast of Florida, as shown over the course of 19 years. Preserving biodiversity is a modern-day challenge of great proportions.

1975 Minimal coral death

1985 Some coral death with no fish present

1995 Coral bleaching with limited chance of recovery

2004 Coral is black from sedimentation; bleaching still evident

b.

1.4 The Process of Science

Learning Outcomes

Upon completion of this section you should be able to

1. Identify the components of the scientific method.
2. Distinguish between a theory and a hypothesis.
3. Analyze a scientific experiment and identify the hypothesis, experiment, control groups, and conclusions.

The process of science pertains to the study of biology. Biology consists of many disciplines and areas of specialty because life has numerous aspects. Some biological disciplines are cytology, the study of cells; anatomy, the study of structure; physiology, the study of function; botany, the study of plants; zoology, the study of animals; genetics, the study of heredity; and ecology, the study of the interrelationships between organisms and their environment.

Religion, aesthetics, ethics, and science are all ways in which human beings seek order in the natural world. Science differs from these other ways of knowing and learning because the scientific process uses the **scientific method,** a standard series of steps used in gaining new knowledge that is widely accepted among scientists. The steps of the scientific method are often applicable to other situations, and begin with observation (Fig. 1.12).

Observation

Scientists believe that nature is orderly and measurable—that natural laws, such as the law of gravity, do not change with time, and that a natural event, or **phenomenon,** can be understood more fully through **observation**—a formal way of "seeing what happens."

Scientists use all of their senses in making observations. The behavior of chimpanzees can be observed through visual means, the disposition of a skunk can be observed through olfactory means, and the warning rattles of a rattlesnake provide auditory information of imminent danger. Scientists also extend the ability of their senses by using instruments; for example, the microscope enables us to see objects that could never be seen by the naked eye. Finally, scientists may expand their understanding even further by taking advantage of the knowledge and experiences of other scientists. For instance, they may look up past studies at the library or on the Internet, or they may write or speak to others who are researching similar topics.

Hypothesis

After making observations and gathering knowledge about a phenomenon, a scientist uses inductive reasoning to formulate a possible explanation. **Inductive reasoning** occurs whenever a person uses creative thinking to combine isolated facts into a cohesive whole. In some cases, chance alone may help a scientist arrive at an idea.

One famous case pertains to the antibiotic penicillin, which was discovered in 1928. While examining a petri dish of bacteria that had become contaminated with the mold *Penicillium,*

Figure 1.12 Flow diagram for the scientific method. On the basis of new and/or previous observations, a scientist formulates a hypothesis, which is then tested by further observations and/or experiments. Experiments provide data that either support or do not support the hypothesis. The return arrow indicates that a scientist often chooses to retest the same hypothesis or to test a related hypothesis. Conclusions from many different but related experiments may lead to the development of a scientific theory.

Alexander Flemming observed an area that was free of bacteria. Flemming, an early expert on antibacterial substances, reasoned that the mold might be producing an antibacterial compound.

We call such a possible explanation for a natural event a **hypothesis.** A hypothesis is not merely a guess; rather, it is an informed statement that can be tested in a manner suited to the processes of science.

All of a scientist's past experiences, no matter what they might be, have the potential to influence the formation of a hypothesis. But a scientist considers only hypotheses that can be tested. Moral and religious beliefs, while very important in the lives of many people, differ between cultures and through time, and these may not be scientifically testable.

Experiments, Observations, and Data

Scientists often perform an **experiment,** which is a series of procedures, to test a hypothesis. To determine how to test a hypothesis, a scientist uses deductive reasoning. **Deductive reasoning** involves "if, then" logic. In designing the experiment, the scientist may make a **prediction,** or an expected outcome, based on knowledge of the factors in the experiment.

The manner in which a scientist intends to conduct an experiment is called the **experimental design.** A good experimental design ensures that scientists are examining the contribution of a specific variable, called the **experimental variable**, to the observation. To ensure that the results will be meaningful, an experiment contains both test groups and a **control** group. A test group is exposed to the environmental variable, but the control group is not. If the control groups and test groups show the same results, the experimenter knows that the hypothesis predicting a difference between them is not supported.

In some cases, scientists may use a **model** as a representation of the actual object because altering the actual object may be physically impossible, very expensive, or morally questionable. Later in this section, a scientist uses bluebird models because it would have been impossible to get live birds to cooperate. As other examples, computer models are used to decide how human activities may affect climate, because of expense, ethical concerns, and physical limitations. Scientists often use mice instead of humans for medical research because of ethical concerns. Bacteria are used in much genetic research because they are inexpensive to grow and reproduce very quickly. Although these models are usually relevant and give useful information, they are themselves still hypotheses in need of testing to ensure that they are valid representations.

The results of an experiment are referred to as the **data**. Data should be observable and objective, rather than subjective. Mathematical data are often displayed in the form of a graph or table. Often, these results include a **standard deviation**, a statistical analysis that is a measure of how much the data in the experiment varies. Many studies, such as the one discussed in the Nature of Science feature on page 13, rely on statistical data.

An Example

As a hypothetical example, let's say an investigator wants to know if eating onions can prevent women from getting osteoporosis (weak bones). The scientist conducts a survey asking women about their onion-eating habits and then correlates this data with the condition of their bones. Other scientists critiquing this study would want to know: How many women were surveyed? How old were the women? What were their exercise habits? What proportion of the diet consisted of onions? And what criteria were used to determine the condition of their bones?

If the investigators conclude that eating onions does protect a woman from osteoporosis, then other scientists might want to know the statistical probability of error. The probability of error is a mathematical calculation based on the conditions and methods of the experiment. If the results are significant at a 0.30 level, then the probability that the correlation is incorrect is 30% or less. (This would be considered a high probability of error.) The greater the variance in the data, the greater the probability of error.

Even if this study had a low probability of error, it would be considered hypothetical until scientists identified one or more active components in onions that have a direct biochemical or physiological effect on bones. Therefore, scientists must be skeptics who always pressure one another to continue investigating a particular topic.

Conclusion

Scientists must analyze the data in order to reach a **conclusion** as to whether the hypothesis is supported or not (see Fig. 1.12). Because science progresses, the conclusion of one experiment can lead to the hypothesis for another experiment, as represented by the return arrow in Figure 1.12. Results that do not support one hypothesis can often help a scientist formulate another hypothesis to be tested.

Scientists report their findings in scientific journals so that their methodology and data are available to other scientists for critique. Experiments and observations must be repeatable—that is, the reporting scientist and any scientist who repeats the experiment must get the same results, or else the data are suspect.

Scientific Theory

The ultimate goal of science is to understand the natural world in terms of **scientific theories,** which are concepts that join together well-supported and related hypotheses. In ordinary speech, the word *theory* refers to a speculative idea. In contrast, a scientific theory is supported by a broad range of observations, experiments, and data often from a variety of disciplines. Some of the basic theories of biology are:

Theory	Concept
Cell	All organisms are composed of cells, and new cells come only from preexisting cells.
Homeostasis	The internal environment of an organism stays relatively constant—within a range that is protective of life.
Gene	Organisms contain coded information that dictates their form, function, and behavior.
Ecosystem	Organisms are members of populations, which interact with each other and the physical environment within a particular locale.
Evolution	All living things have a common ancestor, but each is adapted to a particular way of life.

As stated earlier, the theory of evolution is the unifying concept of biology because it pertains to many different aspects of living things. For example, the theory of evolution enables scientists to understand the history of living things, and the anatomy, physiology, and embryological development of organisms. Even behavior can be described through evolution, as we shall see in a study discussed later in this chapter.

The theory of evolution has been a fruitful scientific theory, meaning that it has helped scientists generate new hypotheses. Because this theory has been supported by so many observations and experiments for over 100 years, some biologists refer to the **principle** of evolution, a term sometimes used for theories that are generally accepted by an overwhelming number of scientists. The term **law** instead of principle is preferred by some. For instance, in a subsequent chapter concerning energy relationships, we will examine the laws of thermodynamics.

THEME   Nature of Science

The Benefits and Limitations of Statistical Studies

Many of the studies published in scientific journals and reported in the news are statistical studies, so it behooves us to be aware of their benefits and limitations. At the start, you should know that a statistical study will gather numerical information from various sources and then try to make sense out of it, for the purpose of coming to a conclusion.

Example of a Statistical Study

Let's take a look at a study that allows us to conclude that babies conceived 18 months to five years after a previous birth are healthier than those conceived at shorter or longer intervals. In other words, spacing children about two to five years apart is a good idea (Fig. 1A). Here is how the authors collected their data and the results they published in the *Journal of the American Medical Association*.[1]

Objective.   To determine whether there is an association between birth spacing and a healthy baby when data are corrected for maternal characteristics or socioeconomic status.

Data.   The authors collected data from studies performed around the world in 1966 through January 2006. The studies were published in various journals, reported on at professional meetings, or were known to the authors by personal contact. The authors gathered a very large pool of data that included over 11 million pregnancies from 67 individual studies. Twenty of the studies were from the United States, with the remaining 47 coming from 61 different countries. The authors attempted to adjust the data (by elimination of certain data) for factors such as mother's age, wealth, access to prenatal care, and breast-feeding. These adjustments allow the findings to be applied to both developed and developing countries.

Conclusion.

1. A pregnancy that begins less than six months after a previous birth has a 77% higher chance of being preterm and a 39% higher chance of lower birth weight.
2. For up to 18 months between pregnancies, the chance of a preterm birth decreases by 2% per month, and the chance of a low-weight birth decreases

Figure 1A Does spacing pregnancies lead to healthier children?   A recent statistical study suggests that it does. If so, which mother, left or right, may have a healthier younger child?

by 3% per month as the 18-month time period is approached.
3. Babies conceived after 59 months have the same risk as those conceived in the less-than-six-months group.
4. The optimum spacing between pregnancies appears to be 18 months to five years after a previous birth.

The study leader, Agustin Conde-Agudelo, said, "Health officials should counsel women who have just given birth to delay their next conception by 18 to 59 months."

Limitations of Experimental Studies

The expression "statistical study" is a bit of a misnomer because most scientists collect quantitative data and use them to come to a conclusion. However, if we compare this study to experimental studies, we can see that the experimental studies include both a control group and test groups. The groups are treated the same except for the experimental variable. Obviously, you wouldn't be able to divide women of the same childbearing age into various groups and tell each group when they will conceive their children for the purpose of deciding the best interval between pregnancies for the health of the newborn. So, what is the next best thing? Do a statistical study utilizing data already available about women who became pregnant at different intervals.

A statistical study is really a correlation study. In our example, the authors studied the correlation between birth spacing and the health of a newborn. The more data collected from more varied sources make a correlation study more reliable. The study by Conde-Agudelo has a very large sample size, which goes a long way to validating the results. Even so, a correlation does not necessarily translate to causation. So, it is not surprising that Dr. Mark A. Klebanoff, director of the National Institute of Child Health and Human Development, commented that many factors will affect birth spacing and that the study is not detailed enough to take all factors into consideration. Is any statistical study detailed enough? Most likely not.

Benefits of Statistical Studies

Before we give up on statistical studies, let's consider that they do provide us with information not attainable otherwise. Regardless of whether we understand the intricacies of statistical analysis, statistical studies do allow scientists to gain information and insights into many problems. True, further study is needed to find out if the observed correlation does mean causation, but science is always a work in progress, with additional findings being published every day.

Questions to Consider

1. Why is a large sample size needed in a statistical study? Why might this be a challenge for scientists?
2. How might both statistical and experimental studies be combined to enhance the validity of a scientific study?

1. Conde-Agudelo, A., Rosas-Bermudez, A., and Kafury-Goeta, A. C. 2006. Birth spacing and risk of adverse perinatal outcomes. Abstract. *JAMA* 295: 1809–23.

Using the Scientific Method

This section demonstrates the use of the scientific method in a controlled study to ensure that the outcome is due to the experimental variable, or independent variable—the component or factor being tested. The result is termed the **responding variable,** or dependent variable, because it is due to the experimental variable:

Experimental Variable (Independent Variable)	Responding Variable (Dependent Variable)
Factor of the experiment being tested	Result or change that occurs due to the experimental variable

Observation

Researchers doing this study knew that in the short run, nitrogen fertilizer enhances yield and increases food supplies. However, excessive nitrogen fertilizer application can cause pollution by adding toxic levels of nitrates to water supplies. Also, applying nitrogen fertilizer year after year may alter soil properties to the point that crop yields may decrease instead of increase. At that point, the only solution is to let the land remain unplanted for several years until the soil recovers naturally.

An alternative to the use of nitrogen fertilizers is the use of legumes, plants such as peas and beans, that increase soil nitrogen. Legumes provide a home for bacteria that convert atmospheric nitrogen to a form usable by the plant. The bacteria live in nodules on the roots (Fig. 1.13). The bacteria supply the plant with nitrogen compounds, and in turn, the plant passes the product of photosyntheis to the nodules.

Numerous legume crops can be rotated (planted every other season) with any number of cereal crops. The nitrogen added to the soil by the legume crop is a natural fertilizer that increases the yield of cereal crops. The particular rotation used by farmers tends to depend on the location, climate, and market demand. In this study, researchers performed an experiment in which method of fertilization is the experimental variable and enhanced yield is the responding variable.

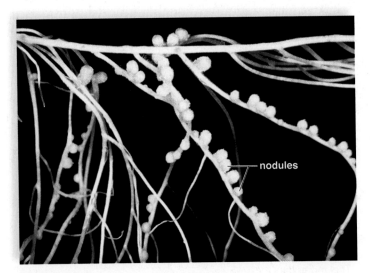

Figure 1.13 Root nodules.   Bacteria that live in nodules on the roots of legumes, such as pea plants, convert nitrogen in the air to a form that land plants can use to make proteins and other nitrogen-containing molecules.

Hypothesis

Researchers doing this study knew that the pigeon pea plant is a legume with a high rate of atmospheric nitrogen conversion. This plant is widely grown as a food crop in India, Kenya, Uganda, Pakistan, and other subtropical countries. Researchers formulated the hypothesis that a pigeon pea/winter wheat rotation would be a reasonable alternative to the use of nitrogen fertilizer to increase the yield of winter wheat.

> HYPOTHESIS: A pigeon pea/winter wheat rotation will cause winter wheat production to increase as well as or better than the use of nitrogen fertilizer.
>
> PREDICTION: Wheat biomass following the growth of pigeon peas will surpass wheat biomass following nitrogen fertilizer treatment.

Experiment and Data

In this study, the investigators decided on the following experimental design (Fig. 1.14a):

CONTROL POTS
- Winter wheat was planted in pots of soil that received no fertilization treatment—that is, no nitrogen fertilizer and no preplanting of pigeon peas.

TEST POTS
- Winter wheat was grown in clay pots in soil treated with nitrogen fertilizer equivalent to 45 kilograms (kg)/hectare (ha).
- Winter wheat was grown in clay pots in soil treated with nitrogen fertilizer equivalent to 90 kg/ha.
- Pigeon pea plants were grown in clay pots in the summer. The pigeon pea plants were then tilled into the soil and winter wheat was planted in the same pots.

To ensure a controlled experiment, the conditions for the control pots and the test pots were identical; the plants were exposed to the same environmental conditions and watered equally. During the following spring, the wheat plants were dried and weighed to determine wheat biomass production in each of the pots.

After the first year, wheat biomass was higher in certain test pots than in the control pots (Fig. 1.14b). Specifically, test pots with 45 kg/ha of nitrogen fertilizer (orange) had only slightly more wheat biomass production than the control pots, but test pots that received 90 kg/ha treatment (green) demonstrated nearly twice the biomass production of the control pots. To the surprise of investigators, wheat production following summer planting of pigeon peas (brown) did not demonstrate as high a biomass production as the control pots.

Conclusion and Further Investigation

Wheat biomass following the growth of pigeon peas is not as great as that obtained with nitrogen fertilizer treatments, meaning that the data from the experiment did not support the investigators' hypothesis. This is not an uncommon event in scientific investigations. However, the investigators decided to continue the experiment using the same design and the same pots as before, to see if the buildup of residual soil nitrogen from pigeon peas would eventually increase wheat biomass. So they proposed a new hypothesis.

a. Control pots and test pots of three types

Figure 1.14 Pigeon pea/winter wheat rotation study.
a. Experiment involves control pots and test pots of three types: test pots that received 45 kg/ha of nitrogen; test pots that received 90 kg/ha of nitrogen; and test pots in which pigeon peas rotated with winter wheat. **b.** The graph compares wheat biomass for each of three years. Wheat biomass in test pots that received the most nitrogen fertilizer (green) declined while wheat biomass in test pots with pigeon pea/winter wheat rotation (brown) increased dramatically.

b. Results

HYPOTHESIS: A sustained pigeon pea/winter wheat rotation will eventually cause an increase in winter wheat production.

PREDICTION: Wheat biomass following two years of pigeon pea/winter wheat rotation will surpass wheat biomass following nitrogen fertilizer treatment.

After two years, the yield following 90 kg/ha nitrogen treatment (green) was not as much as it was the first year (Fig. 1.14*b*). Indeed, wheat biomass following summer planting of pigeon peas (brown) was the highest of all treatments, suggesting that buildup of residual nitrogen from pigeon peas had the potential to provide fertilization for winter wheat growth.

CONCLUSION: The hypothesis is supported. At the end of two years, the yield of winter wheat following a pigeon pea/winter wheat rotation was better than for the other type pots.

The researchers continued their experiment for still another year. After three years, winter wheat biomass production had decreased in the control pots and in the pots treated with nitrogen fertilizer. Pots treated with nitrogen fertilizer still had increased wheat biomass production compared with the control

pots, but not nearly as much as pots following summer planting of pigeon peas. Compared to the first year, wheat biomass increased almost fourfold in pots having a pigeon pea/winter wheat rotation (brown, Fig. 1.14*b*). The researchers suggested that the soil was improved by the organic matter as well as the addition of nitrogen from the pigeon peas. The researchers published their results in a scientific journal.[1]

A Field Study

Researcher David Barash observed the mating behavior of mountain bluebirds (Fig. 1.15*a, b*) and noted that males perform aggressive behavior during the mating season. He was interested in whether this behavior changed during the events of mating and reproduction.

1 Bidlack, J. E., Rao, S. C., and Demezas, D. H. 2001. Nodulation, nitrogenase activity, and dry weight of chickpea and pigeon pea cultivars using different *Bradyrhizobium* strains. *Journal of Plant Nutrition* 24: 549–60.

Hypothesis

Barash formulated the hypothesis that aggression of the male varies during the reproductive cycle. To test this hypothesis, he reasoned that he should evaluate the intensity of male aggression at three stages: after the nest is built, after the first egg is laid, and after the eggs hatch.

HYPOTHESIS: Male bluebird aggression varies during the reproductive cycle.

PREDICTION: Aggression intensity will change after the nest is built, after the first egg is laid, and after hatching.

Experiment and Data

For his experiment, Barash decided to measure aggression intensity by recording the number of approaches per minute a male made toward a rival male and his own female mate. To provide a rival, Barash posted a male bluebird model near the nests while resident males were out foraging. The aggressive behavior (approaches) of the resident male was noted and counted during the first 10 minutes of the male's return (Fig. 1.15c).

To give his results validity, Barash included a control group. For his control, Barash posted a male robin model instead of a male bluebird near certain nests.

Resident males of the control group did not exhibit any aggressive behavior, but resident males of the experimental groups did exhibit aggressive behavior. Barash graphed his mathematical data on number of approaches (Fig. 1.15d). By examining the graph, you can see that the resident male was more aggressive toward the rival male model than toward his female mate, and that he was most aggressive while the nest was under construction, less aggressive after the first egg was laid, and least aggressive after the eggs hatched.

Conclusion

The results allowed Barash to conclude that aggression in male bluebirds is related to their reproductive cycle. Therefore, his hypothesis was supported. If male bluebirds were always aggressive, even toward male robin models, his hypothesis would not have been supported.

CONCLUSION: The hypothesis is supported. Male bluebird aggression does vary during the reproductive cycle.

Barash reported his experiment in *The American Naturalist*.[2] In this article, Barash gave an evolutionary interpretation to his results. It is adaptive, he said, for male bluebirds to be less aggressive after the first egg is laid because by then the male bird is "sure the offspring is his own." It is maladaptive for the male bird to waste energy being aggressive after hatching, because his offspring are already present.

Check Your Progress   1.4

1. Identify the role of the experimental variable in an experiment.
2. Distinguish between the roles of the test group and the control group in an experiment.
3. Describe the process by which a scientist may test a hypothesis about an observation.

2 Barash, D. P. 1976. Male response to apparent female adultery in the mountain bluebird (*Sialia currucoides*): an evolutionary interpretation. *The American Naturalist* 110: 1097–1101.

Figure 1.15 A field study. Observation of normal male bluebird behavior (**a** and **b**) allowed David Barash to formulate a testable hypothesis. He (**c**) collected data, which was (**d**) displayed in a graph. Then, he came to a conclusion.

a. Scientist making observations

b. Normal mountain bluebird nesting behavior

resident male

female mate

c. Resident male attacking a male model near nest

male bluebird model

d. Observation of two experimental nests provided data for graph.

Approaches to male model

Approaches to female mate

— nest 1
— nest 2

2.0
1.5
1.0
0.5
0

Approaches per Minute

nest construction   first egg laid   hatching of eggs

Stage of Nesting Cycle

CONNECTING *the* CONCEPTS *with the* THEMES

Evolution

- Evolution is the core concept of biology, and explains how species develop adaptations to an ever-changing environment.
- Natural selection is the mechanism by which evolutionary change occurs.

Nature of Science

- Science is based on the ability to observe the natural world and then formulate hypotheses as potential explanations for these observations.
- Scientists use an ordered series of events, called the scientific method, to construct experiments that explore the structure of the natural world.

Biological Systems

- All life is based on atoms and molecules, which in turn are involved in the formation of cells, the basic unit of all life.
- Members of a species form populations. Populations of different species in a given area are called a community. The interaction of a community with the environment is called an ecosystem.
- Ecosystems are characterized by energy flow and chemical cycling.

Media Study Tools

www.mhhe.com/maderbiology11

Enhance your study of this chapter with study tools and practice tests. Also ask your instructor about the resources available through ConnectPlus, including the media-rich eBook, interactive learning tools, and animations.

Summarize

1.1 How to Define Life

Although living things are diverse, they have certain characteristics in common. Living things (a) are organized, and their levels of organization extend from the cell to ecosystems; (b) need an outside source of materials and energy; (c) maintain homeostasis; (d) respond to external stimuli; (e) reproduce and develop, passing on genes to their offspring; and (f) have adaptations suitable to their way of life in a particular environment. Together, these characteristics unify life on Earth.

1.2 Evolution, the Unifying Concept of Biology

Life on Earth is diverse, but the theory of evolution unifies life and describes how all living organisms evolved from a common ancestor. Taxonomists assign each living thing an italicized binomial name that consists of the genus and the specific epithet. From the least inclusive to the most inclusive category, each species belongs to a genus, family, order, class, phylum, kingdom, and finally domain. Systematists study the evolutionary relationships between species.

The three domains of life are Archaea, Bacteria, and Eukarya. The first two domains contain prokaryotic organisms that are structurally simple but metabolically complex. Domain Eukarya contains the protists, fungi, plants, and animals. Protists range from unicellular to multicellular organisms and include the protozoans and most algae. Among the fungi are the familiar molds and mushrooms. Plants are well known as the multicellular photosynthesizers of the world, while animals are multicellular and ingest their food. An evolutionary tree shows how the domains are related by way of common ancestors.

Natural selection describes the process by which living organisms are descended from a common ancestor. Mutations occur within a population, creating new traits. The agents of natural selection, present in both biological and physical environments, shape species over time and may create new species from existing ones.

1.3 How the Biosphere Is Organized

Within an ecosystem, populations interact with one another and with the physical environment. Nutrients cycle within and between ecosystems, but energy flows unidirectionally and is eventually lost as an unusable form. Adaptations of organisms allow them to play particular roles within an ecosystem.

1.4 The Process of Science

When studying the natural world, scientists use the scientific process. Observations, along with previous data, are used to formulate a hypothesis. New observations and/or experiments are carried out in order to test the hypothesis. A good experimental design includes an experimental variable and a control group. The experimental and observational results are analyzed, and the scientist comes to a conclusion as to whether the results support the hypothesis or do not support the hypothesis.

Several conclusions in a particular area may allow scientists to arrive at a theory, such as the cell theory, the gene theory, or the theory of evolution. The theory of evolution is a unifying concept of biology.

Key Terms

adaptation 5	domain Bacteria 7
animal 8	domain Eukarya 7
binomial nomenclature 8	ecosystem 9
biodiversity 10	emergent property 2
biology 2	energy 4
biosphere 9	eukaryote 7
cell 2	evolution 5
class 6	experiment 11
community 9	experimental design 11
conclusion 12	experimental variable 12
control 12	extinction 10
data 12	family 6
deductive reasoning 11	fungi 8
domain 6	gene 5
domain Archaea 7	genus 6

homeostasis   4
hypothesis   11
inductive reasoning   11
kingdom   6
law   12
metabolism   4
model   12
multicellular   2
natural selection   8
observation   11
order   6
phenomenon   11
photosynthesis   4
phylum   6
plant   8

population   9
prediction   11
principle   12
prokaryote   7
protist   7
reproduce   5
responding variable   14
scientific method   11
scientific theory   12
species   6
standard deviation   12
systematics   6
taxonomy   6
unicellular   2

Assess

Reviewing This Chapter

1. What are the common characteristics of life?   2–5
2. Describe the levels of biological organization.   2
3. Why do living things require an outside source of nutrients and energy? Describe these sources.   4
4. What is passed from generation to generation when organisms reproduce? What has to happen to the hereditary material DNA for evolution to occur?   5
5. How does evolution explain both the unity and the diversity of life?   5–6
6. What are the categories of classification? How does the domain Eukarya differ from domain Bacteria and domain Archaea?   6
7. Explain the scientific name of an organism.   6
8. How does natural selection result in adaptation to the environment?   8
9. What is an ecosystem, and why should human beings preserve ecosystems?   9–10
10. Describe the series of steps involved in the scientific method.   11–12
11. Give an example of a controlled study. Name the experimental variable and the responding variable.   14–15

Testing Yourself

Choose the best answer for each question.

1. Which of these is not a property of all living organisms?
   a. organization
   b. acquisition of materials and energy
   c. care for their offspring
   d. reproduction
   e. responding to the environment
2. Describe an emergent property that might arise when moving from a single neuron (nerve cell) to nervous tissue.
3. The level of organization that includes cells of similar structure and function would be
   a. an organ.
   b. a tissue.
   c. an organ system.
   d. an organism.

4. Which of the following is an example of adaptation?
   a. In a very wet year, some plants grow unusually tall stalks and large leaves.
   b. Over millions of years, the eyes of cave salamanders lose their function.
   c. An escaped dog joins a pack of wild dogs and begins interbreeding with them.
   d. A harsh winter kills many birds within a population, especially the smallest ones.
5. Energy is brought into ecosystems by which of the following?
   a. fungi and other decomposers
   b. cows and other organisms that graze on grass
   c. meat-eating animals
   d. organisms that photosynthesize, such as plants
   e. All of these are correct.
6. Which of the following statements is a hypothesis?
   a. Will increasing my cat's food increase her weight?
   b. Increasing my cat's food consumption will result in a 25% increase in her weight.
   c. I will feed my cat more food.
   d. My cat has gained weight; therefore, she is eating more food.
7. After formulating a hypothesis, a scientist
   a. proves the hypothesis true or false.
   b. tests the hypothesis.
   c. decides how to best avoid having a control.
   d. makes sure environmental conditions are just right.
   e. formulates a scientific theory.
8. The experimental variable in the bluebird experiment (pages 15-16) was the
   a. use of a model male bluebird.
   b. observations of the experimenter.
   c. various behavior of the males.
   d. identification of what bluebirds to study.
   e. All of these are correct.
9. The control group in the pigeon pea/winter wheat experiment (pages 14-15) was the pots that were
   a. planted with pigeon peas.
   b. treated with nitrogen fertilizer.
   c. not treated.
   d. not watered.
   e. Both c and d are correct.
10. Which of the following are agents of natural selection?
    a. changes in the environment
    b. competition among individuals for food and water
    c. predation by another species
    d. competition among members of a population for prime nesting sites
    e. All of these are correct.
11. Which of the following is an example of natural selection?
    a. In a very wet year, some plants grow unusually tall stalks and large leaves.
    b. After several unusually cold winters, squirrels with an extra layer of fat have more offspring.
    c. Squirrels may have long or short tails.
    d. Dogs with longer legs are able to run faster than dogs with shorter legs.

12. Which of the following statements regarding evolution is false?
    a. Adaptations may be physical or behavioral.
    b. Natural selection always results in organisms becoming more adapted to the environment.
    c. A trait selected for, may suddenly become selected against when the environment changes.
    d. Some traits are neither selected for nor against.

For questions 13–15, write a brief answer.

13. Why is it said that all energy used by living organisms originates from the Sun?

14. Carbon dioxide emissions have been blamed for climate change by many scientists. How might excessive amounts of carbon dioxide affect nutrient cycling?

15. Would the accidental introduction of a new species to an ecosystem necessarily have a negative effect on biodiversity? Why or why not?

Engage

Virtual Lab
Dependent and Independent Variables

The virtual lab "Dependent and Independent Variables" provides an interactive exploration of how scientists construct scientific experiments.

Thinking Scientifically

1. An investigator spills dye on a culture plate and notices that the bacteria live despite exposure to sunlight. He decides to test if the dye is protective against ultraviolet (UV) light. He exposes one group of culture plates containing bacteria and dye and another group containing only bacteria to UV light. The bacteria on all plates die. Complete the following diagram.

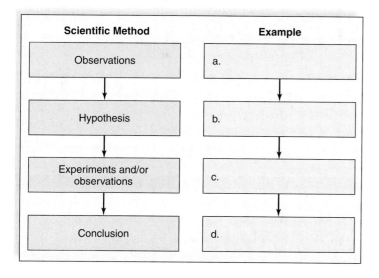

2. You want to grow large tomatoes and notice that a name-brand fertilizer claims to produce larger produce than a generic brand. How would you test this claim?

3. A scientist wishes to test her hypothesis that a commonly used drug causes heart attacks in some individuals. What kind of study should she initiate? What would you expect her experimental and responding variables to be?

Bioethical Issue

Oil Drilling in the Arctic

Established by an act of Congress in 1980, the Arctic National Wildlife Refuge (ANWR) covers a total of 19 million acres of northernmost Alaska far above the Arctic Circle. ANWR is home to a variety of wildlife, such as caribou, migratory birds, grizzly and polar bears, wolves, and musk oxen. But it is also home to substantial oil reserves, which has led to an ongoing contentious debate over its future: Should Congress allow development of ANWR for oil exploration and drilling?

Those who favor oil drilling in ANWR insist that first and foremost, the impact on the land would be minimal. The affected area would be roughly the size of an airport in a total area roughly the size of the state of South Carolina. They contend that the effect would mainly be underground because new techniques allow us to go lower and spread out beneath the surface to get the oil. Waste treatment and disposal methods have also improved. Acquiring the oil, advocates say, would also protect jobs and national security in the United States by lessening dependence on often hostile foreign countries for oil, and would have the added benefit of insulating the U.S. economy from oil price spikes and supply shocks.

Those who do not favor oil drilling in ANWR are eager to point out that at current levels of consumption, the oil coming from ANWR would hardly have a noticeable impact on prices and supply levels. Furthermore, they believe that the best solution to the current energy crunch would be for U.S. citizens to adopt simple energy conservation measures and invest in research on alternative fuels. They suggest that this would save many times the oil that could come from drilling in the Arctic refuge and that, by using a renewable energy resource, the environment in the lower 48 states would be protected, in addition to protecting the wildlife in the Arctic National Wildlife Refuge. Using renewable energy would lessen the need for foreign oil, and would also protect our national security.

Should Congress approve oil drilling in ANWR? Or should Congress invest in alternative and renewable energy forms, and insist that citizens adopt energy conservation measures? Should public tax monies be made available to Congress for oil exploration or for investment in alternative energy sources?

UNIT 1

The Cell

We're going to take a fairly long journey through the various levels of biological organization from atoms to ecosystems, as shown in Figure 1.2. Whenever you get ready to go on a trip, you think about what you should bring with you and how to pack your suitcase. Similarly, you can think of the chapters in Unit I as the necessities you are going to bring with you as we take our biological journey.

The chapters in Unit I will teach you principles of biology that will apply to every chapter in the book. Chapters 2 and 3 introduce you to chemistry because all organisms are composed of chemicals, some of them quite unique to living things. In Chapters 4 and 5, we will see how these chemicals are arranged to form the structure of a cell, the basic unit of life. Some organisms are single cells and some are multicellular, but all are made up of cells. Chapters 6, 7, and 8 are about the physiology of cells—how they stay alive.

Your understanding of these chapters will serve you well as you move through the other parts of this text. Just as building a house first requires a solid foundation, your learning begins with the foundation provided in this first unit.

UNIT OUTLINE

UNIT LEARNING OUTCOMES

The learning outcomes for this unit focus on three major themes in the life sciences.

Evolution	Examine how inanimate elements can be combined to produce a living cell.
Nature of Science	Describe how science is used to investigate cellular phenomena.
Biological Systems	Evaluate how cellular components work together in order to function and live.

Bottle-nosed dolphin (*Tursiops truncatus*).

2

Basic Chemistry

A bottle-nosed dolphin, an amazing and intelligent creature, can tolerate a certain salinity, can stay underwater for only so long, and must eat a particular diet to keep its complex organ systems functioning. Chemistry affects every aspect of the dolphin's life, whether it is playing in the Gulf of Mexico or performing at Sea World. Without molecular chemistry, a dolphin wouldn't be able to live at all.

At one time, people believed that organisms contained a "vital force" that allowed them to live. Over time, science has shown us that living and nonliving things are all composed of the same elements. It is true, though, that living and nonliving things differ as to which elements are most common, as we shall see. This chapter reviews inorganic chemistry, which largely pertains to nonliving things, and also explores the composition and chemistry of water, an inorganic substance that is intimately connected to the life of organisms on planet Earth. Our search for water on other planets further emphasizes the essential role of water in all life.

As you read through the chapter, think about the following questions:

1. What unique properties do chemical elements have?
2. How do elements interact with one another?
3. How is it possible for inanimate chemical elements to produce a living organism?

BEFORE YOU BEGIN

Before beginning this chapter, take a few moments to review the following discussions.

Figure 1.2 Why is it important to understand scale when studying biology?

Figures 1.5-1.8 Why do we organize biological concepts into systems?

Section 1.4 How does scientific study help us to understand the natural world?

FOLLOWING *the* THEMES

CHAPTER 2 BASIC CHEMISTRY

UNIT 1 THE CELL		
	Evolution	Chemicals form the basis of living things, which evolve by changing their chemistry over time.
	Nature of Science	Knowledge of chemicals is used to understand the scientific basis of life.
	Biological Systems	Chemical elements are combined into molecular compounds, which are used to build life systems.

2.1 Chemical Elements

Learning Outcomes

Upon completion of this section, you should be able to

1. Describe how protons, neutrons, and electrons relate to atomic structure.
2. Use the periodic table to evaluate relationships between atomic number and mass number.
3. Describe how variations in an atomic nucleus account for its physical properties.
4. Determine how electrons are configured around a nucleus.

Throw a ball, pat your dog, rake leaves, turn a page; everything we touch—from the water we drink to the air we breathe—is composed of matter. **Matter** refers to anything that takes up space and has mass. Although matter has many diverse forms—anything from molten lava to kidney stones—it only exists in three distinct states: solid, liquid, or gas.

Elements

All matter, both nonliving and living, is composed of certain basic substances called **elements.** An element is a substance that cannot be broken down to simpler substances with different properties (a property is a physical or chemical characteristic, such as density, solubility, melting point, and reactivity) by ordinary chemical means. It is quite remarkable that, in the known universe, there are only 92 naturally occurring elements that serve as the building blocks of matter. Other elements have been artificially constructed by physicists and are not biologically important.

Both the Earth's crust and all organisms are composed of elements, but they differ as to which ones are common. Only six elements—carbon, hydrogen, nitrogen, oxygen, phosphorus, and sulfur—are basic to life and make up about 95% of the body weight of organisms. The acronym CHNOPS helps us remember these six elements. The properties of these elements are essential to the uniqueness of cells and organisms, such as the macaws in Figure 2.1. The macaws have gathered on a salt lick in South America. Salt contains the elements sodium and chlorine and is commonly sought after by many forms of life. Potassium, calcium, iron, and magnesium are still other elements found in living things.

Atoms

In the early 1800s, the English scientist John Dalton (1776-1844) developed the atomic theory, which says that elements consist of tiny particles called **atoms** [Gk. *atomos*, uncut, indivisible]. An atom is the smallest part of an element that displays the properties of the element. An element and its atoms share the same name. One or two letters create the **atomic symbol,** which stands for this name. For example, the symbol H means a hydrogen atom, the symbol Rn stands for radon, and the symbol Na (for *natrium* in Latin) is used for a sodium atom.

Physicists have identified a number of subatomic particles that make up atoms. The three best known subatomic particles include positively charged **protons,** uncharged **neutrons,** and negatively charged **electrons** [Gk. *elektron*, electricity]. Protons and neutrons are located within the nucleus of an atom, and electrons move about the nucleus. Figure 2.2 shows the arrangement of the subatomic particles in a helium atom, which has only two electrons. In Figure 2.2a, the stippling shows the

Figure 2.1 Elements that make up the Earth's crust and its organisms.   Scarlet macaws gather on a salt lick in South America. The graph inset shows the Earth's crust primarily contains the elements silicon (Si), aluminum (Al) and oxygen (O). Living organisms primarily contain the elements oxygen (O), nitrogen (N), carbon (C), and hydrogen (H). Biological molecules also contain the elements sulfur (S) and phosphorus (P).

a.   b.

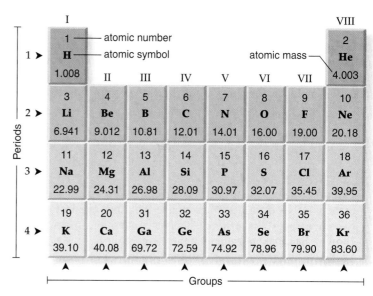

Subatomic Particles			
Particle	Electric Charge	Atomic Mass Unit (AMU)	Location
Proton	+1	1	Nucleus
Neutron	0	1	Nucleus
Electron	−1	0	Electron shell

c.

Figure 2.2 Model of helium (He). Atoms contain subatomic particles, which are located as shown. Protons and neutrons are found within the nucleus, and electrons are outside the nucleus. **a.** The stippling shows the probable location of the electrons in the helium atom. **b.** The average location of an electron is sometimes represented by a circle termed an electron shell. **c.** The electric charge and the atomic mass units (AMU) of the subatomic particles vary as shown.

Figure 2.3 A portion of the periodic table. In the periodic table, elements are listed in the order of their atomic numbers, but arranged so each element is placed in a group (vertical column) and period (horizontal row). All the atoms in a particular group have the same number of valence electrons and therefore share common chemical characteristics. Each period shows the number of electron shells for an element. This abbreviated periodic table contains elements most important in biology; the complete periodic table is in Appendix D.

probable location of electrons, and in Figure 2.2b, the circle represents an **electron shell,** the average location of electrons.

The concept of an atom has changed greatly since Dalton's day. If an atom could be drawn the size of a football field, the nucleus would be like a gumball in the center of the field, and the electrons would be tiny specks whirling about in the upper stands. Most of an atom is empty space. We should also realize that we can only indicate where the electrons are expected to be most of the time. In our analogy, the electrons might very well stray outside the stadium at times.

Atomic Number and Mass Number

Atoms not only have an atomic symbol, they also have an atomic number and mass number. All atoms of an element have the same number of protons housed in the nucleus. This is called the **atomic number,** which accounts for the unique properties of this type of atom.

Each atom also has its own mass number dependent on the number of subatomic particles in that atom. Protons and neutrons are assigned one atomic mass unit (AMU) each. Electrons are so small that their AMU is considered zero in most calculations (Fig. 2.2c). Therefore, the **mass number** of an atom is the sum of protons and neutrons in the nucleus.

The term mass is used, and not *weight*, because mass is constant, while weight changes according to the gravitational force of a body. The gravitational force of the Earth is greater than that of the moon; therefore, substances weigh less on the moon, even though their mass has not changed.

By convention, when an atom stands alone (and not in the periodic table, discussed next), the atomic number is written as a subscript to the lower left of the atomic symbol. The mass number is written as a superscript to the upper left of the atomic

symbol. Regardless of position, the smaller number is always the atomic number, as shown here for carbon.

The Periodic Table

Once chemists discovered a number of the elements, they began to realize that even though each element consists of a different atom, certain chemical and physical characteristics recur. The periodic table, developed by the Russian chemist Dmitri Mendeleev (1834–1907), was constructed as a way to group the elements, and therefore atoms, according to these characteristics.

Figure 2.3 is a portion of the periodic table, which is shown in total in Appendix D. The atoms shown in the periodic table are assumed to be electrically neutral. Therefore, the atomic number not only tells you the number of protons, it also tells you the number of electrons. The **atomic mass** is the average of the AMU for all the isotopes (discussed next) of that atom. To determine the number of neutrons, subtract the number of protons from the atomic mass, and take the closest whole number.

In the periodic table, every atom is in a particular period (the horizontal rows) and in a particular group (the vertical columns). The atomic number of every atom in a period increases by one if you read from left to right. All the atoms in a group share the same binding characteristics. For example, all the atoms in group VII react with one atom at a time, for reasons we will soon explore. The atoms in group VIII are called the noble gases because they are inert and rarely react with another atom. Notice that helium, neon, argon, and krypton are noble gases.

Isotopes

Isotopes [Gk. *isos*, equal, and *topos*, place] are atoms of the same element that differ in the number of neutrons. Isotopes have the same number of protons, but they have different atomic masses. For example, the element carbon has three common isotopes:

$$^{12}_{6}C \qquad ^{13}_{6}C \qquad ^{14}_{6}C*$$

*radioactive

Carbon 12 has six neutrons, carbon 13 has seven neutrons, and carbon 14 has eight neutrons. Unlike the other two isotopes of carbon, carbon 14 is unstable; it changes over time into nitrogen 14, which is a stable isotope of the element nitrogen. As carbon 14 decays, it releases various types of energy in the form of rays and subatomic particles, and therefore it is termed a radioactive isotope. The radiation given off by radioactive isotopes can be detected in various ways. The Geiger counter is an instrument that is commonly used to detect radiation. In 1860, the French physicist Antoine-Henri Becquerel (1852-1908) discovered that a sample of uranium would produce a bright image on a photographic plate even in the dark, and a similar method of detecting radiation is still in use today. Marie Curie (1867-1934), who worked with Becquerel, coined the term "radioactivity" and contributed much to its study. Today, radiation is used by biologists to date objects from our distant past, create images, and trace the movement of substances in the body.

Animation Half-Life

Low Levels of Radiation

The chemical behavior of a radioactive isotope is essentially the same as that of the stable isotopes of an element. This means that you can put a small amount of radioactive isotope in a sample and it becomes a **tracer** by which to detect molecular changes. Melvin Calvin and his co-workers used carbon 14 to detect all the various reactions that occur during the process of photosynthesis (see Chapter 7).

The importance of chemistry to medicine is nowhere more evident than in the many medical uses of radioactive isotopes. Specific tracers are used in imaging the body's organs and tissues. For example, after a patient drinks a solution containing a minute amount of ^{131}I, it becomes concentrated in the thyroid—the only organ to take it up. A subsequent image of the thyroid indicates whether it is healthy in structure and function (Fig. 2.4a).

Positron-emission tomography (PET) is a way to determine the comparative activity of tissues. Radioactively labeled glucose, which emits a subatomic particle known as a positron, is injected into the body. The radiation given off is detected by sensors and analyzed by a computer. The result is a color image that shows which tissues took up glucose and are therefore metabolically active. The red areas surrounded by green in Figure 2.4b indicate which areas of the brain are most active. PET scans of the brain are used to evaluate patients who have memory disorders of an undetermined cause or suspected brain tumors or seizure disorders that could possibly benefit from surgery. PET scans, utilizing radioactive thallium, can detect signs of coronary artery disease and low blood flow to the heart.

Video Nuclear Medicine

a.

b.

Figure 2.4 Low levels of radiation. **a.** Medical scan of the thyroid gland (colored image) indicates the presence of a tumor that does not take up the radioactive iodine. **b.** A PET (positron-emission tomography) scan reveals which portions of the brain are most active (green and red colors).

a.　　　　b.

Figure 2.5 High levels of radiation. **a.** Radiation used to kill bacteria and fungi on peaches helps them spoil less quickly and keep for a longer period of time. **b.** Physicians use targeted radiation therapy to kill cancer cells.

High Levels of Radiation

Radioactive substances in the environment can harm cells, damage DNA, and cause cancer. When Marie Curie was studying radiation, its harmful effects were not known, and she and many of her co-workers developed cancer. The release of radioactive particles following a nuclear power plant accident can have far-reaching and long-lasting effects on human health. The harmful effects of radiation can be put to good use, however (Fig. 2.5). Radiation from radioactive isotopes has been used for many years to sterilize medical and dental products. Now it can be used to sterilize the U.S. mail and other packages to free them of possible pathogens, such as anthrax spores. High radiation is often used to kill cancer cells. Targeted radioisotopes can be introduced into the body so that the subatomic particles emitted destroy only cancer cells, with little risk to the rest of the body.

Electrons and Energy

In an electrically neutral atom, the positive charges of the protons in the nucleus are balanced by the negative charges of electrons moving about the nucleus. Various models in years past have attempted to illustrate the precise location of electrons. Figure 2.6 uses the Bohr model, which is named after the physicist Niels Bohr (1885-1962). The Bohr model is useful as a way to visualize electron location, but we need to realize that today's physicists tell us it is not possible to determine the precise location of any individual electron at any given moment.

In the Bohr model, the electron shells about the nucleus also represent energy levels. Because negatively charged electrons are attracted to the positively charged nucleus, it takes energy to push them away and keep them in their own shell. The more distant the shell, the more energy it takes. Therefore, it is more accurate to speak of electrons as being at particular energy levels in relation to the nucleus. When you study photosynthesis, you will learn that when atoms absorb the energy of the Sun, electrons are boosted to a higher energy level. Later, as the electrons return to their original energy level, energy is released and transformed into chemical energy. This chemical energy supports all life on Earth and therefore our very existence is dependent on the energy of electrons.

You will want to learn to draw a Bohr model for each of the elements that occurs in the periodic table shown in Figure 2.3. Let's begin by examining the models depicted in Figure 2.6. Notice that the first shell (closest to the nucleus) can contain two electrons; thereafter, each additional shell can contain eight electrons. Also, each lower level is filled with electrons before the next higher level contains any electrons.

Animation
Atomic Structure

The sulfur atom, with an atomic number of 16, has two electrons in the first shell, eight electrons in the second shell, and six electrons in the third, or outer, shell. Revisit the periodic table (see Fig. 2.3), and note that sulfur is in the third period. In other words, the period tells you how many shells an atom has. Also note that sulfur is in group VI. The group tells you how many electrons an atom has in its outer shell.

Regardless of how many shells an atom has, the outermost shell is called the valence shell. The valence shell is important because it determines many of an atom's chemical properties. If an atom has only one shell, the outermost valence shell is complete when it has two electrons. But if an atom has more than one shell, the **octet rule** holds. This rule states that the outermost shell is most stable when it has eight electrons. As mentioned previously, atoms in group VIII of the periodic table are called the noble gases because they do not ordinarily react. Stability exists because the valence shell is filled with eight electrons and therefore has less energy. In general, lower energy states represent stability, as we will have an opportunity to point out again in Chapter 6.

Just as you sometimes communicate with and react to other people by using your hands, so atoms use the electrons in their valence shells to undergo reactions. Atoms with fewer than eight electrons in the outer shell react with other atoms in such a way that after the reaction, each has a stable outer shell. As we shall see, the number of electrons in an atom's **valence shell** determines whether the atom gives up, accepts, or shares electrons to acquire eight electrons in the outer shell. Each atom in a group within the periodic table has the same number of electrons in its valence shell.

Check Your Progress   2.1

1. Contrast atomic number and mass number.
2. Examine the periods and groups from the periodic table to determine the electron configuration of chlorine.
3. Explain what would happen if you used low radiation to medically treat cancer.

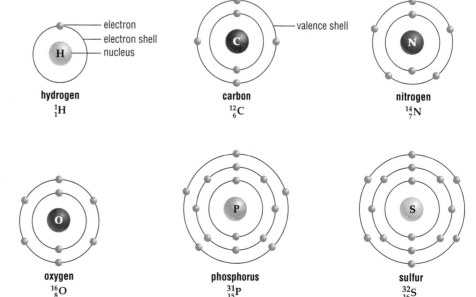

Figure 2.6 Bohr models of atoms.
Electrons orbit the nucleus at particular energy levels (electron shells). The first shell contains up to two electrons, and each shell thereafter can contain up to eight electrons as long as we consider only atoms with an atomic number of 20 or below. Each shell is filled before electrons are placed in the next shell. The outermost, or valence, shell helps determine the atom's chemical properties and how many other elements it can interact with.

hydrogen
$_1^1H$

carbon
$_6^{12}C$

nitrogen
$_7^{14}N$

oxygen
$_8^{16}O$

phosphorus
$_{15}^{31}P$

sulfur
$_{16}^{32}S$

electron
electron shell
nucleus

valence shell

2.2   Molecules and Compounds

Learning Outcomes

Upon completion of this section, you should be able to

1. Describe how elements are combined into molecules and compounds.
2. List different types of bonds that occur between elements.
3. Compare the relative strengths of ionic, covalent, and hydrogen bonds.

A **molecule** [L. *moles,* mass] exists when two or more elements bond together, and is the smallest part of a compound that retains its chemical properties. A **compound** is a molecule containing at least two different elements. In practice, these two terms are used interchangeably, but in biology, we usually speak of molecules. Water (H_2O) is a molecule that contains atoms of hydrogen and oxygen. A **formula** tells you the number of each kind of atom in a molecule. For example, in glucose:

one molecule

$$C_6H_{12}O_6$$

indicates 6 atoms of carbon   indicates 12 atoms of hydrogen   indicates 6 atoms of oxygen

Electrons possess energy, and the bonds that exist between atoms also contain energy. Organisms are directly dependent on chemical-bond energy to maintain their organization. As you may know, organisms routinely break down glucose, the sugar shown to the left, to obtain energy. When a chemical reaction occurs, as when glucose is broken down, electrons shift in their relationship to one another, and energy is released. Spontaneous reactions, which are ones that occur freely, always release energy.

MP3
Chemical Bonding

Ionic Bonding

Sodium (Na), with only one electron in its third shell, tends to be an electron donor (Fig. 2.7*a*). Once it gives up this electron, the second shell, with eight electrons, becomes its outer shell. Chlorine (Cl), on the other hand, tends to be an electron acceptor. Its outer shell has seven electrons, so if it acquires only one more electron it has a completed outer shell. When a sodium atom and a chlorine atom come together, an electron is transferred from the sodium atom to the chlorine atom. Now both atoms have eight electrons in their outer shells.

This electron transfer, however, causes a charge imbalance in each atom. After giving up an electron, the sodium atom has one more proton than it has electrons; therefore, it has a net charge of +1 (symbolized by Na^+). After accepting an electron, the chlorine atom has one more electron than it has protons; therefore, it has a net charge of −1 (symbolized by Cl^-). Such charged particles are called **ions.** Sodium (Na^+) and chloride (Cl^-) are not the only biologically important ions. Some, such as potassium (K^+), are formed by the transfer of a single electron to another atom; others, such as calcium (Ca^{2+}) and magnesium (Mg^{2+}), are formed by the transfer of two electrons.

Ionic compounds are held together by a strong attraction between negatively and positively charged ions called an **ionic bond.** When sodium reacts with chlorine, an ionic compound called sodium chloride (NaCl) results. Sodium chloride is

Figure 2.7 Formation of sodium chloride (table salt).   a. During the formation of sodium chloride, an electron is transferred from the sodium atom to the chlorine atom. At the completion of the reaction, each atom has eight electrons in the outer shell, but each also carries a charge as shown. **b.** In a sodium chloride crystal, ionic bonding between Na^+ and Cl^- causes the atoms to assume a three-dimensional lattice in which each sodium ion is surrounded by six chloride ions, and each chloride ion is surrounded by six sodium ions. The result is crystals of salt as in table salt.

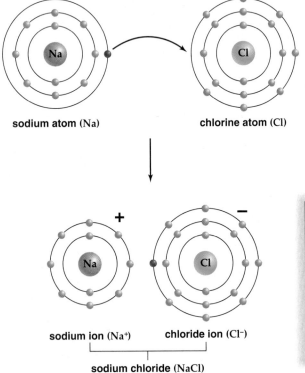

sodium atom (Na)   chlorine atom (Cl)

+   −

sodium ion (Na^+)   chloride ion (Cl^-)

sodium chloride (NaCl)

a.

Na^+ Cl^-

b.

a salt, commonly known as table salt, because it is used to season our food (Fig. 2.7*b*). **Salts** are solid substances that usually separate and exist as individual ions in water, as discussed on page 30.

Animation
Ionic Bonds

Covalent Bonding

A **covalent bond** [L. *co*, together, with, and *valens*, strength] results when two atoms share electrons in such a way that each atom has an octet of electrons in the outer shell (or two electrons, in the case of hydrogen). In a hydrogen atom, the outer shell is complete when it contains two electrons. If hydrogen is in the presence of a strong electron acceptor, it gives up its electron to become a hydrogen ion (H^+). But if this is not possible, hydrogen can share with another atom and thereby have a completed outer shell. For example, one hydrogen atom will share with another hydrogen atom. Their two electron shells overlap and the electrons are shared between them (Fig. 2.8*a*). Because they share the electron pair, each atom has a completed outer shell.

A more common way to symbolize that atoms are sharing electrons is to draw a line between the two atoms, as in the structural formula H—H. Just as a handshake requires two hands, one from each person, a covalent bond between two atoms requires two electrons, one from each atom. In a molecular formula, the line is omitted and the molecule is simply written as H_2.

Sometimes, atoms share more than one pair of electrons to complete their octets. A double covalent bond occurs when two atoms share two pairs of electrons (Fig. 2.8*b*). To show that oxygen gas (O_2) contains a double bond, the molecule can be written as $O = O$. It is also possible for atoms to form triple covalent bonds, as in nitrogen gas (N_2), which can be written as $N \equiv N$. Single covalent bonds between atoms are quite strong, but double and triple bonds are even stronger.

Nonpolar and Polar Covalent Bonds

When the sharing of electrons between two atoms is equal, the covalent bond is said to be a **nonpolar covalent bond.** If one atom is able to attract electrons to a greater degree than the other atom, it is the more electronegative atom. **Electronegativity** is dependent on the number of protons—the greater the number of protons, the greater the electronegativity. When electrons are not shared equally, the covalent bond is a **polar covalent bond.**

Animation
Electronegativity

You can readily see that the bonds in methane (Fig. 2.8*c*) must be polar because carbon has more protons than a hydrogen atom. However, methane is a symmetrical molecule and the polarities cancel each other out—methane is a nonpolar molecule. Not so in water, which has this shape:

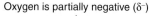
Oxygen is partially negative (δ^-)

Hydrogens are partially positive (δ^+)

In water, the oxygen atom is more electronegative than the hydrogen atoms and the bonds are polar. Moreover, because of its

a. Hydrogen gas

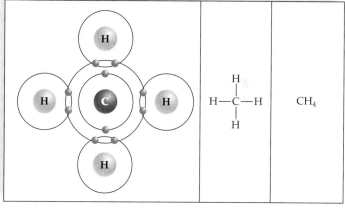

b. Oxygen gas

c. Methane

Figure 2.8 Covalently bonded molecules. In a covalent bond, atoms share electrons, allowing each atom to have a completed outer shell. **a.** A molecule of hydrogen (H_2) contains two hydrogen atoms sharing a pair of electrons. This single covalent bond can be represented in any of the three ways shown. **b.** A molecule of oxygen (O_2) contains two oxygen atoms sharing two pairs of electrons. This results in a double covalent bond. **c.** A molecule of methane (CH_4) contains one carbon atom bonded to four hydrogen atoms.

Electron Model	Structural Formula	Molecular Formula
H—H	H_2
$O = O$	O_2
H—C—H (with H above and below)	CH_4

nonsymmetrical shape, the polar bonds cannot cancel each other, and water is a polar molecule. The more electronegative end of the molecule is designated slightly negative (δ^-), and the hydrogens are designated slightly positive (δ^+).

Water is not the only polar molecule in living things. For example, the amine group ($-NH_2$) is polar, and this causes amino acids and nucleic acids to exhibit polarity, as we shall see in the next chapter. The polarity of molecules affects how they interact with other molecules.

Animation
Ionic vs. Covalent
Bonding

Check Your Progress   2.2

1. Compare and contrast an ionic bond with a covalent bond.
2. Explain why calcium ion carries two positive charges.
3. Describe how the atoms in methane (CH_4) produce a complete outer shell.

2.3 Chemistry of Water

Learning Outcomes

Upon completion of this section, you should be able to

1. Describe how water associates with other molecules in solution.
2. Evaluate which property of water is important for biological life.
3. Analyze how water's solid, liquid, and vapor states allow life to exist on Earth.

Figure 2.9a recaps what we know about the water molecule. The structural formula on the far left shows that when water forms, an oxygen atom is sharing electrons with two hydrogen atoms. The ball-and-stick model in the center shows that the covalent bonds between oxygen and each of the hydrogens are at an angle of 104.5°. Finally, the space-filling molecule gives us the three-dimensional shape of the molecule and indicates its polarity.

The shape of water and of all organic molecules is necessary to the structural and functional roles they play in living things. For example, hormones have specific shapes that allow them to be recognized by the cells in the body. We can stay well only when antibodies recognize the shape of disease-causing agents, like a key fits a lock, and are able to remove them. Similarly, homeostasis is only maintained when enzymes have the proper shape to carry out their particular reactions in cells.

The shape of a water molecule and its polarity make hydrogen bonding possible. A **hydrogen bond** is the attraction of a slightly positive hydrogen to a slightly negative atom in the vicinity. In carbon dioxide, $O = C = O$, a slight difference in polarity between carbon and the oxygens is present, but because carbon dioxide is symmetrical, the opposing charges cancel one another and hydrogen bonding does not occur.

Hydrogen Bonding

The dotted lines in Figure 2.9b indicate that the hydrogen atoms in one water molecule are attracted to the oxygen atoms in other water molecules. Each of these hydrogen bonds is weaker than an ionic or covalent bond. The dotted lines indicate that hydrogen bonds are more easily broken than the other bonds.

Hydrogen bonding is not unique to water. Other biological molecules, such as DNA, have polar covalent bonds involving an electropositive hydrogen and usually an electronegative oxygen or nitrogen. In these instances, a hydrogen bond can occur within the same molecule or between nearby molecules.

Although a single hydrogen bond is more easily broken than a single covalent bond, multiple hydrogen bonds are collectively quite strong. Hydrogen bonds between cellular molecules help maintain their proper structure and function. For example, hydrogen bonds hold the two strands of DNA together.

Electron Model

Ball-and-stick Model

104.5°

Space-filling Model

Oxygen attracts the shared electrons and is partially negative.

δ^-

O

H   H

δ^+ δ^+

Hydrogens are partially positive.

a. Water (H_2O)

Figure 2.9 Water molecule.   **a.** Three models for the structure of water. The electron model does not indicate the shape of the molecule. The ball-and-stick model shows that the two bonds in a water molecule are angled at 104.5°. The space-filling model also shows the V shape of a water molecule. **b.** Hydrogen bonding between water molecules. Each water molecule can hydrogen bond with up to four other molecules, in three dimensions. When in a liquid state, water is constantly forming and breaking hydrogen bonds.

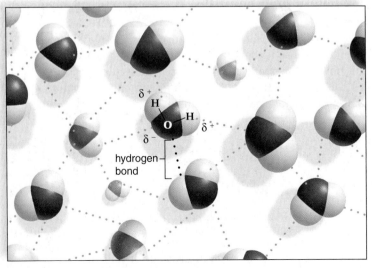

δ^+
H
H δ^+
O
δ^-

hydrogen bond

b. Hydrogen bonding between water molecules

When DNA makes a copy of itself, hydrogen bonds easily break, allowing DNA to unzip. But normally, the hydrogen bonds add stability to the DNA molecule. Similarly, the shape of protein molecules is often maintained by hydrogen bonding between different parts of the same molecule. As we shall see, many of the important properties of water are the result of hydrogen bonding.

Properties of Water

The first cell(s) evolved in water, and all living things are 70–90% water. Because of hydrogen bonding, water molecules cling together, and this association gives water its unique chemical properties. Without hydrogen bonding between molecules, water would freeze at –100°C and boil at –91°C, making most of the water on Earth steam, and life unlikely. Hydrogen bonding is responsible for water being a liquid at temperatures typically found on the Earth's surface. It freezes at 0°C and boils at 100°C. These and other unique properties of water make it essential to the existence of life as we know it. When scientists examine other planets with the hope of finding life, they first look for signs of water.

Animation
Properties of Water

Water Has a High Heat Capacity. A **calorie** is the amount of heat energy needed to raise the temperature of 1 g of water 1°C. In comparison, other covalently bonded liquids require input of only about half this amount of energy to rise in temperature 1°C. The many hydrogen bonds that link water molecules together help water absorb heat without a great change in temperature. Converting 1 g of the coldest liquid water to ice requires the loss of 80 calories of heat energy (Fig. 2.10a). Water holds onto its heat, and its temperature falls more slowly than that of other liquids. This property of water is important not only for aquatic organisms but also for all living things.

Because the temperature of water rises and falls slowly, organisms are better able to maintain their normal internal temperatures and are protected from rapid temperature changes.

Water Has a High Heat of Evaporation. When water boils, it evaporates—that is, vaporizes into the environment. Converting 1 g of the hottest water to a gas requires an input of 540 calories of energy. Water has a high heat of evaporation because hydrogen bonds must be broken before water boils.

Water's high heat of vaporization gives animals in a hot environment an efficient way to release excess body heat. When an animal sweats, or gets splashed, body heat is used to vaporize water, thus cooling the animal (Fig. 2.10b). Because of water's high heat of vaporization and ability to hold onto its heat, temperatures along the coasts are moderate. During the summer, the ocean absorbs and stores solar heat, and during the winter, the ocean releases it slowly. In contrast, the interior regions of continents experience abrupt changes in temperatures.

Water Is a Solvent. Due to its polarity, water facilitates chemical reactions, both outside and within living systems. As

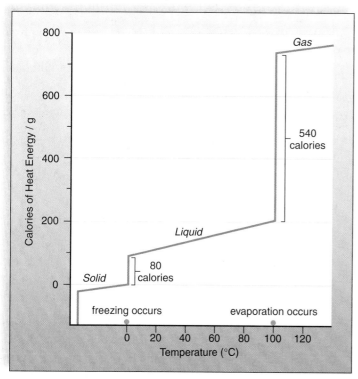

a. Calories lost when 1 g of liquid water freezes and calories required when 1 g of liquid water evaporates.

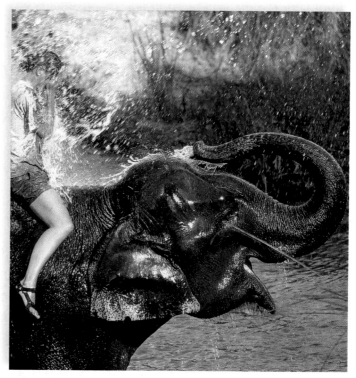

b. Bodies of organisms cool when their heat is used to evaporate water.

Figure 2.10 Temperature and water. a. Water can be a solid, a liquid, or a gas at naturally occurring environmental temperatures. At room temperature and pressure, water is a liquid. When water freezes and becomes a solid (ice), it gives off heat, and this heat can help keep the environmental temperature higher than expected. On the other hand, when water evaporates, it takes up a large amount of heat as it changes from a liquid to a gas. **b.** This means that splashing water on the body will help keep body temperature within a normal range. Can you also see why water's properties help keep the coasts moderate in both winter and summer?

a solvent, it dissolves a great number of substances, especially those that are also polar. A **solution** contains dissolved substances, which are then called **solutes**. When ionic salts—for example, sodium chloride (NaCl)—are put into water, the negative ends of the water molecules are attracted to the sodium ions, and the positive ends of the water molecules are attracted to the chloride ions. This attraction causes the sodium ions and the chloride ions to separate, or dissociate, in water.

An ionic salt dissolves in water.

Water is also a solvent for larger polar molecules, such as ammonia (NH_3).

A polar molecule dissolves in water.

Molecules that can attract water are said to be **hydrophilic** [Gk. *hydrias*, of water, and *phileo*, love]. When ions and molecules disperse in water, they move about and collide, allowing reactions to occur. Nonionized and nonpolar molecules that cannot attract water are said to be **hydrophobic** [Gk. *hydrias*, of water, and *phobos*, fear]. Hydrophilic molecules tend to attract other polar molecules; similarly, hydrophobic substances usually associate with other nonpolar molecules. Gasoline contains nonpolar molecules, and therefore does not mix with water and is hydrophobic.

Water Molecules Are Cohesive and Adhesive.   Cohesion refers to the ability of water molecules to cling to each other due to hydrogen bonding. At any moment in time, a water molecule can form hydrogen bonds with at most four other water molecules. Because of cohesion, water exists as a liquid under the conditions of temperature and pressure present at the Earth's surface. The strong cohesion of water molecules is apparent because water flows freely, yet water molecules do not separate from each other.

Adhesion refers to the ability of water molecules to cling to other polar surfaces. This is a result of water's polarity. Multicellular animals often contain internal vessels in which water assists the transport of nutrients and wastes because the cohesion and adhesion of water allows blood to fill the tubular

vessels of the cardiovascular system. For example, the liquid portion of our blood, which transports dissolved and suspended substances about the body, is 90% water.

Cohesion and adhesion also contribute to the transport of water in plants. Plants have their roots anchored in the soil, where they absorb water, but the leaves are uplifted and exposed to solar energy. Water evaporating from the leaves is immediately replaced with water molecules from transport vessels that extend from the roots to the leaves (Fig. 2.11). Because water molecules are cohesive, a tension is created that pulls the water column up from the roots. Adhesion of water to the walls of the transport vessels also helps prevent the water column

H_2O

Water evaporates, pulling the water column from the roots to the leaves.

Water molecules cling together and adhere to sides of vessels in stems.

H_2O

Water enters a plant at root cells.

Figure 2.11 Water as a transport medium.
How does water rise to the top of tall trees when they have no heart to pump it? Plants have water-filled pipelines that run from the roots to the leaves. When water evaporates from the leaves, the water column is pulled upward due to the cohesion of water molecules to one another and the adhesion of water molecules to the sides of the vessels. This capillary action is critical for plants to function.

from breaking apart. This capillary action is essential to plant life, as will be discussed in chapter 25.

Because water molecules are attracted to each other, they cling together where the liquid surface is exposed to air. The stronger the force between molecules in a liquid, the greater the **surface tension.** Water's high surface tension makes it possible for humans to skip rocks on water. Water striders, a common insect, can even walk on the surface of a pond without breaking the surface.

Frozen Water (Ice) Is Less Dense than Liquid Water.   As liquid water cools, the molecules come closer together. Water is most dense at 4°C, but the water molecules are still moving about (Fig. 2.12). At temperatures below 4°C, only vibrational movement occurs, and hydrogen bonding becomes more rigid but also more open. This means that water expands as it reaches 0°C and freezes, which is why cans of soda burst when placed in a freezer, or why frost heaves make northern roads bumpy in the winter. It also means that ice is less dense than liquid water, and therefore ice floats on liquid water.

If ice did not float on water, it would sink to the bottom, and ponds, lakes, and perhaps even the ocean would freeze solid, making life impossible in the water and also on land. Instead, bodies of water always freeze from the top down. When a body of water freezes on the surface, the ice acts as an insulator to prevent the water below it from freezing. This allows aquatic organisms to survive the winter. As ice melts in the spring, it draws heat from the environment, helping to prevent a sudden change in temperature that might be harmful to life.

Check Your Progress   2.3

1. Explain how water's high heat of vaporization allows coastal cities to have a consistent temperature throughout the year.
2. Analyze which property of water helps children cool off during summertime by playing in a sprinkler.
3. Evaluate what would happen to life if ice sank instead of floating in the winter.

Figure 2.12 A pond in winter.   *Above:* Remarkably, water is more dense at 4°C than at 0°C. Most substances contract when they solidify, but water expands when it freezes because in ice, water molecules form a lattice in which the hydrogen bonds are farther apart than in liquid water. *Below:* The layer of ice that forms at the top of a pond shields the water and protects the protists, plants, and animals so that they can survive the winter. These animals, except for the otter, are ectothermic, which means that they take on the temperature of the outside environment. This might seem disadvantageous until you realize that water remains relatively warm because of its high heat capacity. During the winter, frogs and turtles hibernate and in this way, lower their oxygen needs. Insects survive in air pockets. Fish, as you will learn later in this text, have an efficient means of extracting oxygen from the water, and they need less oxygen than the endothermic otter, which depends on muscle activity to warm its body.

Figure labels: ice lattice · liquid water · Density (g/cm³) · 1.0 · 0.9 · Temperature (°C) · 0 · 4 · 100 · ice layer · Protists provide food for fish. · River otters visit ice-covered ponds. · Aquatic insects survive in air pockets. · Freshwater fish take oxygen from water. · Common frogs and pond turtles hibernate.

2.4 Acids and Bases

Learning Outcomes

Upon completion of this section, you should be able to

1. Identify common acidic and basic substances.
2. Determine pH from a known H⁺ or OH⁻ concentration.
3. Analyze how buffers prevent large pH changes in solutions.

When water ionizes, it releases an equal number of **hydrogen ions (H⁺)** (also called protons[1]) and **hydroxide ions (OH⁻)**:

H—O—H ⇌ H⁺ + OH⁻
water   hydrogen   hydroxide
              ion   ion

Only a few water molecules at a time dissociate, and the actual number of H⁺ and OH⁻ is very small (1×10^{-7} moles/liter).[2]

MP3
Water and pH

Acidic Solutions (High H⁺ Concentrations)

Lemon juice, vinegar, tomatoes, and coffee are all acidic solutions. What do they have in common? **Acids** are substances that dissociate in water, releasing hydrogen ions (H⁺). The acidity of a substance depends on how fully it dissociates in water. For example, hydrochloric acid (HCl) is a strong acid that dissociates almost completely in this manner:

$$HCl \longrightarrow H^+ + Cl^-$$

If hydrochloric acid is added to a beaker of water, the number of hydrogen ions (H⁺) increases greatly.

Basic Solutions (Low H⁺ Concentration)

Milk of magnesia and ammonia are common basic solutions familiar to most people. **Bases** are substances that either take up hydrogen ions (H⁺) or release hydroxide ions (OH⁻). For example, sodium hydroxide (NaOH) is a strong base that dissociates almost completely in this manner:

$$NaOH \longrightarrow Na^+ + OH^-$$

If sodium hydroxide is added to a beaker of water, the number of hydroxide ions increases.

pH Scale

The **pH scale** is used to indicate the acidity or basicity (alkalinity) of a solution.[3] The pH scale (Fig. 2.13) ranges from 0 to 14. A pH of 7 represents a neutral state in which the hydrogen ion and hydroxide ion concentrations are equal. A pH below 7

---

1 A hydrogen atom contains one electron and one proton. A hydrogen ion has only one proton, so it is often simply called a proton.
2 In chemistry, a mole is defined as 6.02 x 10²³ of any atom, molecule, or ion. For example, 6.02 x 10²³ atoms of 12C would have a mass of exactly 12 g. The same number of glucose molecules (1 mole) would have a mass of 180 g.
3 pH is defined as the negative log of the hydrogen ion concentration [H⁺]. A log is the power to which 10 must be raised to produce a given number.

Figure 2.13 The pH scale. The pH scale ranges from 0 to 14 with 0 being the most acidic and 14 being the most basic. pH 7 (neutral pH) has equal amounts of hydrogen ions (H⁺) and hydroxide ions (OH⁻). An acidic pH has more H⁺ than OH⁻ and a basic pH has more OH⁻ than H⁺.

is an acidic solution because the hydrogen ion concentration is greater than the hydroxide concentration. A pH above 7 is basic because the [OH⁻] is greater than the [H⁺]. Further, as we move down the pH scale from pH 14 to pH 0, each unit is 10 times more acidic than the previous unit. As we move up the scale from 0 to 14, each unit is 10 times more basic than the previous unit. Therefore pH 5 is 100 times more acidic than pH 7 and a 100 times more basic than pH 3.

The pH scale was devised to eliminate the use of cumbersome numbers. For example, the possible hydrogen ion concentrations of a solution are on the left of this listing and the pH is on the right:

	[H⁺] (moles per liter)	pH
0.000001	$= 1 \times 10^{-6}$	6
0.0000001	$= 1 \times 10^{-7}$	7
0.00000001	$= 1 \times 10^{-8}$	8

To further illustrate the relationship between hydrogen ion concentration and pH, consider the following question. Which of the pH values listed indicates a higher hydrogen ion concentration [H⁺] than pH 7, and therefore would be an acidic solution? A number with a smaller negative exponent indicates a greater quantity of hydrogen ions than one with a larger negative exponent. Therefore, pH 6 is an acidic solution.

The Biological Systems feature on page 33 describes detrimental environmental consequences to nonliving and living things as rain and snow have become more acidic. In humans, pH needs to be maintained within a narrow range or there are health consequences. The pH of blood is around 7.4, and blood is buffered in the manner described next to keep the pH within a normal range.

THEME Biological Systems

The Interconnectedness of Water, Plants, and People

Acid Deposition

Normally, rainwater has a pH of about 5.6 because the carbon dioxide in the air combines with water to give a weak solution of carbonic acid. Acid deposition includes rain or snow that has a pH of less than 5, as well as dry acidic particles that fall to Earth from the atmosphere.

When fossil fuels such as coal, oil, and gasoline are burned, sulfur dioxide and nitrogen oxides combine with water to produce sulfuric and nitric acids. These pollutants are generally found eastward of where they originated because of wind patterns. The use of very tall smokestacks causes them to be carried even hundreds of miles away. For example, acid rain in southeastern Canada results from the burning of fossil fuels in factories and power plants in the midwestern United States.

Impact on Lakes

Acid rain adversely affects many aspects of biological systems. Aluminum may leach from the soil of lakes, particularly in areas where the soil is thin and lacks limestone (calcium carbonate, or $CaCO_3$) as a buffer. Acid rain may convert mercury in lake bottom sediments to toxic methyl mercury. Methyl mercury accumulates in fish, which wildlife and people eat. Over time, methyl mercury can accumulate in body tissues and cause serious sensory and muscular health problems. Acid rain in Canada and New England has caused hundreds of lakes to be devoid of fish, and in some cases, any life at all.

Impact on Forests

The leaves of plants damaged by acid rain can no longer carry on photosynthesis as before. When plants are under stress, they become susceptible to diseases and pests of all types. Forests on mountaintops re-

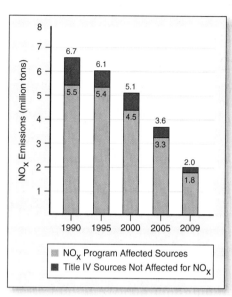

Figure 2A Trends in U.S. acid rain emissions. The burning of fossil fuels in factories, automobiles, and other industrial processes produces chemicals like SO_2 and NO_x that lead to acid deposition and destruction of the environment, Clean air legislation and stricter emission standards over the past 20 years have resulted in steady decreases in SO_2 and NO_x, chemicals that lead to acid rain.

ceive more rain than those at lower levels; therefore, they are more affected by acid rain. Forests are also damaged when toxic chemicals such as aluminum are leached from the soil. These kill soil fungi that assist roots in acquiring the nutrients trees need. In New England, 1.3 million acres of high-elevation forests have been devastated. Sulfur dioxide and nitrogen oxides, the main precursors of acid rain, have been steadily decreasing in the United States due to clean air legislation and strict emission limits (see Figure 2A).

Impact on Humans and Structures

Humans may be affected by acid rain. Inhaling dry sulfate and nitrate particles appears to increase the occurrence of respiratory illnesses, such as asthma. Buildings and monu-

ments made of limestone and marble break down when exposed to acid rain. The paint on homes and automobiles is likewise degraded. However, damage to natural systems and human structures due to acid rain is likely to decrease if we continue efforts to reduce chemicals that contribute to acid rain.

Questions to Consider

1. What acid rain trends are evident from the EPA data?
2. Considering that manufacturing is essential to our national interests, how might we modify industrial processing to reduce sulfur dioxide and nitrogen oxide contamination?
3. How might we prevent methyl mercury from entering biological systems and reduce the amount already present?

Buffers and pH

A **buffer** is a chemical or a combination of chemicals that keeps pH within normal limits. Many commercial products such as shampoos or deodorants are buffered as an added incentive for us to buy them.

In living things, the pH of body fluids is maintained within a narrow range, or else molecules don't function correctly and our

health suffers. The pH of our blood when we are healthy is always about 7.4—that is, just slightly basic (alkaline). If the blood pH drops to about 7, acidosis results. If the blood pH rises to about 7.8, alkalosis results. Both conditions can be life threatening, so the blood pH must be kept around 7.4. Normally, pH stability is possible because the body has built-in mechanisms to prevent pH changes. Buffers are one of these important mechanisms.

Buffers help keep the pH within normal limits because they are chemicals or combinations of chemicals that take up excess hydrogen ions (H⁺) or hydroxide ions (OH⁻). For example, carbonic acid (H_2CO_3) is a weak acid that minimally dissociates and then re-forms in the following manner:

$$H_2CO_3 \underset{\text{re-forms}}{\overset{\text{dissociates}}{\rightleftarrows}} H^+ + HCO_3^-$$

carbonic acid   bicarbonate ion

Blood always contains a combination of some carbonic acid and some bicarbonate ions. When hydrogen ions (H⁺) are added to blood, the following reaction reduces acidity:

$$H^+ + HCO_3^- \longrightarrow H_2CO_3$$

When hydroxide ions (OH⁻) are added to blood, this reaction reduces basicity:

$$OH^- + H_2CO_3 \longrightarrow HCO_3^- + H_2O$$

These reactions prevent any significant change in blood pH.

Check Your Progress   2.4

1. Explain the difference in H⁺ concentration between an acid and a base.
2. Predict what would happen to plant and animal life where you live if the pH of rain dropped to 6.
3. Interpret what would happen to your blood pH if the amount of buffer decreased by a factor of 10.

CONNECTING *the* CONCEPTS *with the* THEMES

This chapter has explored concepts that integrate with the major themes of life science.

Evolution

- Six of the 92 naturally occurring elements—carbon, hydrogen, nitrogen, oxygen, phosphorus, and sulfur (CHNOPS)—make up 95% of the body mass of organisms on Earth.
- Carbon-containing molecules can be modified in numerous ways, and this accounts for life's diversity. Molecules can undergo evolution (change), and this in turn can account for evolution of species.
- Much biological evolution has occurred due to life's interactions with water. Our search for water on other planets underscores the central role that water plays in living matter.

Nature of Science

- Scientific discoveries about chemistry, water, and carbon help us understand substances that are built from these atoms.
- Our understanding of life continues to change over time as we uncover fundamental truths about chemistry. Items we use every day, including food, plastics, and medicine, are products of ongoing research in chemistry.

Biological Systems

- All of life consists of systems, from the atomic and molecular levels to the ecosystem and planet levels.
- Like all systems, chemistry consists of inputs and outputs, with resulting changes in energy.
- The total of all the chemical reactions in our bodies is called metabolism, which is responsible for regulating life-supporting processes.
- Many elements exist as ions in the body, and their functions depend on their charged nature.
- Cells consist largely of water, a molecule that contains only hydrogen and oxygen atoms. Because of oxygen's strong electronegativity, water is a polar molecule, making hydrogen bonding possible.

Media Study Tools

www.mhhe.com/maderbiology11

Enhance your study of this chapter with study tools and practice tests. Also ask your instructor about the resources available through ConnectPlus, including the media-rich eBook, interactive learning tools, and animations.

Summarize

2.1 Chemical Elements

Both living and nonliving things are composed of matter consisting of elements. The most significant elements (atoms) are found in living things: carbon, hydrogen, nitrogen, oxygen, phosphorus, and sulfur (CHNOPS).

Elements contain atoms, and atoms contain subatomic particles. Protons have positive charges, neutrons are uncharged, and electrons have negative charges. Protons and neutrons in the nucleus determine the mass number of an atom. The atomic number indicates the number of protons and the number of electrons in electrically neutral atoms.

Isotopes are atoms of a single element that differ in their numbers of neutrons. Radioactive isotopes have many uses, including serving as tracers in biological experiments and medical procedures.

Electrons occupy energy levels (electron shells) at discrete distances from the nucleus. The number of electrons in the outer shell determines the reactivity of an atom. The first shell is complete when it is occupied by two electrons. In atoms up through calcium, number 20, every shell beyond the first shell is complete when eight electrons are present. The octet rule states that atoms react with one another in order to have a completed outer shell. Most atoms, including those common to living things, do not have filled outer shells and this causes them to react with one another to form compounds and/or molecules. Following the reaction, the atoms have completed outer shells.

2.2 Molecules and Compounds

Compounds and molecules are formed when elements associate with each other. Ions, which are created when atoms lose or gain one or more electrons to achieve a completed outer shell, form ionic bonds between oppositely charged ions.

Covalent compounds form when atoms share one or more pairs of electrons. There are single, double, and triple covalent bonds.

In polar covalent bonds, the sharing of electrons is not equal. If the molecule is polar, the more electronegative atom carries a slightly negative charge and the other atom carries a slightly positive charge.

2.3 Chemistry of Water

Water is an essential molecule for life. The polarity of water molecules allows hydrogen bonding to occur between water molecules. A hydrogen bond is a weak attraction between a slightly positive hydrogen atom and a slightly negative oxygen or nitrogen atom within the same or a different molecule. Hydrogen bonds help maintain the structure and function of cellular molecules.

Water's polarity and hydrogen bonding account for its unique properties. These features allow living things to exist and carry on cellular activities.

2.4 Acids and Bases

pH is a measure of how acidic or basic a substance is. A small fraction of water molecules dissociate to produce an equal number of hydrogen ions and hydroxide ions. Solutions with equal numbers of H^+ and OH^- are termed neutral.

Acidic solutions contain more hydrogen ions than hydroxide ions; these solutions have a pH less than 7. Basic solutions have more hydroxide ions than hydrogen ions; these solutions have a pH greater than 7. Cells are sensitive to pH changes. Biological systems often contain buffers that help keep the pH within a normal range.

Key Terms

acid 32	electron shell 23
atom 22	element 22
atomic mass 23	formula 26
atomic number 23	hydrogen bond 28
atomic symbol 22	hydrogen ion (H^+) 32
base 32	hydrophilic 30
buffer 33	hydrophobic 30
calorie 29	hydroxide ion (OH^-) 32
compound 26	ion 26
covalent bond 27	ionic bond 26
electron 22	isotope 24
electronegativity 27	mass number 23

matter 22	proton 22
molecule 26	salt 27
neutron 22	solute 30
nonpolar covalent bond 27	solution 30
octet rule 25	surface tension 31
pH scale 32	valence shell 25
polar covalent bond 27	

 Assess

Reviewing This Chapter

1. Name the kinds of subatomic particles studied. What is their atomic mass unit, charge, and location in an atom?   21–23
2. What is an isotope? A radioactive isotope? Radioactivity is always considered dangerous. Why?   24–26
3. Using the Bohr model, draw an atomic structure for a carbon that has six protons and six neutrons.   26
4. Draw an atomic representation for $MgCl_2$. Using the octet rule, explain the structure of the compound.   27
5. Explain whether CO_2 ($O = C = O$) is an ionic or a covalent compound. Why does this arrangement satisfy all atoms involved?   27
6. Of what significance is the shape of molecules in organisms?   28
7. Explain why water is a polar molecule. What does the polarity and shape of water have to do with its ability to form hydrogen bonds?   28
8. Name five properties of water, and relate them to the structure of water, including its polarity and hydrogen bonding between molecules.   28–31
9. On the pH scale, which numbers indicate a solution is acidic? Basic? Neutral?   32
10. What are buffers, and why are they important to life?   32–33

Testing Yourself

Choose the best answer for each question.

1. Which of the subatomic particles contributes almost no weight to an atom?
   a. protons in the electron shells
   b. electrons in the nucleus
   c. neutrons in the nucleus
   d. electrons at various energy levels

2. The atomic number tells you the
   a. number of neutrons in the nucleus.
   b. number of protons in the atom.
   c. atomic mass of the atom.
   d. number of its electrons if the atom is neutral.
   e. Both b and d are correct.

3. An atom that has two electrons in the outer shell, such as magnesium, would most likely
   a. share to acquire a completed outer shell.
   b. lose these two electrons and become a negatively charged ion.
   c. lose these two electrons and become a positively charged ion.
   d. bind with carbon by way of hydrogen bonds.
   e. bind with another calcium atom to satisfy its energy needs.

4. Isotopes differ in their
   a. number of protons.   c. number of neutrons.
   b. atomic number.   d. number of electrons.

5. When an atom gains electrons, it
   a. forms a negatively charged ion.
   b. forms a positively charged ion.
   c. forms covalent bonds.
   d. forms ionic bonds.
   e. gains atomic mass.

6. A covalent bond is indicated by
   a. plus and minus charges attached to atoms.
   b. dotted lines between hydrogen atoms.
   c. concentric circles about a nucleus.
   d. overlapping electron shells or a straight line between atomic symbols.
   e. the touching of atomic nuclei.

7. The shape of a molecule
   a. is dependent in part on the angle of bonds between its atoms.
   b. influences its biological function.
   c. is dependent on its electronegativity.
   d. is dependent on its place in the periodic table.
   e. Both a and b are correct.

8. In the molecule

   a. all atoms have eight electrons in the outer shell.
   b. all atoms are sharing electrons.
   c. carbon could accept more hydrogen atoms.
   d. the bonds point to the corners of a square.
   e. All of these are correct.

9. Which of these properties of water cannot be attributed to hydrogen bonding between water molecules?
   a. Water stabilizes temperature inside and outside the cell.
   b. Water molecules are cohesive.
   c. Water is a solvent for many molecules.
   d. Ice floats on liquid water.
   e. Both b and c are correct.

10. Complete this diagram by placing an O for oxygen or an H for hydrogen on the appropriate atoms. Place partial charges where they belong.

11. H_2CO_3/$NaHCO_3$ is a buffer system in the body. What effect will the addition of an acid have on the pH of a solution that is buffered?
    a. The pH will rise.   c. The pH will not change.
    b. The pH will lower.   d. All of these are correct.

12. Acids
    a. release hydrogen ions in solution.
    b. cause the pH of a solution to rise above 7.
    c. take up hydroxide ions and become neutral.
    d. increase the number of water molecules.
    e. Both a and b are correct.

13. If a chemical accepted H^+ from the surrounding solution, the chemical could be
    a. a base.   d. None of the above are correct.
    b. an acid.   e. Both a and c are correct.
    c. a buffer.

14. The periodic table tells us
    a. the atomic number, symbol, and mass.
    b. how many shells an atom has.
    c. how many electrons are in the outer shell.
    d. whether the atom will react or not.
    e. All of these are correct.

15. Which of these best describes the changes that occur when a solution goes from pH 5 to pH 7?
    a. The solution is now 100 times more acidic.
    b. The solution is now 100 times more basic.
    c. The hydrogen ion concentration decreases by only a factor of 20, as the solution goes from basic to acidic.
    d. The hydrogen ion concentration changes by only a factor of 20, as the solution goes from acidic to basic.

For questions 16–19, match the statements with a property of water in the key.

KEY:
   a. Water flows because it is cohesive.
   b. Water holds its heat.
   c. Water has neutral pH.
   d. Water has a high heat of vaporization.

16. Sweating helps cool us off.

17. Our blood is composed mostly of water and cells.

18. Our blood is just about pH 7.

19. We usually maintain a normal body temperature.

Engage

Thinking Scientifically

1. Natural phenomena often require an explanation. Based on how sodium chloride dissociates in water (see pages 29–30) and Figure 2.12, explain why the oceans don't freeze.

2. Melvin Calvin used radioactive carbon (as a tracer) to discover a series of molecules that form during photosynthesis. Explain why carbon behaves chemically the same, even when radioactive.

Bioethical Issue

The Right to Refuse an IV

When a person gets sick or endures physical stress—as, for example, during childbirth—pH levels may dip or rise too far, endangering that person's life. In most U.S. hospitals, doctors routinely administer IVs, or intravenous infusions, of certain fluids to maintain a patient's pH level. Some people who oppose IVs for philosophical reasons may refuse an IV. That's relatively safe, as long as the person is healthy.

Problems arise when hospital policy dictates an IV, even though a patient does not want one. Should a patient be allowed to refuse an IV? Or does a hospital have the right to insist, for health reasons, that patients accept IV fluids? And what role should doctors play—patient advocates or hospital representatives?

Granddaughter Sylvia with azalea plant.

3

The Chemistry of Organic Molecules

BEFORE YOU BEGIN

Before beginning this chapter, take a few moments to review the following discussions.

Figures 1.5–1.8 What are the the major kingdoms of life?

Figure 2.3 What chemical elements are most important for producing organic molecules?

Sections 2.2–2.3 What types of bonds can form between elements in an organic molecule?

All life is interconnected because it uses a common set of chemicals to build larger, more complex molecules that are used as the building blocks of every living thing. In fact, the same organic molecules are used to build a bacterium, a flower, or a little girl. These macromolecules—namely, carbohydrates, lipids, proteins, and nucleic acids—are combined to produce different structures which lead them to have different functions. The similarities in molecules makes it possible for vegetarians to eat only plants and be healthy, as long as they include enough different plants in their diet. When we consume other things, we break down their macromolecules to smaller molecules, and then we use these smaller molecules to build our own types of carbohydrates, lipids, proteins, and nucleic acids. Both the breakdown and building processes are made possible using special catalysts called enzymes.

A bacterium, plant, and human are different because of their genes. All genes are made of DNA, and the way genes function in cells is essentially the same in all organisms. In this chapter, we extend our knowledge of chemistry and consider macromolecules, how their structure and function are related, and how these support life on Earth.

As you read through the chapter, think about the following questions:

1. How can a relatively small number of chemicals be used to build many large, complex, and diverse molecules?
2. Why can one organism use molecules from another organism to build their own?
3. How are organic molecules combined to create the structures and functions necessary to support life?

FOLLOWING *the* THEMES

CHAPTER 3 THE CHEMISTRY OF ORGANIC MOLECULES		
UNIT 1 THE CELL	**Evolution**	The diversity of biological life is the result of changes in DNA sequences.
	Nature of Science	Investigating relationships between a molecule's structure and its function allows discovery of new and useful substances.
	Biological Systems	Macromolecules form the functional basis for all cellular systems.

3.1 Organic Molecules

Learning Outcomes

Upon completion of this section, you should be able to

1. Explain how the properties of carbon enable it to produce diverse organic molecules.
2. Describe how functional groups affect a carbon molecule's chemical reactivity.
3. Compare what is added and what is produced during biomolecule synthesis and degradation reactions.

Table 3.1 Inorganic Versus Organic Molecules

Inorganic Molecules	Organic Molecules
Usually contain positive and negative ions	Always contain carbon and hydrogen
Usually ionic bonding	Always covalent bonding
Always contain a small number of atoms	Often quite large, with many atoms
Often associated with nonliving matter	Usually associated with living organisms

Chemists of the nineteenth century thought that the molecules of cells must contain a vital force, so they divided chemistry into **organic chemistry,** the chemistry of living organisms, and **inorganic chemistry,** the chemistry of nonliving matter. We still use this terminology, even though many types of organic molecules can now be synthesized in the laboratory. Today, we simply define **organic molecules** as molecules that contain both carbon and hydrogen atoms (Table 3.1).

There are only four classes of organic compounds in any living thing: carbohydrates, lipids, proteins, and nucleic acids. Collectively, these are called the **biomolecules** and despite the limited number of types, their functions in a cell are quite diverse. A bacterial cell contains some 5,000 different organic molecules, and a plant or animal cell has twice that number. The diversity of life is possible because of this diversity of organic molecules (Fig. 3.1). Ultimately, the variety of organic molecules is based on the unique chemical properties of the carbon atom.

The Carbon Atom

What is there about carbon that makes organic molecules the same and also different? Carbon is quite small, with only a total of six electrons: two electrons in the first shell and four electrons in the outer shell. To acquire four electrons to complete its outer shell, a carbon atom almost always shares electrons with—you guessed it—CHNOPS, the elements that make up most of the weight of living things (see Fig. 2.1).

Because carbon needs four electrons to complete its outer shell, it can share with as many as four other elements. This flexibility makes carbon an ideal building block for biomolecules, and makes the diversity of molecules we see in nature possible. But even more significant to the shape, and therefore the function, of biomolecules, is the ability of carbon to share electrons with other carbon atoms. The C—C

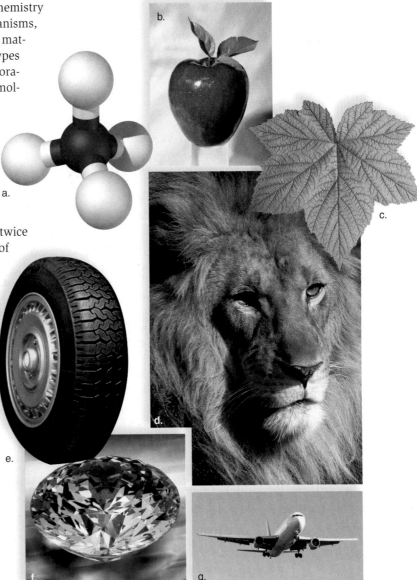

Figure 3.1 Carbon and life. Carbon (**a**) is the basis for many compounds in living things, including (**b**) an apple and other foods, (**c**) plants, and (**d**) animals, as well as nonliving things like (**e**) tires, (**f**) diamonds, and (**g**) airplanes.

bond that is formed is quite stable, and allows formation of long carbon chains. The molecules termed hydrocarbons are chains of carbon atoms that have additional bonds exclusively with hydrogen atoms.

octane

Branching of the chain at any carbon atom is possible, and a hydrocarbon can also turn back on itself to form a ring compound when placed in water:

cyclohexane

In addition to forming single bonds, carbon can form double bonds with itself and other atoms. Double bonds aren't as flexible as single bonds, and they restrict the movement of bonded atoms. Double bonds affect a molecule's shape and therefore influence its function. The presence of double bonds is one way to distinguish between saturated and unsaturated fats, which are important to heart health. Carbon is also capable of forming triple bonds with itself, as in acetylene, $H-C\equiv C-H$, a gas used in industrial welding.

The diversity of organic molecules is further enhanced by the presence of particular functional groups, chemical groups attached to the carbon skeleton or backbone, as discussed next. Contrast the structure of cyclohexane, above, with the structure of glucose in Figure 3.6. Notice how the difference in structure can be attributed to the functional groups added to the same number of carbons.

The Carbon Skeleton and Functional Groups

The carbon chain of an organic molecule is called its skeleton or backbone. Just as a skeleton accounts for your body's shape, so does the carbon skeleton of an organic molecule account for its shape. The diversity of vertebrates, species with a backbone, results from the overall shapes of the organisms and the types of appendages (fins, wings, limbs) they have developed. Likewise, the diversity of organic molecules comes from the attachment of different functional groups to the carbon skeleton.

Table 3.2 Functional groups.

Functional Groups			
Group	**Structure**	**Compound**	**Significance**
Hydroxyl	$R-OH$	Alcohol as in ethanol	Polar, forms hydrogen bond
			Present in sugars, some amino acids
Carbonyl	$R-C{\scriptsize\nearrow O}_{\searrow H}$	Aldehyde as in formaldehyde	Polar
			Present in sugars
	$R-\overset{O}{\underset{\|}{C}}-R$	Ketone as in acetone	Polar
			Present in sugars
Carboxyl (acidic)	$R-C{\scriptsize\nearrow O}_{\searrow OH}$	Carboxylic acid as in acetic acid	Polar, acidic
			Present in fatty acids, amino acids
Amino	$R-N{\scriptsize\nearrow H}_{\searrow H}$	Amine as in tryptophan	Polar, basic, forms hydrogen bonds
			Present in amino acids
Sulfhydryl	$R-SH$	Thiol as in ethanethiol	Forms disulfide bonds
			Present in some amino acids
Phosphate	$R-O-\overset{O}{\underset{\underset{OH}{\|}}{\overset{\|}{P}}}-OH$	Organic phosphate as in phosphorylated molecules	Polar, acidic
			Present in nucleotides, phospholipids

R = remainder of molecule

A **functional group** is a specific combination of bonded atoms that always reacts in the same way, regardless of the particular carbon skeleton. Much of a biomolecule's chemistry can be attributed to its functional groups, rather than to the carbon skeleton to which they are attached. As in Table 3.2, it is even acceptable to use an R to stand for the "remainder" of the molecule, which is the carbon skeleton, because only the functional group is involved in a chemical reaction.

When a particular functional group is added to a carbon skeleton, the molecule becomes a certain type of compound. For example, the addition of an $-OH$ (hydroxyl group) to a carbon skeleton turns that molecule into an alcohol. When an −OH replaces one of the hydrogens in ethane, a 2-carbon hydrocarbon, it becomes ethanol, a type of alcohol that is familiar because humans can consume it. Whereas ethane, like other hydrocarbons, is **hydrophobic** (not soluble in water), ethanol is **hydrophilic** (soluble in water) because the −OH functional group makes the otherwise nonpolar carbon skeleton polar. Because cells are 70–90% water, the ability to interact with and be soluble in water profoundly affects the function of organic molecules in cells.

Organic molecules containing carboxyl (acidic) groups (−COOH) are highly polar. They tend to ionize and release hydrogen ions in solution:

$$-COOH \longrightarrow -COO^- + H^+$$

The attached functional groups determine not only the polarity of an organic molecule, but also the types of reactions it will undergo. You will see that alcohols react with carboxyl groups when a fat forms, and that carboxyl groups react with amino groups during protein formation.

Isomers

Isomers [Gk. *isos*, equal, and *meros*, part, portion] are organic molecules that have identical molecular formulas but a different arrangement of atoms. In essence, isomers are variations in the molecular architecture of a molecule. Isomers are another example of how the chemistry of carbon leads to variations in organic molecules.

The two molecules in Figure 3.2 are isomers of one another; they have the same molecular formula but different functional groups. Therefore, we would expect them to have different properties and react differently in chemical reactions.

The Biomolecules of Cells

You are familiar with the names of biomolecules—carbohydrates, lipids, proteins, and nucleic acids—because certain foods are known to be rich in them, as shown in Figure 3.3. For example, bread is rich in carbohydrates, and meat is rich in proteins. When you digest food, it gets broken down into smaller molecules that are subunits for biomolecules that your body uses. Digestion of bread releases glucose molecules, and digestion of

glyceraldehyde	dihydroxyacetone
H—C—C—C—H with H, H on first/second carbons, O double-bonded to end C, OH OH below	H—C—C—C—H with H, H on carbons, O double-bonded to middle C, OH OH below

Figure 3.2 Isomers. Isomers have the same molecular formula but different atomic configurations. Both of these compounds have the formula $C_3H_6O_3$. In glyceraldehyde, a colorless crystalline solid, oxygen is double-bonded to an end carbon. In dihydroxyacetone, a white crystalline solid, oxygen is double-bonded to the middle carbon.

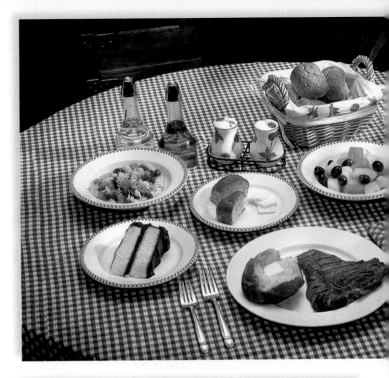

Biomolecules		
Category	**Subunit(s)**	**Polymer**
Carbohydrates*	Monosaccharide ⟶	Polysaccharide
Lipids	Glycerol and fatty acids ⟶	Fat
Proteins*	Amino acids ⟶	Polypeptide
Nucleic acids*	Nucleotide ⟶	DNA, RNA

*Polymers

Figure 3.3 Common foods. Carbohydrates in bread and pasta are digested to sugars; lipids such as oils are digested to glycerol and fatty acids; and proteins in meat are digested to amino acids. Cells use these subunit molecules as a source of energy and to build their own biomolecules.

meat releases amino acids. Your body then takes these subunits and builds from them the particular carbohydrates and proteins that make up your cells (Fig. 3.3).

Polymers

The largest of the biomolecules are called **polymers,** and like all biomolecules, polymers are constructed by linking together a large number of the same type of subunit. However, in the case of polymers, the subunits are called **monomers.** A polysaccharide, a protein, and a nucleic acid are all polymers that contain many monomers. Just as a train increases in length when boxcars are hitched together one by one, so a polymer gets longer as monomers bond to one another.

Synthesis and Degradation

A cell uses a condensation reaction to synthesize (build up) any type of biomolecule. It's called a **dehydration reaction** because the equivalent of a water molecule—that is, an −OH (hydroxyl group) and an −H (hydrogen atom), is removed as subunits are

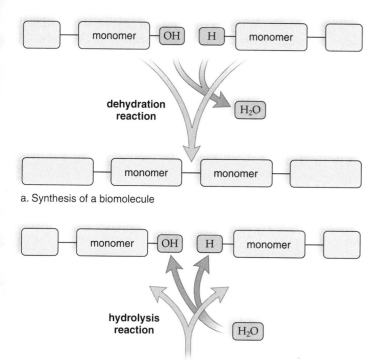

a. Synthesis of a biomolecule

b. Degradation of a biomolecule

Figure 3.4 Synthesis and degradation of biomolecules.
a. In cells, synthesis often occurs when subunits bond during a dehydration reaction (removal of H_2O). **b.** Degradation occurs when the subunits separate during a hydrolysis reaction (the addition of H_2O).

joined. Therefore, water molecules are formed as biomolecules are synthesized (Fig. 3.4a).

To break down biomolecules, a cell uses an opposite type of reaction. During a **hydrolysis** [Gk. *hydro*, water, and *lyse*, break] **reaction,** an −OH group from water attaches to one subunit, and an −H from water attaches to the other subunit. In other words, biomolecules are broken down by adding water to them (Fig. 3.4b).

Enzymes are required for cells to carry out dehydration and hydrolysis reactions. An **enzyme** is a molecule that speeds a reaction by bringing reactants together and helping them to form new molecules. The enzyme partici- pates in the reaction but is unchanged by it.

MP3
Organic Molecules

Check Your Progress   3.1

1. Describe the properties of a carbon atom that make it ideally suited to produce varied carbon skeletons.
2. Compare solubility in water of a 2-carbon alcohol and a 2-carbon carboxylic acid biomolecule.
3. Discuss what would happen if no water was present during degradation of a biomolecule.

3.2 Carbohydrates

Learning Outcomes

Upon completion of this section, you should be able to
1. List several examples of important monosaccharides and polysaccharides.
2. Compare the energy and structural uses of starch, glycogen, and cellulose.

Carbohydrates are almost universally used as an immediate energy source in living things, but they also play structural roles in a variety of organisms (Fig. 3.5). The majority of carbohy- drates have a carbon to hydrogen to oxygen ratio of 1:2:1. The term *carbohydrate* (literally, carbon-water) includes single sugar molecules and chains of sugars. Chain length varies from a few sugars to hundreds of sugars. The monomer subunits, called monosaccharides, are assembled into long polymer chains called polysaccharides.

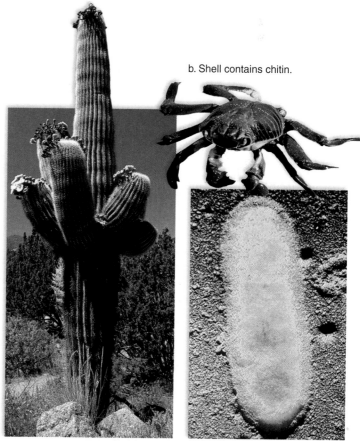

b. Shell contains chitin.

a. Cell walls contain cellulose.   c. Cell walls contain peptidoglycan.

Figure 3.5 Carbohydrates as structural materials.   a. Plants, such as the cactus shown here, have the carbohydrate cellulose in their cell walls. **b.** The shell of a crab contains chitin, a different carbohydrate. **c.** The cell walls of bacteria contain another type of carbohydrate known as peptidoglycan.

Figure 3.6 Glucose. Glucose provides energy for organisms, such as this cheetah. Each of these structural formulas is glucose. **a.** The carbon skeleton and all attached groups are shown. **b.** The carbon skeleton is omitted. **c.** The carbon skeleton and attached groups are omitted. **d.** Only the ring shape, which includes one oxygen atom, remains.

Monosaccharides: Ready Energy

Monosaccharides [Gk. *monos*, single, and *sacchar*, sugar] consist of only a single sugar molecule and are called simple sugars. A simple sugar can have a carbon backbone of three to seven carbons. The molecular formula for a simple sugar is some multiple of CH_2O, suggesting that every carbon atom is bonded to an $-H$ and an $-OH$. This is not strictly correct, as you can see by examining the structural formula for glucose (Fig. 3.6). Still, sugars do have many hydroxyl groups, and this polar functional group makes them soluble in water.

Glucose, with six carbon atoms, is a **hexose** [Gk. *hex*, six] sugar and has a molecular formula of $C_6H_{12}O_6$. Despite the fact that glucose has several isomers, such as fructose and galactose, we usually think of $C_6H_{12}O_6$ as glucose. Glucose is critical to biological function, and is the major source of cellular fuel for all living things. Glucose is transported in the blood of animals, and

it is the molecule that is broken down and converted into stored chemical energy (ATP) during cellular respiration in nearly all types of organisms.

Ribose and **deoxyribose,** with five carbon atoms, are **pentose** [Gk. *pent*, five] sugars that are significant because they are found respectively in the nucleic acids RNA and DNA. RNA and DNA are discussed later in the chapter.

Disaccharides: Varied Uses

A **disaccharide** contains two monosaccharides that have joined during a dehydration reaction. Figure 3.7 shows how the disaccharide maltose (an ingredient used in brewing) arises when two glucose molecules bond together. Note the position of the bond that results when the $-OH$ groups participating in the reaction project below the ring. When our hydrolytic digestive juices break this bond, the result is two glucose molecules.

Sucrose (the structure shown above) is another disaccharide of special interest because it is sugar we use at home to sweeten our food. Sucrose is also the form in which sugar is transported in plants. We acquire sucrose from plants such as sugarcane and sugar beets. You may also have heard of lactose, a disaccharide found in milk. Lactose is glucose combined with galactose. Individuals that are lactose intolerant cannot break this disaccharide down and have subsequent medical problems. To prevent problems they can buy foods in which lactose has been broken down into its subunit monosaccharides.

Polysaccharides: Energy Storage Molecules

Polysaccharides are polymers of monosaccharides. Some types of polysaccharides function as short-term energy storage molecules. When an organism requires energy, the polysaccharide is broken down to release sugar molecules. The helical shape of the polysaccharides in Figure 3.8 exposes the sugar linkages to the hydrolytic enzymes that can break them down.

Figure 3.7 Synthesis and degradation of maltose, a disaccharide. Synthesis of maltose occurs following a dehydration reaction when a bond forms between two glucose molecules, and water is removed. Degradation of maltose occurs following a hydrolysis reaction when this bond is broken by the addition of water.

Amylose:
nonbranched

starch
granule

Amylopectin:
branched

a. Starch   250 µm

glycogen
granule

b. Glycogen   150 nm

Figure 3.8 Starch and glycogen structure and function.   **a.** The electron micrograph shows the location of starch in plant cells. Starch is a chain of glucose molecules that can be branched or unbranched. **b.** The electron micrograph shows glycogen deposits in a portion of a liver cell. Glycogen is a highly branched polymer of glucose molecules.

Plants store glucose as **starch.** The cells of a potato contain granules where starch resides during winter until energy is needed for growth in the spring. Notice in Figure 3.8a that starch exists in two forms: One form (amylose) is nonbranched and the other (amylopectin) is branched. When a polysaccharide is branched, there is no main carbon chain because new chains occur at regular intervals, always at the sixth carbon of the monomer.

Animals store glucose as **glycogen.** In our bodies and those of other vertebrates, liver cells contain granules where glycogen

is stored until needed. The storage and release of glucose from liver cells is controlled by hormones. After we eat, the release of the hormone insulin from the pancreas promotes the storage of glucose as glycogen. Notice in Figure 3.8b that glycogen is even more branched than starch.

Polysaccharides serve as storage molecules because they are not as soluble in water, and are much larger than a simple sugar. Therefore, polysaccharides cannot easily pass through the plasma membrane, a sheetlike structure that encloses cells.

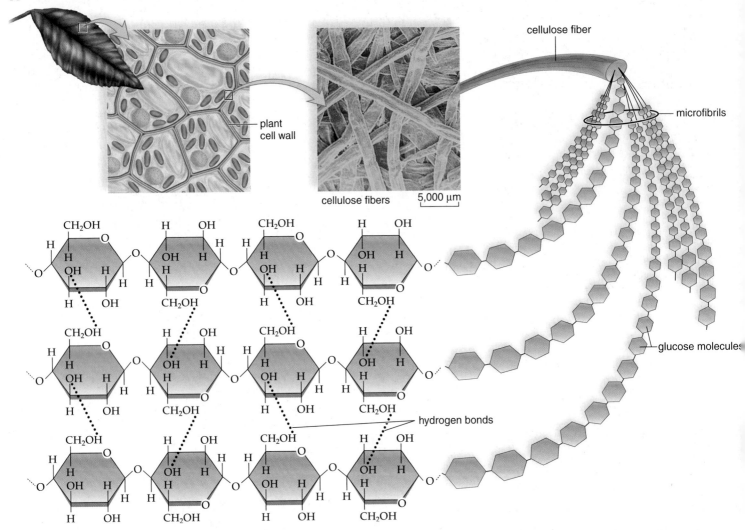

plant cell wall

cellulose fibers

5,000 µm

cellulose fiber

microfibrils

glucose molecules

hydrogen bonds

Figure 3.9 Cellulose fibrils.   Cellulose fibers criss-cross in plant cell walls for added strength. A cellulose fiber contains several microfibrils, each a polymer of glucose molecules—notice that the linkage bonds differ from those of starch. Every other glucose is flipped, permitting hydrogen bonding and greater strength between the microfibrils.

Polysaccharides: Structural Molecules

Structural polysaccharides include **cellulose** in plants, **chitin** in animals and fungi, and **peptidoglycan** in bacteria (see Fig. 3.5). In all three, monomers are joined by the type of bond shown for cellulose in Figure 3.9. The cellulose monomer is simply glucose, but in chitin, the monomer has an attached amino group. The structure of peptidoglycan is even more complex because each monomer also has an amino acid chain. In both cases, the addition of a functional group to the glucose monomer changes its chemical properties.

Cellulose is the most abundant carbohydrate, and in fact, the most abundant organic molecule on Earth—over 100 billion tons of cellulose is produced by plants each year. Wood, a cellulose plant product, is used for construction, and cotton is used for cloth. Microorganisms, but not animals, are able to digest the bond between glucose monomers in cellulose. The protozoans in the gut of termites enable these insects to digest wood. In cows and other ruminants, microorganisms break down cellulose in a special digestive-tract pouch before the "cud" is returned to the mouth for more chewing and reswallowing. In rabbits, microorganisms digest cellulose in a pouch where it is packaged into pellets. In order to make use

of these nutrient pellets, rabbits have to reswallow them as soon as they pass out at the anus. For other animals, including humans, that have no means of digesting cellulose, cellulose serves as dietary fiber, which maintains regularity of fecal elimination.

Chitin [Gk. *chiton*, tunic] is found in fungal cell walls and in the exoskeletons of crabs and related animals, such as lobsters, scorpions, and insects. Chitin, like cellulose, cannot be digested by animals; however, humans have found many other good uses for chitin. Seeds are coated with chitin, and this protects them from attack by soil fungi. Because chitin also has antibacterial and antiviral properties, it is processed and used in medicine as a wound dressing and suture material. Chitin is even useful during the production of cosmetics and various foods.

MP3
Carbohydrates

Check Your Progress   3.2

1. Explain why humans cannot utilize the glucose in cellulose as a nutrient source.
2. Compare and contrast the structure and function of cellulose with chitin.

3.3 Lipids

Learning Outcomes

Upon completion of this section, you should be able to

1. Describe why lipids are essential to living organisms.
2. Explain where fats and oils are produced.
3. Contrast the structures of fats, phospholipids, and steroids.
4. Compare the functions of phospholipids and steroids in cells.

A variety of organic compounds are classified as **lipids** [Gk. *lipos*, fat] (Table 3.3). These compounds are insoluble in water due to their hydrocarbon chains. Hydrogens bonded only to carbon are nonpolar and have no tendency to form hydrogen bonds with water molecules. Fat, a well-known lipid, is used by animals for both insulation and long-term energy storage. Fat below the skin of marine mammals is called blubber; in humans, it is given slang expressions such as "spare tire" and "love handles." Plants use oil instead of fat for long-term energy storage. We are familiar with fats and oils because we use them as foods and for cooking.

Table 3.3 Lipids

Type	Functions	Human Uses
Fats	Long-term energy storage and insulation in animals	Butter, lard
Oils	Long-term energy storage in plants and their seeds	Cooking oils
Phospholipids	Component of plasma membrane	—
Steroids	Component of plasma membrane (cholesterol), sex hormones	Medicines
Waxes	Protection, prevent water loss (cuticle of plant surfaces), beeswax, earwax	Candles, polishes

Phospholipids and steroids are also important lipids found in living things. They serve as major components of the plasma membrane in cells. Steroids are also involved in cell communication. Waxes, which are sticky, not greasy like fats and oils, tend to have a protective function in living things.

THEME Nature of Science

Everyone Needs a Little Fat, Right?

Fats are an essential part of the diet. They provide lots of energy, having more than twice the caloric density of carbohydrates. Fats are needed to build and maintain cell membranes, which are critical to biological life, as well as hormones like testosterone and estrogen, and they provide essential padding for our internal organs. Fats are also a major reason why some foods taste good.

A short time ago, scientists and nutritionists thought that too much fat was bad for you. Now we know that saturated fats, which come from animals and are solid at room temperature, have effects in the body that are different from those of unsaturated fats, which come from plants and are liquid at room temperature. Saturated fats are flat molecules that easily stick together in the blood, and too much saturated fat has been shown by scientists to negatively affect heart health, contributing to clogging of arteries and coronary heart disease (CHD). By comparison, unsaturated fats seem to help prevent CHD because they don't stick together in the blood, and therefore don't clog arteries.

A Food Revolution

Unsaturated fats might be healthier for you, but plant oils can easily go rancid and aren't solid at room temperature, which makes them more difficult to cook with and to use in solid food products. To get around this problem, food manufacturers hydrogenated unsaturated fatty acids by heating the oil and exposing it to hydrogen gas. This treatment made the otherwise liquid plant oils semi-solid at room temperature, and gave foods containing partially hydrogenated oils better shelf life.

An unintended consequence of hydrogenation, however, was the formation of **trans-fats**. Many commercially packaged foods contain trans-fats, which recently have been shown to increase LDL or "bad" cholesterol and lower HDL or "good" cholesterol in the blood. Trans-fat consumption also appears to increase risk of CHD and heart attack.

Scientific Evidence Changes Our Perceptions

Initially, investigators thought that the total amount of lipid in the diet caused coronary and other heart-related diseases. As scientific evidence accumulated showing a distinction between the effects of saturated and unsaturated fats, public perception changed. Until recently, trans-fats were of little concern to the general public, and people readily consumed them without much thought. As science has brought the negative effects of trans-fats to light, perception has changed once again. Public outcry has prompted changes in the food services industry, with clear labeling of trans-fats on all food products and with more restaurants using trans-fat-free oils during cooking.

This example shows how our perceptions change over time based on scientific evidence, and it illustrates the essential role that science plays in the common good. Science constantly refines what we know as new evidence provides greater insights into how we function and live.

Questions to Consider

1. How much trans-fat do you consume daily?
2. What is the chemical structure of a trans-fat compared to a non-trans-fat?
3. How might your new scientific knowledge of fats affect your nutritional decision-making?

Triglycerides: Long-Term Energy Storage

Fats and **oils** contain two types of subunit molecules: fatty acids and glycerol. Each **fatty acid** consists of a long hydrocarbon chain with an even number of carbons and a −COOH (carboxyl) group at one end. Most of the fatty acids in cells contain 16 or 18 carbon atoms per molecule, although smaller ones are also found. Fatty acids are either saturated or unsaturated. **Saturated fatty acids** have no double bonds between the carbon atoms and contain as many hydrogens as they can potentially hold. **Unsaturated fatty acids** have double bonds in the carbon chain, which reduces the number of bonded hydrogen atoms. In addition, double bonds in unsaturated fatty acids may have chemical groups arranged on the same side (termed *cis* configuration) or on opposite sides (termed *trans* configuration) of the double bond. The *cis* or *trans* configuration of an unsaturated fatty acid affects its biological activity.

Glycerol is a 3-carbon compound with three −OH groups. The −OH groups are polar, making glycerol soluble in water. When a fat or oil forms, the −COOH functional groups of three fatty acids react with the −OH groups of glycerol during a dehydration reaction (Fig. 3.10*a*), resulting in a fat molecule and three molecules of water. Fats and oils are degraded during a hydrolysis reaction. Because three fatty acids are attached to each glycerol molecule, fats and oils are sometimes called **triglycerides.** Notice that triglycerides have many non-polar C−H bonds; therefore, they do not mix with water. Even though cooking oils and water are both liquid, they do not mix, even after shaking, because the nonpolar oil and polar water are chemically incompatible.

Triglycerides containing fatty acids with unsaturated bonds melt at a lower temperature than those containing only saturated fatty acids. The reason is that a double bond creates a kink in the fatty acid chain that prevents close packing between the hydrocarbon chains (Fig. 3.10*a*). We can infer that butter, a fat that is solid at room temperature, must contain primarily saturated fatty acids, while corn oil, which is a liquid even when placed in the refrigerator, must contain primarily unsaturated fatty acids (Fig. 3.10*b*). This difference is useful to living things. For example, the feet of reindeer and penguins contain unsaturated triglycerides, and this helps protect those exposed parts from freezing.

In general, fats, which most often come from animals, are solid at room temperature, whereas oils, which come from plants, are liquid at room temperature. Diets high in animal fat have been associated with circulatory disorders because saturated fats and other molecules can accumulate inside the lining of blood vessels and block blood flow. Health organizations have recommended replacing fat with oils such as olive oil and canola oil in our diet whenever possible.

Nearly all animals use fat rather than glycogen for long-term energy storage. Gram for gram, fat stores more energy than glycogen. The C−H bonds of fatty acids make them a richer source of chemical energy than glycogen, because more bonds with stored energy are present in fatty acids; in contrast, glycogen has many C−OH bonds, which are less energetic bonds. Also, fat droplets do not contain water because they are nonpolar. Small birds, like the broad-tailed hummingbird, store a great deal of fat before they start their long spring and fall migratory flights. About 0.15 g of fat per gram of body weight is accumulated each day. If the same amount of energy were stored as glycogen, a bird would be so heavy it would not be able to fly.

Phospholipids: Membrane Components

Phospholipids [Gk. *phos*, light, and *lipos*, fat], as implied by their name, contain a phosphate group. Essentially, a phospholipid is constructed like a fat, except that in place of the third fatty acid attached to glycerol, there is a polar phosphate group. The phosphate group is usually bonded to another organic group, indicated by *R* in Figure 3.11*a*. This portion of the molecule becomes the polar head, while the hydrocarbon chains of the fatty acids become the nonpolar tails. Notice that a double bond causes a tail to kink.

Phospholipids have hydrophilic heads and hydrophobic tails. When exposed to water, phospholipids tend to arrange themselves so that the polar heads are oriented toward water, and the nonpolar fatty acid tails are oriented away from water. In living things, which are made mostly of water, phospholipids tend to become a bilayer (double layer) because the polar heads prefer to interact with other polar molecules like water. Conversely, the nonpolar tails associate together and stay away from polar water molecules. So, phospholipids arrange themselves like a "sandwich," with the polar heads facing to the the outside (the bread slices) and the fatty acid tails on the inside (the filling). This phospholipid bilayer is a key component used to keep cells and the biological compartments within cells separate.

The plasma membrane that surrounds cells consists primarily of a phospholipid bilayer (Fig. 3.11*b*). The presence of kinks in the tails causes the plasma membrane to be fluid across a range of temperatures found in nature. A plasma membrane is absolutely essential to the structure and function of a cell, and this signifies the importance of phospholipids to living things.

Steroids: Four Fused Rings

Steroids are lipids that have entirely different structures from those of fats. Steroid molecules have skeletons of four fused carbon rings (Fig. 3.12*a*). Each type of steroid differs primarily by the types of functional groups attached to the carbon skeleton.

Cholesterol is an essential component of an animal cell's plasma membrane, where it provides physical stability. Cholesterol is the precursor of several other steroids, such as the sex hormones testosterone and estrogen (Fig. 3.12*b, c*). The male sex hormone, testosterone, is formed primarily in the testes, and the female sex hormone, estrogen, is formed primarily in

Figure 3.10 Fat and fatty acids. **a.** Following a dehydration reaction, glycerol is bonded to three fatty acid molecules as fat forms and water is given off. Following a hydrolysis reaction, the bonds are broken due to the addition of water. **b.** A fatty acid has a carboxyl group attached to a long hydrocarbon chain. If there are double bonds between some of the carbons in the chain, the fatty acid is unsaturated and a kink occurs in the chain. If there are no double bonds, the fatty acid is saturated. **c.** Space-filling models of an unsaturated fat and a saturated fat.

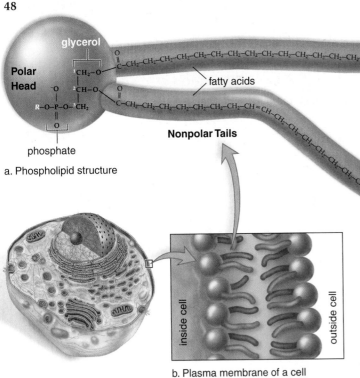

a. Phospholipid structure

b. Plasma membrane of a cell

Figure 3.11 Phospholipids form membranes. **a.** Phospholipids are constructed like fats, except that in place of the third fatty acid, they have a polar phosphate group. The hydrophilic (polar) head is soluble in water, whereas the two hydrophobic (nonpolar) tails are not. A tail has a kink wherever there is an unsaturated bond. **b.** Because of their structure, phospholipids form a bilayer that serves as the major component of a cell's plasma membrane. The fluidity of the plasma membrane is affected by kinks in the phospholipids' tails.

the ovaries. Testosterone and estrogen differ only by the functional groups attached to the same carbon skeleton, and yet each have their own profound effect on the body and sexuality of an animal. Human and plant estrogen are similar in structure, and if estrogen therapy is recommended, some women prefer taking soy products in preference to estrogen from animals.

Cholesterol can also contribute to circulatory disorders. The presence of cholesterol encourages the accumulation of fatty material inside the lining of blood vessels, which decreases the size of the opening and thereby can result in high blood pressure. Cholesterol-lowering medications are available.

Waxes

In **waxes,** long-chain fatty acids bond with long-chain alcohols:

Waxes are solid at normal temperatures because they have a high melting point. Being hydrophobic, they are also waterproof and resistant to degradation. In many plants, waxes, along with other molecules, form a protective cuticle (covering) that prevents the loss of water for all exposed parts (Fig. 3.13a). In

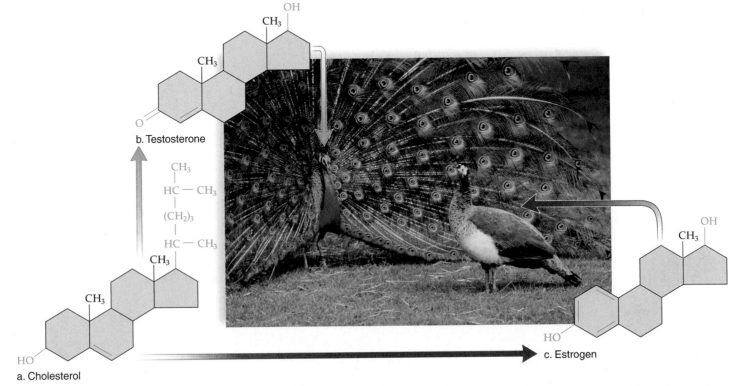

b. Testosterone

a. Cholesterol

c. Estrogen

Figure 3.12 Steroid diversity. **a.** Built like cholesterol, (**b**) testosterone and (**c**) estrogen have different effects on the body due to different functional groups attached to the same carbon skeleton. Testosterone is the male sex hormone active in peacocks (*left*), and estrogen is the female sex hormone active in peahens (*right*). These hormones are present in many living creatures.

a.

b.

Figure 3.13 Waxes. Waxes are a type of lipid. **a.** Fruits are protected by a waxy coating that is visible on these plums. **b.** Bees secrete the wax that allows them to build a comb where they store honey. This bee has collected pollen (yellow) to feed growing larvae.

many animals, waxes are involved in skin and fur maintenance. In humans, wax is produced by glands in the outer ear canal. Earwax contains cerumin, an organic compound that at the very least repels insects, and in some cases even kills them. It also traps dust and dirt, preventing these contaminants from reaching the eardrum.

A honeybee produces beeswax in glands on the underside of its abdomen. Beeswax is used to make the six-sided cells of the comb where honey is stored (Fig. 3.13*b*). Honey contains the sugars fructose and glucose, breakdown products of the sugar sucrose.

Humans have found a myriad of uses for waxes, from making candles to polishing cars, furniture, and floors.   **MP3** Lipids

Check Your Progress   3.3

1. Evaluate why lipids and water do not mix.
2. Contrast a saturated fatty acid with an unsaturated fatty acid. Which of these is preferred in the diet, and why?
3. Explain why phospholipids form a bilayer in water.

3.4 Proteins

Learning Outcomes

Upon completion of this section, you should be able to

1. Describe functions of proteins in cells.
2. Explain how a polypeptide is constructed from amino acids.
3. Compare the four levels of protein structure.
4. Analyze the factors that affect protein structure and function.

Proteins [Gk. *proteios,* first place], as their Greek derivation implies, are of primary importance to the structure and function of cells. As much as 50% of the dry weight of most cells consists of proteins. Presently, several hundred thousand proteins have been identified. Here are some of their many functions in animals:

Metabolism   Enzyme proteins bring reactants together and thereby speed chemical reactions in cells. They are specific for one particular type of reaction and function best at specific body temperatures and pH.

Support   Some proteins have a structural function. For example, keratin makes up hair and nails, while collagen gives strength to ligaments, tendons, and skin.

Transport   Channel and carrier proteins in the plasma membrane regulate what substances enter and exit cells. Other proteins transport molecules in the blood of animals; **hemoglobin** is a complex protein that transports oxygen to tissues and cells.

Defense   Antibodies are proteins of our immune system that combine with foreign substances, called antigens. Antibodies bind and prevent antigens from destroying cells and upsetting homeostasis.

Regulation   Some hormones are proteins that regulate how cells behave. They serve as intercellular messengers that influence cell metabolism. The hormone insulin regulates how much glucose is in the blood and in cells; the presence of growth hormone during childhood and adolescence determines the height of an individual.

Motion   The contractile proteins actin and myosin allow parts of cells to move and cause muscles to contract. Muscle contraction allows animals to travel from place to place. All cells contain proteins that move cell components to different internal locations. Without such proteins, cells would not be able to function.

Figure 3.14 Synthesis and degradation of a peptide. Following a dehydration reaction, a peptide bond joins two amino acids and a water molecule is released. Following a hydrolysis reaction, the bond is broken due to the addition of water.

Proteins are such a major part of living organisms that tissues and cells of the body can sometimes be characterized by the proteins they contain or produce. For example, muscle cells contain large amounts of actin and myosin for contraction; red blood cells are filled with hemoglobin for oxygen transport; and support tissues, such as ligaments and tendons, contain the protein collagen, which is composed of tough fibers.

Peptides

Proteins are polymers constructed from amino acid monomers. Figure 3.14 shows how a dehydration reaction joins the carboxyl group of one amino acid to the amino group of another amino acid. The resulting covalent bond between two amino acids is called a **peptide bond.** The atoms associated with the peptide bond share the electrons unevenly because oxygen is more electronegative than nitrogen. Therefore, the hydrogen attached to the nitrogen has a slightly positive charge, while the oxygen has a slightly negative charge:

The polarity of the peptide bond means that hydrogen bonding is possible between the $-CO$ of one amino acid and the $-NH$ of another amino acid in a polypeptide. This hydrogen bonding influences the structure, or shape, of a protein.

A **peptide** is two or more amino acids bonded together, and a **polypeptide** is a chain of many amino acids joined by peptide bonds. A protein is a polypeptide that has been folded into a particular shape and has function. Some proteins may consist of more than one polypeptide chain, making it possible for some proteins to have a very large number of amino acids.

In 1953, Frederick Sanger developed a method to determine the sequence of amino acids in a polypeptide. Now that we know the sequences of many thousands of polypeptides found in nature, it is clear that the amino acid sequence greatly influences the final three-dimensional shape and function of a protein. Proteins that have an abnormal sequence often have a three-dimensional shape that causes them to function improperly. From an evolutionary perspective, we also know that, for

a particular protein, the sequences of amino acids are highly similar within a species and are different across species.

Amino Acids: Protein Monomers

The name **amino acid** is appropriate because one of these groups is an $-NH_2$ (amino group) and another is a $-COOH$ (an acid group). The third group is called an R group for an amino acid:

Note that the central carbon atom in an amino acid bonds to a hydrogen atom and also to three other groups of atoms, one of which is the R group (Fig. 3.14). Amino acids differ according to their particular R group (Fig. 3.15). The R groups range in complexity from a single hydrogen atom to complicated ring compounds. Some R groups are polar and associate with water, whereas others are nonpolar and do not. Also, the amino acid cysteine has an R group that ends with an $-SH$ (sulfide) group, which often serves to covalently connect one chain of amino acids to another by a disulfide bond, $-S-S-$. Several other amino acids commonly found in cells are shown in Figure 3.15.

Each protein has a sequence of amino acids that is defined by information contained within a gene. This amino acid sequence forms the basis for all levels of protein structure, which directly affect protein function.

Shape of Proteins

A protein can have up to four levels of structure, termed primary, secondary, tertiary, and quaternary; however, not all proteins have all four levels.

Primary Structure

The primary structure of a protein is the sequence of amino acids defined by a gene. Just as millions of different words can be constructed from just 26 letters in the English alphabet, so too can hundreds of thousands of different polypeptides be built from just 20 amino acids. To make a new word in English, all

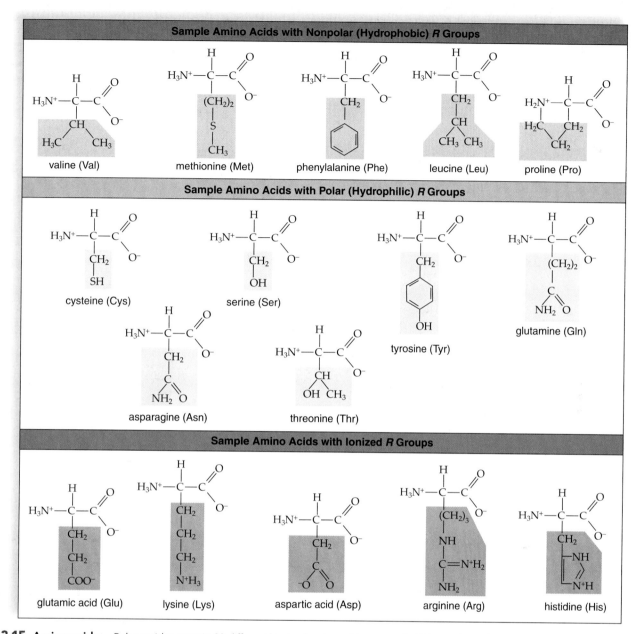

Figure 3.15 Amino acids.   Polypeptides contain 20 different kinds of amino acids, some of which are shown here. Amino acids differ by the particular *R* group (blue) attached to the central carbon. Some *R* groups are nonpolar and hydrophobic (red), some are polar and hydrophilic (light blue), and some are ionized and hydrophilic (dark blue). The amino acids are shown in ionized form.

that is required is to vary the number and sequence of a few letters. Likewise, changing the sequence of 20 amino acids in a polypeptide can produce a huge array of different proteins.

Secondary Structure

The secondary structure of a protein occurs when the polypeptide coils or folds in a particular way (Fig. 3.16).

Linus Pauling and Robert Corey, who began studying the structure of amino acids in the late 1930s, concluded that a coiling they called an α (alpha) helix and a pleated sheet they called the β (beta) sheet were two basic patterns of structure amino acids assumed within a polypeptide. The names came from the

fact that the α helix was the first, and the β sheet the second, pattern they discovered. Each polypeptide can have multiple α helices and β pleated sheets.

The spiral shape of α helices is formed by hydrogen bonding between every fourth amino acid within the polypeptide chain, whereas β sheets are formed when the polypeptide turns back upon itself, allowing hydrogen bonding to occur between extended lengths of the polypeptide. **Fibrous proteins,** which are structural proteins, exist only as helices or pleated sheets that hydrogen-bond to each other. Examples are keratin, a protein in hair, and silk, a protein that forms spider webs. Both of these proteins have only a secondary structure (Fig. 3.17).

Primary Structure

This level of structure is determined by the sequence of amino acids coded by a gene that joins to form a polypeptide.

amino acid

peptide bond

H_3N^+

COO^-

hydrogen bond

hydrogen bond

Secondary Structure

Hydrogen bonding between amino acids causes the polypeptide to form an alpha helix or a pleated sheet.

α (alpha) helix

β (beta) sheet = pleated sheet

Tertiary Structure

Interactions of amino acid side chains with water, covalent bonding between *R* groups, and other chemical interactions determine the folded three-dimensional shape of a protein.

disulfide bond

Quaternary Structure

This level of structure occurs when two or more folded polypeptides interact to perform a biological function.

Figure 3.16 Levels of protein organization.   All proteins have a primary structure. Both fibrous and globular proteins have a secondary structure; they are either helices (keratin, collagen) or pleated sheets (silk). Globular proteins always have a tertiary structure, and most have a quaternary structure (e.g., hemoglobin, and enzymes such as RNAase).

Tertiary Structure

A tertiary structure is the folding that results in the final three-dimensional shape of a polypeptide. **Globular proteins,** which tend to ball up into rounded shapes, have tertiary structure.

The interaction of hydrophobic amino acids in the polypeptide chain with the surrounding water is a major factor in how proteins fold into, and maintain, their final shape. These nonpolar amino acids tend to group together in the interior of a protein, to be as far away from water as possible. In contrast, the polar hydrophilic and ionic amino acids interact well with water, and tend to orient themselves on the protein's surface. These chemical interactions, along with hydrogen

a.   b.   c.

Figure 3.17 Fibrous proteins. Fibrous proteins are structural proteins. **a.** Keratin—found, for example, in hair, horns, and hoofs—exemplifies fibrous proteins that are helical for most of their length. Keratin is a hydrogen-bonded triple helix. In this photo, Drew Barrymore has straight hair. **b.** In order to give her curly hair, water was used to disrupt the hydrogen bonds, and when the hair dried, new hydrogen bonding allowed it to take on the shape of a curler. A permanent-wave lotion induces new covalent bonds within the helix. **c.** Silk made by spiders and silkworms exemplifies fibrous proteins that are pleated sheets for most of their length. Hydrogen bonding between parts of the molecule occurs as the pleated sheet doubles back on itself.

bonds, ionic bonds, and covalent bonds between *R* groups, all contribute to the tertiary structure of a protein. Strong disulfide linkages ($-S-S-$) in particular help maintain the tertiary shape.

Enzymes are globular proteins. Enzymes work best at body temperature, and each one also has an optimal pH at which the rate of the reaction is highest. At this temperature and pH, the enzyme can maintain its normal shape. A high temperature and change in pH can disrupt the interactions that maintain the shape of the enzyme. When a protein loses its natural shape, it is said to be **denatured.** An organism can die if too many proteins become denatured because it can no longer maintain the metabolic processes necessary for life.

Animation
Protein Denaturation

Quaternary Structure

Some proteins have a quaternary structure because they consist of more than one polypeptide. Hemoglobin is a much-studied globular protein that consists of four polypeptides, and therefore it has a quaternary structure. Each polypeptide in hemoglobin has a primary, secondary, and tertiary structure. However, a protein can have only two polypeptides and still have quaternary structure.

MP3
Proteins

Protein-Folding Diseases

Proteins cannot function properly unless they fold into their correct shape. In recent years investigators have found that the cell contains **chaperone proteins,** which help new proteins fold into their normal shape. At first it seemed as if chaperone proteins ensured that proteins folded properly, but now it appears that

they might correct any misfolding of a new protein. These new findings serve as an example of how scientific research helps correct previous misunderstandings about how life works.

In any case, without fully functioning chaperone proteins, a cell's proteins may not be functional because they have misfolded. Several diseases in humans, such as cystic fibrosis and Alzheimer disease, are associated with misshapen proteins. The possibility exists that the diseases are due to missing or malfunctioning chaperone proteins.

Other diseases in humans are due to misfolded proteins, but the cause may be different. For years, investigators have been studying fatal brain diseases, known as TSEs,[1] that have no cure because no infective agent can be found. Mad cow disease is a well-known example of a TSE disease. Now it appears that TSE diseases could be due to misfolded proteins, called **prions,** that cause other proteins of the same type to fold the wrong way too. A possible relationship between prions and the functioning of chaperone proteins is now under investigation.

Animation
How Prions Arise

Check Your Progress   3.4

1. Explain where the information that specifies amino acid sequence in a polypeptide comes from.
2. Examine which types of amino acids are most likely to be found in the interior of a protein and why.
3. Evaluate which factors are most important to protein folding.

1 TSEs: transmissible spongiform encephalopathies.

3.5 Nucleic Acids

Each cell has a storehouse of information that specifies how a cell should behave, respond to the environment, and divide to make new cells. **Nucleic acids,** which are polymers of nucleotides, store information, include instructions for life, and conduct chemical reactions. **DNA (deoxyribonucleic acid)** is one type of nucleic acid that not only stores information about how to copy, or replicate, itself, but also specifies the order in which amino acids are to be joined to make a protein.

RNA (ribonucleic acid) is another diverse type of nucleic acid that has multiple uses. Messenger RNA (mRNA) is a temporary copy of a gene in the DNA that specifies what the amino acid sequence will be during the process of protein synthesis. Transfer RNA (tRNA) is also necessary in synthesizing proteins, and helps to translate the sequence of nucleic acids in a gene into the correct sequence of amino acid during protein synthesis. Ribosomal RNA (rRNA) works as an enzyme to form the peptide bonds between amino acids in a polypeptide. A wide range of other RNA molecules also perform important functions within the cell.

Not all nucleotides are made into DNA or RNA polymers. Some nucleotides are directly involved in metabolic functions in cells. For example, some are components of **coenzymes,** nonprotein organic molecules that help regulate enzymatic reactions. **ATP (adenosine triphosphate)** is a special nucleotide that stores large amounts of energy needed for synthetic reactions and for various other energy-requiring processes in cells.

Structure of DNA and RNA

Every **nucleotide** is comprised of three types of molecules: a pentose sugar, a phosphate (phosphoric acid), and a nitrogen-containing base (Fig. 3.18a). In DNA, the pentose sugar is deoxyribose, and in RNA the pentose sugar is ribose. A difference in the structure of these 5-carbon sugars accounts for their respective names because, as you might guess, deoxyribose lacks an oxygen atom found in ribose (Fig. 3.18b).

Both DNA and RNA contain combinations of four nucleotides, but these differ somewhat between the two nucleic acids (Fig. 3.18c). Nucleotides that have a base with a single ring are called pyrimidines, and nucleotides with a double ring are called purines. In DNA, the pyrimidine bases are cytosine and thymine; in RNA, the pyrimidine bases are cytosine and uracil. Both DNA and RNA contain the purine bases adenine and guanine. These molecules are called bases because their presence raises the pH of a solution.

Nucleotides are joined into a DNA or RNA polymer by a series of dehydration reactions. The resulting polymer is a linear molecule called a strand, in which the backbone is made up of an alternating series of sugar-phosphate-sugar-phosphate molecules. The bases project to one side of the backbone. Nucleotides are joined in an order specified by the strand they are copied from. DNA is double-stranded, and RNA is single-stranded (Fig. 3.19).

The two strands in double-stranded DNA usually twist around each other to form a double helix (Fig. 3.20a, b). The

a. Nucleotide structure

b. Deoxyribose versus ribose

c. Pyrimidines versus purines

Figure 3.18 Nucleotides. **a.** A nucleotide consists of a pentose sugar, a phosphate molecule, and a nitrogen-containing base. **b.** DNA contains the sugar deoxyribose, and RNA contains the sugar ribose. **c.** DNA contains the pyrimidines C and T and the purines A and G. RNA contains the pyrimidines C and U and the purines A and G.

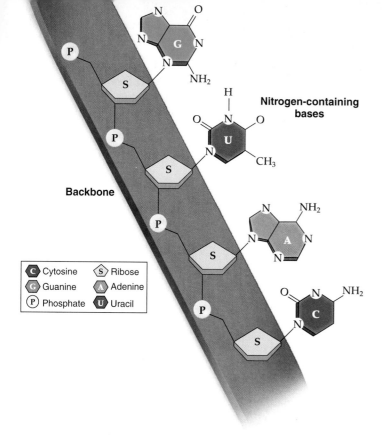

Figure 3.19 RNA structure. RNA is a single-stranded polymer of nucleotides. When the nucleotides join, the phosphate group of one is bonded to the sugar of the next. The bases project out to the side of the resulting sugar-phosphate backbone.

two strands are held together by hydrogen bonds between pyrimidine and purine base pairs. The bases can be in any order within a strand, but between strands, thymine (T) is always paired with adenine (A), and guanine (G) is always paired with cytosine (C). This is called **complementary base pairing.** Therefore, regardless of the order or the quantity of any particular base pair, the number of purine bases (A + G) always equals the number of pyrimidine bases (T + C) (Fig. 3.20c).

Animation
DNA Structure

Table 3.4 summarizes the differences between DNA and RNA.

ATP (Adenosine Triphosphate)

ATP is a special nucleotide comprised of adenine and ribose (adenosine) and three phosphates (triphosphate). The three phosphate groups are attached together and to ribose, the pentose sugar (Fig. 3.21).

Table 3.4 DNA Structure Compared to RNA Structure

	DNA	RNA
Sugar	Deoxyribose	Ribose
Bases	Adenine, guanine, thymine, cytosine	Adenine, guanine, uracil, cytosine
Strands	Double stranded with base pairing	Single stranded
Helix	Yes	No

a. Space-filling model

b. Double helix

c. Complementary base pairing

Figure 3.20 DNA structure. **a.** Space-filling model of DNA. **b.** DNA is a double helix in which the two polynucleotide strands twist about each other. **c.** Hydrogen bonds (dotted lines) occur between the complementarily paired bases: C is always paired with G, and A is always paired with T.

a. **adenosine** **triphosphate**

c.

adenosine   triphosphate   adenosine   diphosphate   phosphate   ENERGY

b.   **ATP**   **ADP**

ATP is a high-energy molecule because the last two phosphate bonds are unstable and are easily broken. In cells, hydrolysis of the terminal phosphate bond produces the molecule **ADP (adenosine diphosphate),** a phosphate molecule Ⓟ, and lots of energy to do cellular work.

The energy that is released by ATP hydrolysis is used to power many cellular processes, including enzyme reactions, cell communication, and cell division. ATP hydrolysis is chemically favored because ADP and Ⓟ are more stable than the original ATP molecule. Even though the third phosphate bond is broken, it is the whole molecule that releases energy.

In many cases, the hydrolysis of the ATP nucleotide is coupled to chemically unfavorable reactions in cells to allow these reactions to proceed. For example, key steps in the synthesis of macromolecules, such as carbohydrates and proteins, are able to proceed because the energy from ATP breakdown is used to pay the energy costs of the chemical reaction. ATP also supplies the energy for muscle contraction and nerve impulse conduction. Just as you spend money when you pay for a product or a service, cells "spend" ATP when they need something. That's why ATP is called the energy currency of cells.

MP3 Nucleic Acids

Check Your Progress   3.5

1. Examine how a nucleic acid stores information.
2. Describe the three components of a nucleotide.
3. Evaluate the properties of ATP that make it an ideal carrier of energy.

CONNECTING *the* CONCEPTS *with the* THEMES

Evolution

- Living cells are built from carbohydrates, lipids, proteins, and nucleic acids.
- DNA in genes specify the amino acid sequences found in all proteins. DNA sequence changes can affect secondary, tertiary, and sometimes quaternary protein structures and therefore function.
- The diversity of life on Earth is partly expained by differences in DNA and protein sequences. Closely related species tend to have similar sequences for many genes, whereas distantly related species show less similarity.
- Mutations are changes in an organism's normal DNA or protein sequences, and may increase, decrease, or have no effect on its biological functions.

Nature of Science

- The term *organic* can refer to food products that have been grown without the use of chemicals or been minimally processed, to molecules that contain carbon and hydrogen, to living things, or to anything that has been previously alive, such as the plants and animals that make up fossil fuels.
- When burned, organic molecules release carbon dioxide into the atmosphere just as we do when we breathe.
- Fossil fuel infrastructure is slowly changing as other energy alternatives are developed. Science plays a key role in this transition.

Biological Systems

- Carbon is central to the chemistry of life. The intake and synthesis of biomolecules is necessary to maintain cellular and life systems.
- Most biomolecules are simply polymers of small organic molecules. Monomers of sugars, amino acids, and nucleotides undergo dehydration reactions to become carbohydrates, proteins, and nucleic acids, respectively. Fats are composed of fatty acids and glycerol.

Media Study Tools

www.mhhe.com/maderbiology11

Enhance your study of this chapter with study tools and practice tests. Also ask your instructor about the resources available through ConnectPlus, including the media-rich eBook, interactive learning tools, and animations.

Summarize

3.1 Organic Molecules

The chemistry of carbon accounts for the diversity of organic molecules found in living things. Carbon can bond with as many as four other atoms. It can also bond with itself to form both chains and rings. Differences in the carbon skeleton and attached functional groups cause organic molecules to have different chemical properties. The chemical properties of a molecule determine how it interacts with other molecules and its role in the cell. Some functional groups are hydrophobic and others are hydrophilic.

There are four classes of biomolecules in cells: carbohydrates, lipids, proteins, and nucleic acids. Polysaccharides, the largest of the carbohydrates, are polymers of simple sugars called monosaccharides. Lipids are diverse hydrophobic molecules made of long chains or ring carbon structures. The polypeptides of proteins are polymers of amino acids, and nucleic acids are polymers of nucleotides. Polymers are formed by the joining together of monomers. For each bond formed during a dehydration reaction, a molecule of water is removed, and for each bond broken during a hydrolysis reaction, a molecule of water is added.

3.2 Carbohydrates

Monosaccharides, disaccharides, and polysaccharides are all carbohydrates. Therefore, the term *carbohydrate* includes both the monomers (e.g., glucose) and the polymers (e.g., starch, glycogen, and cellulose). Glucose is the immediate energy source of cells. Polysaccharides such as starch, glycogen, and cellulose are all polymers of glucose that have different types of chemical bonds. Starch in plants and glycogen in animals are used to store energy, whereas cellulose in plants and chitin in crabs and related animals, as well as fungi, provides structure.

3.3 Lipids

Lipids include a wide variety of compounds that are insoluble in water. Fats and oils, which allow long-term energy storage, contain one glycerol and three fatty acids. Both glycerol and fatty acids have polar groups, but fats and oils are nonpolar, and this accounts for their insolubility in water. Fats tend to contain saturated fatty acids, and oils tend to contain unsaturated fatty acids. Saturated fatty acids do not have carbon–carbon double bonds, but unsaturated fatty acids do have double bonds in their hydrocarbon chain. The double bond causes a kink in the molecule that accounts for the liquid nature of oils at room temperature.

A phospholipid replaces one of the fatty acids with a phosphate group. In water, phospholipids form a bilayer because the head of each molecule is hydrophilic and the tails are hydrophobic. Steroids have the same four-ring structure as cholesterol, but each differs by the attached functional groups. Waxes are composed of a fatty acid with a long hydrocarbon chain bonded to an alcohol.

3.4 Proteins

Proteins carry out many diverse functions in cells and organisms, including support, metabolism, transport, defense, regulation, and motion. Proteins are polymers of amino acids.

A polypeptide is a long chain of amino acids joined by peptide bonds. There are 20 different amino acids in cells, and they differ only by their *R* groups. Whether or not the *R* groups are hydrophilic or hydrophobic helps determine the structure, and therefore the function, of the protein. A polypeptide has up to four levels of structure: The primary level is the linear sequence of the amino acids, which is determined by the DNA; the secondary level contains α helices and β (pleated) sheets held in place by hydrogen bonding between amino acids along the polypeptide chain; and the tertiary level is the final folded polypeptide, which is held in place by internal bonding and hydrophobic interactions between *R* groups. Proteins that contain more than one polypeptide have a quaternary level of structure as well.

Some proteins serve as enzymes, which regulate and carry out body functions. As with other proteins, the shape of an enzyme is important to its function. Both high temperatures and drastic pH change can cause proteins to denature, lose their shape, and decrease their function.

3.5 Nucleic Acids

The nucleic acids DNA and RNA are linear polymers of nucleotides. Nucleotides can be sequenced in any order. Changes in nucleotide sequence produce the diversity of life seen on Earth. Each nucleotide has three components: a 5-carbon sugar, a phosphate (phosphoric acid), and a nitrogen-containing base.

DNA, which contains the sugar deoxyribose, phosphate, and nitrogen-containing bases, is the genetic material that stores information for its own replication and specifies the order in which amino acids are sequenced in proteins. DNA uses mRNA to direct protein synthesis. DNA is a double-stranded helix in which A pairs with T and C pairs with G through hydrogen bonding. RNA is single stranded, contains the sugar ribose and phosphate, and has the same bases as DNA except for uracil. There are many different types of RNA.

ATP is a special nucleotide that, with its unstable phosphate bonds, stores energy to do cellular work. Hydrolysis of ATP to ADP + Ⓟ releases energy needed by the cell to make a product or conduct metabolism.

Key Terms

ADP (adenosine diphosphate) 56	DNA (deoxyribonucleic acid) 54
amino acid 50	enzyme 41
ATP (adenosine triphosphate) 54	fat 46
biomolecule 38	fatty acid 46
carbohydrate 41	fibrous protein 51
cellulose 44	functional group 39
chaperone protein 53	globular protein 52
chitin 44	glucose 42
coenzyme 54	glycerol 46
complementary base pairing 55	glycogen 43
	hemoglobin 49
dehydration reaction 40	hexose 42
denatured 53	hydrolysis reaction 41
deoxyribose 42	hydrophilic 40
disaccharide 42	hydrophobic 40
	inorganic chemistry 38

▮ Assess

Reviewing This Chapter

1. How do the chemical characteristics of carbon affect the structure of organic molecules? 38–39
2. Give examples of functional groups, and discuss the importance of these groups being hydrophobic or hydrophilic. 39–40
3. What biomolecules are monomers of the polymers studied in this chapter? How do monomers join to produce polymers, and how are polymers broken down to monomers? 40
4. Name several monosaccharides, disaccharides, and polysaccharides, and give a function of each. How are these molecules structurally distinguishable? 42–44
5. What is the difference between a saturated and an unsaturated fatty acid? Explain the structure of a fat molecule by stating its components and how they join together. 46
6. How does the structure of a phospholipid differ from that of a fat? How do phospholipids form a bilayer in the presence of water? 46
7. Describe the structure of a generalized steroid. How does one steroid differ from another? 46–48
8. Draw the structure of an amino acid and a peptide, pointing out the peptide bond. 50
9. Discuss the four possible levels of protein structure, and relate each level to particular bonding patterns. 50–53
10. How do nucleotides bond to form nucleic acids? State and explain several differences between the structure of DNA and that of RNA. 54–55
11. Discuss the structure and function of ATP. 55–56

Testing Yourself

Choose the best answer for each question.

1. Which of these is not a characteristic of carbon?
   a. forms four covalent bonds
   b. bonds with other carbon atoms
   c. is sometimes ionic
   d. can form long chains
   e. sometimes shares two pairs of electrons with another atom

2. A hydrophilic group is
   a. attracted to water.
   b. a polar and/or ionized group.
   c. found at the end of fatty acids.
   d. the opposite of a hydrophobic group.
   e. All of these are correct.

3. Which of these is an example of a hydrolysis reaction?
   a. amino acid + amino acid ⟶ dipeptide + H_2O
   b. dipeptide + H_2O ⟶ amino acid + amino acid
   c. denaturation of a polypeptide
   d. Both a and b are correct.
   e. Both b and c are correct.

4. Which of these makes cellulose nondigestible in humans?
   a. a polymer of glucose subunits
   b. a fibrous protein
   c. the linkage between the glucose molecules
   d. the peptide linkage between the amino acid molecules
   e. the carboxyl groups ionize

5. A fatty acid is unsaturated if it
   a. contains hydrogen.
   b. contains carbon–carbon double bonds.
   c. contains a carboxyl (acidic) group.
   d. bonds to glycogen.
   e. bonds to a nucleotide.

6. The difference between one amino acid and another is found in the
   a. amino group.
   b. carboxyl group.
   c. R group.
   d. peptide bond.
   e. carbon atoms.

7. The shape of a polypeptide is
   a. maintained by bonding between parts of the polypeptide.
   b. ultimately dependent on the primary structure.
   c. necessary to its function.
   d. All of these are correct.

8. Nucleotides
   a. contain a sugar, a nitrogen-containing base, and a phosphate group.
   b. are the monomers of fats and polysaccharides.
   c. join together by covalent bonding between the bases.
   d. are present in both DNA and RNA.
   e. Both a and d are correct.

9. ATP
   a. is an amino acid.
   b. has a helical structure.
   c. is a high-energy molecule that can break down to ADP and phosphate.
   d. provides enzymes for metabolism.
   e. is most energetic when in the ADP state.

10. Label the following diagram using the terms H_2O, monomer, hydrolysis reaction, dehydration reaction, and polymer. Terms can be used more than once and a term need not be used.

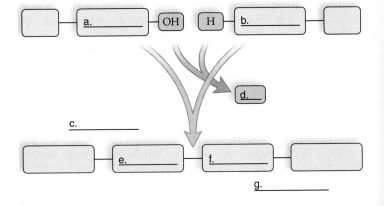

11. The monomer of a carbohydrate is
    a. an amino acid.
    b. a nucleic acid.
    c. a monosaccharide.
    d. a fatty acid.

12. The joining of two adjacent amino acids is called
    a. a peptide bond.
    b. a dehydration reaction.
    c. a covalent bond.
    d. All of these are correct.

13. The shape of a polypeptide
    a. is maintained by bonding between parts of the polypeptide.
    b. is ultimately dependent on the primary structure.
    c. involves hydrogen bonding.
    d. All of these are correct.

14. Which of the following pertains to an RNA nucleotide and not to a DNA nucleotide?
    a. contains the sugar ribose
    b. contains a nitrogen-containing base
    c. contains a phosphate molecule
    d. becomes bonded to other nucleotides following a dehydration reaction

For questions 15–18, match the items to those in the key. Some answers are used more than once.

KEY:
    a. carbohydrate
    b. fats and oils
    c. protein
    d. nucleic acid

15. the 6-carbon sugar, glucose

16. polymer of amino acids

17. glycerol and fatty acids

18. genes

19. Which is a correct statement about carbohydrates?
    a. All polysaccharides serve as energy storage molecules.
    b. Glucose is broken down for immediate energy.
    c. Glucose is not a carbohydrate, only polysaccharides are.
    d. Starch, glycogen, and cellulose have different monomers.
    e. Both a and c are correct.

20. In phospholipids,
    a. heads are polar.
    b. tails are nonpolar.
    c. heads contain phosphate.
    d. All of these are correct.

Engage

Thinking Scientifically

1. The seeds of temperate plants tend to contain unsaturated fatty acids, while the seeds of tropical plants tend to have saturated fatty acids. **a.** How would you test your hypothesis. **b.** Assuming your hypothesis is supported, give an explanation.

2. Chemical analysis reveals that an abnormal form of an enzyme contains a polar amino acid at the location where the normal form has a nonpolar amino acid. Formulate a testable hypothesis concerning the abnormal enzyme.

Bioethical Issue
Organic Pollutants

Organic compounds include the carbohydrates, proteins, lipids, and nucleic acids that make up our bodies. Modern industry also uses all sorts of organic compounds that are synthetically produced. Indeed, our modern way of life wouldn't be possible without synthetic organic compounds.

Pesticides, herbicides, disinfectants, plastics, and textiles contain organic substances that are termed pollutants when they enter the natural environment and cause harm to living things. Global use of pesticides has increased dramatically since the 1950s, and modern pesticides are ten times more toxic than those of the 1950s. The Centers for Disease Control and Prevention in Atlanta reports that 40% of children working in agricultural fields now show signs of pesticide poisoning. The U.S. Geological Survey estimates that 32 million people in urban areas and 10 million people in rural areas are using groundwater that contains organic pollutants. J. Charles Fox, an official of the Environmental Protection Agency, says that "over the life of a person, ingestion of these chemicals has been shown to have adverse health effects such as cancer, reproductive problems, and developmental effects."

At one time, people failed to realize that everything in the environment is connected to everything else. In other words, they didn't know that an organic chemical can wander far from the site of its entry into the environment and that eventually these chemicals can enter our own bodies and cause harm. Now that we are aware of this outcome, we have to decide as a society how to proceed. We might decide to do nothing if the percentage of people dying from exposure to organic pollutants is small. Or we might decide to regulate the use of industrial compounds more strictly than has been done in the past. We could also decide that we need better ways of purifying public and private water supplies so that they do not contain organic pollutants.

4

Cell Structure and Function

Electron micrograph of *Giardia lamblia*, a cause of diarrhea.

BEFORE YOU BEGIN

Before beginning this chapter, take a few moments to review the following discussions.

Figures 3.1 and 3.2 What role do carbon and functional groups serve in biological molecules?

Sections 3.2 to 3.5 What macromolecules are needed to construct a cell?

Figures 3.8, 3.12, 3.17, and 3.21 How does the structure of a macromolecule affect its function?

The Dutch shopkeeper Antonie van Leeuwenhoek (1632–1723) may have been the first person to see living cells. Using a microscope he built himself, he looked at everything possible, including his own stool. He wrote, "I have usually of a morning a well-formed stool. But, hitherto, I have had sometimes a looseness of bowels, so I went to stool some twice, thrice, or four times a day. My excrement being so thin, I was at diverse times constrained to examine it. Wherein I have sometimes seen animalcules a moving prettily. Their bodies were somewhat longer than broad, and the belly, which was flat-lie, furnished with sundry little paws. . . ." [November 9, 1681]

In this way, Antonie van Leeuwenhoek reported seeing the parasite *Giardia lamblia* in his feces. *Giardia* are unicellular organisms, while humans are multicellular organisms. In this chapter, you will see that cells are the fundamental building blocks of organisms, organized to carry out basic metabolic functions and adapt to changing environmental conditions. The presentation concentrates on the generalized bacterial, animal, or plant cell; however, all cells are specialized in particular ways.

As you read through the chapter, think about the following questions:

1. How is a cell more than simply the sum of its macromolecular parts?
2. What characteristics enable cells to be alive and allow them to self-replicate?
3. How are cells able to metabolize and respond to environmental changes so quickly?

FOLLOWING *the* THEMES

CHAPTER 4 CELL STRUCTURE AND FUNCTION		
UNIT 1 THE CELL	**Evolution**	All cells are produced from existing cells, creating an unbroken lineage back to cells from early Earth.
	Nature of Science	Understanding how cells function allows us to discover ways to treat cell-based diseases.
	Biological Systems	Cells metabolize and adapt to changing environmental conditions.

4.1 Cellular Level of Organization

Learning Outcomes

Upon completion of this section, you should be able to

1. Explain why cells are the basic unit of life.
2. List the tenets of cell theory.
3. Compare surface-area-to-volume ratios for large and small cells.

Cells are the basic units of life. All of the chemistry and biomolecules we have discussed to this point are necessary but insufficient on their own to support life. It is only when these components are brought together and organized into a cell that life is possible.

All organisms are made up of cells. When we observe plants, animals, and other organisms, it is important to realize that what we are seeing is a collection of cells that work together in a highly organized, regulated manner, and thus conduct the business of life. Figure 4.1 shows the connection between whole organisms and their component cells. Although the cellular basis of life is clear to us now, scientists were unaware of this fact as recently as two hundred years ago. The link between cells and life became clear to microscopists during the 1830s.

The **cell** is the smallest unit of living matter. The collective work of the 19th century scientists Robert Brown (1773-1858), Matthais Schleiden (1804-1881), and Theodor Schwann (1810-1882) helped determine that plants and animals are composed of cells. Further work by the German physician Rudolph Virchow (1821-1902) showed that cells self-reproduce and "every cell comes from a preexisting cell." Today, we know that various illnesses of the body, such as diabetes and prostate cancer, are due to cellular malfunction. Countless scientific investigations since that time verify these initial findings. From these results, we can infer that all life on Earth today came from cells in ancient times, and that all cells are related in some way. In reality, a continuity of cells has been present from generation to generation, even back to the very first cell (or cells) in the history of life.

Today, some life-forms exist as single cells, whereas others are complex, interconnected systems of cells. When unicellular organisms reproduce, a single cell divides and becomes two new organisms. When multicellular organisms grow, many cells divide. The presence of many cells allows some to specialize to do particular jobs within the multicellular organism, including the cells that create genetic variation through sexual reproduction.

The work of Schleiden, Schwann, and Virchow helped created the **cell theory**. It states that:

1. all organisms are composed of cells,
2. cells are the basic units of structure and function in organisms, and
3. cells come only from preexisting cells because cells are self-reproducing.

Figure 4.1 Organisms and cells. All organisms, including plants and animals, are composed of cells. This is not readily apparent because a microscope is usually needed to see the cells. **a.** Lilac plant. **b.** Light micrograph of a cross section of a lilac leaf showing many individual cells. **c.** Rabbit. **d.** Light micrograph of a rabbit's intestinal lining showing that it, too, is composed of cells. The dark-staining bodies are nuclei.

a.

c.

b.   50 μm

d.   140 μm

Cell Size

Although they range in size, cells are generally quite small. A frog's egg, at about 1 millimeter (mm) in diameter, is large enough to be seen by the human eye. But most cells are far smaller than 1 mm; some are even as small as 1 micrometer (µm)—one thousandth of a millimeter. Cell inclusions and macromolecules are smaller than a micrometer and are measured in terms of nanometers (nm).

Because of their size, very small biological structures can only be viewed with microscopes, which magnify a visual image. Figure 4.2 shows the visual range of the eye, light microscope, and electron microscope; the discussion of microscopy in the Nature of Science feature on pages 63–64 explains why the electron microscope allows us to see so much more detail than the light microscope does.

Why are cells so small? To answer this question, consider that a cell is a system by itself, and as such needs a surface area large enough to allow adequate nutrients to enter and for wastes to be eliminated. Small cells, not large cells, are likely to have an adequate surface area for exchanging wastes for nutrients. As cells increase in size, the surface area becomes inadequate to exchange the materials that the volume of the cell requires.

Figure 4.3 visually demonstrates this relationship; dividing a large cube into smaller cubes provides a lot more surface area per volume. Calculations show that a 1-cm cube has a **surface-area-to-volume ratio** of 6:1, whereas a 4-cm cube has a surface-area-to-volume ratio of 1.5:1. The former ratio allows sufficient transport in and out of the cell to support life; the latter ratio does not.

A mental image might help you visualize the importance of surface-area-to-volume-ratios and why this relationship favors smaller cell size. Imagine a small room and a large room filled with people. The small room, which holds 20 people, has only two doors, and the large room, which holds 80 people, has four doors. If a fire occurred in both rooms, it would be faster to get the people out of the smaller room because it has the more favorable ratio of doors to people. Similarly, a small cell size is more advantageous for exchanging molecules because of its greater surface-area-to-volume ratio.

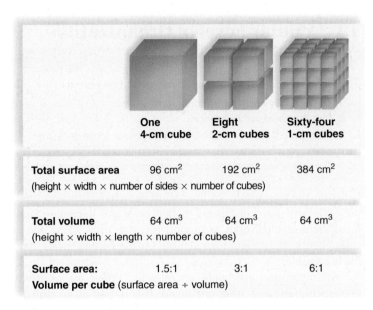

	One 4-cm cube	Eight 2-cm cubes	Sixty-four 1-cm cubes
Total surface area (height × width × number of sides × number of cubes)	96 cm²	192 cm²	384 cm²
Total volume (height × width × length × number of cubes)	64 cm³	64 cm³	64 cm³
Surface area: Volume per cube (surface area ÷ volume)	1.5:1	3:1	6:1

Figure 4.3 Surface-area-to-volume relationships. As cell size decreases from 4 cm³ to 1 cm³, the surface-area-to-volume ratio increases.

Check Your Progress   4.1

1. Describe the major components of cell theory.
2. Evaluate why a cell and a whole organism are both examples of biological systems.
3. Explain why a large surface-area-to-volume ratio is needed for the proper functioning of cells.

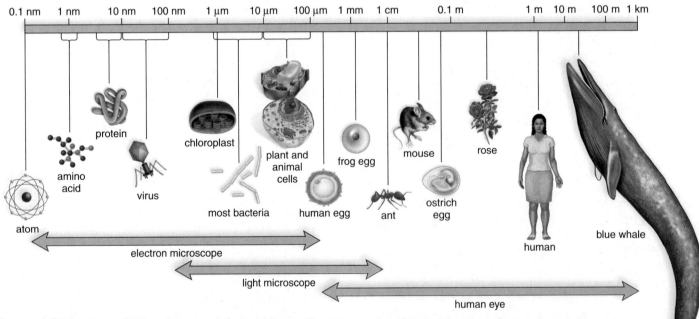

Figure 4.2 The sizes of living things and their components. The unassisted human eye can usually see macroscopic organisms and a few large cells. Microscopic cells are visible with the light microscope, but not in much detail. An electron microscope is necessary to see organelles in detail and to observe viruses and molecules. In the metric system (see back endsheet), each higher unit is ten times greater than the preceding unit. (1 meter = 10² cm = 10³ mm = 10⁶ µm = 10⁹ nm)

Microscopy Today

Since cells are the basic unit of life, the more we learn about cells, the more we understand life. Cells were not discovered until the seventeenth century, when the microscope was invented. Since that time, various types of microscopes have been developed for studying cells and their components.

Many times when scientists don't have suitable tools to investigate natural phenomena, they invent them. Microscopes have given scientists a deeper look into how life works than is possible with the naked eye. Today, there are many types of microscopes. A *compound light microscope* uses a set of glass lenses to focus light rays passing through a specimen to produce an image that is viewed by the human eye. A *transmission electron microscope (TEM)* uses a set of electromagnetic lenses to focus electrons passing through a specimen to produce an image that is projected onto a fluorescent screen or photographic film. A *scanning electron microscope (SEM)* uses a narrow beam of electrons to scan over the surface of a specimen that is coated with a thin metal layer. Secondary electrons given off by the metal are detected and used to produce a three-dimensional image on a television screen. Figure 4A shows these three types of microscopic images.

amoeba, light micrograph

85 µm

pseudopod segment, transmission electron micrograph

200 nm

amoeba, scanning electron micrograph

500 µm

eye
ocular lens
light rays
objective lens
specimen
condenser lens
light source

a. Compound light microscope

electron source
electron beam
electromagnetic condenser lens
specimen
electromagnetic objective lens
electromagnetic projector lens
observation screen or photographic plate

b. Transmission electron microscope

electron gun
electron beam
electromagnetic condenser lenses
scanning coil
final condenser lens
secondary electrons
specimen
electron detector
TV viewing screen

c. Scanning electron microscope

Figure 4A Diagram of microscopes with accompanying micrographs of *Amoeba proteus*.   a. The compound light microscope and **(b)** the transmission electron microscope provide an internal view of an organism. **c.** The scanning electron microscope provides an external view of an organism.

Magnification, Resolution, and Contrast

Magnification is the ratio between the size of an image and its actual size. Electron microscopes magnify to a greater extent than do compound light microscopes. A light microscope can magnify objects about a thousand times, but an electron microscope can magnify them hundreds of thousands of times. The difference lies in the means of illumination. The path of light rays and electrons moving through space is wavelike, but the wavelength of electrons is much shorter than the wavelength of light. This difference in wavelength accounts for the electron microscope's greater magnifying capability and its greater ability to distinguish between two points (resolving power).

Resolution is the minimum distance between two objects that allows them to be seen as two separate objects. A microscope with poor resolution might enable a student to see only one cellular granule, while the microscope with the better resolution would show two granules next to each other. The greater the resolving power, the greater the detail seen.

If oil is placed between the sample and the objective lens of the compound light microscope, the resolving power is increased, and if ultraviolet light is used instead of visible light, it is also increased. But typically, a light microscope can resolve down to 0.2 μm, while the transmission electron microscope can resolve down to 0.0002 μm. If the resolving power of the average human eye is set at 1.0, then the typical compound light microscope is about 500, and the transmission electron microscope is 100,000 (Fig. 4A*b*).

The ability to make out, or resolve, a particular object can depend on *contrast*, a difference in the shading of an object compared to its background. Higher contrast is often achieved by staining cells with colored dyes (light microscopy) or with electron-dense metals (electron microscopy), which make them easier to see. Optical methods such as phase contrast and differential interference contrast (Fig. 4B) can also be used to improve contrast. Using fluorescently tagged antibodies can also help us visualize subcellular components like specific proteins (see Fig. 4.18).

Illumination, Viewing, and Recording

Light rays can be bent (refracted) and brought to focus as they pass through glass lenses, but electrons do not pass through glass. Electrons have a charge that allows them to be brought into focus by electromagnetic lenses. The human eye uses light to see an object but cannot use electrons for the same purpose. Therefore, electrons leaving the specimen in the electron microscope are directed toward a screen or a photographic plate that is sensitive to their presence. Humans can view the image on the screen or photograph.

A major advancement in illumination has been the introduction of *confocal microscopy*, which uses a laser beam scanned across the specimen to focus on a single shallow plane within the cell. The microscopist can "optically section" the specimen by focusing up and down, and a series of optical sections can be combined in a computer to create a three-dimensional image, which can be displayed and rotated on the computer screen.

An image from a microscope may be recorded by placing a television camera where the eye would view the image. The television camera converts the light image into an electronic image, which can be entered into a computer. In *video-enhanced contrast microscopy*, the computer makes the darkest areas of the original image much darker and the lightest areas of the original much lighter. The result is a high-contrast image with deep blacks and bright whites. Even more contrast can be introduced by the computer if shades of gray are replaced by colors.

30 μm

Bright-field. Light passing through the specimen is brought directly into focus. Usually, the low level of contrast within the specimen interferes with viewing all but its largest components.

30 μm

Bright-field (stained). Dyes are used to stain the specimen. Certain components take up the dye more than other components, and therefore contrast is enhanced.

25 μm

Differential interference contrast. Optical methods are used to enhance density differences within the specimen so that certain regions appear brighter than others. This technique is used to view living cells, chromosomes, and organelle masses.

25 μm

Phase contrast. Density differences in the specimen cause light rays to come out of "phase." The microscope enhances these phase differences so that some regions of the specimen appear brighter or darker than others. The technique is widely used to observe living cells and organelles.

25 μm

Dark-field. Light is passed through the specimen at an oblique angle so that the objective lens receives only light diffracted and scattered by the object. This technique is used to view organelles, which appear quite bright against a dark field.

Figure 4B Photomicrographs of cheek cells. Bright-field microscopy is the most common form used with a compound light microscope. Other types of microscopy include differential interference contrast, phase contrast, and dark-field.

4.2 Prokaryotic Cells

Learning Outcomes

Upon completion of this section, you should be able to

1. Examine the evolutionary relatedness of prokaryotes, eukaryotes, and archaeans.
2. Describe the fundamental components of a bacterial cell.

Fundamentally, three different types of cells exist in nature. **Prokaryotic cells** [Gk. *pro*, before, and *karyon*, kernel, nucleus] are so named because they lack a membrane-enclosed nucleus. Another type of cell, called a **eukaryotic cell** [Gk. *eu*, true, and *karyon*, kernel, nucleus], has a nucleus (see Figs. 4.6 and 4.7). A third group of cells, called **archaeans** [Gk. *arkhaios*, ancient], possess qualities of both prokaryotes and eukaryotes. Prokaryotic cells and archaeans were once thought to be closely related because of their similar size and shape. Comparisons of DNA and RNA sequences now show archaeans to be biochemically distinct from prokaryotes and eukaryotes. Although we have learned more about archaeans than was previously known, we have studied prokaryotes and eukaryotes in much greater detail.

Prokaryotes as a group are one of the most abundant and diverse life-forms on Earth, and they are present in great numbers in the air, water, and soil, as well as living in and on other organisms. Although they are structurally less complicated than eukaryotes, their metabolic capabilities as a group far exceed those of eukaryotes. Prokaryotes are an extremely successful group of organisms whose evolutionary history dates back to the first cells on Earth.

Bacteria are well known because they cause some serious diseases, such as tuberculosis, anthrax, tetanus, throat infections, and gonorrhea. But many species of bacteria are important to the environment because they decompose the remains of dead organisms and contribute to ecological cycles. Bacteria also assist humans in still another way—we use them to manufacture all sorts of products, from industrial chemicals to foodstuffs and drugs. For example, today we know how to place human genes in certain cultured bacteria so that they can produce human insulin, a necessary hormone for the treatment of diabetes.

Video
E. coli Wars

The Structure of Prokaryotes

Prokaryotes are quite small; an average size is 1.1–1.5 µm wide and 2.0–6.0 µm long. While other prokaryote shapes have been identified, three basic shapes are most common:

A rod-shaped bacterium is called a **bacillus,** while a spherical-shaped bacterium is a **coccus.** Both of these can occur as pairs or chains, and in addition, cocci can occur as clusters. Some long rods are twisted into spirals, in which case they are **spirilla** if they are rigid or **spirochetes** if they are flexible.

Animation
Prokaryotic Cell Shapes

Figure 4.4 shows the generalized structure of a bacterium. "Generalized" means that not all bacteria have all the structures depicted, and some have more than one of each. Also, for the sake of discussion, we divide the organization of bacteria into the cell envelope, the cytoplasm, and the appendages.

Cell Envelope

In bacteria, the **cell envelope** includes the plasma membrane, the cell wall, and the glycocalyx. The **plasma membrane** is a phospholipid bilayer with embedded proteins:

The plasma membrane has the important function of regulating the entrance and exit of substances into and out of the cytoplasm. Regulating the flow of materials in and out of the cytoplasm is necessary in order to maintain its normal composition.

In prokaryotes, the plasma membrane can form internal pouches called mesosomes. **Mesosomes** most likely increase the internal surface area for the attachment of enzymes that are carrying on metabolic activities.

The **cell wall,** when present, maintains the shape of the cell, even if the cytoplasm should happen to take up an abundance of water. You may recall that the cell wall of a plant cell is strengthened by cellulose; in contrast, the cell wall of a bacterium contains peptidoglycan, a complex molecule containing a unique amino disaccharide and peptide fragments.

Animation
Cell Wall Antibiotics

The **glycocalyx** is a layer of polysaccharides that lies outside the cell wall in some bacteria. When the layer is well organized and not easily washed off, it is called a **capsule.** A slime layer, on the other hand, is not well organized and is easily removed. The glycocalyx aids against drying out and helps bacteria resist a host's immune system. It also helps bacteria attach to almost any surface.

Cytoplasm

The **cytoplasm** is a semifluid solution composed of water and inorganic and organic molecules encased by a plasma membrane. Among the organic molecules are a variety of enzymes, which speed the many types of chemical reactions involved in metabolism.

The DNA of a prokaryote is found in a single, coiled chromosome that is located in a region called the **nucleoid.** Many bacteria also have extrachromosomal pieces of circular DNA called **plasmids.** Plasmids are routinely used in biotechnology

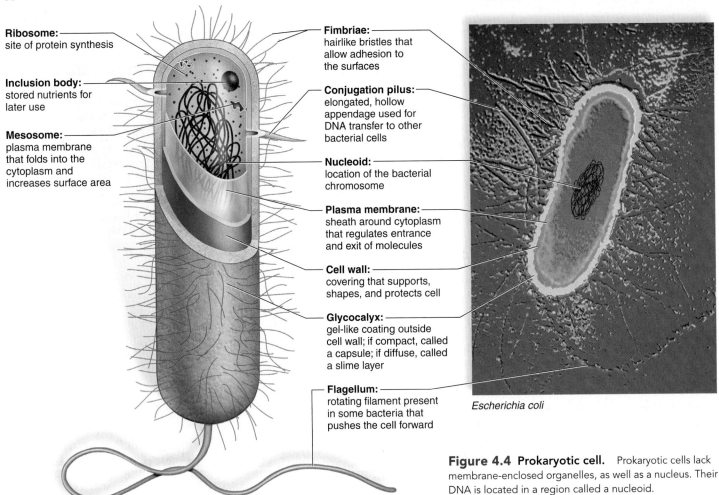

Ribosome:
site of protein synthesis

Inclusion body:
stored nutrients for
later use

Mesosome:
plasma membrane
that folds into the
cytoplasm and
increases surface area

Fimbriae:
hairlike bristles that
allow adhesion to
the surfaces

Conjugation pilus:
elongated, hollow
appendage used for
DNA transfer to other
bacterial cells

Nucleoid:
location of the bacterial
chromosome

Plasma membrane:
sheath around cytoplasm
that regulates entrance
and exit of molecules

Cell wall:
covering that supports,
shapes, and protects cell

Glycocalyx:
gel-like coating outside
cell wall; if compact, called
a capsule; if diffuse, called
a slime layer

Flagellum:
rotating filament present
in some bacteria that
pushes the cell forward

Escherichia coli

Figure 4.4 Prokaryotic cell.   Prokaryotic cells lack membrane-enclosed organelles, as well as a nucleus. Their DNA is located in a region called a nucleoid.

laboratories as a molecular vehicle, also called a **vector**, to transport DNA from different organisms, including humans, into a bacterium. This technique is possible because all life on Earth is constructed from the same four DNA nucleotides: A, G, C, and T. The ability to combine genes from different life-forms is important in the production of new medicines and many commerical products we use every day.

The many proteins encoded by the bacterial DNA are synthesized on tiny structures called **ribosomes.** A bacterial cell contains thousands of ribosomes that are similar in shape and function, but are smaller than eukaryotic ribosomes. Like their eukaryotic counterparts, bacterial ribosomes still contain RNA and protein in two subunits.

Most bacteria carry out metabolism in the same manner as animals, but the **cyanobacteria** are bacteria that are capable of photosynthesis in the same manner as plants. These organisms live in water, in ditches, on buildings, and on the bark of trees. Their cytoplasm contains extensive internal membranes called **thylakoids** [Gk. *thylakon,* small sac], where chlorophyll and other pigments absorb solar energy for the production of carbohydrates. Cyanobacteria are called the blue-green bacteria because some have a pigment that adds a shade of blue to the cell, in addition to the green color of chlorophyll. The cyanobacteria release oxygen as a by-product of photosynthesis, which is one reason why scientists think that ancestral cyanobacteria were the earliest photosynthesizers on Earth. Many sources of evidence show that the composition of the early Earth's atmosphere was changed by addition of oxygen.

Appendages

The appendages of a bacterium, namely the flagella, fimbriae, and conjugation pili, are made of protein. Motile bacteria can propel themselves in water by the means of appendages called **flagella** (usually 20 nm in diameter and 1–70 nm long). The bacterial flagellum is one of the great wonders of nature, and it consists of a filament, a hook, and a basal body. The basal body is a series of rings anchored in the cell wall and membrane. The hook rotates 360° within the basal body, and this rotation propels bacteria—the bacterial flagellum does not move back and forth like a whip. Sometimes flagella occur only at the two ends of a cell, and sometimes they are dispersed randomly over the surface. The number and location of flagella can be used to help distinguish different types of bacteria.

Animation
Bacterial
Locomotion

Fimbriae are small, bristlelike fibers that sprout from the cell surface. They are not involved in locomotion; instead, fimbriae attach bacteria to a surface. **Conjugation pili** are rigid tubular structures used by bacteria to pass DNA from cell to cell. Bacteria reproduce asexually by binary fission, but they can exchange DNA by way of the conjugation pili. They also take up DNA from the external medium or by way of viruses.

Check Your Progress   4.2

1. Explain the major differences between a prokaryotic and eukaryotic cell.
2. Describe the functions of the bacterial cell envelope, cytoplasm, and appendages.

4.3 Introducing Eukaryotic Cells

Learning Outcomes

Upon completion of this section, you should be able to

1. Explain how membranes compartmentalize a cell.
2. Examine how organelles divide cellular work.
3. Apply the endosymbiosis theory to eukaryotic cell structure.

Eukaryotic cells, like prokaryotic cells and archaeans, have a plasma membrane that separates the contents of the cell from the environment and regulates the passage of molecules into and out of the cytoplasm. The plasma membrane is a phospholipid bilayer with embedded proteins. Some scientists have suggested that the nucleus evolved as the result of the invagination, or pocketing, of the plasma membrane (Fig. 4.5). The resulting compartment may have allowed specific functions to occur in the nucleus, freeing up cellular resources in the cytoplasm for other work. An increased ability to metabolize would have given the new cell a comparative advantage over other cells.

Origin of the Eukaryotic Cell

Much scientific evidence also shows that mitochondria and chloroplasts, the two energy-related organelles, arose when a large eukaryotic cell engulfed independent prokaryotes. This relationship is referred to as the **endosymbiotic theory.** This theory explains why mitochondria and chloroplasts are bounded by a double membrane and contain their own genetic material separate from that of the nucleus.

Figure 4.5 shows conceptually how endosymbiosis is thought to have occurred. Figures 4.6 and 4.7 show general features of fully evolved, present day animal and plant cells. Specialized cells, as opposed to generalized cells, do not necessarily contain all the structures depicted and may have more or fewer copies of any particular organelle, depending on their particular function. These generalized depictions of plant and animal cells are useful for study purposes. A baseline understanding of cell structure and function will be helpful when you study the function of specialized cells later in this text.

Structure of a Eukaryotic Cell

As shown in Figures 4.6 and 4.7, eukaryotic cells are compartmentalized. Membranes create internal spaces that divide the labor necessary to conduct life functions. The compartments of a eukaryotic cell, typically called **organelles,** carry out specialized functions that together allow the cell to be more efficient and successful. Nearly all organelles are surrounded by a membrane with embedded proteins, many of which are enzymes. These enzymes make products specific to that organelle, but their action benefits the whole cell system. The cell can be seen as a system of interconnected organelles that work together to metabolize, regulate, and conduct life processes. For example, the nucleus is a compartment that houses the genetic material within eukaryotic chromosomes and contains hereditary information. The nucleus communicates with ribosomes in the cytoplasm, and the organelles of the endomembrane system—notably the endoplasmic reticulum and the Golgi apparatus—communicate with one another.

Production of specific molecules takes place inside or on the surface of organelles. As mentioned, enzymes embedded in the organelles' membranes make these molecules. These products are then transported around the cell by transport **vesicles,** membranous sacs that enclose the molecules and keep them separate from the cytoplasm. For example, the endoplasmic reticulum communicates with the Golgi apparatus by means of transport vesicles. Communication with the energy-related organelles—mitochondria and chloroplasts—is less obvious, but it does occur because they import particular molecules from the cytoplasm.

MP3
Cellular Organelles

Original prokaryotic cell

DNA

1. Cell gains a nucleus by the plasma membrane invaginating and surrounding the DNA with a double membrane.

Nucleus allows specific functions to be assigned, freeing up cellular resources for other work.

2. Cell gains an endomembrane system by proliferation of membrane.

Increased surface area allows higher rate of transport of materials within a cell.

3. Cell gains mitochondria.

Ability to metabolize sugars in the presence of oxygen enables greater function and success.

aerobic bacterium

mitochondrion

4. Cell gains chloroplasts.

Ability to produce sugars from sunlight enables greater function and success.

photosynthetic bacterium

chloroplast

Animal cell has mitochondria, but not chloroplasts.

Plant cell has both mitochondria and chloroplasts.

Figure 4.5 Origin of organelles. Invagination of the plasma membrane could have created the nuclear envelope and an endomembrane system that involves several organelles. The endosymbiotic theory states that mitochondria and chloroplasts were independent prokaryotes that took up residence in a eukaryotic cell. Endosymbiosis was a first step toward the origin of the eukaryotic cell during the evolutionary history of life.

Figure 4.6 Animal cell anatomy. Micrograph of an insect cell (*right*) and drawing of a generalized animal cell (*below*).

2.5 μm

Plasma membrane: outer surface that regulates entrance and exit of molecules

protein

phospholipid

Cytoskeleton: maintains cell shape and assists movement of cell parts:

• **Microtubules:** protein cylinders that move organelles

• **Intermediate filaments:** protein fibers that provide stability of shape

• **Actin filaments:** protein fibers that play a role in cell division and shape

Centrioles*: short cylinders of microtubules

Centrosome: microtubule organizing center that contains a pair of centrioles

Lysosome*: vesicle that digests macromolecules and even cell parts

Vesicle: small membrane-bounded sac that stores and transports substances

Cytoplasm: semifluid matrix outside nucleus that contains organelles

Golgi apparatus: processes, packages, and secretes modified proteins

*not in plant cells

Nucleus: command center of cell

• **Nuclear envelope:** double membrane with nuclear pores that encloses nucleus

• **Chromatin:** diffuse threads containing DNA and protein

• **Nucleolus:** region that produces subunits of ribosomes

Endoplasmic reticulum: protein and lipid metabolism

• **Rough ER:** studded with ribosomes that synthesize proteins

• **Smooth ER:** lacks ribosomes, synthesizes lipid molecules

Peroxisome: vesicle that is involved in fatty acid metabolism

Ribosomes: particles that carry out protein synthesis

Polyribosome: string of ribosomes simultaneously synthesizing same protein

Mitochondrion: organelle that carries out cellular respiration, producing ATP molecules

mitochondrion

chromatin

nucleolus

nuclear envelope

endoplasmic reticulum

Vesicles move around by means of an extensive network or lattice of protein fibers called the **cytoskeleton,** which also maintains cell shape and assists with cell movement. The protein fibers serve as tracks for the transport vesicles that are taking molecules from one organelle to another. Organelles are also moved from place to place using this transport system. Think of the cytoskeleton as a three-dimensional road system inside cells used to transport important cargo from place to place. The cytoskeleton is discussed in detail later in this chapter.

In addition to the plasma membrane, some eukaryotic cells, notably plant cells and those of fungi and many protists, have a cell wall. A plant cell wall contains cellulose fibrils and, therefore, has a different composition from the bacterial cell wall.

Cells can vary the proportion of organelles they have, depending on the specialized function of the cell. For example, a liver cell whose function is partly to detoxify drugs and other ingested compounds contains a greater proportion of smooth

peroxisome
mitochondrion
nucleus
ribosomes
central vacuole
plasma membrane
cell wall
chloroplast

Figure 4.7 Plant cell anatomy. False-colored micrograph of a young plant cell (*left*) and drawing of a generalized plant cell (*below*).

1 μm

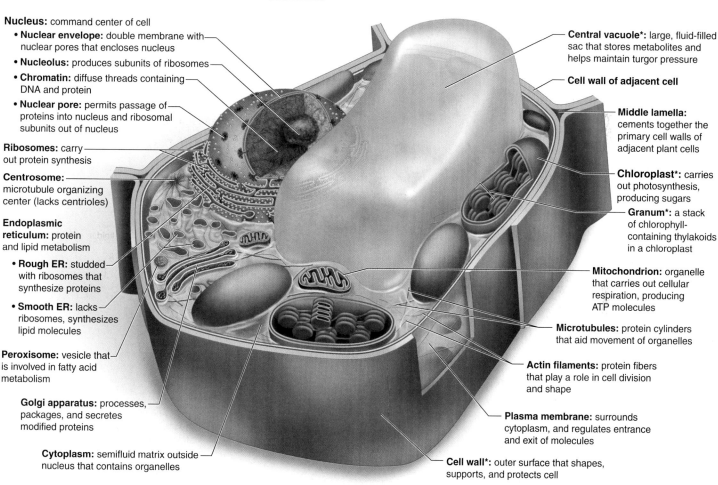

Nucleus: command center of cell
- **Nuclear envelope:** double membrane with nuclear pores that encloses nucleus
- **Nucleolus:** produces subunits of ribosomes
- **Chromatin:** diffuse threads containing DNA and protein
- **Nuclear pore:** permits passage of proteins into nucleus and ribosomal subunits out of nucleus

Ribosomes: carry out protein synthesis

Centrosome: microtubule organizing center (lacks centrioles)

Endoplasmic reticulum: protein and lipid metabolism
- **Rough ER:** studded with ribosomes that synthesize proteins
- **Smooth ER:** lacks ribosomes, synthesizes lipid molecules

Peroxisome: vesicle that is involved in fatty acid metabolism

Golgi apparatus: processes, packages, and secretes modified proteins

Cytoplasm: semifluid matrix outside nucleus that contains organelles

Central vacuole*: large, fluid-filled sac that stores metabolites and helps maintain turgor pressure

Cell wall of adjacent cell

Middle lamella: cements together the primary cell walls of adjacent plant cells

Chloroplast*: carries out photosynthesis, producing sugars

Granum*: a stack of chlorophyll-containing thylakoids in a chloroplast

Mitochondrion: organelle that carries out cellular respiration, producing ATP molecules

Microtubules: protein cylinders that aid movement of organelles

Actin filaments: protein fibers that play a role in cell division and shape

Plasma membrane: surrounds cytoplasm, and regulates entrance and exit of molecules

Cell wall*: outer surface that shapes, supports, and protects cell

*not in animal cells

endoplasmic reticulum, the organelle that accomplishes that task. A nerve cell, whose job is to conduct electrical signals across long distances, contains more plasma membrane relative to other cells. Other cells may specialize so extensively that they completely lose an organelle, like a red blood cell that ejects its nucleus to increase the surface area needed to carry oxygen in the blood. The Nature of Science feature describes the process by which investigators were able to discover the structure and function of various organelles.

Check Your Progress 4.3

1. Describe three benefits of compartmentalization found in cells.
2. Examine why organelles increase cell efficiency and function.
3. Infer how the proportion of organelles might differ between a muscle cell and a nerve cell.

4.4 The Nucleus and Ribosomes

The nucleus is essential to the life of a cell. It contains the genetic information that is passed on from cell to cell and from generation to generation. It specifies the information that ribosomes use to carry out protein synthesis. It also contains instructions for copying itself.

The Nucleus

The nucleus, which has a diameter of about 5 μm, is a prominent structure in the eukaryotic cell (Fig. 4.8). It generally appears as an oval structure located near the center of most cells. Some cells, such as skeletal muscle cells, can have more than one nucleus. The nucleus contains **chromatin** [Gk. *chroma*, color,

and *teino*, stretch] in a semifluid matrix called the **nucleoplasm.** Chromatin looks grainy, but actually it is a network of strands that condenses and undergoes coiling into rodlike structures called **chromosomes** [Gk. *chroma*, color, and *soma*, body], just before the cell divides. All the cells of an individual contain the same number of chromosomes, and the mechanics of nuclear division ensure that each daughter cell receives the normal number of chromosomes, except for the egg and sperm, which usually have half this number. This alone suggested to early investigators that the chromosomes are the carriers of genetic information and that the nucleus is the command center of the cell.

Chromatin, and therefore chromosomes, contains DNA, protein, and some RNA (ribonucleic acid). **Genes,** composed of DNA, are units of heredity located on the chromosomes.

Three types of RNA are produced in the nucleus: *ribosomal RNA (rRNA), messenger RNA (mRNA),* and *transfer RNA (tRNA).* Ribosomal RNA is produced in the **nucleolus,** a dark region of chromatin where rRNA joins with proteins to form the subunits of ribosomes. Ribosomes are small bodies in the cytoplasm that facilitate protein synthesis. Messenger RNA, a mobile molecule, acts as an intermediary for DNA, a sedentary molecule, which specifies the sequence of amino acids in a protein. Transfer RNA participates in the assembly of amino acids into a polypeptide by recognizing both mRNA and amino acids during protein synthesis.

Nuclear envelope:
- inner membrane
- outer membrane
- nuclear pore

- nuclear envelope
- nucleolus
- nuclear pore
- chromatin
- nucleoplasm

phospholipid

Figure 4.8 Anatomy of the nucleus. The nucleus contains chromatin. The nucleolus is a region of chromatin where ribosomal RNA is produced, and ribosomal subunits are assembled. The nuclear envelope contains pores, as shown in the larger micrograph of a freeze-fractured nuclear envelope. Each pore is lined by a complex of eight proteins, as shown in the smaller micrograph and drawing. Nuclear pore complexes serve as passageways for substances to pass into and out of the nucleus.

The nucleus is important to cell structure and function because it specifies the code to make proteins. Although the nucleus is physically separated from the cytoplasm by a double membrane known as the **nuclear envelope,** it is still able to communicate with the cytoplasm through nuclear pores. **Nuclear pores** are of sufficient size (100 nm) to permit the passage of ribosomal subunits and mRNA out of the nucleus into the cytoplasm, and the passage of proteins from the cytoplasm into the nucleus. High-resolution electron micrographs show that nonmembrane components associated with the pores form a nuclear pore complex. Nuclear pore complexes act like gatekeepers to regulate what comes in and goes out of a nucleus.

Ribosomes

Ribosomes are particles where protein synthesis occurs. A large and small ribosomal subunit, each comprised of a mix of proteins and rRNA, are necessary components of a functional ribosome. In eukaryotes, ribosomes are 20 nm by 30 nm, and in prokaryotes they are slightly smaller. The number of ribosomes in a cell varies depending on its functions; for example, pancreatic cells and those of other glands have many ribosomes because they produce secretions that contain proteins.

In eukaryotic cells, some ribosomes occur freely within the cytoplasm, either singly or in groups called **polyribosomes,** whereas others are attached to the endoplasmic reticulum (ER), a membranous system of flattened saccules (small sacs) and tubules,

which is discussed more fully in the next section. In the nucleus, a gene is copied into mRNA, which is exported through a nuclear pore complex into the cytoplasm. Ribosomes receive the mRNA, which carries a coded message from DNA indicating the correct sequence of amino acids in a particular protein. Proteins synthesized by cytoplasmic ribosomes are used in the cytoplasm, and those synthesized by attached ribosomes end up in the ER.

What causes a ribosome to bind to the endoplasmic reticulum? Binding occurs only if the protein being synthesized by a ribosome begins with a sequence of amino acids called a **signal peptide.** The signal peptide binds a particle (signal recognition particle, SRP), which then binds to a receptor on the ER. Once the protein enters the ER, an enzyme cleaves off the signal peptide, and the protein ends up within the lumen (interior) of the ER, where it folds into its final shape (Fig. 4.9).

The sequence of DNA being transcribed into mRNA, and this in turn being translated into a protein, occurs in all living cells, at least during some point in their lifespan. Because of its universality, the DNA—mRNA—protein sequence of events is termed the *central dogma of molecular biology.*

Check Your Progress   4.4

1. Explain the importance of nuclear pore complexes.
2. Describe the sequence of events from a gene to a functional protein.

1. mRNA is first copied from a gene, and then it exits the nucleus through a pore complex. A ribosome attaches and begins protein synthesis, producing a signal peptide.

Nucleus

DNA

mRNA

nuclear pore

mRNA

ribosome

signal peptide

2. Signal recognition particle (SRP) binds to signal peptide and temporarily halts protein synthesis.

signal recognition particle (SRP)

receptor

Cytoplasm

3. SRP binds to receptor (purple); a channel opens; SRP leaves and allows protein synthesis to resume; as polypeptide is synthesized it is simultaneously fed into ER.

SRP

enzyme

Endoplasmic reticulum (ER)

Lumen of ER

ER membrane

4. An enzyme removes the signal peptide from the growing polypeptide.

ribosomal subunits

mRNA

5. Ribosomal subunits and mRNA break away. The polypeptide remains in the ER and folds into a functional protein.

protein

Figure 4.9 Function of ribosomes.   Ribosomes are sites of protein synthesis. An mRNA molecule, serving as a temporary copy of a gene from the nucleus, is read by a ribosome in the cytoplasm. Amino acids are connected together by the ribosome in a sequence specified by the mRNA. When a polypeptide is first translated, it begins with a signal peptide; this combines with a signal recognition particle (SRP), which is brought to the rough ER. The SRP leaves, and the polypeptide is made and pushed into the ER lumen. The signal peptide is removed and the polypeptide folds into its final protein shape.

4.5 The Endomembrane System

Learning Outcomes

Upon completion of this section, you should be able to

1. Explain the importance of the endomembrane system in cellular function.
2. Examine how ER, Golgi, and lysosome membranes differ from one another.
3. Describe how endomembrane vesicles are able to fuse with organelles.

The **endomembrane system** consists of the nuclear envelope, the membranes of the endoplasmic reticulum, the Golgi apparatus, and several types of vesicles. This system compartmentalizes the cell so that particular enzymatic reactions are restricted to specific regions and overall cell efficiency is increased. The vesicles transport molecules from one part of the system to another.

Endoplasmic Reticulum

The **endoplasmic reticulum (ER)** [Gk. *endon,* within; *plasma,* something molded; L. *reticulum,* net], consisting of a complicated system of membranous channels and saccules (flattened vesicles), is physically continuous with the nuclear envelope (Fig. 4.10). The ER consists of rough ER and smooth ER, which have different structures and functions.

Rough ER is studded with ribosomes on the side of the membrane that faces the cytoplasm, giving it the capacity to produce proteins. Inside its lumen, the rough ER allows proteins to fold and take on their final three-dimensional shape. The rough ER also contains enzymes that can add carbohydrate (sugar) chains to proteins, forming glycoproteins, that are important in many cell functions.

Smooth ER, which is continuous with the nuclear envelope and the rough ER, does not have attached ribosomes. Certain organs contain cells with an abundance of smooth ER, depending on the organ's function. In some organs, increased smooth ER helps produce more lipids. For example, in the testes, smooth ER produces testosterone, a steroid hormone. In the liver, smooth ER helps detoxify drugs. The smooth ER of the liver increases in quantity when a person consumes alcohol or takes barbiturates on a regular basis. Regardless of functional differences, both rough and smooth ER form vesicles that transport molecules to other parts of the cell, notably the Golgi apparatus.

The Golgi Apparatus

The **Golgi apparatus** is named for Camillo Golgi (1843-1926), who discovered its presence in cells in 1898. The Golgi apparatus typically consists of a stack of three to twenty slightly curved, flattened saccules whose appearance can be compared to a stack of pancakes (Fig. 4.11). In animal cells, one side of the stack (the *cis* or inner face) is directed toward the ER, and the other side of the stack (the *trans* or outer face) is directed toward the plasma membrane. Vesicles can frequently be seen at the edges of the saccules.

Protein-filled vesicles that bud from the rough ER and lipid-filled vesicles that bud from the smooth ER are received by the Golgi apparatus at its inner face. These substances are altered as they move through the saccules. For example, the Golgi apparatus contains enzymes that modify the carbohydrate chains first attached to proteins in the rough ER. It can change or modify one sugar into another sugar on glycoproteins. In some cases, the modified carbohydrate chain serves as a signal molecule or molecular address label that determines the protein's final destination in the cell.

The Golgi apparatus sorts the modified molecules and packages them into vesicles that depart from the outer face. These vesicles may be transported to various locations within the cell,

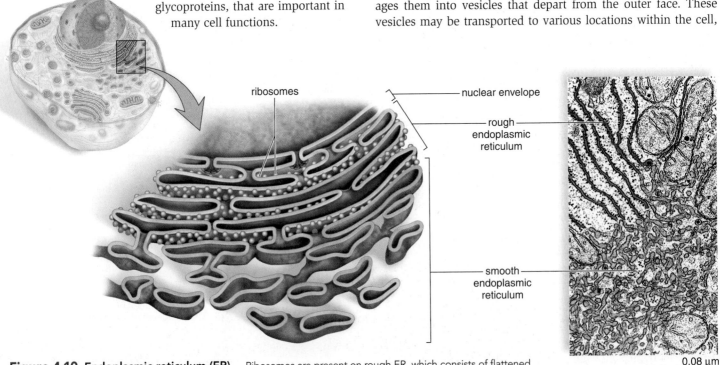

ribosomes

nuclear envelope

rough endoplasmic reticulum

smooth endoplasmic reticulum

0.08 µm

Figure 4.10 Endoplasmic reticulum (ER). Ribosomes are present on rough ER, which consists of flattened saccules, but not on smooth ER, which is more tubular. Proteins are synthesized by rough ER. Smooth ER is involved in lipid synthesis, detoxification reactions, and several other possible functions.

Figure 4.11 **Golgi apparatus.**   The Golgi apparatus is a stack of flattened, curved saccules. It processes proteins and lipids and packages them in transport vesicles that distribute these molecules to various locations within the cell, or secrete them externally.

a. Mitochondrion and a peroxisome in a lysosome

b. Storage bodies in a cell with defective lysosomes

Figure 4.12 **Lysosomes.**   **a.** Lysosomes, which bud off the Golgi apparatus in cells, are filled with hydrolytic enzymes that digest molecules and parts of the cell. Here a lysosome digests a worn mitochondrion and a peroxisome. **b.** The nerve cells of a person with Tay-Sachs disease are filled with membranous cytoplasmic bodies storing a fat that lysosomes are unable to digest.

depending on their molecular address label. In animal cells, some of these vesicles are lysosomes, which are discussed next. Other vesicles may return to the ER or proceed to the plasma membrane, where they merge and discharge their contents to the outside of the cell during **secretion.** Secretion is termed exocytosis because the substance exits the cytoplasm.

Lysosomes

Lysosomes [Gk. *lyo,* loose, and *soma,* body] are membrane-bounded vesicles produced by the Golgi apparatus. They have a very low pH and store powerful hydrolytic-digestive enzymes in an inactive state. Lysosomes act much like your stomach in that they assist in digesting material taken into the cell. They also destroy nonfunctional organelles and portions of cytoplasm (Fig. 4.12).

Materials can be brought into a cell by vesicle or vacuole formation at the plasma membrane. When a lysosome fuses with either, the lysosomal enzymes are activated and digest the material into simpler subunits that are exported into the cytoplasm

and recycled by other cell processes. White blood cells, specialized to protect the body from foreign entities, are well known for engulfing pathogens (e.g., disease-causing viruses and bacteria) that are then broken down in lysosomes. White blood cells have a greater proportion of lysosomes than other cells because their specialized function is digestion of foreign bodies.

A number of human lysosomal storage diseases are due to a missing lysosomal enzyme. In Tay-Sachs disease, the missing enzyme digests a fatty substance that helps insulate nerve cells and increases their efficiency. The fatty substance accumulates in so many storage bodies that nerve cells die off. Affected individuals appear normal at birth but begin to develop neurological problems at four to six months of age. Eventually, the child suffers cerebral degeneration, slow paralysis, blindness, and loss of motor function. Children with Tay-Sachs disease live only about three to four years. In the future, it may be possible to provide the missing enzyme and, in that way, prevent lysosomal storage diseases.

Animation
Lysosomes

Endomembrane System Summary

You have seen that the endomembrane system is a series of membranous organelles that work together and communicate by means of transport vesicles. The endoplasmic reticulum (ER) and the Golgi apparatus are essentially flattened saccules, and lysosomes are specialized vesicles.

Organelles within the endomembrane system can interact because their membranes readily fuse together, and because membrane-associated proteins enable communication and specialized functions. Figure 4.13 shows how the components of the endomembrane system work together. Products of both rough ER and smooth ER are carried in transport vesicles to the Golgi apparatus, where they are further modified. Using signaling sequences and molecular address labels, the Golgi apparatus sorts these products and packages them into vesicles that transport them to various cellular destinations. Secretory vesicles take the proteins

to the plasma membrane, where they exit the cell by exocytosis. For example, secretion into ducts occurs when the mammary glands produce milk or the pancreas produces digestive enzymes.

In animal cells, the Golgi apparatus also produces lysosomes that contain stored hydrolytic enzymes. Lysosomes fuse with incoming vesicles from the plasma membrane and digest macromolecules brought into a cell.

Check Your Progress   4.5

1. Contrast the structure and functions of rough and smooth endoplasmic reticulum.
2. Describe the relationship between the components of the endomembrane system.
3. Examine how cellular function would be affected if the Golgi apparatus ceased to function.

Figure 4.13
Endomembrane system.
The organelles in the endomembrane system work together to carry out the functions noted. Plant cells do not have lysosomes, nor do they have incoming and outgoing (secretory) vesicles.

Consumption

Secretion

5. Secretion

plasma membrane

Incoming vesicle brings substances into the cell that are digested when the vesicle fuses with a lysosome.

4. **Secretory vesicle** fuses with the plasma membrane as secretion occurs.

enzyme

Lysosome contains digestive enzymes that break down worn-out cell parts or substances entering the cell at the plasma membrane.

3. **Golgi apparatus** modifies lipids and proteins from the ER; sorts them and packages them in vesicles.

protein

2. **Transport vesicle** shuttles proteins to various locations such as the Golgi apparatus.

Transport vesicle shuttles lipids to various locations such as the Golgi apparatus.

lipid

Smooth endoplasmic reticulum synthesizes lipids and also performs various other functions.

1. **Rough endoplasmic reticulum** synthesizes proteins and packages them in vesicles; vesicles commonly go to the Golgi apparatus

ribosome

Nucleus

4.6 Other Vesicles and Vacuoles

Learning Outcomes

Upon completion of this section, you should be able to

1. Describe the role of peroxisomes and vacuoles in cell function.

2. Contrast peroxisomes and vacuoles with endomembrane organelles.

Peroxisomes and the vacuoles of cells do not communicate with the organelles of the endomembrane system, and therefore are not part of it.

Peroxisomes

Peroxisomes, similar to lysosomes, are membrane-bounded vesicles that enclose enzymes. However, the enzymes in peroxisomes are synthesized by free ribosomes and transported into a peroxisome from the cytoplasm. All peroxisomes contain enzymes whose actions result in hydrogen peroxide (H_2O_2):

$$RH_2 + O_2 \longrightarrow R + H_2O_2$$

Hydrogen peroxide, a toxic molecule, is immediately broken down to water and oxygen by another peroxisomal enzyme called catalase. When hydrogen peroxide is applied to a wound, bubbling occurs as catalase breaks it down.

Peroxisomes are metabolic assistants to the other organelles. They have varied functions but are especially prevalent in cells that synthesize and break down lipids. In the liver, some peroxisomes produce bile salts from cholesterol, and others break down fats. The 1992 film *Lorenzo's Oil* is based on a medical case of a boy with defective peroxisomes. Lorenzo Odone's peroxisomes lacked a membrane protein

Figure 4.15 Plant cell central vacuole. The large central vacuole of plant cells has numerous functions, from storing molecules to helping the cell increase in size.

100 nm

needed to import a specific enzyme and/or long chain fatty acids from the cytoplasm. As a result, long-chain fatty acids accumulated in his brain, and he suffered neurological damage. This disorder is known as adrenoleukodystrophy (ALD).

Plant cells also have peroxisomes (Fig. 4.14). In germinating seeds, they oxidize fatty acids into molecules that can be converted to sugars needed by the growing plant. In leaves, peroxisomes can carry out a reaction that is opposite to photosynthesis—the reaction uses up oxygen and releases carbon dioxide.

Vacuoles

Like vesicles, **vacuoles** are membranous sacs, but vacuoles are larger than vesicles. The vacuoles of some protists are quite specialized, including contractile vacuoles for ridding the cell of excess water and digestive vacuoles for breaking down nutrients. Vacuoles usually store substances. In general, few animal cells contain vacuoles; however, fat cells contain a very large lipid-engorged vacuole that takes up nearly two-thirds of the volume of the cell!

Vacuoles are essential to plant function. Plant vacuoles contain not only water, sugars, and salts but also water-soluble pigments and toxic molecules. The pigments are responsible for many of the red, blue, or purple colors of flowers and some leaves. The toxic substances help protect a land plant from herbivorous animals.

Plant Cell Central Vacuole

Typically, plant cells have a large **central vacuole** that may take up to 90% of the volume of the cell. The vacuole is filled with a watery fluid called cell sap that gives added support to the cell (Fig. 4.15). The central vacuole maintains hydrostatic pressure or turgor pressure in plant cells, which provides structural

100 nm

Figure 4.14 Peroxisomes. Peroxisomes contain one or more enzymes that can oxidize various organic substances.

support. A plant cell can rapidly increase in size by enlarging its vacuole. Eventually, a plant cell also produces more cytoplasm.

The central vacuole functions in storage of both nutrients and waste products. Metabolic waste products are pumped across the vacuole membrane and stored permanently in the central vacuole. As organelles age and become nonfunctional, they fuse with the vacuole, where digestive enzymes break them down. This is an analogous function to that carried out by lysosomes in animal cells.

Check Your Progress   4.6

1. Compare the structure and functions of a peroxisome with a lysosome.
2. Distinguish between where peroxisome and lysosome proteins are produced.

Figure 4.16 Chloroplast structure. Chloroplasts carry out photosynthesis. **a.** Electron micrograph of a longitudinal section of a chloroplast. **b.** Generalized drawing of a chloroplast in which the outer and inner membranes have been cut away to reveal the grana, each of which is a stack of membranous sacs called thylakoids. In some grana, but not all, thylakoid spaces are interconnected.

a.

500 nm

double membrane — outer membrane / inner membrane — grana — stroma — thylakoid space — thylakoid membrane

b.

4.7 The Energy-Related Organelles

Learning Outcomes

Upon completion of this section, you should be able to

1. Compare the energy management of cellular respiration versus photosynthesis.
2. Describe the evidence that suggests chloroplasts and mitochondria are derived from ancient bacteria and endosymbiosis.
3. Explain why increased membrane surface area is necessary for chloroplast and mitochondrial function.

Life is possible only because a constant input of energy maintains the structure of cells. Chloroplasts and mitochondria are the two eukaryotic membranous organelles that specialize in converting energy to a form that can be used by the cell. Although animal cells contain only mitochodria, plant cells contain both mitochondria and chloroplasts.

During photosynthesis, **chloroplasts** [Gk. *chloros,* green, and *plastos,* formed, molded] use solar energy to synthesize carbohydrates, which serve as organic nutrient molecules for plants and all living things on Earth. *Photosynthesis* can be represented by this equation:

solar energy + carbon dioxide + water → carbohydrate + oxygen

Plants, algae, and cyanobacteria are capable of conducting photosynthesis in this manner, but only plants and algae have chloroplasts because they are eukaryotes.

In cellular respiration, **mitochondria** (sing., mitochondrion) break down carbohydrate-derived products to produce ATP (adenosine triphosphate). *Cellular respiration* can be represented by this equation:

carbohydrate + oxygen → carbon dioxide + water + energy

Here the word *energy* stands for ATP molecules. When a cell needs energy, ATP supplies it. The energy of ATP is used to drive synthetic reactions, active transport, and all energy-requiring processes in cells.

Chloroplasts

Some algal cells have only one chloroplast, while some plant cells have as many as a hundred. Chloroplasts can be quite large, being twice as wide and as much as five times the length of a mitochondrion.

Chloroplasts have a three-membrane system (Fig. 4.16). They are bounded by a double membrane, which includes an outer membrane and an inner membrane. The double membrane encloses the semifluid **stroma,** which contains enzymes and **thylakoids,** disk-like sacs formed from a third chloroplast membrane. A stack of thylakoids is a **granum.** The lumens of the thylakoids are believed to form a large internal compartment called the thylakoid space. Chlorophyll and the other pigments that capture solar energy are located in the thylakoid membrane, and the enzymes that synthesize carbohydrates are located outside the thylakoid in the fluid of the stroma.

The endosymbiotic theory holds that chloroplasts are derived from a photosynthetic bacterium that was engulfed by a eukaryotic cell. This certainly explains why a chloroplast is bounded by a double membrane—one membrane is derived from the vesicle that brought the prokaryote into the cell, while the inner membrane is derived from the prokaryote. The endosymbiotic theory is also supported by the finding that chloroplasts have their own prokaryotic-type chromosome and ribosomes, and they produce some of their own enzymes even today.

Other Types of Plastids

A chloroplast is a type of plastid. **Plastids** are plant organelles that are surrounded by a double membrane and have varied functions. **Chromoplasts** contain pigments that result in a yellow, orange, or red color. Chromoplasts are responsible for the color of autumn leaves, fruits, carrots, and some flowers. **Leucoplasts** are generally colorless plastids that synthesize and store starches and oils. A microscopic examination of potato tissue reveals a number of leucoplasts.

Mitochondria

Nearly all eukaryotic cells, and certainly all plant and algal cells in addition to animal cells, contain mitochondria. Even though mitochondria are smaller than chloroplasts, they can usually be seen using a light microscope. The number of mitochondria can vary depending on the metabolic activities and energy needed within a cell. Some cells, such as liver cells, may have as many as 1,000 mitochondria.

We think of mitochondria as having a shape like that shown in Figure 4.17, but actually they often change shape to be longer and thinner or shorter and broader. Mitochondria can form long, moving chains, or they can remain fixed in one location—typically where energy is most needed. For example, they are packed between the contractile elements of cardiac cells and wrapped around the interior of a sperm's flagellum. In contrast, fat cells contain few mitochondria—they function in fat storage, which does not require energy.

Mitochondria have two membranes, the outer membrane and the inner membrane. The inner membrane is highly convoluted into folds called **cristae** that project into the matrix. These cristae increase the surface area of the inner membrane so much that in a liver cell they account for about one-third the total membrane in the cell. The inner membrane encloses a semifluid **matrix,** which contains mitochondrial DNA and ribosomes. Again, the presence of a double membrane and mitochondrial genes is consistent with the endosymbiotic theory regarding the origin of mitochondria, which was illustrated in Figure 4.5.

Mitochondria are often called the powerhouses of the cell because they produce most of the ATP utilized by the cell. The procedure described in the Nature of Science feature on page 63 allowed investigators to separate the inner membrane, the outer membrane, and the matrix from each other. Then they discovered that the matrix is a highly concentrated mixture of enzymes that break down carbohydrates and other nutrient molecules. These reactions supply the chemical energy needed for a chain of proteins on the inner membrane to create the conditions that allow ATP synthesis to take place. The entire process, which also involves the cytoplasm, is called cellular respiration because oxygen is used and carbon dioxide is given off, as shown at the beginning of this section.

Animation
Endosymbiosis

**Figure 4.17
Mitochondrion
structure.** Mitochondria are involved in cellular respiration. **a.** Electron micrograph of a longitudinal section of a mitochondrion. **b.** Generalized drawing in which the outer membrane and portions of the inner membrane have been cut away to reveal the cristae.

a.   200 nm

double membrane ⎧ outer membrane / inner membrane ⎫   cristae   matrix

b.

Mitochondrial Diseases

So far, more than 40 different mitochondrial diseases that affect the brain, muscles, kidneys, heart, liver, eyes, ears, or pancreas have been identified. The common factor among these genetic diseases is that the patient's mitochondria are unable to completely metabolize organic molecules to produce ATP. As a result, toxins accumulate inside the mitochondria and the body. The toxins can be free radicals (substances that readily form harmful compounds when they react with other molecules), and these compounds damage mitochondria over time. In the United States, between 1,000 and 4,000 children per year are born with a mitochondrial disease. In addition, it is possible that many diseases of aging are due to malfunctioning mitochondria.

Video
Aging Secret

Check Your Progress   4.7

1. Discuss the evidence that chloroplasts and mitochondria are derived from ancient bacteria.
2. Explain the role of ATP in photosynthesis and cellular respiration.

4.8 The Cytoskeleton

Cells are exposed to many physical forces. Cell shape, movement, and internal transport all require structural support provided by the cytoskeleton. The protein components of the cytoskeleton [Gk. *kytos,* cell, and *skeleton,* dried body] interconnect and extend from the nucleus to the plasma membrane in eukaryotic cells. Prior to the 1970s, it was believed that the cytoplasm was an unorganized mixture of organic molecules. Then, high-voltage electron microscopes, which can penetrate thicker specimens, showed instead that the cytoplasm was highly organized. The technique of immunofluorescence microscopy identified the makeup of the protein components within the cytoskeletal network (Fig. 4.18).

The cytoskeleton contains actin filaments, intermediate filaments, and microtubules, which maintain cell shape and allow the cell and its organelles to move. Therefore, the cytoskeleton is often compared to the bones and muscles of an animal. However, the cytoskeleton is dynamic, and can rearrange its protein components as necessary in response to changes in internal and external environments. A number of different mechanisms appear to regulate this process, including protein phosphatases, which remove phosphates from proteins and bring about assembly, and protein kinases, which phosphorylate proteins and lead to disassembly.

Actin Filaments

Actin filaments (formerly called microfilaments) are long, extremely thin, flexible fibers (about 7 nm in diameter) that occur in bundles or meshlike networks. Each actin filament contains two chains of globular actin monomers twisted about one another in a helical manner.

Actin filaments provide structural support as a dense, complex web just under the plasma membrane, to which they are anchored by special proteins. Sometimes, actin filaments can dynamically rearrange themselves and facilitate cellular movement, such as when an amoeba moves over a surface with pseudopods [L. *pseudo,* false, and *pod,* feet], or when intestinal cell microvilli lengthen and shorten into the gut lumen (the space where ingested food is processed). In plant cells, actin filaments form the tracks along which chloroplasts circulate in a particular direction in a process called cytoplasmic streaming.

Actin filaments move the cell and its organelles by interacting with **motor molecules,** which are proteins that can attach, detach, and reattach farther along an actin filament. The motor molecule myosin uses ATP to pull actin filaments along in this way. Myosin has both a head and a tail. In muscle cells, the tails of several myosin molecules are joined to form a thick filament. In non-muscle cells, cytoplasmic myosin tails are bound to membranes, but the heads still interact with actin:

During animal cell division, the two new cells form when actin, in conjunction with myosin, pinches off the cells from one another.

Intermediate Filaments

Intermediate filaments (8–11 nm in diameter) are so named because they are intermediate in size between actin filaments and microtubules. They form a ropelike assembly of fibrous polypeptides, but the specific filament type varies according to the tissue. Some intermediate filaments support the nuclear envelope, whereas others support the plasma membrane and take part in the formation of cell-to-cell junctions. In the skin, intermediate filaments made of the protein keratin give great mechanical strength to skin cells. Like other cytoskeletal components, intermediate filaments are highly dynamic and disassemble when phosphate is added to them by a kinase.

Microtubules

Microtubules [Gk. *mikros,* small, little; L. *tubus,* tube] are small, hollow cylinders about 25 nm in diameter and from 0.2 to 25 μm in length.

Microtubules are made of a globular protein called tubulin, which is of two types called α and β. Alpha tubulin has a slightly different amino acid sequence than β tubulin. When assembly occurs, α and β tubulin molecules come together as dimers, and the dimers arrange themselves in rows. Microtubules have 13 rows of tubulin dimers, surrounding what appears in electron micrographs to be an empty central core.

Microtubule assembly is under the regulatory control of a microtubule organizing center (MTOC). In most eukaryotic cells, the main MTOC is in the **centrosome** [Gk. *centrum,* center, and *soma,* body], which lies near the nucleus. Microtubules radiate from the centrosome, helping to maintain the shape of the cell and acting as tracks along which organelles can be moved. Whereas the motor molecule myosin is associated with actin filaments, the motor molecules kinesin and dynein are associated with microtubules:

vesicle moves, not microtubule

a. Actin filaments

b. Intermediate filaments

c. Microtubules

Figure 4.18 The cytoskeleton. The cytoskeleton maintains a cell's shape and allows its parts to move. Three types of protein components make up the cytoskeleton. They can be detected in cells by using labeling and fluorescence microscopy. **a.** *Left to right:* Animal cells showing a twisted double chain of actin filaments (green fibers). The giant cells of the green alga *Chara* use actin filaments to move organelles within the cell. **b.** *Left to right:* Animal cells showing fibrous, ropelike intermediate filaments (blue fibers). A peacock's colorful feathers are strengthened by intermediate filaments. **c.** *Left to right:* Animal cells showing hollow microtubules made of tubulin dimers (orange fibers). A chameleon's skin cells use microtubules to move pigment granules around so that they take on the color of their environment.

There are different types of kinesin proteins, each specialized to move one kind of vesicle or cellular organelle. Kinesin moves vesicles or organelles in an opposite direction from dynein. Cytoplasmic dynein is closely related to the molecule dynein found in flagella.

Before a cell divides, microtubules disassemble and then reassemble into a structure called a spindle that distributes chromosomes in an orderly manner. At the end of cell division, the spindle disassembles, and microtubules reassemble once again into their former array. In the "arms race" between plants and herbivores, plants have evolved various types of poisons that prevent them from being eaten. Colchicine is a plant poison that binds tubulin and blocks the assembly of microtubules.

Centrioles

Centrioles [Gk. *centrum*, center] are short cylinders with a 9 + 0 pattern of microtubule triplets—nine sets of triplets are arranged in an outer ring, but the center of a centriole does not contain a microtubule. In animal cells and most protists, a centrosome contains two centrioles lying at right angles to each other. A centrosome, as mentioned previously, is the major microtubule-organizing center for the cell. Therefore, it is possible that centrioles are also involved in the process by which microtubules assemble and disassemble.

Before an animal cell divides, the centrioles replicate, and the members of each pair are at right angles to one another (Fig. 4.19). Then each pair becomes part of a separate centrosome. During cell division, the centrosomes move apart and most likely function to organize the mitotic spindle. In any case, each new cell has its own centrosome and pair of centrioles. Plant and fungal cells have the equivalent of a centrosome, but this structure does not contain centrioles, suggesting that centrioles are not necessary to the assembly of cytoplasmic microtubules.

A **basal body** is an organelle that lies at the base of cilia and flagella and may direct the organization of microtubules within these structures. In other words, a basal body may do for a cilium or flagellum what the centrosome does for the cell. In cells with cilia and flagella, centrioles are believed to give rise to basal bodies.

Cilia and Flagella

Cilia [L. *cilium*, eyelash, hair] and **flagella** [L. *flagello*, whip] are hairlike projections that can move either in an undulating fashion, like a whip, or stiffly, like an oar. In free cells, cilia (or flagella) move the cell through liquid. For example, unicellular paramecia are organisms that move by means of cilia, whereas sperm cells move by means of flagella. If the cell is attached to other cells, cilia (or flagella) are capable of moving liquid over the cell. The cells that line our upper respiratory tract have cilia that sweep debris trapped within mucus back up into the throat, where it can be swallowed or expelled. This action helps keep the lungs clean.

In eukaryotic cells, cilia are much shorter than flagella, but they have a similar construction. Both are membrane-bounded cylinders enclosing a matrix area. In the matrix are nine microtubule doublets arranged in a circle around two central microtubules; this is called the 9 + 2 pattern of microtubules (Fig. 4.20). Cilia and flagella move when the microtubule doublets slide past one another using motor molecules.

As mentioned, each cilium and flagellum has a basal body lying in the cytoplasm at its base. Basal bodies have the same circular arrangement of microtubule triplets as centrioles and are believed to be derived from them. It is possible that basal bodies organize the microtubules within cilia and flagella, but this idea is not supported by the observation that cilia and flagella grow by the addition of tubulin dimers to their tips.

empty center of centriole

one microtubule triplet

one centrosome: one pair of centrioles

two centrosomes: two pairs of centrioles   200 nm

Figure 4.19 Centrioles.   In a nondividing animal cell, a single pair of centrioles is present in the centrosome located just outside the nucleus. Just before a cell divides, the centrioles replicate, producing two centrosomes. During cell division, the centrosomes separate so that each new cell has one centrosome containing one pair of centrioles.

Check Your Progress   4.8

1. Differentiate between the components of the cytoskeleton and how they provide support to the cell.
2. Explain how ATP is used to produce movement in a cell.
3. Describe the role of motor molecules in cilia and flagella.

Flagellum

shaft

The shaft of the flagellum has a ring of nine microtubule doublets anchored to a central pair of microtubules.

Sperm

plasma membrane

outer microtubule doublet

radial spoke

central microtubules

dynein side arm

Flagellum cross section   25 nm

The side arms of each doublet are composed of dynein, a motor molecule.

dynein side arms

ATP

In the presence of ATP, the dynein side arms reach out to their neighbors, and bending occurs.

Basal body

triplets

Basal body cross section   100 nm

The basal body of a flagellum has a ring of nine microtubule triplets with no central microtubules.

Figure 4.20 Structure of a flagellum. *Below, left:* The basal body of a flagellum has a 9 + 0 pattern of microtubule triplets. Notice the ring of nine triplets, with no central microtubules. *Above, left:* In sperm, the shaft of the flagellum has a 9 + 2 pattern (a ring of nine microtubule doublets surrounds a central pair of microtubules). *Middle, right:* In place of the triplets seen in a basal body, a flagellum's outer doublets have side arms of dynein, a motor molecule. *Below, right:* In the presence of ATP, the dynein side arms reach out and attempt to move along their neighboring doublet. Because of the radial spokes connecting the doublets to the central microtubules and motor molecules, bending occurs.

CONNECTING *the* CONCEPTS *with the* THEMES

Evolution

- Cells self-replicate. All modern day cells are descendants of the first cells on Earth.
- Endosymbiosis gave previously separate prokaryotic cells a metabolic advantage, which allowed them to become more numerous.
- Over time, specialized functions became associated with separate, membrane-enclosed spaces within the cell. This compartmentalization allowed previously incompatible chemical reactions to occur simultaneously, making cells more efficient.

Nature of Science

- Our knowledge of cell anatomy has been gathered by studying micrographs of cells. Cytologists (biologists who study cells) have arrived at a picture of generalized cells, such as those depicted for the animal and plant cells in Figures 4.6 and 4.7.
- The Nature of Science feature on page 63–64 describes tools used for studying the function of cells and organelles. Many other techniques have provided additional detail and insight into cell structure and function.

Biological Systems

- Cells are integrated systems of assembled macromolecules that collectively support life. Organelles are assemblies that carry out specialized functions within the cell.
- All cellular systems must function normally to maintain the metabolic activity necessary for life. Cellular systems must also be able to adapt to rapidly changing environmental conditions.

Media Study Tools

www.mhhe.com/maderbiology11

Enhance your study of this chapter with study tools and practice tests. Also ask your instructor about the resources available through ConnectPlus, including the media-rich eBook, interactive learning tools, and animations.

Summarize

4.1 Cellular Level of Organization

All organisms are composed of cells, the smallest units of living matter. Cells self-reproduce, and existing cells come only from preexisting cells. Cells are very small (measured in micrometers) and must remain small in order to have an adequate surface area to volume ratio. The plasma membrane regulates exchange of materials between the cell interior and the external environment.

4.2 Prokaryotic Cells

Prokaryotic cells lack the nucleus of eukaryotic cells. The cell envelope of bacteria includes a plasma membrane, a cell wall, and an outer glycocalyx. The cytoplasm contains ribosomes, inclusion bodies, and a nucleoid without a nuclear envelope. The cytoplasm of cyanobacteria also includes thylakoids. The appendages of a bacterium are flagella, fimbriae, and conjugation pili.

4.3 Introducing Eukaryotic Cells

Eukaryotic cells are much larger than prokaryotic cells, and contain compartmentalized structures called organelles that each have a specific structure and function (Table 4.1) that increases cell efficiency. Endosymbiont theory helps explain the evolutionary origins of many membrane-enclosed organelles. Most membranous organelles are in constant communication.

4.4 The Nucleus and Ribosomes

The nucleus of eukaryotic cells is bounded by a nuclear envelope containing pores that regulate transport between the cytoplasm and the nucleoplasm. The nucleus contains DNA that is organized into chromosomes.

Ribosomes are organelles that function in protein synthesis. In order to make a protein, mRNA is copied exactly from the DNA, processed, and exits the nucleus through a nuclear pore. After a ribosome attaches to an mRNA, most of the time this assembly goes to the rough ER to make a protein.

4.5 The Endomembrane System

The endomembrane system includes the ER (both rough and smooth), the Golgi apparatus, the lysosomes (in animal cells), and transport vesicles. Newly produced proteins made in the rough ER are modified before they are packaged in transport vesicles, many of which go to the Golgi apparatus. The smooth ER has various metabolic functions, depending on the cell type, but it generally makes lipids that are carried by vesicles to different locations, particularly the Golgi apparatus. The Golgi apparatus modifies, sorts, and repackages proteins and also processes lipids. Some proteins are tagged for transport to different cellular destinations; others are secreted from the cell.

Table 4.1 Comparison of Prokaryotic Cells and Eukaryotic Cells

	Prokaryotic Cells (1–20 μm in diameter)	Eukaryotic Cells (10–100 μm in diameter)	
		Animal	Plant
Cell wall	Usually (peptidoglycan)	No	Yes (cellulose)
Plasma membrane	Yes	Yes	Yes
Nucleus	No	Yes	Yes
Nucleolus	No	Yes	Yes
Ribosomes	Yes (smaller)	Yes	Yes
Endoplasmic reticulum	No	Yes	Yes
Golgi apparatus	No	Yes	Yes
Lysosomes	No	Yes	No
Mitochondria	No	Yes	Yes
Chloroplasts	No	No	Yes
Peroxisomes	No	Usually	Usually
Cytoskeleton	No	Yes	Yes
Centrioles	No	Yes	No
9 + 2 cilia or flagella	No	Often	No (in flowering plants) Yes (sperm of bryophytes, ferns, and cycads)

4.6 Other Vesicles and Vacuoles

Cells contain numerous vesicles and vacuoles, some of which, such as lysosomes, have already been discussed. Peroxisomes are vesicles that are involved in the metabolism of long chain fatty acids. The large central vacuole in plant cells functions in storage and also in the breakdown of molecules and cell parts.

4.7 The Energy-Related Organelles

Cells require a constant input of energy to maintain their structure. Chloroplasts capture the energy of the sun and conduct photosynthesis, which produces carbohydrates. Carbohydrate-derived products are broken down in mitochondria in the presence of oxygen via cellular respiration, and ATP is produced as a result.

4.8 The Cytoskeleton

The cytoskeleton contains actin filaments, intermediate filaments, and microtubules. These maintain cell shape and help transport orgenelles from place to place within the cell. Actin, the thinnest filaments, interact with motor proteins to allow a range of functions from muscular contraction to cellular division. Intermediate filaments support the nuclear and plasma membranes and participate in the cell-to-cell junctions that produce tissues. Microtubules radiate out from the centrosome and are present in centrioles, cilia, and flagella. They serve as an internal transport system along which vesicles and other organelles move.

Key Terms

actin filament 78
archaean 65
bacillus 65
basal body 80
capsule 65
cell 61
cell envelope 65
cell theory 61
cell wall 65
central vacuole 75
centriole 79
centrosome 78
chloroplast 76
chromatin 70
chromoplast 77
chromosome 70
cilium 80
coccus 65
conjugation pili 66
cristae 77
cyanobacteria 66
cytoplasm 65
cytoskeleton 68
endomembrane system 72
endoplasmic reticulum (ER) 72
endosymbiotic theory 67
eukaryotic cell 65
fimbriae 66
flagellum (pl., flagella) 66, 80
gene 70
glycocalyx 65
Golgi apparatus 72
granum 76
intermediate filament 78

leucoplast 77
lysosome 73
matrix 77
mesosome 65
microtubule 78
mitochondrion 76
motor molecule 78
nuclear envelope 71
nuclear pore 71
nucleoid 65
nucleolus 70
nucleoplasm 70
organelle 67
peroxisome 75
plasma membrane 65
plasmid 65
plastid 77
polyribosome 71
prokaryotic cell 65
ribosome 66, 71
rough ER 72
secretion 73
signal peptide 71
smooth ER 72
spirillum 65
spirochete 65
stroma 76
surface-area-to-volume ratio 62
thylakoid 66, 76
vector 66
vacuole 75
vesicle 67

Assess

Reviewing This Chapter

1. What are the three basic principles of the cell theory? 60
2. Why is it advantageous for cells to be small? 61
3. Roughly sketch a bacterial (prokaryotic) cell, label its parts, and state a function for each of these. 65
4. How do eukaryotic and prokaryotic cells differ? 66
5. Describe how the nucleus, the chloroplast, and the mitochondrion may have become a part of the eukaryotic cell. 66
6. What does it mean to say that the eukaryotic cell is compartmentalized? 66–67
7. Describe the structure and the function of the nuclear envelope and the nuclear pores. 70–71
8. Distinguish between the nucleolus, rRNA, and ribosomes. 70–71
9. Name organelles that are a part of the endomembrane system and explain the term. 72
10. Trace the path of a protein from rough ER to the plasma membrane. 74
11. Give the overall equations for photosynthesis and cellular respiration, contrast the two, and tell how they are related. 76
12. Describe the structure and function of chloroplasts and mitochondria. How are these two organelles related to one another? 76–77
13. What are the three components of the cytoskeleton? What are their structures and functions? 78–79
14. Relate the structure of flagella (and cilia) to centrioles, and discuss the function of both. 80

Testing Yourself

Choose the best answer for each question.

1. The small size of cells best correlates with
   a. the fact that they are self-reproducing.
   b. their prokaryotic versus eukaryotic nature.
   c. an adequate surface area for exchange of materials.
   d. the fact that they come in multiple sizes.
   e. All of these are correct.

2. Which of these is not a true comparison of the compound light microscope and the transmission electron microscope?

	LIGHT	ELECTRON
a.	Uses light to "view" object	Uses electrons to "view" object
b.	Uses glass lenses for focusing	Uses magnetic lenses for focusing
c.	Specimen must be killed and stained	Specimen may be alive and nonstained
d.	Magnification is not as great	Magnification is greater
e.	Resolution is not as great	Resolution is greater

3. Which of these best distinguishes a prokaryotic cell from a eukaryotic cell?
   a. Prokaryotic cells have a cell wall, but eukaryotic cells never do.
   b. Prokaryotic cells are much larger than eukaryotic cells.
   c. Prokaryotic cells have flagella, but eukaryotic cells do not.
   d. Prokaryotic cells do not have a membrane-bounded nucleus, but eukaryotic cells do have such a nucleus.
   e. Prokaryotic cells have ribosomes, but eukaryotic cells do not have ribosomes.

4. Which of these is not found in the nucleus?
   a. functioning ribosomes
   b. chromatin that condenses to chromosomes
   c. nucleolus that produces rRNA
   d. nucleoplasm instead of cytoplasm
   e. all forms of RNA

5. Vesicles from the ER most likely are on their way to
   a. the rough ER.
   b. the lysosomes.
   c. the Golgi apparatus.
   d. the plant cell vacuole only.
   e. the location suitable to their size.

6. Lysosomes function in
   a. protein synthesis.   d. lipid synthesis.
   b. processing and packaging.   e. production of hydrogen
   c. intracellular digestion.   peroxide.

7. Mitochondria
   a. are involved in cellular respiration.
   b. break down ATP to release energy for cells.
   c. contain grana and cristae.
   d. are present in animal cells but not plant cells.
   e. All of these are correct.

8. Which organelle releases oxygen?
   a. ribosome   c. chloroplast
   b. Golgi apparatus   d. smooth ER

9. Which of these is not true?
   a. Actin filaments are found in muscle cells.
   b. Microtubules radiate out from the ER.
   c. Intermediate filaments sometimes contain keratin.
   d. Motor molecules use microtubules as tracks.

10. Cilia and flagella
    a. have a 9 + 0 pattern of microtubules, same as basal bodies.
    b. contain myosin that pulls on actin filaments.
    c. are organized by basal bodies derived from centrioles.
    d. are constructed similarly in prokaryotes and eukaryotes.
    e. Both a and c are correct.

11. Which of the following organelles contains its (their) own DNA,
    suggesting they were once independent prokaryotes?
    a. Golgi apparatus   d. ribosomes
    b. mitochondria   e. Both b and c are correct.
    c. chloroplasts

12. Which organelle most likely originated by invagination of the
    plasma membrane?
    a. mitochondria   d. chloroplasts
    b. flagella   e. All of these are correct.
    c. nucleus

13. Which structures are found in a prokaryotic cell?
    a. cell wall, ribosomes, thylakoids, chromosome
    b. cell wall, plasma membrane, nucleus, flagellum
    c. nucleoid, ribosomes, chloroplasts, capsule
    d. plasmid, ribosomes, enzymes, DNA, mitochondria
    e. chlorophyll, enzymes, Golgi apparatus, plasmids

14. Study the example given in (a) below. Then for each other
    organelle listed, state another that is structurally and
    functionally related. Tell why you paired these two organelles.
    a. The nucleus can be paired with nucleoli because nucleoli
       are found in the nucleus. Nucleoli occur where chromatin is
       producing rRNA.
    b. mitochondria
    c. centrioles
    d. ER

Engage

Thinking Scientifically

1. The protists that cause malaria contribute to infections
   associated with AIDS. Scientists have discovered that an
   antibiotic that inhibits prokaryotic enzymes will kill the parasite
   because it is effective against the plastids in the protist. What
   can you conclude about the origin of the plastids?

2. For your cytology study, you have decided to label and,
   thereby, detect the presence of the base uracil in an animal
   cell. In what parts of the cell do you expect to find your
   radioactive tracer?

Bioethical Issue

Stem Cells

A stem cell is an immature cell capable of producing many different
types of differentiated mature cells. Stem cells exist in the various
organs of the human body; however, they are difficult to obtain,
except for those that reside in red bone marrow and produce all
types of blood cells. A rich source of stem cells is an umbilical cord;
another, less controversial source is adult stem cells from, say, skin.
Since the nucleus contains the genetic information, it is possible to
take a 2n adult nucleus, manipulate it genetically, and put it in an
enucleated egg cell. Under the right conditions, the new cells can
be grown and used to make neurological tissues that could possibly
cure Alzheimer or Parkinson disease or any other type of neurological disorder. However, if development were to continue, a clone of
the human that donated the 2n nucleus could possibly result.

   Is it bioethical to continue investigating such research? Especially when you consider that the "embryo" that provided the stem
cells was not produced by the normal method of having a sperm
fertilize an egg? Or, is it wrong to produce an embryo only to serve
as a source of stem cells?

Plants appear green because chlorophyll reflects green light (*left*). Otherwise, plants would be black (*right*).

Photosynthesis

BEFORE YOU BEGIN

Before beginning this chapter, take a few moments to review the following discussions.

Figure 6.1 How does energy flow in biological systems?

Section 6.3 What role do enzymes play in regulating metabolic processes?

Section 6.4 How are redox reactions and membranes used to conduct cellular work?

unlight, the kind that shines down on us every day, contains many different colors, from violet to green, yellow, orange, and red. Plants use all the colors of light, except green, when they photosynthesize—that's why most plants are green! They are reflecting the green light back to our eyes. Does this mean that if plants used green light, in addition to all the other colors, they would appear black to us? In fact, yes. As a result natural areas like the one pictured above would be black, as shown on the right.

How did it happen that plants do not use green light for photosynthesis? When the ancestors of plants evolved in the ocean, green light was already being absorbed by other photosynthesizers, so natural selection favored the evolution of a pigment such as chlorophyll, which does not absorb green light. When plants moved onto land, chlorophyll remained as the primary pigment, but because there is plentiful sunlight on land, the selective pressure relaxed, allowing for the evolution of additional pigments.

Photosynthesis, as discussed in this chapter, consists of two interconnected pathways that allow chloroplasts to produce carbohydrate while releasing oxygen. This remarkable process is the basis for much life on Earth.

As you read through the chapter, think about the following questions:

1. Why are plants so important to most life on Earth?

2. What relationships do heterotrophs have with the photosynthesizing autotrophs?

3. How might the increased destruction of plants affect our environment, climate, and lives in the future?

FOLLOWING *the* THEMES

UNIT 1 THE CELL	CHAPTER 7 PHOTOSYNTHESIS	
	Evolution	Plants have adapted and spread to nearly every environment and climate on Earth.
	Nature of Science	Researchers have created new plant varieties that produce more food and commercially useful products.
	Biological Systems	Most ecosystems on Earth depend on photosynthesizing autotrophs as the basis of their food webs.

7.1 Photosynthetic Organisms

Learning Outcomes

Upon completion of this section, you should be able to

1. Explain how autotrophs are able to produce their own food.
2. Describe the components of a chloroplast.
3. Compare the role of carbon dioxide in autotrophs and heterotrophs.

Photosynthesis converts solar energy into the chemical energy of a carbohydrate. Photosynthetic organisms, including land plants, algae, and cyanobacteria, are called **autotrophs** because they produce their own food (Fig. 7.1). Globally, photosynthesis produces an enormous amount of carbohydrate—so much that, if it were instantly converted to coal and the coal were loaded into standard railroad cars (each car holding about 50 tons), the photosynthesizers of the biosphere would fill more than 100 cars per second with coal.

No wonder photosynthetic organisms are able to sustain themselves and all other living things on Earth. With few exceptions, it is possible to trace any food chain back to plants and algae. In other words, producers, which have the ability to synthesize carbohydrates, feed not only themselves but also consumers, which must take in preformed organic molecules. Collectively, consumers are called **heterotrophs.** Both autotrophs and heterotrophs use organic molecules produced by photosynthesis as a source of building blocks for growth and repair and as a source of chemical energy for cellular work.

Photosynthesizers also produce copious amounts of oxygen gas (O_2) as a by-product. Oxygen, which is required by organisms when they carry on cellular respiration, rises high into the atmosphere, where it forms an ozone shield that filters out ultraviolet radiation and makes terrestrial life possible.

Our analogy about photosynthetic products becoming coal is apt because the bodies of many ancient plants did become the coal we burn today, usually to produce electricity. Coal formation happened several hundred million years ago, and that is why coal is called a fossil fuel. Today's trees are also commonly used as fuel. Fermentation of plant materials produces ethanol, which can be used to fuel automobiles directly or as a gasoline additive.

The products of photosynthesis are critical to humankind in a number of other ways. They serve as a source of building materials, fabrics, paper, and pharmaceuticals. Of course, we also appreciate green plants for the simple beauty of a magnolia blossom, the scent of a rose, or the majesty of the Earth's forests.

Figure 7.1 Photosynthetic organisms. Photosynthetic organisms include plants, such as trees, garden plants, and mosses, which typically live on land; photosynthetic protists, such as *Euglena*, diatoms, and kelp, which typically live in water; and cyanobacteria, a type of bacterium that lives in water, damp soil, and rocks.

mosses

kelp

trees

garden plants

Euglena

cyanobacteria

diatoms

Flowering Plants as Photosynthesizers

Photosynthesis takes place in the green portions of plants. The leaves of a flowering plant contain mesophyll tissue in which cells are specialized for photosynthesis (Fig. 7.2). The raw materials for photosynthesis are water and carbon dioxide. The roots of a plant absorb water, which then moves in vascular tissue up the stem to a leaf by way of the leaf veins. Carbon dioxide in the air enters a leaf through small openings called **stomata** (sing., stoma). After entering a leaf, carbon dioxide and water diffuse into **chloroplasts** [Gk. *chloros*, green, and *plastos*, formed, molded], the organelles that carry on photosynthesis.

Video Plants

A double membrane surrounds a chloroplast, and its semifluid interior called the **stroma** [Gk. *stroma*, bed, mattress]. A different membrane system within the stroma forms flattened sacs called **thylakoids** [Gk. *thylakos*, sack, and *eides*, like, resembling], which in some places are stacked to form **grana** (sing., granum), so called because they looked like piles of seeds to early microscopists. The space of each thylakoid is thought to be connected to the space of every other thylakoid within a chloroplast, thereby forming an inner compartment within chloroplasts called the thylakoid space. Overall, chloroplast membranes provide tremendous surface area for photosynthesis to occur.

3D Animation Structure of Chloroplasts

The thylakoid membrane contains **chlorophyll** and other pigments that are capable of absorbing solar energy, the type of energy that drives photosynthesis. The stroma contains an enzyme-rich solution where carbon dioxide is first attached to an organic compound and is then reduced to a carbohydrate.

Therefore, it is proper to associate the absorption of solar energy with the thylakoid membranes making up the grana and to associate the reduction of carbon dioxide to a carbohydrate with the stroma of a chloroplast.

Human beings, and indeed nearly all organisms, release carbon dioxide into the air when they respire. Some of these same carbon dioxide molecules enter a leaf through the stoma and are converted to carbohydrate. Carbohydrate, in the form of glucose, is the chief source of chemical energy for most organisms. Thus, an interdependent relationship exists between organisms that make their own food (autotrophs) and those that consume their food (heterotrophs).

Check Your Progress   7.1

1. Describe three major groups of photosynthetic organisms.
2. Distinguish the part of a chloroplast that absorbs solar energy from the part that forms a carbohydrate.

Leaf cross section

cuticle

upper epidermis

mesophyll

lower epidermis

CO_2

O_2

leaf vein

stoma

outer membrane

inner membrane

stroma

granum

stroma

Chloroplast

37,000×

thylakoid space

thylakoid membrane

independent thylakoid in a granum

overlapping thylakoid in a granum

Grana

Figure 7.2 Leaves and photosynthesis.
The raw materials for photosynthesis are carbon dioxide and water. Water, which enters a leaf by way of leaf veins, and carbon dioxide, which enters by way of the stomata, diffuse into chloroplasts. Chloroplasts have two major parts. The grana are made up of thylakoids, which are membranous disks. Their membrane contains photosynthetic pigments such as chlorophylls *a* and *b*. These pigments absorb solar energy. The stroma is a semifluid interior where carbon dioxide is enzymatically reduced to a carbohydrate.

7.2 The Process of Photosynthesis

Learning Outcomes

Upon completion of this section, you should be able to:

1. Describe the overall process of photosynthesis.
2. Compare energy input and output of the light reaction.
3. Compare carbon input and output of the Calvin cycle reaction.

Figure 7.3 Photosynthesis releases oxygen. Bubbling indicates that the aquatic plant *Elodea* releases O_2 gas when it photosynthesizes.

The overall process of photosynthesis can be represented by an equation:

$$6CO_2 + 12H_2O \xrightarrow{\text{solar energy}} 6(CH_2O) + 6H_2O + 6O_2$$

In this equation, (CH_2O) represents carbohydrate. If the equation were multiplied by six, the carbohydrate would be $C_6H_{12}O_6$, or glucose.

The overall equation implies that photosynthesis involves oxidation-reduction (redox) and the movement of electrons from one molecule to another. Recall that oxidation is the loss of electrons, and reduction is the gain of electrons. In living things, as discussed in Chapter 6, the electrons are very often accompanied by hydrogen ions so that oxidation is the loss of hydrogen atoms ($H^+ + e^-$), and reduction is the gain of hydrogen atoms. This simplified rewrite of the above equation makes it clear that carbon dioxide has been reduced, and water has been oxidized:

$$CO_2 + H_2O \xrightarrow[\text{Oxidation}]{\overset{\text{Reduction}}{\text{solar energy}}} (CH_2O) + O_2$$

It takes hydrogen atoms and a lot of energy to reduce carbon dioxide. From your study of energy and enzymes in Chapter 6, you probably expect that solar energy is not used directly during photosynthesis; rather, it is converted to ATP molecules. ATP is the energy currency of cells and, when cells need something, they spend ATP. In this case, solar energy is used to generate the ATP needed to reduce carbon dioxide to a carbohydrate. Of course, we always want to keep in mind that this carbohydrate represents the food produced by land plants, algae, and cyanobacteria that feeds the biosphere.

The Role of NADP⁺/NADPH

A review of Section 6.4 will also lead you to suspect that the electrons needed to reduce carbon dioxide are carried by a coenzyme. $NADP^+$ is the coenzyme of oxidation-reduction (redox coenzyme) active during photosynthesis. When $NADP^+$ is reduced, it has accepted two electrons and one hydrogen atom, and when NADPH is oxidized, it gives up its electrons:

$$NADP^+ + 2\,e^- + H^+ \longrightarrow NADPH$$

What molecule supplies the electrons that reduce $NADP^+$ during photosynthesis? Put a sprig of *Elodea* in a beaker, and supply it with light, and you will observe a bubbling (Fig. 7.3). The bubbling occurs because the plant is releasing oxygen as it photosynthesizes.

A very famous experiment performed by C. B. van Niel of Stanford University found that the oxygen given off by photosynthesizers comes from water. Van Niel performed two separate experiments. When an isotope of oxygen, ^{18}O, was a part of water, the O_2 given off by the plant contained ^{18}O. When ^{18}O was a part of carbon dioxide supplied to a plant, the O_2 given off by a plant did not contain the ^{18}O. Why not? Because the oxygen in carbon dioxide doesn't come from water, it comes from the air. This was the first step toward discovering that water splits during photosynthesis. When water splits, oxygen is released, and the hydrogen atoms ($H^+ + e^-$) are taken up by $NADP^+$. Later, NADPH reduces carbon dioxide to a carbohydrate.

Two Sets of Reactions

Many investigators have contributed to our understanding of the overall equation of photosynthesis and to our current realization that photosynthesis consists of two separate sets of reactions. F. F. Blackman (1866-1947) was the first to suggest, in 1905, that enzymes must be involved in the reduction of carbon dioxide to a carbohydrate and that the process must consist of two separate sets of reactions. We call the two sets of reactions the light reactions and the Calvin cycle reactions.

Light Reactions

The **light reactions** are so named because they only occur when solar energy is available (during daylight hours). The overall equation for photosynthesis gives no hint that the green pigment chlorophyll, present in thylakoid membranes, is largely responsible for absorbing the solar energy that drives photosynthesis.

During the light reactions, solar energy energizes electrons that move down an electron transport chain (see Fig. 6.12). As the electrons move down the chain, energy is released and captured to produce ATP molecules. Energized electrons are also taken up by NADP$^+$, which is reduced and becomes NADPH. This equation can be used to summarize the light reactions because, during the light reactions, solar energy is converted to chemical energy:

$$\text{solar energy} \longrightarrow \text{chemical energy} \\ \text{(ATP, NADPH)}$$

Calvin Cycle Reactions

The **Calvin cycle reactions** are named for Melvin Calvin, who received a Nobel Prize for discovering the enzymatic reactions that reduce carbon dioxide to a carbohydrate in the stroma of chloroplasts (Fig. 7.4). The enzymes that speed the reduction of carbon dioxide during both day and night are located in the semifluid substance of the chloroplast stroma.

During the Calvin cycle reactions, CO_2 is taken up and then reduced to a carbohydrate that can later be converted to glucose. This equation can be used to summarize the Calvin cycle reactions because during these reactions, the ATP and NADPH formed during the light reactions are used to reduce carbon dioxide:

$$\text{chemical energy} \longrightarrow \text{chemical energy} \\ \text{(ATP, NADPH)} \qquad \text{(carbohydrate)}$$

Summary

Figure 7.5 summarizes our discussion so far and shows that during the light reactions, (1) solar energy is absorbed, (2) water is split so that oxygen is released, and (3) ATP and NADPH are produced.

During the Calvin cycle reactions, (1) CO_2 is absorbed and (2) reduced to a carbohydrate (CH_2O) by utilizing ATP and

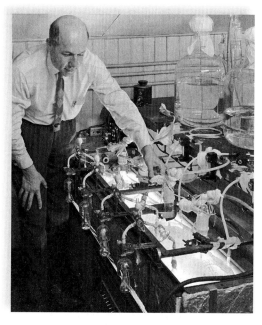

Figure 7.4 Melvin Calvin in the laboratory. Melvin Calvin used tracers to discover the cycle of reactions that reduce CO_2 to a carbohydrate.

NADPH from the light reactions (see bottom set of red arrows). The top set of red arrows takes ADP + Ⓟ and NADP$^+$ back to light reactions, where they become ATP and NADPH once more so that carbohydrate production can continue.

Check Your Progress   7.2

1. Explain how redox reactions are used in photosynthesis.
2. Describe the role of enzymes during photosynthesis.

Figure 7.5 Overview of photosynthesis. The process of photosynthesis consists of the light reactions and the Calvin cycle reactions. The light reactions, which produce ATP and NADPH, occur in the thylakoid membrane. These molecules are used in the Calvin cycle reactions which take place in the stroma. The Calvin cycle reactions reduce carbon dioxide to a carbohydrate.

7.3 Plants as Solar Energy Converters

Learning Outcomes

Upon completion of this section, you should be able to

1. Describe the relationship between wavelength and energy in the electromagnetic spectrum.
2. Explain the role of photosynthetic pigments in harnessing solar energy.
3. Examine how ATP and NADPH are produced from redox reactions and membrane gradients.

Solar energy can be described in terms of its wavelength and its energy content. Figure 7.6a lists the different types of radiant energy from the shortest wavelength, gamma rays, to the longest, radio waves. Most of the radiation reaching the Earth is within the visible-light range. Higher-energy wavelengths are screened out by the ozone layer in the atmosphere, and lower-energy wavelengths are screened out by water vapor and carbon dioxide, before they reach the Earth's surface. Because visible light is the most prevalent in the environment, we can conclude that organic molecules and processes within organisms, such as vision and photosynthesis, are chemically adapted to the radiation associated with visible light (Fig. 7.6a).

3D Animation Properties of Light

Pigments and Photosystems

Pigment molecules absorb wavelengths of light. Most pigments absorb only some wavelengths; they reflect or transmit the other wavelengths. The pigments found in chloroplasts are capable of absorbing various portions of visible light. This is called their **absorption spectrum.**

Photosynthetic organisms differ in the type of chlorophyll they contain. In plants, chlorophyll *a* and chlorophyll *b* play prominent roles in photosynthesis. **Carotenoids** play an accessory role. Both chlorophylls *a* and *b* absorb violet, blue, and red light better than the light of other colors. Because green light is transmitted and reflected by chlorophyll, plant leaves appear green to us. The carotenoids, which are shades of yellow and orange, are able to absorb light in the violet-blue-green range. These pigments become noticeable in the fall when chlorophyll breaks down.

Animation Absorption of Light

How do you determine the absorption spectrum of pigments? To identify the absorption spectrum of a particular pigment, a purified sample is exposed to different wavelengths of light inside an instrument called a spectrophotometer. A spectrophotometer measures the amount of light that passes through the sample, and from this it is possible to calculate how much was absorbed. The amount of light absorbed at each wavelength is plotted on a graph, and the result is a record of the pigment's absorption spectrum (Fig. 7.6b).

A **photosystem** consists of a pigment complex (molecules of chlorophyll *a*, chlorophyll *b*, and the carotenoids) and electron acceptor molecules within the thylakoid membrane. The pigment complex serves as an "antenna" for gathering solar energy.

The Electron Flow in the Light Reactions

The light reactions utilize two photosystems, called photosystem I (PS I) and photosystem II (PS II). The photosystems are named for the order in which they were discovered, not for the order in which they occur in the thylakoid membrane or participate in the photosynthetic process.

During the light reactions, electrons usually, but not always, follow a **noncyclic pathway** that begins with photosystem II (Fig. 7.7). The pigment complex absorbs solar energy, which is then passed from one pigment to the other until it is concentrated in a particular pair of chlorophyll *a* molecules, called the *reaction center*. Electrons (e^-) in the reaction center become so energized that they escape from the reaction center and move to nearby electron acceptor molecules.

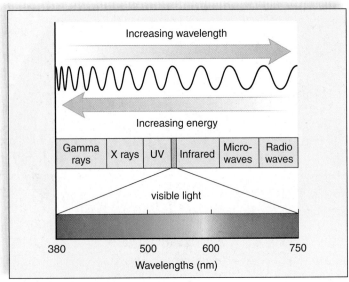

a. The electromagnetic spectrum includes visible light.

b. Absorption spectrum of photosynthetic pigments.

Figure 7.6 Photosynthetic pigments and photosynthesis. **a.** The wavelengths in visible light differ according to energy content and color. **b.** The photosynthetic pigments in chlorophylls *a* and *b* and the carotenoids absorb certain wavelengths within visible light. This is their absorption spectrum.

PS II would disintegrate without replacement electrons, and these are removed from water, which splits, releasing oxygen to the atmosphere. Notice that with the loss of electrons, water has been oxidized, and that indeed, the oxygen released during photosynthesis does come from water. Many organisms, including plants themselves and human beings, use this oxygen within their mitochondria to make ATP. The hydrogen ions (H^+) stay in the thylakoid space and contribute to the formation of a hydrogen ion gradient.

An electron acceptor sends energized electrons, received from the reaction center, down an **electron transport chain (ETC)**, a series of carriers that pass electrons from one to the other (see Fig. 6.13). As the electrons pass from one carrier to the next, energy is captured and stored in the form of a hydrogen ion (H^+) gradient. When these hydrogen ions flow down their electrochemical gradient through ATP synthase complexes, ATP production occurs (see Fig. 7.8). Notice that this ATP is then used by the Calvin cycle reactions in the stroma to reduce carbon dioxide to a carbohydrate.

When the PS I pigment complex absorbs solar energy, energized electrons leave its reaction center and are captured by electron acceptors. (Low-energy electrons from the *electron transport chain* adjacent to PS II replace those lost by PS I.) The electron acceptors in PS I pass their electrons to $NADP^+$ molecules. Each $NADP^+$ accepts two electrons and an H^+ to become reduced and forms NADPH. This NADPH is then used by the Calvin cycle reactions in the stroma along with ATP in the reduction of carbon dioxide to a carbohydrate.

3D Animation
Light-Dependent Reactions

ATP and NADPH are not made in equal amounts during the light reactions, and more ATP than NADPH is required during the Calvin cycle. Where does this extra ATP come from? Every so often, an electron moving down the noncyclic pathway is rerouted back to an earlier point in the electron transport chain. This cyclic pathway enables electrons to participate in additional redox reactions, moving more H^+ across the thylakoid membrane and through ATP synthase, and ultimately producing more ATP.

Figure 7.7 Noncyclic pathway: Electrons move from water to $NADP^+$. Energized electrons (replaced from water, which splits, releasing oxygen) leave photosystem II and pass down an electron transport chain, leading to the formation of ATP. Energized electrons (replaced by photosystem II by way of the ETC) leave photosystem I and pass to $NADP^+$, which then combines with H^+, becoming NADPH.

The Organization of the Thylakoid Membrane

As we have discussed, the following molecular complexes are present in the thylakoid membrane (Fig. 7.8):

PS II, which consists of a pigment complex and electron-acceptor molecules, receives electrons from water as water splits, releasing oxygen.

The electron transport chain (ETC), consisting of Pq (plastoquinone) and cytochrome complexes, carries electrons from PS II to PS I via redox reactions. Pq also pumps H^+ from the stroma into the thylakoid space.

PS I, which also consists of a pigment complex and electron-acceptor molecules, is adjacent to NADP reductase, which reduces $NADP^+$ to NADPH.

The **ATP synthase** complex, which has a channel and a protruding ATP synthase, is an enzyme that joins ADP + $\textcircled{P}$.

Animation
Photosynthetic Electron and ATP Synthesis

ATP Production

The thylakoid space acts as a reservoir for many hydrogen ions (H^+). First, each time water is oxidized, two H^+ remain in the thylakoid space. Second, as the electrons move from carrier to carrier via redox reactions along the electron transport chain, the electrons give up energy, which is used to pump H^+ from the stroma into the thylakoid space. Therefore, there are more H^+ in the thylakoid space than in the stroma. This difference and the resulting flow of H^+ (often referred to as protons in this context) from high to low concentration provides kinetic energy that allows an ATP synthase complex enzyme to enzymatically produce ATP from ADP + $\textcircled{P}$. This method of producing ATP is called **chemiosmosis** because ATP production is tied to the establishment of an H^+ gradient (see Fig. 6.13).

Animation
Proton Pump

Video
Spinach Battery

Check Your Progress   7.3

1. Distinguish visible light from the electromagnetic spectrum.
2. Evaluate the energy level of molecules that go in and come out of the light reaction.

Figure 7.8 Organization of a thylakoid. Each thylakoid membrane within a granum produces NADPH and ATP. Electrons move through sequential molecular complexes within the thylakoid membrane, and the last one passes electrons to $NADP^+$, after which it becomes NADPH. A carrier at the start of the electron transport chain pumps hydrogen ions from the stroma into the thylakoid space. When hydrogen ions flow back out of the space into the stroma through an ATP synthase complex, ATP is produced from ADP + $\textcircled{P}$.

THEME Biological Systems

Tropical Rain Forest Destruction and Climate Change

Al Gore, former presidential candidate, won the 2007 Nobel Peace Prize for raising public awareness concerning climate change. The Nobel Committee said that "global warming could induce large-scale migrations and lead to greater competition for the Earth's resources. As such, it may increase the danger of violent conflicts and wars, within and between countries."

Climate change refers to an expected rise in the average global temperature during the twenty-first century due to the introduction of certain gases into the atmosphere. For at least a thousand years prior to 1850, atmospheric carbon dioxide (CO_2) levels remained fairly constant at 0.028%. Since the 1850s, when industrialization began, the amount of CO_2 in the atmosphere has increased to 0.038% (Fig. 7A).

Role of Carbon Dioxide

In much the same way as the panes of a greenhouse, CO_2 and other gases in our atmosphere trap radiant heat from the Sun. Therefore, these gases are called greenhouse gases. Without any greenhouse gases, the Earth's temperature would be about 33°C cooler than it is now. Likewise, increasing the concentration of greenhouse gases is predicted to affect climate change.

Certainly, the burning of fossil fuels adds CO_2 to the atmosphere. But another factor that contributes to an increase in atmospheric CO_2 is tropical rain forest destruction.

Role of Tropical Rain Forests

Tropical rain forests are considered by many scientists to be the "lungs" of the Earth. Between 10 and 30 million hectares of rain forests are lost every year to ranching, logging, mining, and otherwise developing areas of the forest for human needs.

Each year, deforestation in tropical rain forests accounts for 20–30% of all CO_2 in the atmosphere. With your body, if you lose lung capacity, you lose body function. Similarly, the consequence of losing forests is greater trouble for climate change because burning a forest adds CO_2 to the atmosphere and removes trees that would ordinarily absorb CO_2.

The Earth Is a System

Carbon dioxide is removed from the air via photosynthesis, which takes place in forests, oceans, and other terrestrial and marine ecosystems. In fact, photosynthesis produces organic matter that is 300 to 600 times the mass of people currently living on Earth this year. Thus, these environments act as a sink for CO_2, preventing too much from accumulating in the atmosphere where CO_2 can affect global temperatures and bring about climate change.

Despite their reduction in size from an original 14% to 6% of land surface today, tropical rain forests make a substantial contribution to global CO_2 removal. They are a critical element of the Earth's systems, and, like any biological system, are essential for normal, healthy function. Tropical rain forests contribute greatly to the uptake of CO_2 and the productivity of photosynthesis because they are the most efficient of all terrestrial ecosystems.

Tropical rain forests occur near the equator. They can exist wherever temperatures are above 26°C and rainfall is heavy (from 100–200 cm) and regular. Huge trees with buttressed trunks and broad, undivided, dark-green leaves predominate. Nearly all land plants in a tropical rain forest are woody, and woody vines are also abundant.

It might be hypothesized that an increased amount of CO_2 in the atmosphere would cause photosynthesis to increase in the remaining portion of the forest. To study this possibility, investigators measured atmospheric CO_2 levels, daily temperature levels, and tree girth in La Selva, Costa Rica, for 16 years. The results demonstrated relatively lower forest productivity at higher temperatures. These findings suggest that, as temperatures rise, tropical rain forests may add to ongoing atmospheric CO_2 accumulation and accelerated climate change rather than the reverse.

These and other studies show that, as with any biological system, equilibrium and balance are necessary for healthy function. As a biological system, the Earth is sensitive to environmental change. Learning how to properly balance human activity with the needs of the biosphere requires that people become educated about how the Earth functions.

Questions to Consider

1. Are you concerned about climate change?
2. What actions can a person take to learn more about the facts of climate change?

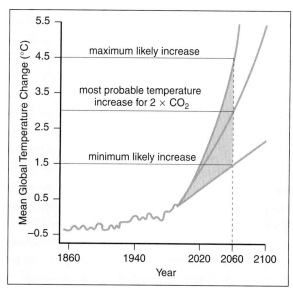

Figure 7A Climate change. Mean global temperature change is expected to rise due to the introduction of greenhouse gases into the atmosphere.

7.4 Plants as Carbon Dioxide Fixers

Learning Outcomes

Upon completion of this section, you should be able to

1. Describe the three phases of the Calvin cycle and when ATP and/or NADPH are needed.
2. Evaluate the significance of RuBP carboxylase enzyme to photosynthesis.
3. Explain how glyceraldehyde-3-phosphate (G3P) is used to produce other necessary plant molecules.

The Calvin cycle is a series of reactions that occur after the light reactions. The Calvin cycle produces carbohydrate before returning to its starting point, ready to accept more carbon dioxide (CO_2) (Fig. 7.9). The cycle is named for Melvin Calvin, who,

with colleagues, used the radioactive isotope ^{14}C as a tracer to discover the reactions making up the cycle.

This series of reactions uses carbon dioxide from the atmosphere to produce carbohydrate. How does carbon dioxide get into the atmosphere? We and most other organisms take in oxygen from the atmosphere and release carbon dioxide to the atmosphere. The Calvin cycle includes (1) carbon dioxide fixation, (2) carbon dioxide reduction, and (3) regeneration of RuBP (pronounced "ruby-P"; described shortly).

3D Animation
Calvin Cycle

Fixation of Carbon Dioxide

Carbon dioxide fixation is the first step of the Calvin cycle. During this reaction, a molecule of carbon dioxide from the atmosphere is attached to RuBP (ribulose-1,5-bisphosphate), a 5-carbon molecule. The result is one 6-carbon molecule, which splits into two 3-carbon molecules.

The enzyme that speeds this reaction, called **RuBP carboxylase,** is a protein that makes up about 20–50% of the protein content in chloroplasts. The reason for its abundance may be

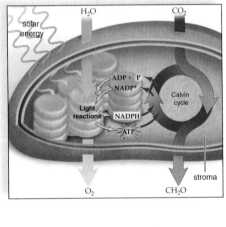

Figure 7.9 The Calvin cycle reactions.   The Calvin cycle is divided into three portions: CO_2 fixation, CO_2 reduction, and regeneration of RuBP. Because five G3P are needed to re-form three RuBP, it takes three turns of the cycle to have a net gain of one G3P. Two G3P molecules are needed to form glucose.

Metabolites of the Calvin Cycle	
RuBP	ribulose-1,5-bisphosphate
3PG	3-phosphoglycerate
BPG	1,3-bisphosphoglycerate
G3P	glyceraldehyde-3-phosphate

that it is unusually slow—it processes only a few molecules of substrate per second compared to thousands per second for a typical enzyme—and so there has to be a lot of it to keep the Calvin cycle going.

Reduction of Carbon Dioxide

The first 3-carbon molecule in the Calvin cycle is called 3PG (3-phosphoglycerate). Each of two 3PG molecules undergoes reduction to G3P (glyceraldehyde-3-phosphate) in two steps:

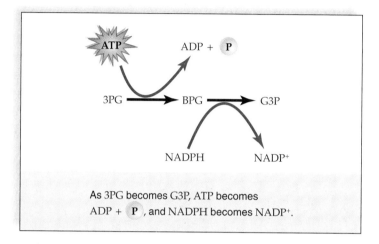

As 3PG becomes G3P, ATP becomes ADP + P , and NADPH becomes NADP$^+$.

This is the sequence of reactions that uses some ATP and NADPH from the light reactions. This sequence signifies the reduction of carbon dioxide to a carbohydrate because R—CO_2 has become R—CH_2O. Energy and electrons are needed for this reduction reaction, and these are supplied by ATP and NADPH.

Regeneration of RuBP

Notice that the Calvin cycle reactions in Figure 7.9 are multiplied by three because it takes three turns of the Calvin cycle to allow one G3P to exit. Why? Because, for every three turns of the Calvin cycle, five molecules of G3P are used to re-form three molecules of RuBP, and the cycle continues. Notice that 5×3 (carbons in G3P) = 3×5 (carbons in RuBP):

As five molecules of G3P become three molecules of RuBP, three molecules of ATP become three molecules of ADP + P .

This reaction also uses some of the ATP produced by the light reactions.

 Animation
How the Calvin
Cycle Works

The Importance of the Calvin Cycle

G3P is the product of the Calvin cycle that can be converted to other molecules a plant needs. Notice that glucose phosphate is

among the organic molecules that result from G3P metabolism (Fig. 7.10). This is of interest to us because glucose is the molecule that plants and animals most often metabolize to produce the ATP molecules they require for their energy needs.

Glucose phosphate can be combined with fructose (and the phosphate removed) to form sucrose, the molecule that plants use to transport carbohydrates from one part of the plant to the other.

Glucose phosphate is also the starting point for the synthesis of starch and cellulose. Starch is the storage form of glucose. Some starch is stored in chloroplasts, but most starch is stored in amyloplasts in roots. Cellulose is a structural component of plant cell walls and becomes fiber in our diet because we are unable to digest it.

A plant can use the hydrocarbon skeleton of G3P to form fatty acids and glycerol, which are combined in plant oils. We are all familiar with corn oil, sunflower oil, or olive oil used in cooking. Also, when nitrogen is added to the hydrocarbon skeleton derived from G3P, amino acids are formed, allowing the plant to produce protein.

Check Your Progress   7.4

1. Describe the three major steps of the Calvin cycle.
2. Illustrate why it takes 3 turns of the Calvin cycle to produce 1 G3P.

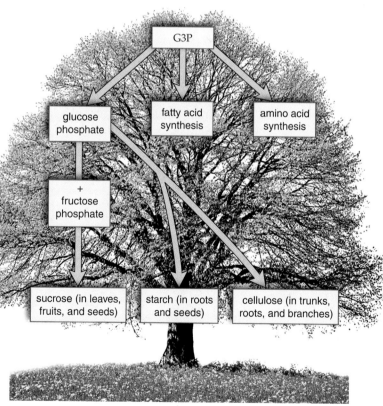

Figure 7.10 Fate of G3P. G3P is the first reactant in a number of plant cell metabolic pathways. Two G3Ps are needed to form glucose phosphate; glucose is often considered the end product of photosynthesis. Sucrose is the transport sugar in plants; starch is the storage form of glucose; and cellulose is a major constituent of plant cell walls.

7.5 Other Types of Photosynthesis

The majority of land plants, such as azaleas, maples, and tulips, carry on photosynthesis as described and are called **C_3 plants** (Fig. 7.11a). C_3 plants use the enzyme RuBP carboxylase to fix CO_2 to RuBP in mesophyll cells. The first detected molecule following fixation is the 3-carbon molecule 3PG:

$$\text{RuBP} + CO_2 \xrightarrow{\text{RuBP carboxylase}} 2\ 3\text{PG}$$

As shown in Figure 7.2, leaves have small openings called stomata through which water can leave and carbon dioxide (CO_2) can enter. If the weather is hot and dry, the stomata close, conserving water. (Water loss might cause the plant to wilt and die.) Now the concentration of CO_2 decreases in leaves, while O_2, a by-product of photosynthesis, increases. When O_2 rises in C_3 plants, RuBP carboxylase combines it with RuBP instead of CO_2. The result is one molecule of 3PG and the eventual release of CO_2. This is called **photorespiration** because in the presence of light (*photo*), oxygen is taken up and CO_2 is released (*respiration*).

An adaptation called C_4 photosynthesis enables some plants to avoid photorespiration.

C_4 Photosynthesis

In a C_3 plant, the mesophyll cells contain well-formed chloroplasts and are arranged in parallel layers. In a C_4 leaf, the bundle sheath cells, as well as the mesophyll cells, contain chloroplasts. Further, the mesophyll cells are arranged concentrically around the bundle sheath cells:

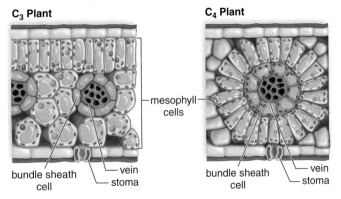

C_4 plants fix CO_2 to PEP (phosphoenolpyruvate, a C_3 molecule) using the enzyme PEP carboxylase (PEPCase). The result is oxaloacetate, a C_4 molecule:

$$\text{PEP} + CO_2 \xrightarrow{\text{PEPCase}} \text{oxaloacetate}$$

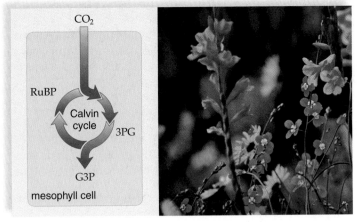

a. CO_2 fixation in a C_3 plant, wildflowers

b. CO_2 fixation in a C_4 plant, corn, *Zea mays*

Figure 7.11 Carbon dioxide fixation in C_3 and C_4 plants.
a. In C_3 plants, CO_2 is taken up by the Calvin cycle directly in mesophyll cells. **b.** C_4 plants form a C_4 molecule in mesophyll cells prior to releasing CO_2 to the Calvin cycle in bundle sheath cells.

In a C_4 plant, CO_2 is taken up in mesophyll cells, and then malate, a reduced form of oxaloacetate, is pumped into the bundle sheath cells (Fig. 7.11b). Here, and only here, does CO_2 enter the Calvin cycle.

Because it takes energy to pump molecules, you would think that the C_4 pathway would be disadvantageous. Yet in hot, dry climates, the net photosynthetic rate of C_4 plants, such as sugarcane, corn, and Bermuda grass, is about two to three times that of C_3 plants (e.g., wheat, rice, and oats). Why do C_4 plants enjoy such an advantage? The answer is that they can avoid photorespiration, discussed previously. Photorespiration is wasteful because it is not part of the Calvin cycle. Photorespiration does not occur in C_4 leaves because PEPCase, unlike RuBP carboxylase, does not combine with O_2. Even when stomata are closed, CO_2 is delivered to the Calvin cycle in the bundle sheath cells.

When the weather is moderate, C_3 plants ordinarily have the advantage, but when the weather becomes hot and dry, C_4 plants have the advantage, and we can expect them to predominate. In the early summer, C_3 plants such as Kentucky bluegrass and creeping bent grass predominate in lawns in the cooler parts of the United States, but by midsummer, crabgrass, a C_4 plant, begins to take over.

CO₂ fixation in a CAM plant, pineapple, *Ananas comosus*

Figure 7.12 Carbon dioxide fixation in a CAM plant. CAM plants, such as pineapple, fix CO_2 at night, forming a C_4 molecule that is released to the Calvin cycle during the day.

CAM Photosynthesis

CAM stands for crassulacean-acid metabolism; the Crassulaceae is a family of flowering succulent (water-containing) plants that live in warm, dry regions of the world. CAM was first discovered in these plants, but now it is known to be prevalent among other groups of plants.

Whereas a C_4 plant represents partitioning in space—carbon dioxide fixation occurs in mesophyll cells while the Calvin cycle occurs in bundle sheath cells—CAM is partitioning by the use of time. During the night, CAM plants use PEPCase to fix some CO_2, forming C_4 molecules, which are stored in large vacuoles in mesophyll cells. During the day, C_4 molecules (malate) release CO_2 to the Calvin cycle when NADPH and ATP are available from the light reactions (Fig. 7.12). The primary advantage for this partitioning again has to do with the conservation of water. CAM plants open their stomata only at night, and therefore only at that time does atmospheric CO_2 enter the plant. During the day, the stomata close; this conserves water, but CO_2 cannot enter the plant.

Photosynthesis in a CAM plant is minimal because a limited amount of CO_2 is fixed at night, but it does allow CAM plants to live under stressful conditions.

Photosynthesis and Adaptation to the Environment

The different types of photosynthesis give us an opportunity to consider that organisms are metabolically adapted to their environment. Each method of photosynthesis has its advantages and disadvantages, depending on the climate.

C_4 plants most likely evolved in, and are adapted to, areas of high light intensities, high temperatures, and limited rainfall. C_4 plants, however, are more sensitive to cold, and C_3 plants do better than C_4 plants below 25°C. CAM plants, on the other hand, compete well with either type of plant when the environment is extremely arid. Surprisingly, CAM is quite widespread and has evolved in 23 families of flowering plants, including some lilies and orchids! And it is found among nonflowering plants, including some ferns and cone-bearing trees.

Check Your Progress 7.5

1. Describe some plants that use a method of photosynthesis other than C_3 photosynthesis.
2. Explain why C_4 photosynthesis is advantageous in hot, dry conditions.

CONNECTING *the* CONCEPTS *with the* THEMES

Evolution

- Plants have evolved to capture solar energy and store it in carbon-based organic nutrients. These are passed on to organisms that have evolved to feed on plants, and in turn to organisms that have evolved to feed on the plant-eaters, and so on in a food web.
- Plants are called autotrophs because they make their own organic food. Heterotrophs are organisms that take in organic food made by other organisms.

Nature of Science

- The amount of carbon dioxide in the atmosphere is increasing steadily, in part because of burning fossil fuels. This buildup of carbon dioxide can contribute to climate change.
- We can use the tools of science to understand the scope of global climate change, learn about our atmosphere and how to keep it healthy, and make informed choices about how best to maintain the Earth.

Biological Systems

- Autotrophs take in carbon dioxide when they photosynthesize. Carbon dioxide is returned to the atmosphere when autotrophs and heterotrophs carry on cellular respiration. In this way, carbon atoms cycle through living things.
- Energy does not cycle, and therefore all life is dependent on the ability of plants to capture solar energy and produce carbohydrate molecules from CO_2.

Media Study Tools

www.mhhe.com/maderbiology11

Enhance your study of this chapter with study tools and practice tests. Also ask your instructor about the resources available through

ConnectPlus, including the media-rich eBook, interactive learning tools, and animations.

3D Animation For a detailed examination of the process of
Photosynthesis photosynthesis, including a description of the
properties of light, watch McGraw-Hill's new 3D animation
"Photosynthesis."

Summarize

7.1 Photosynthetic Organisms

Photosynthesis produces carbohydrates and releases oxygen, both of which are used by the majority of living things. Cyanobacteria, algae, and land plants carry on photosynthesis. In plants, photosynthesis takes place in chloroplasts. A chloroplast is bounded by a double membrane and contains two main components: the semifluid stroma and the membranous grana made up of thylakoids.

7.2 The Process of Photosynthesis

The overall equation for photosynthesis shows that it is a redox reaction. Carbon dioxide is reduced, and water is oxidized. During photosynthesis, the light reactions take place in the thylakoid membranes, and the Calvin cycle reactions take place in the stroma.

7.3 Plants as Solar Energy Converters

Photosynthesis uses solar energy in the visible-light range. Specifically, chlorophylls *a* and *b* absorb violet, blue, and red wavelengths best and reflect green light, whereas the carotenoids absorb violet-blue-green light and reflect yellow-to-orange light.

In the light reactions, noncyclic electron flow begins when solar energy enters PS II and energizes chlorophyll *a* electrons. The oxidation (splitting) of water replaces these electrons in the reaction-center chlorophyll *a* molecules. Oxygen is released to the atmosphere, and hydrogen ions (H^+) remain in the thylakoid space. Electrons are ultimately passed to PS I via an electron transport chain, which pumps hydrogen ions across the thylakoid membrane and contributes to the chemiosmotic gradient used to make ATP via ATP synthetase. Light-energized electrons from PS I are captured by $NADP^+$, which combines with H^+ from the stroma to become NADPH. Cyclic electron flow in the light reactions pumps additional hydrogen ions and also contributes to ATP production.

7.4 Plants as Carbon Dioxide Fixers

The energy yield of the light reactions is stored in ATP and NADPH. These molecules are used by the Calvin cycle reactions to reduce CO_2 to carbohydrate, namely G3P, which is then converted to all the organic molecules a plant needs.

During the first stage of the Calvin cycle, the enzyme RuBP carboxylase fixes CO_2 to RuBP, producing a 6-carbon molecule that immediately breaks down to two C_3 molecules. During the second stage, CO_2 (incorporated into an organic molecule) is reduced to carbohydrate (CH_2O). This step requires the NADPH and some of the ATP from the light reactions. For every three turns of the Calvin cycle, the net gain is one G3P molecule; the other five G3P molecules are used to re-form three molecules of RuBP, which also requires ATP. It takes two G3P molecules to make one glucose molecule.

7.5 Other Types of Photosynthesis

Plants have adapted ways other than the C3 process just described to photosynthesize in various environments. In C_4 plants, carbon dioxide is first fixed in mesophyll cells via PEPCase, is transported to a different location in bundle sheath cells, and then released to the Calvin cycle. PEPCase has an advantage over RuBP carboxylase because it doesn't participate in photorespiration. C_4 plants avoid the photorespiration complication by dividing where carbon fixation occurs from where the Calvin cycle occurs.

CAM plants, which live in hot, dry environments, cannot leave their stomata open during the day, or they will die from loss of water. CAM plants fix carbon only at night, conserving water. Stores of CO_2 are released to the Calvin cycle during the day, when photosynthesis is possible. CAM plants avoid drying out by dividing when they bring in carbon dioxide from when they release it to the Calvin cycle.

Key Terms

absorption spectrum   124
ATP synthase   126
autotroph   120
C_3 plant   130
C_4 plant   130
Calvin cycle reactions   123
CAM   131
carbon dioxide (CO_2)
   fixation   128
carotenoid   124
chemiosmosis   126
climate change 127
chlorophyll   121

chloroplast   121
electron transport chain 125
grana (sing., granum)   121
heterotroph   120
light reactions   122
noncyclic pathway   124
photorespiration   130
photosynthesis   120
photosystem   124
RuBP carboxylase   128
stomata   121
stroma   121
thylakoid   121

 Assess

Reviewing This Chapter

1. Why is it proper to say that almost all living things are dependent on solar energy?   120
2. Name the two major components of chloroplasts, and associate each with one of two sets of reactions that occur during photosynthesis. How are the two sets of reactions related?   121–23
3. Write the overall equation of photosynthesis and associate each participant with either the light reactions or the Calvin cycle reactions.   122–23
4. Discuss the electromagnetic spectrum and the combined absorption spectrum of chlorophylls *a* and *b* and the carotenoids. Why is chlorophyll a green pigment, and the carotenoids a yellow-orange pigment?   124
5. Trace the noncyclic electron pathway, naming and explaining all the events that occur as the electrons move from water to $NADP^+$.   124–25
6. How is the thylakoid membrane organized? Name the main complexes in the membrane. Give a function for each.   126
7. Explain what is meant by chemiosmosis, and relate this process to the electron transport chain present in the thylakoid membrane.   126
8. Describe the three stages of the Calvin cycle. Which stage uses the ATP and NADPH from the light reactions?   128–29
9. Compare C_3 and C_4 photosynthesis, contrasting the actions of RuBP carboxylase and PEPCase.   130
10. Explain CAM photosynthesis, contrasting it to C_4 photosynthesis in terms of partitioning a pathway.   131

Testing Yourself

Choose the best answer for each question.

1. The absorption spectrum of chlorophyll
   a. is not the same as that of carotenoids.
   b. approximates the action spectrum of photosynthesis.
   c. explains why chlorophyll is a green pigment.
   d. shows that some colors of light are absorbed more than others.
   e. All of these are correct.

2. The final acceptor of electrons during the noncyclic electron pathway is
   a. PS I.
   b. PS II.
   c. ATP.
   d. NADP$^+$.
   e. water.

3. A photosystem contains
   a. pigments, a reaction center, and electron acceptors.
   b. ADP, $\textcircled{P}$, and hydrogen ions (H$^+$).
   c. protons, photons, and pigments.
   d. cytochromes only.
   e. Both b and c are correct.

For questions 4–8, match each item to those in the key. Use an answer more than once, if possible.

KEY:

   a. solar energy
   b. chlorophyll
   c. chemiosmosis
   d. Calvin cycle

4. light energy

5. ATP synthase

6. thylakoid membrane

7. green pigment

8. RuBP

For questions 9–11, indicate whether the statement is true (T) or false (F).

9. RuBP carboxylase is the enzyme that fixes carbon dioxide to RuBP in the Calvin cycle. _____

10. When 3PG becomes G3P during the light reactions, carbon dioxide is reduced to carbohydrate. _____

11. NADPH and ATP cycle between the Calvin cycle and the light reactions constantly. _____

12. The NADPH and ATP from the light reactions are used to
    a. split water.
    b. cause RuBP carboxylase to fix CO$_2$.
    c. re-form the photosystems.
    d. cause electrons to move along their pathways.
    e. convert 3PG to G3P.

13. Chemiosmosis
    a. depends on complexes in the thylakoid membrane.
    b. depends on an electrochemical gradient.
    c. depends on a difference in H$^+$ concentration between the thylakoid space and the stroma.
    d. results in ATP formation.
    e. All of these are correct.

14. The function of the light reactions is to
    a. obtain CO$_2$.
    b. make carbohydrate.
    c. convert light energy into a usable form of chemical energy.
    d. regenerate RuBP.

15. Label the following diagram of a chloroplast:

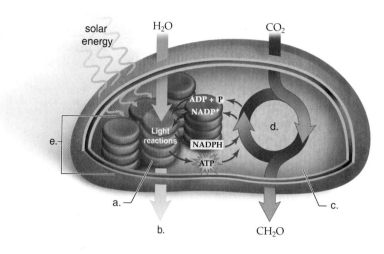

   f. The light reactions occur in which part of a chloroplast?
   g. The Calvin cycle reactions occur in which part of a chloroplast?

16. The oxygen given off by photosynthesis comes from
    a. H$_2$O.
    b. CO$_2$.
    c. glucose.
    d. RuBP.

17. The glucose formed by photosynthesis can be used by plants to make
    a. starch.
    b. cellulose.
    c. lipids and oils.
    d. proteins.
    e. All of these are correct.

18. The Calvin cycle reactions
    a. produce carbohydrate.
    b. convert one form of chemical energy into a different form of chemical energy.
    c. regenerate more RuBP.
    d. use the products of the light reactions.
    e. All of these are correct.

19. CAM photosynthesis
    a. is the same as C$_4$ photosynthesis.
    b. is an adaptation to cold environments in the Southern Hemisphere.
    c. is prevalent in desert plants that close their stomata during the day.
    d. occurs in plants that live in marshy areas.
    e. stands for chloroplasts and mitochondria.

20. C$_4$ photosynthesis
    a. is the same as C$_3$ photosynthesis because it takes place in chloroplasts.
    b. occurs in plants whose bundle sheath cells contain chloroplasts.
    c. takes place in plants such as wheat, rice, and oats.
    d. is an advantage when the weather is hot and dry.
    e. Both b and d are correct.

Engage

Thinking Scientifically

1. In 1882, T. W. Engelmann carried out an ingenious experiment to demostrate that chlorophyll absorbs light in the blue and red portions of the spectrum. He placed a single filament of a green alga in a drop of water on a microscope slide. Then he passed light through a prism and onto the string of algal cells. The slide also contained aerobic bacterial cells. After some time, he peered into the microscope and saw the bacteria clustered around the regions of the algal filament that were receiving blue light and red light, as shown in the illustration. Why do you suppose the bacterial cells were clustered in this manner?

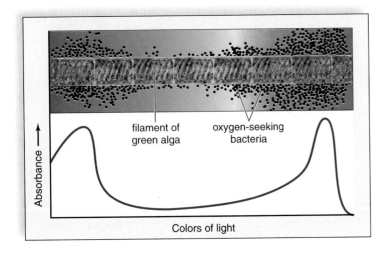

filament of
green alga

oxygen-seeking
bacteria

Absorbance →

Colors of light

2. In the fall of the year, the leaves of many trees change from green to red or yellow. Two hypotheses can explain this color change: (a) In the fall, chlorophyll degenerates, and red or yellow pigments that were earlier masked by chlorophyll become apparent. (b) In the fall, red or yellow pigments are synthesized, and they mask the color of chlorophyll. How could you test these two hypotheses?

Bioethical Issue
The World's Food Supply

The Food and Agriculture Organization of the United Nations warns that the world's food supply is dwindling rapidly and food prices are soaring to historic levels. They estimate that approximately 1 billion people currently live in hunger. Their records show that the reserves of cereals are severely depleted, and presently only 12 weeks of the world's total consumption is stored, which is much less than the average of 18 weeks consumption in storage during the years 2000-2005. Only 8 weeks of corn are in storage compared to 11 weeks during this same time period. Various reasons are offered for a possible calamitous shortfall in the world's grain supplies in the near future. Possible causes are an ever larger world population, water shortages, climate change, and the growing costs of fertilizer. Also of concern is the converting of corn into ethanol as a fuel source, although this is becoming less of a concern as better fuel crops are developed. There are apparently no quick fixes to boost supplies. In years past, newly-developed hybrid crops led to enormous increases in yield per acre, but they also caused pollution problems that degrade the environment. Even if the promised biotech advances in drought, cold, and disease resistant crops are made, they will not immediately boost food supplies. Recent weather fluctuations, including widespread flooding and regional temperature fluctuations, are adding pressure to an already compressed food production situation. Possible solutions have been offered. Rather than exporting food to needy countries, it may be better to improve their ability to grow their own food, especially when you consider that transportation costs are soaring. Also, it would be beneficial to achieve zero population growth as quickly as possible and use renewable energy supplies other than converting corn to ethanol. The use of ethanol only contributes to climate change, which is expected to be a contributing factor to producing less grain. What do you think should be done to solve the expected shortage in the world's food supply, and how should your solution be brought about?

UNIT 2

Genetic Basis of Life

This unit provides an opportunity to become acquainted with the basics of cellular reproduction and Mendelian and molecular genetics. Cellular reproduction is one of the basic characteristics of life: the processes of mitosis and meiosis allow organisms to reproduce, grow, and repair damaged tissues. An understanding of cellular reproduction has led to the study of stem cells, which have the potential to offer treatments for many human diseases.

Mendelian genetics explains the patterns of inheritance that are founded in the process of meiosis. Among the many applications of knowledge of these patterns is the ability to predict the chances of having a child with a specific genetic disorder. An understanding of molecular genetics has led to the development of DNA technologies that have the potential to cure genetic diseases and produce crops to feed an ever-increasing human population.

The field of genetics is making progress in other areas too. We are beginning to understand how cell division is regulated by numerous genes, and how a failure of these regulatory mechanisms may lead to cancer. Many other human diseases are the result of mutations in genes as well. Thus, at every turn, it is clear that you can't fully appreciate the happenings of the twenty-first century without a knowledge of genetics, and this is your chance to become a part of the action.

UNIT OUTLINE

UNIT LEARNING OUTCOMES

The learning outcomes for this unit focus on three major themes in the life sciences.

Evolution	Explain how the process of meiosis introduces the variation necessary for evolutionary change.
Nature of Science	Discuss how an understanding of cellular reproduction and molecular biology can be used to treat human disease.
Biological Systems	Evaluate how the information contained with the DNA is responsible for the physical characteristics of an organism.

A cell may become cancerous when regulation of cell division fails.

9

The Cell Cycle and Cellular Reproduction

CHAPTER OUTLINE

9.1 The Cell Cycle 154
9.2 Mitosis and Cytokinesis 157
9.3 The Cell Cycle and Cancer 163
9.4 Prokaryotic Cell Division 166

The process of cell division is highly regulated. In humans, life begins as a single cell, yet in a very short period of time the process of cell division produces trillions of cells, each specialized for a special function. Over 200 different types of cells are found in the human body, and although each is specialized, they all work together in harmony.

But what happens when the regulation of cell division fails? In the United States this year, over 68,000 individuals will be diagnosed with melanoma, a form of skin cancer, and around 8,000 people will die from this disease. In many instances of melanoma, exposure to ultraviolet radiation (UV) from the Sun has caused a mutation in the regulatory mechanisms of the cell cycle. Without proper regulation, cell division occurs continuously, a characteristic of cancer. For melanoma, this loss of cell cycle control results from a mutation in a gene known as *CDKN2A*. This gene is an example of a tumor suppressor gene, one of the key regulatory mechanisms of the cell cycle. In this chapter we describe the process of cell division, how it is regulated, and how cancer may develop when regulatory mechanisms malfunction.

As you read through the chapter, think about the following questions:

1. What is the normal sequence of events in the process of cellular reproduction?
2. What are the roles of the checkpoints in a cell cycle?
3. How do tumor suppressor genes regulate the cell cycle?

BEFORE YOU BEGIN

Before beginning this chapter, take a few moments to review the following discussions.

Section 3.5 What is the role of the DNA in a cell?

Sections 4.2 and 4.3 What are the major differences between prokaryotic and eukaryotic cells?

Section 4.8 What is the role of the cytoskeleton in a eukaryotic cell?

FOLLOWING *the* THEMES

CHAPTER 9 THE CELL CYCLE AND CELLULAR REPRODUCTION

UNIT 2 GENETIC BASIS OF LIFE		
	Evolution	As eukaryotic cells became increasingly complex, a similarly complex series of events evolved to separate their multiple chromosomes, located within a membrane-bound nucleus, into new daughter cells.
	Nature of Science	By studying the regulatory mechanisms of the cell cycle, scientists are able to gather a deeper understanding of why cancer occurs.
	Biological Systems	For unicellular organisms, cell division results in the formation of two new organisms, while in multicellular organisms, cell division is the basis of growth and tissue repair.

9.1 The Cell Cycle

The **cell cycle** is an orderly set of stages that take place between the time a eukaryotic cell divides and the time the resulting daughter cells also divide. When a cell is going to divide, it grows larger, the number of organelles doubles, and the amount of DNA doubles as DNA replication occurs. The two portions of the cell cycle are interphase, which includes a number of stages, and the mitotic stage when mitosis and cytokinesis occur.

Animation
Overview of Cell Division

Interphase

As Figure 9.1 shows, most of the cell cycle is spent in **interphase.** This is the time when a cell performs its usual functions, depending on its location in the body. The amount of time the cell takes for interphase varies widely. Embryonic cells complete the entire cell cycle in just a few hours. For adult mammalian cells, interphase lasts for about 20 hours, which is 90% of the cell cycle. In the past, interphase was known as the resting stage. However, today it is known that interphase is very busy, and that preparations are being made for mitosis. Interphase consists of three stages, referred to as G_1, S, and G_2.

3D Animation
Interphase

G_1 Stage

Cell biologists named the stage before DNA replication G_1, and they named the stage after DNA replication G_2. G stood for "gap," but now that we know how metabolically active the cell is, it is better to think of G as standing for "growth." During G_1, the cell recovers from the previous division. The cell grows in size, increases the number of organelles (such as mitochondria and ribosomes), and accumulates materials that will be used for DNA synthesis. Otherwise, cells are constantly performing their normal daily functions during G_1, including communicating with other cells, secreting substances, and carrying out cellular respiration.

Some cells, such as nerve and muscle cells, typically do not complete the cell cycle and are permanently arrested. These cells exit interphase and enter a stage called G_0. While in the G_0 stage, the cells continue to perform normal everyday processes, but no preparations are being made for cell division. Cells may not leave the G_0 stage without proper signals from other cells and other parts of the body. Thus, completion of the cell cycle is very tightly controlled.

S Stage

Following G_1, the cell enters the S stage, when DNA synthesis or replication occurs. At the beginning of the S stage, each chromosome is composed of one DNA double helix. Following DNA replication, each chromosome is composed of two identical DNA double helix molecules. Each double helix is called a **chromatid,** and the two identical chromatids are referred to as **sister chromatids.** The sister chromatids remain attached until they are separated during mitosis.

G_2 Stage

Following the S stage, G_2 is the stage from the completion of DNA replication to the onset of mitosis. During this stage, the cell synthesizes proteins that will assist cell division. For example, it makes the proteins that form microtubules. Microtubules are used during the mitotic stage to form the mitotic spindle that is critical during M stage.

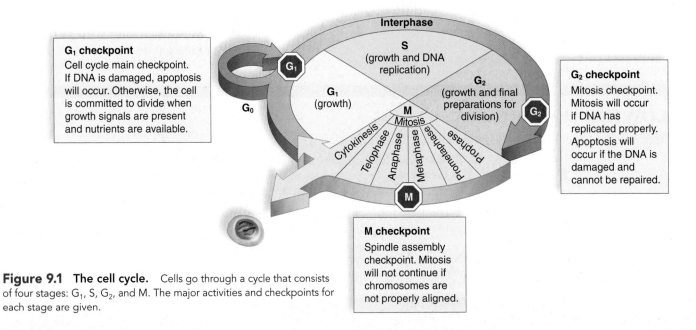

Figure 9.1 **The cell cycle.** Cells go through a cycle that consists of four stages: G_1, S, G_2, and M. The major activities and checkpoints for each stage are given.

G_1 checkpoint
Cell cycle main checkpoint. If DNA is damaged, apoptosis will occur. Otherwise, the cell is committed to divide when growth signals are present and nutrients are available.

G_2 checkpoint
Mitosis checkpoint. Mitosis will occur if DNA has replicated properly. Apoptosis will occur if the DNA is damaged and cannot be repaired.

M checkpoint
Spindle assembly checkpoint. Mitosis will not continue if chromosomes are not properly aligned.

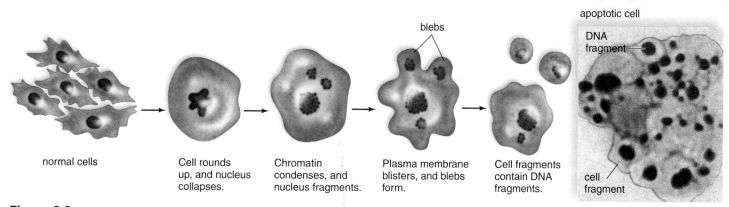

Figure 9.2 Apoptosis. Apoptosis is a sequence of events that results in a fragmented cell. The fragments are phagocytized (engulfed) by white blood cells and neighboring tissue cells.

M (Mitotic) Stage

Following interphase, the cell enters the M (for mitotic) stage. This cell division stage includes **mitosis** (nuclear division) and **cytokinesis** (division of the cytoplasm). During mitosis, daughter chromosomes are distributed by the **mitotic spindle** to two daughter nuclei. When division of the cytoplasm is complete, two daughter cells are present.

Control of the Cell Cycle

A **signal** is an agent that influences the activities of a cell. **Growth factors** are signaling proteins received at the plasma membrane. Even cells arrested in G_0 will finish the cell cycle if stimulated to do so by growth factors. In general, signals ensure that the cell cycle stages follow one another in the normal sequence.

Animation
Cell Proliferation
Signaling Pathway

Cell Cycle Checkpoints

The red barriers in Figure 9.1 represent three checkpoints at which the cell cycle either stops or continues on, depending on the internal signals received. Researchers have identified a family of internal signaling proteins called **cyclins** that increase and decrease as the cell cycle continues. Specific cyclins must be present for the cell to proceed from the G_1 stage to the S stage and from the G_2 stage to the M stage.

3D Animation
Checkpoints

As discussed in the Nature of Science feature "The G_1 Checkpoint," the primary checkpoint of the cell cycle is the G_1 checkpoint. In mammalian cells, the signaling protein **p53** stops the cycle at the G_1 checkpoint when DNA is damaged. (In the name p53, p stands for *protein* and 53 represents its molecular weight in kilodaltons.) First, p53 attempts to initiate DNA repair, but rising levels of p53 can bring about **apoptosis,** which is programmed cell death (Fig. 9.2). Another protein, called **RB,** is responsible for interpreting growth signals and also nutrient availability signals. RB stands for *retino*blastoma, a cancer of the retina that occurs when the *RB* gene undergoes a mutation.

The cell cycle may also stop at the G_2 checkpoint if DNA has not finished replicating. This checkpoint prevents the initiation of the M stage before completion of the S stage. If DNA is physically damaged, such as from exposure to solar radiation or X-rays, the G_2 checkpoint also offers the opportunity for DNA to be repaired.

Another cell cycle checkpoint occurs during the mitotic stage. The cycle stops if the chromosomes are not properly attached to the mitotic spindle. Normally, the mitotic spindle ensures that the chromosomes are distributed accurately to the daughter cells.

Animation
Control of the Cell
Cycle

Apoptosis

Apoptosis is often defined as programmed cell death because the cell progresses through a typical series of events that bring about its destruction (Fig. 9.2). The cell rounds up, causing it to lose contact with its neighbors. The nucleus fragments, and the plasma membrane develops blisters. Finally, the cell fragments are engulfed by white blood cells and/or neighboring cells.

A remarkable finding of the past few years is that the enzymes that bring about apoptosis, called *caspases,* are always present in the cell. The enzymes are ordinarily held in check by inhibitors, but they can be unleashed by either internal or external signals.

Apoptosis and Cell Division. In living systems, opposing events keep the body in balance and maintain homeostasis. cell division and apoptosis are two opposing processes that keep the number of cells in the body at an appropriate level. Cell division increases and apoptosis decreases the number of **somatic** (body) **cells.** Both are normal parts of growth and development. An organism begins as a single cell that repeatedly divides to produce many cells, but eventually some cells must die for the organism to take shape. For example, when a tadpole becomes a frog, the tail disappears as apoptosis occurs. In a human embryo, the fingers and toes are at first webbed, but then they are usually freed from one another as a result of apoptosis.

Cell division occurs during your entire life. Even now, your body is producing thousands of new red blood cells, skin cells, and cells that line your respiratory and digestive tracts. Also, if you suffer a cut, cell division repairs the injury. Apoptosis occurs all the time too, particularly if an abnormal cell that could become cancerous appears, or a cell becomes infected with a virus. Death through apoptosis prevents a tumor from developing and helps to limit the spread of viruses.

Check Your Progress 9.1

1. List, in order, the four stages of the cell cycle and briefly summarize what is happening at each stage.
2. Explain what conditions might cause a cell to halt the cell cycle.
3. Discuss how apoptosis represents a regulatory event of the cell cycle.

The G₁ Checkpoint

Cell division is very tightly regulated so that only certain cells in an adult body are actively dividing. After cell division occurs, cells enter the G_1 stage. Upon completing G_1, they will divide again, but before this happens they have to pass through the G_1 checkpoint.

The G_1 checkpoint ensures that conditions are right for making the commitment to divide by evaluating the meaning of growth signals, determining the availability of nutrients, and assessing the integrity of DNA. Failure to meet any one of these criteria results in a cell's halting the cell cycle and entering G_0 stage, or undergoing apoptosis if the problems are severe.

Evaluating Growth Signals

Multicellular organisms tightly control cell division so that it occurs only when needed. Signaling molecules, such as hormones, may be sent from nearby cells or distant tissues to encourage or discourage cells from entering the cell cycle. Such signals may cause a cell to enter a G_0 stage, or complete G_1 and enter the S stage. Growth signals that promote cell division cause a cyclin-dependent-kinase (CDK) to add a phosphate group to the RB protein, a major regulator of the G_1 checkpoint.

Ordinarily, a protein called E2F is bound to RB, but when RB is phosphorylated, its shape changes and it releases E2F. Now, E2F binds to DNA, activating certain genes whose products are needed to complete the cell cycle (Fig. 9Aa). Likewise, growth signals prompt cells that are in G_0 stage to reenter the G_1 stage, complete it, and enter the S stage. If growth signals are sufficient, a cell passes through the G_1 checkpoint and cell division occurs.

Determining Nutrient Availability

Just as experienced hikers ensure that they have sufficient food for their journey, a cell ensures that nutrient levels are adequate before committing to cell division. For example, scientists know that starving cells in culture enter G_0. At that time, phosphate groups are removed from RB (see reverse arrows in Figure 9Aa); RB does not release E2F; and the proteins needed to complete the cell cycle are not produced. When nutrients become available, CDKs bring about the phosphorylation of RB, which then releases E2F (see forward arrows in Figure 9Aa). After E2F binds to DNA, proteins needed to complete the cell cycle are produced. Therefore, you can see that cells do not commit to divide until conditions are conducive for them to do so.

Assessing DNA Integrity

For cell division to occur, DNA must be free of errors and damage. The p53 protein is involved in this quality control function. Ordinarily, p53 is broken down because it has no job to do. In response to DNA damage, CDK phosphorylates p53 (Fig. 9Ab). Now, the molecule is not broken down as usual, and instead its level in the nucleus begins to rise. Phosphorylated p53 binds to DNA; certain genes are activated; and DNA repair proteins are produced. If the DNA damage cannot be repaired, p53 levels continue to rise, and apoptosis is triggered. If the damage is successfully repaired, p53 levels fall, and the cell is allowed to complete G_1 stage—as long as growth signals and nutrients are present, for example.

Actually, many criteria must be met for a cell to commit to cell division, and the failure to meet any one of them may cause the cell cycle to be halted and/or apoptosis to be initiated. The G_1 checkpoint is currently an area of intense research because understanding it holds the key to possibly curing cancer, and for unleashing the power of normal, healthy cells to regenerate tissues, which could be used to cure many other human conditions.

Questions to Consider

1. What potentially could be the effect of an abnormally high level of a growth hormone on the regulation of the cell cycle?
2. Why might some cancers be associated with a mutation in the gene encoding the p53 protein?

a.

b.

Figure 9A Regulation of the G1 checkpoint.   a. When CDK (cyclin-dependent-kinase) is not present, RB retains E2F. When CDK is present, a phosphorylated RB releases E2F, and after it binds to DNA, proteins necessary to completing cell division are produced. **b.** If DNA is damaged, p53 is not broken down, and instead is involved in the production of DNA repair enzymes and in triggering apoptosis when repair is impossible.

9.2 Mitosis and Cytokinesis

Learning Outcomes

Upon completion of this section you should be able to

1. Explain how the cell prepares the chromosomes and centrosomes prior to nuclear division.
2. Summarize the major events that occur during mitosis and cytokinesis.
3. Discuss why human stem cells continuously conduct mitosis.

As mentioned, cell division in eukaryotes involves mitosis, which is nuclear division, and cytokinesis, which is division of the cytoplasm. During mitosis, the sister chromatids are separated and distributed to two daughter cells.

Eukaryotic Chromosomes

The DNA in the chromosomes of eukaryotes is associated with various proteins, including **histones** that are especially involved in organizing chromosomes. When a eukaryotic cell is not undergoing division, the DNA (and associated proteins) are located within **chromatin,** which has the appearance of a tangled mass of thin threads. Before mitosis begins, chromatin becomes highly coiled and condensed, and it is easy to see the individual chromosomes.

When the chromosomes are visible, it is possible to photograph and count them. Each species has a characteristic chromosome number (Table 9.1). This is the full or **diploid (2n)** number [Gk. *diplos,* twofold, and *-eides,* like] of chromosomes that is found in all cells of the individual. The diploid number includes two chromosomes of each kind. Half the diploid number, called the **haploid (n)** number [Gk. *haplos,* single, and *-eides,* like] of chromosomes, contains only one chromosome of each kind. Typically, only sperm and eggs have the haploid number of chromosomes in the life cycle of animals.

Preparations for Mitosis

During interphase, a cell must make preparations for cell division. These arrangements include replicating the chromosomes and duplicating most cellular organelles, including the centrosome, which will organize the spindle apparatus necessary for movement of chromosomes.

Chromosome Duplication

During mitosis, a 2n nucleus divides to produce daughter nuclei that are also 2n. The dividing cell is called the *parent cell,* and the resulting cells are called the *daughter cells.* Before nuclear division takes place, DNA replicates, duplicating the chromosomes in the parent cell. This occurs during the S stage of interphase. Now each chromosome has two identical double helical molecules. Each double helix is a *chromatid,* and the two identical chromatids are called *sister chromatids* (Fig. 9.3). Sister chromatids are constricted and attached to each other at a region called the **centromere.** Protein complexes called **kinetochores** develop on either side of the centromere during cell division.

Table 9.1 Diploid Chromosome Numbers of Some Eukaryotes

Type of Organism	Name of Chromosome	Chromosome Number
Fungi	*Saccharomyces cerevisiae* (yeast)	32
Plants	*Pisum sativum* (garden pea)	14
	Solanum tuberosum (potato)	48
	Ophioglossum vulgatum (Southern adder's tongue fern)	1,320
Animals	*Drosophila melanogaster* (fruit fly)	8
	Homo sapiens (human)	46
	Carassius auratus (goldfish)	94

During nuclear division, the two sister chromatids separate at the centromere, and in this way each duplicated chromosome gives rise to two daughter chromosomes. Each daughter chromosome has only one double helix molecule. The daughter chromosomes are distributed equally to the daughter cells. In this way, each daughter nucleus gets a copy of each chromosome that was in the parent cell.

Division of the Centrosome

The **centrosome** [Gk. *centrum,* center, and *soma,* body], the main microtubule-organizing center of the cell, also divides before mitosis begins. Each centrosome in an animal cell contains a pair

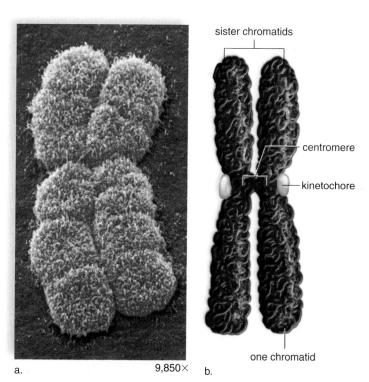

a.   9,850×   b.

Figure 9.3 Duplicated chromosomes. A duplicated chromosome contains two sister chromatids, each with a copy of the same genes. **a.** Electron micrograph of a highly coiled and condensed chromosome, typical of a nucleus about to divide. **b.** Diagrammatic drawing of a condensed chromosome. The chromatids are held together at a region called the centromere.

of barrel-shaped organelles called **centrioles.** Centrioles are not found in plant cells.

The centrosomes organize the mitotic spindle, which contains many fibers, each of which is composed of a bundle of microtubules. Microtubules are hollow cylinders made up of the protein tubulin. They assemble when tubulin subunits join, and when they disassemble, tubulin subunits become free once more. The microtubules of the cytoskeleton disassemble when spindle fibers begin forming. Most likely, this provides tubulin for the formation of the spindle fibers, or it may allow the cell to change shape as needed for cell division.

Figure 9.4 Phases of mitosis in animal and plant cells. The blue chromosomes were inherited from one parent and the red from the other parent.

Phases of Mitosis

Mitosis is a continuous process that is arbitrarily divided into five phases for convenience of description: prophase, prometaphase, metaphase, anaphase, and telophase (Fig. 9.4).

Prophase

It is apparent during **prophase** that nuclear division is about to occur because chromatin has condensed and the chromosomes are visible. Recall that DNA replication occurred during interphase, and therefore the *parental chromosomes are already duplicated and composed of two sister chromatids held together at a centromere.* Counting the number of centromeres in diagrammatic drawings gives the number of chromosomes for the cell depicted.

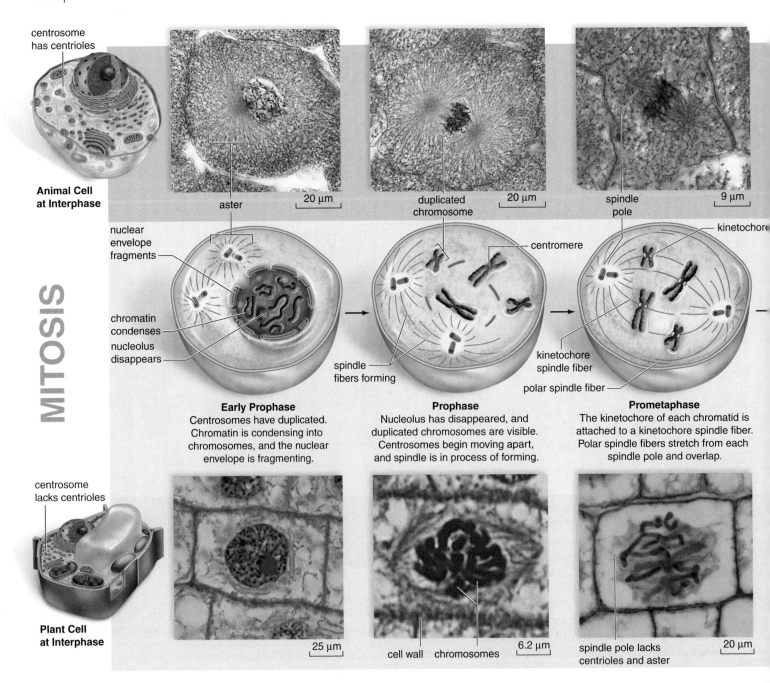

MITOSIS

centrosome has centrioles

Animal Cell at Interphase

aster   20 μm

duplicated chromosome   20 μm

spindle pole   9 μm

nuclear envelope fragments

centromere   kinetochore

chromatin condenses

nucleolus disappears

spindle fibers forming

kinetochore spindle fiber

polar spindle fiber

Early Prophase
Centrosomes have duplicated. Chromatin is condensing into chromosomes, and the nuclear envelope is fragmenting.

Prophase
Nucleolus has disappeared, and duplicated chromosomes are visible. Centrosomes begin moving apart, and spindle is in process of forming.

Prometaphase
The kinetochore of each chromatid is attached to a kinetochore spindle fiber. Polar spindle fibers stretch from each spindle pole and overlap.

centrosome lacks centrioles

Plant Cell at Interphase

25 μm

cell wall   chromosomes   6.2 μm

spindle pole lacks centrioles and aster   20 μm

During prophase, the nucleolus disappears and the nuclear envelope fragments. The spindle begins to assemble as the two centrosomes migrate away from one another. In animal cells, an array of microtubules radiates toward the plasma membrane from the centrosomes. These structures are called **asters.** It is thought that asters serve to brace the centrioles during later stages of cell division. Notice that the chromosomes have no particular orientation because the spindle has not yet formed.

Prometaphase (Late Prophase)

During **prometaphase,** preparations for sister chromatid separation are evident. Kinetochores appear on each side of the centromere, and these attach sister chromatids to the *kinetochore spindle fibers.* These fibers extend from the poles to the chromosomes, which will soon be located at the center of the spindle.

The kinetochore fibers attach the sister chromatids to opposite poles of the spindle, and the chromosomes are pulled first toward one pole and then toward the other before the chromosomes come into alignment. Notice that even though the chromosomes are attached to the spindle fibers in prometaphase, they are still not in alignment.

Metaphase

During **metaphase,** the centromeres of chromosomes are now in alignment on a single plane at the center of the cell. The chromosomes usually appear as a straight line across the middle of the cell when viewed under a light microscope. An imaginary plane that is perpendicular and passes through this circle is called the **metaphase plate.** It indicates the future axis of cell division.

chromosomes at metaphase plate   20 µm

daughter chromosome   20 µm

cleavage furrow   16 µm

nucleolus

kinetochore spindle fiber

Metaphase
Centromeres of duplicated chromosomes are aligned at the metaphase plate (center of fully formed spindle). Kinetochore spindle fibers attached to the sister chromatids come from opposite spindle poles.

Anaphase
Sister chromatids part and become daughter chromosomes that move toward the spindle poles. In this way, each pole receives the same number and kinds of chromosomes as the parent cell.

Telophase
Daughter cells are forming as nuclear envelopes and nucleoli reappear. Chromosomes will become indistinct chromatin.

spindle fibers   6.2 µm

6.2 µm

cell plate   6.6 µm

Several nonattached spindle fibers called *polar spindle fibers* reach beyond the metaphase plate and overlap. A cell cycle checkpoint, the M checkpoint, delays the start of anaphase until the kinetochores of each chromosome are attached properly to spindle fibers and the chromosomes are properly aligned along the metaphase plate.

Anaphase

At the start of **anaphase,** the two sister chromatids of each duplicated chromosome separate at the centromere, giving rise to two daughter chromosomes. Daughter chromosomes, each with a centromere and single chromatid composed of a single double helix, appear to move toward opposite poles. Actually, the daughter chromosomes are being pulled to the opposite poles as the kinetochore spindle fibers disassemble at the region of the kinetochores.

Even as the daughter chromosomes move toward the spindle poles, the poles themselves are moving farther apart because the polar spindle fibers are sliding past one another. Microtubule-associated proteins such as the motor molecules kinesin and dynein are involved in the sliding process. Anaphase is the shortest phase of mitosis.

Telophase

During **telophase,** the spindle disappears as new nuclear envelopes form around the daughter chromosomes. Each daughter nucleus contains the same number and kinds of chromosomes as the original parent cell. Remnants of the polar spindle fibers are still visible between the two nuclei.

The chromosomes become more diffuse chromatin once again, and a nucleolus appears in each daughter nucleus. Division of the cytoplasm requires cytokinesis, which is discussed in the next section.

Cytokinesis in Animal and Plant Cells

As mentioned previously, cytokinesis is division of the cytoplasm. Cytokinesis accompanies mitosis in most cells but not all. When mitosis occurs but cytokinesis doesn't occur, the result is a multinucleated cell. For example, you will see in Chapter 27 that the embryo sac in flowering plants is multinucleated.

Division of the cytoplasm begins in anaphase, continues in telophase, but does not reach completion until the following interphase begins. By the end of mitosis each newly forming cell has received a share of the cytoplasmic organelles that duplicated during interphase. Cytokinesis proceeds differently in plant and animal cells because of differences in cell structure.

Animation Cytokinesis

Cytokinesis in Animal Cells

In animal cells a **cleavage furrow,** which is an indentation of the membrane between the two daughter nuclei, forms just as anaphase draws to a close. By that time, the newly forming cells have received a share of the cytoplasmic organelles that duplicated during the previous interphase.

The cleavage furrow deepens when a band of actin filaments, called the contractile ring, slowly forms a circular constriction between the two daughter cells. The action of the contractile ring can be likened to pulling a drawstring ever tighter about the

middle of a balloon. As the drawstring is pulled tight, the balloon constricts in the middle as the material on either side of the constriction gathers in folds. These folds are represented by the longitudinal lines in Figure 9.5.

A narrow bridge between the two cells can be seen during telophase, and then the contractile ring continues to separate the cytoplasm until there are two independent daughter cells (Fig. 9.5).

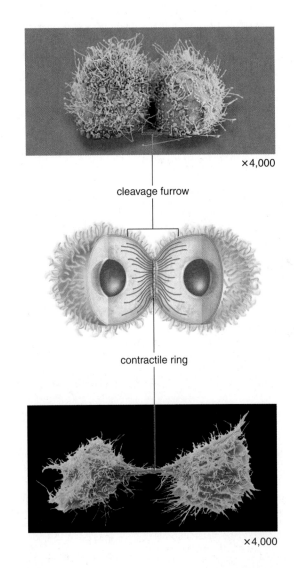

×4,000

cleavage furrow

contractile ring

×4,000

Figure 9.5 Cytokinesis in animal cells. A single cell becomes two cells by a furrowing process. A contractile ring composed of actin filaments gradually gets smaller, and the cleavage furrow pinches the cell into two cells.

Cytokinesis in Plant Cells

Cytokinesis in plant cells occurs by a process different from that seen in animal cells (Fig. 9.6). The rigid cell wall that surrounds plant cells does not permit cytokinesis by furrowing. Instead, cytokinesis in plant cells involves the building of new cell walls between the daughter cells.

Cytokinesis is apparent when a small, flattened disk appears between the two daughter plant cells near the site where the metaphase plate once was. In electron micrographs, it is possible to see that the disk is at right angles to a set of microtubules that radiate outward from the forming nuclei. The Golgi apparatus produces vesicles, which move along the microtubules to the region of the disk. As more vesicles arrive and fuse, a cell plate can be seen. The **cell plate** is simply newly formed plasma membrane that expands outward until it reaches the old plasma membrane and fuses with this membrane.

The new membrane releases molecules that form the new plant cell walls. These cell walls, known as primary cell walls, are later strengthened by the addition of cellulose fibrils. The space between the daughter cells becomes filled with middle lamella, which cements the primary cell walls together.

3D Animation Cytokinesis

The Functions of Mitosis

Mitosis permits growth and repair. In both plants and animals, mitosis is required during development as a single cell develops into an individual. In plants, the individual could be a fern or daisy, while in animals, the individual could be a grasshopper or a human being.

In flowering plants, meristematic tissue retains the ability to divide throughout the life of a plant. Meristematic tissue at the shoot tip accounts for an increase in the height of a plant for as long as it lives. Then, too, lateral meristem accounts for the ability of trees to increase their girth each growing season.

In human beings and other mammals, mitosis is necessary as a fertilized egg becomes an embryo and as the embryo becomes a fetus. Mitosis also occurs after birth as a child becomes an adult. Throughout life, mitosis allows a cut to heal or a broken bone to mend.

Video
Mitosis

Stem Cells

Earlier, you learned that the cell cycle is tightly controlled, and that most cells of the body at adulthood are permanently arrested in the G_0 stage. However, mitosis is needed to repair injuries, such as a cut or a broken bone. Many mammalian organs contain stem cells (often called adult stem cells) that retain the ability to divide. As one example, red bone marrow stem cells repeatedly divide to produce millions of cells that go on to become various types of blood cells.

Researchers are learning to manipulate the production of various types of tissues from adult stem cells in the laboratory. If successful, these tissues could be used to cure illnesses. As discussed in the Nature of Science feature "Reproductive and Therapeutic Cloning," **therapeutic cloning,** which is used to produce human tissues, can begin with either adult stem cells or embryonic stem cells. Embryonic stem cells can also be used for **reproductive cloning,** the production of a new individual.

Video
Heart Stem Cells

Video
Stem Cells

Check Your Progress   9.2

1. Describe the major events that occur during each phase of mitosis.
2. Summarize the differences between cytokinesis in animal and plant cells and explain why the differences are necessary.
3. Discuss the importance of stem cells in the human body.

daughter cells

Figure 9.6 Cytokinesis in plant cells. During cytokinesis in a plant cell, a cell plate forms midway between two daughter nuclei and extends to the plasma membrane.

cell plate formation

daughter nucleus

vesicles containing membrane components fusing to form cell plate

nucleoli

daughter nucleus

THEME Nature of Science

Reproductive and Therapeutic Cloning

Our knowledge of how the cell cycle is controlled has yielded major technological breakthroughs, including reproductive cloning—the ability to clone an adult animal from a normal body cell, and therapeutic cloning, which allows the rapid production of mature cells of a specific type. Both types of cloning are a direct result of recent discoveries about how the cell cycle is controlled.

Reproductive cloning, or the cloning of adult animals, was once thought to be impossible because investigators found it difficult to have the nucleus of an adult cell "start over" with the cell cycle, even when it was placed in an egg cell that had its own nucleus removed.

In 1997, Dolly the sheep demonstrated that reproductive cloning is indeed possible. The donor cells were starved before the cell's nucleus was placed in an enucleated egg. This caused them to stop dividing and go into a G_0 (resting) stage, and this made the nuclei amenable to cytoplasmic signals for initiation of development (Fig. 9Ba). This advance has made it possible to clone all sorts of farm animals that have desirable traits and even to clone rare animals that might otherwise become extinct. Despite the encouraging results, however, there are still obstacles to be overcome, and a ban on the use of federal funds in experiments to clone human beings remains firmly in place.

In therapeutic cloning, however, the objective is to produce mature cells of various cell types rather than an individual organism. The purpose of therapeutic cloning is (1) to learn more about how specialization of cells occurs and (2) to provide cells and tissues that could be used to treat human illnesses, such as diabetes, or major injuries like strokes or spinal cord injuries.

There are two possible ways to carry out therapeutic cloning. The first way is to use the exact same procedure as reproductive cloning, except that *embryonic stem cells (ESCs)* are separated and each is subjected to a treatment that causes it to develop into a particular type of cell, such as red blood cells, muscle cells, or nerve cells (Fig. 9Bb). Some have ethical concerns about this type of therapeutic cloning, which is still experimental, because if the embryo were allowed to continue development, it would become an individual.

The second way to carry out therapeutic cloning is to use *adult stem cells*. Stem cells are found in many organs of the adult's body; for example, the bone marrow has stem cells that produce new blood cells. However, adult stem cells are limited in the possible number of cell types that they may become. Nevertheless, scientists are beginning to overcome this obstacle. In 2006, by adding just four genes to adult skin stem cells, Japanese scientists were able to coax the cells, called fibroblasts, into becoming induced pluripotent stem cells (iPS), a type of stem cell that is similar to an ESC. The researchers were then able to create heart and brain cells from the adult stem cells. Other researchers have used this technique to reverse Parkinson-like symptoms in rats.

Although questions exist on the benefits of iPS cells, these advances demonstrate that scientists are actively investigating methods of overcoming the current limitations and ethical concerns of using embryonic stem cells.

Questions to Consider

1. How might the study of therapeutic cloning benefit scientific studies of reproductive cloning?
2. What types of diseases might not be treatable using therapeutic cloning?

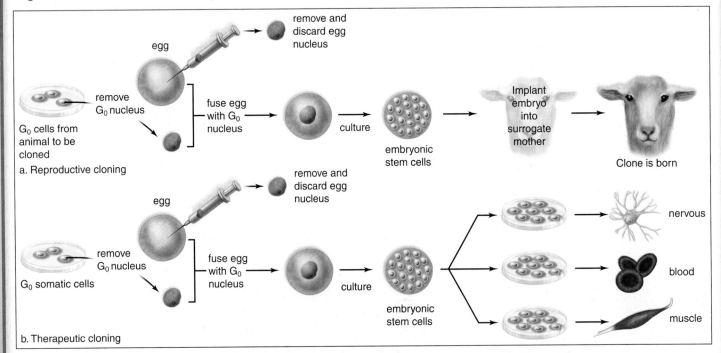

Figure 9B Two types of cloning. **a.** The purpose of somatic cell cloning is to produce an individual that is genetically identical to the one that donated a nucleus. The nucleus is placed in an enucleated egg, and, after several mitotic divisions, the embryo is implanted into a surrogate mother for further development. **b.** The purpose of therapeutic cloning is to produce specialized tissue cells. A nucleus is placed in an enucleated egg, and, after several mitotic divisions, the embryonic cells (called embryonic stem cells) are separated and treated to become specialized cells.

9.3 The Cell Cycle and Cancer

Learning Outcomes

Upon completion of this section, you should be able to

1. Describe the basic characteristics of cancer cells.
2. Distinguish between the roles of the tumor-suppressor genes and proto-oncogenes in the regulation of the cell cycle.

Cancer is a cellular growth disorder that occurs when cells divide uncontrollably. Although causes widely differ, most cancers are the result of accumulating mutations that ultimately cause a loss of control of the cell cycle.

Although cancers vary greatly, they usually follow a common multi-step progression (Fig. 9.7). Most cancers begin as an abnormal cell growth that is **benign,** or not cancerous, and usually does not grow larger. However, additional mutations may occur, causing the abnormal cells to fail to respond to inhibiting signals that control the cell cycle. When this occurs, the growth becomes **malignant,** meaning that it is cancerous and possesses the ability to spread.

Characteristics of Cancer Cells

The development of cancer is gradual. A mutation in a cell may cause it to become precancerous, but many other regulatory processes within the body prevent it from becoming cancerous. In fact, it may be decades before a cell possesses most or all of the characteristics of a cancer cell (Table 9.2 and Fig. 9.7). Although cancers vary greatly, cells that possess the following characteristics are generally recognized as cancerous:

Cancer cells lack differentiation. Cancer cells are not specialized and do not contribute to the functioning of a tissue. Although cancer cells may still possess many of the characteristics of surrounding normal cells, they usually look distinctly abnormal. Normal cells can enter the cell cycle about 50 times before they are incapable of dividing again. Cancer cells can enter the cell cycle an indefinite number of times, and in this way seem immortal.

Cancer cells have abnormal nuclei. The nuclei of cancer cells are enlarged and may contain an abnormal number of chromosomes. Often, extra copies of one or more chromosomes may be present. Often, there are also duplicated portions of some chromosomes present, which causes gene amplification,

New mutations arise, and one cell (brown) has the ability to start a tumor.

primary tumor

lymphatic vessel

blood vessel

Cancer in situ. The tumor is at its place of origin. One cell (purple) mutates further.

lymphatic vessel

blood vessel

Cancer cells now have the ability to invade lymphatic and blood vessels and travel throughout the body.

New metastatic tumors are found some distance from the primary tumor.

Figure 9.7 Progression of cancer. The development of cancer requires a series of mutations leading first to a localized tumor and then to metastatic tumors. With each successive step toward cancer, the most genetically altered and aggressive cell becomes the dominant type of tumor. The cells take on characteristics of embryonic cells; they are not differentiated, they can divide uncontrollably; and they are able to metastasize and spread to other tissues.

or extra copies of specific genes. Some chromosomes may also possess deleted portions.

Cancer cells do not undergo apoptosis. Ordinarily, cells with damaged DNA undergo apoptosis, or programmed cell death. The immune system can also recognize abnormal cells and trigger apoptosis, which normally prevents tumors from developing. Cancer cells fail to undergo apoptosis even though they are abnormal cells.

Cancer cells form tumors. Normal cells anchor themselves to a substratum and/or adhere to their neighbors. They exhibit contact inhibition—in other words, when they come in contact with a neighbor, they stop dividing. Cancer cells have lost all restraint and do not exhibit contact inhibition. The abnormal cancer cells pile on top of one another and grow in multiple

Table 9.2 Cancer Cells Versus Normal Cells

Cancer Cells	Normal Cells
Nondifferentiated cells	Differentiated cells
Abnormal nuclei	Normal nuclei
Do not undergo apoptosis	Undergo apoptosis
No contact inhibition	Contact inhibition
Disorganized, multilayered	One organized layer
Undergo metastasis	

layers, forming a **tumor.** During carcinogenesis, the most aggressive cell becomes the dominant cell of the tumor.

Cancer cells undergo metastasis and angiogenesis. Additional mutations may cause a benign tumor, which is usually contained within a capsule and cannot invade adjacent tissue, to become malignant, and spread throughout the body, forming new tumors distant from the primary tumor. These cells now produce enzymes that they normally do not express, allowing tumor cells to invade underlying tissues. Then, they travel through the blood and lymph, to start tumors elsewhere in the body. This process is known as **metastasis.**

Tumors that are actively growing soon encounter another obstacle—the blood vessels supplying nutrients to the tumor cells become insufficient to support the rapid growth of the tumor. In order to grow further, the cells of the tumor must receive additional nutrition. Thus, the formation of new blood vessels is required to bring nutrients and oxygen to support further growth. Additional mutations occurring in tumor cells allow them to direct the growth of new blood vessels into the tumor in a process called **angiogenesis.** Some modes of cancer treatment are aimed at preventing angiogenesis from occurring.

Origin of Cancer

Normal growth and maintenance of body tissues depend on a balance between signals that promote and inhibit cell division. When this balance is upset, conditions such as cancer may occur. Thus, cancer is usually caused by mutations affecting genes that directly or indirectly affect this balance, such as those shown in Figure 9.8. These two types of genes are usually affected:

1. **Proto-oncogenes** code for proteins that promote the cell cycle and prevent apoptosis. They are often likened to the gas pedal of a car because they cause the cell cycle to speed up.
2. **Tumor suppressor genes** code for proteins that inhibit the cell cycle and promote apoptosis. They are often likened to the brakes of a car because they cause the cell cycle to go more slowly or even stop.

Proto-oncogenes Become Oncogenes

Proto-oncogenes are normal genes that promote progression through the cell cycle. They are often at the end of a *stimulatory pathway* extending from the plasma membrane to the nucleus. A stimulus, such as an injury, results in the release of a growth factor that binds to a receptor protein in the plasma membrane. This sets in motion a whole series of enzymatic reactions leading to the activation of genes that promote the cell cycle, both directly and indirectly. Proto-oncogenes include the receptors and signal molecules that make up these pathways.

When mutations occur in proto-oncogenes, they become **oncogenes,** or cancer-causing genes. Oncogenes are under constant stimulation and keep on promoting the cell cycle regardless of circumstances. For example, an oncogene may code for a faulty receptor in the stimulatory pathway such that the cell cycle is stimulated, even when no growth factor is present! Or, an oncogene may specify either an abnormal protein product or

produce abnormally high levels of a normal product that stimulate the cell cycle to begin or to go to completion. As a result, uncontrolled cell division may occur.

Researchers have identified perhaps 100 oncogenes that can cause increased growth and lead to tumors. The oncogenes most frequently involved in human cancers belong to the *ras* gene family. Mutant forms of the *BRCA1* oncogene (breast cancer predisposition gene 1) are associated with certain hereditary forms of breast and ovarian cancer.

Tumor Suppressor Genes Become Inactive

Tumor suppressor genes, on the other hand, directly or indirectly inhibit the cell cycle and prevent cells from dividing uncontrollably. Some tumor suppressor genes prevent progression of the cell cycle when DNA is damaged. Other tumor suppressor genes may promote apoptosis as a last resort.

A mutation in a tumor suppressor gene is much like brake failure in a car; when the mechanism that slows down and stops cell division does not function, the cell cycle accelerates and does not halt. Researchers have identified about a half-dozen tumor suppressor genes. Among these are the *RB* and *p53* genes that code for the RB and p53 proteins. The Nature of Science feature "The G_1 Checkpoint" discusses the function of these proteins in controlling the cell cycle. The *RB* tumor suppressor gene was discovered when the inherited condition retinoblastoma was being studied, but malfunctions of this gene have now been identified in many other cancers as well, including breast, prostate, and bladder cancers. The *p53* gene turns on the expression of other genes that inhibit the cell cycle. The p53 protein can also stimulate apoptosis. It is estimated that over half of human cancers involve an abnormal or deleted *p53* gene.

Other Causes of Cancer

As mentioned previously, cancer develops when the delicate balance between promotion and inhibition of cell division is tilted toward uncontrolled cell division. Other mutations may occur within a cell that affect this balance. For example, while a mutation affecting the cell's DNA repair system will not immediately cause cancer, it leads to a much greater chance of a mutation occurring within a proto-oncogene or tumor suppressor gene. And in some cancer cells, mutation of the telomerase enzyme that regulates the length of **telomeres,** or the ends of chromosomes, causes the telomeres to remain at a constant length. Because cells with shortened telomeres normally stop dividing, keeping the telomeres at a constant length allows the cancer cells to continue dividing over and over again.

Check Your Progress   9.3

1. List the major characteristics of cancer cells that distinguish them from normal cells.
2. Distinguish between a malignant and benign tumor.
3. Compare and contrast the effect on the cell cycle of **(a)** a mutation in a proto-oncogene; **(b)** a mutation in a tumor suppressor gene.

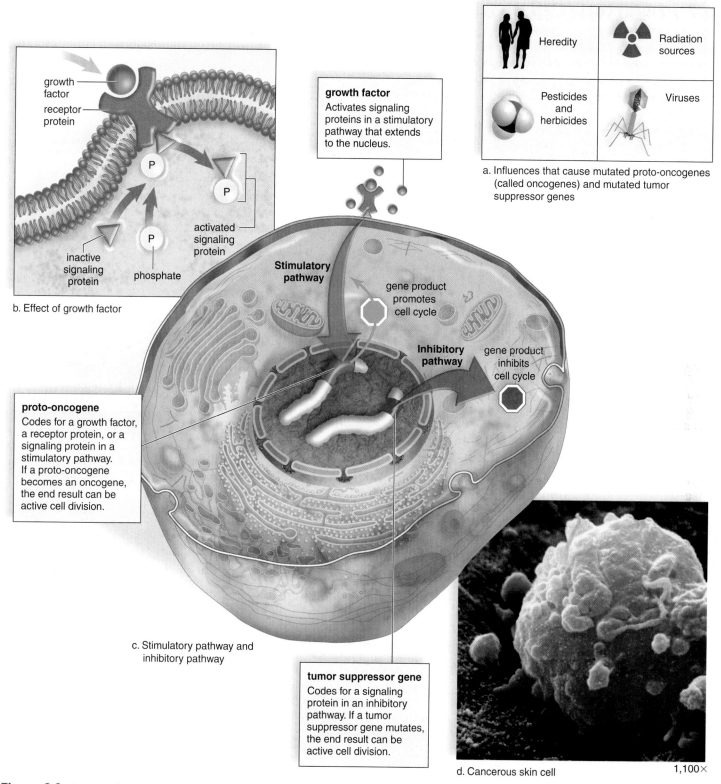

growth factor — receptor protein

growth factor
Activates signaling proteins in a stimulatory pathway that extends to the nucleus.

Heredity

Radiation sources

Pesticides and herbicides

Viruses

a. Influences that cause mutated proto-oncogenes (called oncogenes) and mutated tumor suppressor genes

P

P

P

activated signaling protein

inactive signaling protein

phosphate

b. Effect of growth factor

Stimulatory pathway

gene product promotes cell cycle

Inhibitory pathway

gene product inhibits cell cycle

proto-oncogene
Codes for a growth factor, a receptor protein, or a signaling protein in a stimulatory pathway. If a proto-oncogene becomes an oncogene, the end result can be active cell division.

c. Stimulatory pathway and inhibitory pathway

tumor suppressor gene
Codes for a signaling protein in an inhibitory pathway. If a tumor suppressor gene mutates, the end result can be active cell division.

d. Cancerous skin cell

1,100×

Figure 9.8 Causes of cancer. **a.** Mutated genes that cause cancer can be due to the influences noted. **b.** A growth factor that binds to a receptor protein initiates a reaction that triggers a stimulatory pathway. **c.** A stimulatory pathway that begins at the plasma membrane turns on proto-oncogenes. The products of these genes promote the cell cycle and double back to become part of the stimulatory pathway. When proto-oncogenes become oncogenes, they are turned on all the time. An inhibitory pathway begins with tumor suppressor genes whose products inhibit the cell cycle. When tumor suppressor genes mutate, the cell cycle is no longer inhibited. **d.** Cancerous skin cell.

9.4 Prokaryotic Cell Division

Learning Outcomes

Upon completion of this section you should be able to

1. Distinguish between the structure of a prokaryotic and eukaryotic chromosome.
2. Describe the events that occur during binary fission.

Cell division in unicellular organisms, such as prokaryotes, produces two new individuals. This is **asexual reproduction** in which the offspring are genetically identical to the parent. In prokaryotes, reproduction consists of duplicating the single chromosome and distributing a copy to each of the daughter cells. Unless a mutation has occurred, the daughter cells are genetically identical to the parent cell.

The Prokaryotic Chromosome

Prokaryotes (bacteria and archaea) lack a nucleus and other membranous organelles found in eukaryotic cells. Still, they do have a chromosome, which is composed of DNA and a limited number of associated proteins. The single chromosome of prokaryotes contains just a few proteins and is organized differently from eukaryotic chromosomes. A eukaryotic chromosome has many more associated proteins than does a prokaryotic chromosome.

In electron micrographs, the bacterial chromosome appears as an electron-dense, irregularly shaped region called the **nucleoid** [L. *nucleus*, nucleus, kernel; Gk. *-eides*, like], which is not enclosed by membrane. When stretched out, the chromosome is seen to be a circular loop with a length that is up to about a thousand times the length of the cell. Special enzymes and proteins help coil the chromosome so that it will fit within the prokaryotic cell.

Animation Bacterial Chromosome Compaction

Binary Fission

Prokaryotes reproduce asexually by binary fission. The process is termed **binary fission** because division (fission) produces two (binary) daughter cells that are identical to the original parent cell. Before division takes place, the cell enlarges, and after DNA replication occurs, there are two chromosomes. These chromosomes attach to a special plasma membrane site and separate by an elongation of the cell that pulls them apart. During this period, new plasma membrane and cell wall develop and grow inward to divide the cell. When the cell is approximately twice its original length, the new cell wall and plasma membrane for each cell are complete (Fig. 9.9).

Animation Binary Fission

1. Attachment of chromosome to a special plasma membrane site indicates that this bacterium is about to divide.

2. The cell is preparing for binary fission by enlarging its cell wall, plasma membrane, and overall volume.

3. DNA replication has produced two identical chromosomes. Cell wall and plasma membrane begin to grow inward.

4. As the cell elongates, the chromosomes are pulled apart. Cytoplasm is being distributed evenly.

5. New cell wall and plasma membrane has divided the daughter cells.

chromosome
cell wall
plasma membrane
cytoplasm

SEM 2,345×

Figure 9.9 Binary fission.   First, DNA replicates, and as the cell lengthens, the two chromosomes separate, and the cells become divided. The two resulting bacteria are identical.

Escherichia coli, which lives in our intestines, has a generation time (the time it takes the cell to divide) of about 20 minutes under favorable conditions. In about seven hours, a single cell can increase to over 1 million cells! The division rate of other bacteria varies depending on the species and conditions.

Comparing Prokaryotes and Eukaryotes

Both binary fission and mitosis ensure that each daughter cell is genetically identical to the parent cell. The genes are portions of DNA found in the chromosomes. Prokaryotes (bacteria and archaea), protists (many algae and protozoans), and some fungi (yeasts) are unicellular. Cell division in unicellular organisms produces two new individuals:

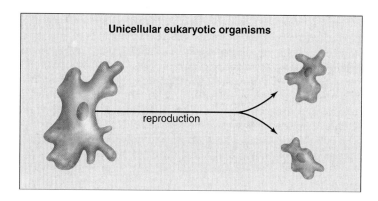

This is a form of asexual reproduction because one parent has produced identical offspring (Table 9.3).

Table 9.3 Functions of Cell Division

Type of Organism	Cell Division	Function
Prokaryotes		
Bacteria and archaea	Binary fission	Asexual reproduction
Eukaryotes		
Protists, and some fungi (yeast)	Mitosis and cytokinesis	Asexual reproduction
Other fungi, plants, and animals	Mitosis and cytokinesis	Development, growth, and repair

In multicellular fungi (molds and mushrooms), plants, and animals, cell division is part of the growth process. It produces the multicellular form we recognize as the mature organism. Cell division is also important in multicellular forms for renewal and repair:

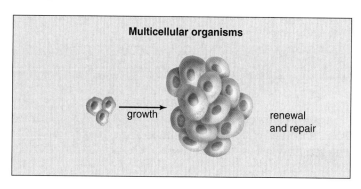

The chromosomes of eukaryotic cells are composed of DNA and many associated proteins. The histone proteins organize a chromosome, allowing it to extend as chromatin during interphase and to coil and condense just prior to mitosis. Each species of multicellular eukaryotes has a characteristic number of chromosomes in the nuclei. As a result of mitosis, each daughter cell receives the same number and kinds of chromosomes as the parent cell. The spindle, which appears during mitosis, is involved in distributing the daughter chromosomes to the daughter nuclei. Cytokinesis, either by the formation of a cell plate (plant cells) or by furrowing (animal cells), is division of the cytoplasm.

In prokaryotes, the single chromosome consists largely of DNA with a few associated proteins. During binary fission, this chromosome duplicates, and each daughter cell receives one copy as the parent cell elongates, and a new cell wall and plasma membrane form between the daughter cells. No spindle is involved in binary fission.

Check Your Progress   9.4

1. Explain how binary fission in prokaryotes differs from mitosis and cytokinesis in eukaryotes.
2. Distinguish between the structure of a prokaryotic and eukaryotic chromosome.

CONNECTING *the* CONCEPTS *with the* THEMES

Evolution

- Eukaryotic cells have evolved the process of mitosis to sort chromosomes into daughter cells.
- The stages of mitosis are the same for all eukaryotic cells, suggesting a common evolutionary lineage.
- Plants and animals have evolved different strategies for cytokinesis that compensates for the presence or lack of a cell wall.

Nature of Science

- An understanding of the regulatory mechanisms of the cell cycle has led to insight into the causes of cancer.
- The advances in stem cell technologies, specifically reproductive and therapeutic cloning, have been made possible by research on the cell cycle.

Biological Systems

- In prokaryotic organisms and unicellular eukaryotes, binary fission provides for cellular reproduction and the formation of new individuals.
- In eukaryotic organisms, mitosis provides for growth of tissues and the repair of damage.

Summarize

9.1 The Cell Cycle

The cell cycle of a eukaryotic cell includes (1) interphase and (2) a mitotic stage that consists of mitosis and cytokinesis. Interphase, in turn, is composed of three stages: G_1 (growth as certain organelles double), S (the synthesis stage, where the chromosomes are duplicated), and G_2 (growth as the cell prepares to divide). Cells of the body that are no longer dividing are said to be arrested in a G_0 state. During the mitotic stage (M), the chromosomes are sorted into two daughter cells so that each receives a full complement of chromosomes.

The cell cycle is regulated by three well-known checkpoints—the G_1 checkpoint, the G_2 checkpoint prior to the M stage, and the M stage checkpoint, or spindle assembly checkpoint, immediately before anaphase. The G_1 checkpoint ensures that conditions are favorable and that the proper signals are present, and also checks the DNA for damage. If the DNA is damaged beyond repair, apoptosis may occur. Cell division and apoptosis are two opposing processes that keep the number of healthy cells in balance.

9.2 Mitosis and Cytokinesis

Interphase represents the portion of the cell cycle between nuclear divisions, and during this time, preparations are made for cell division. These preparations include duplication of most cellular contents, including the centrosome, which organizes the mitotic spindle. The DNA is duplicated during S stage, at which time the chromosomes, which consisted of a single chromatid each, are duplicated. The G_2 checkpoint ensures that DNA has replicated properly. This results in a nucleus containing the same number of chromosomes, with each now consisting of two chromatids attached at the centromere. During interphase, the chromosomes are not distinct and are collectively called chromatin. Each eukaryotic species has a characteristic number of chromosomes. The total number is called the diploid number, and half this number is the haploid number.

Among eukaryotes, cell division involves both mitosis (nuclear division) and division of the cytoplasm (cytokinesis). As a result of mitosis, the chromosome number stays constant because each chromosome is duplicated and gives rise to two daughter chromosomes that consist of a single chromatid each.

Mitosis consists of five phases:

Prophase—The nucleolus disappears, the nuclear envelope fragments, and the spindle forms between centrosomes. The chromosomes condense and become visible under a light microscope. In animal cells, asters radiate from the centrioles within the centrosomes. Plant cells lack centrioles and, therefore, asters. Even so, the mitotic spindle forms.

Prometaphase (late prophase)—The kinetochores of sister chromatids attach to kinetochore spindle fibers extending from opposite poles. The chromosomes move back and forth until they are aligned at the metaphase plate.

Metaphase—The spindle is fully formed, and the duplicated chromosomes are aligned at the metaphase plate. The spindle consists of polar spindle fibers that overlap at the metaphase plate and kinetochore spindle fibers that are attached to chromosomes. The M stage checkpoint, or spindle assembly checkpoint, must be satisfied before progressing to the next phase.

Anaphase—Sister chromatids separate, becoming daughter chromosomes that move toward the poles. The polar spindle fibers slide past one another, and the kinetochore spindle fibers disassemble. Cytokinesis by furrowing begins.

Telophase—Nuclear envelopes re-form, chromosomes begin changing back to chromatin, the nucleoli reappear, and the spindle disappears. Cytokinesis continues, and is complete by the end of telophase.

Cytokinesis in animal cells is a furrowing process that divides the cytoplasm. Cytokinesis in plant cells involves the formation of a cell plate from which the plasma membrane and cell wall are completed.

9.3 The Cell Cycle and Cancer

The development of cancer is primarily due to the mutation of genes involved in control of the cell cycle. Cancer cells lack differentiation, have abnormal nuclei, do not undergo apoptosis, form tumors, and undergo metastasis and angiogenesis. Cancer often follows a progression in which mutations accumulate, gradually causing uncontrolled growth and the development of a tumor.

Proto-oncogenes stimulate the cell cycle after they are turned on by environmental signals such as growth factors. Oncogenes are mutated proto-oncogenes that stimulate the cell cycle without need of environmental signals. Tumor suppressor genes inhibit the cell cycle. Mutated tumor suppressor genes no longer inhibit the cell cycle, allowing unchecked cell division.

9.4 Prokaryotic Cell Division

Binary fission (in prokaryotes) and mitosis (in unicellular eukaryotic protists and fungi) allow organisms to reproduce asexually. Mitosis in multicellular eukaryotes is primarily for the purpose of development, growth, and repair of tissues.

The prokaryotic chromosome has a few proteins and a single, long loop of DNA. When binary fission occurs, the chromosome attaches to the inside of the plasma membrane and replicates. As the cell elongates, the chromosomes are pulled apart. Inward growth of the plasma membrane and formation of new cell wall material divide the cell in two.

Key Terms

anaphase 160	kinetochore 157
angiogenesis 164	malignant 163
apoptosis 155	metaphase 159
asexual reproduction 166	metaphase plate 159
aster 159	metastasis 164
benign 163	mitosis 155
binary fission 166	mitotic spindle 155
cancer 163	nucleoid 166
cell cycle 154	oncogene 164
cell plate 161	p53 155
centriole 158	prometaphase 159
centromere 157	prophase 158
centrosome 157	proto-oncogene 164
chromatid 154	RB 155
chromatin 157	reproductive cloning 161
cleavage furrow 160	signal 155
cyclin 155	sister chromatids 154
cytokinesis 155	somatic cell 155
diploid (2n) 157	telomere 164
growth factor 155	telophase 160
haploid (n) 157	therapeutic cloning 161
histone 157	tumor 164
interphase 154	tumor suppressor gene 164

Assess

Reviewing This Chapter

1. Describe the cell cycle, including its different stages.   154–55
2. Describe three checkpoints of the cell cycle.   155
3. What is apoptosis, and what are its functions?   155
4. Distinguish between chromosome, chromatin, chromatid, centromere, and kinetochore.   154–57
5. Describe the events that occur during the phases of mitosis.   158–60
6. Contrast cytokinesis in animal cells and plant cells.   160–61
7. List and discuss characteristics of cancer cells that distinguish them from normal cells.   163–64
8. Compare and contrast the functions of proto-oncogenes and tumor suppressor genes in controlling the cell cycle.   164–65
9. Describe the prokaryotic chromosome and the process of binary fission.   166
10. Contrast the function of cell division in prokaryotic and eukaryotic cells.   167

Testing Yourself

Choose the best answer for each question.

1. In contrast to a eukaryotic chromosome, a prokaryotic chromosome
   a. is shorter and fatter.
   b. has a single loop of DNA.
   c. never replicates.
   d. contains many histones.
   e. All of these are correct.

2. The diploid number of chromosomes
   a. is the 2n number.
   b. is in a parent cell and therefore in the two daughter cells following mitosis.
   c. varies according to the particular organism.
   d. is in every somatic cell.
   e. All of these are correct.

For questions 3–5, match the descriptions that follow to the terms in the key.

KEY:
   a. centrosome
   b. chromosome
   c. centromere
   d. cyclin

3. Point of attachment for sister chromatids
4. Found at a spindle pole in the center of an aster
5. Coiled and condensed chromatin
6. If a parent cell has 14 chromosomes prior to mitosis, how many chromosomes will each daughter cell have?
   a. 28 because each chromatid is a chromosome
   b. 14 because the chromatids separate
   c. only 7 after mitosis is finished
   d. any number between 7 and 28
   e. 7 in the nucleus and 7 in the cytoplasm, for a total of 14
7. In which phase of mitosis are the kinetochores of the chromosomes being attached to spindle fibers?
   a. prophase
   b prometaphase
   c. metaphase
   d. anaphase
   e. telophase
8. Interphase
   a. is the same as prophase, metaphase, anaphase, and telophase.
   b. is composed of G_1, S, and G_2 stages.
   c. requires the use of polar spindle fibers and kinetochore spindle fibers.
   d. is the majority of the cell cycle.
   e. Both b and d are correct.
9. At the metaphase plate during metaphase of mitosis, there are
   a. single chromosomes.
   b. duplicated chromosomes.
   c. G_1 stage chromosomes.
   d. always 23 chromosomes.
10. During which mitotic phases are duplicated chromosomes present?
   a. all but telophase
   b. prophase and anaphase
   c. all but anaphase and telophase
   d. only during metaphase at the metaphase plate
   e. Both a and b are correct.
11. Which of these is paired incorrectly?
   a. prometaphase—the kinetochores become attached to spindle fibers
   b. anaphase—daughter chromosomes are located at the spindle poles
   c. prophase—the nucleolus disappears and the nuclear envelope disintegrates
   d. metaphase—the chromosomes are aligned in the metaphase plate
   e. telophase—a resting phase between cell division cycles
12. When cancer occurs,
   a. cells cannot pass the G_1 checkpoint.
   b. control of the cell cycle is impaired.
   c. apoptosis has occurred.
   d. the cells can no longer enter the cell cycle.
   e. All of these are correct.

13. Which of the following is not characteristic of cancer cells?
    a. Cancer cells often undergo angiogenesis.
    b. Cancer cells tend to be nonspecialized.
    c. Cancer cells undergo apoptosis.
    d. Cancer cells often have abnormal nuclei.
    e. Cancer cells can metastasize.

14. Which of the following statements is true?
    a. Proto-oncogenes cause a loss of control of the cell cycle.
    b. The products of oncogenes may inhibit the cell cycle.
    c. Tumor-suppressor-gene products inhibit the cell cycle.
    d. A mutation in a tumor suppressor gene may inhibit the cell cycle.
    e. A mutation in a proto-oncogene may convert it into a tumor suppressor gene.

For questions 15–18, match the descriptions to a stage in the key.

KEY:
    a. G_1 stage
    b. S stage
    c. G_2 stage
    d. M (mitotic) stage

15. At the end of this stage, each chromosome consists of two attached chromatids.

16. During this stage, daughter chromosomes are distributed to two daughter nuclei.

17. The cell doubles its organelles and accumulates the materials needed for DNA synthesis.

18. The cell synthesizes the proteins needed for cell division.

19. Which is not true of the cell cycle?
    a. The cell cycle is controlled by internal/external signals.
    b. Cyclin is a signaling molcule that increases and decreases as the cycle continues.
    c. DNA damage can stop the cell cycle at the G_1 checkpoint.
    d. Apoptosis occurs frequently during the cell cycle.

20. Label this diagram. What phase of mitosis does it represent?

a. _____
b. _____
c. _____
d. _____

Engage

Virtual Lab
Cell Reproduction
The virtual lab "Cell Reproduction" provides an interactive examination of the cell cycle and provides for a comparison of normal and cancer cells.

Thinking Scientifically

1. After DNA is duplicated in eukaryotes, it must be bound to histones. This requires the synthesis of hundreds of millions of new protein molecules. With reference to Figure 9.1, when in the cell cycle would histones be made?

2. The survivors of the atomic bombs that were dropped on Hiroshima and Nagasaki have been the subjects of long-term studies of the effects of ionizing radiation on cancer incidence. The frequencies of different types of cancer in these individuals varied across the decades. In the 1950s, high levels of leukemia and cancers of the lung and thyroid gland were observed. The 1960s and 1970s brought high levels of breast and salivary gland cancers. In the 1980s, rates of colon cancer were especially high. Why do you suppose the rates of different types of cancer varied across time?

Bioethical Issue
Paying for Cancer Treatment

The risk factors for developing cancer are generally well known. Many lifestyle factors, such as smoking, poor dietary habits, obesity, physical inactivity, risky sexual behavior, and alcohol abuse, among others, have all been linked to higher risks of developing cancer. The greatly increasing rates of cancer over the past few decades have been decried as a public health epidemic. But aside from the cost in human life, the rising tide of cancer is causing a major crisis in today's society—how to pay for it all.

Despite increasing cure rates, effective new drugs, and novel treatments for various types of cancer, the costs of treatment continue to skyrocket. Nowhere is this more apparent than in the pharmaceutical industry. For example, new cancer drugs, while effective, are extremely expensive. Drug companies claim that it costs them between $500 million and $1 billion to bring a single new medicine to market. This cost may seem overblown, especially when you consider that the National Cancer Institute funds basic research into cancer biology and that drug companies often benefit indirectly from the findings. But the drug companies tell us that they need one successful drug to pay for the many drugs they try to develop that do not pay off.

Still, it does seem as if successful drug companies try to keep lower-cost competitors out of the market. The question of how much drug companies can charge for drugs and who should pay for them is a thorny one. If drug companies don't show a profit, they may go out of business and there will be no new drugs. The same is true for insurance companies if they can't raise the cost of insurance to pay for expensive drugs. If the government buys drugs for Medicare patients, taxes may go up dramatically.

But how should the cost of treatment be met? Cancer is an illness that can be the direct result of poor lifestyle choices, but it can also occur in otherwise healthy individuals who make proper choices. And with increasing life spans, the incidence of cancer can only be expected to increase in future years. Should people who develop cancer due to poor lifestyle choices be held fully or partly responsible for paying for treatment? And if so, how? And how should the cost of developing new drugs and treatments be borne? There are no easy answers for any of these questions, but as cancer continues to extract a high toll in both human life and financial resources, future generations may face some difficult choices.

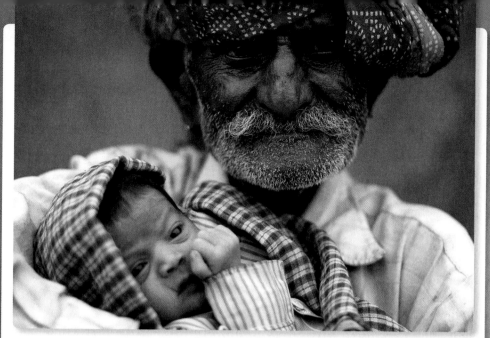

Nanu Ram Jogi, one of the world's oldest fathers.

10

Meiosis and Sexual Reproduction

Nanu Ram Jogi, at 90 years old, recently became a new father. As he hoisted his newborn daughter into the air amid a throng of cameras, microphones, and reporters, he boasted that he plans to continue fathering children with his wife, Saburi, now 50, until he is 100. He cannot even recall how many children he has fathered over the many years of his life, but it is estimated that he has at least twelve sons, nine daughters, and twenty grandchildren. Ramjit Raghavanu, at 94 years old, is now thought to be the world's oldest new father. Nadya Suleman, the so-called Octo-mom, gave birth to 8 babies in 2009. Extreme cases such as these remind us of the huge reproductive potential of most species.

This chapter discusses meiosis, the process that occurs during sexual reproduction and ensures that offspring will have a different combination of genes than their parents. This genetic diversity is essential for survival of a species, but occasionally, offspring inherit a detrimental combination of genes and chromosomes. Such events do not detract from the success of a species overall because they allow a species to evolve and become adapted to an ever-changing environment.

As you read through the chapter, think about the following questions:

1. What is the role of meiosis in introducing new variation?
2. Why is genetic variation necessary for species survival?
3. What effects are seen when different combinations of chromosomes are produced?

CHAPTER OUTLINE

10.1 Halving the Chromosome Number 172

10.2 Genetic Variation 174

10.3 The Phases of Meiosis 176

10.4 Meiosis Compared to Mitosis 177

10.5 The Cycle of Life 180

10.6 Changes in Chromosome Number and Structure 183

BEFORE YOU BEGIN

Before beginning this chapter, take a few moments to review the following discussions.

Figures 3.19 and 3.20 How is genetic information stored in nucleic acids?

Section 4.8 What are microtubules and how do they interact with chromosomes?

Section 9.2 How are eukaryotic chromosomes organized and replicated prior to cell division?

FOLLOWING *the* THEMES

CHAPTER 10 MEIOSIS AND SEXUAL REPRODUCTION

UNIT 2 GENETIC BASIS OF LIFE		
	Evolution	Variation introduced during meiosis can produce permanent changes in a species over time.
	Nature of Science	Research in reproductive technology enables couples who can't conceive to have children.
	Biological Systems	The cells of reproductive systems undergo meiosis, which functions to mix versions of genes and increase genetic diversity.

10.1 Halving the Chromosome Number

Learning Outcomes

Upon completion of this section, you should be able to

1. Contrast haploid and diploid chromosome numbers.
2. Explain what is meant by homologous chromosomes.
3. Describe the central concept of meiosis.

a.

b.

Figure 10.1 Homologous chromosomes. In diploid body cells, the chromosomes occur in pairs called homologous chromosomes. **a.** In this micrograph of stained chromosomes from a human cell, the pairs have been numbered 1–23. Note that chromosome pairs 1–22 are autosomes, coding for non-sex traits, whereas pair 23 include the sex chromosomes, and help determine human gender. **b.** These chromosomes are duplicated, and each chromosome in the homologous pair is composed of two chromatids. The sister chromatids contain the exact same genes; the nonsister chromatids contain genes for the same traits (e.g., type of hair, color of eyes), but they may differ in that one could have DNA that codes for trait variations, such as dark hair versus light hair.

In sexually reproducing organisms, **meiosis** [Gk. *mio,* less, and *-sis,* act or process of] is the type of nuclear division that reduces the chromosome number from the diploid (2n) number [Gk. *diplos,* twofold, and *-eides,* like] to the haploid (n) number [Gk. *haplos,* single, and *-eides,* like]. The **diploid (2n) number** refers to the total number of chromosomes, which exists in two sets. The **haploid (n) number** of chromosomes is half the diploid number, or a single set of chromosomes. In humans, the diploid number of 46 is reduced to the haploid number of 23.

Gametes, or reproductive cells, (often the sperm and egg) usually have the haploid number of chromosomes. In **sexual reproduction**, haploid gametes are produced during meiosis that subsequently merge into a diploid cell called a **zygote.** In plants and animals, the zygote undergoes development to become an adult organism.

Meiosis is necessary in sexually reproducing organisms because the diploid number of chromosomes has to be reduced by half in each of the parents in order to produce diploid offspring. Otherwise, the number of chromosomes would double with each new generation. Within a few generations, the cells of an animal would be nothing but chromosomes! For example, in humans with a diploid number of 46 chromosomes, in five generations the chromosome number would increase to 1,472 chromosomes (46×2^5). In 10 generations this number would increase to a staggering 47,104 chromosomes (46×2^{10}). The early cytologists (biologists who study cells) realized this, and Pierre-Joseph van Beneden (1809-1894), a Belgian, was gratified to find in 1883 that the sperm and the egg of the roundworm *Ascaris* each contain only two chromosomes, while the zygote and subsequent embryonic cells always have four chromosomes.

Homologous Pairs of Chromosomes

In diploid body cells, the chromosomes occur in pairs. Figure 10.1*a,* a pictorial display of human chromosomes called a karyotype, shows the chromosomes arranged according to pairs. The members of each pair are called homologous chromosomes. **Homologous chromosomes** or **homologues** [Gk. *homologos,* agreeing, corresponding] look alike; they have the same length and centromere position. When stained, homologues have a similar banding pattern because they contain genes for the same traits in the same order in the same locations on both chromosomes in the homologous pair. But while homologous chromosomes have genes for the same traits, such as finger length, the DNA (deoxyribonucleic acid) sequence for the gene on one homologue may code for short fingers and the gene at the same location on the other homologue may code for long fingers. Alternate forms of a gene (as for long fingers and short fingers) are called **alleles.** The DNA sequences of alleles are highly similar, but different enough to produce alternative physical traits like long or short fingers.

To properly produce a haploid number of chromsomes in gametes, you first have to double the amount of DNA. The chromosomes in Figure 10.1*a* are duplicated as they would be just before nuclear division. Recall that during the S stage of the cell cycle, DNA replicates and the chromosomes become duplicated. The results of the duplication process are depicted in Figure 10.1*b.* When duplicated, a chromosome is composed of two identical parts called sister chromatids, each containing one DNA double helix molecule. The sister chromatids are held together at a common region called the centromere.

Why does the zygote have paired chromosomes? One member of a homologous pair was inherited from the male parent, and the other was inherited from the female parent when the haploid sperm and egg fused together. In Figure 10.1*b* and throughout this chapter, the paternal chromosome is colored blue, and the maternal chromosome is colored red. *However, this is simply a conventional distinction. Geneticists generally use chromosome length and centromere location, not color, to recognize homologues.* You will see shortly how meiosis reduces the chromosome number. Whereas the zygote and body cells have homologous pairs of chromosomes, the gametes have only one chromosome of each kind—derived from either the paternal or maternal homologue.

Overview of Meiosis

The central purpose of meiosis is to reduce the chromosome number from 2n to n. Meiosis requires two nuclear divisions and produces four haploid daughter cells, each having one of each kind of chromosome. The process begins by replicating the chrosomosomes, then splitting the matched homologous pairs to go from 2n to n chromosomes during the first division. The second division reduces the amount of DNA in n chromosomes to an amount appropriate for each gamete. Once the DNA has been replicated and chromosomes become a pair, they may exchange genes, creating a genetic mixture different from the parent. The first nuclear division separates each homologous pair, reducing the chromosome number from 2n to n. Even though each daughter cell now has n chromosomes, each chromosome still has a sister chromatid, making a second nuclear division necessary. The end result of meiosis is four gametes with n chromosomes.

Figure 10.2 presents an overview of meiosis, indicating the two nuclear divisions, meiosis I and meiosis II. Prior to meiosis I, DNA replication has occurred; therefore, each chromosome has two sister chromatids. During meiosis I, something new happens that does not occur in mitosis. The homologous chromosomes come together and line up side by side, forming a **synaptonemal complex.** This process is called **synapsis** [Gk. *synaptos,* united, joined together] and results in a **bivalent** [L. *bis,* two, and *valens,* strength]—that is, two homologous chromosomes that stay in close association during the first two phases of meiosis I. Sometimes the term tetrad [Gk. *tetra,* four] is used instead of bivalent because, as you can see, a bivalent contains four chromatids. Chromosomes may recombine or exchange genetic information during this association (see Section 10.2).

Following synapsis, homologous pairs align at the metaphase plate, and then the members of each pair separate. This separation means that only one duplicated chromosome from each homologous pair reaches a daughter nucleus, reducing the chromosome number from 2n to n. It is important for each daughter nucleus to have a member from each pair of homologous chromosomes because only in that way can there be a copy of each *kind* of chromosome in the daughter nuclei. Notice in Figure 10.2 that two possible combinations of chromosomes in the daughter cells are shown: short red with long blue and short blue with long red. Knowing that all daughter cells have to have one short chromosome and one long chromosome, what are the other two possible combinations of chromosomes for these particular cells?

Notice that DNA replication occurs only once during meiosis; no replication is needed between meiosis I and meiosis II because the chromosomes are already duplicated; they already

Figure 10.2 Overview of meiosis. Following DNA replication, each chromosome is duplicated and consists of two chromatids. During meiosis I, homologous chromosomes pair and separate. During meiosis II, the sister chromatids of each duplicated chromosome separate. At the completion of meiosis, there are four haploid daughter cells. Each daughter cell has one of each kind of chromosome.

have two sister chromatids. During meiosis II, the sister chromatids separate, becoming daughter chromosomes that move to opposite poles. The chromosomes in each of the four daughter cells now contain only one DNA double helix molecule in the form of a haploid chromosome.

The number of centromeres can be counted to verify that the parent cell has the diploid number of chromosomes. At the end of meiosis I, the chromosome number has been reduced because there are half as many centromeres present, even though each chromosome still consists of two chromatids each. Each daughter cell that forms has the haploid number of chromosomes. At the end of meiosis II, sister chromatids separate, and each daughter cell that forms still contains the haploid number of chromosomes, each consisting of a single chromatid.

 Animation How Meiosis Works

 MP3 Meiosis

Fate of Daughter Cells

In the plant life cycle, the daughter cells become haploid spores that germinate to become a haploid generation. This generation produces the gametes by mitosis. The plant life cycle is studied in Chapter 27. In the animal life cycle, the daughter cells become the gametes, either sperm or eggs. The body cells of an animal normally contain the diploid number of chromosomes due to the fusion of sperm and egg during fertilization. If meiotic events go wrong, the gametes can contain the wrong number of chromosomes or altered chromosomes. This possibility and its consequences are discussed in Section 10.6.

Check Your Progress   **10.1**

1. Describe what is meant by a homologous pair of chromosomes.
2. Examine how chromosome number changes during meiosis I and meiosis II.
3. Explain the purpose of a bivalent in chromosome pairing.

10.2 Genetic Variation

Learning Outcomes

Upon completion of this section, you should be able to

1. Contrast the effects of asexual and sexual reproduction on genetic variation.
2. Explain how crossing-over contributes to genetic variation.
3. Examine how independent assortment contributes to genetic variation in the offspring.

We have seen that meiosis provides a way to keep the chromosome number constant generation after generation. Without meiosis, the chromosome number of the next generation would continually increase. The events of meiosis also help ensure that genetic variation occurs with each generation.

Genetic variation is essential for a species to be able to evolve and adapt in a changing environment. Asexually reproducing organisms, such as the prokaryotes, depend primarily on mutations to generate variation among offspring. This is sufficient for their survival because they produce great numbers of offspring very quickly. Although mutations also occur among sexually reproducing organisms, the reshuffling of genetic material during sexual reproduction ensures that offspring will have a different combination of genes from their parents. Meiosis brings about genetic variation in two key ways: crossing-over and independent assortment of homologous chromosomes.

Genetic Recombination

Crossing-over is an exchange of genetic material between nonsister chromatids of a bivalent during meiosis I. It is estimated that an average of two or three crossovers occur per human chromosome. At synapsis, homologues line up side by side, and a nucleoprotein lattice appears between them (Fig. 10.3). This lattice holds the bivalent together in such a way that the DNA of the duplicated chromosomes of each homologue pair is aligned. This ensures that the genes contained on the nonsister

Figure 10.3 Crossing-over occurs during meiosis I.   a. The homologous chromosomes pair up, and a nucleoprotein lattice develops between them. This is an electron micrograph of the lattice. It "zippers" the members of the bivalent together so that corresponding genes on paired chromosomes are in alignment. **b.** This visual representation shows only two places where nonsister chromatids 1 and 3 have come into contact. Actually, the other two nonsister chromatids most likely are also crossing-over. **c.** Chiasmata indicate where crossing-over has occurred. The exchange of color represents the exchange of genetic material. **d.** Following meiosis II, daughter chromosomes have a new combination of genetic material due to crossing-over, which occurred between nonsister chromatids during meiosis I.

nucleoprotein lattice | sister chromatids of a chromosome | sister chromatids of its homologue

chiasmata of nonsister chromatids 1 and 3

12   34
Bivalent forms
a.   b.

1 2 3 4
Crossing-over has occurred
c.

1   2   3   4
Daughter chromosomes
d.

chromatids are directly aligned. Now crossing-over may occur. As the lattice breaks down, homologues are temporarily held together by *chiasmata* (sing., chiasma), regions where the non-sister chromatids are attached due to DNA strand exchange and crossing-over. After exchange of genetic information between the mother's and father's chromosomes, the homologues separate and are distributed to different daughter cells.

Crossing-over has been shown to be essential for the normal segregation of chromosomes during meiosis. For example, reduced levels of crossing-over have been linked to Down syndrome, which is caused by an extra copy of chromosome 21.

To appreciate the significance of crossing-over, keep in mind that the members of a homologous pair can carry slightly different instructions for the same genetic traits. In the end, due to a swapping of genetic material during crossing-over, the chromatids held together by a centromere are no longer identical. Therefore, when the chromatids separate during meiosis II, some of the daughter cells receive daughter chromosomes with recombined alleles. Due to **genetic recombination,** the offspring have a different set of alleles, and therefore genes, than their parents. This increases the genetic variation of the offspring.

 Animation Meiosis with Crossing-Over

Independent Assortment of Homologous Chromosomes

During **independent assortment,** the homologous chromosome pairs separate independently, or in a random manner. When homologues align at the metaphase plate, the maternal or paternal homologue may be oriented toward either pole. Figure 10.4 shows the possible chromosome orientations for a cell that contains only three pairs of homologous chromosomes. Once all possible alignments of independent assortment are considered for these three pairs, the result will be 2^3, or eight, combinations of maternal and paternal chromosomes in the resulting gametes from this cell, simply due to independent assortment of homologues.

Animation Random Orientation of Chromosomes During Meiosis

Significance of Genetic Variation

In humans, who have 23 pairs of chromosomes, the possible chromosomal combinations in the gametes is a staggering 2^{23}, or

8,388,608. The variation that results from meiosis is enhanced by **fertilization,** the union of the male and female gametes. The chromosomes donated by the parents are combined, and in humans, this means that there are $(2^{23})^2$, or 70,368,744,000,000, chromosomally different zygotes possible, even assuming no crossing-over. If crossing-over occurs once, then $(4^{23})^2$, or 4,951,760,200,000,000,000,000,000,000, genetically different zygotes are possible for every couple. Keep in mind that crossing-over can occur several times in each chromosome!

 Animation Genetic Diversity

The staggering amount of genetic variation achieved through meiosis is particularly important to the long-term survival of a species because it increases genetic variation within a population. (Asexual reproduction passes on exactly the same combination of chromosomes and genes.) The process of sexual reproduction brings about genetic recombinations among members of a population.

If a parent is already successful in a particular environment, is asexual reproduction advantageous? It would seem so as long as the environment remains unchanged. However, if the environment changes, genetic variability among offspring introduced by sexual reproduction may be advantageous. Under the new conditions, some offspring may have a better chance of survival and reproductive success than others in a population. For example, suppose the ambient temperature were to rise due to climate change. Perhaps a dog with genes for the least amount of fur may have an advantage over other dogs of its generation.

In a changing environment, sexual reproduction, with its reshuffling of genes due to meiosis and fertilization, might give a few offspring a better chance to survive and reproduce, thereby increasing the possibility of passing on their genes to the next generation.

Check Your Progress   10.2

1. Describe the two main ways in which meiosis contributes to genetic variation.
2. Examine how many combinations of chromosomes are possible in the gametes in a cell with four pairs of homologous chromosomes.
3. Evaluate why meiosis and sexual reproduction are important in responding to the changing environment.

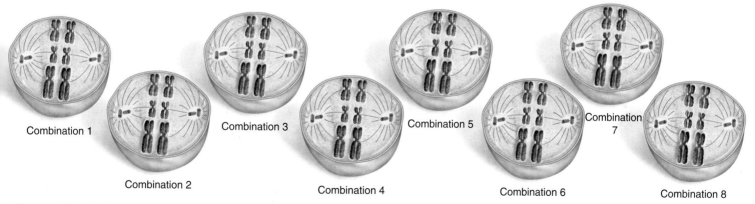

Combination 1   Combination 2   Combination 3   Combination 4   Combination 5   Combination 6   Combination 7   Combination 8

Figure 10.4 Independent assortment.   When a parent cell has three pairs of homologous chromosomes, there are 2^3, or 8, possible chromosome alignments at the metaphase plate due to independent assortment. Among the 16 daughter nuclei resulting from these alignments, there are 8 different combinations of chromosomes. Each possible combination is shown, one in each cell.

10.3 The Phases of Meiosis

Learning Outcomes

Upon completion of this section, you should be able to

1. Describe the phases of meiosis and the major events that occur during each phase.
2. Identify the phase of meiosis where chromosome number is reduced from diploid to haploid.

Meiosis consists of two unique, consecutive cell divisions, meiosis I and meiosis II. DNA is replicated in S phase of the cell cycle prior to meiosis I but not meiosis II. Both meiosis I and meiosis II each contain a prophase, metaphase, anaphase, and telophase.

Animation
Stages of Meiosis

Prophase I

It is apparent during prophase I that nuclear division is about to occur because a spindle forms as the centrosomes migrate away from one another. The nuclear envelope fragments, and the nucleolus disappears.

The homologous chromosomes, each having replicated during S phase of the cell cycle, consist of two sister chromatids. The homologous chromsomes undergo synapsis to form bivalents. At this time crossing-over may occur between the non-sister chromatids (Fig. 10.3). As described earlier, crossing-over increases the genetic diversity of the daughter cells, because after crossing-over, the sister chromatids are no longer identical.

Throughout prophase I, the homologous chromosomes have been condensing so that by now they have the appearance of compacted metaphase chromosomes.

Metaphase I

During metaphase I, the bivalents held together by chiasmata (see Fig. 10.3) have moved toward the metaphase plate (equator of the spindle). Metaphase I is characterized by a fully formed spindle and alignment of the bivalents at the metaphase plate. As in mitosis, kinetochores are seen, but the two kinetochores of a duplicated chromosome are attached to the same kinetochore spindle fiber.

Bivalents independently align themselves at the metaphase plate of the spindle. Either the maternal or paternal homologue of each bivalent may be oriented toward either pole of the cell. The orientation of one bivalent is not dependent on the orientation of the other bivalents. This independent assortment of chromosomes contributes to the genetic variability of the daughter cells because all possible combinations of chromosomes can occur in the daughter cells.

Anaphase I

During anaphase I, the homologues of each bivalent separate and move to opposite poles, but sister chromatids do not separate. This splitting of the homologous pair reduces the chromosome number from 2n to n. However, each chromosome still has two chromatids (see Fig. 10.5).

Telophase I

Completion of telophase I is not necessary during meiosis. That is, the spindle disappears, but new nuclear envelopes need not form before the daughter cells proceed to meiosis II. Also, this phase may or may not be accompanied by cytokinesis, which is separation of the cytoplasm. Figure 10.5 shows only two of the four possible combinations of haploid chromosomes when the parent cell has two homologous pairs of chromosomes. Can you determine what the other two possible combinations of chromosomes are?

Animation
Meiosis I

Interkinesis

Following telophase, the cells enter interkinesis, a short rest period prior to beginning the second nuclear division, meiosis II. The process of **interkinesis** is similar to interphase between mitotic divisions except that DNA replication does not occur because the chromosomes are already duplicated.

Meiosis II and Gamete Formation

At the beginning of meiosis II, the two daughter cells contain the haploid number of chromosomes, or one chromosome from each homologous pair. Note that these chromosomes still consist of duplicated sister chromatids at this point. During metaphase II, the chromosomes align at the metaphase plate, but do not align in homologous pairs as in meiosis I because only one chromosome of each homologous pair is present (see Fig. 10.5). Thus, the alignment of the chromosomes at the metaphase plate is similar to what is observed during mitosis.

During anaphase II, the sister chromatids separate, becoming daughter chromosomes that are not duplicated. These daughter chromosomes move toward the poles. At the end of telophase II and cytokinesis, there are four haploid cells. Because of crossing-over of chromatids during meiosis I, each gamete most likely contains chromosomes with a mixture of maternal and paternal genes.

Animation
Meiosis II

As mentioned, following meiosis II, the haploid cells become gametes in animals (see Section 10.5). In plants, they become **spores,** reproductive cells that develop into new multicellular structures without the need to fuse with another reproductive cell. The multicellular structure is the haploid generation, which produces gametes. The resulting zygote develops into a diploid generation. Therefore, plants have both haploid and diploid phases in their life cycle, and plants are said to exhibit an **alternation of generations.** In most fungi and algae, the zygote undergoes meiosis, and the daughter cells develop into new individuals. Therefore, the organism is always haploid.

Check Your Progress   **10.3**

1. Explain what would cause daughter cells following meiosis II to contain identical chromosomes or nonidentical chromosomes.
2. Examine what might happen if homologous chromosomes lined up top to bottom instead of side by side during meiosis I.

10.4 Meiosis Compared to Mitosis

Learning Outcomes

Upon completion of this section, you should be able to

1. Contrast changes in chromosome number, genetic variability, and number of daughter cells between meiosis and mitosis.
2. Distinguish the events that occur during prophase I of meiosis that do not occur during prophase of mitosis.
3. Compare chromosome alignment during meiosis I to mitosis.

Figure 10.6 graphically compares meiosis and mitosis. Several of the fundamental differences between the two processes include:

- Meiosis requires two nuclear divisions, but mitosis requires only one nuclear division.
- Meiosis produces four daughter nuclei. Following cytokinesis there are four daughter cells. Mitosis followed by cytokinesis results in two daughter cells.
- Following meiosis, the four daughter cells are haploid and have half the chromosome number as the diploid parent cell. Following mitosis, the daughter cells have the same chromosome number as the parent cell.
- Following meiosis, the daughter cells are neither genetically identical to each other nor to the parent cell. Following mitosis, the daughter cells are genetically identical to each other and to the parent cell.

In addition to the fundamental differences between meiosis and mitosis, two specific differences between the two types of nuclear divisions can be categorized. These differences involve occurrence and process.

Occurrence

Meiosis occurs only at certain times in the life cycle of sexually reproducing organisms. In humans, meiosis occurs only in the reproductive organs and produces the gametes. Mitosis is more common because it occurs in all tissues during growth and repair.

Animation
Comparison of Meiosis and Mitosis

Process

We now compare the processes of both meiosis I and meiosis II to mitosis.

Meiosis I Compared to Mitosis

Notice that these events distinguish meiosis I from mitosis:

- During prophase I, bivalents form and crossing-over occurs. These events do not occur during mitosis.
- During metaphase I of meiosis, bivalents independently align at the metaphase plate. The paired chromosomes have a total of four chromatids each. During metaphase in mitosis, individual chromosomes align at the metaphase plate. They each have two chromatids.

Table 10.1 Meiosis I Compared to Mitosis

Meiosis I	Mitosis
Prophase I	**Prophase**
Pairing of homologous chromosomes	No pairing of chromosomes
Metaphase I	**Metaphase**
Bivalents at metaphase plate	Duplicated chromosomes at metaphase plate
Anaphase I	**Anaphase**
Homologues of each bivalent separate and duplicated chromosomes move to poles	Sister chromatids separate, becoming daughter chromosomes that move to the poles
Telophase I	**Telophase**
Two haploid daughter cells, not identical to the parent cell	Two diploid daughter cells, identical to the parent cell

Table 10.2 Meiosis II Compared to Mitosis

Meiosis II	Mitosis
Prophase II	**Prophase**
No pairing of chromosomes	No pairing of chromosomes
Metaphase II	**Metaphase**
Haploid number of duplicated chromosomes at metaphase plate	Diploid number of duplicated chromosomes at metaphase plate
Anaphase II	**Anaphase**
Sister chromatids separate, becoming daughter chromosomes that move to the poles	Sister chromatids separate, becoming daughter chromosomes that move to the poles
Telophase II	**Telophase**
Four haploid daughter cells, not genetically identical	Two diploid daughter cells, identical to the parent cell

- During anaphase I of meiosis, homologues of each bivalent separate and duplicated chromosomes (with centromeres intact) move to opposite poles. During anaphase of mitosis, sister chromatids separate, becoming daughter chromosomes that move to opposite poles.

Meiosis II Compared to Mitosis

The events of meiosis II are similar to those of mitosis except that in meiosis II, the nuclei contain the haploid number of chromosomes. In mitosis, the original number of chromosomes is maintained. Meiosis II produces two daughter cells from each parent cell that completes meiosis I, for a total of four daughter cells. These daughter cells contain the same number of chromosomes as they did at the end of meiosis I. Tables 10.1 and 10.2 compare meiosis I and II to mitosis.

Check Your Progress   10.4

1. Compare chromosome alignment between metaphase I of meiosis and metaphase of mitosis.
2. Explain how meiosis II is more similar to mitosis than to meiosis I.

Plant Cell at Interphase

centrosome has centrioles

Animal Cell at Interphase

Prophase I
Chromosomes have duplicated. Homologous chromosomes pair during synapsis and crossing-over occurs.

2n = 4

Metaphase I
Homologous pairs align independently at the metaphase plate.

kinetochore

Anaphase I
Homologous chromosomes separate and move toward the poles.

MEIOSIS I

Figure 10.5 Meiosis I and II in plant cell micrographs and animal cell drawings. When diploid homologous chromosomes pair during meiosis I, crossing-over occurs as represented by the exchange of color. Pairs of homologous chromosomes separate during meiosis I, and chromatids separate, becoming haploid daughter chromosomes with two copies of each during meiosis II. Following meiosis II and the separation of sister chromatids, four haploid daughter cells are produced.

n = 2

n = 2

Prophase II
Cells have one chromosome from each homologous pair.

Metaphase II
Chromosomes align at the metaphase plate.

Anaphase II
Sister chromatids separate and become daughter chromosomes.

MEIOSIS II

Telophase I
Daughter cells have one chromosome
from each homologous pair.

Interkinesis
Chromosomes still
consist of two chromatids.

n = 2

n = 2

MEIOSIS I cont'd

n = 2

Telophase II
Spindle disappears, nuclei form,
and cytokinesis takes place.

Daughter cells
Meiosis results in four
haploid daughter cells.

n = 2

MEIOSIS II cont'd

MEIOSIS I

Prophase I
Synapsis and
crossing-over occur.

2n = 4

Metaphase I
Homologous pairs align
independently at the metaphase plate.

Anaphase I
Homologous chromosomes
separate and move toward the poles.

MITOSIS

Prophase

2n = 4

Metaphase
Chromosomes align
at the metaphase plate.

Anaphase
Sister chromatids separate and
become daughter chromosomes.

10.5 The Cycle of Life

Learning Outcomes

Upon completion of this section, you should be able to

1. Contrast the life cycle of plants with the life cycle of animals.
2. Describe spermatogenesis and oogenesis in humans.

The term **life cycle** refers to all the reproductive events that occur from one generation to the next similar generation. In animals, including humans, the individual is always diploid, and meiosis produces the gametes, the only haploid phase of the life cycle (Fig. 10.7). In contrast, plants have a haploid phase that alternates with a diploid phase. The haploid generation, known as the **gametophyte,** may be larger or smaller than the diploid generation, called the **sporophyte.**

Mosses growing on bare rocks and forest floors are the haploid generation, and the diploid generation is short-lived.

In most fungi and algae, the zygote is the only diploid portion of the life cycle, and it undergoes meiosis. Therefore, the black mold that grows on bread and the green scum that floats on a pond are haploid.

The majority of plant species, including pine, corn, and sycamore, are usually diploid, and the haploid generation is short-lived. In plants, algae, and fungi, the haploid phase of the life cycle produces gamete nuclei without the need for meiosis because it has occurred earlier.

Animals are diploid, and meiosis occurs during the production of gametes **(gametogenesis).** In males, meiosis is a part of **spermatogenesis** [Gk. *sperma*, seed; L. *genitus*, producing], which occurs in the testes and produces sperm. In females, meiosis is a part of **oogenesis** [Gk. *oon*, egg; L. *genitus*, producing], which occurs in the ovaries and produces eggs. A sperm and egg join at fertilization, restoring the diploid chromosome number. The resulting zygote undergoes mitosis during development of the fetus. After birth, mitosis is involved in the continued growth of the child and repair of tissues at any time.

Telophase I
Daughter cells are forming and will go on to divide again.

Sister chromatids separate and become daughter chromosomes.

Daughter cells

n = 2

n = 2

n = 2

Four haploid daughter cells. Their nuclei are genetically different from the parent cell.

MEIOSIS I cont'd   **MEIOSIS II**

Daughter cells

Telophase
Daughter cells are forming.

Two diploid daughter cells. Their nuclei are genetically identical to the parent cell.

MITOSIS cont'd

Figure 10.6 Meiosis compared to mitosis. Why does meiosis produce daughter cells with half the number of chromosomes, while mitosis produces daughter cells with the same number of chromosomes as the parent cell? Compare metaphase I of meiosis to metaphase of mitosis. Only in metaphase I of meiosis are the homologous chromosomes paired at the metaphase plate. Members of homologous chromosome pairs separate during anaphase I, and therefore the daughter cells are haploid. The exchange of color between nonsister chromatids represents the crossing-over that occurred during meiosis I. The blue chromosomes were inherited from the paternal parent, and the red chromosomes were inherited from the maternal parent.

Spermatogenesis and Oogenesis in Humans

In human males, spermatogenesis occurs within the testes, and in females, oogenesis occurs within the ovaries.

Spermatogenesis

The testes contain stem cells called spermatogonia, and these cells keep the testes supplied with primary spermatocytes that undergo spermatogenesis as described in Figure 10.8, *top.* Primary spermatocytes with 46 chromosomes undergo meiosis I to form two secondary spermatocytes, each with 23 duplicated chromosomes. Secondary spermatocytes undergo meiosis II to produce four spermatids with 23 daughter chromosomes. Spermatids then differentiate into viable sperm (spermatozoa). Upon sexual arousal, the sperm enter ducts and exit the penis upon ejaculation.

Animation Spermatogenesis

Oogenesis

The ovaries contain stem cells called oogonia that produce many primary oocytes with 46 chromosomes during fetal development.

They even begin oogenesis, but only a few continue when a female has become sexually mature. The result of meiosis I is two haploid cells with 23 chromosomes each (Fig. 10.8, *bottom*). One of these cells, termed the **secondary oocyte** [Gk, *oon,* egg, and *kytos,* cell], receives almost all the cytoplasm. The other is a **polar body** that may either disintegrate or divide again.

The secondary oocyte begins meiosis II but stops at metaphase II. Then the secondary oocyte leaves the ovary and enters an oviduct, where sperm may be present. If no sperm are in the oviduct, or if a sperm does not enter the secondary oocyte, it eventually disintegrates without completing meiosis. If a sperm does enter the oocyte, some of its contents trigger the completion of meiosis II in the secondary oocyte, and another polar body forms.

At the completion of oogenesis, following entrance of a sperm, there is one egg and two to three polar bodies. The polar bodies are a way to "dispose" of chromosomes while retaining much of the cytoplasm in the egg. Cytoplasmic molecules and organelles are needed by a developing embryo following

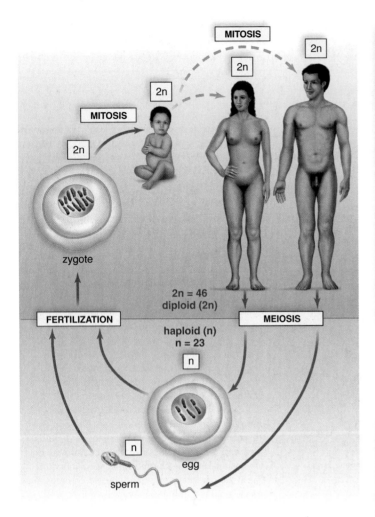

Figure 10.7 Life cycle of humans.   Meiosis in males is a part of sperm production, and meiosis in females is a part of egg production. When a haploid sperm fertilizes a haploid egg, the zygote is diploid. The zygote undergoes mitosis as it develops into a newborn child. Mitosis continues throughout life during growth and repair.

fertilization. Some zygote components, such as the centrosome, are contributed by the sperm.

The mature egg has 23 chromosomes, but the zygote formed when the sperm and egg nuclei fuse has 46 chromosomes. Therefore, fertilization restores the diploid number of chromosomes. The production of haploid gametes and subsequent fusion of those gametes into a diploid zygote completes a human life cycle.

Check Your Progress   10.5

1. Describe where cells that undergo meiosis are located in humans.
2. Compare the number of gametes produced during oogenesis and spermatogenesis in humans.

Figure 10.8 Spermatogenesis and oogenesis in mammals. Spermatogenesis produces four viable sperm, whereas oogenesis produces one egg and at least two polar bodies. In humans, both sperm and egg have 23 chromosomes each; therefore, following fertilization, the zygote has 46 chromosomes.

10.6 Changes in Chromosome Number and Structure

Learning Outcomes

Upon completion of this section, you should be able to

1. Distinguish between euploidy and aneuploidy.
2. Explain how nondisjunction can cause monosomy and trisomy aneuploidy.
3. Describe human diseases caused by changes in the number of sex chromosomes.
4. Examine how changes in chromosome structure can lead to human diseases.

We have seen that crossing-over creates variation within a population and is essential for the normal separation of chromosomes during meiosis. Furthermore, the proper separation of homologous chromosomes during meiosis I and the separation of sister chromatids during meiosis II are essential for the maintenance of normal chromosome numbers in living organisms. Although meiosis almost always proceeds normally, failure of chromosomes to separate, or **nondisjunction,** may occur, resulting in gain or loss of chromosomes. Errors in crossing-over may result in extra or missing parts of chromosomes.

Aneuploidy

The correct number of chromosomes in a species is known as **euploidy.** A change in the chromosome number resulting from nondisjunction during meiosis is called **aneuploidy.** Aneuploidy is seen in both plants and animals. Monosomy and trisomy are two aneuploid states.

Monosomy $(2n - 1)$ occurs when an individual has only one of a particular type of chromosome when they should have two, and **trisomy** $(2n + 1)$ occurs when an individual has three of a particular type of chromosome when they should have two. Both monosomy and trisomy are the result of nondisjunction during mitosis or meiosis. *Primary nondisjunction* occurs during meiosis I when both members of a homologous pair go into the same daughter cell (Fig. 10.9a). *Secondary nondisjunction* occurs during meiosis II when the sister chromatids fail to separate and both daughter chromosomes go into the same gamete (Fig. 10.9b).

Notice that when secondary nondisjunction occurs, there are two normal gametes and two aneuploid gametes. In contrast, when primary nondisjunction occurs, no normal gametes are produced. Therefore, primary nondisjunction tends to have more deleterious effects than secondary nondisjunction.

In animals, monosomies and trisomies of non-sex, or autosomal, chromosomes are generally lethal, but a trisomic individual is more likely to survive than a monosomic one. In humans,

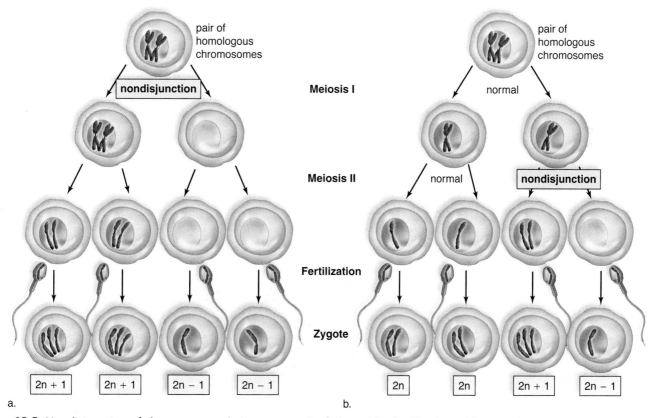

Figure 10.9 Nondisjunction of chromosomes during oogenesis, followed by fertilization with normal sperm. a. Nondisjunction can occur during meiosis I (primary nondisjunction) and results in abnormal eggs that also have one more or one less than the normal number of chromosomes. Fertilization of these abnormal eggs with normal sperm results in a zygote with abnormal chromosome numbers. 2n = diploid number of chromosomes. **b.** Nondisjunction can also occur during meiosis II (secondary nondisjunction) if the sister chromatids separate but the resulting daughter chromosomes go into the same daughter cell. Then the egg will have one more or one less than the usual number of chromosomes. Fertilization of these abnormal eggs with normal sperm produces a zygote with abnormal chromosome numbers.

only three autosomal trisomic conditions are known to be viable beyond birth: trisomy 13, 18, and 21. Only trisomy 21 is viable beyond early childhood, and is characterized by a distinctive set of physical and mental abnormalities. In comparison, sex chromosome aneuploids are better tolerated in animals and have a better chance of producing survivors.

Trisomy 21

The most common autosomal trisomy seen among humans is trisomy 21, also called Down syndrome. This syndrome is easily recognized by these characteristics: short stature; an eyelid fold; a flat face; stubby fingers; a wide gap between the first and second toes; a large, fissured tongue; a round head; a distinctive palm crease; heart problems; and some degree of mental retardation, which can sometimes be severe. Individuals with Down syndrome also have a greatly increased risk of developing leukemia and tend to age rapidly, resulting in a shortened life expectancy. In addition, these individuals have an increased chance of developing Alzheimer disease later in life.

Many scientists agree that the symptoms of Down syndrome are caused by gene dosage effects resulting from the presence of the extra chromosome. Recent studies indicate that not all of the genes on the chromosome are expressed at a level of 150%, challenging this theory; however, scientists have identified several genes that have been linked to increased risk of leukemia, cataracts, aging, and mental retardation.

The chances of a woman having a child with Down syndrome increase rapidly with age. In women ages 20 to 30, the incidence of trisomy 21 is 1 in 1,400 births, and in women 30 to 35, the incidence is about 1 in 750 births. It is thought that the longer the oocytes are stored in the female, the greater the chances of nondisjunction occurring. However, even though an older woman is more likely to have a Down syndrome child, most babies with Down syndrome are born to women younger than age 40 because this is the age group having the most babies. Furthermore, some recent research also indicate that in 23% of the cases studied, the sperm contributed the extra chromosome. A **karyotype,** a visual display of the chromosomes arranged by size, shape, and banding pattern, may be performed to identify babies with Down syndrome and other aneuploid conditions (Fig. 10.10).

Changes in Sex Chromosome Number

An abnormal sex chromosome number is the result of inheriting too many or too few X or Y chromosomes. Nondisjunction during oogenesis or spermatogenesis can result in gametes with an abnormal number of sex chromosomes. However, extra copies of the sex chromosomes are much more easily tolerated in humans than are extra copies of autosomes.

A person with Turner syndrome (XO) is a female, and a person with Klinefelter syndrome (XXY) is a male. However, deletion of the *SRY* gene on the short arm of the Y chromosome results in Swyer syndrome, or an "XY female." Individuals with Swyer syndrome lack a hormone called testis-determining factor, which plays a critical role in the development of male genitals. Furthermore, movement of this same gene onto the X chromosome may result in de la Chapelle syndrome, or an "XX male." Men with de la Chapelle syndrome exhibit undersized testes, sterility, and rudimentary breast development. Together, these observations suggest that in humans, the presence of the *SRY* gene, not the number of X chromosomes, determines maleness. In its absence, a person develops as a female.

a.

b.

extra chromosome 21

Figure 10.10 Trisomy 21.   Persons with Down syndrome, or trisomy 21, have an extra chromosome 21. **a.** Common characteristics of the syndrome include a wide, rounded face and a fold on the upper eyelids. Mental disabilities, along with an enlarged tongue, may make it difficult for a person with Down syndrome to speak distinctly. **b.** The karyotype of an individual with Down syndrome shows three copies of chromosome 21. Therefore, the individual has three copies instead of two copies of each gene on chromosome 21. Researchers are using new techniques to discover which genes on chromosome 21 are causing the syndrome's disabilities.

Why are newborns with an abnormal sex chromosome number more likely to survive than those with an abnormal autosome number? Because females have two X chromosomes and males have only one, we might expect females to produce twice the amount of each gene from this chromosome, but both males and females produce roughly the same amount. In reality, both males and females only have one functioning X chromosome. In females, and in males with extra X chromosomes, any additional X chromosomes become an inactive mass called a **Barr body,** named after Murray Barr, the person who discovered it. This inactivation provides a natural method for gene dosage compensation of the sex chromosomes and explains why extra sex chromosomes are more easily tolerated than extra autosomes.

Turner Syndrome. From birth, an XO individual with Turner syndrome has only one sex chromosome, an X; the O signifies the absence of a second sex chromosome (Fig. 10.11a). Therefore, the nucleus does not contain a Barr body. The approximate incidence is 1 in 10,000 females.

Turner females are short, with a broad chest and widely spaced nipples. These individuals also have a low posterior hairline and neck webbing. The ovaries, oviducts, and uterus are very small and underdeveloped. Turner females do not undergo puberty or menstruate, and their breasts do not develop. However, some have given birth following in vitro fertilization using donor eggs. They usually are of normal intelligence and can lead fairly normal lives if they receive hormone supplements.

Klinefelter Syndrome. A male with Klinefelter syndrome has two or more X chromosomes in addition to a Y chromosome (Fig. 10.11b). The extra X chromosomes become Barr bodies. The approximate incidence for Klinefelter syndrome is 1 in 500 to 1,000 males.

In Klinefelter males, the testes and prostate gland are underdeveloped and facial hair is lacking. They may exhibit some breast development. Affected individuals have large hands and feet and very long arms and legs. They are usually slow to learn but not mentally retarded unless they inherit more than two X chromosomes. No matter how many X chromosomes there are, an individual with a Y chromosome is a male.

While males with Klinefelter syndrome exhibit no other major health abnormalities, they have an increased risk of some disorders, including breast cancer, osteoporosis, and lupus, which disproportionately affect females. Although men with

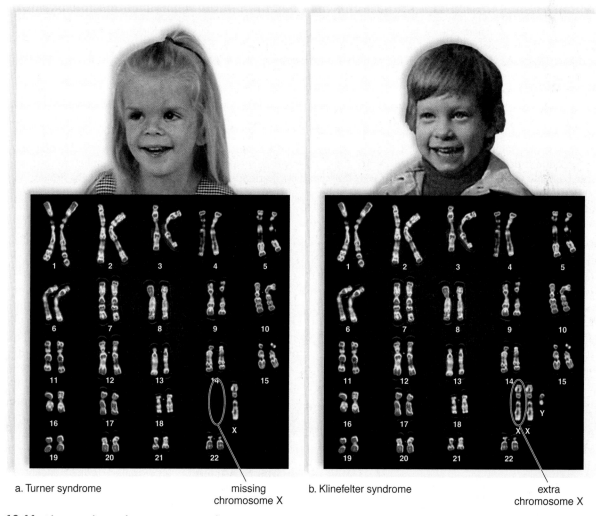

a. Turner syndrome   missing chromosome X   b. Klinefelter syndrome   extra chromosome X

Figure 10.11 Abnormal sex chromosome number. Nondisjunction of sex chromosomes is tolerated better than with autosomes. People with **(a)** Turner syndrome, who have only one X chromosome, as shown, and **(b)** Klinefelter syndrome, who have more than one X chromosome plus a Y chromosome, as shown, can look relatively normal (especially as children) and can lead relatively normal lives.

Living with Klinefelter Syndrome

In 1996, at the age of 25, I was diagnosed with Klinefelter syndrome (KS). Being diagnosed has changed my life for the better.

I was a happy baby, but when I was still very young, my parents began to believe that there was something wrong with me. I knew something was different about me, too, as early on as five years old. I was very shy and had trouble making friends. One minute I'd be well behaved, and the next I'd be picking fights and flying into a rage. Many psychologists, therapists, and doctors tested me because of school and social problems and severe mood changes. Their only diagnosis was "learning disabilities" in such areas as reading comprehension, abstract thinking, word retrieval, and auditory processing.

No one could figure out what the real problem was, and I hated the tutoring sessions I had. In the seventh grade, a psychologist told me that I was stupid and lazy, I would probably live at home for the rest of my life, and I would never amount to anything. For the next five years, he was basically right, and I barely graduated from high school.

I believe, though, that I have succeeded because I was told that I would fail. I quit the tutoring sessions when I enrolled at a community college; I decided I could figure things out on my own. I received an associate degree there, then transferred to a small liberal arts college. I never told anyone about my learning disabilities and never sought special help. However, I never had a semester below a 3.0, and I graduated with two B.S. degrees. I was accepted into a graduate program but decided instead to accept a job as a software engineer even though I did not have an educational background in this field. As I later learned, many KS'ers excel in computer skills. I had been using a computer for many years and had learned everything I needed to know on my own, through trial and error.

Around the time I started the computer job, I went to my physician for a physical. He sent me for blood tests because he noticed that my testes were smaller than usual. The results were conclusive: Klinefelter syndrome with sex chromosomes XXY. I initially felt denial, depression, and anger, even though I now had an explanation for many of the problems I had experienced all my life. But then I decided to learn as much as I could about the condition and treatments available. I now give myself a testosterone injection once every two weeks, and it has made me a different person, with improved learning abilities and stronger thought processes in addition to a more outgoing personality.

I found, though, that the best possible path I could take was to help others live with the condition. I attended my first support group meeting four months after I was diagnosed. By spring 1997, I had developed an interest in KS that was more than just a part-time hobby. I wanted to be able to work with this condition and help people forever. I have been very involved in KS conferences and have helped to start support groups in the United States, Spain, and Australia.

Since my diagnosis, it has been my dream to have a son with KS, although when I was diagnosed, I found out it was unlikely that I could have biological children. Through my work with KS, I had the opportunity to meet my wife, Chris. She has two wonderful children: a daughter, and a son who has the same condition that I do. There are a lot of similarities between my stepson and me, and I am happy I will be able to help him get the head start in coping with KS that I never had. I also look forward to many more years of helping other people seek diagnosis and live a good life with Klinefelter syndrome.

—Stefan Schwarz

Questions to Consider

1. If you discovered you had a genetic disease, how would you deal with it?
2. Why have genetic diseases persisted over time in the human population?
3. With scientific advances like the Human Genome Project, what treatments might be available to treat genetic diseases?

Klinefelter syndrome typically do not need medical treatment, some have found that testosterone therapy may help increase muscle strength, sex drive, and concentration ability. Testosterone treatment, however, does not reverse the sterility associated with Klinefelter syndrome due to the incomplete testicle development.

The Evolution feature in this chapter describes the personal experiences of a person with Klinefelter syndrome. The essay suggests that it is best for parents to know right away that they have a child with this abnormality because much can be done to help the child lead a normal life.

Poly-X Females.   A poly-X female, sometimes called a superfemale, has more than two X chromosomes and, therefore, extra Barr bodies in the nucleus. Females with three X chromosomes have no distinctive phenotype aside from a tendency to be tall and thin. Although some have delayed motor and language development, as well as learning problems, most poly-X females are not mentally retarded. Some may have menstrual difficulties, but many menstruate regularly and are fertile. Children usually have a normal karyotype. The incidence for poly-X females is about 1 in 1,500 females.

Females with more than three X chromosomes occur rarely. Unlike XXX females, XXXX females are usually tall and severely mentally retarded. Various physical abnormalities are seen, but they may menstruate normally.

Jacobs Syndrome.   XYY males, termed Jacobs syndrome, can result only from nondisjunction during spermatogenesis. These individuals are sometimes called supermales. Among all live male births, the frequency of the XYY karyotype is about 1 in 1,000. Affected males are usually taller than average, suffer from persistent acne, and tend to have speech and reading problems, but are fertile and may have children. Based upon the number of XYY individuals in prisons and mental facilities, it was suggested at one time that these men were likely to be criminally aggressive, but it has since been shown that the incidence of such behavior among them may be no greater than among XY males.

Changes in Chromosome Structure

Changes in chromosome structure are another type of chromosomal mutation. Some, but not all, changes in chromosome structure can be detected microscopically. Various agents in the environment, such as radiation, certain organic chemicals, or even viruses, can cause chromosomes to break. Ordinarily, when breaks occur in chromosomes, the two broken ends reunite to give the same sequence of genes. Sometimes, however, the broken ends of one or more chromosomes do not rejoin in the same pattern as before, and the result is various types of chromosomal mutations.

Changes in chromosome structure include deletions, duplications, translocations, and inversions of chromosome segments. A **deletion** occurs when an end of a chromosome breaks off or when two simultaneous breaks lead to the loss of an internal segment (Fig. 10.12*a*). Even when only one member of a pair of chromosomes is affected, a deletion often causes abnormalities.

Animation
Changes in Chromosome Structure

A **duplication** is the presence of a chromosomal segment more than once in the same chromosome (Fig. 10.12*b*). Duplications may or may not cause visible abnormalities, depending on the size of the duplicated region. An **inversion** has occurred when a segment of a chromosome is turned around 180° (Fig. 10.12*c*). Most individuals with inversions exhibit no abnormalities, but this reversed sequence of genes can result in duplications or deletions being passed on to their children, as described in Figure 10.13.

A **translocation** is the movement of a chromosome segment from one chromosome to another, nonhomologous chromosome. The translocation shown in Figure 10.12*d* is *balanced*, meaning that there is a reciprocal swap of one piece of the chromosome

a. Deletion

b. Duplication

c. Inversion

d. Translocation

Figure 10.12 Types of chromosomal mutations.   a. Deletion is the loss of a chromosome piece. **b.** Duplication occurs when the same piece is repeated within the chromosome. **c.** Inversion occurs when a piece of chromosome breaks loose and then rejoins in the reversed direction. **d.** Translocation is the exchange of chromosome pieces between nonhomologous pairs.

deletion

lost

Figure 10.13 Deletion.

a. When chromosome 7 loses an end piece, the result is Williams syndrome. **b.** These children, although unrelated, have the same appearance, health, and behavioral problems.

a.

b.

for the other. Often, there are no visible effects of the swap, but if the individual has children, they receive one normal copy of the chromosome from the normal parent, and one of the abnormal chromosomes. The translocation is now *unbalanced*, with extra material from one chromosome and missing material from another chromosome. Embryos with unbalanced translocations usually result in miscarriage, but those individuals who are born often have severe symptoms.

Some Down syndrome cases are caused by an unbalanced translocation between chromosomes 21 and 14. In other words, because a portion of chromosome 21 is now attached to a portion of chromosome 14, the individual has three copies of the genes that bring about Down syndrome when they are present in triplet copy. In these cases, Down syndrome is not caused by nondisjunction during meiosis, but is passed on normally like any other genetic trait as described in Chapter 11.

Human Syndromes

Changes in chromosome structure occur in humans and lead to various syndromes, many of which are just now being discovered. Sometimes changes in chromosome structure can be detected in humans by doing a karyotype. They may also be discovered by studying the inheritance pattern of a disorder in a particular family.

Deletion Syndromes. Williams syndrome occurs when chromosome 7 loses a tiny end piece (Fig. 10.13). Children who have this syndrome look like pixies, with turned-up noses, wide mouths, a small chin, and large ears. Although their academic skills are poor, they exhibit excellent verbal and musical abilities. The gene that governs the production of the protein elastin is missing, and this affects the health of the cardiovascular system and causes their skin to age prematurely. Such individuals are very friendly but need an ordered life, perhaps because of the loss of a gene for a protein that is normally active in the brain.

Cri du chat (cat's cry) syndrome is seen when chromosome 5 is missing an end piece. The affected individual has a small head, is mentally retarded, and has facial abnormalities. Abnormal development of the glottis and larynx results in the most characteristic symptom—the infant's cry resembles that of a cat.

Translocation Syndromes. A person who has both of the chromosomes involved in a translocation has the normal amount of genetic material and is healthy, unless the chromosome exchange breaks an allele into two pieces. The person who inherits only one of the translocated chromosomes no doubt has only one copy of certain alleles and three copies of certain other alleles. A genetic counselor begins to suspect a translocation has occurred when spontaneous abortions are commonplace and family members suffer from various syndromes. A special microscopic technique allows a technician to determine that a translocation has occurred.

Figure 10.14 shows a person who has a translocation between chromosomes 2 and 20. Although they have the normal amount of genetic material, they have the distinctive face, abnormalities of the eyes and internal organs, and severe itching characteristic of Alagille syndrome. People with this syndrome ordinarily have a deletion on chromosome 20 (Fig. 10.14a), which can lead to a congenital heart condition called Tetralogy of Fallot that produces digital clubbing of the fingers (Fig. 10.14b). The symptoms of Alagille syndrome range from mild to severe, so some people may not be aware they have the syndrome until after they've had children

Translocations can also be responsible for a variety of other disorders including certain types of cancer. In the 1970s, new staining techniques identified that a translocation from a portion of chromosome 22 to chromosome 9 was responsible for many cases of chronic myelogenous leukemia. This translocated chromosome was called Philadelphia chromosome. In Burkitt lymphoma, a cancer common in children in equatorial Africa, a large tumor develops from lymph glands in the region of the jaw. This disorder involves a translocation from a portion of chromosome 8 to chromosome 14.

Check Your Progress   10.6

1. Explain the kinds of changes in chromosome number that can be caused by nondisjunction in meiosis.
2. Examine why sex chromosome aneuploidy is more common than autosome aneuploidy.
3. Compare structural changes between an inversion and a translocation.

Figure 10.14
Translocation.

a. When chromosomes 2 and 20 exchange segments, (**b**) Alagille syndrome, with distinctive body features, sometimes results because of organ malfunction caused by the chromosome 20 translocation.

a.

b.

CONNECTING *the* CONCEPTS *with the* THEMES

Evolution

- Meiosis is a key process in sexual reproduction, with both evolutionary costs and benefits.
- Although mutations during meiosis can produce faulty gametes, greater genetic diversity is also possible, and this diversity can benefit the species.
- Understanding chromosomal behavior during meiosis is critical to understanding how genes segregate during gamete formation and how this contributes to patterns of inheritance.

Nature of Science

- Researching meoisis provides a deeper understanding of chromosome transmission, leading to the possiblity of treating genetic diseases like Down syndrome prior to birth.
- Greater understanding of how chromosomes match up and exchange genetic information during meiosis can help us understand one of the foundations of genetic diversity.

Biological Systems

- Meiosis and mitosis use similar processes to separate chromosomes.
- Like the cell cycle and mitosis, meiosis is tightly controlled. Regulatory mechanisms ensure that homologous chromosomes first pair and then separate during the first division, and that sister chromatids do not separate until the second division.
- Meiosis occurs only in certain types of cells during a restricted period of an organism's life span.

Media Study Tools

www.mhhe.com/maderbiology11

Enhance your study of this chapter with study tools and practice tests. Also ask your instructor about the resources available through ConnectPlus, including the media-rich eBook, interactive learning tools, and animations.

Summarize

10.1 Halving the Chromosome Number

Meiosis ensures that the chromosome number in offspring stays constant generation after generation. The nucleus contains pairs of chromosomes, called homologous chromosomes (homologues).

Meiosis requires two cell divisions and results in four daughter cells. Replication of DNA takes place before meiosis begins. During meiosis I, the homologues undergo synapsis (resulting in a bivalent) and align independently at the metaphase plate. The daughter cells receive one member of each pair of homologous chromosomes. There is no replication of DNA during interkinesis, the pause between meiosis I and II. During meiosis II, the sister chromatids separate, becoming daughter chromosomes that move to opposite poles as they do in mitosis. The four daughter cells contain the haploid number of chromosomes and only one of each kind.

10.2 Genetic Variation

Sexual reproduction ensures that the offspring have a different genetic makeup than the parents, and increases the ability of a species to survive. Meiosis contributes to genetic variability in two ways: crossing-over and independent assortment of the homologous chromosomes. When homologous chromosomes lie side by side during synapsis, nonsister chromatids may exchange genetic material. Due to crossing-over, the chromatids that separate during meiosis II have a different combination of genes.

When the homologous chromosomes align at the metaphase plate during metaphase I, either the maternal or the paternal chromosome can be facing either pole. Therefore, there will be all possible combinations of chromosomes in the gametes.

10.3 The Phases of Meiosis

Meiosis I, which splits pairs of homologous chromosomes and reduces the chromosome number from 2n to n, is divided into four phases:

Prophase I—Bivalents form, and crossing-over occurs as chromosomes condense; the nuclear envelope fragments.

Metaphase I—Bivalents independently align at the metaphase plate.

Anaphase I—Homologous chromosomes separate, and duplicated chromosomes move to poles.

Telophase I—Nuclei become haploid, having received one duplicated chromosome from each homologous pair.

Meiosis II, which reduces the amount of DNA in half from previously replicated 1n chromosomes, is divided into four phases:

Prophase II—Chromosomes condense, and the nuclear envelope fragments.

Metaphase II—The haploid number of still duplicated chromosomes align at the metaphase plate.

Anaphase II—Sister chromatids separate, becoming daughter chromosomes that move to the poles.

Telophase II—Four haploid daughter cells are genetically different from the parent cell.

10.4 Meiosis Compared to Mitosis

Mitosis and meiosis can be compared in this manner:

Meiosis I	Mitosis
Prophase	
Pairing of homologous chromosomes	No pairing of chromosomes
Metaphase	
Bivalents at metaphase plate	Duplicated chromosomes at metaphase plate
Anaphase	
Homologous chromosomes separate and move to poles	Sister chromatids separate, becoming daughter chromosomes that move to the poles
Telophase	
Daughter nuclei have the haploid number of chromosomes	Daughter nuclei have the parent cell chromosome number

Meiosis II is like mitosis except the nuclei are haploid.

10.5 The Cycle of Life

Meiosis occurs in any life cycle that involves sexual reproduction. In the animal life cycle, only the gametes are haploid; in plants, meiosis produces spores that develop into a multicellular haploid adult that produces the gametes. In unicellular protists and fungi, the zygote undergoes meiosis, and spores become a haploid adult that gives rise to gametes.

During the life cycle of humans and other animals, meiosis is involved in spermatogenesis and oogenesis. Whereas spermatogenesis produces four sperm per meiosis, oogenesis produces one egg and two to three nonfunctional polar bodies. Spermatogenesis occurs in males, and oogenesis occurs in females. When a sperm fertilizes an egg, the zygote has the diploid number of chromosomes. Mitosis, which is involved in growth and repair, also occurs during the life cycle of all animals.

10.6 Changes in Chromosome Number and Structure

Nondisjunction during meiosis I or meiosis II may result in aneuploidy (extra or missing copies of chromosomes). Monosomy occurs when an individual has only one of a particular type of chromosome ($2n - 1$) and is usually lethal; trisomy occurs when an individual has three of a particular type of chromosome ($2n + 1$). Down syndrome is a well-known trisomy in human beings resulting from an extra copy of chromosome 21.

Aneuploidy of the sex chromosomes is tolerated more easily than aneuploidy of the autosomes. Turner syndrome, Klinefelter syndrome, poly-X females, and Jacobs syndrome are examples of sex chromosome aneuploidy.

Abnormalities in crossing-over may result in deletions, duplications, inversions, and translocations within chromosomes. Many human syndromes, including Williams syndrome, cri du chat syndrome, and Alagille syndrome, result from changes in chromosome structure.

Key Terms

allele 172	interkinesis 176
alternation of generations 176	inversion 187
aneuploidy 183	karyotype 184
Barr body 185	life cycle 180
bivalent 173	meiosis 172
crossing-over 174	monosomy 183
deletion 187	nondisjunction 183
diploid (2n) number 172	oogenesis 180
duplication 187	polar body 181
euploidy 183	secondary oocyte 181
fertilization 175	sexual reproduction 172
gamete 172	spermatogenesis 180
gametogenesis 180	spore 176
gametophyte 180	sporophyte 180
genetic recombination 175	synapsis 173
haploid (n) number 172	synaptonemal complex 173
homologous	translocation 187
chromosome 172	trisomy 183
homologue 172	zygote 172
independent assortment 175	

Assess

Reviewing This Chapter

1. Why did early investigators predict that there must be a reduction division in the sexual reproduction process?   172
2. What are homologous chromosomes? Contrast the genetic makeup of sister chromatids with that of nonsister chromatids.   172–74
3. Draw and explain a diagram that illustrates crossing-over and another that shows all possible results from independent assortment of homologous pairs. How do these events ensure genetic variation among the gametes?   174–75
4. Draw and explain a series of diagrams that illustrate the stages of meiosis I and meiosis II.   177–81
5. What accounts for **(a)** the genetic similarity between daughter cells and the parent cell following mitosis, and **(b)** the genetic dissimilarity between daughter cells and the parent cell following meiosis?   180–81
6. Explain the human (animal) life cycle and the roles of meiosis and mitosis.   180–81
7. Compare spermatogenesis in males to oogenesis in females.   181
8. How does aneuploidy occur? Why is sex chromosome aneuploidy more common than autosomal aneuploidy? What are some human syndromes associated with aneuploidy?   183–87
9. Name and explain four types of changes in chromosome structure.   187–88
10. Name some syndromes that occur in humans due to changes in chromosome structure.   188

Testing Yourself

Choose the best answer for each question.

1. A bivalent is
   a. a homologous chromosome.
   b. the paired homologous chromosomes.
   c. a duplicated chromosome composed of sister chromatids.
   d. the two daughter cells after meiosis I.
   e. the two centrioles in a centrosome.

2. If a parent cell has 16 chromosomes, then each of the daughter cells following meiosis will have
   a. 48 chromosomes.   c. 16 chromosomes.
   b. 32 chromosomes.   d. 8 chromosomes.

3. At the metaphase plate during metaphase I of meiosis, there are
   a. chromosomes consisting of one chromatid.
   b. unpaired duplicated chromosomes.
   c. bivalents.
   d. homologous pairs of chromosomes.
   e. Both c and d are correct.

4. At the metaphase plate during metaphase II of meiosis, there are
   a. chromosomes consisting of one chromatid.
   b. unpaired duplicated chromosomes.
   c. bivalents.
   d. homologous pairs of chromosomes.
   e. Both c and d are correct.

5. Crossing-over occurs between
   a. sister chromatids of the same chromosome.
   b. two different kinds of bivalents.
   c. two different kinds of chromosomes.
   d. nonsister chromatids of a bivalent.
   e. two daughter nuclei.

6. During which phase of meiosis do homologous chromosomes separate?
   a. prophase I   c. anaphase I
   b. telophase I   d. anaphase II

7. Nondisjunction during meiosis I of oogenesis will result in eggs that have
   a. the normal number of chromosomes.
   b. one too many chromosomes.
   c. one less than the normal number of chromosomes.
   d. Both b and c are correct.

8. Which two of these chromosomal mutations are most likely to occur when an inverted chromosome is undergoing synapsis?
   a. deletion and translocation
   b. deletion and duplication
   c. duplication and translocation
   d. inversion and duplication

9. A male with underdeveloped testes and some breast development most likely has
   a. Down syndrome.   c. Turner syndrome.
   b. Jacobs syndrome.   d. Klinefelter syndrome.

For questions 10–13, fill in the blanks.

10. If the parent cell has 24 chromosomes, the daughter cells following mitosis will have _____ chromosomes and following meiosis will have _____ chromosomes.

11. Meiosis in males is a part of _____, and meiosis in females is a part of _____.

12. Oogenesis will not go to completion unless _____ occurs.

13. During oogenesis, the primary oocyte has the _____ and the secondary oocyte has the _____ number of chromosomes.

For questions 14–19, match the statements that follow to the items in the key. Answers may be used more than once, and more than one answer may be used.

KEY:
   a. mitosis
   b. meiosis I
   c. meiosis II
   d. Both meiosis I and meiosis II are correct.
   e. All of these are correct.

14. A parent cell with ten duplicated chromosomes will produce daughter cells with five duplicated chromosomes each.

15. Involves pairing of duplicated homologous chromosomes.

16. A parent cell with five duplicated chromosomes will produce daughter cells with five chromosomes consisting of one chromatid each.

17. Nondisjunction may occur, causing abnormal gametes to form.

18. A parent cell with ten duplicated chromosomes will produce daughter cells with ten chromosomes consisting of one chromatid each.

19. Involved in growth and repair of tissues.

Engage

Thinking Scientifically

1. Why is the first meiotic division considered to be the reduction division for chromosome number?

2. Recall that during interphase, the G_2 checkpoint ensures that the DNA has been faithfully replicated before the cell is allowed to divide by mitosis. Would you expect this checkpoint to be active during interkinesis? How might you set up an experiment to test your hypothesis?

3. A man has a balanced translocation between chromosome 2 and 6. If he reproduces with a normal woman could the child have the same translocation? Why or why not?

Bioethical Issue

The Risks of Advanced Maternal Age

In today's society, it is commonplace for women to embark on careers and pursue higher education, delaying marriage and childbirth until later years. Between 1991 and 2001, the birthrate among women aged 35 to 39 increased over 30%, while the birthrate among women aged 40 to 44 leaped by almost 70%. The U.S. Census Bureau indicates the average age at which a woman first gives birth is now 25.1 years, as compared to 21.1 years in 1970. These increases have occurred as society has changed, spurred by the elimination of the social stigmas, better prenatal care, and new medical technologies that can overcome the decline in fertility associated with age and treat at-risk children.

The decision to delay childbirth does carry risks. Although the reasons are not well understood, the risk of many disorders associated with meiotic nondisjunction, such as Down syndrome, increase greatly with age, rising from nearly 1 in 900 at age 30 to 1 in 109 by age 40. The risk of complications to the mother, such as gestational diabetes, are also much higher in women over 30. Thus, the medical community has embarked on a campaign to ensure that women who are pregnant and over age 35 are offered more intensive prenatal care. Many people are concerned about the ultimate cost to society, through increased insurance premiums and increased costs to governments to pay for it.

Although definite risks are associated with advanced maternal age, some people contend that having children later in life provides many advantages. Women over age 35 are usually at a later stage in their careers and have higher salaries, lessening the need for many social welfare programs. Furthermore, women over 35 often have a more stable living situation, are less likely to experience unplanned pregnancy, and are often able to devote more time to the child than are younger women. Therefore, while older mothers may require more medical attention, the overall costs to society are lower.

Considering both the benefits and the disadvantages, are we as a society obligated to fund intense screening and prenatal care for women of advanced maternal age, and to pay for treating the maladies associated with it? As birthrates among women over age 30 continue to soar, the debate over advanced maternal age is not likely to abate any time soon.

11

Mendelian Patterns of Inheritance

BEFORE YOU BEGIN

Before beginning this chapter, take a few moments to review the following discussions.

Figure 10.1 How is DNA-based genotype related to protein-based phenotype?

Section 10.3 How are chromosomes segregated during meiosis I and II?

Figure 10.9 What genetic changes are possible in gametes when chromosomes fail to segregate properly?

Trimethylaminuria is a genetic disorder that produces a fishy body odor.

Camille was painfully aware of her foul body odor because children teased her relentlessly, calling her "Miss Fishy" and other nasty names. She had no idea that she suffers from trimethylaminuria, or "fish odor syndrome," an extremely rare genetic disorder she shares with only 1 in 10,000 people. People with this syndrome have a defective gene that makes a nonfunctional protein unable to break down the smelly chemical trimethylamine, which accumulates in the body and ends up in their urine, sweat, and sometimes even in their breath.

Like the rest of us, you are the product of your family tree. The DNA you inherit from your parents directly affects the proteins that enable your body to function properly. Rare genetic disorders like Camille's pique our curiosity about how traits are inherited from one generation to the next. In this chapter, you will learn that the process of meiosis can be used to predict the inheritance of a trait, and that the genetic diversity produced through meiosis can sometimes create cases like Camille's. Through patterns of inheritance discovered by Mendel, you will also learn that certain traits, such as trimethylaminuria, are recessive and it takes two nonfunctional copies of that gene before you are affected. This chapter will introduce you to observable patterns of inheritance, including human genetic disorders that are linked to specific genes on the chromosomes.

As you read through the chapter, think about the following questions:

1. How does the collection of chromosomes we inherit from our parents affect our body's appearance and function?

2. What patterns of inheritance can be observed across generations?

3. How does meiosis help predict the probability of producing gametes and inheriting a trait?

FOLLOWING *the* THEMES

CHAPTER 11 MENDELIAN PATTERNS OF INHERITANCE		
UNIT 2 GENETIC BASIS OF LIFE	**Evolution**	Inheritance of genes within a population is a cornerstone of a species' ability to change over time.
	Nature of Science	Researchers now have the technology to permanently change inheritance patterns and potentially cure genetic diseases.
	Biological Systems	Inheriting abnormal genes can affect many aspects of body function.

11.1 Gregor Mendel

Learning Outcomes

Upon completion of this section you should be able to

1. Describe how Mendel's scientific approach enabled his genetic experiments to be successful.
2. Contrast blending and the particulate concept of inheritance.

The science of genetics explains the stability of inheritance (why you are human, as are your parents) and also variations between offspring from one generation to the next (why you have a different combination of traits than your parents). Virtually every culture in history has attempted to explain observed inheritance patterns. An understanding of these patterns has always been important to agriculture, animal husbandry (the science of breeding animals), and medicine.

The Blending Concept of Inheritance

Until the late nineteenth century, most plant and animal breeders believed that traits were inherited by the blending concept of inheritance, which stated that an offspring's genetic makeup was intermediate to that of its parents. While they acknowledged that both sexes contribute equally to a new individual, they believed that parents of contrasting appearance always produce offspring of intermediate appearance.

If the blending concept were true, a cross between plants with red flowers and plants with white flowers would yield only plants with pink flowers. However, scientists who supported the blending theory could not explain, for example, why pink flowers were able to produce offspring with red and white flowers in later generations. The breeders mistakenly attributed this to instability of the genetic material.

The blending concept of inheritance offered little help to Charles Darwin, the father of evolution, whose treatise on natural selection lacked a strong genetic basis. If populations contained only intermediate individuals and normally lacked variations, how could diverse forms evolve?

Mendel's Particulate Theory of Inheritance

Gregor Mendel was an Austrian monk who developed a particulate theory of inheritance after performing a series of ingenious experiments in the 1860s (Fig. 11.1). Mendel studied science and mathematics at the University of Vienna, and at the time of his research in genetics, he was a substitute natural science teacher at a local high school.

Mendel was a successful scientist for several reasons. First, he was one of the first scientists to apply mathematics to biology. Most likely his background in mathematics prompted him to apply statistical methods and the laws of probability to his breeding experiments. He was also a careful, deliberate scientist who followed the scientific method very closely and kept

Figure 11.1 Gregor Mendel, 1822–84. Mendel grew and tended the pea plants he used for his experiments. For each experiment, he observed as many offspring as possible. For a cross that required him to calculate the ratio of round seeds to wrinkled seeds, he observed and counted a total of 7,324 peas!

very detailed, accurate records. He prepared for his experiments carefully and conducted many preliminary studies with various animals and plants.

Mendel's theory of inheritance is called a particulate theory because it is based on the existence of minute particles or hereditary units we now call genes. Inheritance involves the reshuffling of the same genes from generation to generation. The two laws he proposed, the law of segregation and the law of independent assortment, which we will discuss shortly, describe the behavior of these particulate units of heredity as they are passed from one generation to the next. Much of modern genetics is based upon Mendel's theories, which have withstood the test of time and have been supported by innumerable experiments.

Mendel Worked with the Garden Pea

Mendel's preliminary experiments prompted him to choose the garden pea, *Pisum sativum* (Fig. 11.2a), as his experimental organism. The garden pea was a good choice for many reasons. The plants were easy to cultivate and had a short generation time. Although peas normally self-pollinate (pollen only goes to the same flower), they could be cross-pollinated by hand by

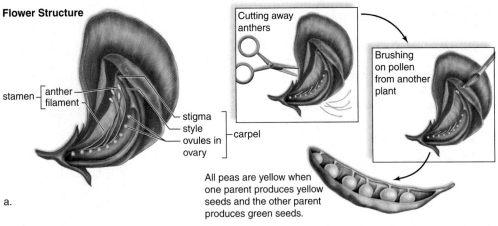

Flower Structure

a.

All peas are yellow when one parent produces yellow seeds and the other parent produces green seeds.

Figure 11.2 Garden pea anatomy and a few traits. **a.** In the garden pea, *Pisum sativum*, pollen grains produced in the anther contain sperm, and ovules in the ovary contain eggs. When Mendel performed crosses, he brushed pollen from one plant onto the stigma of another plant. This cross-pollination allowed sperm to fertilize eggs, and ovules to develop into seeds (peas). The open pod shows the seed color trait that resulted from a cross between plants with yellow seeds and plants with green seeds. **b.** Mendel selected traits to study that were one form or another, and not a blend of two traits. In his research, Mendel observed a dominant, or more prevalent form, as well as a recessive or less prevalent form, in the pea's physical appearance. The text and Figure 11.3 explain the approach Mendel used and how he interpreted his results to discover basic patterns of inheritance.

Trait	Characteristics		
	Dominant		**Recessive**
Stem length	Tall		Short
Pod shape	Inflated		Constricted
Seed shape	Round		Wrinkled
Seed color	Yellow		Green
Flower position	Axial		Terminal
Flower color	Purple		White
Pod color	Green		Yellow

b.

transferring pollen from the anther (male part of a flower) to the stigma (female part of a flower).

Many varieties of peas were available, and Mendel chose 22 for his experiments. When these varieties self-pollinated, over generations they became *true-breeding*—meaning that all the offspring were the same and exactly like the parent plants. Unlike his predecessors, Mendel studied the inheritance of relatively simple and discrete traits that were not subjective and were easy to observe, such as seed shape, seed color, and flower

color. In his crosses, Mendel observed either dominant or recessive characteristics but no intermediate ones (Fig. 11.2b).

Check Your Progress   11.1

1. Describe Gregor Mendel's scientific approach and how it helped make his experiments successful.
2. Explain why the garden pea was a good choice for Mendel's experiments.

11.2 Mendel's Laws

After ensuring that his pea plants were true-breeding—for example, that his tall plants always had tall offspring and his short plants always had short offspring—Mendel was ready to perform cross-pollination experiments (see Fig. 11.2a). These crosses allowed Mendel to formulate his law of segregation.

Law of Segregation

For these initial experiments, Mendel chose varieties that differed in only one trait (e.g. plant height). If the blending theory of inheritance were correct, the cross should yield plants with an intermediate appearance of medium height compared to the parents that were all tall or all short.

Mendel's Experimental Design and Results

Mendel called the original, true-breeding all tall or all short parents the *P generation*. The first generation of offspring were called the *F₁*, or *filial* [L. *filius*, sons and daughters] *generation* (Fig. 11.3). He performed *reciprocal crosses*: First he dusted the pollen of tall plants onto the stigmas of short plants, and then he dusted the pollen of short plants onto the stigmas of tall plants. In both cases, all F₁ offspring resembled the tall parent.

Certainly, these results were contrary to those predicted by the blending theory of inheritance. Rather than being intermediate, the F₁ plants were all tall and resembled only one parent. Did these results mean that the other characteristic (i.e., shortness) had disappeared permanently? Apparently not, because when Mendel allowed the F₁ plants to self-pollinate, ³/₄ of the next generation of offspring, or *F₂ generation*, were tall and ¹/₄ were short, a 3:1 ratio (Fig. 11.3).

Mendel inferred that the F₁ plants were able to pass on a factor for shortness—it didn't disappear, it just skipped a generation. Because the F₁ plants were tall but clearly still contained the shortness characteristic, Mendel deduced that tallness was dominant to shortness (Fig 11.2b and 11.3).

Mendel counted many plants in his plant height and other experiments. When he allowed the F₁ pea plants (which were all tall but carried the characteristic for shortness) to self-fertilize and produce offspring, he counted a total of 1,064 plants, of which 787 were tall and 277 were short. This type of experiment is called a **monohybrid cross** [L. *mono*, single, and *hybrida*, mixture] because it is a cross of a single trait (i.e., plant height)

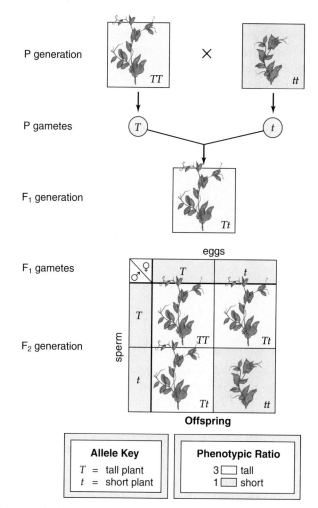

Figure 11.3 Monohybrid cross done by Mendel. The P generation pea plants differ in only one trait—length of the stem. The F₁ generation plants are all tall, but the factor for short has not disappeared because ¹/₄ of the F₂ generation plants are short. The 3:1 ratio allowed Mendel to deduce that individuals have two discrete and separate genetic factors for each trait.

with organisms that are a hybrid (i.e., tall and short characteristics). In fact, in all monohybrid crosses that he performed for the traits shown in Figure 11.2b, he found a 3:1 ratio in the F₂ generation. The characteristic for shortness that had disappeared in the F₁ generation reappeared in ¹/₄ of the F₂ offspring. *Today, we know that the expected phenotypic results of a monohybrid cross are always 3:1.*

Mendel's Conclusion

Mendel's mathematical approach led him to interpret his results differently from previous breeders. He knew that the same ratio was obtained among the F₂ generation time and time again when he did a monohybrid cross involving one of the seven traits he was studying. Eventually Mendel arrived at this explanation: A 3:1 ratio among the F₂ offspring was possible if (1) the

F_1 parents contained two separate copies of each hereditary factor, one of these being dominant and the other recessive; (2) the factors separated when the gametes were formed, and each gamete carried only one copy of each factor; and (3) random fusion of all possible gametes occurred upon fertilization. Only in this way could shortness reoccur in the F_2 generation. Thinking this, Mendel arrived at the first of his laws of inheritance—the law of segregation. The law of segregation is a cornerstone of his particulate theory of inheritance.

> The **law of segregation** states the following:
> - Each individual has two factors for each trait.
> - The factors segregate (separate) during the formation of the gametes.
> - Each gamete contains only one factor from each pair of factors.
> - Fertilization gives each new individual two factors for each trait.

Mendel's Cross as Viewed by Classical Genetics

Figure 11.3 also shows how classical scientists interpreted the results of Mendel's experiments on inheritance of stem length in peas. Stem length in peas is controlled by a single gene. This gene occurs on a homologous pair of chromosomes at a particular location that is called the gene **locus** (Fig. 11.4). Alternative versions of a gene are called **alleles** [Gk. *allelon*, reciprocal, parallel]. The **dominant allele** is so named because the DNA sequence that comprises that gene makes a fully functional protein. The **recessive allele** contains a slightly different DNA sequence and produces a protein with little or no function.

Figure 11.4 Classical view of homologous chromosomes.
a. The letters represent alleles; that is, alternative forms of a gene. Each allelic pair, such as *Gg* or *Tt*, is located on homologous chromosomes at a particular physical location called a gene locus. **b.** Sister chromatids carry the same alleles in the same order. Proteins made from each allele determine the observable traits.

When dominant and recessive alleles for a gene are present in a cell, the resulting mixture of functional and nonfunctional protein allows the dominant physical trait to be shown and the recessive trait to be masked. The dominant allele is identified by a capital letter, and the recessive allele by the same letter but lowercase. Usually, the first letter designating a trait is chosen to identify the allele. Using the plant height example, there is an allele for tallness (*T*) and an allele for shortness (*t*).

As described in the preceding chapter, meiosis is the type of cell division that reduces the chromosome number from diploid (2n) to haploid (n). During meiosis I, the members of bivalents (homologous chromosomes each having sister chromatids) separate. This means that the two alleles for each gene separate from each other during meiosis (see Fig. 11.7). Therefore, the process of meiosis gives an explanation for Mendel's law of segregation, and why only one allele for each trait is in a gamete.

In Mendel's cross, the original parents (P generation) were true-breeding; therefore, the tall plants had two alleles for tallness (*TT*), and the short plants had two alleles for shortness (*tt*). When an organism has two identical alleles, as these had, we say it is **homozygous** [Gk. *homo*, same, and *zygos*, balance, yoke]. Because the parents were homozygous, all gametes produced by the tall plant contained the allele for tallness (*T*), and all gametes produced by the short plant contained an allele for shortness (*t*).

After cross-pollination between different pea plants, all the individuals of the resulting F_1 generation had one allele for tallness and one for shortness (*Tt*). When an organism has two different alleles at a gene locus, we say that it is **heterozygous** [Gk. *hetero*, different, and *zygos*, balance, yoke]. Although the plants of the F_1 generation had one of each type of allele, they were all tall. The allele that is expressed in a heterozygous individual is the dominant allele. The allele that is not expressed in a heterozygote is the recessive allele. This explains why shortness, the recessive trait, skipped a generation in Mendel's experiment.

Continuing with the discussion of Mendel's cross (see Fig. 11.3), the F_1 plants produce gametes in which 50% have the dominant allele *T* and 50% have the recessive allele *t*. During the process of fertilization, we assume that all types of sperm (i.e., *T* or *t*) have an equal chance to fertilize all types of eggs (i.e., *T* or *t*). When this occurs, such a monohybrid cross always produces a 3:1 (dominant to recessive) ratio among the offspring. Figure 11.5 gives Mendel's results for several monohybrid crosses, and you can see that the results were always close to 3:1.

Genotype Versus Phenotype

It is obvious from our discussion that two organisms with different allelic combinations for a trait can have the same outward appearance. (That is, *TT* and *Tt* pea plants are both tall.) For this reason, it is necessary to distinguish between the alleles present in an organism and the appearance of that organism.

The word **genotype** [Gk. *genos*, birth, origin, race, and *typos*, image, shape] refers to the alleles an individual receives

Trait	Characteristics				F₂ Results		
	Dominant		Recessive		Dominant	Recessive	Ratio
Stem length	Tall		Short		787	277	2.84:1
Pod shape	Inflated		Constricted		882	299	2.95:1
Seed shape	Round		Wrinkled		5,474	1,850	2.96:1
Seed color	Yellow		Green		6,022	2,001	3.01:1
Flower position	Axial		Terminal		651	207	3.14:1
Flower color	Purple		White		705	224	3.15:1
Pod color	Green		Yellow		428	152	2.82:1
				Totals:	14,949	5,010	2.98:1

Figure 11.5 Relationship between observed phenotype and F₂ offspring.   Mendel was fortunate in choosing the pea plant because the traits he observed were quite distinct and easily classified. After crossing F₁ hybrids and counting hundreds of F₂ pea plants for each trait, Mendel discovered that each showed a 3:1 ratio.

at fertilization. Genotype may be indicated by letters or by short, descriptive phrases, and represents the DNA sequence for a particular gene. Genotype TT is called homozygous dominant, and genotype tt is called homozygous recessive. Genotype Tt is called heterozygous. These refer to the different ways that alleles can be combined in a cell.

The word **phenotype** [Gk. *phaino*, appear, and *typos*, image, shape] refers to the physical appearance of the individual, which is made from the proteins produced by the corresponding alleles. The homozygous dominant (TT) individual and the heterozygous (Tt) individual both show the dominant phenotype and are tall because they make fully functional proteins that build the tall trait, while the homozygous recessive individual that shows the recessive phenotype and makes less or nonfunctional protein for that trait is short. Thus, the DNA

that makes up the genotype produces the proteins that make up the phenotype.

Check Your Progress   **11.2A**

1. State all possible gametes, noting the proportion of each for the individual, for these genotypes: **a.** *WW* **b.** *Ww* **c.** *Tt* **d.** *TT*
2. Interpret which of these genotypes (*Bb, BB, bb*) a white rabbit would have if B = black and b = white.
3. What would be the expected phenotypic ratio of the offspring if two heterozygous rabbits mate? If they produced 20 offspring, how many would you expect to be white?

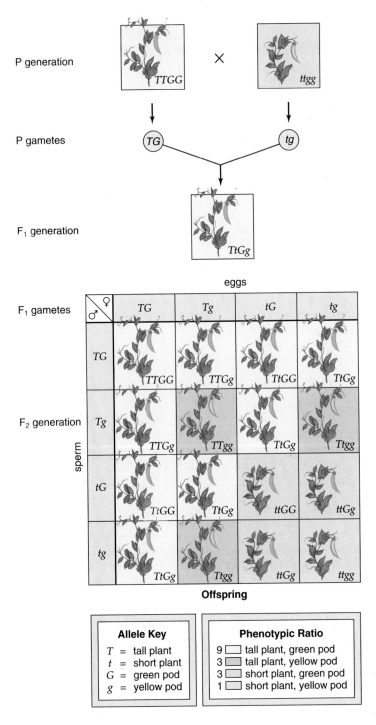

Offspring

Allele Key
T = tall plant
t = short plant
G = green pod
g = yellow pod

Phenotypic Ratio	
9 ☐	tall plant, green pod
3 ☐	tall plant, yellow pod
3 ☐	short plant, green pod
1 ☐	short plant, yellow pod

Figure 11.6 Dihybrid cross done by Mendel. P generation plants differ in two traits: —length of the stem, and color of the pod. The F_1 generation shows only the dominant traits, but all possible phenotypes appear among the F_2 generation because the F_1 parents are hybrids. The 9:3:3:1 ratio allowed Mendel to deduce that factors segregate into gametes independently of other factors.

Mendel's Law of Independent Assortment

Mendel performed a second series of crosses in which true-breeding pea plants differed in two traits. For example, he crossed tall plants having green pods with short plants having yellow pods (Fig. 11.6). The F_1 plants showed both dominant characteristics. As before, Mendel then allowed the F_1 plants to self-pollinate. This F_1 cross is known as a **dihybrid cross** [L. *di*, two, and *hybrida*, mixture] because the plants are hybrid in two ways. Two possible results could occur in the F_2 generation:

1. If the dominant factors (*TG*) always segregate into the F_1 gametes together, and the recessive factors (*tg*) always stay together, then there would be two phenotypes among the F_2 plants—tall plants with green pods and short plants with yellow pods.
2. If the four factors segregate into the F_1 gametes independently, then there would be four phenotypes among the F_2 plants—tall plants with green pods, tall plants with yellow pods, short plants with green pods, and short plants with yellow pods.

Figure 11.6 shows that Mendel observed four phenotypes among the F_2 plants, supporting the second hypothesis. This is how Mendel formulated his second law of heredity—the law of independent assortment.

> The **law of independent assortment** states the following:
> - Each pair of factors segregates (assorts) independently of the other pairs.
> - All possible combinations of factors can occur in the gametes.

The law of independent assortment applies only to alleles on different chromosomes. Each chromosome carries a large number of alleles.

We know that the process of meiosis explains why the F_1 plants produced every possible type of gamete and, therefore, four phenotypes appear among the F_2 generation of plants. Figure 11.7 shows a parent cell with two homologous pairs of chromosomes, with alleles *A*, *a* on one pair and *B*, *b* on the other pair. Following duplication of the chromosomes during interphase, the parent cell undergoes meiosis I. At metaphase I, the homologous pairs line up independently of one another, such that the chromosomes with *A* alleles have an equal chance of lining up with the *B* alleles or the *b* alleles. The subsequent segregation of the homologous pairs during anaphase I reduces the chromosome number from 2n to n. Because *A* alleles can be sorted with *B* or *b*, and so can the *a* allele, it is possible to create gametes with *AB*, *Ab*, *aB*, and *ab* allele combinations with equal probability.

Animation
Random Orientation of Chromosomes During Meiosis

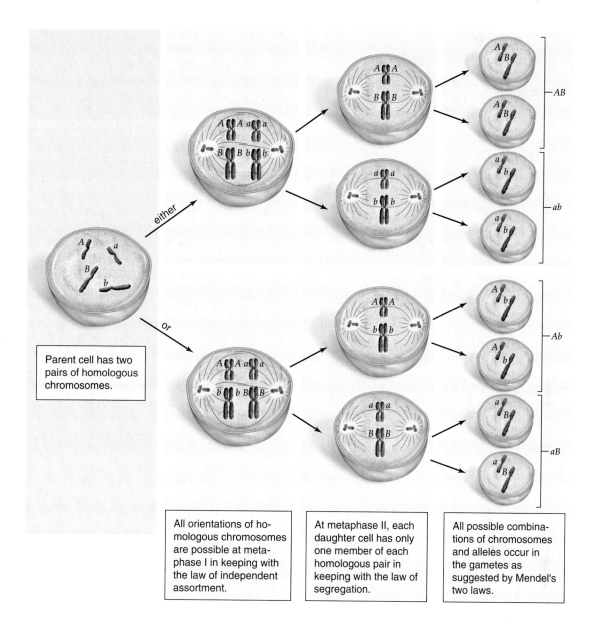

Figure 11.7 Independent assortment and segregation during meiosis.   Mendel's laws hold because of the events of meiosis. The homologous pairs of chromosomes line up randomly at the metaphase plate during meiosis I. It doesn't matter which member of a homologous pair faces which spindle pole. In this example, A alleles can segregate with B or with b alleles. Likewise, a alleles can segregate with B or with b alleles. Therefore, the homologous chromosomes, and alleles they carry, segregate independently during gamete formation. All possible combinations of chromosomes and alleles, that is, AB, Ab, aB, and ab, occur in the gametes.

The same rule of independent assortment applies for the pea plant example in Figure 11.6. In that case, the possible gametes are the two dominants (such as *TG*), the two recessives (such as *tg*), and the ones that have a dominant and a recessive (such as *Tg* and *tG*). Regardless of whether we are using the A and B chromosome or the T and G chromosome examples, when all possible sperm have an opportunity to fertilize all possible eggs, *the expected phenotypic ratio of a dihybrid cross is always 9:3:3:1.*

Check Your Progress   **11.2B**

1. Identify all possible gametes for a heterozygote in fruit flies where *L* = long wings and *l* = short wings; *G* = gray body and *g* = black body.
2. Describe the expected phenotypic ratio when two heterozygous dihybrids reproduce.

Labels within figure:

- Parent cell has two pairs of homologous chromosomes.
- either
- or
- All orientations of homologous chromosomes are possible at metaphase I in keeping with the law of independent assortment.
- At metaphase II, each daughter cell has only one member of each homologous pair in keeping with the law of segregation.
- All possible combinations of chromosomes and alleles occur in the gametes as suggested by Mendel's two laws.
- AB
- ab
- Ab
- aB

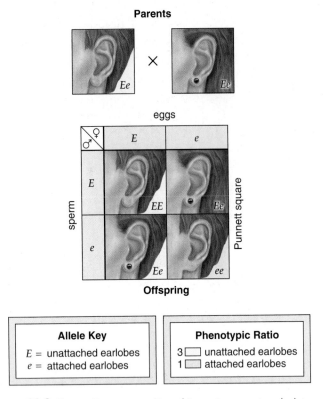

Figure 11.8 Punnett square. Use of Punnett square to calculate probable results; in this case, a 3:1 phenotypic ratio.

Mendel's Laws of Probability

The diagram we have been using to calculate the results of a cross is called a Punnett square. The **Punnett square** allows us to easily calculate the chances, or the probability, of genotypes and phenotypes among the offspring. Like flipping a coin, an offspring of the cross illustrated in the Punnett square in Figure 11.8 has a 50% (or ½) chance of receiving an E for unattached earlobe or an e for attached earlobe from each parent:

The chance of E = ½
The chance of e = ½

How likely is it that an offspring will inherit a specific set of two alleles, one from each parent? The *product rule* of probability tells us that we have to multiply the chances of independent events to get the answer:

1. The chance of EE = ½ × ½ = ¼
2. The chance of Ee = ½ × ½ = ¼
3. The chance of eE = ½ × ½ = ¼
4. The chance of ee = ½ × ½ = ¼

The Punnett square does this for us because we can easily see that each of these is ¼ of the total number of squares.

How do we get the phenotypic results? The *sum rule* of probability tells us that when the same event can occur in more than one way, we can add the results. Because 1, 2, and 3 all result in unattached earlobes, we add them up to know that the chance of unattached earlobes is ¾, or 75%. The chance of

attached earlobes is ¼, or 25%. The Punnett square doesn't do this for us—we have to add the results ourselves.

The statement "Chance has no memory" is important when considering inheritance across offspring. Every time a couple produces an offspring, the child has the same chances of inheriting the different allele combinations. So, for a heterozygous (Ee) couple, each child has a 25% chance of having attached (ee) earlobes. Inheriting a recessive trait may not seem significant if we are considering earlobes. However, it becomes quite significant when we consider a recessive genetic disorder such as cystic fibrosis, a debilitating respiratory illness. For a heterozygous couple, there is a 25% chance that a child they have will inherit two recessive alleles and exhibit the disease. And because each child is an independent event, it is possible that all their children—or none of them—could exhibit cystic fibrosis.

We can use the product rule and the sum rule of probability to predict the results of a dihybrid cross, such as the one shown in Figure 11.6. The Punnett square carries out the multiplication for us, and we add the results to find that the phenotypic ratio is 9:3:3:1. We expect these same results for each and every dihybrid cross. Therefore, it is not necessary to do a Punnett square over and over again for either a monohybrid or a dihybrid cross. Instead, we can simply remember the probable results of 3:1 and 9:3:3:1. But we have to remember that the 9 represents the two dominant phenotypes together, the 3's are a dominant phenotype with a hidden recessive, and the 1 stands for the double recessive phenotype.

This tells you the probable phenotypic ratio among the offspring, but not the chances for each possible phenotype. Because the dihybrid Punnett square has 16 squares, the chances are ⁹⁄₁₆ for the two dominants together, ³⁄₁₆ for the dominants with each recessive, and ¹⁄₁₆ for the two recessives together.

Mendel counted the results of many similar crosses to get the probable results, and in the laboratory, we too have to count the results of many individual crosses to get the probable results for a monohybrid or a dihybrid cross. Why? Consider that each time you toss a coin, you have a 50% chance of getting heads or tails. If you tossed the coin only a couple of times, you might very well have heads or tails both times. However, if you toss the coin many times, your results are more likely to approach 50% heads and 50% tails.

Testcrosses

To confirm that the F_1 plants of his one-trait crosses were in fact heterozygous, Mendel crossed his F_1 generation tall pea plants with true-breeding short (homozygous recessive) plants; such a mating is termed a **testcross.** These crosses provided Mendel with further support for his law of segregation.

For the cross in Figure 11.9, Mendel reasoned that half the offspring should be tall and half should be short, producing a 1:1 phenotypic ratio. His results supported the hypothesis that alleles segregate when gametes are formed. In Figure 11.9a, the homozygous recessive parent can produce only one type of gamete—t—and so the Punnett square has only one column. The use of one column signifies that all the gametes carry a t. *The expected phenotypic ratio for this type of one-trait cross (heterozygous × recessive) is always 1:1.*

One-Trait Testcross

Today, a one-trait testcross is used to determine if an individual with the dominant phenotype is homozygous dominant (e.g., TT) or heterozygous (e.g., Tt). Because both of these genotypes produce the dominant phenotype, it is not possible to determine the genotype by observation. Figure 11.9b shows that if the individual is homozygous dominant, all the offspring will be tall. Each parent has only one type of gamete and, therefore, a Punnett square is not required to determine the results.

Two-Trait Testcross

When doing a two-trait testcross, an individual with the dominant phenotype is crossed with one having the recessive phenotype. Suppose you are working with fruit flies in which:

L = long wings	G = gray bodies
l = vestigial (short) wings	g = black bodies

You wouldn't know by examination whether the fly on the left was homozygous or heterozygous for wing and body color. To find out the genotype of the test fly, you cross it with the one on the right. You know by examination that this vestigial-winged and black-bodied fly is homozygous recessive for both traits.

If the test fly is homozygous dominant for both traits with the genotype $LLGG$, it will form only one gamete: LG. Therefore, all the offspring from the proposed cross would have long wings and a gray body.

However, if the test fly is heterozygous for both traits with the genotype $LlGg$, it will form four different types of gametes:

Gametes: LG Lg lG lg

and could have four different offspring:

| $LlGg$ | $Llgg$ | $llGg$ | $llgg$ |

The presence of the offspring with vestigial wings and a black body shows that the test fly is heterozygous for both traits and has the genotype $LlGg$. Otherwise, it could not produce this offspring. In general, you want to remember that *the expected phenotypic ratio for this type of two-trait cross (heterozygous for two traits × recessive for both traits) is always 1:1:1:1.*

Check Your Progress   11.2C

1. State the percentage of pea plants that would have **a.** yellow seeds, and **b.** green seeds in a cross of two heterozygous plants where yellow seed color is dominant over green seed color.
2. State the chances of producing offspring with long wings and a black body from a testcross of a heterozygous ($LlGg$) fruit fly and a homozygous recessive ($llgg$) fruit fly.
3. State the genotype of all the horses if trotter (T) is dominant over pacer (t), and a pacer is produced when a trotter is mated to a pacer.

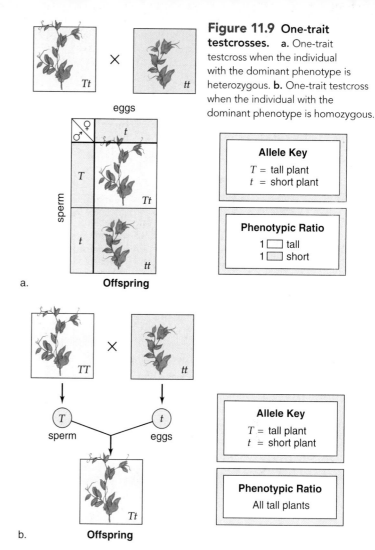

Figure 11.9 One-trait testcrosses. a. One-trait testcross when the individual with the dominant phenotype is heterozygous. **b.** One-trait testcross when the individual with the dominant phenotype is homozygous.

Allele Key
T = tall plant
t = short plant

Phenotypic Ratio
1 ☐ tall
1 ☐ short

Allele Key
T = tall plant
t = short plant

Phenotypic Ratio
All tall plants

Mendel's Laws and Human Genetic Disorders

Many traits and disorders in humans, and other organisms also, are genetic in origin and follow Mendel's laws. These traits are controlled by a single pair of alleles on the autosomal chromosomes. An **autosome** is any chromosome other than a sex (X or Y) chromosome.

Autosomal Patterns of Inheritance

When a genetic disorder is autosomal dominant, the normal allele (a) is recessive, and an individual with the alleles AA or Aa has the disorder. When a genetic disorder is autosomal recessive, the normal allele (A) is dominant, and only individuals with the alleles aa have the disorder. A pedigree shows the pattern of inheritance for a particular condition and can be used by genetic counselors to determine whether a condition is dominant or recessive. Consider these two possible patterns of inheritance:

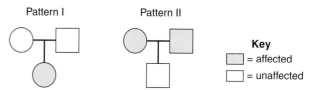

Pattern I   Pattern II

Key
☐ = affected
☐ = unaffected

In a pedigree, males are designated by squares and females by circles. Shaded circles and squares are the affected individuals. The shaded boxes do not indicate whether the condition is

Figure 11.10 Autosomal recessive pedigree. The list gives ways to recognize an autosomal recessive disorder. How would you know the individual at the asterisk is heterozygous? (See Appendix A for answer.)

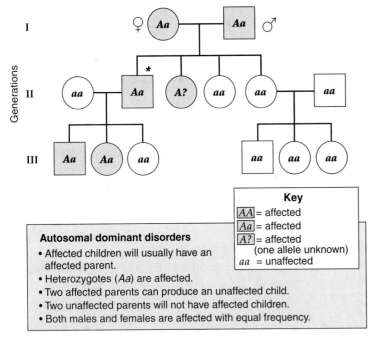

Figure 11.11 Autosomal dominant pedigree. The list gives ways to recognize an autosomal dominant disorder. How would you know the individual at the asterisk is heterozygous? (See Appendix A for answer.)

dominant or recessive, only that the individual exhibits the trait. A line between a square and a circle represents a union. In the patterns on page 201, a vertical line going downward leads to a single child. (If there are more children, they are lined up horizontally.) From page 201, which pattern of inheritance (I or II) do you suppose represents an autosomal dominant characteristic, and which represents an autosomal recessive characteristic?

In pattern I, the child is affected, but neither parent is; this can happen if the condition is recessive and both parents are *Aa*.

Notice that the parents are **carriers** because they appear normal (do not express the trait) but are capable of having a child with the genetic disorder. In pattern II, the child is unaffected, but the parents are affected. This can happen if the condition is dominant and the parents are *Aa*.

Figure 11.10 shows other ways to recognize an autosomal recessive pattern of inheritance, and Figure 11.11 shows other ways to recognize an autosomal dominant pattern of inheritance. In these pedigrees, generations are indicated by Roman numerals placed on the left side. Notice in the third generation of Figure 11.10 that two closely related individuals have produced three children, two of which have the affected phenotype. In this case, a double line denotes consanguineous reproduction, or inbreeding, which is reproduction between two closely related individuals. This illustrates that inbreeding significantly increases the chances of children inheriting two copies of a potentially harmful recessive allele.

Autosomal Recessive Disorders

In humans, a number of autosomal recessive disorders have been identified. Here, we discuss methemoglobinemia and cystic fibrosis.

Methemoglobinemia

Methemoglobinemia is a relatively harmless disorder that results from an accumulation of methemoglobin in the blood. This disorder has been documented for centuries, but the exact cause and genetic link had remained mysterious. Although rarely mentioned, hemoglobin, the main oxygen-carrying protein in the blood, is usually converted at a slow rate to an alternate form called methemoglobin. Unlike hemoglobin, which is bright red when carrying oxygen, methemoglobin has a bluish color, similar to that of oxygen-poor blood. Although this process is harmless, individuals with methemoglobinemia are unable to clear the abnormal blue protein from their blood, causing their skin to appear bluish-purple in color (Fig. 11.12).

A persistent and determined physician finally solved the age-old mystery of what causes methemoglobinemia by doing blood tests and pedigree analysis involving a family known as the "blue Fugates" of Troublesome Creek, Kentucky. Enzyme tests indicated that the blue Fugates lacked the enzyme diaphorase, coded for by a gene on chromosome 22. The enzyme normally converts methemoglobin back to hemoglobin.

The physician treated the disorder in a simple, but rather unconventional manner. He injected the Fugates with a dye called methylene blue! This unusual dye can donate electrons to other compounds, successfully converting the excess methemoglobin back into normal hemoglobin. The results were striking but immediate—the patient's skin quickly turned pink after treatment.

A pedigree analysis of the Fugate family indicated that the trait is common in the family because so many members carried the recessive allele.

Cystic Fibrosis

Cystic fibrosis (CF) is the most common lethal genetic disease among Caucasians in the United States (Fig. 11.13). About 1 in 20 Caucasians is a carrier, and about 1 in 2,000 newborns has the disorder. CF patients exhibit a number of characteristic symptoms, the most obvious being extremely salty sweat. In

Figure 11.12 Methemoglobinemia. The hands of the woman on the right appear blue due to chemically induced methemoglobinemia.

Figure 11.13 Cystic fibrosis. Cystic fibrosis is due to a faulty protein that is supposed to regulate the flow of chloride ions into and out of cells through a channel protein.

children with CF, the mucus in the bronchial tubes and pancreatic ducts is particularly thick and viscous, interfering with the function of the lungs and pancreas. To ease breathing, the thick mucus in the lungs has to be loosened periodically, but still the lungs frequently become infected. The clogged pancreatic ducts prevent digestive enzymes from reaching the small intestine, and to improve digestion, patients take digestive enzymes mixed with applesauce before every meal.

Cystic fibrosis is caused by a defective chloride ion channel that is encoded by the *CFTR* allele on chromosome 7. Research has demonstrated that chloride ions (Cl^-) fail to pass through the defective version of the CFTR chloride ion channel, which is located on the plasma membrane. Ordinarily, after chloride ions have passed through the channel to the other side of the membrane, sodium ions (Na^+) and water follow. It is believed that lack of water is the cause of the abnormally thick mucus in the bronchial tubes and pancreatic ducts.

In the past few years, new treatments have raised the average life expectancy for CF patients to as much as 35 years of age. It is hoped that other novel treatments, such as gene therapy, may be able to correct the defect by replacing a faulty copy of the gene with a normal one. Some scientists have suggested that the mutated *CFTR* allele has persisted in the human population as a means of surviving potentially fatal diseases, such as cholera.

Autosomal Dominant Disorders

A number of autosomal dominant disorders have been identified in humans. Two relatively well-known autosomal dominant disorders include osteogenesis imperfecta and hereditary spherocytosis.

Osteogenesis Imperfecta

Osteogenesis [L. *os*, bone, and *genesis*, origin] imperfecta is an autosomal dominant genetic disorder that results in weakened, brittle bones. Although at least nine types of the disorder are known, most are linked to mutations in two genes necessary to the synthesis of a type I collagen—one of the most abundant proteins in the human body. Collagen has many roles, including providing strength and rigidity to bone and forming the framework for most of the body's tissues. Osteogenesis imperfecta leads to a defective collagen I that causes the bones to be brittle and weak. Because the mutant collagen can cause structural defects even when combined with normal collagen I, osteogenesis imperfecta is generally considered to be dominant.

Osteogenesis imperfecta, which has an incidence of approximately 1 in 5,000 live births, affects all racial groups similarly

and has been documented as long as 300 years ago. Some historians think that the Viking chieftain Ivar Ragnarsson, who was known as Ivar the Boneless and was often carried into battle on a shield, had this condition. In most cases, the diagnosis is made in young children who visit the emergency room frequently due to broken bones. Some children with the disorder have an unusual blue tint in the sclera, the white portion of the eye; reduced skin elasticity; weakened teeth; and occasionally heart valve abnormalities. Currently, the disorder is treatable with a number of drugs that help to increase bone mass, but these drugs must be taken long-term.

Hereditary Spherocytosis

Hereditary spherocytosis is an autosomal dominant genetic blood disorder that results from a defective copy of the ankyrin-1 gene found on chromosome 8. The protein encoded by this gene serves as a structural component of red blood cells, and is responsible for maintaining their disklike shape. The abnormal spherocytosis protein is unable to perform its usual function, causing the affected person's red blood cells to adopt a spherical rather than disklike shape. As a result, the abnormal cells are fragile and burst easily, especially under osmotic stress. Enlargement of the spleen is also commonly seen in people with the disorder.

With an incidence of approximately 1 in 5,000, hereditary spherocytosis is one of the most common hereditary blood disorders. Roughly one-fourth of these cases result from new mutations and are not inherited from either parent. Hereditary spherocytosis exhibits incomplete penetrance, so not all individuals who inherit the mutant allele will actually show the trait. The cause of incomplete penetrance in these cases and others remains poorly understood.

Check Your Progress   11.2D

1. State the genotype of the child in Figure 11.13 and the genotypes of his parents if neither parent has cystic fibrosis. (Use this key: *C* = normal; *c* = cystic fibrosis)
2. Identify the chance that the parents in the above problem will have a child with cystic fibrosis.
3. Construct a pedigree of Ivar Ragnarsson's family tree assuming that his mother, and both her parents, were normal and that Ivar's father's father had osteogenesis imperfecta (mother was normal).

THEME   Nature of Science

Testing for Genetic Disorders

Many human genetic disorders such as Huntington disease and cystic fibrosis are the result of inheriting faulty genes. Huntington disease is a devastating neurological disease caused by the inheritance of a single dominant allele; in contrast, cystic fibrosis, being a recessive disorder, requires the inheritance of two recessive alleles. In each case, mutated sequences in these genes that have been inherited lead to defective proteins, which disrupt normal biological function.

Genetic tests have been developed that can detect a particular sequence of bases for all your genes, and these sequences tell whether you have a particular genetic disorder. When researchers set out to develop a test for Huntington disease, they first obtained multiple **family pedigrees,** such as the one shown in Figure 11A. This pedigree meets the requirements for a dominant allele and autosomal inheritance: Every individual who is affected (shaded box or circle) has a parent who is also affected, heterozygotes are affected, and both males and females are affected in equal numbers. Each offspring of an affected individual has a 50% chance of having received the faulty gene and developing Huntington disease, which doesn't appear until later in life. Thus, a person could already have produced children before they know about the disease.

The letters under the square or circle mean the individual has undergone a blood test that resulted in an analysis of their DNA. A computer analysis of these individuals' DNA found that a large number of them had a sequence designated as J, K, or L. Only the sequence of bases designated as L appears in all the individuals with Huntington disease. A closer look at the pedigree indicates that sequence L is not in the gene for Huntington because at least one individual has the sequence but does not have Huntington disease.

When genes occur on the same chromosome in close proximity, their alleles are said to be linked. The closer linked alleles are on a chromosome, the greater the chance that they will be inherited together. This is the reason that alleles must be on separate chromosomes for the law of independent assortment to hold. Still, even genes that are closely linked can undergo crossing-over and become unlinked on occasion. Testable sequences that are closely linked to that of the faulty gene are called genetic markers, and these may be used as indicators of genetic disorders, such as Huntington disease. Association studies are another way for researchers to find possible sequences that indicate someone has a genetic disorder. During an association study, the DNA of a diverse sample of the general population is tested to find similar DNA sequences. The use of genetic markers and association studies has made it possible to successfully identify many genes involved in human disease.

The mapping of disorders to genes within the human genome has yielded much valuable information to the scientific and medical communities. The information has a variety of uses including prenatal genetic testing, diagnosis of disorders in individuals before symptoms occur, carrier testing of recessive disorders, and to further understand the origin, progression, and pathology of a disorder. This may lead to the development of novel treatment methods. New techniques and technologies have greatly accelerated this process, but the tried and true methods of family pedigrees and association studies are still the primary techniques used by geneticists in pursuing the cure for many human genetic ailments.

Questions to Consider

1. Considering how quickly cell and molecular technology is emerging, what implications does this have for curing genetic diseases?
2. If you or someone you knew suffered from a genetic disease, would you choose to use emerging technologies to treat the disease?

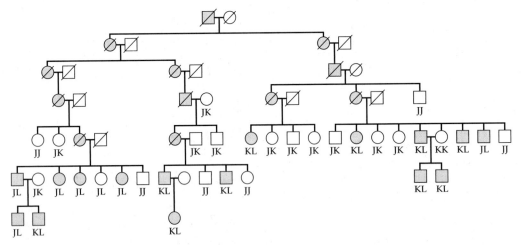

Figure 11A Blood sample testing and pedigree analysis.   In individuals with Huntingon disease, a particular sequence of DNA bases (L) is always present. The pedigree chart shows that the L sequence is not present unless an ancestor exhibited Huntington disease. A slash indicates that the ancestor is deceased.

11.3 Extending the Range of Mendelian Genetics

Learning Outcomes

Upon completion of this section you should be able to

1. Explain the inheritance pattern of traits where more than two alleles for the trait exist.
2. Contrast incomplete dominance and incomplete penetrance.
3. Describe the effects of pleiotropy on phenotypic traits.
4. Distinguish the inheritance of polygenic traits.
5. Examine X-linked inheritance and its gender-based effects.

Mendelian genetics can also be applied to complex patterns of inheritance, such as multiple alleles, incomplete dominance, pleiotropy, and polygenic inheritance.

Multiple Allelic Traits

When a trait is controlled by **multiple alleles,** the gene exists in several allelic forms within a population. For example, although a person's ABO blood type is controlled by a single gene pair, there are three possible alleles within the human population that determine the blood type. Each person receives two of these alleles (one from each parent) to determine the presence or absence of antigens on their red blood cells.

I^A = A antigen on red blood cells
I^B = B antigen on red blood cells
i = Neither A nor B antigen on red blood cells

The possible phenotypes and genotypes for blood type are as follows:

Phenotype	Genotype
A	$I^A I^A$, $I^A i$
B	$I^B I^B$, $I^B i$
AB	$I^A I^B$
O	ii

The inheritance of the ABO blood group in humans is also an example of **codominance** because both I^A and I^B are fully expressed in the presence of the other. A person who inherits chromosomes with I^A and I^B alleles will make fully functional A and B protein, and because these alleles are codominant, the resulting mixture of AB protein will give the red blood cell an AB phenotype. On the other hand, both I^A and I^B are dominant over i. Therefore, two genotypes are possible for type A blood, and two genotypes are possible for type B blood.

Use a Punnett square to confirm that reproduction between a heterozygote with type A blood and a heterozygote with type B blood can result in any one of the four blood types. Such a cross makes it clear that an offspring can have a different blood type from either parent, and for this reason, DNA fingerprinting is now used to identify the parents of an individual, instead of blood type.

Incomplete Dominance and Incomplete Penetrance

Incomplete dominance is exhibited when the heterozygote has an intermediate phenotype between that of either homozygote. In a cross between a true-breeding, red-flowered four-o'clock plant strain and a true-breeding, white-flowered strain, the offspring have pink flowers. Although this outcome might appear to be an example of the blending theory of inheritance, it is not. Here's why. When the pink plants self-pollinate, the offspring plants have a phenotypic ratio of 1 red-flowered : 2 pink-flowered : 1 white-flowered. The reappearance of the three phenotypes in this generation makes it clear that we are still dealing with a single pair of alleles (Fig. 11.14).

Incomplete dominance in four-o'clocks actually has more to do with the amount of pigment protein produced in the plant cells: A double dose of pigment results in red flowers; a single dose of pigment results in pink flowers; and a lack of any pigment produces white flowers.

Human Examples of Incomplete Dominance

In humans, familial hypercholesterolemia (FH) is an example of incomplete dominance. An individual with two alleles for this disorder develops fatty deposits in the skin and tendons and may have a heart attack as a child. An individual with one normal allele and one *FH* allele may suffer a heart attack as a young adult, and an individual with two normal alleles does not have the disorder.

Perhaps the inheritance pattern of other human disorders should be considered one of incomplete dominance. To detect the carriers of cystic fibrosis, for example, it is customary to determine the amount of cellular activity of the gene. When the activity is one-half that of the dominant homozygote, the individual is a carrier, even though the individual does not exhibit the genetic disease. In other words, at the level of gene

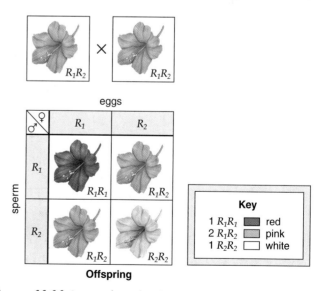

Figure 11.14 Incomplete dominance. When pink four-o'clocks self-pollinate, the results show three phenotypes. This is only possible if the pink parents had an allele for red pigment (R_1) and an allele for no pigment (R_2). Note that alleles involved in incomplete dominance are both given a capital letter.

expression, the homozygotes and heterozygotes do differ in the same manner as four-o'clock plants.

In some cases, a dominant allele may not always lead to the dominant phenotype in a heterozygote, even when the alleles show a true dominant/recessive relationship. The dominant allele in this case does not always determine the phenotype of the individual, so we describe these traits as showing **incomplete penetrance.** In other words, just because a person inherits a dominant allele doesn't mean they will fully express the gene or show the dominant phenotype. Many dominant alleles exhibit varying degrees of penetrance.

The best-known example of incomplete penetrance is polydactyly, the presence of one or more extra digits on hands, feet, or both. Polydactyly is inherited in an autosomal dominant manner; however, not all individuals who inherit the dominant allele exhibit the trait. The reasons for this are not clear, but expression of polydactyly may require additional environmental factors or be influenced by other genes, as discussed later.

Pleiotropic Effects

Pleiotropy occurs when a single mutant gene affects two or more distinct and seemingly unrelated traits. For example, persons with Marfan syndrome have disproportionately long arms, legs, hands, and feet; a weakened aorta; poor eyesight; and other characteristics (Fig. 11.15). All of these characteristics are due to the production of abnormal connective tissue.

Marfan syndrome has been linked to a mutated gene (*FBN1*) on chromosome 15 that ordinarily specifies a functional protein called fibrillin. Fibrillin is essential for the formation of elastic fibers in connective tissue. Without the structural support of normal connective tissue, the aorta can burst, particularly if the person is engaged in a strenuous sport, such as volleyball or basketball. Flo Hyman may have been the best American woman volleyball player ever, but she fell to the floor and died at the age of only 31 because her aorta gave way during a game. Now that coaches are aware of Marfan syndrome, they are on the lookout for it among very tall basketball players. Chris Weisheit, whose career was cut short after he was diagnosed with Marfan syndrome, said, "I don't want to die playing basketball."

Many other disorders, including porphyria and sickle-cell disease, are examples of pleiotropic traits. Porphyria is caused by a chemical insufficiency in the production of hemoglobin, the pigment that makes red blood cells red. The symptoms of porphyria are photosensitivity, strong abdominal pain, port-wine-colored urine, and paralysis in the arms and legs. Many members of the British royal family in the late 1700s and early 1800s suffered from this disorder, which can lead to epileptic convulsions, bizarre behavior, and coma.

In a person suffering from sickle-cell disease (Hb^SHb^S), the cells are sickle-shaped. The underlying mutation is in a gene that codes for a type of polypeptide chain in hemoglobin. Of 146 amino acids, the gene mutation changes only one amino acid, but the result is a less soluble polypeptide chain that stacks up and causes

1,600×, colorized SEM

Sickled red blood cell

Figure 11.15 Marfan syndrome. Marfan syndrome illustrates the multiple effects a single gene can have. Marfan syndrome is due to any number of defective connective tissue defects.

Connective tissue defects

Skeleton — Chest wall deformities / Long, thin fingers, arms, legs / Scoliosis (curvature of the spine) / Flat feet / Long, narrow face / Loose joints

Heart and blood vessels — Mitral valve prolapse / Enlargement of aorta → Aneurysm / Aortic wall tear

Eyes — Lens dislocation / Severe nearsightedness

Lungs — Collapsed lungs

Skin — Stretch marks in skin / Recurrent hernias / Dural ectasia: stretching of the membrane that holds spinal fluid red blood cells to be sickle-shaped. The abnormally shaped sickle cells slow down blood flow and clog small blood vessels. In addition, sickled red blood cells have a shorter life span than normal red blood cells. Affected individuals may exhibit a number of symptoms, including severe anemia, physical weakness, poor circulation, impaired mental function, pain and high fever, rheumatism, paralysis, spleen damage, low resistance to disease, and kidney and heart failure. All of these effects are due to the tendency of sickled red blood cells to break down and to the resulting decreased oxygen-carrying capacity of the blood and the damage the body suffers as a result of the condition.

Although sickle-cell disease is a devastating disorder, from an evolutionary perspective it provides heterozygous individuals with a survival advantage. People who have sickle-cell trait are resistant to the protozoan parasite that causes malaria. The parasite spends part of its life cycle in red blood cells feeding on hemoglobin, but it cannot complete its life cycle when sickle-shaped cells form and break down earlier than usual. Because of this survival benefit, the sickle-cell allele has been maintained in the human population over evolutionary time.

Polygenic Inheritance

Polygenic inheritance [Gk. *poly*, many; L. *genitus*, producing] occurs when a trait is governed by two or more sets of alleles. Examples include human height and prevalence of diabetes. The individual has a copy of all allelic pairs, possibly located on many different pairs of chromosomes. Each dominant allele has a quantitative effect on the phenotype, and these effects are additive. Therefore, a population is expected to exhibit continuous phenotypic variations, such as a wide variation in human height and weight. In Figure 11.16, a cross between genotypes *AABBCC* and *aabbcc* yields F$_1$ hybrids with the genotype *AaBbCc*. A range of genotypes and phenotypes results in the F$_2$ generation that can be depicted as a bell-shaped curve (Fig. 11.16).

Polygenic traits are controlled by many genes and may be influenced by environmental factors. We observed previously (see Fig. 6.9) that the coat color of a Siamese cat is darker in color at the ears, nose, paws, and tail because an enzyme involved in the production of melanin is active only at a low temperature. Similarly, polygenic traits like prevalence of diabetes are influenced by environmental factors like nutrition.

Human Examples of Multifactorial Inheritance

Human skin color and height are examples of polygenic traits affected by the environment. For example, exposure to the sun can affect skin color, and nutrition can affect human height. Just how many pairs of alleles control skin color is not known, but a range in colors can be explained on the basis of just two pairs when *each capital letter contributes equally to the pigment in the skin.*

Genotypes	Phenotypes
AABB	Very dark
AABb or *AaBB*	Dark
AaBb or *AAbb* or *aaBB*	Medium brown
Aabb or *aaBb*	Light
aabb	Very light

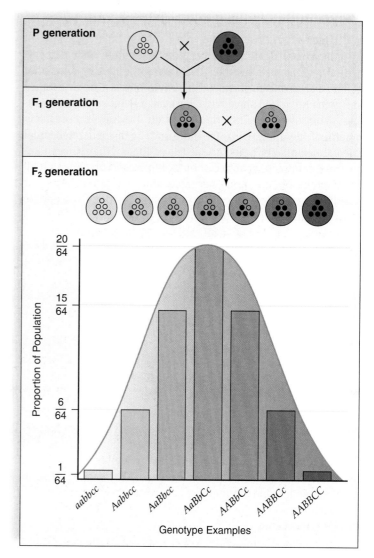

Figure 11.16 Polygenic inheritance. In polygenic inheritance, a number of pairs of genes control the trait. *Above:* Black dots and intensity of blue shading stand for the number of dominant alleles. *Below:* Orange shading shows the degree of environmental influences.

Eye color is also a polygenic trait. The amount of melanin deposited in the iris increases the darker color of the eye. Different eye colors from the brightest of blue to nearly black eyes are thought to be the result of two genes with alleles each interacting in an additive manner.

Many human disorders, such as cleft lip and/or palate, clubfoot, congenital dislocations of the hip, hypertension, diabetes, schizophrenia, and even allergies and cancers, are most likely due to the combined action of many genes plus environmental influences. In recent years, reports have surfaced that all sorts of behavioral traits, such as alcoholism, phobias, and even suicide, can be associated with particular genes.

The relative importance of genetic and environmental influences on the phenotype can vary, but in some instances the role of the environment is clear. For example, cardiovascular disease is more prevalent among those whose biological or adoptive parents have cardiovascular disease. Can you suggest environmental reasons for this correlation, based on your study of Chapter 3?

Many investigators are trying to determine what percentage of various traits is due to nature (inheritance) and what percentage is due to nurture (the environment). Some studies use twins separated since birth, because if identical twins in different environments share the same trait, the trait is most likely inherited. Identical twins are more similar in their intellectual talents, personality traits, and levels of lifelong happiness than are fraternal twins separated at birth. Biologists conclude that all behavioral traits are partly heritable, and that genes exert their effects by acting together in complex combinations susceptible to environmental influences.

Check Your Progress 11.3A

1. Interpret the genotype of the heterozygote if the inheritance pattern for a genetic disorder is shown to be incompletely dominant.
2. Examine the genotype of the child, the mother, and the possible genotypes of the father for a child with type O blood who is born to a mother with type A blood.

X-Linked Inheritance

The X and Y chromosomes in mammals determine the gender of the individual. Females are XX and males are XY. These chromosomes carry genes that control development and, in particular, if the Y chromosome contains an *SRY* gene, the embryo becomes a male. The term **X-linked** is used for genes that have nothing to do with gender, and yet they are carried on the X chromosome. The Y chromosome does not carry these genes and indeed carries very few genes.

This type of inheritance was discovered in the early 1900s by a group at Columbia University headed by Thomas Hunt Morgan. Morgan performed experiments with fruit flies, whose scientific name is *Drosophila melanogaster*. Fruit flies are even better subjects for genetic studies than garden peas. They can be easily and inexpensively raised in simple laboratory glassware; after mating, females lay hundreds of eggs during their lifetimes; and, the generation time is short, taking only about ten days from egg to adult. Fruit flies have a sex chromosome pattern similar to that of humans, and therefore Morgan's experiments with X-linked genes apply directly to humans.

Video Why a Guy Is a Guy

Morgan's Experiment

Morgan took a newly discovered mutant male with white eyes and crossed it with a red-eyed female:

	♀		♂
P	red-eyed	×	white-eyed
F₁	red-eyed		red-eyed

From these results, he knew that red eyes are the dominant characteristic and white eyes are the recessive characteristic. He then crossed the F₁ flies. In the F₂ generation, there was the expected

3 red-eyed : 1 white-eyed ratio, but it struck him as odd that all of the white-eyed flies were males:

	♀		♂
F₁ × F₁	red-eyed	×	red-eyed
F₂	red-eyed		1 red-eyed : 1 white-eyed

Obviously, a major difference between the male flies and the female flies was their sex chromosomes. Could it be possible that an allele for eye color was on the Y chromosome but not on the X? This idea could be quickly discarded because usually females have red eyes, and they have no Y chromosome. Perhaps an allele for eye color was on the X, but not on the Y, chromosome. Figure 11.17 indicates that this explanation would match the results obtained in the experiment. These results support the chromosome theory of inheritance by showing that the

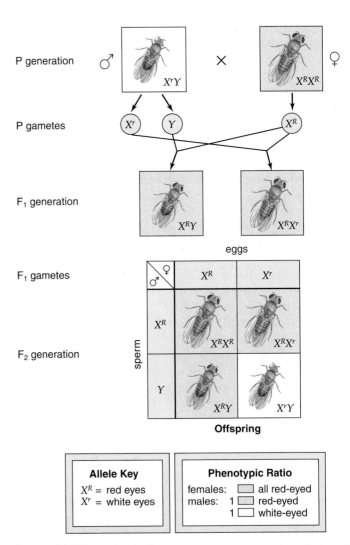

Figure 11.17 X-linked inheritance. Once researchers deduced that the alleles for red/white eye color are on the X chromosome in *Drosophila*, they were able to explain their experimental results. Males with white eyes in the F₂ generation inherit the recessive allele only from the female parent; they receive a Y chromosome lacking the allele for eye color from the male parent.

behavior of a specific allele corresponds exactly with that of a specific chromosome—the X chromosome in *Drosophila*.

Notice that X-linked alleles have a different pattern of inheritance than alleles that are on the autosomes because the Y chromosome is lacking for these alleles, and the inheritance of a Y chromosome cannot offset the inheritance of an X-linked recessive allele. For the same reason, males always receive an X-linked recessive mutant allele from the female parent—they receive only the Y chromosome from the male parent, and therefore sex-linked recessive traits appear much more frequently in males than in females.

Solving X-Linked Genetics Problems

Recall that when solving autosomal genetics problems, the allele key and genotypes can be represented as follows:

Allele key	Genotypes
L = long wings	LL, Ll
l = short wings	ll

When predicting inheritance of sex-linked traits, however, it is necessary to indicate the sex chromosomes of each individual. As noted in Figure 11.17, however, the allele key for an X-linked gene shows an allele attached to the X:

Allele key

X^R = red eyes
X^r = white eyes

The possible genotypes and phenotypes in both males and females are as follows:

Genotype	Phenotype
$X^R X^R$	red-eyed female
$X^R X^r$	red-eyed female
$X^r X^r$	white-eyed female
$X^R Y$	red-eyed male
$X^r Y$	white-eyed male

Notice that there are three possible genotypes for females but only two for males. Females can be heterozygous $X^R X^r$, in which case they are carriers. Carriers usually do not show a recessive abnormality, but they are capable of passing on a recessive allele for an abnormality. But unlike autosomal traits, males cannot be carriers for X-linked traits; if the dominant allele is on the single X chromosome, they show the dominant phenotype, and if the recessive allele is on the single X chromosome, they show the recessive phenotype. For this reason, males are considered **hemizygous** for X-linked traits, because a male only possesses one allele for the trait and, therefore, expresses whatever allele is present on the X chromosome.

We know that male fruit flies have white eyes when they receive the mutant recessive allele from the female parent. What is the inheritance pattern when females have white eyes? Females can have white eyes only when they receive a recessive allele from both parents.

Human X-Linked Disorders

Several X-linked recessive disorders occur in humans, including color blindness, Menkes syndrome, muscular dystrophy, adrenoleukodystrophy, and hemophilia.

Color Blindness. In humans, the receptors for color vision in the retina of the eyes are three different classes of cone cells. Only one type of pigment protein is present in each class of cone cell; there are blue-sensitive, red-sensitive, and green-sensitive cone cells. The allele for the blue-sensitive protein is autosomal, but the alleles for the red- and green-sensitive pigments are on the X chromosome. About 8% of Caucasian men have red-green color blindness. Most of these see brighter greens as tans, olive greens as browns, and reds as reddish browns. A few cannot tell reds from greens at all. They see only yellows, blues, blacks, whites, and grays.

Pedigrees can also reveal the unusual inheritance pattern seen in sex-linked traits. For example, the pedigree in Figure 11.18 shows the usual pattern of inheritance for color blindness. More males than females have the trait because recessive alleles on the X chromosome are expressed in males. The disorder often passes from grandfather to grandson through a carrier daughter.

Menkes Syndrome. Menkes syndrome, or kinky hair syndrome, is caused by a defective allele on the X chromosome. Normally, the gene product controls the movement of the metal

Figure 11.18 X-linked recessive pedigree. This pedigree for color blindness exemplifies the inheritance pattern of an X-linked recessive disorder. The list gives various ways of recognizing the X-linked recessive pattern of inheritance.

copper in and out of cells. The symptoms of Menkes syndrome are due to accumulation of copper in some parts of the body, and the lack of the metal in other parts.

Symptoms of Menkes syndrome include poor muscle tone, seizures, abnormally low body temperature, skeletal anomalies, and the characteristic brittle, steely hair associated with the disorder. Although the condition is relatively rare, affecting approximately 1 in 100,000, mostly males, the prognosis for people with Menkes syndrome is poor, and most individuals die within the first few years of life. In recent years, some people with Menkes syndrome have been treated with injections of copper directly underneath the skin, but with mixed results, and treatment must begin very early in life to be effective.

Muscular Dystrophy. Muscular dystrophy, as the name implies, is characterized by a wasting away of the muscles. The most common form, Duchenne muscular dystrophy, is X-linked and occurs in about 1 out of every 3,600 male births (Fig. 11.19). Symptoms, such as waddling gait, toe walking, frequent falls, and difficulty in rising, may appear as soon as the child starts to walk. Muscle weakness intensifies until the individual is confined to a wheelchair. Death usually occurs by age 20; therefore, affected males are rarely fathers. The recessive allele remains in the population through passage from carrier mother to carrier daughter.

The allele for Duchenne muscular dystrophy has been isolated, and it has been discovered that the absence of a protein called dystrophin causes the disorder. Much investigative work has determined that dystrophin is involved in the release of calcium from the sarcoplasmic reticulum in muscle fibers. The lack of dystrophin causes calcium to leak into the cell, which promotes the action of an enzyme that dissolves muscle fibers. When the body attempts to repair the tissue, fibrous tissue forms, and this cuts off the blood supply so that more and more cells die.

A test is now available to detect carriers of Duchenne muscular dystrophy. Also, various treatments have been tried. Immature muscle cells can be injected into muscles, and for every 100,000 cells injected, dystrophin production occurs in 30–40% of muscle fibers. The allele for dystrophin has been inserted into thigh muscle cells, and about 1% of these cells then produced dystrophin.

Adrenoleukodystrophy. Adrenoleukodystrophy, or ALD, is an X-linked recessive disorder due to the failure of a carrier protein to move either an enzyme or very long chain fatty acid (24–30 carbon atoms) into peroxisomes. As a result, these fatty acids are not broken down, and they accumulate inside the cell; the result is severe nervous system damage.

Children with ALD fail to develop properly after age 5, lose adrenal gland function, exhibit very poor coordination, and show a progressive loss of hearing, speech, and vision. The condition is usually fatal, with no known cure, but the onset and severity of symptoms in patients not yet showing symptoms may be mitigated by treatment with a mixture of lipids derived from olive oil. The disease was made well-known by the 1992 movie *Lorenzo's Oil*, detailing a mother's and father's determination to devise a treatment for their son who was suffering from ALD.

Hemophilia. About 1 in 10,000 males is a hemophiliac. There are two common types of hemophilia: Hemophilia A is due to the absence or minimal presence of a clotting factor known as factor VIII, and hemophilia B is due to the absence of clotting factor IX. Hemophilia is called the bleeder's disease because the affected person's blood either does not clot or clots very slowly. Although hemophiliacs bleed externally after an injury, they also bleed internally, particularly around joints. Hemorrhages can be stopped with transfusions of fresh blood (or plasma) or concentrates of the clotting protein. Also, clotting factors are now available as biotechnology products.

At the turn of the century, hemophilia was prevalent among the royal families of Europe, and all of the affected males could trace their ancestry to Queen Victoria of England. Of Queen Victoria's 26 grandchildren, four grandsons had hemophilia and four granddaughters were carriers. Because none of Queen Victoria's relatives were affected, it seems that the faulty allele she carried arose by mutation either in Victoria or in one of her parents. Her carrier daughters Alice and Beatrice introduced the allele into the ruling houses of Russia and Spain, respectively. Alexis, the last heir to the Russian throne before the Russian Revolution, was a hemophiliac. There are no hemophiliacs in the present British royal family because Victoria's eldest son, King Edward VII, did not receive the allele.

Check Your Progress   11.3B

1. Describe the possible genotypes if a homozygous red-eyed *Drosophila* female is crossed with a red-eyed male.
2. Explain the chances that a color-blind woman who is married to a man with normal vision will produce
   a. color-blind sons b. color-blind daughters c. carrier daughters.
3. Identify the genotype of all individuals involved in a cross between a brown-haired woman and a black-haired man that produce all brown-haired male offspring and all black-haired female offspring, assuming X-linkage.

Figure 11.19 Muscular dystrophy. In muscular dystrophy, an X-linked recessive disorder, calves enlarge because fibrous tissue develops as muscles waste away, due to lack of the protein dystrophin.

CONNECTING *the* CONCEPTS *with the* THEMES

Evolution	Nature of Science	Biological Systems
• Although humans usually produce small numbers of offspring, it is clear from years of research that Mendel's laws apply to humans in many instances.	• A good experimental design and careful data analysis allowed Mendel to discover his laws of inheritance.	• The work of Morgan and others showed that the sex chromosomes contain genes unrelated to gender.
• Good historical records of inheritance in large families, such as Mormon families, have shown a number of human genetic disorders are indeed controlled by a single allelic pair.	• Mendel was fortunate in that he chose to study an organism, namely the garden pea, whose observable traits are often determined by a single allelic pair.	• Geneticists later discovered that some human genetic diseases, such as hemophilia, are caused by faulty genes on the X chromosome.
• The persistence of such genetic diseases over evolutionary time may confer some biological benefit to humans. For example, heterozygous sickle-cell anemia individuals are more resistant to malaria, one of the world's most deadly diseases.	• In most cases, however, traits are determined by several genes or are affected by additional factors, such as the environment.	• With the help of Mendelian genetics, pedigree analysis, and statistics, scientists have been able to link many human diseases to specific genes on certain chromosomes.
	• In the future, emerging technologies will allow humans to sequence personal genomes, showing us the entirety of individual biological potential and providing a mechanism for customized medicine.	• Projects like the human genome project are beginning to decipher how genes affect the whole body, not just single traits.

Media Study Tools

www.mhhe.com/maderbiology11

Enhance your study of this chapter with study tools and practice tests. Also ask your instructor about the resources available through ConnectPlus, including the media-rich eBook, interactive learning tools, and animations.

Summarize

11.1 Gregor Mendel

Gregor Mendel used the garden pea as the subject in his genetic studies. In contrast to preceding plant breeders, his study involved nonblending traits of the garden pea. Mendel applied mathematics, followed the scientific method very closely, and kept careful records. His results supported a particulate theory of inheritance, effectively disproving the blending theory of inheritance.

11.2 Mendel's Laws

When Mendel crossed heterozygous plants with other heterozygous plants, he found that the recessive phenotype reappeared in about ¼ of the F_2 plants; there was a 3:1 phenotypic ratio. This allowed Mendel to propose his law of segregation, which states that the individual has two factors for each trait, and the factors segregate with equal probability into the gametes.

Mendel conducted two-trait crosses, in which the F_1 individuals showed both dominant characteristics, but there were four phenotypes among the F_2 offspring. (The actual phenotypic ratio was 9:3:3:1.) This allowed Mendel to deduce the law of independent assortment, which states that the members of one pair of factors separate independently of those of another pair. Therefore, all possible combinations of parental factors can occur in the gametes.

The laws of probability can be used to calculate the expected phenotypic ratio of a cross. A large number of offspring must be counted in order to observe the expected results, and to ensure that all possible types of sperm have fertilized all possible types of eggs, as is done in a Punnett square. The Punnett square uses the product law of probability to arrive at possible genotypes among the offspring, and then the sum law can be used to arrive at the phenotypic ratio.

Mendel also crossed the F_1 plants having the dominant phenotype with homozygous recessive plants. The 1:1 results indicated that the recessive factor was present in these F_1 plants (i.e., that they were heterozygous). Today, we call this a testcross, because it is used to test whether an individual showing the dominant characteristic is homozygous dominant or heterozygous. The two-trait testcross allows an investigator to test whether an individual showing two dominant characteristics is homozygous dominant for both traits or for one trait only, or is heterozygous for both traits.

Studies have shown that many human traits and genetic disorders can be explained on the basis of simple Mendelian inheritance. When studying human genetic disorders, biologists often construct pedigrees to show the pattern of inheritance of a characteristic within a family. The particular pattern indicates the manner in which a characteristic is inherited. Sample pedigrees for autosomal recessive and autosomal dominant patterns appear in Figures 11.10 and 11.11.

11.3 Extending the Range of Mendelian Genetics

Other patterns of inheritance have been discovered since Mendel's original contribution. For example, some genes have multiple alleles, although each individual organism has only two alleles, as in the inheritance of blood type in human beings. Inheritance of blood type also illustrates codominance. With incomplete dominance, the phenotype of F_1 individuals are intermediate between the parent phenotypes; this does not support the blending theory because the parent phenotypes reappear in F_2. With incomplete penetrance, some traits that are dominant may not be expressed due to unknown reasons.

In pleiotropy, one gene has multiple effects as with Marfan syndrome and sickle-cell disease. Polygenic traits are controlled by several genes that have an additive effect on the phenotype, resulting in quantitative variations within a population. A bell-shaped curve is seen because environmental influences bring about many intervening phenotypes, as in the inheritance of height in human beings. Skin color and eye color are also examples of polygenic inheritance (multiple genes plus the environment).

In *Drosophila*, as in humans, the sex chromosomes determine the sex of the individual, with XX being female and XY being male. Experimental support for the chromosome theory of inheritance came when Morgan and his group were able to determine that the gene for a trait unrelated to sex determination, the white-eyed allele in *Drosophila*, is on the X chromosome.

Alleles on the X chromosome are called X-linked alleles. Therefore, when doing X-linked genetics problems, it is the custom to indicate the sexes by using sex chromosomes and to indicate the alleles by superscripts attached to the X. The Y is blank because it does not carry these genes. Color blindness, Menkes syndrome, adrenoleukodystrophy, and hemophilia are X-linked recessive disorders in humans.

Key Terms

allele 196	law of segregation 196
autosome 201	locus 196
carrier 202	monohybrid cross 195
codominance 205	multiple alleles 205
dihybrid cross 198	phenotype 197
dominant allele 196	pleiotropy 206
family pedigree 204	polygenic inheritance 207
genotype 196	polygenic trait 207
hemizygous 209	Punnett square 200
heterozygous 196	recessive allele 196
homozygous 196	testcross 200
incomplete dominance 205	X-linked 208
incomplete penetrance 206	
law of independent assortment 198	

▓▓▓ Assess

Reviewing This Chapter

1. How did Mendel's procedure differ from that of his predecessors? What is his theory of inheritance called?   193
2. How does the F_2 of Mendel's one-trait cross refute the blending concept of inheritance? Using Mendel's one-trait cross as an example, trace his reasoning to arrive at the law of segregation.   195–96
3. Using Mendel's two-trait cross as an example, trace his reasoning to arrive at the law of independent assortment.   198

4. What are the two laws of probability, and how do they apply to a Punnett square?   200
5. What is a testcross, and when is it used?   200–01
6. How might you distinguish an autosomal dominant trait from an autosomal recessive trait when viewing a pedigree?   201–02
7. For autosomal recessive disorders, what are the chances of two carriers having an affected child?   202
8. For most autosomal dominant disorders, what are the chances of a heterozygote and a normal individual having an affected child?   202
9. Explain inheritance by multiple alleles. List the human blood types, and give the possible genotypes for each.   205
10. Explain the inheritance of incompletely dominant alleles and why this is not an example of blending inheritance.   205–06
11. Explain why traits controlled by polygenes show continuous variation and produce a distribution in the F_2 generation that follows a bell-shaped curve.   207
12. How do you recognize a pedigree for an X-linked recessive allele in human beings?   208–09

Testing Yourself

Choose the best answer for each question. For questions 1–4, match each item to those in the key.

KEY:
   a. 3:1
   b. 9:3:3:1
   c. 1:1
   d. 1:1:1:1
   e. 3:1:3:1

1. *TtYy* × *TtYy*
2. *Tt* × *Tt*
3. *Tt* × *tt*
4. *TtYy* × *ttyy*
5. Which of these could be a normal gamete?
   a. *GgRr*
   b. *GRr*
   c. *Gr*
   d. *GgR*
   e. None of these are correct.
6. Which of these properly describes a cross between an individual who is homozygous dominant for hairline but heterozygous for finger length, and an individual who is recessive for both characteristics? (*W* = widow's peak, *w* = straight hairline, *S* = short fingers, *s* = long fingers)
   a. *WwSs* × *WwSs*
   b. *WWSs* × *wwSs*
   c. *Ws* × *ws*
   d. *WWSs* × *wwss*
7. In peas, yellow seed (*Y*) is dominant over green seed (*y*). In the F_2 generation of a monohybrid cross that begins when a dominant homozygote is crossed with a recessive homozygote, you would expect
   a. three plants with yellow seeds to every plant with green seeds.
   b. plants with one yellow seed for every green seed.
   c. only plants with the genotype *Yy*.
   d. only plants that produce yellow seeds.
   e. Both c and d are correct.

8. In humans, pointed eyebrows (*B*) are dominant over smooth eyebrows (*b*). Mary's father has pointed eyebrows, but she and her mother have smooth. What is the genotype of the father?
   a. *BB*
   b. *Bb*
   c. *bb*
   d. *BbBb*
   e. Any one of these is correct.

9. In guinea pigs, smooth coat (*S*) is dominant over rough coat (*s*), and black coat (*B*) is dominant over white coat (*b*). In the cross *SsBb* × *SsBb*, how many of the offspring will have a smooth black coat on average?
   a. 9 only
   b. about ⁹⁄₁₆
   c. ¹⁄₁₆
   d. ⁶⁄₁₆
   e. ²⁄₆

10. In horses, *B* = black coat, *b* = brown coat, *T* = trotter, and *t* = pacer. A black trotter that has a brown pacer offspring would have which of the following genotypes?
    a. *BT*
    b. *BbTt*
    c. *bbtt*
    d. *BBtt*
    e. *BBTT*

11. In tomatoes, red fruit (*R*) is dominant over yellow fruit (*r*), and tallness (*T*) is dominant over shortness (*t*). A plant that is *RrTT* is crossed with a plant that is *rrTt*. What are the chances of an offspring possessing both recessive traits?
    a. none
    b. ½
    c. ¼
    d. ¾

12. In the cross *RrTt* × *rrtt*,
    a. all the offspring will be tall with red fruit.
    b. 75% (¾) will be tall with red fruit.
    c. 50% (½) will be tall with red fruit.
    d. 25% (¼) will be tall with red fruit.

13. A boy is color-blind (X-linked recessive) and has a straight hairline (autosomal recessive). Which could be the genotype of his mother?
    a. *bbww*   d. *XBXbWw*
    b. *XbYWw*   e. *XwXwBb*
    c. *bbXwXw*

14. Which of the following would you *not* find in a pedigree when a male has an X-linked recessive disorder?
    a. Neither parent has the disorder.
    b. Only males in the pedigree have the disorder.
    c. Only females in the pedigree have the disorder.
    d. The sons of a female with the disorder all have the disorder.
    e. Both a and c would not be seen.

For questions 15–17, match the statements to the items in the key.

KEY:
   a. multiple alleles
   b. polygenes
   c. pleiotropic gene

15. People with sickle-cell disease have many cardiovascular complications.

16. Although most people have an IQ of about 100, IQ generally ranges from about 50 to 150.

17. In humans, there are three possible alleles at the chromosomal locus that determine blood type.

18. Alice and Henry are at the opposite extremes for a polygenic trait. Their children will
    a. be bell-shaped.
    b. be a phenotype typical of a 9:3:3:1 ratio.
    c. have the middle phenotype between their two parents.
    d. look like one parent or the other.

19. Determine whether the characteristic possessed by the shaded squares (males) and circles (females) is an autosomal dominant, autosomal recessive, or X-linked recessive.

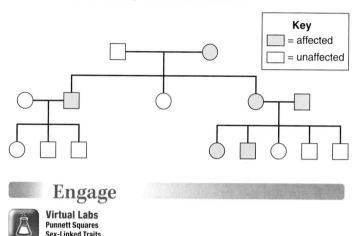

Key
☐ = affected
☐ = unaffected

Engage

Virtual Labs
Punnett Squares
Sex-Linked Traits

The virtual labs "Punnett Squares" and "Sex-linked Traits" both provide you with the ability to test your knowledge of Mendelian and sex-linked patterns of inheritance.

Thinking Scientifically

1. You want to determine whether a newly found *Drosophila* characteristic is dominant or recessive. Would you wait to cross this male fly with another of its own kind or cross it now with a fly that lacks the characteristic?

2. You want to test whether the leaf pattern of a plant is influenced by the amount of fertilizer in the environment. What would you do?

12

Molecular Biology of the Gene

BEFORE YOU BEGIN

Before beginning this chapter, take a few moments to review the following discussions.

Figures 3.18 and 3.20 What are the components of a nucleotide and the structure of the DNA molecule?

Figure 11.4 How are genes organized on chromosomes, and how are alleles related to genes?

Section 11.2 What is the relationship between genotype and phenotype?

The diversity of life is dependent on gene activity.

All life on Earth has the four bases of DNA—A, G, C, and T—in common. Considering up to 1.8 million different species have been discovered and named, with only a fraction of the total discovered, what makes one species different from another? It is largely due to differences in the DNA sequences that make up genes within each species.

How do DNA sequence differences determine the uniqueness of a species—for example, whether an individual is a snow leopard, a crab, or a flower? Or the variation within a species, such as whether a human has blue, brown, or hazel eyes? The diversity of life is based on the flow of genetic information from genes to proteins to observable traits, that is, from genotype to phenotype. This expression of genes is responsible for producing proteins, the molecules that carry out life functions every day.

As DNA sequences change via mutation and other mechanisms over evolutionary time, so do the proteins that are made from genes. Likewise, as proteins change, so do the life forms and diversity we see on Earth. Given that different mixtures of genes and alleles can be inherited over generations, and that life has been in existence for millions of generations, it is not surprising to see how diverse life has become.

As you read through the chapter, think about the following questions:

1. How does the flow of genetic information from DNA to protein to trait work?
2. What mechanisms are in place to ensure that genetic information is accurately expressed?
3. How might the expression of a gene change in response to environmental conditions?

FOLLOWING *the* THEMES

CHAPTER 12 MOLECULAR BIOLOGY OF THE GENE

UNIT 2 GENETIC BASIS OF LIFE		
	Evolution	Changes in DNA sequence produce different proteins that change organismal structure and function.
	Nature of Science	Research in gene expression enables scientists to discover new, effective ways to treat disease.
	Biological Systems	The flow of genetic information in biological systems is highly regulated and responsive to environmental changes.

12.1 The Genetic Material

Learning Outcomes

Upon completion of this section, you should be able to

1. Describe the properties a substance must possess in order to serve as the genetic material.
2. Examine how historical researchers demonstrated that DNA was the genetic material.
3. Explain the chemical structure of DNA as defined by the Watson and Crick model.

The middle of the twentieth century was an exciting period of scientific discovery. On one hand, geneticists were busy determining that *DNA (deoxyribonucleic acid)* is the genetic material of living things. On the other hand, biochemists were in a frantic race to describe the structure of DNA. The classic experiments performed during this era set the stage for an explosion in our knowledge of modern molecular biology.

When researchers began their work, they knew that the genetic material must be

1. able to *store information* that pertains to the development, structure, and metabolic activities of the cell or organism;
2. stable so that it *can be replicated* with high accuracy during cell division and be transmitted from generation to generation;
3. able to *undergo rare changes* called mutations [L. *muta*, change] that provide the genetic variability required for evolution to occur.

This chapter will show, as the researchers of the twentieth century did, that DNA can fulfill these functions.

Transformation of Bacteria

During the late 1920s, the bacteriologist Frederick Griffith (1879-1941) was attempting to develop a vaccine against *Streptococcus pneumoniae* (pneumococcus), which causes pneumonia in mammals. In 1931, he performed a classic experiment with the bacterium. He noticed that when these bacteria are grown on culture plates, some, called S strain bacteria, produce shiny, smooth colonies, and others, called R strain bacteria, produce colonies that have a rough appearance. Under the microscope, S strain bacteria have a capsule (mucous coat) that makes them smooth but R strain bacteria do not.

When Griffith injected mice with the S strain of bacteria, the mice died, and when he injected mice with the R strain, the mice did not die (Fig. 12.1). In an effort to determine whether the capsule alone was responsible for the virulence (ability to kill) of the S strain bacteria, he injected mice with heat-killed S strain bacteria. The mice did not die.

Finally, Griffith injected the mice with a mixture of heat-killed S strain and live R strain bacteria. Most unexpectedly, the mice died—and living S strain bacteria were recovered from the bodies! Griffith concluded that some substance necessary for the bacteria to produce a capsule and be virulent must have passed from the dead S strain bacteria to the living R strain bacteria so that the R strain bacteria were *transformed* (Fig. 12.1*d*). This change in the phenotype of the R strain bacteria must be due to a change in their genotype. Indeed, couldn't the transforming substance that passed from S strain to R strain be genetic material? Reasoning such as this prompted investigators at the time to begin looking for the transforming substance to determine the chemical nature of the genetic material.

DNA: The Transforming Substance

By the time the next group of investigators, led by Oswald Avery (1877-1955) in the 1940s, began their work, it was known that the genes are on the chromosomes and that the chromosomes contain both proteins and nucleic acids. Investigators were having a much heated debate about whether protein or DNA was the genetic material. Many thought that the protein component of chromosomes must be the genetic material because proteins contain up to 20 different amino acids that can be sequenced in

a. Injected live S strain has capsule and causes mice to die.

b. Injected live R strain has no capsule and mice do not die.

c. Injected heat-killed S strain does not cause mice to die.

d. Injected heat-killed S strain plus live R strain causes mice to die. Live S strain is withdrawn from dead mice.

capsule

Figure 12.1 Griffith's transformation experiment. **a.** Encapsulated S strain is virulent and kills mice. **b.** Nonencapsulated R strain is not virulent and does not kill mice. **c.** Heat-killed S strain bacteria do not kill mice. **d.** If heat-killed S strain and R strain are both injected into mice, they die because the R strain bacteria have been transformed into the virulent S strain.

any particular way. On the other hand, nucleic acids—DNA and RNA—contain only four types of nucleotides as basic building blocks. Some argued that DNA did not have enough variability to be able to store information and be the genetic material.

In 1944, after 16 years of research, Oswald Avery and his coinvestigators, Colin MacLeod and Maclyn McCarty, published a paper demonstrating that the transforming substance that allows *Streptococcus* to produce a capsule and be virulent is DNA. This meant that DNA is the genetic material. Here is what they found out:

1. DNA from S strain bacteria causes R strain bacteria to be transformed so that they can produce a capsule and be virulent.
2. The addition of DNase, an enzyme that digests DNA, prevents transformation from occurring. This supports the hypothesis that DNA is the genetic material.
3. The molecular weight of the transforming substance is large. This suggests the possibility of genetic variability.
4. The addition of enzymes that degrade proteins has no effect on the transforming substance nor does RNase, an enzyme that digests RNA. This shows that neither protein nor RNA is the genetic material.

These experiments showed that DNA is the transforming substance and, therefore, the genetic material. Although some scientists remained skeptical, many felt that the evidence for DNA being the genetic material was overwhelming.

An experiment by Alfred Hershey and Martha Chase in the early 1950s helped to firmly establish DNA as the genetic material. Hershey and Chase used a virus called a T phage, composed of radioactively labeled DNA and capsid coat proteins, to infect *E. coli* bacteria. They discovered that the radioactive tracers for DNA, but not protein, ended up inside the bacterial cells, causing them to become transformed. Since only the genetic material could have caused this transformation, Hershey and Chase determined that DNA must be the genetic material.

Animation Hershey and Chase Experiment

Transformation of Organisms Today

Because the code for living things is based on the same four nucleic acid bases of A, G, C, and T, and genes are made from this code, it is conceivable to take genes from one organism and put them into another. Transformation of organisms, resulting in *genetically modified organisms* (GMOs), is an invaluable tool in modern biotechnology today. As discussed further in the next chapter, transformation of bacteria and other organisms has resulted in commercial products that are used every day.

Early biotechnologists seeking a dramatic way to show the possibility of gene transfer between different organisms took a jellyfish gene that codes for a green fluorescent protein (GFP) and started transforming different organisms with it. When this gene is transferred to another organism, the organism glows in the dark! (Fig. 12.2.) The basic technique is relatively simple. First, isolate the jellyfish gene and then transfer it to a bacterium, or the embryo of a plant, pig, or mouse. The result is a bioluminescent organism.

Figure 12.2 Transformation of organisms. When bacteria, plants, pigs, and mice are genetically transformed with a gene from the jellyfish *Aequorea victoria* for green fluorescent protein (GFP), these organisms glow in the dark.

Because living organisms are coded by the same four bases, genes should theoretically have no difficulty crossing the species barrier. Mammalian genes can potentially be transferred to bacteria, and an invertebrate gene, such as the GFP gene, can be transferred to a bacterium, plant, or animal. Although it is possible and relatively easy to perform, cross-species gene transfer does not always result in the host organism producing the new protein because of the innate complexity of each species.

Animation
Bacterial
Transformation

The Structure of DNA

By the early 1950s, DNA was widely accepted as the genetic material of living things. However. the structure of DNA was not known. How can a molecule with only four different nucleotides produce the great diversity of life on Earth?

To understand the structure of DNA, we need to understand how the bases in DNA are composed. Investigators knew that DNA contains four different types of nucleotides: two with *purine* bases, **adenine (A)** and **guanine (G),** which have a double ring; and two with *pyrimidine* bases, **thymine (T)** and **cytosine (C),** which have a single ring (Fig. 12.3a, b). Erwin Chargaff used new chemical techniques developed in the 1940s to analyze in detail the base content of DNA.

A sample of Chargaff's data is seen in Figure 12.3c. You can see that while some species—*E. coli* and *Zea mays* (corn), for example—do have approximately 25% of each type of nucleotide, most do not. Further, the percentage of each type of nucleotide differs from species to species. Therefore, the nucleotide content of DNA is not fixed across species, and DNA does have the *variability* between species required for it to be the genetic material.

Within each species, however, DNA was found to have the *constancy* required of the genetic material—that is, all members of a species have the same base composition. Also, the percentage of A always equals the percentage of T, and the percentage of G equals the percentage of C. It follows that if the percentage of A + G equals 40%, then the percentage of T + C would equal 60%. (Do you see why?) These relationships are called Chargaff's rules.

Chargaff's rules:

1. The amount of A, T, G, and C in DNA varies from species to species.
2. In each species, the amount of A = T and the amount of G = C.

a. Purine nucleotides

b. Pyrimidine nucleotides

DNA Composition in Various Species (%)			
Species	**A**	**T**	**G**	**C**
Homo sapiens (human)	31.0	31.5	19.1	18.4
Drosophila melanogaster (fruit fly)	27.3	27.6	22.5	22.5
Zea mays (corn)	25.6	25.3	24.5	24.6
Neurospora crassa (fungus)	23.0	23.3	27.1	26.6
Escherichia coli (bacterium)	24.6	24.3	25.5	25.6
Bacillus subtilis (bacterium)	28.4	29.0	21.0	21.6

c. Chargaff's data

Figure 12.3 Nucleotide composition of DNA. All nucleotides contain phosphate, a 5-carbon sugar, and a nitrogen-containing base. In DNA, the sugar is called deoxyribose because it lacks an oxygen atom in the 2′ position, compared to ribose. The nitrogen-containing bases are **(a)** the purines adenine and guanine, which have a double ring, and **(b)** the pyrimidines thymine and cytosine, which have a single ring. **c.** Chargaff's data show that the DNA of various species differs. For example, in humans the A and T percentages are about 31%, but in fruit flies these percentages are about 27%. Note that by convention, the carbon atoms in the sugar rings are labeled with a number and a prime symbol to distinguish them from the carbon atoms in the base, which are labeled with a number only (numbers in bases not shown).

Although only one of four bases is possible at each nucleotide position in DNA, the sheer number of bases and the length of most DNA molecules is more than sufficient to provide for variability. For example, it has been calculated that each human chromosome typically contains about 140 million base pairs. This provides for a staggering number of possible sequences of nucleotides. Because any of the four possible nucleotides can be present at each nucleotide position, the total number of possible nucleotide sequences is $4^{(140 \times 10^6)}$ or $4^{140,000,000}$. No wonder each species has its own unique base percentages!

X-Ray Diffraction of DNA

Rosalind Franklin (Fig. 12.4*a*), a researcher at King's College in London, studied the structure of DNA using X-rays. She found that if a concentrated, viscous solution of DNA is made, it can be separated into fibers. Under the right conditions, the fibers are enough like a crystal (a solid substance whose atoms are arranged in a definite manner) that when X-rayed, an X-ray diffraction pattern results (Fig. 12.4*b*).

The X-ray diffraction pattern of DNA shows that DNA is a double helix. The helical shape is indicated by the crossed (X) pattern in the center of the photograph in Figure 12.4*c*. The dark portions at the top and bottom of the photograph indicate that some portion of the helix is repeated. Maurice H. F. Wilkins, a colleague of Franklin's, showed one of her crystallographic patterns to James Watson, who immediately grasped its significance.

Video DNA Dark Lady

The Watson and Crick Model

James Watson, an American, was on a postdoctoral fellowship at Cavendish Laboratories in Cambridge, England, and while there he began to work with the biophysicist Francis H. C. Crick. Using the data provided from X-ray diffraction and other sources, they constructed a model of DNA for which they received a Nobel Prize in 1962.

Based on previous work of other scientists, Watson and Crick knew that DNA is a polymer of nucleotides, but they did not know how the nucleotides were arranged within the molecule. However, they deduced that DNA is a **double helix** with sugar-phosphate backbones on the outside and paired bases on the inside. This arrangement fits the mathematical measurements provided by Franklin's X-ray diffraction data for the spacing between the base pairs (0.34 nm) and for a complete turn of the double helix (3.4 nm).

According to Watson and Crick's model, the two DNA strands of the double helix are *antiparallel*, meaning the sugar-phosphate groups that are chained together to make each strand are oriented in opposite directions. As explained on page 217, each nucleotide possesses a phosphate group located at the 5′ position of the sugar. Nucleotides are joined together by linking the 5′ phosphate of one nucleotide to a free hydroxyl (−OH) located at the 3′ position on the sugar of the preceding nucleotide, giving the molecule directionality. Antiparallel simply means that while one DNA strand runs 5′ to 3′, the other strand runs in a parallel but opposite direction.

Figure 12.4 X-ray diffraction of DNA.   **a.** Rosalind Franklin, 1920–1958. **b.** When a crystal is X-rayed, the way in which the beam is diffracted reflects the pattern of the molecules in the crystal. The closer together two repeating structures are in the crystal, the farther from the center the beam is diffracted. **c.** The diffraction pattern of DNA produced by Rosalind Franklin. The crossed (X) pattern in the center told investigators that DNA is a helix, and the dark portions at the top and the bottom told them that some feature is repeated over and over. Watson and Crick determined that this feature was the hydrogen-bonded bases.

This model also agreed with Chargaff's rules, which states that A = T and G = C. Figure 12.5 shows that A is hydrogen-bonded to T, and G is hydrogen-bonded to C. This so-called **complementary base pairing** means that a purine (large, two-ring base) is always bonded to a pyrimidine (smaller, one-ring base). This antiparallel pairing arrangement of the two strands ensures that the bases are oriented properly so that they can interact. The consistent spacing between the two strands of the DNA was detected by Franklin's X-ray diffraction pattern, because two pyrimidines together are too narrow, and two purines together are too wide (Fig. 12.5).

The information stored within DNA must always be read in the 5′ to 3′ direction. Thus, a DNA strand is usually replicated in a 5′ to 3′ direction.

Check Your Progress   12.1

1. Discuss how it is possible to take a gene from one organism and express it in another organism.
2. Explain the major features of DNA structure.

Figure 12.5 Watson and Crick model of DNA.
a. Space-filling model of DNA. **b.** The double helix molecules. **c.** The two strands of the molecule are antiparallel. **d.** James Watson (*left*) and Francis Crick (*right*) deduced the molecular configuration of DNA.

12.2 Replication of DNA

Learning Outcomes

Upon completion of this section, you should be able to

1. Explain why the replication of DNA is semiconservative.
2. Examine the steps of DNA replication.
3. Contrast DNA replication in eukaryotes and prokaryotes.

The term **DNA replication** refers to the process of copying a DNA molecule. Following replication, there is usually an exact copy of the parental DNA double helix. As soon as Watson and Crick developed their double-helix model, they commented, "It has not escaped our notice that the specific pairing we have postulated immediately suggests a possible copying mechanism for the genetic material."

A **template** is most often a mold used to produce a shape complementary to itself. During DNA replication, each DNA strand of the parental double helix serves as a template for a new strand in a daughter molecule (Fig. 12.6). DNA replication is termed **semiconservative replication** because each daughter DNA double helix contains an old strand from the parental DNA double helix and a new strand.

> **Animation**
> Meselson and
> Stahl Experiment

Replication requires the following steps:

1. *Unwinding.* The old strands that make up the parental DNA molecule are unwound and "unzipped" (i.e., the weak hydrogen bonds between the paired bases are broken). A special enzyme called helicase unwinds the molecule.
2. *Complementary base pairing.* New free nucleotides, always present in the nucleus, are paired with nucleotides on the parental strands, A with T, and G with C.
3. *Joining.* The complementary nucleotides paired with the parental strands are connected to each other to form a connected chain. Each daughter DNA molecule now contains an old strand and a newly synthesized strand.

Steps 2 and 3 are carried out by an enzyme complex called **DNA polymerase.** DNA polymerase works in the test tube as well as in cells.

In Figure 12.6, the backbones of the parental DNA molecule are blue, and each base is given a particular color. Following replication, the daughter molecules each have a green backbone (new strand) and a blue backbone (old strand). Because A pairs with T, and G pairs with C, A daughter DNA double helix has the same sequence of bases as the parental DNA double helix had originally. Although we have described DNA replication simply here, it is actually a complicated process. Some of the more precise molecular events are discussed in the Biological Systems feature on page 221.

> **Animation**
> DNA Replication

You may recall from Chapters 10 and 11 that DNA must be copied before mitosis or meiosis can begin. Because the goal of these processes is to create either an exact cell copy (mitosis) or to make a gamete for reproduction (meiosis), in either case you have to double the DNA before you can separate it during cell division. DNA replication must occur before a cell can divide. Cancer, which is characterized by rapid, uncontrolled cell division, is sometimes treated with chemotherapeutic drugs that mimic one of the four nucleotides in DNA. When these are mistakenly used by the cancer cells to synthesize DNA, replication stops and the cells die off.

region of parental DNA double helix

DNA polymerase enzyme

region of replication: new nucleotides are pairing with those of parental strands

region of completed replication

old strand   new strand

daughter DNA double helix

new strand   old strand

daughter DNA double helix

Figure 12.6 Semiconservative replication (simplified). After the DNA double helix unwinds, each parental strand serves as a template for the formation of the new daughter strands. Complementary free nucleotides hydrogen bond to a matching base (e.g., A with T; G with C) in each parental strand, and are joined to form a complete daughter strand. Two helices, each with a daughter and parental strand, are produced following replication.

THEME Biological Systems

Aspects of DNA Replication

DNA replication is an example of a complex, highly regulated biological system that requires many parts in order to function properly.

During replication, DNA polymerase needs a place to start joining new nucleotides together. In this case, it recognizes the –OH chemical group at the 3' end of an existing nucleic acid chain, which can be DNA or RNA, and it begins synthesiz-

ing from there. During DNA replication, an RNA-producing enzyme makes a short primer that has the necessary 3' –OH group on the end. DNA polymerase recognizes that target and begins DNA synthesis, allowing new nucleotides to form complementary base pairs with the old strand and connecting the new nucleotides together in a chain.

3 As a helicase enzyme unwinds DNA, it creates two replication forks that move away from each other. Each of the parental strands in a fork is accessible for complementary base pairing with new nucleotides and therefore synthesis of a new strand. (Binding proteins coat the newly formed, single-stranded regions and prevent them from reattaching to each other.)

The parental strands are antiparallel to each other, and each of the new daughter strands must also be antiparallel to their matching parental strand—which creates a problem. **4** The new strand that gets made in the same direction as the fork is moving is called the leading strand. The other new strand in the fork must be synthesized in a direction opposite fork movement, which requires DNA polymerase to periodically start and stop. This strand is called the lagging strand. **5** Replication of this lagging strand is therefore made in segments called **6** Okazaki fragments, after the Japanese scientist Reiji Okazaki, who discovered them.

Replication is complete only when the RNA primers are removed. This works out well for the lagging strand. While checking to make sure bases are properly matched up (proofreading), DNA polymerase removes the RNA primers and replaces them with the proper DNA nucleotides. **7** Another enzyme, called DNA ligase, joins the fragments, creating a seamless DNA molecule.

However, in eukaryotic organisms, which have linear chromosomes, there is no way for DNA polymerase to replicate all the way to the 5' ends of both new strands after RNA primers are removed. This means that the DNA in each chromosome can get shorter for each cycle of replication. The ends of the DNA in eukaryotic chromosomes have a special nucleotide sequence called a telomere that is repeated a number of times. **Telomeres** do not code for proteins and use a repeat sequence such as TTAGGG.

Mammalian cells grown in a culture have a built-in lifespan; they can divide about 50 times before they stop. The loss of telomeres apparently signals the cell to stop dividing. Ordinarily, telomeres are maintained at their proper length by an enzyme called telomerase. Misfunctional telomerase can result in chromosome shortening, leading to premature aging and loss of cellular function. Thus, controlling telomerase activity is important to normal cell function. As you might expect, telomerase is often mistakenly turned on in cancer cells, which in effect enables them to divide indefinitely.

Questions to Consider

1. What are some potential mechanisms of regulating DNA replication?
2. How might we repair DNA when errors in replication are made?

3D Animation DNA Replication Fork

3D Animation Discontinuous Synthesis

3D Animation DNA Synthesis

OH ← **P** is attached here
base is attached here

5' CH₂

4' C O OH ←

H   H H   C 1'

H   H

3' C —— C 2'

OH   H

1

Deoxyribose molecule

5' end

2 DNA polymerase attaches a new nucleotide to the 3' carbon of the previous nucleotide.

P

P   A ---- T

P

P

P   G ---- C

3' end

P   C ---- G   P

P   T ---- A   P

P   C ---- G   P

3' end   5' end   P
template strand   new strand

Direction of replication

5'
3'

template strand

4 leading new strand

3'

DNA polymerase

3 helicase at replication fork

3'

5'

parental DNA helix

template strand

6 Okazaki fragment

RNA primer

5 lagging strand

5'

3'

7 DNA ligase

DNA polymerase

Replication fork introduces complications

Figure 12A More detailed model of DNA replication.

Prokaryotic Versus Eukaryotic Replication

The process of DNA replication is distinctly different in prokaryotic and eukaryotic cells, although many of these organisms' basic functions are similar (Fig. 12.7).

Prokaryotic DNA Replication

Bacteria have a single circular loop chromosome whose DNA must be replicated before the cell divides. In some circular DNA molecules, replication moves around the DNA molecule in one direction only. In others, as shown in Figure 12.7*a*, replication occurs in two directions. The process always occurs in the 5′ to 3′ direction.

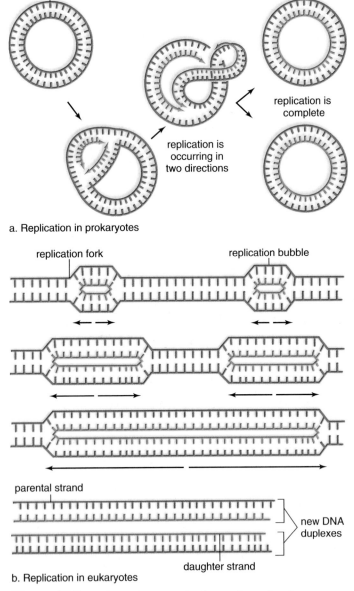

a. Replication in prokaryotes

parental strand

new DNA duplexes

daughter strand

b. Replication in eukaryotes

Figure 12.7 Prokaryotic versus eukaryotic replication. a. In prokaryotes, replication can occur in two directions at once because the DNA molecule is circular. **b.** In eukaryotes, replication occurs at numerous replication bubbles, each with two forks. The forks move away from each other until they meet again and the two new daughter helices have been completed.

The process begins at the *origin of replication*, a specific site on the bacterial chromosome. The strands are separated and unwound, and a DNA polymerase enzyme binds to each side of the opening and begins the copying process. When the two DNA polymerases meet at a termination region, replication is halted, and the two copies of the chromosome are separated.

Bacterial cells require about 40 minutes to replicate the complete chromosome. Because bacterial cells are able to divide as often as once every 20 minutes, it is possible for a new round of DNA replication to begin even before the previous round is completed!

Eukaryotic DNA Replication

In eukaryotes, DNA replication begins at numerous origins of replication along the length of the linear chromosome, and the so-called replication bubbles spread bidirectionally until they meet. Notice in Figure 12.7*b* that there is a V shape wherever DNA is being replicated. This is called a **replication fork.**

The chromosomes of eukaryotes are long, making replication a more time-consuming process. Eukaryotes replicate their DNA at a slower rate—500 to 5,000 base pairs per minute—but there are many individual origins of replication to accelerate the process. Therefore, eukaryotic cells complete the replication of the diploid amount of DNA (in humans, over 6 billion base pairs) in a matter of hours!

The linear chromosomes of eukaryotes also pose another problem: DNA polymerase is unable to replicate the ends of the chromosomes. The ends of eukaryotic chromosomes are composed of telomeres, which are short DNA sequences that are repeated over and over. Telomeres are not copied by DNA polymerase; rather, they are added by an enzyme called telomerase, which adds the correct number of repeats after the chromosome is replicated. In stem cells, this process preserves the ends of the chromosomes and prevents the loss of DNA after successive rounds of replication. Unregulated telomerase activity can negatively affect cell function, as is seen with uncontrolled cell division in cancer cells.

Accuracy of Replication

A DNA polymerase is very accurate and makes a mistake approximately once per 100,000 base pairs at most. This error rate, however, would result in many errors accumulating over the course of several cell divisions. DNA polymerase is also capable of checking for accuracy, or proofreading the daughter strand it is making. It can recognize a mismatched nucleotide and remove it from a daughter strand by reversing direction and removing several nucleotides. Once it has removed the mismatched nucleotide, it changes direction again and resumes making DNA. Overall, the error rate for the bacterial DNA polymerase is only one in 100 million base pairs!

Check Your Progress   12.2

1. Explain the three major steps in DNA replication.
2. Compare DNA replication in prokaryotes and eukaryotes.
3. Examine how eukaryotic cells use telomerase to fully copy linear chromosomes.

12.3 The Genetic Code of Life

Learning Outcomes

Upon completion of this section, you should be able to

1. Explain the central dogma of molecular biology.
2. Determine the amino acid sequence specified by an mRNA sequence.

Evidence began to mount in the 1900s that metabolic disorders can be inherited. An English physician, Sir Archibald Garrod, called them "inborn errors of metabolism." Investigators George Beadle and Edward Tatum, working with red bread mold, proposed what they called the "one gene, one enzyme hypothesis," based on the observation that a defective gene caused a defective enzyme.

This and many other examples illustrate the flow of genetic information from DNA to RNA to protein to an observed trait. We now turn our attention to the transfer of information from DNA to RNA, the next component in the system.

RNA Carries the Information

Like DNA, *RNA (ribonucleic acid)* is a polymer composed of nucleotides. The nucleotides in RNA, however, contain the sugar ribose and the bases adenine (A), cytosine (C), guanine (G), and **uracil (U).** In RNA, the base uracil replaces the thymine found in DNA. Finally, RNA is single stranded and does not form a double helix in the same manner as DNA (Table 12.1 and Fig. 12.8).

Table 12.1 RNA Structure Compared to DNA Structure

	RNA	DNA
Sugar	Ribose	Deoxyribose
Bases	Adenine, guanine, uracil, cytosine	Adenine, guanine, thymine, cytosine
Strands	Single stranded	Double stranded with base pairing
Helix	No	Yes

There are three major classes of RNA. Each class of RNA has its own unique size, shape, and function in protein synthesis.

Messenger RNA (mRNA) takes a message from DNA in the nucleus to the ribosomes in the cytoplasm.

Transfer RNA (tRNA) transfers amino acids to the ribosomes.

Ribosomal RNA (rRNA), along with ribosomal proteins, makes up the ribosomes, where polypeptides are synthesized.

The Genetic Code

In the genetic flow of information, two major steps are needed to convert the information stored in DNA into a protein that supports body function (Fig. 12.9). First, the DNA undergoes **transcription** [L. *trans*, across, and *scriptio*, a writing], a process by which an RNA molecule is produced based on a DNA template. DNA is transcribed, or copied base by base, into mRNA, tRNA, and rRNA.

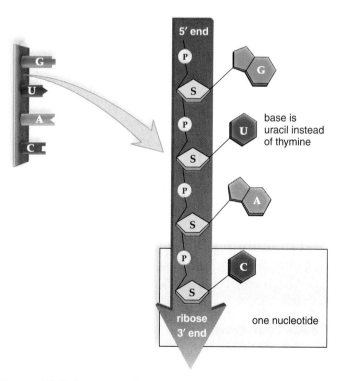

Figure 12.8 Structure of RNA. Like DNA, RNA is a polymer of nucleotides. RNA, however, is single stranded, the pentose sugar (S) is ribose, and uracil replaces thymine as one of the bases.

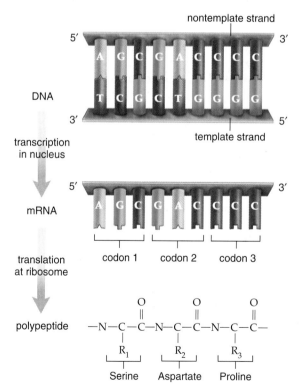

Figure 12.9 The central dogma of molecular biology. One strand of DNA acts as a template for mRNA synthesis, and the sequence of bases in mRNA determines the sequence of amino acids in a polypeptide.

Second, during **translation** [L. *trans*, across, and *latus*, carry or bear], the mRNA transcript is read by a ribosome and converted into the sequence of amino acids in a polypeptide. Like a translator who understands two languages, the cell changes a nucleotide sequence into an amino acid sequence. Together, the flow of information from DNA to RNA to protein to trait is known as the **central dogma** of molecular biology.

Now that we know that the DNA sequence within a gene is transcribed into an RNA molecule, and, for genes that code for proteins, the mRNA sequence determines the sequence of amino acids in a protein, it becomes necessary to identify the specific **genetic code** for each of the 20 amino acids found in proteins. Although scientists knew that DNA somehow directed protein production, they did not initially know specifically how the code was translated. This discovery was made in the 1960s.

Finding the Genetic Code

Logically, the genetic code would have to be at least a **triplet code**; that is, each coding unit, or **codon,** would need to be made up of three nucleotides. The reason is that fewer nucleotides would not provide sufficient variety to encode 20 different amino acids.

In 1961, Marshall Nirenberg and J. Heinrich Matthei performed an experiment that laid the groundwork for cracking the genetic code. First, they found that a cellular enzyme could be used to construct a synthetic RNA (one that does not occur in cells), and then they found that the synthetic RNA polymer could be translated in a test tube that contains the cytoplasmic contents of a cell. Their first synthetic RNA was composed only of uracil, and the protein that resulted was composed only of the amino acid phenylalanine. Therefore, the mRNA codon for phenylalanine was known to be UUU. Later, they were able to translate just three nucleotides at a time; in that way, it was possible to assign an amino acid to each of the mRNA codons (Fig. 12.10).

Like the periodic table and other major works, the genetic code seen in Figure 12.10 is a masterpiece of scientific discovery because it is a key that unlocks the very basis of biological life. Here are some of its features:

1. The genetic code is *degenerate*. This term means that most amino acids have more than one codon; leucine, serine, and arginine have six different codons, for example. The degeneracy of the code helps protect against potentially harmful mutations.
2. The genetic code is *unambiguous*. Each triplet codon has only one meaning.
3. The code has *start and stop signals*. There is only one start signal, but there are three stop signals.

The Code Is Universal

With a few exceptions, the genetic code (Fig. 12.10) is universal to all living things. In 1979, however, researchers discovered that the genetic code used by mammalian mitochondria and chloroplasts differs slightly from the more familiar genetic code.

First Base	Second Base				Third Base
	U	C	A	G	
U	UUU phenylalanine	UCU serine	UAU tyrosine	UGU cysteine	U
	UUC phenylalanine	UCC serine	UAC tyrosine	UGC cysteine	C
	UUA leucine	UCA serine	UAA *stop*	UGA *stop*	A
	UUG leucine	UCG serine	UAG *stop*	UGG tryptophan	G
C	CUU leucine	CCU proline	CAU histidine	CGU arginine	U
	CUC leucine	CCC proline	CAC histidine	CGC arginine	C
	CUA leucine	CCA proline	CAA glutamine	CGA arginine	A
	CUG leucine	CCG proline	CAG glutamine	CGG arginine	G
A	AUU isoleucine	ACU threonine	AAU asparagine	AGU serine	U
	AUC isoleucine	ACC threonine	AAC asparagine	AGC serine	C
	AUA isoleucine	ACA threonine	AAA lysine	AGA arginine	A
	AUG *(start)* methionine	ACG threonine	AAG lysine	AGG arginine	G
G	GUU valine	GCU alanine	GAU aspartate	GGU glycine	U
	GUC valine	GCC alanine	GAC aspartate	GGC glycine	C
	GUA valine	GCA alanine	GAA glutamate	GGA glycine	A
	GUG valine	GCG alanine	GAG glutamate	GGG glycine	G

Figure 12.10 Messenger RNA codons. Notice that in this chart, each of the codons (in boxes) is composed of three letters representing the first base, second base, and third base. For example, find the box where C for the first base and A for the second base intersect. You will see that U, C, A, or G can be the third base. The bases CAU and CAC are codons for histidine; the bases CAA and CAG are codons for glutamine.

The universal nature of the genetic code provides strong evidence that all living things share a common evolutionary heritage. Because the same genetic code is used by all living things, it is possible to transfer genes from one organism to another. Many commercial and medicinal products, such as human insulin, can be produced in this manner. Earlier, we showed that the gene for GFP could be transferred from jellyfish to a number of other organisms to cause a fluorescent green color (see Fig. 12.2). This is only made possible because the genetic code is universal.

Check Your Progress 12.3

1. Examine the flow of genetic information in a cell.
2. Describe the three major classes of RNA; what is the function of each class?
3. Explain why the genetic code is said to be degenerate.

12.4 First Step: Transcription

Learning Outcomes

Upon completion of this section, you should be able to

1. Distinguish the events of transcription that occur during formation of an mRNA molecule.
2. Describe how eukaryotic mRNA molecules are processed and exported to the cytoplasm.

During *transcription*, a segment of the DNA serves as a template for the production of an RNA molecule. Although mRNA, tRNA, and rRNA are all produced by transcription, we focus here on transcription to make mRNA, the type of RNA that eventually leads to building a protein.

MP3
Protein Synthesis

Messenger RNA Is Produced

The sequences of bases in a gene are transcribed into an mRNA molecule based on complementary base pairing: the T base in the DNA pairs with A in the mRNA, G with C, and A with U (note that uracil replaces T in the newly formed mRNA) (Fig. 12.11). When a gene is transcribed, a segment of the DNA helix unwinds and unzips, and complementary RNA nucleotides pair with DNA nucleotides of the strand opposite the gene. This strand is known as the *template strand*; the other strand is the gene strand. An **RNA polymerase** joins the nucleotides together in the 5′ ⟶ 3′ direction. Like DNA polymerase, an RNA polymerase adds a nucleotide only to the 3′ end of the polymer under construction.

Transcription begins when RNA polymerase attaches to a region of DNA called a promoter (see Fig. 12.11). A **promoter** defines the start of transcription, the direction of transcription,

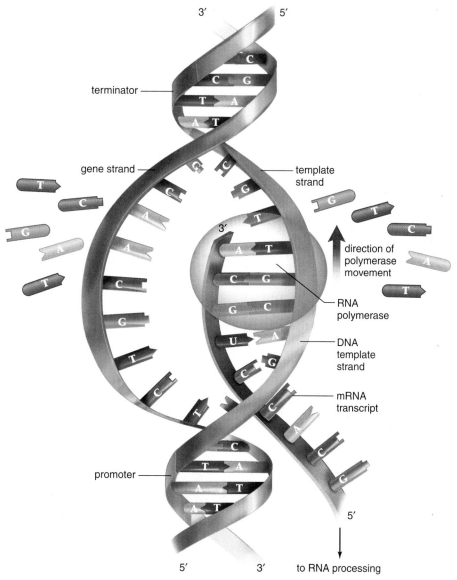

Figure 12.11 Transcription.   During transcription, complementary RNA is made from a DNA template. At the point of attachment of RNA polymerase, the DNA helix unwinds and unzips, and complementary RNA nucleotides are joined together. After RNA polymerase has passed by, the DNA strands rejoin and the mRNA transcript dangles to the side.

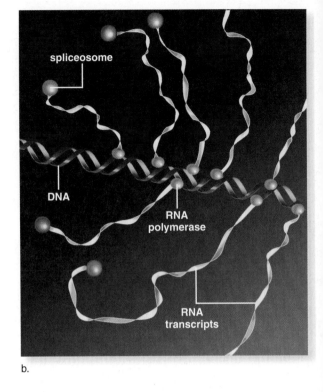

Figure 12.12 RNA polymerase.   a. Numerous RNA transcripts extend from a horizontally oriented gene in an amphibian egg cell. **b.** The strands get progressively longer because transcription begins to the left. The dots along the DNA are RNA polymerase molecules. The dots at the end of the strands are spliceosomes involved in RNA processing (see Fig. 12.13).

and the strand to be transcribed. The binding of RNA polymerase to the promoter is the *initiation* of transcription. The RNA-DNA association is not as stable as the two strands in the DNA helix. Therefore, only the newest portion of an RNA molecule that is associated with RNA polymerase is bound to the DNA, and the rest dangles off to the side.

Elongation of the mRNA molecule occurs as the RNA polymerase reads down the DNA template strand in a 5′ to 3′ direction, and continues until RNA polymerase comes to a DNA stop sequence, where *termination* occurs. The stop sequence causes RNA polymerase to stop transcribing the DNA and to release the mRNA molecule, now called an **mRNA transcript.**

It is not necessary for RNA polymerase to finish making one mRNA transcript before it starts another. As long as they have access to the gene's promoter, many RNA polymerase molecules can be working one after the other to produce mRNA transcripts at the same time (Fig. 12.12). This allows the cell to produce many thousands of copies of the same mRNA molecule, and eventually many copies of the same protein, within a shorter period of time than if a single mRNA copy were used to direct protein synthesis. This ability to rapidly express the gene enables the cell (and the organism) to better respond to changing environmental conditions and have a greater chance at survival.

Note that, for a given gene, either strand of the DNA can be a template strand. The example above uses one strand as the template, but for another gene, the opposite strand may be the template. Assuming both genes are on the same chromosome, and therefore the same piece of DNA, can you think what the orientation of template strand in the second gene might be? (Hint: Consider the directionality of RNA polymerase.)

RNA Molecules Undergo Processing

A newly formed RNA transcript, called a pre-mRNA, is modified before leaving the eukaryotic nucleus. For example, the molecule receives a cap at the 5′ end and a tail at the 3′ end (Fig. 12.13). The *cap* is a modified guanine (G) nucleotide that helps tell a ribosome where to attach when translation begins. The tail consists of a chain of 150–200 adenine (A) nucleotides. This *poly-A tail* facilitates the transport of mRNA out of the nucleus, helps initiate loading of ribosomes and the start of translation, and also delays degradation of mRNA by hydrolytic enzymes.

When the mRNA is first made by RNA polymerase from the gene, it is in a rough form. Called pre-mRNA, it contains a mix of **exons** (protein-coding regions) and **introns** (non-protein coding regions), particularly in multicellular eukaryotes. Because only the exons of the pre-mRNA will be contained in the mature mRNA, the introns, which occur in between the exons, must be spliced out.

In lower eukaryotes, introns are removed by "self-splicing"—that is, the intron itself has the capability of enzymatically splicing itself out of a pre-mRNA. In higher eukaryotes, the RNA splicing is done by spliceosomes, which contain *small nuclear RNAs (snRNAs)*. By means of complementary base pairing, snRNAs are capable of identifying the introns to be removed. A spliceosome utilizes a **ribozyme** (enzyme made of RNA rather than just protein) to cut and remove the introns. Following splicing of the exons together and the addition of the 5′ cap and 3′ poly-A tail, an mRNA is ready to leave the nucleus and be translated into a protein.

Animation
How Spliceosomes Process RNA

Function of Introns

For many years, scientists thought that introns were simply wasted space within genes. Now, we realize they serve several key functions in the cell. The presence of introns allows a cell to pick and choose which exons will go into a particular mRNA (see Chapter 13). Just because an mRNA has all the exons in its pre-mRNA doesn't mean they will all make it to the final product. For example, if a gene has 3 exons, then depending on cell need and environmental conditions, it may produce an mRNA with exons 1 and 2 only, or 1 and 3 only, or 1, 2, and 3. This ability is called *alternative mRNA splicing*, and it increases the flexibility and efficiency of the cell. The snRNAs of the spliceosomes that excise the introns play an important role in alternative splicing in eukaryotes.

Some introns give rise to *microRNAs (miRNAs)*, which are small molecules involved in regulating the translation of mRNAs. These molecules bind with the mRNA through complementary base pairing and, in that way, prevent translation from occurring.

Video
Drug Discovery

Video
New Cancer Clue

It is also possible that the presence of introns encourages crossing-over during meiosis, and this permits a phenomenon termed *exon shuffling*, which can play a role in the evolution of new genes.

Animation
Exon Shuffling

3D Animation
mRNA Modifications

Check Your Progress 12.4

1. Explain the orientation of the DNA template strand relative to both the DNA gene strand and the new mRNA molecule.
2. Describe the three major modifications that occur during the processing of an mRNA.
3. Distinguish between the introns and exons of a gene.
4. Predict the sequence of nucleotides given a strand of DNA.
5. Explain the potential evolutionary benefits of alternative mRNA splicing.

Figure 12.13 Messenger RNA (mRNA) processing in eukaryotes. DNA contains both exons (protein-coding sequences) and introns (non-protein-coding sequences). Both of these are transcribed and are present in pre-mRNA. During processing, a cap and a poly-A tail (a series of adenine nucleotides) are added to the molecule. Also, introns get cut out and the exons get spliced together by complexes called spliceosomes. Once processing is complete the mRNA molecule is ready to leave the nucleus.

12.5 Second Step: Translation

Translation, which takes place in the cytoplasm of eukaryotic cells, is the second step needed to express a gene into a protein. During translation, the sequence of codons (nucleotide triplets) in the mRNA is read by a ribosome, which connects the sequence of amino acids dictated by the mRNA into a polypeptide. The process is called translation because it requires the conversion of information from a nucleic acid language (DNA and RNA) into an amino acid language (protein).

The Role of Transfer RNA

Transfer RNA (tRNA) molecules transfer amino acids to the ribosomes. A tRNA molecule is a single-stranded nucleic acid that doubles back on itself to create regions where complementary bases are hydrogen-bonded to one another. The structure of a tRNA molecule is generally drawn as a flat cloverleaf (Fig 12.14a), but a space-filling model shows the molecule's actual three-dimensional shape (Fig. 12.14b).

There is at least one tRNA molecule for each of the 20 amino acids found in proteins. The amino acid binds to the 3′ end. The opposite end of the molecule contains an **anticodon,** a group of three bases that is complementary and antiparallel to a specific mRNA codon. For example, a tRNA that has the anticodon 5′ AAG 3′ binds to the mRNA codon 5′ CUU 3′ and carries the amino acid leucine. In the genetic code, 61 codons specify amino acids; the other three serve as stop sequences (see Fig. 12.10).

Approximately 40 different tRNA molecules are found in most cells. There are fewer tRNAs than codons because some

a.

b.

Figure 12.14 Structure of a transfer RNA (tRNA) molecule.   a. Complementary base pairing indicated by hydrogen bonding occurs between nucleotides within the molecule, and this causes it to form its characteristic loops. The anticodon that base-pairs with a particular messenger RNA (mRNA) codon occurs at one end of the folded molecule; the other two loops help hold the molecule at the ribosome. An appropriate amino acid is attached at the 3′ end of the molecule in the cytoplasm by a tRNA charging enzyme. For this mRNA codon and tRNA anticodon, the specific amino acid is leucine. **b.** Space-filling model of tRNA molecule.

tRNAs can pair with more than one codon. In 1966, Francis Crick observed this phenomenon and called it the **wobble hypothesis.** He stated that the first two positions in a tRNA anticodon pair obey the A–U/G–C configuration rule. However, the third position can be variable. Some tRNA molecules can recognize as many as four separate codons differing only in the third nucleotide. The wobble effect helps ensure that despite changes in DNA base sequences, the resulting sequence of amino acids will produce a correct protein. This is one of the reasons the genetic code is said to be degenerate.

How does the correct amino acid become attached to the correct tRNA molecule? This task is carried out by amino acid–charging enzymes, generically called aminoacyl-tRNA synthetases. Just as a key fits a lock, each enzyme has a recognition site for a particular amino acid to be joined to a specific tRNA. For example, leucine-tRNA synthetase attaches the leucine amino acid to a tRNA with the correct anticodon. This is an energy-requiring process that uses ATP. A tRNA with its amino acid attached is termed a *charged tRNA*. Once the amino acid–tRNA

complex is formed, it is added to the large pool of charged tRNAs that exist in the cytoplasm, where it can now be accessed by a ribosome during protein synthesis.

The Role of Ribosomal RNA

As with so many cellular structures, the structure of a ribosome is essential to its function.

Structure of a Ribosome

In eukaryotes, ribosomal RNA (rRNA) is produced from a DNA template in the nucleolus of a nucleus. The rRNA is packaged with a variety of proteins into two ribosomal subunits, one of which is larger than the other. The subunits then move separately through nuclear envelope pores into the cytoplasm, where they join together at the start of translation (Fig. 12.15a). Once translation begins, ribosomes can remain in the cytoplasm, or they can become attached to endoplasmic reticulum.

large subunit

small subunit

a. Structure of a ribosome

5′ 3′

mRNA

E P A

tRNA binding sites

b. Binding sites of ribosome

polypeptide

incoming tRNA

mRNA

outgoing tRNA

c. Function of ribosomes

d. Polyribosome

Figure 12.15 Ribosome structure and function. **a.** Side view of a ribosome shows a small subunit and a large subunit. **b.** Frontal view of a ribosome shows its binding sites. mRNA is bound to the small subunit, and the large subunit has three binding sites for tRNAs. **c.** Overview of protein synthesis. The tRNA bearing the growing polypeptide passes the entire chain to the new amino acid carried by the tRNA occupying the A site. The ribosome shifts, and freed of its burden, the "empty" tRNA exits. The new peptide-bearing tRNA moves over one binding site, making the A site accessible once again to a new tRNA. This cycle is repeated until the ribosome reaches the termination codon. **d.** Electron micrograph of a polyribosome, a number of ribosomes all translating the same mRNA molecule.

Function of a Ribosome

Both prokaryotic and eukaryotic cells contain thousands of ribosomes per cell because they play such a significant role in protein synthesis. Ribosomes have a binding site for mRNA and three binding sites for transfer RNA (tRNA) molecules (Fig. 12.15*b*). The tRNA binding sites facilitate complementary base pairing between tRNA anticodons and mRNA codons. The large ribosomal subunit has enzyme activity from rRNA (i.e., a ribozyme) that creates the peptide bond between adjacent amino acids. This peptide bond is created many times to produce a polypeptide, which in turn folds into its three-dimensional shape and becomes a protein.

When a ribosome moves down an mRNA molecule, the polypeptide increases by one amino acid at a time (Fig. 12.15*c*). Translation terminates at a stop codon. Once translation is complete, the polypeptide dissociates from the translation complex and folds into its normal shape. Recall from Chapter 3 that a polypeptide twists and bends into a definite shape based on the makeup of its amino acids. This folding process begins as soon as the polypeptide emerges from a ribosome. Chaperone molecules that are often present in the cytoplasm and the ER ensure protein folding proceeds as it should. For proteins that contain more than one polypeptide, each subunit is folded first, and then subunits join together into a final, functional protein complex.

Like RNA polymerase during transcription, multiple ribosomes often attach and translate the same mRNA at one time. As soon as the initial portion of mRNA has been translated by one ribosome, and the ribosome has begun to move down the mRNA, another ribosome can attach to the mRNA. The entire complex of mRNA and multiple ribosomes is called a **polyribosome** (Fig. 12.15*d*) and it greatly increases the efficiency of translation.

Translation Requires Three Steps

During translation, the codons of an mRNA base-pair with the anticodons of tRNA molecules carrying specific amino acids. The order of the codons determines the order of the tRNA molecules at a ribosome and the corresponding sequence of amino acids in a polypeptide. The process of translation must be extremely orderly so that the amino acids of a polypeptide are sequenced correctly. Even a single amino acid change has the potential to dramatically affect a protein's function, as is the case with individuals who carry the alleles for sickle cell anemia.

Animation
How Translation Works

Protein synthesis involves three steps: initiation, elongation, and termination. Enzymes are required for each of the three steps to function properly. The first two steps, initiation and elongation, require energy.

Initiation

Initiation is the step that brings all the translation components together. Proteins called initiation factors are required to

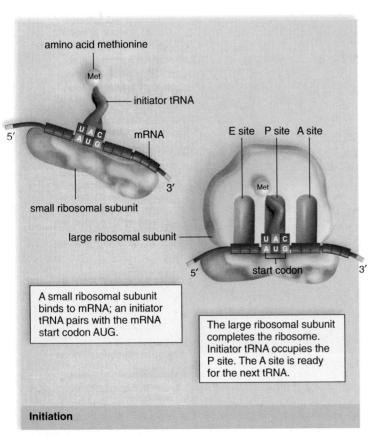

Initiation

Figure 12.16 Initiation.   In prokaryotes, participants in the translation process assemble as shown. The first amino acid is typically a special form of methionine.

Elongation

Figure 12.17 Elongation.   Note that a polypeptide is already at the P site. During elongation, polypeptide synthesis occurs as amino acids are added one at a time to the growing chain.

assemble the small ribosomal subunit, mRNA, initiator tRNA, and the large ribosomal subunit for the start of protein synthesis.

Initiation is shown in Figure 12.16. In prokaryotes, a small ribosomal subunit attaches to the mRNA in the vicinity of the *start codon* (AUG). The first or initiator tRNA pairs with this codon. Then, a large ribosomal subunit joins to the small subunit (Fig. 12.16). Although similar in many ways, initiation in eukaryotes is much more complex.

As already discussed, a ribosome has three binding sites for tRNAs. One of these is called the E (for exit) site, second is the P (for peptide) site, and the third is the A (for amino acid) site. The initiator tRNA binds to the P site, even though it carries only the amino acid methionine (see Fig. 12.10). The A site is where tRNA carrying the next amino acid enter the ribosome, and the E site is for any tRNAs that are leaving a ribosome. Following initiation, translation continues with elongation and then termination.

Elongation

Elongation is the stage during protein synthesis when a polypeptide increases in length one amino acid at a time. In addition to the necessary tRNAs, elongation requires elongation factors, which facilitate the binding of tRNA anticodons to mRNA codons within a ribosome.

❶ Elongation is shown in Figure 12.17, where a tRNA with an attached peptide is already at the P site, and a tRNA carrying its appropriate amino acid is just arriving at the A site. ❷ Once a ribosome has verified that the incoming tRNA matches the codon and is firmly in place at the A site, the entire growing peptide will be transferred to the amino acid on the tRNA in the A site. A ribozyme, an rRNA-based enzyme which is a part of the large ribosomal subunit, uses energy to transfer the growing peptide and create a new peptide bond. ❸ Following peptide bond formation, the peptide is one amino acid longer than it was before. ❹ Next, **translocation** occurs: The ribosome moves forward, and the peptide-bearing tRNA is now in the P site of the ribosome. The spent tRNA, now at the E site, exits the ribosome. A new codon is now exposed at the A site and is ready to receive another tRNA.

The complete cycle—complementary base pairing of new tRNA, transfer of peptide chain, and translocation—is repeated at a rapid rate (about 15 times each second in the bacterium *Escherichia coli*).

Eventually, the ribosome reaches a stop codon, and termination occurs, during which the polypeptide is released.

Termination

Termination is the final step in protein synthesis. During termination, as shown in Figure 12.18, the polypeptide and the assembled components that carried out protein synthesis are separated from one another.

Termination of polypeptide synthesis occurs at a *stop codon*—that is, a codon that does not code for an amino acid.

3 Peptide bond formation attaches the peptide chain to the newly arrived amino acid.

4 The ribosome moves forward; the "empty" tRNA exits from the E site; the next amino acid–tRNA complex is approaching the ribosome.

The ribosome comes to a stop codon on the mRNA. A release factor binds to the site.

The release factor hydrolyzes the bond between the last tRNA at the P site and the polypeptide, releasing them. The ribosomal subunits dissociate.

Termination

Figure 12.18 Termination. During termination, the finished polypeptide is released, as is the mRNA and the last tRNA.

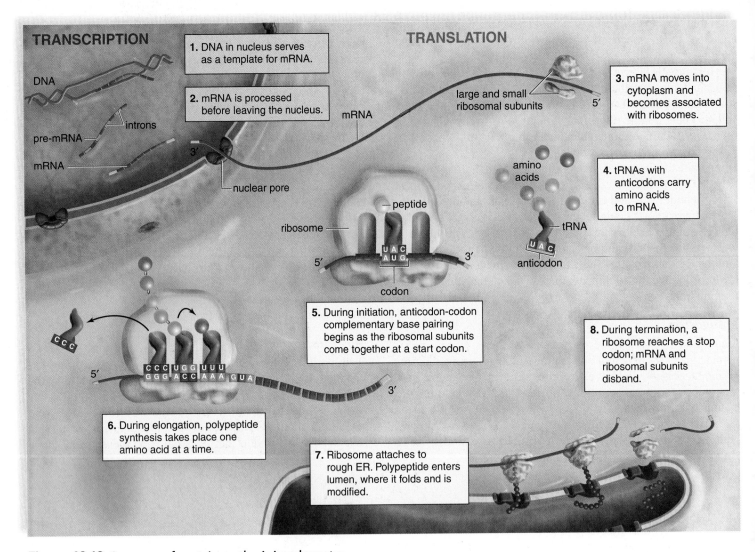

Figure 12.19 Summary of protein synthesis in eukaryotes.

Termination requires a protein called a release factor, which can bind to a stop codon and also cleave the polypeptide from the last tRNA. After this occurs, the polypeptide is set free and begins to fold and take on its three-dimensional shape. The ribosome dissociates into its two subunits, which are returned to the cytoplasmic pool of large and small subunits, to be used again as necessary.

The next section reviews the entire process of protein synthesis (recall that a protein contains one or more polypeptides) and the role of the rough endoplasmic reticulum in the production of a polypeptide. Proteins do the work of the cell, whether they reside in a cellular membrane or are free in the cytoplasm. A whole new field of biology called **proteomics** is now dedicated to understanding the structure of proteins and how they function in metabolic pathways. One of the important goals of proteomics is to understand how proteins are modified in the endoplasmic reticulum and the Golgi apparatus.

MP3
Translation

3D Animation
Translation

Gene Expression

A gene has been expressed once its product, a protein (or an RNA), is made and is operating in the cell. For a protein, gene expression requires transcription and translation (Fig. 12.19) and it also requires that the protein be active as discussed in the next chapter.

Translation occurs at ribosomes. Some ribosomes (polyribosomes) remain free in the cytoplasm, and some become attached to rough ER. The first few amino acids of a polypeptide act as a signal peptide that indicates where the polypeptide belongs in the cell or if it is to be secreted from the cell. Polypeptides that are to be secreted enter the lumen of the ER by way of a channel, and are then folded and further processed by the addition of sugars, phosphates, or lipids. Transport vesicles carry the proteins between organelles and to the plasma membrane as appropriate for that protein.

Animation
Processing of Gene Information in Prokaryotes and Eukaryotes

Check Your Progress   12.5

1. Explain the role of transfer RNA in translation.
2. Describe how the structure of a ribosome contributes to polypeptide synthesis.
3. Examine the events that occur during the three major steps of translation.

12.6 Structure of the Eukaryotic Chromosome

Learning Outcomes

Upon completion of this section, you should be able to

1. Explain how DNA becomes sufficiently compacted to fit inside a nucleus.

Only in recent years have investigators been able to produce models suggesting how chromosomes are organized. A eukaryotic chromosome contains a single double helix DNA molecule, but it is composed of more than 50% protein. Some of these proteins are concerned with DNA and RNA synthesis, but a large majority, termed **histones,** play primarily a structural role.

The five primary types of histone molecules are designated H1, H2A, H2B, H3, and H4 (see Fig. 13.5*b*). Remarkably, the amino acid sequences of H3 and H4 vary little between organisms. For example, the H4 of peas is only two amino acids different from the H4 of cattle. This similarity suggests that few mutations in the histone proteins have occurred during the course of evolution and that the histones, therefore, have essential functions for survival.

A human cell contains at least 2 m of DNA. Yet, all of this DNA is packed into a nucleus that is about 5 μm in diameter. The histones are responsible for packaging the DNA so that it can fit into such a small space. First, the DNA double helix is wound at intervals around a core of eight histone molecules (two copies each of H2A, H2B, H3, and H4), giving the appearance of a string of beads (Fig. 12.20*a*). Each bead is called a **nucleosome,** and the nucleosomes are said to be joined by "linker" DNA.

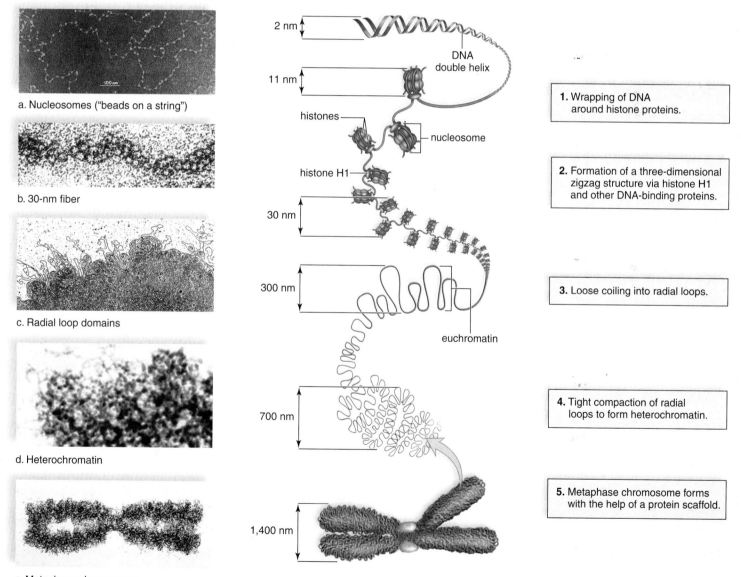

a. Nucleosomes ("beads on a string")

b. 30-nm fiber

c. Radial loop domains

d. Heterochromatin

e. Metaphase chromosome

1. Wrapping of DNA around histone proteins.

2. Formation of a three-dimensional zigzag structure via histone H1 and other DNA-binding proteins.

3. Loose coiling into radial loops.

4. Tight compaction of radial loops to form heterochromatin.

5. Metaphase chromosome forms with the help of a protein scaffold.

Figure 12.20 Structure of eukaryotic chromosomes. The DNA molecule of a chromosome is compacted at several levels. Structural changes in the DNA influence its ability to express genes. **a.** The DNA strand is wound around histones to form nucleosomes. **b.** The strand is further shortened by folding it into a zigzag structure. **c.** The fiber loops back and forth into radial loops. **d.** In heterochromatin, additional proteins further compact the radial loops. **e.** A metaphase chromosome forms.

This string is compacted by folding into a zigzag structure, further shortening the DNA strand (Fig. 12.20*b*). Histone H1 appears to mediate this coiling process. The fiber then loops back and forth into radial loops (Fig. 12.20*c*). This loosely coiled **euchromatin** represents the active chromatin containing genes that are being transcribed. The DNA of euchromatin may be accessed by RNA polymerase and other factors that are needed to promote transcription. In fact, recent research seems to indicate that regulating the level of compaction of the DNA is an important method of controlling gene expression in the cell.

Under a microscope, one often observes dark-stained fibers within the nucleus of the cell. These areas within the nucleus represent a more highly compacted form of the chromosome called **heterochromatin** (Fig. 12.20*d*). Most chromosomes exhibit both levels of compaction in a living cell, depending on which portions of the chromosome are being used more frequently. Heterochromatin is considered inactive chromatin because the genes contained on it are infrequently transcribed, if at all.

Prior to cell division, a protein scaffold helps to further condense the chromosome into a form that is characteristic of metaphase chromosomes (Fig. 12.20*e*). No doubt, compact chromosomes are easier to move about than extended chromatin.

Check Your Progress   12.6

1. Examine how regulation of gene expression might be accomplished by changing the compaction of chromatin.

CONNECTING *the* CONCEPTS *with the* THEMES

Evolution

- Genes specify proteins through the steps of transcription and translation. During transcription, a strand of DNA is used as a template for the production of an mRNA molecule.
- The actions of RNA polymerase, the enzyme that carries out transcription, and DNA polymerase, which is required for DNA replication, are similar enough to suggest that both enzymes evolved from a common ancestral enzyme.
- Specifically, it now appears that RNA may play a prominent role in the regulation of the genome. Some believe this is evidence that RNA may have preceded DNA in the evolutionary history of cells.

Nature of Science

- Early investigators who did their work between 1950 and 1990 came to the conclusion that DNA is organized into discrete units called genes.
- Scientists are now discovering that the rest of the DNA that does not specify proteins may also have valuable functions.
- Many biologists believe that we need a new definition of a gene that recognizes that much of our DNA results in RNA molecules rather than protein products.

Biological Systems

- Both protein-coding and non-protein-coding DNA provides the blueprint for building and developing an entire organism.
- But just as a blueprint is useless without a team of engineers, architects, and construction workers to execute it, the expression of genes requires a large system of proteins and other factors to control it.
- As described in the following chapter, regulatory proteins may turn genes on or off, and genes can be combined in many different ways to alter the proteins that are made. Together, these mechanisms contribute to the great complexity and diversity of living organisms.

Media Study Tools

www.mhhe.com/maderbiology11

Enhance your study of this chapter with study tools and practice tests. Also ask your instructor about the resources available through ConnectPlus, including the media-rich eBook, interactive learning tools, and animations.

 3D Animations
DNA Replication For an interactive examination of the
Molecular Biology processes of DNA replication and gene
of the Gene expression, review the 3D animations "DNA Replication" and "Molecular Biology of the Gene."

Summarize

12.1 The Genetic Material

Early work illustrated that DNA was the hereditary material. Griffith injected strains of pneumococcus into mice and observed that when heat-killed S strain bacteria were injected along with live R strain bacteria, virulent S strain bacteria were recovered from the dead mice. Griffith said that the R strain had been transformed by some substance passing from the dead S strain to the live R strain. Twenty years later, Avery and his colleagues reported that the transforming substance is DNA.

To study the structure of DNA, Chargaff performed a chemical analysis of DNA and found that A = T and G = C, and that the amount of purine equals the amount of pyrimidine. Franklin prepared an X-ray photograph of DNA that showed it is helical, has repeating structural features, and has certain dimensions. Watson and Crick built a model of DNA in which the sugar-phosphate molecules made up the sides of a twisted ladder, and the complementary-paired bases were the rungs of the ladder.

12.2 Replication of DNA

The Watson and Crick model immediately suggested a method by which DNA could be replicated. Basically, the two strands unwind and unzip, and each parental strand acts as a template for a new (daughter) strand. In the end, each new helix is like the other and like the parental helix.

The enzyme DNA polymerase joins the nucleotides together and proofreads them to make sure the bases have been paired correctly. Incorrect base pairs that survive the process are a mutation. Replication in prokaryotes typically proceeds in both directions from one point of origin to a termination region until there are two copies of the circular chromosome. Replication in eukaryotes has many points of origin and many bubbles (places where the DNA strands are separating and replication is occurring). Replication occurs at the ends of the bubbles—at replication forks. Since eukaryotes have linear chromosomes, they cannot replicate the very ends of them. Therefore, the ends (telomeres) get shorter with each replication. Telomerase enzyme helps to ensure that chromosomes maintain their proper length.

12.3 The Genetic Code of Life

The central dogma of molecular biology says that the flow of genetic information is from DNA to RNA to protein to traits. More specifically, (1) DNA is a template for its own replication and also for RNA formation during transcription, and (2) the sequence of nucleotides in mRNA directs the correct sequence of amino acids of a polypeptide during translation.

The genetic code is a triplet code, and each codon (code word) consists of three bases. The code is degenerate—that is, more than one codon exists for most amino acids. There are also one start and three stop codons. The genetic code is considered universal, but there are a few exceptions.

12.4 First Step: Transcription

Transcription to produce messenger RNA (mRNA) begins when RNA polymerase attaches to the promoter of a gene. Elongation occurs until RNA polymerase reaches a stop sequence. The mRNA is processed following transcription. A cap is put onto the 5′ end, a poly-A tail is put onto the 3′ end, and introns are removed in eukaryotes by spliceosomes.

Small nuclear RNAs (snRNAs) present in spliceosomes help identify the introns to be removed. These snRNAs play a role in alternative mRNA splicing, which allows a single eukaryotic gene to code for different proteins, depending on which segments of the gene serve as introns and which serve as exons.

Some introns serve as microRNAs (miRNAs), which help regulate the translation of mRNAs. Research is now directed to discovering the many ways small RNAs influence the production of proteins in a cell.

12.5 Second Step: Translation

Translation requires mRNA, transfer RNA (tRNA), and ribosomal RNA (rRNA). Each tRNA has an anticodon at one end and an amino acid at the other; amino acid–charging enzymes ensure that the correct amino acid is attached to the correct tRNA. When tRNAs bind with their codon at a ribosome, the amino acids are correctly sequenced in a polypeptide according to the order predetermined by DNA.

In the cytoplasm, many ribosomes move along the same mRNA at a time. Collectively, these are called a polyribosome.

Translation requires these steps: During initiation, mRNA, the first (initiator) tRNA, and the two subunits of a ribosome all come together in the proper orientation at a start codon. During elongation, as the tRNA anticodons bind to their codons, the growing pep-

tide chain is transferred by peptide bonding to the next amino acid in a polypeptide. During termination at a stop codon, the polypeptide is cleaved from the last tRNA. The ribosome now dissociates.

12.6 Structure of the Eukaryotic Chromosome

Eukaryotic cells contain nearly 2 m of DNA, yet must pack it all into a nucleus no more than 20 μm in diameter. Thus, the DNA is compacted by winding it around DNA-binding proteins called histones to make nucleosomes. The nucleosomes are further compacted into a zigzag structure, which is then folded upon itself many times to form radial loops, which is the usual compaction state of euchromatin. Heterochromatin is further compacted by scaffold proteins, and further compaction can be achieved prior to mitosis and meiosis.

Key Terms

adenine (A) 217
anticodon 228
central dogma 224
codon 224
complementary base
  pairing 219
cytosine (C) 217
DNA polymerase 220
DNA replication 220
double helix 218
elongation 231
euchromatin 234
exon 226
genetic code 224
guanine (G) 217
heterochromatin 234
histone 233
initiation 230
intron 226
messenger RNA (mRNA) 223
mRNA transcript 226

nucleosome 233
polyribosome 230
promoter 225
proteomics 232
replication fork 222
ribosomal RNA (rRNA) 223
ribozyme 227
RNA polymerase 225
semiconservative
  replication 220
telomere 221
template 220
termination 231
thymine (T) 217
transcription 223
transfer RNA (tRNA) 223
translation 224
translocation 231
triplet code 224
uracil (U) 223
wobble hypothesis 229

 Assess

Reviewing This Chapter

1. List and discuss the requirements for genetic material. 215
2. How did Avery and his colleagues demonstrate that the transforming substance is DNA? 215–16
3. Describe the Watson and Crick model of DNA structure. How did it fit the data provided by Chargaff and the X-ray diffraction patterns of Franklin? 218–19
4. Explain how DNA replicates semiconservatively. What role does DNA polymerase play? What role does helicase play? 220–21
5. List and discuss differences between prokaryotic and eukaryotic replication of DNA. 222
6. How did investigators reason that the code must be a triplet code, and in what manner was the code cracked? Why is it said that the code is degenerate, unambiguous, and almost universal? 224
7. What two steps are required for the expression of a gene? 225, 228
8. What specific steps occur during transcription of RNA off a DNA template? 225–26
9. How is messenger RNA (mRNA) processed before leaving the eukaryotic nucleus? 226–27

10. What is the role of snRNAs in the nucleus?   227
11. Compare the functions of mRNA, transfer RNA (tRNA), and ribosomal RNA (rRNA) during protein synthesis. What are the specific events of translation?   228–32
12. What are the various levels of chromosome structure?   233–34

Testing Yourself

Choose the best answer for each question.

1. If 30% of an organism's DNA is thymine, then
   a. 70% is purine.   d. 70% is pyrimidine.
   b. 20% is guanine.   e. Both c and d are correct.
   c. 30% is adenine.

2. The double-helix model of DNA resembles a twisted ladder in which the rungs of the ladder are
   a. a purine paired with a pyrimidine.
   b. A paired with G and C paired with T.
   c. sugar-phosphate paired with sugar-phosphate.
   d. a 5′ end paired with a 3′ end.
   e. Both a and b are correct.

3. DNA replication is said to be semiconservative because
   a. one of the new molecules conserves both of the original DNA strands.
   b. the new DNA molecule contains two new DNA strands.
   c. both of the new molecules contain one new strand and one old strand.
   d. DNA polymerase conserves both of the old strands.

4. If the sequence of bases in one strand of DNA is 5′ TAGCCT 3′, then the sequence of bases in the other strand will be
   a. 3′ TCCGAT 5′.   c. 3′ TAGCCT 5′.
   b. 3′ ATCGGA 5′.   d. 3′ AACGGUA 5′.

5. Transformation occurs when
   a. DNA is transformed into RNA.
   b. DNA is transformed into protein.
   c. bacteria cannot grow on penicillin.
   d. organisms receive foreign DNA and thereby acquire a new characteristic.

6. Pyrimidines
   a. are always paired with a purine.
   b. are thymine and cytosine.
   c. keep DNA from replicating too often.
   d. are adenine and guanine.
   e. Both a and b are correct.

7. A nucleotide
   a. is smaller than a base.
   b. is a subunit of nucleic acids.
   c. has a lot of variable parts.
   d. has at least four phosphates.
   e. always joins with other nucleotides.

8. This is a segment of a DNA molecule. What are (a) the RNA codons, (b) the matching tRNA anticodons, and (c) the sequence of amino acids in the eventual protein?

nontemplate strand

template strand

9. In prokaryotes,
   a. replication can occur in two directions at once because their DNA molecule is circular.
   b. bubbles thereby created spread out until they meet.
   c. replication occurs at numerous replication forks.
   d. a new round of DNA replication cannot begin before the previous round is complete.
   e. Both a and b are correct.

10. The central dogma of molecular biology
    a. states that DNA is a template for all RNA production.
    b. states that DNA is a template only for DNA replication.
    c. states that translation precedes transcription.
    d. states that RNA is a template for DNA replication.
    e. All of these are correct.

11. Because there are more codons than amino acids,
    a. some amino acids are specified by more than one codon.
    b. some codons specify more than one amino acid.
    c. some codons do not specify any amino acid.
    d. some amino acids do not have codons.

12. If the sequence of bases in the coding strand of a DNA is TAGC, then the sequence of bases in the mRNA will be
    a. AUCG.   c. UAGC.
    b. TAGC.   d. CGAU.

13. During protein synthesis, an anticodon on transfer RNA (tRNA) pairs with
    a. DNA nucleotide bases.
    b. ribosomal RNA (rRNA) nucleotide bases.
    c. messenger RNA (mRNA) nucleotide bases.
    d. other tRNA nucleotide bases.
    e. Any one of these can occur.

14. If the sequence of DNA on the template strand of a gene is AAA, the mRNA codon produced by transcription will be _____ and will specify the amino acid _____ .
    a. AAA, lysine   d. UUU, phenylalanine
    b. AAA, phenylalanine   e. TTT, lysine
    c. TTT, arginine

15. Euchromatin
    a. is organized into radial loops.
    b. is less condensed than heterochromatin.
    c. contains nucleosomes.
    d. All of these are correct.

Engage

Thinking Scientifically

1. How would you test a hypothesis that a genetic condition, such as cancer, is due to mistakes in transcription and translation?

2. Knowing that a plant will grow from a single cell in tissue culture, how could you transform a plant so that it glows in the dark?

Individual neurons, shown in pink in this electron micrograph, may use unique forms of the DSCAM proteins in their plasma membranes to identify themselves.

13

Regulation of Gene Expression

It was once estimated that the human genome may contain as many as a million genes. At the start of the Human Genome Project, that number was considered to be closer to 100,000. We now know that the human genome probably contains less than 23,000 genes. So how do a mere 23,000 genes account for the variety of proteins found in human cells? The answer, surprisingly, may lie in the regulation of pre-mRNA splicing to allow the production of a myriad of proteins from a single gene. *DSCAM* is a gene associated with Down Syndrome that is present in the brain of many animals. In fruit flies *DSCAM* has four regions of alternative exons. The result is over 38,000 different possible combinations of functional mRNAs, and therefore, the *DSCAM* gene is able to specify 38,000 different proteins. Such a huge number of proteins is sufficient to provide each nerve cell with a unique identity as it communicates with others within a brain.

Complex alternative splicing, and other regulatory mechanisms, could very well account for how humans generate so many different proteins from so few genes. This chapter introduces you to regulatory mechanisms in both prokaryotes and eukaryotes, allowing you to see how these mechanisms influence the processes of transcription and translation that you learned about in the previous chapter.

As you read through this chapter, think about the following questions:

1. How does gene regulation differ between prokaryotes and eukaryotes?
2. Where in the process of gene expression does regulation occur in a eukaryotic organism?
3. How might mutations influence the ability of a cell to regulate gene expression?

BEFORE YOU BEGIN

Before starting this chapter, take a few moments to review these earlier concepts

Figure 12.9 What is the central dogma of biology?

Section 12.4 What is the purpose of transcription and where does it occur in both prokaryotic and eukaryotic cells?

Section 12.5 What is the role of translation in gene expression?

FOLLOWING *the* THEMES

CHAPTER 13 REGULATION OF GENE EXPRESSION

UNIT 2 GENETIC BASIS OF LIFE		
	Evolution	Whereas prokaryotic gene regulation operates primarily at the level of the gene, eukaryotes have evolved mechanisms to regulate gene expression at multiple levels.
	Nature of Science	By understanding how cells regulate gene expression it is possible to better understand the basis of many human diseases.
	Biological Systems	Mutations in the genetic material may have a profound impact on the function of a cell or the health of an organism.

13.1 Prokaryotic Regulation

Because their environment is ever changing, bacteria do not always need to express their entire complement of enzymes and proteins. In 1961, French microbiologists François Jacob and Jacques Monod showed that *Escherichia coli* is capable of regulating the expression of its genes. They observed that the genes for a metabolic pathway, called **structural genes,** are grouped on a chromosome and subsequently are transcribed at the same time. Jacob and Monod, therefore, proposed the **operon** [L. *opera*, works] model to explain gene regulation in prokaryotes. They later received a Nobel Prize for their investigations.

An operon (Fig. 13.1) typically includes the following elements:

A **regulator gene**—Normally located outside the operon, this codes for a DNA-binding protein that acts as a **repressor.** The repressor controls whether the operon is active or not.

Promoter—A short sequence of DNA where RNA polymerase first attaches to begin transcription of the grouped genes.

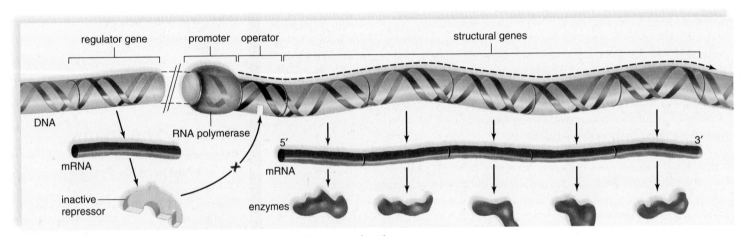

a. **Tryptophan absent.** Enzymes needed to synthesize tryptophan are produced.

b. **Tryptophan present.** Presence of tryptophan prevents production of enzymes used to synthesize tryptophan.

Figure 13.1 The *trp* operon. **a.** The regulator gene codes for a repressor protein that is normally inactive. RNA polymerase attaches to the promoter, and the structural genes are expressed. **b.** When the nutrient tryptophan is present, it binds to the repressor, changing its shape. Now the repressor is active and can bind to the operator. RNA polymerase cannot attach to the promoter, and the structural genes are not expressed.

Basically, a promoter signals the start of the operon and the location where transcription begins.

Operator—A short portion of DNA where an active repressor binds. When an active repressor binds to the operator, RNA polymerase cannot attach to the promoter, and transcription cannot occur. In this way, the operator controls transcription of structural genes.

Structural genes—These genes code for the enzymes and proteins that are involved in the metabolic pathway of the operon. The structural genes are transcribed as a unit.

Next, we will briefly review the findings of Jacob and Monod in their studies of two *E. coli* operons: the *trp* operon and the *lac* operon.

The *trp* Operon

Many investigators, including Jacob and Monod, found that some operons in *E. coli* usually exist in the "on" rather than "off" condition. For example, in the *trp* operon, the regulator codes for a repressor that ordinarily is unable to attach to the operator. Therefore, RNA polymerase can bind to the promoter, and the structural genes of the operon are ordinarily expressed (Fig. 13.1). Their products, five different enzymes, are part of an anabolic pathway for the synthesis of the amino acid tryptophan.

If tryptophan happens to be already present in the medium, these enzymes are not needed by the cell, and the operon is turned off by the following method. Tryptophan binds to the repressor. A change in shape now allows the repressor to bind to the operator and prevent RNA polymerase from binding to the promoter, and the structural genes are not expressed. The enzymes are said to be repressible, and the entire unit is called a *repressible operon*. Tryptophan is called the **corepressor**. Repressible operons are usually involved in anabolic pathways that synthesize a substance needed by the cell.

Animation
The Tryptophan Repressor

The *lac* Operon

Bacteria metabolism is remarkably efficient; when there is no need for certain proteins or enzymes, the genes that are used to make them are usually inactive. For example, if the milk sugar lactose is not present, there is no need to express genes for enzymes involved in lactose catabolism. But when *E. coli* is denied glucose and is instead given lactose, the cell immediately begins to make the three enzymes needed for lactose metabolism.

The enzymes that break down lactose are encoded by three genes (Fig. 13.2): One gene is for an enzyme called β-galactosidase, which breaks down the disaccharide lactose to glucose and galactose; a second gene codes for a permease that facilitates the entry of lactose into the cell; and a third gene codes for an enzyme called transacetylase, which has an accessory function in lactose metabolism.

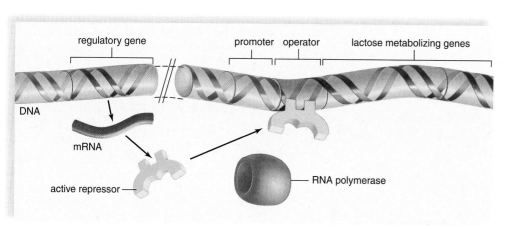

a.

b.

Figure 13.2 The *lac* operon.
a. The regulator gene codes for a repressor that is normally active. When it binds to the operator, RNA polymerase cannot attach to the promoter, and structural genes are not expressed. **b.** When lactose is present, it binds to the repressor, changing its shape so that it is inactive and cannot bind to the operator. Now, RNA polymerase binds to the promoter, and the structural genes are expressed.

The three structural genes are adjacent to one another on the chromosome and are under the control of a single promoter and a single operator. The regulator gene codes for a *lac* operon repressor that ordinarily binds to the operator and prevents transcription of the three genes. But when glucose is absent and lactose (or more correctly, allolactose, an isomer formed from lactose) is present, lactose binds to the repressor, and the repressor undergoes a change in shape that prevents it from binding to the operator. Because the repressor is unable to bind to the operator, RNA polymerase is better able to bind to the promoter. After RNA polymerase carries out transcription, the three enzymes of lactose metabolism are synthesized.

Because the presence of lactose brings about expression of genes, it is called an **inducer** of the *lac* operon: The enzymes are said to be inducible enzymes, and the entire unit is called an *inducible operon*. Inducible operons are usually found in catabolic pathways that break down a nutrient. Why is that beneficial? Because these enzymes need to be active only when the nutrient is present.

Further Control of the lac *Operon*

E. coli preferentially breaks down glucose, and the bacterium has a way to ensure that the lactose operon is maximally turned on only when glucose is absent. A molecule called *cyclic AMP (cAMP)* accumulates when glucose is absent. Cyclic AMP, which is derived from ATP, has only one phosphate group, which is attached to ribose at two locations:

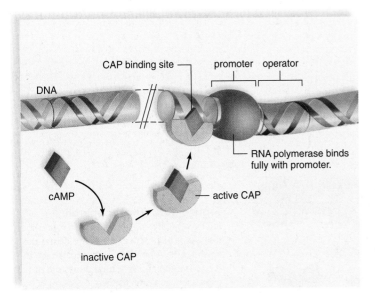

cyclic AMP
(cAMP)

Cyclic AMP binds to a molecule called a *catabolite activator protein (CAP)*, and the complex attaches to a CAP binding site next to the *lac* promoter. When CAP binds to DNA, DNA bends, exposing the promoter to RNA polymerase. RNA polymerase is now better able to bind to the promoter so that the *lac* operon structural genes are transcribed, leading to their expression (Fig. 13.3).

When glucose is present, there is little cAMP in the cell; CAP is inactive, and the lactose operon does not function maximally. CAP affects other operons as well and takes its name for activating the catabolism of various other metabolites when glucose is absent. A cell's ability to encourage the metabolism of lactose and other metabolites when glucose is absent provides a backup system for survival when the preferred energy source glucose is absent.

Animation
Combination of Switches:
The *lac* Operon

The CAP protein's regulation of the *lac* operon is an example of positive control. Why? Because when this molecule is active, it promotes the activity of an operon. The use of repressors, on the other hand, is an example of negative control because when active they shut down an operon. A positive control mechanism allows the cell to fine-tune its response. In the case of the *lac* operon, the operon is only maximally active when glucose is absent and lactose is present. If both glucose and lactose are present, the cell preferentially metabolizes glucose.

Check Your Progress   13.1

1. Explain the difference between the roles of the promoter and operator of an operon.
2. Summarize how gene expression differs in an inducible operon versus a repressible operon and give an example of each.
3. Describe the difference between positive control and negative control of gene expression.

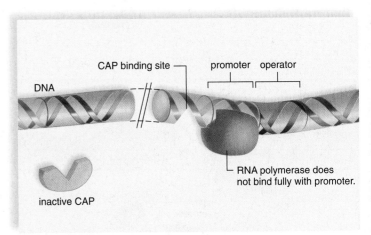

a. **Lactose present, glucose absent (cAMP level high)**

b. **Lactose present, glucose present (cAMP level low)**

Figure 13.3 Action of CAP.   When active CAP binds to its site on DNA, the RNA polymerase is better able to bind to the promoter so that the structural genes of the *lac* operon are expressed. **a.** CAP becomes active in the presence of cAMP, a molecule that is prevalent when glucose is absent. Therefore, transcription of lactose enzymes increases, and lactose is metabolized. **b.** If glucose is present, CAP is inactive, and RNA polymerase does not completely bind to the promoter. Therefore, transcription of lactose enzymes decreases, and less metabolism of lactose occurs.

13.2 Eukaryotic Regulation

Learning Outcomes

Upon completion of this section, you should be able to

1. List the levels of control of gene expression in eukaryotes.

2. Summarize how chromatin structure may be involved in regulation of gene expression in eukaryotes.

3. Identify the mechanisms of transcriptional, posttranscriptional, and translational control of gene expression.

With a few minor exceptions, each cell of a multicellular eukaryote has a complete complement of genes; the differences in cell types are determined by the different genes that are actively expressed in each cell. For example, in muscle cells a different set of genes is turned on in the nucleus and a different set of proteins is active in the cytoplasm compared to nerve cells.

Like prokaryotic cells, a variety of mechanisms regulate gene expression in eukaryotic cells. These mechanisms can be grouped under five primary levels of control; three of them pertain to the nucleus, and two pertain to the cytoplasm (Fig. 13.4). In other words, control of gene activity in eukaryotes extends from transcription to protein activity. These are the types of control in eukaryotic cells that can modify the amount of the gene product:

Animation Control of Gene Expression in Eukaryotes

1. *Chromatin structure:* Chromatin packing is used as a way to keep genes turned off. If genes are not accessible to RNA polymerase, they cannot be transcribed. Chromatin structure is one method of **epigenetic inheritance** [Gk. *epi*, besides], the transmission of genetic information outside the coding sequences of a gene.

2. *Transcriptional control:* The degree to which a gene is transcribed into mRNA determines the amount of gene product. In the nucleus, transcription factors may promote or repress transcription, the first step in gene expression.

3. *Posttranscriptional control:* Posttranscriptional control involves mRNA processing and how fast mRNA leaves the nucleus.

4. *Translational control:* Translational control occurs in the cytoplasm and affects when translation begins and how long it continues. Any condition that can cause the persistence of the 5′ cap and 3′ poly-A tail can affect the length of translation. Excised introns may also have effects on the life span of mRNA.

5. *Posttranslational control:* Posttranslational control, which also takes place in the cytoplasm, occurs after protein synthesis. Only a functional protein is an active gene product.

We now explore each of these types of control in greater depth.

Chromatin Structure

The DNA in eukaryotes is always associated with a variety of proteins, and together they make up a stringy material called **chromatin.** Chromatin is most evident in the nucleus during interphase of the cell cycle.

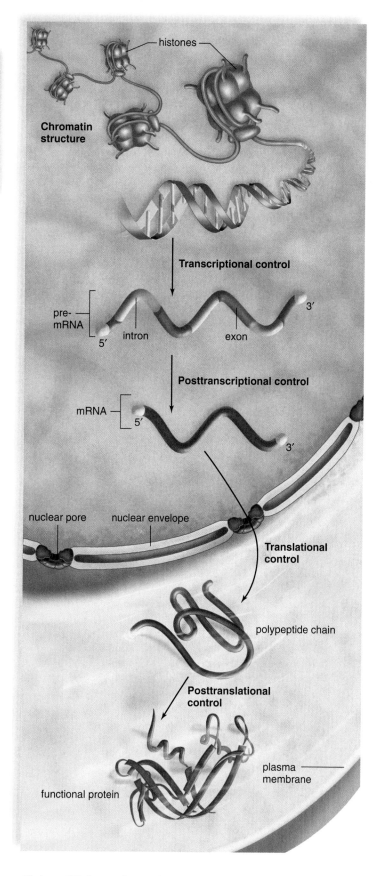

Figure 13.4 Levels at which control of gene expression occurs in eukaryotic cells. The five levels of control are (1) chromatin structure, (2) transcriptional control, and (3) posttranscriptional control, which occur in the nucleus; and (4) translational and (5) posttranslational control, which occur in the cytoplasm.

In Chapter 12 you learned that one class of these DNA-associated proteins are the histones. Histones play an important role in the compaction of the DNA (see Figure 12.20) as well as in eukaryotic gene regulation. Without histones, the DNA would not fit inside the nucleus. Each human cell contains around 2 meters of DNA, yet the nucleus is only 5 to 8 micrometers (μm) in diameter.

The degree to which chromatin is compacted greatly affects the accessibility of the chromatin to the transcriptional machinery of the cell, and thus the expression levels of the genes. Active genes in eukaryotic cells are associated with more loosely packed chromatin called *euchromatin,* while the more tightly packed DNA, called *heterochromatin,* contains mostly inactive genes. Under a microscope, the more densely compacted heterochromatin stains darker than euchromatin (Fig. 13.5*a*).

What regulates whether chromatin exists as heterochromatin or euchromatin? In Chapter 12 you learned that a *nucleosome* consists of a portion of DNA wrapped around a group of histone molecules. Histone molecules have *tails,* strings of amino acids that extend beyond the main portion of a nucleosome (Fig. 13.5*b*). In heterochromatin, the histone tails tend to bear methyl groups ($-CH_3$); in euchromatin, the histone tails tend to be acetylated and have attached acetyl groups ($-COCH_3$).

Histones regulate accessibility to DNA; euchromatin becomes genetically active when histones no longer bar access to DNA. When DNA in euchromatin is transcribed, a so-called *chromatin remodeling complex* pushes aside the histone portion of a nucleosome so that access to DNA is not barred and transcription can begin (Fig. 13.5*c*). After *unpacking* occurs,

a. Darkly stained heterochromatin and lightly stained euchromatin

heterochromatin   nucleolus   euchromatin

1 μm

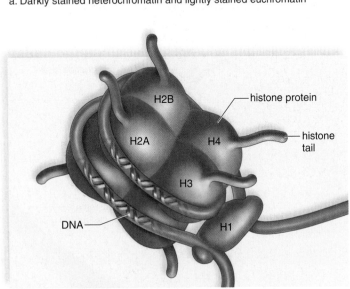

b. A nucleosome

H2B
H2A   H4
H3
DNA
H1
histone protein
histone tail

c. DNA unpacking

nucleosome
inaccessible promoter
chromatin remodeling complex
accessible promoter
DNA to be transcribed

Figure 13.5 Chromatin structure regulates gene expression. **a.** A eukaryotic nucleus contains highly condensed heterochromatin (darkly stained) and euchromatin (lightly stained), which is not as condensed. **b.** Nucleosomes ordinarily prevent access to DNA so that transcription cannot take place. If histone tails are acetylated, access can be achieved; if the tails are methylated, access is more difficult. **c.** A chromatin remodeling complex works on euchromatin to make a promoter accessible for transcription.

many decondensed loops radiate from the central axis of the chromosome. These chromosomes have been named lampbrush chromosomes because their feathery appearance resembles the brushes that were once used to clean kerosene lamps.

In addition to physically moving nucleosomes aside to expose promoters, chromatin remodeling complexes may also affect gene expression by adding acetyl or methyl groups to histone tails.

Heterochromatin Is Not Transcribed

In general, highly condensed heterochromatin is inaccessible to RNA polymerase, and the genes contained within are seldom or never transcribed. A dramatic example of heterochromatin is the **Barr body** in mammalian females, first mentioned in Chapter 10. This small, darkly staining mass of condensed chromatin adhering to the inner edge of the nuclear membrane is an inactive X chromosome. To compensate for the fact that female mammals have two X chromosomes (XX), while males only have one (XY), one of the X chromosomes in the cells of female embryos undergoes inactivation. The inactive X chromosome does not produce gene products, allowing both males and females to produce the same amount of gene product from a single X chromosome.

Animation
X-Inactivation

How do we know that Barr bodies are inactive X chromosomes that are not producing gene products? In a heterozygous female, 50% of the cells have one X chromosome active and 50% have the other X chromosome active. The body of a heterozygous female would therefore be a mosaic, with "patches" of genetically different cells. Investigators have discovered that human females who are heterozygous for an X-linked recessive

form of ocular albinism have patches of pigmented and nonpigmented cells at the back of the eye.

As other examples, women who are heterozygous for X-linked hereditary absence of sweat glands have patches of skin lacking sweat glands. And, the female tortoiseshell cat exhibits a difference in X-inactivation in its cells. In these cats, an allele for black coat color is on one X chromosome, and a corresponding allele for orange coat color is on the other. The patches of black and orange in the coat can be related to which X chromosome is in the Barr bodies of the cells found in the patches (Fig. 13.6).

Epigenetic Inheritance

Histone modification is sometimes linked to a phenomenon termed *epigenetic inheritance*, in which variations in the the pattern of inheritance is not due to changes in the sequence of the DNA nucleotides. For example, when histones are methylated, sometimes the DNA itself becomes methylated as well.

During *genomic imprinting*, either the mother's or the father's gene (but not both) is methylated during gamete formation. If an inherited allele is highly methylated, the gene is not expressed, even if it is a normal gene in every other respect. For traits that exhibit genomic imprinting, the expression of the gene depends on whether the unmethylated allele was inherited from the mother or the father.

The term *epigenetic inheritance* is now used broadly for other inheritance patterns that do not depend on the genes themselves. Epigenetic inheritance explains unusual inheritance patterns and also may play an important role in growth, aging, and cancer. Researchers are even hopeful that it will be easier to develop drugs to modify this level of inheritance rather than trying to change the DNA itself.

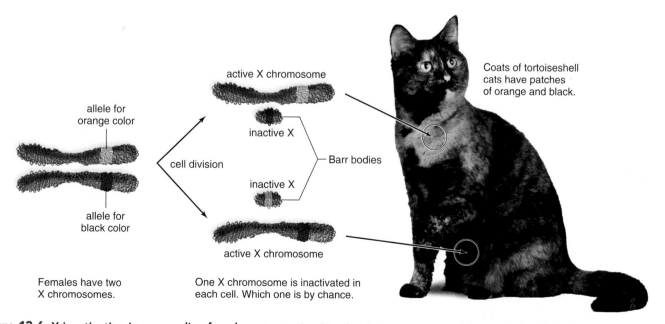

Figure 13.6 X-inactivation in mammalian females.   In cats, the alleles for black or orange coat color are carried on the X chromosomes. Random X-inactivation occurs in females. Therefore, in heterozygous females, 50% of the cells have an allele for black coat color and 50% of cells have an allele for orange coat color. The result is tortoiseshell cats that have coats with patches of both black and orange.

Transcriptional Control

Although eukaryotes have various levels of genetic control (see Fig. 13.4), **transcriptional control** remains the most critical of these levels. The first step toward transcription is availability of DNA, which involves chromatin structure. Transcriptional control also involves the participation of transcription factors, activators, and repressors.

Transcription Factors, Activators, and Repressors

Although some operons like those of prokaryotic cells have been found in eukaryotic cells, transcription in eukaryotes is still controlled by DNA-binding proteins. Every cell contains many different types of **transcription factors,** proteins that help regulate transcription by assisting the binding of the RNA polymerase to the promotor. A cell has many different types of transcription factors, and often a variety of transcription factors may be active at a single promoter. Thus, the absence of one can prevent transcription from occurring.

Animation
Transcription Factors

Even if all of the transcription factors are present, transcription may not begin without the assistance of a DNA-binding protein called a **transcription activator.** These bind to regions of DNA called **enhancers,** which may be located some distance from the promoter. A hairpin loop in the DNA brings the transcription activators attached to the enhancer into contact with the transcription factor complex (Fig. 13.7). Likewise, the binding of repressors to silencers within the promoter may prohibit the transcription of certain genes. Most genes are subject to regulation by both activators and repressors also.

Animation
Transcription Complex
and Enhancers

The promoter structure of eukaryotic genes is often very complex, and a large variety of regulatory proteins may interact with each other and with transcription factors to affect a gene's transcription level. Mediator proteins act as a bridge between transcription factors and transcription activators at the promoter. Now RNA polymerase can begin the transcription process (Fig. 13.7). Such protein-to-protein interactions are a hallmark of eukaryotic gene regulation. Together, these mechanisms can fine-tune a gene's transcription level in response to a large variety of conditions.

Transcription factors, activators, and repressors are always present in the nucleus of a cell, but they most likely have to be activated in some way before they will bind to DNA. Activation often occurs when they are phosphorylated by a kinase. *Kinases,* which add a phosphate group to molecules, and *phosphatases,* which remove a phosphate group, are known to be signaling proteins involved in a growth regulatory network that reaches from receptors in the plasma membrane to the genes in the nucleus.

Posttranscriptional Control

Posttranscriptional control of gene expression occurs in the nucleus and includes alternative mRNA splicing and controlling the speed with which mRNA leaves the nucleus.

During pre-mRNA splicing, introns (noncoding regions) are excised, and exons (expressed regions) are joined together to

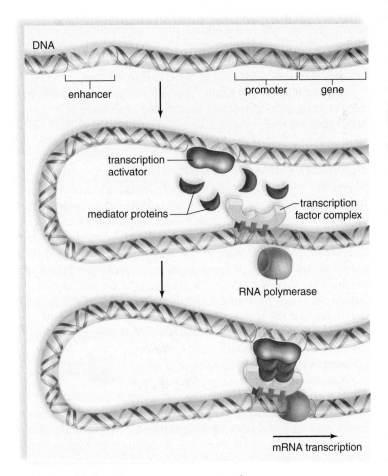

Figure 13.7 Eukaryotic transcription factors. Transcription in eukaryotic cells requires that transcription factors bind to the promoter and transcription activators bind to an enhancer. The enhancer may be far from the promoter, but the DNA loops and mediator proteins act as a bridge joining activators to factors. Only then does transcription begin.

form an mRNA (see Fig. 12.13). When introns are removed from pre-mRNA, differential splicing of exons can occur, and this affects gene expression. For example, an exon that is normally included in an mRNA transcript may be skipped, and it is excised along with the flanking introns (Fig. 13.8). The resulting mature mRNA has an altered sequence, and the protein it encodes is altered. Sometimes introns remain in an mRNA transcript; when this occurs, the protein-coding sequence is also changed.

Animation
Exon-Shuffling

Examples of alternative pre-mRNA splicing abound. Both the hypothalamus and the thyroid gland produce a protein hormone called calcitonin, but the mRNA that leaves the nucleus is not the same in both types of cells. This results in the thyroid's releasing a slightly different version of calcitonin than does the hypothalamus. Evidence of alternative mRNA splicing is found in other cells, such as those that produce neurotransmitters, muscle regulatory proteins, and antibodies.

Alternative pre-mRNA splicing allows humans and other complex organisms to recombine their genes in novel ways to create the great variety of proteins found in these organisms. Researchers are busy determining how small nuclear RNAs (snRNAs) affect the splicing of pre-mRNA. They also know that, sometimes, alternative mRNA splicing can result in the inclusion

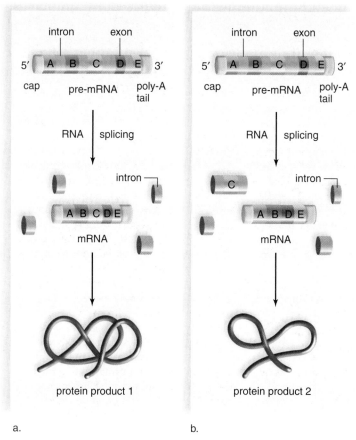

a.   b.

Figure 13.8 Alternative processing of pre-mRNA. Because the pre-mRNAs are processed differently in these two cells (**a** and **b**), distinct proteins result. This is a form of posttranscriptional control of gene expression.

of an intron that brings about destruction of the mRNA before it leaves the nucleus.

Further posttranscriptional control of gene expression is achieved by modifying the speed of transport of mRNA from the nucleus into the cytoplasm. Evidence indicates there is a difference in the length of time it takes various mRNA molecules to pass through a nuclear pore, affecting the amount of gene product realized per unit time following transcription.

Small RNA (sRNA) Molecules Regulate Gene Expression

For a long time, scientists were faced with a mystery: a cell appeared to contain vastly more DNA than was needed to account for the number of expressed proteins. The DNA that was not transcribed into proteins was initially termed "junk" DNA, but recently scientists have begun to understand the role of this DNA in the cell. Although only about 1.5% of the transcribed DNA codes for protein, the remainder is used to form small RNA (sRNA) molecules. We now know that these sRNA molecules represent an important form of gene regulation that functions at multiple levels of gene expression.

How do these RNA molecules regulate gene expression? Notice in Figure 13.9 that transcribed RNA can form loops as hydrogen bonding occurs between its bases. The double-stranded RNA (dsRNA) is diced up by enzymes in the cell to form sRNA molecules. Some of these sRNA molecules regulate transcription, while others are involved in the regulation of translation. Three ways have been found by which sRNA may regulate gene expression:

1. sRNA molecules have been known to alter the compaction of DNA so that some genes are inaccessible to the transcription machinery of the cell.

Figure 13.9 Function of small RNA molecules. Transcription of the DNA ① may lead to looped and double-stranded RNA (dsRNA). ② The cleavage of the dsRNA produces many small RNA (sRNA) molecules. ③ An sRNA can double-back to increase DNA compaction, or may become an miRNA or siRNA. ④ miRNA reduces translation by binding to complementary mRNA molecules. ⑤ siRNA forms a complex with RISC, which then degrades any mRNA with a sequence of bases that are complementary to the siRNA.

THEME Nature of Science

Alternative mRNA Splicing in Disease

The ability to combine the exons and introns of genes into new and novel combinations through alternative mRNA splicing is one of the mechanisms that allow humans to achieve a higher degree of complexity than simpler organisms without a huge increase in the number of genes. In more advanced organisms, the number of alternatively spliced mRNAs increases greatly. Recently, medical science has discovered that when this process goes awry, disease may result.

Figure 13A Skin tumors in patient with Gorlin syndrome.

Gorlin syndrome is an autosomal dominant syndrome that includes aggressive skin cancer (Fig. 13A), multiple other tumors, either benign or cancerous, and cysts in various organs. Gorlin syndrome is linked to the tumor suppressor gene called *patched* located on chromosome 9. But a recent finding demonstrated that several new mutations in *patched* were not within the gene's exons, but within its introns. These mutations caused the mRNA to be spliced incorrectly, rendering the protein nonfunctional. Because at least 95% of most human genes consists of introns, many more such mutations are likely to be discovered in other genetic disorders.

Defective pre-mRNA splicing is also a major cause of spinal muscular atrophy (SMA), an autosomal recessive disorder that is a common cause of childhood mortality. Recent research shows that exon 7 of the *SMN2* gene tends to be left out of the mature mRNA in SMA patients, rendering the protein nonfunctional. The end result is a progressive loss of spinal cord motor neurons, and eventually paralysis and skeletal muscle atrophy. Scientists at Cold Spring Harbor Laboratories turned to antisense oligonucleotide technology, a relatively new technique, in an attempt to reverse the defect. The results were stunning—several of the oligonucleotides tested were able to promote the inclusion of exon 7 in the mature mRNA both in vitro and in cultured cells. These results raise the possibility that targeting aberrant pre-mRNA splicing may ultimately be a viable treatment for many disorders.

Alternative pre-mRNA splicing is also causing scientists to rethink strategies in disease treatment. For example, recent research indicates that the common drug acetaminophen actually targets an alternative version of the COX-1 protein in neurons. This protein variant arises from alternative splicing of the mRNA encoding COX-1 that only occurs in certain neurons. Ultimately, such new findings may allow investigators to design more powerful pain relievers with fewer and less severe side effects.

Geneticists estimate that 80% or more of human genes undergo alternative mRNA splicing, and the estimate is constantly being revised upward. It is perhaps not surprising that this new frontier in gene regulation is redefining the standard approach to identifying the causes of illness and presenting new targets for the development of therapeutics.

Questions to Consider

1. What is the normal role of a tumor-suppressor gene in a cell?
2. How might the use of small RNA molecules be used to treat Gorlin syndrome?

2. Small RNAs are the source of **microRNAs (miRNAs)**, small snippets of RNA that can bind to and dampen the translation of mRNA in the cytoplasm.
3. Small RNAs are also the source of **small-interfering RNAs (siRNAs)** that join with an enzyme (an RNA-induced silencing complex, or RISC) to form an active silencing complex. This activated complex targets specific mRNAs in the cell for breakdown, preventing them from being expressed.

By using a combination of miRNA and siRNA molecules, a cell can fine-tune the amount of gene product being expressed, much like the way in which a dimmer switch on a light regulates the brightness of the room. Because both miRNA and siRNA molecules interfere with the normal gene expression pathways, the process is often referred to as **RNA interference.**

The first scientists to artifically construct miRNA and siRNA molecules to supress the expression of a specific gene were Andrew Fire and Craig Mello. Following this discovery, medical scientists recognized that it may be possible to use sRNA molecules as therapeutic agents to supress the expression of disease-causing genes. For their discovery, Fire and Mello received the 2006 Nobel Prize in Physiology and Medicine.

Translational Control

Translational control begins when the processed mRNA molecule reaches the cytoplasm and before there is a protein product. Translational control involves the activity of mRNA for translation at the ribosome.

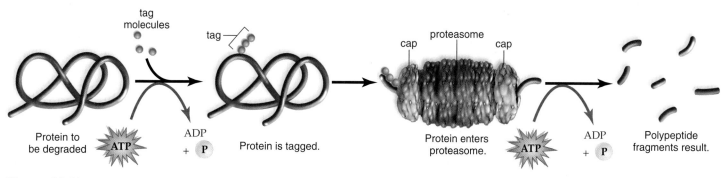

Figure 13.10 Proteasomes degrade proteins in a cell. Proteins to be degraded are first tagged with a signaling molecule. They then enter the proteasome where they are broken down to polypeptide fragments.

Presence or absence of the 5′ cap and the length of the poly-A (adenine nucleotide) tail at the 3′ end of a mature mRNA transcript can determine whether translation takes place and how long the mRNA is active. The long life of mRNAs that code for hemoglobin in mammalian red blood cells is attributed to the persistence of their 5′ end caps and their long 3′ poly-A tails. Therefore any condition that affects the length of the poly-A tail or leads to removal of the cap may trigger the destruction of an mRNA.

Posttranslational Control

Posttranslational control begins once a protein has been synthesized and has become active. Posttranslational control represents the last chance a cell has for influencing gene expression.

Some proteins are not immediately active after synthesis. For example, at first bovine proinsulin is a single, long polypeptide that folds into a three-dimensional structure. Cleavage results in two smaller chains that are bonded together by disulfide (S—S) bonds. Only then is active insulin present. This ensures that some proteins become active only when it is appropriate for them to do so.

Just how long a protein remains active in a cell is usually regulated by the use of **proteases**, enzymes that breakdown proteins. To protect the cell, proteases are typically confined to the lysosomes or special structures called **proteasomes**. For a protein to enter a proteasome, it has to be tagged with a signaling protein that is recognized by the proteasome cap (Fig. 13.10). When the cap recognizes the tag, it opens and allows the protein to enter the core of the structure, where it is digested to peptide fragments. Notice that proteasomes help regulate gene expression because they help control the amount of protein product in the cytoplasm.

Check Your Progress 13.2

1. Describe the five levels of genetic control in eukaryotes.
2. Explain how chromatin structure influences gene expression.
3. Discuss how small RNA molecules and proteasomes regulate gene expression.

13.3 Gene Mutations

Learning Outcomes

Upon completion of this section you should be able to
1. Distinguish between spontaneous and induced mutations.
2. Identify how mutations influence protein structure.
3. Summarize how mutations may cause cancer.

A **gene mutation** is a permanent change in the sequence of bases in DNA. The effect of a DNA base sequence change on protein activity can range from no effect to complete inactivity. Germ-line mutations are those that occur in sex cells and can be passed to subsequent generations. Somatic mutations occur in body cells and, therefore, they may affect only a small number of cells in a tissue. Somatic mutations are not passed on to future generations, but they can lead to the development of cancer.

Causes of Mutations

Some mutations are spontaneous—they happen for no apparent reason—while others are induced by environmental influences. In most cases, **spontaneous mutations** arise as a result of abnormalities in normal biological processes. **Induced mutations** may result from exposure to toxic chemicals or radiation, which induce (cause) changes in the base sequence of DNA.

Spontaneous Mutations

Spontaneous mutations can be associated with any number of normal processes. For example, a movable piece of DNA, termed a *transposon,* may jump from one location to another, disrupting one or more genes and leading to an abnormal product (see Chapter 14). On rare occasions, a base in DNA can undergo a chemical change that leads to a mispairing during replication. A subsequent base pair change may be carried forth in future generations. Spontaneous mutations due to DNA replication errors, however, are rare. DNA polymerase, the enzyme that carries out replication, proofreads the new strand against the old strand and detects any mismatched nucleotides, and each is usually replaced with a correct nucleotide. In the end, only about one mistake occurs for every 1 billion nucleotide pairs replicated.

Induced Mutations

Induced mutations are caused by **mutagens,** environmental factors that can alter the base composition of DNA. Among the best-known mutagens are radiation and organic chemicals. Many mutagens are also **carcinogens** (cancer-causing).

Chemical mutagens are present in many sources, including some of the food we eat and many industrial chemicals. The mutagenic potential of AF-2, a food additive once widely used in Japan, and of safrole, a flavoring agent once used to flavor root beer, caused them to be banned. Surprisingly, many naturally occurring substances like aflatoxin, produced in moldy grain and peanuts (and present in peanut butter at an average level of 2 parts per billion), and acrylamide, a natural product found in French fries, are also suspected mutagens.

Tobacco smoke contains a number of organic chemicals that are known carcinogens, and it is estimated that one-third of all cancer deaths can be attributed to smoking. Lung cancer is the most frequent lethal cancer in the United States, and smoking is also implicated in the development of cancers of the mouth, larynx, bladder, kidney, and pancreas. The greater the number of cigarettes smoked per day, the earlier the habit starts, and the higher the tar content, the greater is the possibility of these cancers. When smoking is combined with drinking alcohol, the risk of these cancers increases even more.

Scientists use the Ames test for mutagenicity to hypothesize that a chemical can be carcinogenic (Fig. 13.11). In the Ames test, a histidine-requiring strain of bacteria is exposed to a chemical. If the chemical is mutagenic, the bacteria can grow without histidine. A large number of chemicals used in agriculture and industry give a positive Ames test. Examples are ethylene dibromide (EDB), which is added to leaded gasoline (to vaporize lead deposits in the engine and send them out the exhaust), and ziram, which is used to prevent fungus disease on crops. Some drugs, such as isoniazed (used to prevent tuberculosis), are mutagenic according to the Ames test.

Aside from chemicals, certain forms of radiation, such as X-rays and gamma rays, are called ionizing radiation because they create free radicals, ionized atoms with unpaired electrons. Free radicals react with and alter the structure of other molecules, including DNA. Ultraviolet (UV) radiation is easily absorbed by the pyrimidines in DNA. Wherever there are two thymine molecules next to one another, ultraviolet radiation may cause them to bond together, forming *thymine dimers.* A kink results in the DNA. Usually, these dimers are removed by **DNA repair enzymes,** which constantly monitor DNA and fix any irregularities. One enzyme excises a portion of DNA that contains the dimer; another makes a new section by using the other strand as a template; and still another seals the new section in place.

The importance of these repair enzymes is exemplified by individuals with the condition known as xeroderma pigmentosum. They lack some of the repair enzymes, and as a consequence, these individuals have a high incidence of skin cancer because of the large number of mutations that accumulate over time. Also, repair enzymes can fail, as when skin cancer develops because of excessive sunbathing or prolonged exposure to X-rays.

Animation
Thymine Dimers: Formation and Repair

Figure 13.11 The Ames test for mutagenicity.   A bacterial strain that requires histidine as a nutrient is exposed to a suspected chemical mutagen, but a control is not exposed. The bacteria are plated on a medium that lacks histidine and only the bacteria exposed to the chemical show growth. A mutation allowed the bacteria to grow; therefore, the chemical can be carcinogenic.

Effect of Mutations on Protein Activity

Point mutations involve a change in a single DNA nucleotide and, therefore, a possible change in a specific amino acid. The base change in the second row of Figure 13.12*a* has no effect on the resulting amino acid in hemoglobin; the change in the third row, however, codes for the amino acid valine instead of glutamic acid. This base change accounts for the genetic disorder sickle-cell disease because the incorporation of valine instead of glutamic acid causes hemoglobin molecules to form semirigid rods, and the red blood cells to become sickle shaped. (Compare Figure 13.12*b* to Figure 13.12*c*.) Sickle-shaped cells clog blood vessels and die off more quickly than normal-shaped cells. The base change in the fourth row of Figure 13.12*a* may also have drastic results because the DNA now codes for a stop codon.

Animation
Mutation by Base Substitution

Frameshift mutations occur most often when one or more nucleotides are either inserted or deleted from DNA. The result of a frameshift mutation can be a completely new sequence of codons and nonfunctional protein. Here is how this occurs: The sequence of codons is read from a specific starting point, as in this sentence, THE CAT ATE THE RAT. If the letter C is deleted from this sentence, shifting the reading frame, we read THE ATA TET HER AT—something that doesn't make sense.

Animation
Addition and Deletion Mutations

b. Normal red blood cell   c. Sickled red blood cell

Figure 13.12 Point mutations in hemoglobin. The effect of a point mutation can vary. **a.** Starting at the *top*: Normal sequence of bases in hemoglobin; next, the base change has no effect; next, due to base change, DNA now codes for valine instead of glutamic acid, and the result is that normal red blood cells **(b)** become sickle shaped **(c)**; next, a different base change causes DNA to code for termination, and the protein will be incomplete.

Nonfunctional Proteins

A single nonfunctioning protein can have a dramatic effect on the phenotype, because enzymes are often a part of metabolic pathways. One particular metabolic pathway in cells is as follows:

$$
\underset{\text{(phenylalanine)}}{A} \xrightarrow{\;E_A\;} \underset{\text{(tyrosine)}}{B} \xrightarrow{\;E_B\;} \underset{\text{(melanin)}}{C}
$$

If a faulty code for enzyme E_A is inherited, a person is unable to convert the molecule A to B. Phenylalanine builds up in the system, and the excess causes mental retardation and the other symptoms of the genetic disorder phenylketonuria (PKU). In the same pathway, if a person inherits a faulty code for enzyme E_B, then B cannot be converted to C, and the individual is an albino.

A rare condition called androgen insensitivity is due to a faulty receptor for androgens, which are male sex hormones such as testosterone. In a male with this condition, plenty of testosterone is present in the blood, but the cells are unable to respond to it. Female instead of male external genitals form, and female instead of male secondary sex characteristics occur at puberty. The individual, who appears to be a normal female, may be prompted to seek medical advice when menstruation never occurs. The karyotype is that of a male rather than a female, and the individual does not have the internal sexual organs of a female.

Mutations Can Cause Cancer

It is estimated that one in three people will develop cancer at some time in their lives. Of these affected individuals, one-third of the females and one-fourth of the males will die due to cancer. In the United States, the three deadliest forms of cancer are lung cancer, colon and rectal cancer, and breast cancer.

The development of cancer involves a series of accumulating mutations that can be different for each type of cancer. As discussed in Chapter 9, tumor suppressor genes ordinarily act as brakes on cell division, especially when it begins to occur abnormally. Proto-oncogenes stimulate cell division but are usually turned off in fully differentiated, nondividing cells. When proto-oncogenes mutate, they become oncogenes that are active all the time. Carcinogenesis begins with the loss of tumor suppressor gene activity and/or the gain of oncogene activity. When tumor suppressor genes are inactive and oncogenes are active, cell division occurs uncontrollably because a cell signaling pathway that reaches from the plasma membrane to the nucleus no longer functions as it should (Fig. 13.13 and Fig. 13.14).

It often happens that tumor suppressor genes and proto-oncogenes code for transcription factors or proteins that control transcription factors. As we have seen, transcription factors are a part of the rich and diverse types of mechanisms that control gene expression in cells. They are of fundamental importance to DNA replication and repair, cell growth and division, control of apoptosis, and cellular differentiation. Therefore, it is not surprising that inherited or acquired defects in transcription factor structure and function contribute to the development of cancer.

As examples, the major tumor suppressor gene called *p53* is more frequently mutated in human cancers than any other known gene. It has been found that the p53 protein acts as a transcription factor, and as such is involved in turning on the expression of genes whose products are cell cycle inhibitors (see Chapter 9). *p53* also promotes apoptosis (programmed cell death) when it is needed. The retinoblastoma protein (RB) controls the activity of a transcription factor for cyclin D and other genes whose products promote entry into the S stage of the cell cycle. When the tumor suppressor gene *p16* mutates, the RB

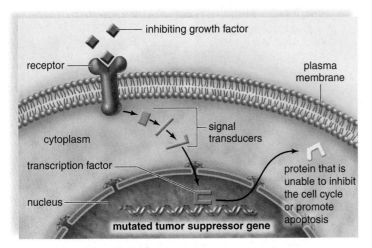

Figure 13.13 Cell signaling pathway that stimulates a mutated tumor suppressor gene.   A mutated tumor suppressor gene codes for a product that directly or indirectly stimulates the cell cycle.

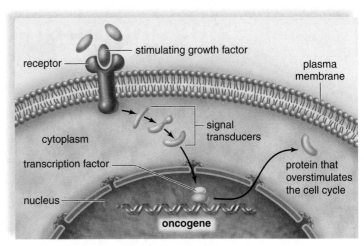

Figure 13.14 Cell signaling pathway that stimulates an oncogene.   An oncogene codes for a product that either directly or indirectly overstimulates the cell cycle.

protein is always available, and the result is too much active cyclin D in the cell.

Mutations in many other genes also contribute to the development of cancer. Several proto-oncogenes code for ras proteins, which are needed for cells to grow, to make new DNA, and to not grow out of control. A point mutation is sufficient to turn a normally functioning *ras* proto-oncogene into an oncogene. Abnormal growth results.

Check Your Progress   13.3

1. List some common causes of spontaneous and induced mutations.
2. Explain how a frameshift mutation may disrupt a gene's function.
3. Discuss how a mutation in a tumor suppressor gene and in proto-oncogenes disrupts the cell cycle.

CONNECTING *the* CONCEPTS *with the* THEMES

Evolution

- In prokaryotes, regulation of gene expression occurs primarily through the regulation of the operon.
- Eukaryotes have evolved a variety of regulatory mechanisms that allows them to fine-tune gene expression and produce a large number of proteins from a relatively small number of genes.
- All living things are subject to genetic mutations or changes in the base sequence of DNA. DNA repair mechanisms have evolved to reduce the impact of mutations. Mutation is a source of genetic variability that is acted on by natural selection, allowing for evolutionary change over time.

Nature of Science

- By studying the structure of the prokaryotic operon, scientists have developed a basic understanding of gene regulation that allows them to better understand gene expression in eukaryotes.
- The discovery of small RNA molecules has caused scientists to rethink the concept of "junk" DNA. New findings may lead to development of new treatments for human diseases.

Biological Systems

- In eukaryotes, gene regulation may occur at a number of different levels, all of which influence the amount of end-product protein found in a cell.
- Mutations cause changes in the DNA and may have a significant influence on the structure and function of the cell, as is the case with cancer.

Media Study Tools

www.mhhe.com/maderbiology11

Enhance your study of this chapter with study tools and practice tests. Also ask your instructor about the resources available through ConnectPlus, including the media-rich eBook, interactive learning tools, and animations.

Summarize

13.1 Prokaryotic Regulation

Prokaryotes often organize genes that are involved in a common process or pathway into operons in which the genes are coordinately regulated. Gene expression in prokaryotes is usually regulated at the level of transcription. The operon model states that a regulator gene codes for a repressor. When the repressor binds to the operator RNA polymerase is unable to bind to the promoter, and transcription of the structural genes of the operon cannot take place. Operons may also be regulated by both activators and repressors.

The *trp* operon is an example of a repressible operon because when tryptophan, the corepressor, is present, it binds to the repressor. The repressor is then able to bind to the operator, and transcription of structural genes does not take place.

The *lac* operon is an example of an inducible operon because when lactose, the inducer, is present, it binds to the repressor. The repressor is unable to bind to the operator, and transcription of structural genes takes place if glucose is absent.

Both the *lac* and *trp* operons exhibit negative control, because a repressor is involved; however, some pathways also provide examples of positive control. The structural genes in the *lac* operon are not maximally expressed unless glucose is absent and lactose is present. At that time, cAMP attaches to a molecule called CAP, and then CAP binds to a site next to the promoter. Now RNA polymerase is better able to bind to the promoter, and transcription occurs.

13.2 Eukaryotic Regulation

The following levels of control of gene expression are possible in eukaryotes: chromatin structure, transcriptional control, posttranscriptional control, translational control, and posttranslational control.

Chromatin structure helps regulate transcription. Highly condensed heterochromatin is genetically inactive, as exemplified by Barr bodies. Less-condensed euchromatin is genetically active, as exemplified by lampbrush chromosomes in vertebrates.

Regulatory proteins called transcription factors, as well as DNA sequences called enhancers and silencers, play a role in controlling transcription in eukaryotes. Transcription factors bind to the promoter, and transcription activators bind to an enhancer. Small RNA molecules, such as microRNAs and small-interferring RNAs, are involved in RNA interference and play a role in gene expression.

Posttranscriptional control is achieved by creating variations in messenger RNA (mRNA) splicing, which may yield multiple mRNA messages from the same gene, and by altering the speed with which a particular mRNA molecule leaves the nucleus.

Translational control affects mRNA translation and the length of time it is translated, primarily by altering the stability of an mRNA.

Posttranslational control affects whether or not an enzyme is active and how long it is active. Proteasomes are specialized structures containing proteases that break down protein molecules and participate in the regulation of gene expression.

13.3 Gene Mutations

In molecular terms, a gene is a sequence of DNA nucleotide bases, and a genetic mutation is a change in this sequence. Mutations can be spontaneous or due to environmental mutagens such as radiation and organic chemicals. Carcinogens are mutagens that cause cancer.

Point mutations can have a range of effects, depending on the particular codon change. Sickle-cell disease is an example of a point mutation that greatly changes the activity of the affected gene. Frameshift mutations result when one or more bases are added or deleted, and the result is usually a nonfunctional protein. Most cases of cystic fibrosis are due to a frameshift mutation. Nonfunctional proteins can affect the phenotype drastically, as in a form of albinism that is due to a single faulty enzyme, and androgen insensitivity, which is due to a faulty receptor for testosterone.

Cancer is often due to an accumulation of genetic mutations among genes that code for regulatory proteins. The cell cycle occurs inappropriately when proto-oncogenes become oncogenes and tumor suppressor genes are no longer effective. Mutations that affect transcription factors and other regulators of gene expression are frequent causes of cancer.

Key Terms

Barr body 243	posttranscriptional control 244
carcinogen 248	posttranslational control 247
chromatin 241	promoter 238
corepressor 239	protease 247
DNA repair enzyme 248	proteasome 247
enhancers 244	regulator gene 238
epigenetic inheritance 241	repressor 238
frameshift mutation 248	RNA interference 246
gene mutation 247	small-interfering RNA
induced mutation 247	(siRNA) 246
inducer 240	spontaneous mutation 247
microRNA (miRNA) 246	structural gene 238
mutagen 248	transcription activator 244
operator 239	transcriptional control 244
operon 238	transcription factor 244
point mutation 248	translational control 246

Assess

Reviewing This Chapter

1. Name and state the function of the three components of operons.   238–39
2. Explain the operation of the *trp* operon, and note why it is considered a repressible operon.   239
3. Explain the operation of the *lac* operon, and note why it is considered an inducible operon.   239–40
4. What are the five levels of genetic regulatory control in eukaryotes?   241

5. Relate heterochromatin and euchromatin to levels of chromatin organization.   242–43
6. With regard to transcriptional control in eukaryotes, explain how Barr bodies show that heterochromatin is genetically inactive.   243
7. What do transcription factors do in eukaryotic cells? What are enhancers?   244
8. Explain how alternative mRNA processing may create multiple mRNAs from a single gene.   244–45
9. Describe the role of small RNA molecules in gene regulation.   245–46
10. Give examples of translational and posttranslational control in eukaryotes.   246–47
11. Name some causes of mutations.   247–48
12. What are two major types of mutations, and what effect can they have on protein activity?   247–48
13. Mutations in what types of genes, in particular, can cause cancer?   249

Testing Yourself

Choose the best answer for each question.

1. Which of the following illustrates negative control?
   a. A repressor that becomes active when bound to a corepressor and inhibits transcription.
   b. A gene that binds a repressor and becomes active.
   c. An activator that becomes active when bound to a coactivator and activates transcription.
   d. A repressor that binds a gene and becomes inactive.
2. In regulation of the *lac* operon, when lactose is present and glucose is absent,
   a. the repressor is able to bind to the operator.
   b. the repressor is unable to bind to the operator.
   c. transcription of structural genes occurs.
   d. transcription of lactose occurs.
   e. Both b and c are correct.
3. In regulation of the *trp* operon, when tryptophan is present,
   a. the repressor is able to bind to the operator.
   b. the repressor is unable to bind to the operator.
   c. transcription of the repressor in inhibited.
   d. transcription of the structural genes, operator, and promoter occurs.
4. In operon models, the function of the promoter is to
   a. code for the repressor protein.
   b. bind with RNA polymerase.
   c. bind to the repressor.
   d. code for the regulator gene.
5. Which of the following statements is/are true regarding operons?
   a. The regulator gene is transcribed with the structural genes.
   b. The structural genes are always transcribed.
   c. All genes are always transcribed.
   d. The regulator gene has its own promoter.
6. Which of the following regulate gene expression in the eukaryotic nucleus?
   a. posttranslational control
   b. transcriptional control
   c. translational control
   d. posttranscriptional control
   e. Both b and d are correct.

7. Which of the following mechanisms may create multiple mRNAs from the same gene?
   a. posttranslational control
   b. alternative mRNA splicing
   c. binding of a transcription factor
   d. chromatin remodeling
   e. miRNAs
8. Translational control of gene expression occurs within the
   a. nucleus.   c. nucleolus.
   b. cytoplasm.   d. mitochondria.
9. Alternative mRNA splicing is an example of which type of regulation of gene expression?
   a. transcriptional   c. translational
   b. posttranscriptional   d. posttranslational
10. A scientist adds radioactive uridine (label for RNA) to a culture of cells and examines an autoradiograph. Which type of chromatin is apt to show the label?
    a. heterochromatin   d. the DNA, not the histones
    b. euchromatin   e. Both a and d are correct.
    c. the histones, not the DNA
11. Barr bodies are
    a. genetically active X chromosomes in males.
    b. genetically inactive X chromosomes in females.
    c. genetically active Y chromosomes in males.
    d. genetically inactive Y chromosomes in females.
12. Which of these might cause a proto-oncogene to become an oncogene?
    a. exposure of the cell to radiation
    b. exposure of the cell to certain chemicals
    c. viral infection of the cell
    d. exposure of the cell to pollutants
    e. All of these are correct.
13. A cell is cancerous. You might find an abnormality in
    a. a proto-oncogene.   d. tumor cells.
    b. a tumor suppressor gene.   e. All of these are correct.
    c. regulation of the cell cycle.
14. A tumor suppressor gene
    a. inhibits cell division.   d. is subject to mutations.
    b. opposes oncogenes.   e. All of these are correct.
    c. prevents cancer.
15. Label this diagram of an operon.

structural genes

16. If the DNA codons are CAT CAT CAT, and a guanine base is added at the beginning, which would result?
    a. CAT CAT CAT G
    b. G CAT CAT CAT
    c. GCA TCA TCA T
    d. GC ATC ATC AT

17. A mutation in a DNA molecule involving the replacement of one nucleotide base pair with another is called a(n)
    a. frameshift mutation.
    b. transposon.
    c. deletion mutation.
    d. point mutation.
    e. insertion mutation.

18. Which of these is characteristic of cancer?
    a. It may involve a lack of mutations over a length of time.
    b. It cannot be tied to particular environmental factors.
    c. Apoptosis is one of the first developmental effects.
    d. Mutations in certain types of genes.
    e. It typically develops within a short period of time.

19. Which is not evidence that eukaryotes control transcription?
    a. euchromatin/heterochromatin
    b. existence of transcription factors
    c. lampbrush chromosomes
    d. occurrence of mutations
    e. All of these are correct.

Engage

Virtual Lab
DNA and Genes

The virtual lab "DNA and Genes" provides an interactive tutorial for understanding the influence of mutations on protein structure.

Thinking Scientifically

1. In patients with chronic myelogenous leukemia, an odd chromosome is seen in all the cancerous cells. A small piece of chromosome 9 is connected to chromosome 22. This 9:22 translocation has been termed the Philadelphia chromosome. How could a translocation cause genetic changes that result in cancer?

2. New findings indicate that mutations outside of genes may cause disease, such as in some cases of Hirschsprung disease and multiple endocrine neoplasia. Explain how such a mutation might alter the expression of a gene.

Bioethical Issue
Environmental Estrogens and Mutation

You have learned from this chapter that many types of carcinogens, such as those found in cigarette smoke, may alter the base sequence of DNA. However, environmental estrogens are a recently identified type of carcinogen that is generating much attention and concern in recent years. Environmental estrogens are estrogen-like compounds that can disrupt normal endocrine system function in animals by competing with normal sex hormones for receptors, inadvertently activating and inactivating transcription factors and greatly affecting gene expression. They have been linked to increased mutation rates, to deformed genitals in alligators and fish, to promotion of cell division in cultured breast cancer cells, and to inhibition of sperm development in humans.

Environmental estrogens are sometimes found naturally at low concentrations in foods such as soybeans and flax seeds. However, many of these compounds are artificial, originating from chemicals such as polychlorinated biphenyls (PCBs), phthalates (found extensively in many plastics), and atrazine, a compound found in many commercial weed killers. Many people, including scientists at the EPA, contend that these artificial compounds, even at very low doses, are a major threat to the environment, to many animal species, and to human health.

However, some critics contend that the concentrations of these compounds in the soil, air, and water are far below concentrations necessary to cause problems in most animal species, including humans. They also tout studies showing high concentrations of environmental estrogens in many grains, fruits, and vegetables, and that many of these compounds are rendered harmless by the body before they have a chance to cause mutations.

Should known environmental estrogens, such as those found in plastics, herbicides, and insecticides, be closely monitored by the government, and maximal permissible levels set for their emission into the environment? And where should money to fund these regulations be derived? Or, as some critics insist, are we worried about a problem that simply does not exist?

14

Biotechnology and Genomics

A biotechnology product derived from corn may someday replace plastics produced from oil.

BEFORE YOU BEGIN

Before starting this chapter, take a few moments to review these earlier concepts.

Section 12.1 What is the basic structure of a DNA molecule?

Section 12.4 What is the difference between an intron and an exon in a gene?

Section 13.2 What is the role of microRNA molecules in a cell?

Biotechnology is the study and application of living organisms and processes to manufacture products, or improves the characteristics of bacteria, plants or animals. As a few examples, biotechnologists are actively investigating ways of making our world less dependent on fossil fuels, such as oil. Some bacteria produce biodegradable plastic granules inside of their cells. By introducing these genes into plants, such as the corn plants above, it may be possible someday to produce large quantities of biodegradable plastic. In addition to plastic-producing plants, biotechnology has made it possible for bioengineers and medical scientists to alter the genotype, and subsequently the phenotype, of other organisms—bacteria, animals, and humans. Genetically modified crops are resistant to disease and able to grow under stressful conditions. Farm animals can be made to grow larger than usual, and humans may be supplied with normal genes to make up for ones that do not function as they should.

But many people worry that genetically modified bacteria and plants might harm the environment and that the products produced by altered organisms might not be healthy for humans. Other ethical concerns abound. Is it ethical to give a cat a gene that makes it glow in the dark? To what extent would it be proper to improve the human genome? Everyone should be knowledgeable about modern genetics and biotechnology so they can participate in deciding these issues.

As you read through this chapter, think about the following questions:

1. What procedures are used to introduce a bacterial gene into a plant?
2. What is the difference between a genetically-modified and transgenic organism?
3. How are animals being genetically modified?

FOLLOWING *the* THEMES

CHAPTER 14 BIOTECHNOLOGY AND GENOMICS

UNIT 2 GENETIC BASIS OF LIFE		
	Evolution	The comparison of the genomes of humans and model organisms, such as the mouse, is providing insights into the evolution of our species.
	Nature of Science	The development of recombinant DNA technology has enabled scientists to produce genetically-modified and transgenic organisms that benefit human society.
	Systems Biology	Recombinant DNA technology may be used to modify individual cells, as is the case in gene therapy, or produce organisms that assist in the cleanup of polluted ecosystems.

14.1 DNA Cloning

Learning Outcomes

Upon completion of this section you should be able to

1. Describe the steps involved in making a recombinant DNA molecule.
2. Explain the purpose of the polymerase chain reaction (PCR).
3. Identify how PCR may be used to analyze DNA.

In biology, **cloning** is the production of genetically identical copies of DNA, cells, or organisms through some asexual means. When an underground stem or root sends up new shoots, the resulting plants are clones of one another. The members of a bacterial colony on a petri dish are clones because they all came from the division of a single original cell. Human identical twins are also considered clones. Early in embryonic development the cells separate, and each becomes a complete individual.

DNA cloning can be done to produce many identical copies of the same gene; that is, for the purpose of **gene cloning.** Scientists clone genes for a number of reasons. They might want to determine the difference in base sequence between a normal gene and a mutated gene. Or they might use the genes to genetically modify organisms in a beneficial way. When cloned genes are used to modify a human, the process is called **gene therapy.** Otherwise, the organisms are called **transgenic organisms** [L. *trans,* across, through; Gk. *genic,* producing]. Transgenic organisms are frequently used today to produce a product desired by humans.

Recombinant DNA (rDNA) technology and the polymerase chain reaction (PCR) are two procedures that scientists can use to clone DNA.

Recombinant DNA Technology

Recombinant DNA (rDNA) contains DNA from two or more different sources, such as a human cell and a bacterial cell, as shown in Figure 14.1. To make rDNA, a technician needs a **vector** [L. *vehere,* to carry] by which rDNA will be introduced into a host cell. One common vector is a plasmid. **Plasmids** are small accessory rings of DNA found in bacteria that were first discovered in the bacterium *Escherichia coli* (*E. coli*). The ring is not part of the main bacterial chromosome, and it replicates on its own.

Two enzymes are needed to introduce foreign DNA into vector DNA: (1) a **restriction enzyme,** which cleaves DNA, and (2) an enzyme called **DNA ligase** [L. *ligo,* bind], which seals DNA into an opening created by the restriction enzyme. Hundreds of restriction enzymes occur naturally in bacteria, where they cut up any viral DNA that enters the cell. They are called restriction enzymes because they *restrict* the growth of viruses, but they also act as molecular scissors to cleave any piece of DNA at a specific site.

Notice that the restriction enzyme creates a gap in the DNA (Fig. 14.2), into which a piece of foreign DNA can be placed if it ends in bases complementary to those exposed by the restriction enzyme. The single-stranded, but complementary, ends of the two DNA molecules are called "sticky ends" because they can bind a piece of foreign DNA by complementary base-pairing. Sticky ends

Animation
Restriction Endonucleases

Animation
Construction of a Plasmid Vector

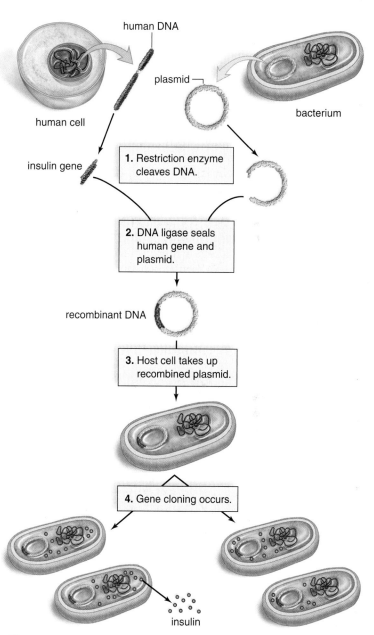

Figure 14.1 **Cloning a human gene.** This figure shows the basic steps in the cloning of a human gene. Human DNA and plasmid DNA are cleaved by a specific type of restriction enzyme. Then the human DNA, perhaps containing the insulin gene, is spliced into a plasmid by the enzyme DNA ligase. Gene cloning is achieved after a bacterium takes up the plasmid. If the gene functions normally as expected, the product (e.g., insulin) may also be retrieved.

Figure 14.2 Restriction enzymes cut DNA at specific locations. Each restriction enzyme recognizes a specific sequence of nucleotides. After the enzyme cuts the DNA, "sticky ends" may be formed that are useful in the cloning of DNA sequences.

facilitate the insertion of foreign DNA into vector DNA as long as both are cleaved by the same restriction enzyme.

Next, genetic engineers use the enzyme DNA ligase to seal the foreign piece of DNA into the vector. DNA splicing is now complete; an rDNA molecule has been prepared (see Fig. 14.1). Bacterial cells take up recombinant plasmids, especially if they are treated to make their cell membranes more permeable. Thereafter, as the plasmid replicates, DNA is cloned.

For bacteria to express a human gene, the cloned gene has to be accompanied by regulatory regions unique to bacteria. Also, the gene should not contain introns because bacteria don't have introns. However, it is possible to make a human gene that lacks introns. The enzyme called reverse transcriptase can be used to make a DNA copy of human mRNA. The DNA molecule, called **complementary DNA (cDNA)**, does not

contain introns. Bacteria may then transcribe and translate the cloned cDNA to produce a human protein because the genetic code is the same in humans and bacteria.

The Polymerase Chain Reaction

The **polymerase chain reaction (PCR)**, developed by Kary Mullis in 1985, is widely used in research laboratories to create copies of a segment of DNA quickly in a test tube. The process mimics DNA replication in the cell (see Section 12.2), except that PCR is very specific—it amplifies (makes copies of) only a targeted DNA sequence. The targeted sequence can be less than one part in a million of the total DNA sample!

PCR requires the use of DNA polymerase, the enzyme that carries out DNA replication, and a supply of nucleotides for the new DNA strands. The DNA polymerase used in the reaction is a heat-stable (thermostable) polymerase that has been extracted from the bacterium *Thermus aquaticus,* which lives in hot springs. The enzyme can withstand the high temperature used to separate double-stranded DNA; therefore, replication does not have to be interrupted by the need to add more enzyme. PCR is a chain reaction because the targeted DNA is repeatedly replicated as long as the process continues. The colors in Figure 14.3 distinguish the old strand from the new DNA strand. Notice that the amount of DNA doubles with each replication cycle.

Analyzing DNA

DNA amplified by PCR can be analyzed for various purposes. For example, mitochondrial DNA taken from modern living populations was used to decipher the evolutionary history of

Figure 14.3 Polymerase chain reaction (PCR). PCR allows the production of many identical copies of DNA in a laboratory setting.

a. DNA band patterns

b. Automated DNA fingerprinting

Figure 14.4 The use of STR profiling to establish paternity. **a.** In this method, DNA fragments containing STRs are separated by gel electrophoresis. Male 1 is the father. **b.** Each person's fingerprint pattern (only one is shown) can also be printed out by a machine that detects fluorescence.

human populations. For identification purposes, DNA taken from a corpse burned beyond recognition can be matched to that on the bristles of the person's toothbrush!

Analysis of DNA following PCR has undergone improvements over the years. At first, the entire genome was treated with restriction enzymes, resulting in a unique collection of different-sized fragments because each person has their own restriction enzyme sites. A process called **gel electrophoresis,** which separates DNA fragments according to their size, was then employed; the result of fragment sorting was a pattern of distinctive bands that identified the person.

Now, **short tandem repeat (STR) profiling** is the method of choice. STRs are short sequences of DNA bases that recur several times, as in TCGTCGTCG. STR profiling is advantageous because it doesn't require the use of restriction enzymes. The chromosomal locations for STRs are known, and therefore it is possible to subject only these locations to PCR and use gel electrophoresis to arrive at a band pattern that is different for each person. The band patterns are different because each person has their own number of repeats at the different locations. The greater the number of STRs at a location, the longer the DNA fragment amplified by PCR. The more STR locations employed, the more confident scientists can be of distinctive results for each person (Fig. 14.4a).

The newest method of producing DNA profiles, or "fingerprints," does away with the need to use gel electrophoresis: the DNA fragments are fluorescently labeled. A laser then excites the fluorescent STRs, and a detector records the amount of emission for each DNA fragment in terms of peaks and valleys. Therefore, the greater the fluorescence, the greater the number of repeats at a location. The printout, such as the one shown in

Figure 14.4b, is the DNA fingerprint, and each person has their own unique printout.

Other Applications

Applications of PCR are limited only by the imagination.

- A viral infection, a genetic disorder, or cancer can be confirmed when the DNA tested matches that of a known virus or mutated gene.
- DNA fingerprinted from blood or tissues at a crime scene has been successfully used in screening suspects, convicting criminals, and in exonerating those wrongly convicted.
- DNA fingerprinting through STR profiling has been extensively used to identify the victims of the natural disasters, such as the tsunamis in Indonesia and Japan.
- Relatives can be found, paternity suits can be settled (Fig. 14.4a), genetic disorders can be detected, and illegally poached ivory and fish can be recognized using this technology (see Chapter 19).
- PCR has also shed new light on evolutionary studies by comparing extracted DNA from ancient specimens with that of living organisms.

Video **World Trade Center DNA**

Check Your Progress 14.1

1. Describe the process for creating a rDNA molecule.
2. List the scientific benefits of using the polymerase chain reaction.
3. Explain how DNA profiling can be used to analyze DNA molecules.

14.2 Biotechnology Products

Today, transgenic bacteria, plants, and animals are often called **genetically modified organisms (GMOs),** and the products they produce are called **biotechnology products.**

Genetically Modified Bacteria

Many uses have been found for genetically modified bacteria, besides the production of proteins. Biotechnology products from bacteria include insulin, clotting factor VIII, human growth hormone, t-PA (tissue plasminogen activator), and hepatitis B vaccine.

Transgenic bacteria have many other uses as well. Some have been produced to promote the health of plants. For example, bacteria that normally live on plants and encourage the formation of ice crystals have been changed from frost-plus to frost-minus bacteria. As a result, new crops such as frost-resistant strawberries are being developed. Also, a bacterium that normally colonizes the roots of corn plants has now been endowed with genes (from another bacterium) that code for an insect toxin. The toxin protects the roots from insects. **Animation** Early Genetic Engineering Experiment

Bacteria can be selected for their ability to degrade a particular substance, and this ability can then be enhanced by bioengineering. For instance, naturally occurring bacteria that eat oil have been genetically engineered to clean up beaches (Fig. 14.5) after oil spills, such as the 2010 Deep Water Horizon spill

Figure 14.5 Genetically modified bacteria. Bacteria capable of decomposing oil have been engineered and patented. Recently, scientists used these bacteria extensively in treating the environmental impacts of the Deep Water Horizon oil spill in the Gulf of Mexico.

in the Gulf of Mexico. Bacteria can also remove sulfur from coal before it is burned and help clean up toxic waste dumps. One such strain was given genes that allowed it to clean up levels of toxins that would have killed other strains. Further, these bacteria were given "suicide" genes that caused them to self-destruct when the job had been accomplished.

Organic chemicals are often synthesized by having catalysts act on precursor molecules or by using bacteria to carry out the synthesis. Today, it is possible to go one step further and manipulate the genes that code for these enzymes. For instance, biochemists discovered a strain of bacteria that is especially good at producing phenylalanine, an organic chemical needed to make aspartame, the dipeptide sweetener better known as NutraSweet®. They isolated, altered, and formed a vector for the appropriate genes so that various other bacteria could be genetically engineered to produce phenylalanine.

Genetically Modified Plants

Techniques have been developed to introduce foreign genes into immature plant embryos or into plant cells called *protoplasts* that have had the cell wall removed. The protoplasts are treated with an electric current while they are suspended in a liquid containing foreign DNA. The current creates tiny, self-sealing holes in the plasma membrane through which the DNA can enter. These treated protoplasts go on to develop into mature plants.

Foreign genes transferred to strains of cotton, corn, potato, and even bananas, have made these plants resistant to pests such as fungi and insects, because their cells now produce a chemical that is toxic to the pest species. Similarly, soybeans have been made resistant to a common herbicide. Some corn and cotton plants are both pest- and herbicide-resistant. These and other genetically modified crops that are expected to have increased yields are now sold commercially.

Like bacteria, plants are also being engineered to produce human proteins, such as hormones, clotting factors, and antibodies, in their seeds. One type of antibody made by corn can deliver radioisotopes to tumor cells, and another made by soybeans can be used to treat genital herpes. **Video** Good Tobacco / **Video** Potato Vaccine

Genetically Modified Animals

Techniques have been developed to insert genes into the eggs of animals. It is possible to microinject foreign genes into eggs by hand, but another method uses vortex mixing. The eggs are placed in an agitator with DNA and silicon-carbide needles, and the needles make tiny holes through which the DNA can enter. When these eggs are fertilized, the resulting offspring are transgenic animals. Using this technique, many types of animal eggs have taken up the gene for bovine growth hormone (bGH). The procedure has been used to produce larger fishes, cows, pigs, rabbits, and sheep. **Video** Cloned Milk / **Video** Firefly Rx

Gene pharming, the use of transgenic farm animals to produce pharmaceuticals, is being pursued by a number of firms. Genes that code for therapeutic and diagnostic proteins are

a.

b.

Figure 14.6 Transgenic mammals produce a product. This figure illustrates the basic procedure for generating a transgenic animal. **a.** A bioengineered egg develops in a host to create a transgenic goat that produces a biotechnology product in its milk. **b.** Nuclei from the transgenic goat are transferred into donor eggs, which develop into cloned transgenic goats.

incorporated into an animal's DNA, and the proteins appear in the animal's milk. Trials are under way for drugs that treat cystic fibrosis, cancer, blood diseases, and other disorders. Figure 14.6a outlines the procedure for producing transgenic mammals: DNA containing the gene of interest is injected into donor eggs. Following in vitro fertilization, the zygotes are placed in host females, where they develop. After female offspring mature, the product is secreted in their milk.

Cloning Transgenic Animals

For many years, researchers believed that adult vertebrate animals could not be cloned because cloning requires that all the

Figure 14.7 Experimental use of mice. Bioengineered mice showed that maleness is due to *SRY* DNA.

genes of an adult cell be turned on if development is to proceed normally. This had long been thought impossible.

In 1997, however, Scottish scientists announced that they had produced a cloned sheep, which they called Dolly. Since then, calves, goats, pigs, rabbits, and even cats have also been cloned. The techniques can be applied to produce populations of transgenic animals.

As shown in Figure 14.6*b*, after enucleated eggs from a donor are microinjected with 2n nuclei from a single transgenic animal, they are coaxed to begin development in vitro. Development continues in host females until the clones are born. The female clones have the same product in their milk as does the donor of the eggs. Now that scientists have a way to clone animals, this procedure will undoubtedly be used routinely to procure biotechnology products. However, animal cloning is a difficult process with a low success rate (usually 1–2 viable embryos per 100 attempts). The vast majority of cloning attempts are unsuccessful, resulting in the early death of the clone.

Applications of Transgenic Animals

Researchers are using transgenic mice for many different research projects. Figure 14.7 shows how this technology has demonstrated that a section of DNA called *SRY* (sex determining region of the *Y* chromosome) produces a male animal. The *SRY* gene was cloned, and then one copy was injected into single-celled mouse embryos. Injected embryos developed into males, but any that were not injected developed into females.

Eliminating a gene is another way to study a gene's function. A *knockout mouse* has had both alleles of a gene removed or made nonfunctional. For example, scientists have constructed a knockout mouse lacking the *CFTR* gene, the same gene mutated in cystic fibrosis patients. The mutant mouse has a phenotype similar to a human with cystic fibrosis and can be used to test new drugs for the treatment of the disease.

Check Your Progress   14.2

1. List some of the beneficial applications of transgenic bacteria, animals, and plants.
2. Distinguish between a transgenic animal and a cloned animal.

14.3 Gene Therapy

Learning Outcomes

Upon completion of this section, you should be able to

1. Distinguish between in vivo and ex vivo gene therapy in humans.
2. List examples of how in vivo and ex vivo gene therapy has been used to treat human disease.

The manipulation of an organism's genes can be extended to humans in a process called **gene therapy.** Gene therapy is an accepted therapy for the treatment of a disorder and has been used to cure inborn errors of metabolism, as well as to treat more generalized disorders such as cardiovascular disease and cancer (Fig. 14.8).

Viruses genetically modified to be safe can be used to ferry a normal gene into the body, and so can liposomes, which are microscopic globules of lipids specially prepared to enclose the normal gene. Sometimes the gene may be injected directly into a particular region of the body. Below we give examples of *ex vivo gene therapy,* in which the gene is inserted into cells that have been removed and then returned to the body, and *in vivo gene therapy,* in which the gene is delivered directly into the body.

Ex Vivo Gene Therapy

Children who have SCID (severe combined immunodeficiency) lack the enzyme ADA (adenosine deaminase), which is involved in the maturation of immune cells. Therefore, these children are prone to constant infections and may die unless they receive treatment. To carry out gene therapy, bone marrow stem cells are removed from the bone marrow of the patient and are infected with a virus that carries a normal gene for the enzyme into their DNA. Then the cells are returned to the patient, where it is hoped they will divide to produce more blood cells with the same genes.

One of the earliest uses of ex vivo gene therapy was for familial hypercholesterolemia, a condition that develops when liver cells lack a receptor protein for removing cholesterol from the blood. The high levels of blood cholesterol make the patient subject to fatal heart attacks at a young age. In this procedure, a small portion of the liver was surgically excised and then infected with a virus containing a normal gene for the receptor before being returned to the patient. Patients experienced lowered serum cholesterol levels following this procedure. Scientists are investigating using ex vivo gene therapy to treat other human diseases, including some forms of hemophilia.

In Vivo Gene Therapy

Cystic fibrosis patients lack a gene that codes for a transmembrane carrier of the chloride ion. They often suffer from numerous and potentially deadly infections of the respiratory tract. In gene therapy trials, the gene needed to cure cystic fibrosis is sprayed into the nose or delivered to the lower respiratory tract

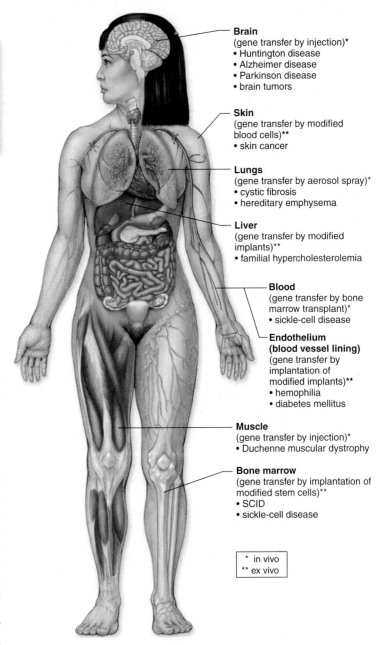

Brain
(gene transfer by injection)*
• Huntington disease
• Alzheimer disease
• Parkinson disease
• brain tumors

Skin
(gene transfer by modified blood cells)**
• skin cancer

Lungs
(gene transfer by aerosol spray)*
• cystic fibrosis
• hereditary emphysema

Liver
(gene transfer by modified implants)**
• familial hypercholesterolemia

Blood
(gene transfer by bone marrow transplant)**
• sickle-cell disease

Endothelium (blood vessel lining)
(gene transfer by implantation of modified implants)**
• hemophilia
• diabetes mellitus

Muscle
(gene transfer by injection)*
• Duchenne muscular dystrophy

Bone marrow
(gene transfer by implantation of modified stem cells)**
• SCID
• sickle-cell disease

*   in vivo
** ex vivo

Figure 14.8 Gene therapy.   Sites of ex vivo and in vivo gene therapy to cure the conditions noted.

by adenoviruses or by the use of a liposome. So far, this treatment has resulted in limited success.

In cancer patients, genes are being used to make healthy cells more tolerant of chemotherapy and to make tumors more vulnerable to chemotherapy. The gene *p53* brings about apoptosis, and there is much interest in introducing it into cancer cells that no longer have the gene and in that way killing them off.

Check Your Progress   14.3

1. Describe the methods that are being used to introduce genes into human beings for gene therapy.
2. Discuss an example of ex vivo and of in vivo gene therapy.

14.4 Genomics

Learning Outcomes

Upon completion of this section, you should be able to

1. Distinguish between the sciences of genomics, proteomics, and bioinformatics.
2. Identify the function of repetitive elements, transposons, and unique noncoding RNA sequences in the human genome.
3. Explain how DNA microarrays are used in the study of genomics.

In the preceding century, researchers discovered the structure of DNA, how DNA replicates, and how DNA and RNA are involved in the process of protein synthesis. Genetics in the twenty-first century concerns **genomics,** the study of genomes—our complete genetic makeup and also that of other organisms. Knowing the sequence of bases in genomes is the first step, and thereafter we want to understand the function of our genes and their introns, as well as the intergenic sequences. The enormity of the task can be appreciated by knowing that there are approximately 6 billion base pairs in the 2n human genome. Many other organisms have a larger number of protein-coding genes but fewer noncoding regions compared to the human genome.

Sequencing the Genome

We now know the order of the base pairs in the human genome. This feat, which has been likened to arriving at the periodic table of the elements in chemistry, was accomplished by the **Human Genome Project (HGP),** a 13-year effort that involved both university and private laboratories around the world.

In the beginning, investigators developed a laboratory procedure that would allow them to decipher a short sequence of base pairs, and then instruments became available that could carry out sequencing automatically. Over the 13-year span, DNA sequencers were constantly improved, and now modern instruments can automatically analyze up to 2 million base pairs of DNA in a 24-hour period.

Sperm DNA was the material of choice for analysis because it has a much higher ratio of DNA to protein than other types of cells. (Recall that sperm do provide both X and Y chromosomes.) However, white cells from the blood of female donors were also used in order to include female-originated samples. The male and female donors were of European, African, American (both North and South), and Asian ancestry.

Many small regions of DNA that vary among individuals, termed polymorphisms, were identified during the HGP. Most of these are *single nucleotide polymorphisms (SNPs);* these vary by only one nucleotide. Many SNPs have no effect; others may contribute to enzymatic differences affecting the phenotype. It's possible that certain SNP patterns change an individual's susceptibility to disease and alter their response to medical treatments (see Chapter 16).

Determining the number of genes in the human genome required a number of techniques, many of which relied on identifying RNAs in cells and then working backward to find the DNA that can pair with that RNA. **Structural genomics**—knowing the sequence of the bases and how many genes we have—is now being followed by functional genomics.

Estimates place the number of human genes between 23,000 and 25,000. The majority of these genes are expected to code for proteins. However, much of the human genome was formerly described as "junk" because it does not specify the order of amino acids in a polypeptide. However, recall from Chapter 12 that it is possible for RNA molecules to have a regulatory effect in cells. We examine this in more detail in the next section.

Structure of the Eukaryotic Genome

Historically, genes were defined as discrete units of heredity that corresponded to a locus on a chromosome (see Fig. 11.4). Prokaryotes typically possess a single circular chromosome with genes that are packed together very closely; eukaryotic chromosomes, in contrast, are much more complex: The genes are seemingly randomly distributed along the length of a chromosome and are fragmented into exons, with intervening sequences called introns scattered throughout the length of the gene (Fig. 14.9).

Figure 14.9 Chromosomal DNA. A genome contains protein-coding DNA (exons) and noncoding DNA, including introns (light blue), and other intergenic sequences (red). Only the exons are present in mRNA and specify protein synthesis.

In general, more complex organisms have more complex genes with more and larger introns. In humans, 95% or more of the average protein-coding gene is introns. Once a gene is transcribed, the introns must be removed and the exons joined together to form a functional mRNA transcript (see Fig. 12.13).

Once regarded as merely intervening sequences, introns are now attracting attention as regulators of gene expression. The presence of introns allows exons to be put together in various sequences so that different mRNAs and proteins can result from a single gene. Introns might also function to regulate gene expression and help determine which genes are to be expressed and how they are to be spliced. In fact, entire genes have been found embedded within the introns of other genes.

Intergenic Sequences

DNA sequences occur between genes and are referred to as **intergenic sequences.** In general, as the complexity of an organism increases, so does the proportion of its noncoding DNA sequences. Intergenic sequences are now known to comprise the vast majority of human chromosomes, and protein-coding genes represent only about 1.5 to 2% of our total DNA. The remainder of this DNA, once dismissed as "junk DNA," is now thought to serve many important functions. Several basic types of intergenic sequences are found in the human genome, including (1) repetitive elements, (2) transposons, and (3) unique noncoding DNA. The majority of intergenic sequences belong to this last class.

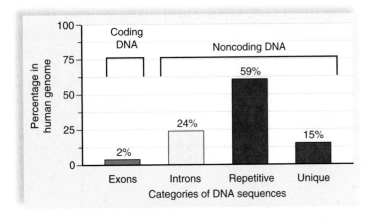

Repetitive DNA Elements

Repetitive DNA elements occur when a sequence of two or more nucleotides is repeated many times along the length of one or more chromosomes. Repetitive elements are very common—comprising nearly half of the human genome—and therefore, many scientists believe that their true significance has yet to be discovered. Although many scientists still dismiss them as having no function, others point out that the centromeres and telomeres of chromosomes are composed of repetitive elements, suggesting that repetitive DNA elements may not be as useless as once thought. For one thing, those of the centromere could possibly help with segregating the chromosomes during cell division.

Repetitive DNA elements include tandem repeats and interspersed repeats. **Tandem repeat** means that the repeated sequences are next to each other on the chromosome. Tandem repeats are often referred to as satellite DNA, because they have a different density than the rest of the DNA within the chromosome. The number and types of tandem repeats may vary significantly from one individual to another, making them invaluable as indicators of heritage. One type of tandem repeat sequence, referred to as *short tandem repeats,* or STRs, has become a standard method in forensic science for distinguishing one individual from another and for determining familial relationships (see page 257).

The second type of repetitive DNA element is called an **interspersed repeat,** meaning that the repetitions may be placed intermittently along a single chromosome, or across multiple chromosomes. For example, a repetitive DNA element, known as the *Alu* sequence, is interspersed every 5,000 base pairs in human DNA and comprises nearly 5–6% of total human DNA. Because of their common occurrence, interspersed repeats are thought to play a role in the evolution of new genes.

Transposons

Transposons are specific DNA sequences that have the remarkable ability to move within and between chromosomes. Their movement to a new location sometimes alters neighboring genes, particularly decreasing their expression. In other words, a transposon sometimes acts like a regulator gene. The movement of transposons throughout the genome is thought to be a driving force in the evolution of living things. The *Alu* repetitive element is an example of a transposon. In fact, many scientists now think that many repetitive DNA elements were originally derived from transposons.

Although Barbara McClintock first described these "movable elements" in corn over 60 years ago, it took time for the scientific community to fully appreciate this revolutionary idea. In fact, their significance was only realized within the past few decades. Transposons, sometimes termed "jumping genes," have now been discovered in bacteria, fruit flies, humans, and many other organisms. McClintock received a Nobel Prize in 1983 for her discovery of transposons and for her pioneering work in genetics.

Animation
Transposons

Unique Noncoding DNA

Genes comprise an estimated 1.5% of the human genome, and repetitive DNA elements make up about 44%; the function of the remaining half, or *unique noncoding DNA*, remains a mystery. Even though this DNA does not appear to contain any protein-coding genes, it has been highly conserved through evolution. In the many millions of years that separate humans from mice, large tracts of this mysterious DNA have remained almost unchanged. But if this DNA has no relevant function, then why has it been so meticulously maintained?

Recently, scientists observed that between 74% and 93% of the genome is transcribed into RNA, including many of these unknown sequences. Thus, what was once thought to be a vast "junk DNA" wasteland may be much more important than once thought and may play active roles in the cell. Small-sized

RNAs may be able to carry out regulatory functions more easily than proteins at times. Therefore, a previously overlooked RNA signaling network may be what allows humans, for example, to achieve structural complexity far beyond anything seen in the unicellular world. Together, these findings have revealed a much more complex, dynamic genome than was envisioned merely a few decades ago.

Revisiting the Definition of a Gene

Perhaps the modern definition of a gene should take the emphasis away from the chromosome and place it on the results of transcription. Previously, molecular genetics considered a gene to be a nucleic acid sequence that codes for the sequence of amino acids in a protein. In contrast to this definition, geneticists have known for some time that all three types of RNA are transcribed from DNA, and that these RNAs are useful products. We also know that protein-coding regions can be interrupted by regions that do not code for a protein but do produce RNAs with various functions. Taking this into consideration, an alternative definition was suggested by Mark Gerstein and associates in 2007: "A gene is a genomic sequence (either DNA or RNA) directly encoding functional products, either RNA or protein."[1]

This definition merely expands on the central dogma of genetics and recognizes that a gene product need not be a protein, and a gene need not be a particular locus on a chromosome. The DNA sequence that results in a gene product can be split and be present on one or several chromosomes. Also, any DNA sequence can result in one or more products. Furthermore, this definition recognizes that some prokaryotes have RNA genes. In other words, the genetic material need not be DNA. Again, we can view this as a simple expansion of the central dogma of genetics.

However, the definition does not spell out what is meant by functional product. It would seem, then, that sequences of DNA resulting in regulatory RNAs or proteins could be considered

genes. According to this definition, "coding" no longer necessarily indicates a DNA sequence that codes for a sequence of amino acids. Instead, it simply means a sequence of DNA bases that are transcribed. The gene product can be RNA molecules, or it can be a protein.

Functional and Comparative Genomics

Since we now know the structure of our genome, the emphasis today is on functional genomics and also on comparative genomics. The aim of **functional genomics** is to understand the exact role of the genome in cells or organisms.

The Nature of Science feature on page 264 discusses the importance of a new technology that can be used to monitor the expression of thousands of genes simultaneously. **DNA microarrays,** also known as DNA chips or genome chips, contain microscopic amounts of known DNA sequences fixed onto a small glass slide or silicon chip in known locations (see Fig. 14A). The use of a microarray can tell you what genes are turned on in a specific cell or organism at a particular time and under what particular environmental circumstances. When mRNA molecules of a cell or organism bind through complementary base pairing with the various DNA sequences on an array, then that gene is active in the cell.

DNA microarrays are increasingly available that rapidly identify all the mutations in the genome of an individual. This information is called the person's **genetic profile.** The genetic profile can indicate if any genetic illnesses are likely and what type of drug therapy for an illness might be most appropriate for that individual.

▶ **Animation** Microarray

Aside from the protein-coding regions, researchers also want to know how SNPs and non-protein-coding regions, including repeats, affect which proteins are active in cells. As already discussed at length in Chapter 12, much research is now devoted to knowing the function of DNA regions that do not code for proteins.

The aim of **comparative genomics** is to compare the human genome to the genome of other organisms, such as the model organisms listed in Table 14.1. Model organisms are used in

1 Gerstein, M. B., Bruce, C., Rozowsky, J. S., et al. 2007. What is a gene, post-ENCODE? History and updated definition. *Genomic Research* 17: 669–81.

Table 14.1 Comparison of Sequenced Genomes

Organism	Homo sapiens (human)	Mus musculus (mouse)	Drosophila melanogaster (fruit fly)	Arabidopsis thaliana (flowering plant)	Caenorhabditis elegans (roundworm)	Saccharomyces cerevisiae (yeast)
Estimated Size	3,200 million bases	2,500 million bases	180 million bases	125 million bases	97 million bases	12 million bases
Estimated Number of Genes	~25,000	~25,000	13,600	25,500	19,100	6,300
Chromosome Number	46	40	8	10	12	32

DNA Microarray Technology

With advances in robotic technology, it is now possible to place the entire human genome onto a single microarray (Fig. 14A). The mRNA from the organism or the cell to be tested is labeled with a fluorescent dye and added to the chip. When the mRNAs bind to the microarray, a fluorescent pattern results that is recorded by a computer. Now the investigator knows what DNA is active in that cell or organism. A researcher can use this method to determine the difference in gene expression between two different cell types, such as between liver cells and muscle cells. **Animation** DNA Microarray

Genetic Profiles

A mutation microarray, the most common type, can be used to generate a person's genetic profile. The microarray contains hundreds to thousands of known disease-associated mutant gene alleles. Genomic DNA from the individual to be tested is labeled with a fluorescent dye, and then added to the microarray. The spots on the microarray fluoresce if the individual's DNA binds to the mutant genes on the chip, indicating that the individual may have a particular disorder or is at risk for developing it later in life. This technique can generate a genetic profile much more quickly and inexpensively than older methods involving DNA sequencing.

Diseased Tissues

DNA microarrays also promise to hasten the identification of genes associated with diseased tissues. In the first instance, mRNA derived from diseased tissue and normal tissue is labeled with different fluorescent dyes. The normal tissue serves as a control.

The investigator applies the mRNA from both normal and abnormal tissue to the microarray. The relative intensities of fluorescence from a spot on the microarray indicate the amount of mRNA originating from that gene in the diseased tissue relative to the normal tissue. If a gene is activated in the disease, more copies of mRNA will bind to the microarray than from the control tissue, and the spot will appear more red than green.

Genomic microarrays are also used to identify links between disease and chromosomal variations. In this instance, the chip contains genomic DNA that is cut into fragments. Each spot on the microarray corresponds to a known chromosomal location. Labeled genomic DNA from diseased and control tissues bind to the DNA on the chip,

and the relative fluorescence from both dyes is determined. If the number of copies of any particular target DNA has increased, more sample DNA will bind to that spot on the microarray relative to the control DNA, and a difference in fluorescence of the two dyes will be detected. Researchers are currently using this technique to identify disease-associated copy number variations, such as those discussed in the Evolution feature on page 266.

Questions to Consider

1. Why might a researcher want to know what genes are being expressed in different cell types?
2. How might the information from a DNA microarray be used to develop new drugs to treat disease?

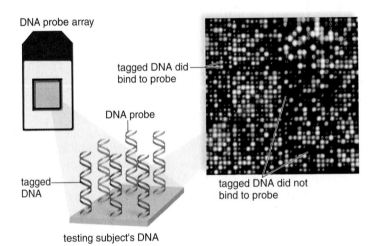

Figure 14A DNA microarray technology.
A DNA microarray contains many microscopic samples of DNA bound to known locations on a silicon chip. A fluorescently labeled mRNA from a tissue or organism binds to the DNA on the chip by complementary base pairing. The fluorescent spots indicate that binding has occurred and that the gene functions in that cell.

genetic analysis because they have many genetic mechanisms and cellular pathways in common with each other and with humans. Functional genomics has also been advanced through the study of these genomes.

Much has been learned by genetically modifying mice; however, other model organisms can also sometimes be used. Scientists inserted a human gene associated with early-onset Parkinson disease into *Drosophila melanogaster*, and the flies

showed symptoms similar to those seen in humans with the disorder. This outcome suggested that we might be able to use these organisms instead of mice to test therapies for Parkinson disease.

Comparative genomics also offers a way to study changes in a genome over time because the model organisms have a shorter generation time than humans. Comparing genomes can also help us understand the evolutionary relationships between organisms. One surprising discovery is that the genomes of all vertebrates are highly similar. Researchers were not surprised to find that the genes of chimpanzees and humans are 98% alike, but they did not expect to find that our sequence is also 85% like that of a mouse. Genomic comparisons will likely reveal evolutionary relationships between organisms never previously considered.

Proteomics

The entire collection of a species' proteins is the **proteome.** At first, it may be surprising to learn that the proteome is larger than the genome until we consider all the many regulatory mechanisms, such as alternative pre-mRNA splicing, that increase the number of possible proteins in an organism.

Proteomics is the study of the structure, function, and interaction of cellular proteins. Specific regulatory mechanisms differ between cells, and these differences account for the specialization of cells. One goal of proteomics is to identify and determine the function of the proteins within a particular cell type. Each cell produces thousands of different proteins that can vary not only between cells but also within the same cell, depending on circumstances. Therefore, the goal of proteomics is an overwhelming endeavor. Microarray technology can assist with this project and so can today's supercomputers.

Computer modeling of the three-dimensional shape of cellular proteins is also an important part of proteomics. If the primary structure of a protein is known, it should be possible to predict its final three-dimensional shape, and even the effects of DNA mutations on the protein's shape and function.

The study of protein function is viewed as essential to the discovery of new and better drugs. Also, it may be possible in the future to correlate drug treatment to the particular proteome of the individual to increase efficiency and decrease side effects. Proteomics will be a critical field of endeavor for many years to come.

Bioinformatics

Bioinformatics is the application of computer technologies, specially developed software, and statistical techniques to the study of biological information, particularly databases that contain much genomic and proteomic information (Fig. 14.10). The new, raw data produced by structural genomics and proteomics is stored in databases that are readily available to research scientists. It is called raw data because, as yet, it has little meaning. Functional genomics and proteomics are dependent on computer analysis to find significant patterns in the raw data. For example, BLAST, which stands for *basic local alignment search tool,* is a computer program that can identify homologous genes among the genomic sequences of model organisms. **Homologous genes** are genes that code for the same proteins, although the base sequences may be slightly different. Finding these differences can help trace the history of evolution among a group of organisms.

Figure 14.10 Bioinformatics. New computer programs are being used to make sense out of the raw data generated by genomics and proteomics. Bioinformatics allows researchers to study both functional and comparative genomics in a meaningful way.

Bioinformatics also has various applications in human genetics. For example, researchers found the function of the protein that causes cystic fibrosis by using the computer to search for genes in model organisms that have the same sequence. Because they knew the function of this gene in model organisms, they could deduce the function in humans. This was a necessary step toward possibly developing specific treatments for cystic fibrosis.

The human genome has 3 billion known base pairs, and without the computer it would be almost impossible to make sense of these data. For example, it is now known that an individual's genome often contains multiple copies of a gene. But individuals may differ as to the number of copies—called *copy number variations,* as discussed in the Evolution feature on page 266. Now it seems that the number of copies in a genome can be associated with specific diseases. The computer can help make correlations between genomic differences among large numbers of people and disease.

It is safe to say that without bioinformatics, our progress in determining the function of DNA sequences, comparing our genome to model organisms, knowing how genes and proteins interact in cells, and so forth, would be extremely slow. Instead, with the help of bioinformatics, progress should proceed rapidly in these and other areas.

Check Your Progress   14.4

1. Distinguish between the genome and the proteome of a cell.
2. Summarize the difference between a short tandem repeat and a transposon.
3. Explain how the use of microarrays and bioinformatics aids in the study of genomics and proteomics.

Copy Number Variations

Geneticists have long been aware of large chromosomal duplications, deletions, and rearrangements detectable microscopically (see Fig. 10.13*a, b*). However, over the past decade scientists have become aware of duplications and deletions in the DNA called *copy number variations* (CNVs). Unlike shorter duplications, CNVs are sequences of DNA, usually greater than one kilobase (1,000 nucleotides) in size, that are repeated in varying numbers compared to a reference genome.

This repetition may arise from errors by the DNA polymerase during replication. For example, DNA damage or some other difficulty may cause the replication fork to stall. To continue, the replication machinery can switch to nearby chromosomal material of the same sequence. The replication fork is soon transferred back to the normal template, but the end result is extra or missing copies of small DNA segments. The fact that repetitive elements facilitate template switching suggests a new function for such sequences in our genome.

Some CNVs have known links to disease. Research shows that individuals with fewer copies of the *CCL3L1* gene are more susceptible to HIV infection than those with more copies. The disease Lupus is much more common among people with fewer copies of the complement component *C4* gene. But more surprising was a study that suggested at least some cases of autism can be linked to CNVs. The scientists who published the study examined the total chromosomal content of 1,441 autistic children and compared their DNA to more than 2,800 normal individuals. They found that in some of the autistic children, a 25-gene region of chromosome 16 was missing. Furthermore, analysis of other DNA databases revealed the same result: Approximately 1% of autism cases could be directly linked to the same deletion.[1]

CNVs are also emerging as a possible driving force in evolution. One study utilized DNA microarrays to examine the chromosomal structure of 47 individuals from many ethnic backgrounds, and found 119 regions where copy number variations existed. More surprising, none of the CNVs were found exclusively in one ethnic group,

suggesting that these variants existed well before the human population spread across the Earth. Perhaps they contributed to the phenotypic variations that developed thereafter. Furthermore, many scientists are suggesting that it may be advantageous for a species to have multiple copies of genes; if one or both normal copies of an allele fail to function properly, having a third allele available might be advantageous because it could restore normal function.

Conversely, an organism's two normal alleles would free an extra gene copy from having to maintain normal function. This situation would allow the gene to accumulate mutations without major consequence, which could ultimately lead to the formation of a new, unique gene. Copy number variations may contribute to evolution because they are yet another mechanism for organisms to achieve genetic innovation.

Questions to Consider

1. Why might a CNV in the coding region of a gene change the function of the protein?
2. From an evolutionary perspective, how might variations in CNV allow an organism to adapt to a new environment?

1 Weiss, L. A., et al. 2008. Association between microdeletion and microduplication at 16p11.2 and Autism. *New England Journal of Medicine*, 358: 667–75.

CONNECTING *the* CONCEPTS *with the* THEMES

Evolution

- Repetitive elements and transposons, once considered to be "junk DNA" are now believed to play a role in genome evolution.
- The field of comparative genomics is yielding valuable new insights into the relationships between species, impacting taxonomy and evolutionary biology.

Nature of Science

- Basic research into the nature and organization of genes in various organisms allowed geneticists to produce recombinant DNA molecules and transgenic organisms.
- Using model organisms as a guide, scientists are able to better understand the role of the elements of the genome.

Biological Systems

- Recombinant DNA technology is being used to generate genetically modified bacteria that can assist in protecting plants from pest species or restoring a polluted ecosystem.
- Techniques such as recombinant DNA technology, PCR, and DNA microarrays are allowing scientists to better understand the structure of the genome and to develop new treatments, such as gene therapy, for a number of human diseases.

Media Study Tools

www.mhhe.com/maderbiology11

Enhance your study of this chapter with study tools and practice tests. Also ask your instructor about the resources available through ConnectPlus, including the media-rich eBook, interactive learning tools, and animations.

Summarize

14.1 DNA Cloning

DNA cloning can isolate a gene and produce many copies of it. The gene can be studied in the laboratory or inserted into a bacterium, plant, or animal. Then, this gene may be transcribed and translated to produce a protein, which can become a commercial product or used as a medicine.

Two methods are currently available for making copies of DNA: recombinant DNA technology and the polymerase chain reaction (PCR). Recombinant DNA contains DNA from two different sources. A restriction enzyme is used to cleave plasmid DNA and to cleave foreign DNA. The resulting "sticky ends" facilitate the insertion of foreign DNA into vector DNA. The foreign gene is sealed into the vector DNA by DNA ligase. Both bacterial plasmids and viruses can be used as vectors to carry foreign genes into bacterial host cells.

PCR uses the enzyme DNA polymerase to quickly make multiple copies of a specific piece (target) of DNA. PCR is a chain reaction because the targeted DNA is replicated over and over again. Analysis of DNA segments following PCR has all sorts of uses from assisting genomic research to doing DNA fingerprinting for the purpose of identifying individuals and confirming paternity.

14.2 Biotechnology Products

Transgenic organisms have had a foreign gene inserted into them. Genetically modified bacteria, agricultural plants, and farm animals now produce commercial products of interest to humans, such as hormones and vaccines. Bacteria usually secrete the product. The seeds of plants and the milk of animals contain the product.

Transgenic bacteria have also been engineered to promote the health of plants, perform bioremediation, extract minerals, and produce chemicals. Transgenic crops, engineered to resist herbicides and pests, are commercially available. Transgenic animals have been given various genes, in particular the one for bovine growth hormone (bGH). Cloning of animals is now possible.

14.3 Gene Therapy

Gene therapy, by either ex vivo or in vivo methods, is used to correct the genotype of humans and to cure various human ills. Ex vivo gene therapy has been used to treat diseases such as SCID and cystic fibrosis. A number of in vivo therapies are being employed in the fight against cancer and other human illnesses, such as cardiovascular disease.

14.4 Genomics

Researchers now know the sequence of all the base pairs along the length of the human chromosomes. So far, researchers have identi-fied around 25,000 human genes that code for proteins; the rest of our DNA consists of regions that do not code for a protein. Currently, researchers are placing an emphasis on functional and comparative genomics.

Genes comprise only 1.5% of the human genome. The rest of this DNA is surprisingly more active than once thought. About half of this DNA consists of repetitive DNA elements, which may be in tandem or interspersed throughout several chromosomes. Some of this DNA is made up of mobile DNA sequences called transposons, which are a driving evolutionary force within the genome. The role of the remaining portion of the genome is actively being investigated, but it is believed that these DNA sequences may play an important role in regulation of gene expression, thus challenging the classical definition of the gene. Functional genomics aims to understand the function of protein-coding regions and noncoding regions of our genome. To that end, researchers are utilizing tools such as DNA microarrays. Microarrays can also be used to create an individual's genetic profile, which is becoming helpful in predicting illnesses and how a person will react to particular medications.

Comparative genomics has revealed that little difference exists between the DNA sequence of our bases and those of many other organisms. Genome comparisons have revolutionized our understanding of evolutionary relationships by revealing previously unknown similarities between organisms.

Proteomics is the study of which genes are active in producing proteins in which cells under which circumstances. Bioinformatics is the use of computer technology to assist proteomics and functional and comparative genomics.

Key Terms

bioinformatics 265
biotechnology products 258
cloning 255
comparative genomics 263
complementary DNA
    (cDNA) 256
DNA ligase 255
DNA microarray 263
functional genomics 263
gel electrophoresis 257
gene cloning 255
gene pharming 258
gene therapy 255, 260
genetic profile 263
genetically modified organism
    (GMO) 258
genomics 261
homologous gene 265
Human Genome Project
    (HGP) 261

intergenic sequence 262
interspersed repeat 262
plasmid 255
polymerase chain reaction
    (PCR) 256
proteome 265
proteomics 265
recombinant DNA (rDNA) 255
repetitive DNA element 262
restriction enzyme 255
short tandem repeat (STR)
    profiling 257
structural genomics 261
tandem repeat 262
transgenic organism 255
transposon 262
vector 255

Assess

Reviewing This Chapter

1. What is the methodology for producing recombinant DNA? 255
2. What is the polymerase chain reaction (PCR), and how is it carried out to produce multiple copies of a DNA segment? 256
3. How does STR profiling produce a DNA fingerprint? 257

4. What are some practical applications of DNA segment analysis following PCR?   257
5. For what purposes have bacteria, plants, and animals been genetically altered?   258–59
6. Explain and give examples of ex vivo and in vivo gene therapies in humans.   260
7. What was the purpose of the Human Genome Project? What is the goal of functional genomics?   261–63
8. Describe the various types of intergenic DNA sequences found within the genome.   262–63
9. What insights into evolutionary relationships between organisms are arising from comparative genomics?   263–65
10. What are the goals of proteomics and bioinformatics?   265

Testing Yourself

Choose the best answer for each question.

1. Using this key, put the phrases in the correct order to form a plasmid-carrying recombinant DNA.

KEY:
  (1) use restriction enzymes
  (2) use DNA ligase
  (3) remove plasmid from parent bacterium
  (4) introduce plasmid into new host bacterium
  a. 1, 2, 3, 4   c. 3, 1, 2, 4
  b. 4, 3, 2, 1   d. 2, 3, 1, 4

2. Restriction enzymes found in bacterial cells are ordinarily used
   a. during DNA replication.
   b. to degrade the bacterial cell's DNA.
   c. to degrade viral DNA that enters the cell.
   d. to attach pieces of DNA together.

3. A genetic profile can
   a. assist in maintaining good health.
   b. be accomplished utilizing bioinformatics.
   c. show how many genes are normal.
   d. be accomplished utilizing a microarray.
   e. Both a and d are correct.

4. Bacteria are able to successfully transcribe and translate human genes because
   a. both bacteria and humans contain plasmid vectors.
   b. bacteria can replicate their DNA, but humans cannot.
   c. human and bacterial ribosomes are vastly different.
   d. the genetic code is nearly universal.

5. Bioinformatics can
   a. assist genomics and proteomics.
   b. compare our genome to that of a monkey.
   c. depend on computer technology.
   d. match up genes with proteins.
   e. All of these are correct.

6. The polymerase chain reaction
   a. uses RNA polymerase.
   b. takes place in huge bioreactors.
   c. uses a temperature-insensitive enzyme.
   d. makes lots of nonidentical copies of DNA.
   e. All of these are correct.

7. Which is a true statement?
   a. Genomics would be slow going without bioinformatics.
   b. Genomics is related to the field of proteomics.
   c. Genomics has now moved on to functional and comparative genomics.
   d. Genomics shows that we are related to all other organisms tested so far.
   e. All of these are correct.

8. DNA amplified by PCR and then used for fingerprinting could come from
   a. any diploid or haploid cell.
   b. only white blood cells that have been karyotyped.
   c. only skin cells after they are dead.
   d. only purified animal cells.
   e. Both b and d are correct.

9. Which was used to find the function of the cystic fibrosis gene?
   a. microarray
   b. proteomics
   c. comparative genomics and bioinformatics
   d. sequencing the gene

10. Which of these pairs is incorrectly matched?
   a. DNA ligase—mapping human chromosomes
   b. protoplast—plant cell engineering
   c. DNA fragments—DNA fingerprinting
   d. DNA polymerase—PCR

11. Which matches best to proteomics?
   a. Start with known gene sequences and build proteins.
   b. Use a microarray to discover what proteins are active in particular cells.
   c. Use bioinformatics to discover the proteins in the cells of other organisms.
   d. Match up known proteins with known genes.

12. Which is not a correct association with regard to bioengineering?
   a. plasmid as a vector—bacteria
   b. protoplast as a vector—plants
   c. RNA virus as a vector—human stem cells
   d. All of these are correct.

13. Proteomics is used to discover
   a. what genes are active in what cells.
   b. what proteins are active in what cells.
   c. the structure and function of proteins.
   d. how proteins interact.
   e. All but a are correct.

14. Which of these is an incorrect statement?
   a. Bacteria usually secrete the biotechnology product into the medium.
   b. Plants are being engineered to have human proteins in their seeds.
   c. Animals are engineered to have a human protein in their milk.
   d. Animals can be cloned, but plants and bacteria cannot.

15. Repetitive DNA elements
   a. may be tandem or spread across several chromosomes.
   b. are found in centromeres and telomeres.
   c. make up nearly half of human chromosomes.
   d. may be present just a few to many thousands of copies.
   e. All of these are correct.

16. Because of the Human Genome Project, we now know
    a. the sequence of the base pairs of our DNA.
    b. the sequence of all genes along the human chromosomes.
    c. all the mutations that lead to genetic disorders.
    d. All of these are correct.
    e. Only a and c are correct.
17. Which of the following delivery methods is not used in gene therapy?
    a. virus
    b. nasal sprays
    c. liposomes
    d. electric currents

Engage

Virtual Labs
Knocking Out Genes
Gene Splicing
Classifying Using Biotechnology

The virtual labs "Knocking Out Genes," "Gene Splicing," and "Classifying Using Biotechnology" all provide an interactive examination of the material found in this chapter.

Thinking Scientifically

1. Transposons are considered by many researchers to have played a major role in the evolution of life on Earth. Explain how the movement of genetic material within the genome may produce some organisms with a selective advantage.

2. The Evolution feature on page 266 describes copy number variations within the genome. Copy number variations do not always contain genes. How might having extra or missing copies of intergenic DNA sequences be beneficial? How might it be harmful?

Bioethical Issue
Transgenic Crops

Transgenic plants can possibly allow crop yields to keep up with the ever-increasing worldwide demand for food. And some of these plants have the added benefit of requiring less fertilizer and/or pesticides, which are harmful to human health and the environment.

Some scientists believe transgenic crops pose their own threat to the environment, however, and many activists believe transgenic plants are themselves dangerous to our health. Studies have shown that wind-carried pollen can cause transgenic crops to hybridize with nearby weedy relatives. Although it has not happened yet, some fear that characteristics acquired in this way might cause weeds to become uncontrollable pests. Or perhaps a toxin produced by transgenic crops could possibly hurt other organisms in the habitat. Many researchers are conducting tests to see if this might occur. And, although transgenic crops have not caused any illnesses in humans so far, some scientists concede the possibility that people could be allergic to a transgene's protein product.

Already, transgenic plants must be approved by the Food and Drug Administration before they are considered safe for human consumption, and they must meet certain Environmental Protection Administration standards. Some people believe safety standards for transgenic crops should be further strengthened, while others fear stricter standards would result in less food produced. Another possibility is to retain the current standards but require all biotech foods to be clearly labeled so the buyer can choose whether or not to eat them. Which approach do you prefer?

UNIT 7

Comparative Animal Biology

In contrast to plants, which are autotrophic and make their own organic food, animals are heterotrophic and feed on organic molecules made by other organisms. An animal's mobility, which is dependent upon nerve and muscle fibers, is essential to escaping predators, finding a mate, and acquiring food. Food is then digested, and the nutrients are distributed to the body's cells. Finally, waste products are expelled.

In complex animals, a distinct division of labor among organs exists, and each of the organ systems is specialized to carry out specific functions. A cardiovascular system transports materials from one body part to another; a respiratory system carries out gas exchange; and a urinary system filters the blood and removes its wastes. The immune system, along with the lymphatic system, protects the body from infectious diseases. The nervous system and endocrine system coordinate the activities of the other systems.

Our comparative study will show how the different organ systems evolved and how they function to maintain homeostasis, the relative constancy of the internal environment.

UNIT OUTLINE

UNIT LEARNING OUTCOMES

The learning outcomes for this unit focus on three major themes in the life sciences.

Evolution	Explain how various anatomical and physiological adaptations that have evolved in animals confer selective advantages.
Nature of Science	Analyze how specific scientific research studies are advancing our understanding of how animal systems function.
Biological Systems	Review the fundamental structures and functions that are uniquely found in animals.

Astronauts need a special suit to take a walk outside their spacecraft.

31

Animal Organization and Homeostasis

T he fact that an astronaut needs to wear a special suit to take a space walk reminds us that organ systems function best if the internal environment stays within normal limits. For example, a warm temperature speeds enzymatic reactions, a moderate blood pressure helps circulate blood, and a sufficient oxygen concentration facilitates ATP production. Working in harmony and under the coordination of the nervous and endocrine systems, healthy organ systems are capable of maintaining homeostasis, a dynamic equilibrium of the internal environment. Swim the English Channel, cross the Sahara Desert by camel, visit the South Pole, or take a space walk—your body temperature will stay at just about 37°C as long as you take proper precautions. An astronaut depends on artificial systems in addition to natural systems to maintain homeostasis.

This chapter discusses homeostasis after a look at the body's organization. Just as in other complex animals, each organ system of the human body contains a particular set of organs. The circulatory system contains the heart and blood vessels and the nervous system contains the brain and nerves. Organs are composed of tissues, and each type of tissue has like cells that perform specific functions. We begin the chapter by examining several of the major types of tissues.

As you read through the chapter, think about the following questions:

1. How did the evolution of specialized tissues, organs, and organ systems allow animals to better adapt to their environment?
2. What are some of the most important functions of animal skin?
3. How does the disruption of homeostasis lead to disease?

BEFORE YOU BEGIN

Before beginning this chapter, take a few moments to review the following discussions.

Figure 1.2 What levels of biological organization are found in animals?

Section 24.2 What types of tissues are found in flowering plants?

Section 28.1 Which types of tissues are most characteristic of animals?

FOLLOWING *the* THEMES

CHAPTER 31 ANIMAL ORGANIZATION AND HOMEOSTASIS

UNIT 7 COMPARATIVE ANIMAL BIOLOGY		
	Evolution	The degree of cell specialization seen in tissues, organs, and organ systems provides evolutionary advantages for animals.
	Nature of Science	Scientific research is increasing our understanding of how tissues and organs can regenerate.
	Biological Systems	Most animals, especially vertebrates, have similar types of tissues, organs, and organ systems.

31.1 Types of Tissues

Learning Outcomes

Upon completion of this section, you should be able to

1. List and describe the four major types of tissues found in animals.
2. Identify the common locations of the various types of animal tissues.
3. Explain how specialization of cells in tissues enhances tissue function.

Like all living things, animals are highly organized. Animals begin life as a single cell, the fertilized egg or *zygote*. The zygote undergoes cell division, producing cells that will eventually form the variety of tissues that make up organs and organ systems. Although all of these cells carry out a number of common functions—such as obtaining nutrients, synthesizing basic cellular constituents, and in most cases, reproducing themselves—the cells of multicellular organisms further differentiate so that they can perform additional, unique functions.

A **tissue** is composed of specialized cells of the same or similar type that perform a common function in the body. The tissues of most complex animals can be categorized into four major types:

1. *Epithelial tissue* covers body surfaces, lines body cavities, and forms glands.
2. *Connective tissue* binds and supports body parts.
3. *Muscular tissue* moves the body and its parts.
4. *Nervous tissue* receives stimuli and transmits nerve impulses.

 MP3
Overview of Tissues

Epithelial Tissue

Epithelial tissue, also called *epithelium* (pl., epithelia), consists of tightly packed cells that form a continuous layer. Epithelial tissue covers surfaces and lines body cavities. Usually, it has a protective function, but it can also be modified to carry out secretion, absorption, excretion, and filtration.

Epithelial cells may be connected to one another by three types of junctions composed of proteins (see Fig. 5.14). Regions where proteins join them together are called tight junctions. In the intestine, the gastric juices stay out of the body, and in the kidneys, the urine stays within kidney tubules because epithelial cells are joined by tight junctions. In the skin, adhesion junctions add strength and allow epithelial cells to stretch and bend, whereas gap junctions are protein channels that permit the passage of molecules between two adjacent cells. (These junctions are described in more detail in Section 5.4.)

Epithelial tissues are often exposed to the environment on one side, but on the other side they are attached to a *basement membrane.* The basement membrane is simply a thin layer of various types of proteins that anchors the epithelium to the extracellular matrix, which is often a type of connective tissue. The basement membrane should not be confused with the plasma membrane or with the body membranes we will be discussing.

Simple Epithelia

Epithelial tissue is either simple or complex. Simple epithelia have only a single layer of cells (Fig. 31.1) and are classified according to cell type. **Squamous epithelium,** which is composed of flattened cells, is found lining blood vessels and the air sacs of lungs. **Cuboidal epithelium** contains cube-shaped

Figure 31.1 Types of epithelial tissues in vertebrates. Basic epithelial tissues found in vertebrates are shown, along with locations of the tissue and the primary function of the tissue at these locations.

Simple squamous
- lining of lungs, blood vessels
- allows diffusion

basement membrane

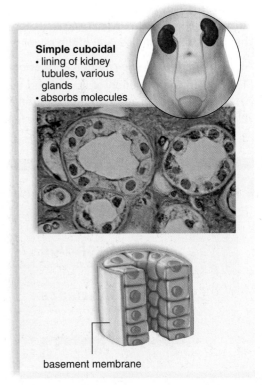

Simple cuboidal
- lining of kidney tubules, various glands
- absorbs molecules

basement membrane

cells and is found lining the kidney tubules and various glands. **Columnar epithelium** has cells resembling rectangular pillars or columns, with nuclei usually located near the bottom of each cell. This epithelium is found lining the digestive tract, where it efficiently absorbs nutrients from the small intestine because of minute cellular extensions called microvilli. Ciliated columnar epithelium is found lining the oviducts, where it propels the egg toward the uterus.

When an epithelium is pseudostratified, it appears to be layered, but true layers do not exist because each cell touches the basement membrane. The lining of the windpipe, or trachea, is pseudostratified ciliated columnar epithelium. A secreted covering of mucus traps foreign particles, and the upward motion of the cilia carries the mucus to the back of the throat, where it may be either swallowed or expectorated. Smoking can cause a change in mucus secretion and inhibit ciliary action, resulting in a chronic inflammatory condition called bronchitis.

Stratified Epithelia

Stratified epithelia have layers of cells piled one on top of the other. Only the bottom layer touches the basement membrane. The nose, mouth, esophagus, anal canal, and vagina are all lined with stratified squamous epithelium. As you'll see, the outer layer of skin is also stratified squamous epithelium, but the cells have been reinforced by keratin, a protein that provides strength. Stratified cuboidal and stratified columnar epithelia also occur in the body.

Glandular Epithelia

When an epithelium secretes a product, it is said to be glandular. A **gland** can be a single epithelial cell, as in the case of mucus-secreting goblet cells within the columnar epithelium lining the

digestive tract, or a gland can contain many cells. Glands that secrete their product into ducts are called **exocrine glands.**

Glands that have no duct are known as **endocrine glands.** Endocrine glands (e.g., pituitary gland and thyroid) secrete hormones internally, so they are transported by the bloodstream (see Chapter 40).

MP3 Epithelial Tissue

Connective Tissue

Connective tissue is the most abundant and widely distributed tissue in complex animals. It is quite diverse in structure and function, but, even so, all types have three components: specialized cells, ground substance, and protein fibers (Fig. 31.2).

The ground substance is a noncellular material that separates the cells and varies in consistency from solid to semifluid to fluid. The fibers[1] are of three possible types. White **collagen fibers** contain collagen, a protein that gives them flexibility and strength. **Reticular fibers** are very thin collagen fibers that are highly branched and form delicate supporting networks. Yellow **elastic fibers** contain elastin, a protein that is not as strong

---

1 In connective tissue, a fiber is a component of the matrix; in muscular tissue, a fiber is a muscle cell; in nervous tissue, a nerve fiber is an axon and its myelin sheath.

Simple columnar
- lining of small intestine, oviducts
- absorbs nutrients

goblet cell secretes mucus

basement membrane

Pseudostratified, ciliated columnar
- lining of trachea
- sweeps impurities toward throat

cilia

goblet cell secretes mucus

basement membrane

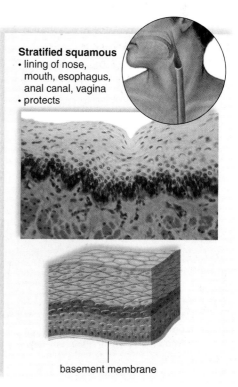

Stratified squamous
- lining of nose, mouth, esophagus, anal canal, vagina
- protects

basement membrane

Adipose cell: stores fat

Ground substance: fills spaces between cells and fibers

Elastic fiber: branched and stretchable

Blood vessel

Stem cell: divides to produce other types of cells

Collagen fiber: unbranched, strong but flexible

Fibroblast: divides to produce other types of cells

Reticular fiber: branched, thin, and forms network

White blood cell: engulfs pathogens or produces antibodies

Figure 31.2 Diagram of fibrous connective tissue.

as collagen but is more elastic. The ground substance plus the fibers together are referred to as the connective tissue *matrix*.

Connective tissue is classified into three major categories: fibrous, supportive, and fluid. Each category includes a number of different types of tissues.

Fibrous Connective Tissue

Both loose fibrous and dense fibrous connective tissues have cells called **fibroblasts** [L. *fibra*, thread, and Gk. *blastos*, bud] that are located some distance from one another and are separated by a jellylike matrix containing white collagen fibers and yellow elastic fibers.

Loose fibrous connective tissue supports epithelium and also many internal organs (Fig. 31.3a). Its presence in lungs, arteries, and the urinary bladder allows these organs to expand.

It forms a protective covering enclosing many internal organs, such as muscles, blood vessels, and nerves.

Adipose tissue [L. *adipalis*, fatty] serves as the body's primary energy reservoir (Fig. 31.3b). It is loose fibrous connective tissue composed mostly of enlarged fibroblasts that store fat. These specialized fibroblasts are called *adipocytes*. Adipose tissue also insulates the body, contributes to body contours, and provides cushioning. In mammals, adipose tissue is found particularly beneath the skin, around the kidneys, and on the surface of the heart.

The number of adipocytes in an individual is fixed. When a person gains weight, the cells become larger, and when weight is lost, the cells shrink. In obese people, the individual cells may be up to five times larger than normal. Most adipose tissue is white, but in newborns and hibernating mammals, some is brown due to an increased number of mitochondria that can produce heat.

Dense fibrous connective tissue contains many collagen fibers that are packed together (Fig. 31.3c). This type of tissue has more specific functions than does loose connective tissue. For example, dense fibrous connective tissue is found in **tendons** [L. *tendo*, stretch], which connect muscles to bones, and in **ligaments** [L. *ligamentum*, band], which connect bones to other bones at joints.

Supportive Connective Tissue

Cartilage and bone are the two main supportive connective tissues that provide structure, shape, protection, and leverage for movement. Generally cartilage is more flexible than bone because it lacks mineralization of the matrix.

Cartilage.   In **cartilage,** the cells lie in small chambers called lacunae (sing., **lacuna**), separated by a matrix that is solid yet flexible. Unfortunately, because this tissue lacks a direct blood

Figure 31.3 Types of connective tissue in vertebrates. Pertinent information about each type of connective tissue is given.

Loose fibrous connective tissue
• has space between components.
• occurs beneath skin and most epithelial layers.
• functions in support and binds organs.

fibroblast

elastic fiber   collagen fiber   50 μm

a.

Adipose tissue
• cells are filled with fat.
• occurs beneath skin, around heart and other organs.
• functions in insulation, stores fat.

nucleus   50 μm

b.

Dense fibrous connective tissue
• has collagenous fibers closely packed.
• in dermis of skin, tendons, ligaments.
• functions in support.

collagen fibers   nuclei of fibroblasts   400×

c.

supply, it heals very slowly. There are three types of cartilage, distinguished by the type of fiber in the matrix.

Hyaline cartilage (Fig. 31.3*d*), the most common type of cartilage, contains only very fine collagen fibers. The matrix has a white, translucent appearance. Hyaline cartilage is found in the nose and at the ends of the long bones and the ribs, and it forms rings in the walls of respiratory passages. The fetal skeleton also is made of this type of cartilage. Later, the cartilaginous fetal skeleton is replaced by bone.

Elastic cartilage has more elastic fibers than hyaline cartilage. For this reason, it is more flexible and is found, for example, in the framework of the outer ear.

Fibrocartilage has a matrix containing strong collagen fibers. Fibrocartilage is found in structures that withstand tension and pressure, such as the pads between the vertebrae in the backbone and the wedges in the knee joint.

Bone. Of all the connective tissues, **bone** is the most rigid. It consists of an extremely hard matrix of inorganic salts, notably calcium salts, deposited around protein fibers, especially collagen fibers. The inorganic salts give bones rigidity, and the protein fibers provide elasticity and strength, much as steel rods do in reinforced concrete.

Compact bone makes up the shaft of a long bone (Fig. 31.3*e*). It consists of cylindrical structural units called osteons (Haversian systems). The central canal of each osteon is surrounded by rings of hard matrix. Bone cells are located in spaces called lacunae between the rings of matrix. Blood vessels in the central canal carry nutrients that allow bone to renew itself. Thin extensions of bone cells within canaliculi (minute canals) connect the cells to each other and to the central canal. The hollow shaft of long bones such as the femur (thigh bone) is filled with yellow bone marrow (see Chapter 39).

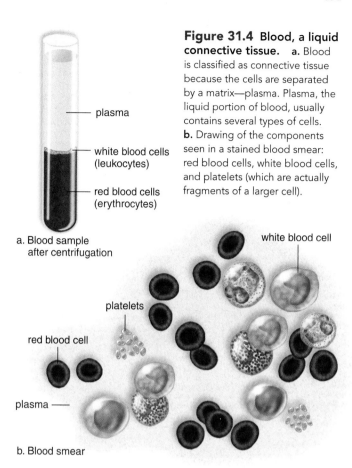

Figure 31.4 Blood, a liquid connective tissue. a. Blood is classified as connective tissue because the cells are separated by a matrix—plasma. Plasma, the liquid portion of blood, usually contains several types of cells. **b.** Drawing of the components seen in a stained blood smear: red blood cells, white blood cells, and platelets (which are actually fragments of a larger cell).

plasma

white blood cells (leukocytes)

red blood cells (erythrocytes)

a. Blood sample after centrifugation

white blood cell

platelets

red blood cell

plasma

b. Blood smear

The ends of a long bone contain spongy bone, which has an entirely different structure. **Spongy bone** contains numerous bony bars and plates, separated by irregular spaces. Although lighter than compact bone, spongy bone is still designed for strength. Just as braces are used for support in buildings, the solid portions of spongy bone follow lines of stress. Spongy bone is also the site of red bone marrow, which is critical to production of blood cells (see Chapters 32 and 33).

Fluid Connective Tissues

Blood, which consists of formed elements and plasma, is a fluid connective tissue located in blood vessels (Fig. 31.4). Formed elements in the blood consist of the many kinds of blood cells and the platelets.

The internal environment of the body consists of blood and **tissue fluid.** The systems of the body help keep blood composition and chemistry within normal limits, and blood in turn creates tissue fluid. Blood transports nutrients and oxygen to tissue fluid and removes carbon dioxide and other wastes. It helps distribute heat and also plays a role in fluid, ion, and pH balance. The formed elements, discussed following, each have specific functions.

The **red blood cells** are small, disk-shaped cells without nuclei. The absence of a nucleus makes the cells biconcave. The presence of the red pigment hemoglobin

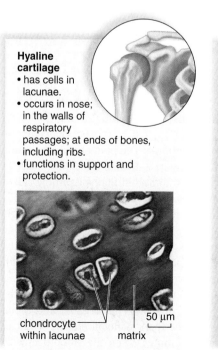

Hyaline cartilage
• has cells in lacunae.
• occurs in nose; in the walls of respiratory passages; at ends of bones, including ribs.
• functions in support and protection.

chondrocyte within lacunae   matrix   50 μm

d.

Compact bone
• has cells in concentric rings.
• occurs in bones of skeleton.
• functions in support and protection.

central canal   osteon

osteocyte within a lacuna   canaliculi   320×

e.

Skeletal muscle
- has striated cells with multiple nuclei.
- occurs in muscles attached to skeleton.
- functions in voluntary movement of body.

striation   nucleus   250×

a.

Smooth muscle
- has spindle-shaped cells, each with a single nucleus.
- cells have no striations.
- functions in movement of substances in lumens of body.
- is involuntary.
- is found in blood vessel walls and walls of the digestive tract.

smooth muscle cell   nucleus   400×

b.

Cardiac muscle
- has branching, striated cells, each with a single nucleus.
- occurs in the wall of the heart.
- functions in the pumping of blood.
- is involuntary.

intercalated disk   nucleus   250×

c.

Figure 31.5 Muscular tissue. **a.** Skeletal muscle is voluntary and striated. **b.** Smooth muscle is involuntary and nonstriated. **c.** Cardiac muscle is involuntary and striated. Cardiac muscle cells branch and fit together at intercalated disks.

makes them red, and in turn, makes the blood red. Hemoglobin is composed of four units; each unit is composed of the protein globin and a complex iron-containing structure called heme. The iron forms a loose association with oxygen, and in this way red blood cells transport oxygen and readily give it up in the tissues.

White blood cells may be distinguished from red blood cells by the fact that they are usually larger, have a nucleus, and without staining would appear translucent. When blood is smeared onto a microscope slide and stained, the nucleus of a white blood cell typically looks blue or purple. White blood cells fight infection, primarily in two ways. Some white blood cells are phagocytic and engulf infectious **pathogens,** while other white blood cells either produce antibodies, molecules that combine with foreign substances to inactivate them, or they kill cells outright.

Platelets are not complete cells; rather, they are fragments of large cells present only in bone marrow. When a blood vessel is damaged, platelets help to form a plug that seals the vessel, and injured tissues release molecules that help the clotting process.

Lymph is a fluid connective tissue located in lymphatic vessels. Lymphatic vessels absorb excess tissue fluid and return it to the cardiovascular system. Special lymphatic capillaries, called lacteals, also absorb fat molecules from the small intestine. Lymph nodes, composed of fibrous connective tissue plus specialized white blood cells called lymphocytes, occur along the length of lymphatic vessels. These lymphocytes and other cells remove any foreign material from the lymph as it passes through lymph nodes. Lymph nodes may enlarge when these cells respond to an infection.

MP3
Connective Tissue

Muscular Tissue

Muscular (contractile) tissue is composed of cells called muscle fibers. Muscle fibers contain actin filaments and myosin filaments, whose interaction accounts for movement. The muscles are also important in the generation of body heat. There are three distinct types of muscle tissue: skeletal, smooth, and cardiac. Each type differs in appearance, physiology, and function.

Skeletal muscle, also called voluntary muscle (Fig. 31.5a), is attached by tendons to the bones of the skeleton, and when it contracts, body parts move. Contraction of skeletal muscle is under voluntary control and occurs faster than in the other muscle types. Skeletal muscle fibers are cylindrical and quite long—sometimes they run the length of the muscle. They arise during development when several cells fuse, resulting in one fiber with multiple nuclei. The nuclei are located at the periphery of the cell, just inside the plasma membrane. The fibers have alternating light and dark bands that give them a **striated** appearance, due to the position of actin filaments and myosin filaments in the cell.

Smooth (visceral) muscle is so named because the cells lack striations. The spindle-shaped cells, each with a single nucleus, form layers in which the thick middle portion of one cell is opposite the thin ends of adjacent cells. Consequently, the nuclei form an irregular pattern in the tissue (Fig. 31.5b). Smooth muscle is not under voluntary control and therefore is said to be involuntary. Smooth muscle, found in the walls of viscera (intestine, stomach, and other internal organs) and blood vessels, contracts more slowly than skeletal muscle but can remain contracted for a longer time. When the smooth muscle of the intestine contracts, food moves along its lumen (central cavity). When the smooth muscle of the blood vessels contracts, blood vessels constrict, helping to raise blood pressure. Small amounts of smooth muscle are also found in the iris of the eye and in the skin.

Cardiac muscle (Fig. 31.5c) is found only in the walls of the heart. Its contraction pumps blood and accounts for the heartbeat. Cardiac muscle combines features of both smooth muscle and skeletal muscle. Like skeletal muscle, it has striations, but the contraction of the heart is involuntary for the most part. Cardiac muscle cells also differ from skeletal muscle cells in that they usually have a single, centrally placed nucleus. The cells are branched and seemingly fused one with the other, and the heart appears to be composed of one large interconnecting mass of muscle cells. Actually, cardiac muscle cells are separate and individual, but they are bound end to end at *intercalated disks*, areas where folded plasma membranes between two cells contain adhesion junctions and gap junctions.

MP3
Muscle Tissue

Nervous Tissue

Nervous tissue contains nerve cells called neurons and supporting cells called neuroglia. An average human body has about 1 trillion neurons. The nervous system conveys signals termed nerve impulses throughout the body.

Neurons

A **neuron** is a specialized cell that has three parts: dendrites, a cell body, and an axon (Fig. 31.6a). A dendrite is a process that conducts signals toward the cell body. The cell body contains the major portion of the cytoplasm and the nucleus of the neuron. An axon is a process that typically conducts nerve impulses away from the cell body. Long axons are covered by myelin, a white, fatty substance. The term *fiber* is used here to refer to an axon along with its myelin sheath if it has one. Outside the brain and spinal cord, fibers bound by connective tissue form **nerves.**

The nervous system has just three functions: sensory input, integration of data, and motor output. Nerves conduct impulses from sensory receptors to the spinal cord and the brain, where integration occurs. The phenomenon called sensation occurs only in the brain, however. Nerves also conduct nerve impulses away from the spinal cord and brain to the muscles and glands, causing them to contract and secrete, respectively. In this way, a coordinated response to the stimulus is achieved.

Neuroglia

In addition to neurons, nervous tissue contains cells called **neuroglia**. In the human brain, these cells outnumber neurons as much as ten to one, and make up approximately half the volume of the organ. Although the primary function of neuroglia is to support and nourish neurons, recent research has shown that some neuroglia directly contribute to brain function.

Several types of neuroglia are found in the brain. Microglia, astrocytes, and oligodendrocytes are shown in Figure 31.6a. Microglia, in addition to supporting neurons, engulf bacterial and cellular debris. Astrocytes provide nutrients to neurons and produce a hormone known as glial cell-derived growth factor, which is being studied as a possible treatment for Parkinson disease and other diseases caused by neuron degeneration. Oligodendrocytes form myelin in the brain.

a. Neuron and neuroglia

b. Micrograph of a neuron   200×

Figure 31.6 Neurons and neuroglia. Neurons conduct nerve impulses. Neuroglia consist of cells that support and service neurons and have various functions: Microglia become mobile in response to inflammation and phagocytize debris. Astrocytes lie between neurons and a capillary; therefore, nutrients must first pass through astrocytes before entering neurons. Oligodendrocytes form the myelin sheaths around fibers in the brain and spinal cord.

THEME Nature of Science

Regenerative Medicine

The ability of salamanders and a few other animals to regenerate amputated tails, limbs, and other organs has fascinated scientists for centuries. Although many invertebrate species can regenerate missing parts (some decapitated snails can regrow a new head!), most vertebrates can regenerate body parts only during embryonic stages of development. The salamander is an exception to this rule, however, with many species retaining the ability to replace lost limbs, tails, and even jaws throughout their lives. Unlike salamanders, humans who lose limbs or organs must either get by without them, or rely on artificial limbs, machines, or transplanted organs.

Much like human arms or legs, salamander limbs contain many different tissue types: bone, muscle, nerve, connective tissue, blood vessels, and skin. Until quite recently, most scientists believed that when a salamander limb is severed, the cells that migrate to the site of the injury revert to being truly undifferentiated, pluripotent stem cells capable of becoming any kind of tissue. That hypothesis leads to a number of questions: How did an injury cause the cells to become "reprogrammed"? And how do the cells know which types of tissues to become?

Some recent research has cast doubt on the idea that the cells that regrow a salamander's limb are true stem cells. In a 2009 study, scientists in a German laboratory devised a new method to track the fate of cells rebuilding the severed limb. The researchers first inserted a gene coding for a jellyfish protein called green fluorescent protein (GFP) into the genome of embryonic axolotl salamanders. The result was transgenic salamanders, in which every cell of the animal gave off a detectable green glow when illuminated with ultraviolet light (Figure 31A).

Different tissues from these transgenic salamanders could then be transplanted into nontransgenic salamanders of the same species. When the researchers were certain that the transplanted tissues had survived, different limb amputations were performed. As the limb regenerated, the fate of the transplanted cells could be easily followed by examining the regenerating limb for GFP+ (green) cells. This tracking allowed the researchers to answer the question of whether the GFP+ donor cells would be found throughout the regenerating limb, or only in the same type of tissue that was originally transplanted (Figure 31B).

Somewhat surprisingly, the results showed that most GFP+ tissue types gave rise only to the same tissue type, or to a very limited set of tissues (Figure 31B). For example, when GFP+ skin was transplanted, GFP+ cells were found only in skin or cartilage, but never in muscle. Similarly, when GFP+ cartilage was transplanted, GFP+ cells were found in cartilage but never in muscle, and GFP+ muscle tissue never produced cartilage. Additionally, although previous research had suggested that neuroglia-type cells present in the regenerating limb might revert to pluripotent cells capable of forming many types of tissues, in these experiments GFP+ neuroglia-type cells gave rise only to nerve tissue.

Although the ability to regenerate human limbs and organs is still far in the future, the key to teaching human cells how to regenerate may lie in experiments like these. Beyond regenerating limbs and organs, scientists working in the field of regenerative medicine are closing in on ways to replace insulin-producing cells in type 1 diabetes, to grow new blood vessels to replace blocked ones in failing hearts, and even to replace damaged nerves as well as bone, muscle, and cartilage. Although a

Figure 31A Creating a new type of salamander for limb regeneration research.   *Left:* Wild type axolotl salamander showing normal coloration. *Right:* Researchers used genetic engineering techniques to produce an axolotl whose cells would fluoresce green under UV illumination.

One fundamental difference between neurons and neuroglia is that the neurons of adult animals usually cannot undergo cell division, but neuroglial cells retain this capacity. As a result, the majority of brain tumors in adults involve actively dividing neuroglial cells. Most of these tumors have to be treated with surgery or radiation therapy because a large number of tight juctions in the epithelial cells of brain capillaries prevent many substances (including anti-cancer drugs) from entering the brain tissue.

MP3
Nervous Tissue

Check Your Progress   31.1

1. List five types of epithelium and identify an example of where each type could be found.
2. Compare and contrast the three major types of connective tissue.
3. Describe the structure and function of skeletal, smooth, and cardiac muscle.
4. Recall the three parts of a neuron, and explain the function of each.

large amount of financial support for this research is needed initially, regenerative medicine offers the potential to cure many conditions that currently can only be managed over the lifetime of a patient.

Questions to Consider

1. Certain primitive invertebrate animals, such as sponges and hydras, can regenerate their entire body from one or a few cells. How does this phenomenon complicate the definition of what constitutes an "animal" versus a single-celled life-form?

2. Even in humans, certain cell types (e.g., neurons) are relatively less likely to regenerate after an injury than other types (e.g., skin). What are some relevant differences between these two types of cells that might explain this observation?

3. Beyond regenerating limbs, what are some other potential human diseases that could be treated or cured if we completely understood regeneration?

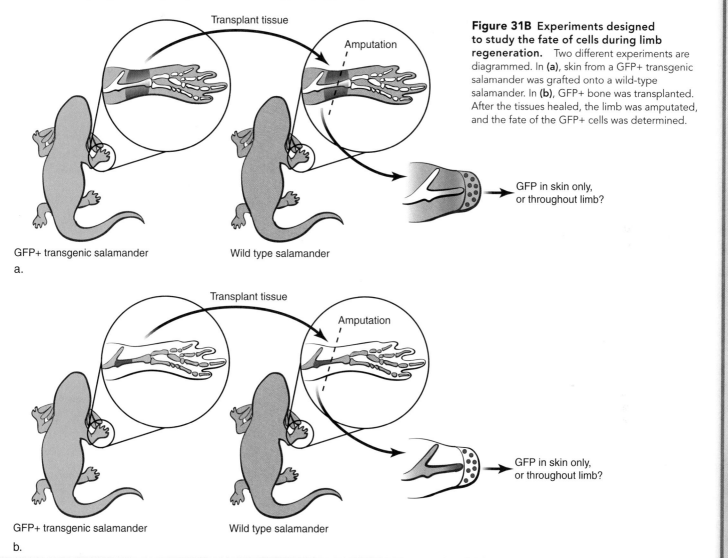

Figure 31B Experiments designed to study the fate of cells during limb regeneration. Two different experiments are diagrammed. In **(a)**, skin from a GFP+ transgenic salamander was grafted onto a wild-type salamander. In **(b)**, GFP+ bone was transplanted. After the tissues healed, the limb was amputated, and the fate of the GFP+ cells was determined.

31.2 Organs, Organ Systems, and Body Cavities

Learning Outcomes

Upon completion of this section, you should be able to

1. Distinguish between tissues, organs, and organ systems.
2. List the major life processes carried out by each organ system in vertebrate animals.
3. Describe the two main cavities of the human body, and the major organs found in each.

Tissues have four main types; however, two or more of these types may be arranged together in a structure termed an organ that has a specific function; in turn, several organs may work together in an organ system to accomplish a general process. The evolution of organs and organ systems allowed animals to localize these processes to certain areas of the body, and to accomplish them more efficiently.

Organs

We first described the concept of organs in Chapter 24 when we discussed the vegetative and reproductive organs of flowering plants. An **organ** is composed of two or more types of tissues working together to perform a particular function. For example, a kidney is an organ that contains a variety of epithelial and connective tissues, and these tissues are specialized for the function of eliminating waste products from the blood.

Organ Systems

In most animals, individual organs function as part of an organ system. An **organ system** contains many different organs that cooperate to carry out a general process, such as the digestion of food. Similar types of organ systems are found in most invertebrates, and in all vertebrate animals. These organ systems carry out the life processes that all of these animals, including humans, must carry out.

Life Processes	Organ Systems
Coordinate body activities	Nervous system Endocrine system
Acquire materials and energy (food)	Skeletal system Muscular system Digestive system
Maintain body shape	Skeletal system Muscular system
Exchange gases	Respiratory system
Transport materials	Cardiovascular system
Eliminate wastes	Urinary system Digestive system
Protect the body from pathogens	Lymphatic system Immune system
Produce offspring	Reproductive system

Body Cavities

Each organ system has a particular distribution within the body. Vertebrates have two main **body cavities:** the smaller dorsal cavity and the larger ventral cavity (Fig. 31.7a). The brain and the spinal cord are in the dorsal cavity.

During development, the ventral cavity develops from the coelom. In humans and other mammals, the coelom is divided by a muscular diaphragm that assists breathing. The heart and the lungs are located in the upper (thoracic or chest) cavity (Fig. 31.7b). The major portions of the digestive system, including the accessory organs (e.g., the liver and pancreas) are located in the abdominal cavity, as are the kidneys of the urinary system. The urinary bladder, the female reproductive organs, or certain of the male reproductive organs, are located in the pelvic cavity.

MP3 Body Cavities

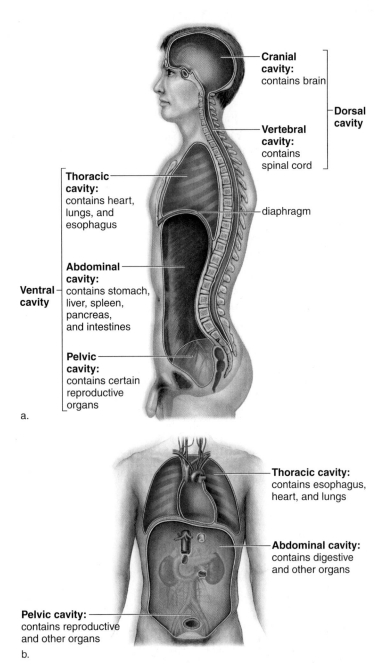

Figure 31.7 Mammalian body cavities. **a.** Side view. The dorsal (toward the back) cavity contains the cranial cavity and the vertebral canal. The brain is in the cranial cavity, and the spinal cord is in the vertebral canal. The well-developed ventral (toward the front) cavity is divided by the diaphragm into the thoracic cavity and the abdominopelvic cavity (abdominal cavity and pelvic cavity). The heart and lungs are in the thoracic cavity, and most other internal organs are in the abdominal cavity. **b.** Frontal view of the thoracic cavity.

Check Your Progress 31.2

1. Explain the difference between an organ and an organ system.
2. Identify two organ systems that protect the body from disease.
3. List and locate the two major body cavities in humans, as well as the two cavities found in each of these.

31.3 The Integumetary System

Learning Outcomes

Upon completion of this section, you should be able to

1. Distinguish between the functions of skin that are common to all animals versus those that are unique to specific groups.
2. Identify the two main regions of skin, and how these differ from the subcutaneous layer.
3. Explain the function of melanocytes in the skin and the effects of UV radiation.
4. Describe the makeup and function of the accessory structures of human skin.

The integumentary system, consisting of the skin, its derivatives, and its accessory organs, is the largest and most conspicuous organ system in the body. The skin of an average human covers an area of 21 square feet and accounts for nearly 15% of the body weight.

Derivatives of the skin differ throughout the vertebrate world. Most fishes have protective outgrowths of the skin called scales. Amphibian skin is usually covered with mucous glands. Scales are characteristic of reptiles, and are also found on the legs and feet of birds, but only birds have feathers, which grow from specialized follicles in the skin. Hair is found only on the skin of mammals, and all mammals (even whales) have hair at some stage of their life.

Functions of Skin

Skin covers the body, protecting underlying parts from dessication, physical trauma, and pathogen invasion. It is also important in regulating body temperature. The skin of small aquatic or semiaquatic animals is often involved in the exchange of gases with the environment (see Chapter 35). In contrast, the dry, scaly skin of reptiles is very poor at gas exchange, but prevents water loss and thus was probably an important evolutionary adaptation to life on land. Feathers are unique appendages of bird skin that function in insulation, waterproofing, and of course, flight. Skin is also equipped with a variety of sensory structures that monitor touch, pressure, temperature, and pain. In addition, skin cells manufacture precursor molecules that are converted to vitamin D after exposure to UV (ultraviolet) light.

Regions of Skin

The **skin** has two main regions: the epidermis and the dermis (Fig. 31.8). A *subcutaneous layer*, also known as the hypodermis, is found between the skin and any underlying structures, such as muscle or bone.

Figure 31.8 Human skin anatomy. Skin consists of two regions, the epidermis and the dermis. A subcutaneous layer, or hypodermis, lies below the dermis.

hair shaft

sweat pore
melanocytes
sensory receptor
capillaries
oil gland
arrector pili muscle
free nerve endings
hair follicle
hair root
sweat gland
artery
vein
nerve
adipose tissue

Epidermis

Dermis

Subcutaneous layer

The Epidermis

The **epidermis** [Gk. *epi,* over, and *derma,* skin] is made up of stratified squamous epithelium. Human skin can be described as thin skin or thick skin based on the thickness of the epidermis. Thin skin covers most of the body and is associated with hair follicles, sebaceous (oil) glands, and sweat glands. Thick skin appears in regions of wear and tear, such as the palms of the hands and soles of the feet. Thick skin has sweat glands but no sebaceous glands or hair follicles.

In both types of skin, new cells derived from stem (basal) cells become flattened and hardened as they push to the surface (Fig. 31.9*a*). Hardening takes place because the cells produce keratin, a waterproof protein. It is estimated that 1.5 million of these cells are shed from the human body every day! A thick layer of dead keratinized cells, arranged in spiral and concentric patterns, forms fingerprints (and toe prints, too), which are thought to increase friction and aid in gripping objects.

Specialized cells in the epidermis called **melanocytes** produce melanin, the pigment responsible for skin color. The amount of melanin varies throughout the body. It is concentrated in freckles and moles. Tanning occurs after a lighter-skinned person is exposed to sunlight because melanocytes produce more melanin, which is distributed to epidermal cells before they rise to the surface. Although we tend to associate a tan with health, in reality it signifies that the body is trying to protect itself from the dangerous rays of the Sun. Some ultraviolet (UV) radiation can benefit health, however. As mentioned, certain cells in the epidermis convert a steroid related to

cholesterol into *vitamin D* only with the aid of ultraviolet radiation. Vitamin D is required for proper bone growth, and perhaps for many other bodily functions.

In contrast to its beneficial effects, UV radiation can cause mutations in the DNA of skin cells, leading to skin cancer. Basal cell carcinoma (Fig. 31.9*b*) derived from stem cells gone awry is the more common type of skin cancer and the most curable. Melanoma (Fig. 31.9*c*), the type of skin cancer derived from melanocytes, is the most deadly form. New melanoma treatments are being developed that activate the immune system to fight the tumors more effectively.

The Dermis

The **dermis** [Gk. *derma,* skin] is a region of dense fibrous connective tissue beneath the epidermis. As seen in Figure 31.9*a*, the deeper epidermis forms ridges that interact with projections of the dermis. The dermis contains collagen and elastic fibers. The collagen fibers are flexible but offer great resistance to overstretching; they prevent the skin from being torn. Stretching of the dermis, as occurs in obesity and pregnancy, can produce stretch marks, or striae.

The elastic fibers maintain normal skin tension but also stretch to allow movement of underlying muscles and joints. (The number of collagen and elastic fibers decreases with age and with exposure to the Sun, causing the skin to become less supple and more prone to wrinkling.) The dermis also contains blood vessels that nourish the skin. When blood rushes into these vessels, a person blushes, and when blood is minimal in them, a person turns "blue."

Sensory receptors are specialized nerve endings in the dermis that respond to external stimuli. There are sensory receptors for touch, pressure, pain, and temperature. The fingertips contain the most touch receptors, and these add to our ability to use our fingers for delicate tasks.

The Subcutaneous Layer

Technically speaking, the subcutaneous layer (the hypodermis) beneath the dermis is not a part of skin. It is composed of loose connective tissue and adipose tissue. Subcutaneous adipose tissue helps to thermally insulate the body from either gaining heat from the outside or losing heat from the inside. Excessive development of the subcutaneous layer accompanies obesity.

Accessory Structures of Human Skin

Nails, hair, and glands are of epidermal origin, even though some parts of hair and glands are largely found in the dermis.

Nails are a protective covering of the distal part of fingers and toes, collectively called digits. Nails grow from special epithelial cells at the base of the nail in the portion called the nail root. The cuticle is a fold of skin that hides the nail root. The whitish color of the half-moon-shaped base, or lunula, results

a. Photomicrograph of skin

b. Basal cell carcinoma

c. Melanoma

Figure 31.9 The epidermis. **a.** Epidermal ridges following dermal projections are clearly visible. Stem cells and melanocytes are in this region. Types of skin cancers include **(b)** basal cell carcinoma derived from stem cells, and **(c)** melanoma derived from melanocytes.

from the thick layer of cells in this area. The cells of a nail become keratinized as they grow out over the nail bed. The appearance of nails can reveal clues about a person's health. For example, in clubbing of the nails, the nails turn down instead of lying flat. This condition is associated with a deficiency of oxygen in the blood.

Hair follicles begin in the dermis and continue through the epidermis, where the hair shaft extends beyond the skin. Contraction of the arrector pili muscles attached to hair follicles causes the hairs to "stand on end" and goose bumps to develop. Epidermal cells form the root of hair, and their division causes a hair to grow. The cells become keratinized and die as they are pushed farther from the root.

Hair, except for the root, is formed of dead, hardened epidermal cells; the root is alive and resides at the base of a follicle in the dermis. A person's scalp has about 100,000 hair follicles on average. The number of follicles varies from one body region to another. The texture of hair is dependent on the shape of the hair shaft. In wavy hair, the shaft is oval, and in straight hair, the shaft is round. Hair color is determined by pigmentation. Dark hair is due to melanin concentration, and blond hair has scanty amounts of melanin. Red hair is caused mainly by the presence of an iron-containing pigment called pheomelanin. Gray or white hair results from a lack of pigment. A hair on the scalp grows about 1 mm every three days.

Each hair follicle has one or more **oil glands,** also called sebaceous glands, which secrete sebum, an oily substance that lubricates the hair within the follicle and the skin itself. If the sebaceous glands fail to discharge, the secretions collect and form "whiteheads" or "blackheads." The color of blackheads is due to oxidized sebum. Acne is an inflammation of the sebaceous glands that most often occurs during adolescence due to hormonal changes.

On average, a person's skin has about 250,000 **sweat glands,** which are present in all regions of skin. A sweat gland is a tubule that begins in the dermis and either opens into a hair follicle, or more often opens onto the surface of the skin. Sweat glands located all over the body play a role in modifying body temperature. When the body temperature starts to rise, sweat glands become active. Sweat absorbs body heat as it evaporates. Once the body temperature lowers, sweat glands are no longer active. Other sweat glands occur in the groin and axillary regions and are associated with distinct scents.

MP3 Human Skin

Check Your Progress   31.3

1. List one function of skin that is common to all animals, and one that is unique to a single group.
2. Compare the structure and function of the epidermal and dermal layers of the skin.
3. Discuss why a dark-skinned individual living in northern Canada might develop bone problems.
4. Describe the structure of nails, hair, sweat glands, and oil glands.

31.4 Homeostasis

Learning Outcomes

Upon completion of this section, you should be able to

1. Define homeostasis, and explain why it is an essential feature of all living organisms.
2. Evaluate the evolutionary benefits of regulating an internal variable, such as body temperature, versus the cost.
3. Differentiate between positive and negative feedback mechanisms, and list one specific example of each in animals.

All organ systems of animals contribute to **homeostasis,** the ability of an organism to maintain a relatively constant internal environment. Although all organisms must carry out some degree of homeostasis, animals vary in the degree to which they regulate these internal variables.

Examples of Homeostatic Regulation

With respect to body temperature, all invertebrates, as well as fish, amphibians, and reptiles, are "cold-blooded," or **poikilothermic,** meaning their body temperature fluctuates depending on their environmental temperature. This approach saves energy, but it also may restrict the ability of these species to live in extremely cold or hot environments.

Birds and mammals tend to be "warm-blooded," or **homeothermic,** and they have mechanisms for regulating their body temperature toward an optimum. This approach is energetically expensive, but provides the evolutionary advantage of being able to adapt to many different environments.

Homeostasis does not mean a rigid or unvarying stability, but rather a dynamic fluctuation around a set point. Besides temperature, animal systems regulate pH, salt balance, and the concentrations of many other body constituents such as glucose, oxygen, CO_2, and various minerals. All organ systems participate in this regulation:

- The digestive system takes in and digests food, providing nutrient molecules to replace those constantly being consumed by the body cells.
- The respiratory system adds oxygen to the blood and removes carbon dioxide, to meet body needs.
- The liver removes glucose from the blood and stores it as glycogen; later, glycogen is broken down to supply the needs of body cells. Blood glucose levels remain fairly constant.
- The pancreas secretes insulin in response to elevated blood glucose; insulin helps regulate glycogen storage.
- Under hormonal control, the kidneys excrete wastes and salts, substances that can affect the pH of the blood.

When homeostasis fails, disease or death often results.

 MP3 Homeostasis

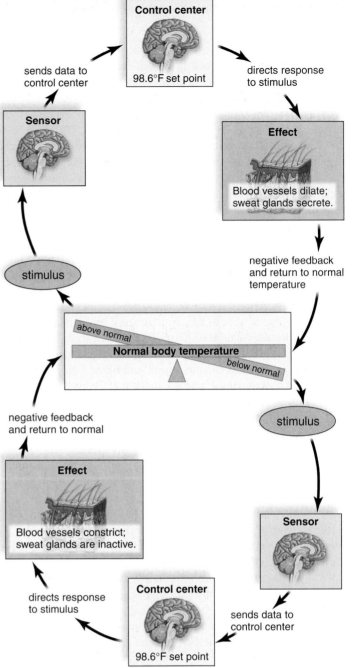

Figure 31.10 Regulation of room temperature using negative feedback. Room temperature is returned to normal when the room becomes too hot (*above*) or too cold (*below*). The thermostat contains both the sensor and the control center. *Above:* The sensor detects that the room is too hot, and the control center turns the furnace off. The room cools, removing the stimulus (negative feedback). *Below:* The sensor detects that the room is too cold, and the control center turns the furnace on. When the temperature returns to normal, the stimulus is no longer present.

Figure 31.11 Regulation of body temperature by negative feedback. *Above:* When body temperature rises above normal, the hypothalamus senses the change and causes blood vessels to dilate and sweat glands to secrete so that body temperature returns to normal. *Below:* When body temperature falls below normal, the hypothalamus senses the change and causes blood vessels to constrict. In addition, shivering may occur to bring body temperature back to normal. In this way, the original stimulus was removed (negative feedback).

Although homeostasis is, to a degree, controlled by hormones, it is ultimately controlled by the nervous system. In humans, the brain contains regulatory centers that control the function of other organs, maintaining homeostasis. These regulatory centers are often a part of negative feedback systems.

Negative Feedback

Negative feedback is the primary homeostatic mechanism that keeps a variable, such as the blood glucose level, close to a particular value, or set point.

A homeostatic mechanism has at least two components: a sensor and a control center. The sensor detects a change in the internal environment; the control center then initiates an action to bring conditions back to normal again. When normal conditions are reached, the sensor is no longer activated. In other words, a negative feedback mechanism is present when the output of the system dampens the original stimulus. As an example, when blood pressure rises, sensory receptors signal a control center in the brain. The center stops sending nerve impulses to the arterial walls, and they relax. Once the blood pressure drops, signals no longer go to the control center.

A home heating system is often used to illustrate how a more complicated negative feedback mechanism works (Fig. 31.10).

You set the thermostat at, say, 68°F. This is the *set point*. The thermostat contains a thermometer, a sensor that detects when the room temperature is above or below the set point. The thermostat also contains a control center; it turns the furnace off when the room is warm and turns it on when the room is cool. When the furnace is off, the room cools a bit, and when the furnace is on, the room warms a bit. In other words, typical of negative feedback mechanisms, there is a fluctuation above and below normal.

Human Example: Regulation of Body Temperature

The sensor and control center for body temperature are located in a part of the brain called the hypothalamus.

Above Normal Temperature. When the body temperature is above normal, the control center directs the blood vessels of the skin to dilate. The result is that more blood flows near the surface of the body, where heat can be lost to the environment. In addition, the nervous system activates the sweat glands, and the evaporation of sweat helps lower body temperature. Gradually, body temperature decreases to 37.0 degrees C (98.6°F). Body temperature does not get colder and colder because a body temperature below normal brings about a change toward a warmer body temperature.

Below Normal Temperature. When the body temperature falls below normal, the control center directs (via nerve impulses) the blood vessels of the skin to constrict (Fig. 31.11). This action conserves heat. If body temperature falls even lower, the control center sends nerve impulses to the skeletal muscles, and shivering occurs. Shivering generates heat, and gradually body temperature rises to 37.0°C. When the temperature rises to normal, the control center is inactivated.

MP3 Temperature Regulation

Positive Feedback

Positive feedback is a mechanism that brings about a continually greater change in the same direction (Fig. 31.12).

When a woman is giving birth, the head of the baby begins to press against the cervix (opening to the birth canal) stimulating sensory receptors there. When nerve impulses reach the brain, the brain causes the pituitary gland to secrete the hormone

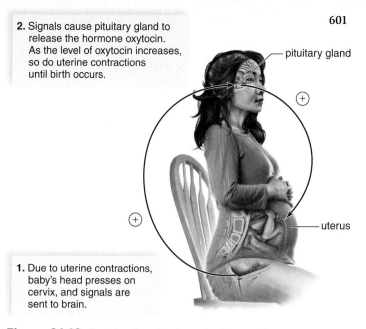

2. Signals cause pituitary gland to release the hormone oxytocin. As the level of oxytocin increases, so do uterine contractions until birth occurs.

pituitary gland

(+)

(+)

uterus

1. Due to uterine contractions, baby's head presses on cervix, and signals are sent to brain.

Figure 31.12 Positive feedback. This diagram shows how positive feedback works. The signal causes a change in the same direction until there is a definite cutoff point, such as birth of a child.

oxytocin. Oxytocin travels in the blood and causes the uterus to contract. As labor continues, the cervix is increasingly more stimulated and uterine contractions become stronger until birth occurs.

A positive feedback mechanism can be harmful, as when a fever causes metabolic changes that push the fever still higher. Death occurs at a body temperature of 113°F because cellular proteins denature at this temperature and metabolism stops. Still, positive feedback loops such as those involved in childbirth, blood clotting, and the stomach's digestion of protein assist the body in completing a process that has a definite cutoff point.

Animation Feedback Mechanisms

Check Your Progress   31.4

1. Define homeostasis and discuss why is it important to body function.
2. Explain how the circulatory, respiratory, and urinary systems specifically contribute to homeostasis.
3. Discuss how negative feedback is similar to the way a thermostat works.

CONNECTING *the* CONCEPTS *with the* THEMES

Evolution

- With the evolution of multicellularity, cell differentiation became possible.
- The development of organs—tissues combined into a structure with a particular function—gave animals the ability to more efficiently localize a function, such as waste elimination (kidneys) and respiration (lungs).
- The evolution of the skin and its derivatives, such as feathers and fur, facilitated movement into new environments and aided homeostasis.

Nature of Science

- Cells of many tissues continue to divide throughout life; for example, skin, hair, and nails. Other tissues are limited in their ability to regenerate.
- Certain animals are able to regenerate various parts of their body. Study of these organisms may someday lead to the ability to stimulate regeneration of human tissues and organs.

Biological Systems

- The organs of complex animals are comprised of four major types of tissues: epithelial, connective, muscular, and nervous.
- The integumentary system serves many functions for animals, including protection, temperature regulation, and detecting sensations.
- Homeostatic mechanisms, especially negative feedback mechanisms, help ensure optimum internal conditions for the body's metabolic functions.

Media Study Tools

www.mhhe.com/maderbiology11

Enhance your study of this chapter with study tools and practice tests. Also ask your instructor about the resources available through ConnectPlus, including the media-rich eBook, interactive learning tools, and animations.

Summarize

31.1 Types of Tissues

During development, the zygote divides to produce cells that go on to form tissues composed of similar cells specialized for a particular function. Tissues make up organs, and organ systems make up the organism. This sequence describes the levels of organization within an organism.

Tissues are categorized into four groups. Epithelial tissue, which covers the body and lines cavities, is of three types: squamous, cuboidal, and columnar epithelium. Each type can be simple or stratified; it can also be glandular or have modifications, such as cilia. In all cases, epithelial tissues are attached to a basement membrane. Epithelial tissue protects, absorbs, secretes, and excretes.

Connective tissue contains cells and a matrix containing fibers and ground substance. The three major categories of connective tissue are fibrous, supportive, and fluid. Loose fibrous and dense fibrous connective tissues contain cells called fibroblasts. Loose fibrous connective tissue has both collagen and elastic fibers. Dense fibrous connective tissue, like that of tendons and ligaments, contains closely packed collagen fibers. Adipose tissue contains cells called adipocytes that enlarge and store fat.

Supportive connective tissue includes cartilage and bone. Both have cells within lacunae, but the matrix for cartilage is more flexible than that for bone, which contains calcium salts. In bone, the lacunae lie in concentric circles within an osteon (or Haversian system) about a central canal. Blood is a fluid connective tissue in which the matrix is a liquid called plasma.

Muscular (contractile) tissue can be smooth or striated, and involuntary (smooth and cardiac) or voluntary (skeletal). In humans, skeletal muscle is attached to bone, smooth muscle is in the wall of internal organs, and cardiac muscle makes up the heart.

Nervous tissue has one main type of conducting cell, the neuron, and several types of neuroglia. The majority of neurons have dendrites, a cell body, and an axon. The brain and spinal cord contain complete neurons, while nerves contain only axons. Axons are specialized to conduct nerve impulses.

31.2 Organs, Organ Systems, and Body Cavities

Organs contain two or more tissues. Organ systems are made up of several organs that function together in a particular life process.

The human body has two main cavities. The dorsal cavity contains the brain and spinal cord. The ventral cavity is divided into the thoracic cavity (containing the heart and lungs) and the abdominal cavity (containing most other internal organs).

31.3 The Integumentary System

The integumentary system includes the skin and its derivatives, such as scales (in fish, reptiles, and birds), feathers (birds only), and hair (mammals only). This organ system protects underlying tissues against dessication, trauma, and pathogens, plus functions in thermoregulation, sensory perception, and vitamin D synthesis.

Skin itself has two regions. Epidermis (stratified squamous epithelium) overlies the dermis (fibrous connective tissue containing sensory receptors, hair follicles, blood vessels, and nerves). The epidermis contains melanocytes, cells that produce a pigment called melanin that helps protect against the harmful effects of UV light. A subcutaneous layer is composed of loose connective tissue and adipose tissue.

31.4 Homeostasis

Homeostasis is the ability of an organism to maintain a relatively constant internal environment. Animals differ in their approach to regulating certain variables like body temperature, but all must be capable of maintaining a certain degree of homeostasis.

All organ systems contribute to homeostasis, but special contributions are made by the liver, which keeps the blood glucose constant, and the kidneys, which regulate the pH. The nervous and hormonal systems regulate the other body systems. Both of these are controlled by negative feedback mechanisms, which result in slight fluctuations above and below desired levels. Less commonly, positive feedback mechanisms can bring about an increasingly greater change it the same direction.

Key Terms

adipose tissue 590	lymph 592
blood 591	melanocyte 598
body cavity 596	muscular (contractile)
bone 591	tissue 592
cardiac muscle 593	nail 598
cartilage 590	negative feedback 600
collagen fiber 589	nerve 593
columnar epithelium 589	nervous tissue 593
compact bone 591	neuroglia 593
connective tissue 589	neuron 593
cuboidal epithelium 588	oil gland 599
dense fibrous connective	organ 596
tissue 590	organ system 596
dermis 598	pathogen 592
elastic cartilage 591	platelet 592
elastic fiber 589	poikilothermic 599
endocrine gland 589	positive feedback 601
epidermis 598	red blood cell 591
epithelial tissue 588	reticular fiber 589
exocrine gland 589	skeletal muscle 592
fibroblast 590	skin 597
fibrocartilage 591	smooth (visceral) muscle 592
gland 589	spongy bone 591
hair follicle 599	squamous epithelium 588
homeostasis 599	striated 592
homeothermic 599	sweat gland 599
hyaline cartilage 591	tendon 590
lacuna 590	tissue 588
ligament 590	tissue fluid 591
loose fibrous connective	white blood cell 592
tissue 590	

Assess

Reviewing This Chapter

1. Name the four major types of tissues. 588
2. Describe the structure and the functions of three types of simple epithelial tissue. 588–89
3. Describe the structure and the functions of six major types of connective tissue. 590–92
4. Describe the structure and the functions of three types of muscular tissue. 592–93
5. Nervous tissue contains what types of cells? 593
6. In general terms, describe the locations of the human organ systems. 596
7. Describe the structure of skin, and state five functions of the integumentary system. 597–99
8. Tell how the various systems of the body contribute to homeostasis. 599
9. What are the functions of sensors, the regulatory center, and effectors in a negative feedback mechanism? Why is it called negative feedback? 600–1

Testing Yourself

Choose the best answer for each question.

1. Which of these is not a type of epithelial tissue?
   a. simple cuboidal
   b. cartilage
   c. stratified squamous
   d. striated
   e. All of these are epithelial tissue.

2. Tendons and ligaments
   a. are dense fibrous connective tissue.
   b. are associated with the bones.
   c. are found in vertebrates.
   d. contain collagen.
   e. All of these are correct.

3. Which tissue has cells in lacunae?
   a. epithelial tissue
   b. cartilage
   c. bone
   d. smooth muscle
   e. Both b and c are correct.

4. Cardiac muscle is
   a. striated.
   b. involuntary.
   c. smooth.
   d. many fibers fused together.
   e. Both a and b are correct.

5. Which of these components of blood fights infection?
   a. red blood cells
   b. white blood cells
   c. platelets
   d. hydrogen ions
   e. All of these are correct.

6. Which of these body systems contribute to homeostasis?
   a. digestive and urinary systems
   b. respiratory and nervous systems
   c. nervous and endocrine systems
   d. immune and cardiovascular systems
   e. All of these are correct.

7. In a negative feedback mechanism,
   a. the output cancels the input.
   b. there is a fluctuation above and below the average.
   c. there is self-regulation.
   d. a regulatory center communicates with other body parts.
   e. All of these are correct.

8. When a human being is cold, the superficial blood vessels
   a. dilate, and the sweat glands are inactive.
   b. dilate, and the sweat glands are active.
   c. constrict, and the sweat glands are inactive.
   d. constrict, and the sweat glands are active.
   e. contract so that shivering occurs.

9. Give the name, the location, and the function for each of the illustrated tissues in the human body.
   a. type of epithelial tissue _____
   b. type of muscular tissue _____
   c. type of connective tissue _____

10. Which of these is a function of skin?
    a. temperature regulation
    b. manufacture of vitamin D
    c. collection of sensory input
    d. protection from invading pathogens
    e. All of these are correct.

11. Which of these is an example of negative feedback?
    a. Air conditioning switches off when room temperature lowers.
    b. Insulin decreases blood sugar levels after eating a meal.
    c. Heart rate increases when blood pressure drops.
    d. All of these are examples of negative feedback.

12. Which of these correctly describes a layer of the skin?
    a. The epidermis is simple squamous epithelium in which hair follicles develop and blood vessels expand when we are hot.
    b. The subcutaneous layer lies between the epidermis and the dermis. It contains adipose tissue, which keeps us warm.
    c. The dermis is a region of connective tissue that contains sensory receptors, nerve endings, and blood vessels.
    d. The skin has a special layer, still unnamed, in which there are all the accessory structures such as nails, hair, and various glands.

13. The _____ separates the thoracic cavity from the abdominal cavity.
    a. liver
    b. pancreas
    c. diaphragm
    d. pleural membrane
    e. intestines

In questions 14–16, match each type of muscle tissue to as many terms in the key as possible.

KEY:
   a. voluntary
   b. involuntary
   c. striated
   d. nonstriated
   e. spindle-shaped cells
   f. branched cells
   g. long, cylindrical cells

14. skeletal muscle

15. smooth muscle

16. cardiac muscle

In questions 17–20, match each description to the tissues in the key.

KEY:
   a. loose fibrous connective tissue
   b. hyaline cartilage
   c. adipose tissue
   d. compact bone

17. occurs in nose and walls of respiratory passages

18. occurs only within bones of skeleton

19. occurs beneath most epithelial layers

20. occurs beneath skin, and around organs, including the heart

Engage

Virtual Lab
Virtual Frog Dissection

The Virtual Lab "Virtual Frog Dissection" provides an interactive look at the major organ systems found in vertebrate animals.

Thinking Scientifically

1. Many cancers develop from epithelial tissue. These include lung, colon, and skin cancers. What are two attributes of this tissue type that make cancer more likely to develop?

2. Bacterial or viral infections can cause a fever. Fevers occur when the hypothalamus changes its temperature set point. Signaling of the hypothalamus could be direct (from the infectious agent itself) or indirect (from the immune system). Which of these would enable the hypothalamus to respond to the greatest variety of infectious agents? Is there any disadvantage to such a signaling system?

Bioethical Issue
Organ Transplants

Despite widespread efforts to convince people of the need for organ donors, supply continues to lag far behind demand. One proposed strategy to bring supply and demand into better balance is to develop an "insurance" program for organs. In this program, participants would pay the "premium" by promising to donate their organs at death. They, in turn, would receive priority for transplants as their "benefit." To avoid the problem of too many high-risk people applying for this type of insurance, a medical exam would be required so that only people with a normal risk of requiring a transplant would be accepted. Do you suppose this system would be an improvement over the current system in which organ donation is voluntary, with no tangible benefit? Can you think of any other strategy that would be more effective for increasing organ donations?

Movie and television star John Ritter died unexpectedly at a relatively young age due to a sudden failure of his circulatory system.

32

Circulation and Cardiovascular Systems

John Ritter was an actor best known for his roles on the TV sitcoms *Three's Company* and *8 Simple Rules for Dating My Teenage Daughter*. In September of 2003, Ritter, then age 54, complained of nausea and chest pains while rehearsing for the latter show. He was taken to a hospital across the street, where he died later that evening.

On autopsy, Ritter's death was confirmed to have been due to an aortic dissection, a condition in which the walls of the body's largest blood vessel, the aorta, separate and fill with blood. This can affect blood flow through the aorta, which may also rupture, filling the chest cavity with blood. Deaths due to aortic dissection are uncommon, with an estimated 5 to 30 such cases per million people per year. Interestingly, evidence of some aortic dissection is found in 1% to 3% of all autopsies performed in the United States; clearly many people are unaware that they have this defect.

After her husband's death, John Ritter's widow filed a $67 million wrongful death lawsuit against the doctors who she believed failed to diagnose and treat his condition properly. In 2008, a Los Angeles jury split 9 to 3 in favor of the doctors, but the plaintiff felt that she had helped to educate people about the condition. Indeed, after Ritter died, his brother was diagnosed with a similar condition, which was then surgically corrected. This tragic situation demonstrates the critical importance of the circulatory system, the topic of this chapter.

As you read through the chapter, think about the following questions:

1. What are the essential components of any circulatory system, and their functions?

2. Through what major blood vessels does a human red blood cell normally pass as it travels from the aorta to a capillary in the lower leg, and back to the heart?

3. Why are the processes that occur in capillaries essential to life?

CHAPTER OUTLINE

BEFORE YOU BEGIN

Before beginning this chapter, take a few moments to review the following discussions.

Figure 8.1 Animal cells use glucose and oxygen for what specific purpose(s)? Where is carbon dioxide generated?

Figure 29.9 How do the circulatory pathways of fishes, amphibians, reptiles, birds, and mammals resemble each other? How are they different?

Section 31.3 What types of tissues comprise the various parts of the cardiovascular system?

FOLLOWING *the* THEMES

CHAPTER 32 CIRCULATION AND CARDIOVASCULAR SYSTEMS

UNIT 7 COMPARATIVE ANIMAL BIOLOGY		
	Evolution	The circulatory systems of animals show a distinct pattern of evolution, from no discrete system, to open systems, to closed cardiovascular systems.
	Nature of Science	Experimentation and observation have increased our understanding of circulatory systems, in some cases resulting in the ability to treat or prevent cardiovascular disease.
	Biological Systems	Circulatory systems carry out critical functions in most animals, helping to provide cells of the body with oxygen and nutrients, and to remove wastes.

32.1 Transport in Invertebrates

Learning Outcomes

Upon completion of this section, you should be able to

1. Describe the common features that determine why invertebrates, such as sponges, cnidarians, and flatworms, do not require a circulatory system.
2. Explain two differences between blood and hemolymph.
3. Compare and contrast the open circulatory system of an arthropod with the closed system of an annelid.

All animal cells require a steady supply of oxygen and nutrients, and their waste products must be removed. In most animals these tasks are facilitated by a **circulatory system**, which moves fluid between various parts of the body. However, some invertebrates, such as sponges, cnidarians (e.g., hydras, sea anemones), and flatworms (e.g., planarians) lack a circulatory system (Fig. 32.1a, b). Their thin body wall makes a circulatory system unnecessary.

In hydras, cells are either part of an external layer, or they line the gastrovascular cavity. Each cell is exposed to water and can independently exchange gases and rid itself of wastes. The cells that line the gastrovascular cavity are specialized to complete the digestive process. They pass nutrient molecules to other cells by diffusion. In planarians, a trilobed gastrovascular cavity branches throughout the small, flattened body. No cell is very far from one of the three digestive branches, so nutrient molecules can diffuse from cell to cell. Similarly, diffusion meets the respiration and elimination needs of the cells.

Pseudocoelomate invertebrates, such as nematodes, use the coelomic fluid of their body cavity for transport purposes. The coelomate echinoderms also rely on movement of coelomic fluid within a body cavity as a circulatory system (Fig. 32.1c).

Invertebrates with a Circulatory System

Most invertebrates have a circulatory system that transports oxygen and nutrients, such as glucose and amino acids, to their cells. There it picks up wastes, which are later excreted from the body by the lungs or kidneys. There are two types of circulatory fluids: **blood,** which is always contained within blood vessels, and **hemolymph,** a mixture of blood and tissue fluid, which fills the body cavity and surrounds the internal organs.

Open Circulatory Systems

Hemolymph is seen in animals that have an **open circulatory system** that consists of blood vessels plus open spaces. Open circulatory systems were likely the first to evolve, as they are present in simpler and evolutionarily older animals. For example, in most molluscs and arthropods, the heart pumps hemolymph via vessels into tissue spaces that are sometimes enlarged into saclike sinuses (Fig. 32.2a). Eventually, hemolymph drains back to the heart. In the grasshopper, an arthropod, the dorsal tubular heart pumps hemolymph into a dorsal aorta, which empties into the hemocoel. When the heart contracts, openings called ostia (sing., ostium) are closed; when the heart relaxes, the hemolymph is sucked back into the heart by way of the ostia.

a. Hydra

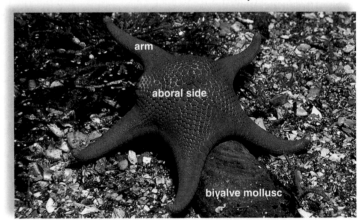

b. Flatworm

c. Red sea star, *Mediastar*

Figure 32.1 Aquatic animals without a circulatory system.
a. In a hydra, a cnidarian, the gastrovascular cavity makes digested material available to the cells that line the cavity. These cells can also acquire oxygen from the watery contents of the cavity and discharge their wastes there. **b.** In a planarian, a flatworm, the gastrovascular cavity branches throughout the body, bringing nutrients to body cells. **c.** In a sea star, the coelomic fluid distributes oxygen and picks up wastes.

The hemolymph of a grasshopper is colorless because it does not contain hemoglobin or any other respiratory pigment. It carries nutrients but no oxygen. Oxygen is taken to cells, and carbon dioxide is removed from them, by way of air tubes called tracheae, which are found throughout the body. The tracheae provide efficient transport and delivery of respiratory gases, while at the same time restricting water loss.

Closed Circulatory Systems

Blood is seen in animals that have a **closed circulatory system,** in which blood does not leave the vessels. For example, in annelids, such as earthworms, and in some molluscs, such as squid and octopuses, blood consisting of cells and plasma (a liquid) is pumped by the heart into a system of blood vessels (Fig. 32.2*b*). Valves prevent the backward flow of blood.

In the segmented earthworm, five pairs of anterior hearts (aortic arches) pump blood into the ventral blood vessel (an artery), which has a branch called a lateral vessel in every segment of the worm's body. Blood moves through these branches into capillaries, the thinnest of the blood vessels, where exchanges with tissue fluid take place. Both gas exchange and nutrient-for-waste exchange occur across the capillary walls. (Most cells in the body of an animal with a closed circulatory system are not far from a capillary.) In an earthworm, after leaving a capillary, blood moves from small veins into the dorsal blood vessel (a vein). This dorsal blood vessel returns blood to the heart for repumping.

The earthworm has red blood that contains the respiratory pigment hemoglobin. Hemoglobin is dissolved in the blood and is not contained within blood cells. The earthworm has no specialized organ, such as lungs, for gas exchange with the external environment. Gas exchange takes place across the body wall, which must always remain moist for this purpose.

Check Your Progress   32.1

1. List the general functions of all circulatory systems.
2. Explain how blood differs from hemolymph.
3. Regarding oxygen transport, deduce the specific additional step that must occur in animals with a closed circulatory system, compared to those with an open system.

a. Open circulatory system

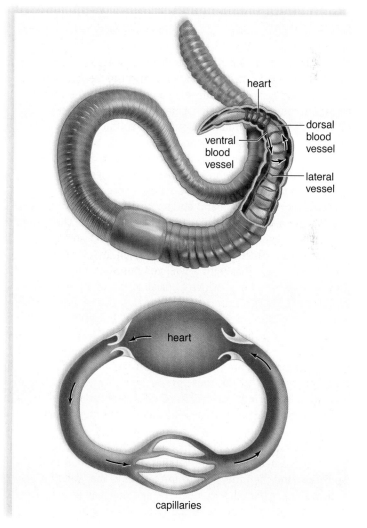

b. Closed circulatory system

Figure 32.2 Open versus closed circulatory systems.   **a.** *Top:* The grasshopper, an arthropod, has an open circulatory system. *Bottom:* A hemocoel is a body cavity filled with hemolymph, which freely bathes the internal organs. The heart, a pump, sends hemolymph out through vessels and collects it through ostia (openings). This open system probably could not supply oxygen to wing muscles rapidly enough. These muscles receive oxygen directly from tracheae (air tubes). **b.** *Top:* The earthworm, an annelid, has a closed circulatory system. The dorsal and ventral blood vessels are joined by five pairs of anterior hearts, which pump blood. *Bottom:* The lateral vessels distribute blood to the rest of the worm.

32.2 Transport in Vertebrates

Learning Outcomes

Upon completion of this section, you should be able to

1. Distinguish the structure and functions of arteries, veins, and capillaries.
2. Compare the path of blood in animals with a one-circuit circulatory pathway vs. a two-circuit pathway.
3. Identify the number of atria and ventricles in each type of vertebrate animal: fish, amphibians, most reptiles, crocodilians, birds, and mammals.

All vertebrate animals have a closed circulatory system, which is called a **cardiovascular system** [Gk. *kardia*, heart; L. *vascular*, vessel]. It consists of a strong, muscular heart in which the atria (sing., atrium) receive blood and the muscular ventricles pump blood through the blood vessels. There are three kinds of blood vessels: **arteries,** which carry blood away from the heart; **capillaries** [L. *capillus*, hair], which exchange materials with tissue fluid; and **veins** [L. *vena*, blood vessel], which return blood to the heart (Fig. 32.3).

An artery or a vein has three distinct layers (Fig. 32.3*a, c*). The outer layer consists of fibrous connective tissue, which is rich in elastic and collagen fibers. The middle layer is composed of smooth muscle and elastic tissue. The innermost layer, called the endothelium, is similar to squamous epithelium.

Arteries have thick walls, and those attached to the heart are resilient, meaning that they are able to expand and accommodate the sudden increase in blood volume that results after each heartbeat. **Arterioles** are small arteries whose diameter can be regulated by the nervous and endocrine systems. Arteriole constriction and dilation affect blood pressure in general. The greater the number of vessels dilated, the lower the blood pressure.

Arterioles branch into capillaries, which are extremely narrow, microscopic tubes with a wall composed of only one layer of cells. Capillary beds, which consist of many interconnected capillaries (Fig. 32.4), are so prevalent that in humans, almost all cells are within 60–80 μm of a capillary. But only about 5% of the capillary beds are open at the same time. After an animal has eaten, precapillary sphincters relax, and the capillary beds in the digestive tract are usually open. During muscular exercise, the capillary beds of the muscles are open. Capillaries, which are usually so narrow that red blood cells pass through in single file, allow exchange of nutrient and waste molecules across their thin walls.

Venules and veins collect blood from the capillary beds and take it to the heart. First, the venules drain the blood from the capillaries, and then they join to form a vein. The wall of a vein is much thinner than that of an artery, and this may be associated with a lower blood pressure in the veins. Valves within the veins point, or open, toward the heart, preventing a backflow of blood when they close (Fig. 32.3*c*).

MP3 Classification of Blood Vessels

Comparison of Circulatory Pathways

Two different types of circulatory pathways are seen among vertebrate animals. In fishes, blood follows a one-circuit (single-loop)

a. Artery

b. Capillary

c. Vein

Figure 32.3 Transport in vertebrates. **a.** Arteries have well-developed walls with a thick middle layer of elastic tissue and smooth muscle. **b.** Capillary walls are only one cell thick. **c.** Veins have flabby walls, particularly because the middle layer is not as thick as in arteries. Veins have valves, which ensure one-way flow of blood back to the heart.

circulatory pathway through the body. The heart has a single atrium and a single ventricle (Fig. 32.5*a*).

The pumping action of the ventricle sends blood under pressure to the gills, where gas exchange occurs. After passing through the gills, blood returns to the dorsal aorta, which distributes blood throughout the body. Veins return oxygen (O_2)-poor blood to an enlarged chamber called the sinus venosus that leads to the atrium. The atrium pumps blood back to the ventricle. This single circulatory loop has an advantage in that the gill capillaries receive oxygen-poor blood and the capillaries of the body, called systemic capillaries, receive fully oxygen-rich blood. It is disadvantageous in that after leaving the gills, the blood is under reduced pressure.

As a result of evolutionary changes, other vertebrates have a two-circuit (double-loop) circulatory pathway. The heart pumps blood to the tissues through a **systemic circuit,** and also pumps blood to the lungs through a **pulmonary circuit** [L. *pulmonarius*, of the lungs]. This double-pumping action is an adaptation to breathing air on land.

In amphibians, the heart has two *atria* and a single *ventricle* (Fig. 32.5*b*). Oxygen-poor blood from the systemic veins returns to the right atrium. Oxygen-rich blood returning from the lungs passes to the left atrium. Both of the atria empty into the single ventricle. Oxygen-rich and oxygen-poor blood are kept somewhat separate because oxygen-poor blood is pumped out of the ventricle before the oxygen-rich blood enters. When the ventricle contracts, the division of the main artery also helps keep the blood somewhat separated. More oxygen-rich blood is distributed to the body, and more oxygen-poor blood is delivered to the lungs, and perhaps to the skin, for recharging with oxygen.

In most reptiles, a septum partially divides the ventricle. In these animals, mixing of oxygen-rich and oxygen-poor blood is kept to a minimum. In crocodilians (alligators and crocodiles), the septum completely separates the ventricle. These reptiles have a four-chambered heart. The heart of birds and mammals is also divided into left and right halves (Fig. 32.5*c*). The right ventricle pumps blood to the lungs, and the larger left ventricle pumps blood to the rest of the body. This arrangement provides adequate blood pressure for both the pulmonary and systemic circuits.

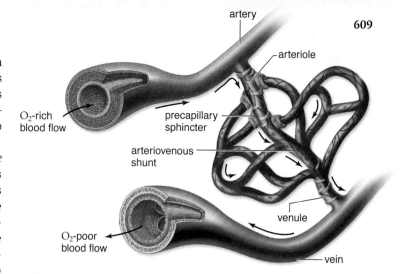

Figure 32.4 Anatomy of a capillary bed. When a capillary bed is open, sphincter muscles are relaxed and blood flows through the capillaries. When precapillary sphincter muscles are contracted, the bed is closed and blood flows through an arteriovenous shunt that carries blood directly from an arteriole to a venule.

Check Your Progress 32.2

1. List and describe the functions of three types of vessels in a cardiovascular system.
2. Identify which of the three types of vessels listed in Question 1 contain valves, and analyze why.
3. Examine the evolutionary benefits of a two-circuit circulatory pathway compared to a one-circuit pathway, especially for animals that breathe air on land.

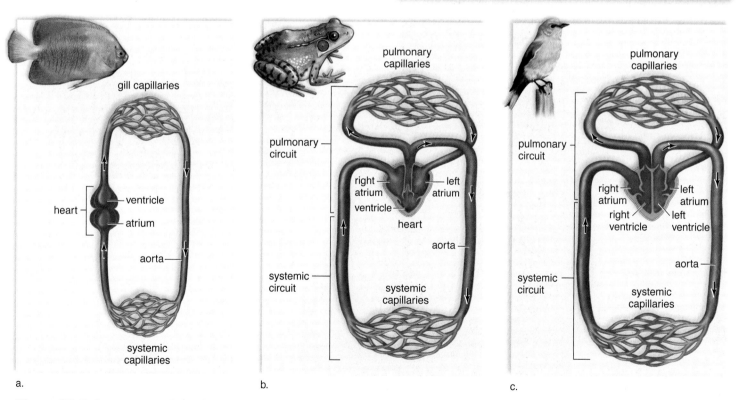

Figure 32.5 Comparison of circulatory circuits in vertebrates. **a.** In fishes, the blood moves in a single circuit. Blood pressure created by the pumping of the heart is dissipated after the blood passes through the gill capillaries. This is a disadvantage of this one-circuit system. **b.** Amphibians and most reptiles have a two-circuit system in which the heart pumps blood to both the pulmonary capillaries in the lungs and the systemic capillaries in the body itself. Although there is a single ventricle, little mixing of oxygen-rich and oxygen-poor blood takes place. **c.** The pulmonary and systemic circuits are completely separate in crocodiles (a reptile) and in birds and mammals, because the heart is divided by a septum into right and left halves. The right side pumps blood to the lungs, and the left side pumps blood to the rest of the body.

32.3 The Human Cardiovascular System

Learning Outcomes

Upon completion of this section, you should be able to

1. List the major components of the human heart, including the four chambers and four valves.
2. Trace the path of blood through the human heart, lungs, and major vessels leading to the lower leg.
3. Discuss how the SA and AV nodes control the contractions of the heart muscle, and how these electrical changes result in the characteristic patterns seen in an ECG.
4. Describe the major categories of cardiovascular disease that occur in the United States.

In the cardiovascular system of humans, the pumping of the heart keeps blood moving primarily in the arteries. Skeletal muscle contraction pressing against veins is the main force responsible for the movement of blood in the veins.

The Human Heart

The **heart** is a cone-shaped, muscular organ about the size of a fist (Fig. 32.6). It is located between the lungs directly behind the sternum (breastbone) and is tilted so that the apex (the pointed end) is oriented to the left.

Structure of the Heart

The major portion of the heart, called the myocardium, consists largely of cardiac muscle tissue. The myocardium receives oxygen and nutrients from the coronary arteries, not from the blood it pumps. The muscle fibers of the myocardium are branched and tightly joined to one another at intercalated disks.

The heart lies within the pericardium, a thick, membranous sac that secretes a small quantity of lubricating liquid. The inner surface of the heart is lined with endocardium, a membrane composed of connective tissue and endothelial tissue. The lining is continuous with the endothelium lining of the blood vessels.

Internally, a wall called the **septum** separates the heart into a right side and a left side (Fig. 32.7). The heart has four chambers. The two upper, thin-walled atria (sing., **atrium**) have wrinkled, protruding appendages called auricles. The two lower

Figure 32.6 External heart anatomy.   a. The venae cavae and the pulmonary trunk are attached to the right side of the heart. The aorta and the pulmonary veins are attached to the left side of the heart. Blood vessels are colored red if they carry oxygen-rich blood and blue if they carry oxygen-poor blood. **b.** Photograph of a heart in its natural position in the chest.

chambers are the thick-walled **ventricles,** which pump the blood away from the heart.

The heart also has four valves, which direct the flow of blood and prevent its backward movement. The two valves that lie between the atria and the ventricles are called the **atrioventricular valves.** These valves are supported by strong fibrous strings called chordae tendineae. The chordae, which are attached to muscular projections of the ventricular walls, support the valves and prevent them from inverting when the heart contracts. The atrioventricular valve on the right side is called the tricuspid valve because it has three flaps, or cusps. The valve on the left side is called the bicuspid (or the mitral) because it has two flaps.

The remaining two valves are the **semilunar valves,** whose flaps resemble half-moons, between the ventricles and their attached vessels. The pulmonary semilunar valve lies between the right ventricle and the pulmonary trunk. The aortic semilunar valve lies between the left ventricle and the aorta.

Path of Blood Through the Heart

Even though both atria and then both ventricles contract simultaneously due to the presence of intercalated disks (Fig. 32.7*b*),

we can trace the path of blood through the heart in the following manner:

- The superior vena cava and the inferior vena cava, which carry oxygen (O_2)-poor blood that is relatively high in carbon dioxide, empty into the right atrium.
- The right atrium sends blood through an atrioventricular valve (the tricuspid valve) to the right ventricle.
- The right ventricle sends blood through the pulmonary semilunar valve into the pulmonary trunk and the two pulmonary arteries to the lungs.
- Four pulmonary veins, which carry oxygen-rich blood, empty into the left atrium.
- The left atrium sends blood through an atrioventricular valve (the bicuspid or mitral valve) to the left ventricle.
- The left ventricle sends blood through the aortic semilunar valve into the aorta and to the rest of the body.

From this description, it is obvious that oxygen-poor blood never mixes with oxygen-rich blood, and that blood must go through the lungs in order to pass from the right side to the left side of the heart, as is typical in a double-loop circulatory system. Because

left subclavian artery
left common carotid artery
brachiocephalic artery

superior vena cava
aorta
left pulmonary artery

pulmonary trunk
left pulmonary veins
right pulmonary artery

right pulmonary veins

semilunar valve
left atrium
right atrium
atrioventricular (bicuspid) valve
atrioventricular (tricuspid) valve

chordae tendineae
papillary muscles
right ventricle
septum
left ventricle
inferior vena cava

a.

cardiac muscle cell
mitochondrion
intercalated disk

gap junction

b.

Figure 32.7 Internal view of the heart. a. The heart has four chambers; the two chambers on the right are separated from the two chambers on the left by a septum. When the atrioventricular valves open, blood passes from the atria to the ventricles, and when the semilunar valves open, blood passes out of the heart. **b.** Intercalated disks contain gap junctions and these allow muscle cells to contract simultaneously. Desmosomes at the same location allow the cells to bend and stretch.

the left ventricle has the harder job of pumping blood to the entire body, its walls are thicker than those of the right ventricle, which pumps blood a relatively short distance to the lungs.

People often associate oxygen-rich blood with all arteries and oxygen-poor blood with all veins, but this idea is incorrect: Pulmonary arteries and pulmonary veins are just the reverse. That is why pulmonary arteries are colored blue and pulmonary veins are colored red in Figures 32.6 and 32.7.

The pumping of the heart sends blood out under pressure into the arteries. Because the left side of the heart is the stronger pump, blood pressure is greatest in the aorta. Blood pressure then decreases as the cross-sectional area of arteries and then arterioles increases. Therefore, a different mechanism is needed to move blood in the veins, as we shall discuss later.

The Heartbeat

The average human heart contracts, or beats, about 70 times a minute, so each heartbeat lasts about 0.85 second. This adds up to about 100,000 beats per day, and over a 70-year lifespan, the average human heart will have contracted about 2.5 billion times! The term **systole** [Gk. *systole*, contraction] refers to contraction of the heart chambers, and the word **diastole** [Gk. *diastole*, dilation, spreading] refers to relaxation of these chambers. Each heartbeat, or **cardiac cycle,** consists of the following phases, which are also depicted in Figure 32.8:

Cardiac Cycle		
Time	**Atria**	**Ventricles**
0.15 sec	Systole	Diastole
0.30 sec	Diastole	Systole
0.40 sec	Diastole	Diastole

First the atria contract (while the ventricles relax), then the ventricles contract (while the atria relax), and then all chambers rest. Note that the heart is in diastole about 50% of the time. The short systole of the atria is appropriate because the atria send blood only into the ventricles. It is the muscular ventricles that actually pump blood out into the cardiovascular system proper.

The volume of blood that the left ventricle pumps per minute into the systemic circuit is called the **cardiac output.** A person with a heartbeat of 70 beats per minute has a cardiac output of 5.25 liters a minute. This is almost equivalent to the amount of blood in the body, and adds up to about 2,000 gallons a day. During heavy exercise, the cardiac output can increase manyfold.

When the heart beats, the familiar lub-dub sound is heard as the valves of the heart close. The longer and lower-pitched

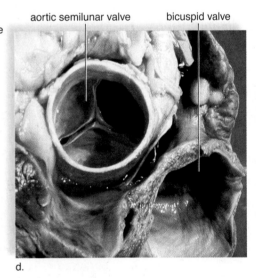

Figure 32.8 Stages in the cardiac cycle.
a. When the atria contract, the ventricles are relaxed and filling with blood. The atrioventricular valves are open, and the semilunar valves are closed. **b.** When the ventricles contract, the atrioventricular valves are closed, the semilunar valves are open, and the blood is pumped into the pulmonary trunk and aorta. **c.** When the heart is relaxed, both the atria and the ventricles are filling with blood. The atrioventricular valves are open, and the semilunar valves are closed. **d.** Aortic semilunar valve and bicuspid valve, an atrioventricular valve on left.

lub is caused by vibrations of the heart when the atrioventricular valves close due to ventricular contraction. The shorter and sharper *dub* is heard when the semilunar valves close due to back pressure of blood in the arteries. A heart murmur, a slight slush sound after the lub, is often due to ineffective valves, which allow blood to pass back into the atria after the atrioventricular valves have closed.

The **pulse** is a wave effect that passes down the walls of the arterial blood vessels when the aorta expands and then recoils following ventricular systole. Because there is one arterial pulse per ventricular systole, the arterial pulse rate can be used to determine the heart rate.

The rhythmic contraction of the atria and ventricles is due to the internal (intrinsic) conduction system of the heart. Nodal tissue, which has both muscular and nervous characteristics, is a unique type of cardiac muscle located in two regions of the heart. The *SA (sinoatrial) node* is found in the upper dorsal wall of the right atrium; the *AV (atrioventricular) node* is found in the base of the right atrium very near the septum (Fig. 32.9a). The SA node initiates the heartbeat about every 0.85 second by automatically sending out an excitation impulse, which causes the atria to contract. Therefore, the SA node is called the **pacemaker** because it usually keeps the heartbeat regular. When the impulse reaches the AV node, the AV node signals the ventricles to contract by way of large fibers terminating in the more numerous and smaller Purkinje fibers.

Although the heart muscle will contract without any external nervous stimulation, input from the brain can increase or decrease the rate and strength of heart contractions. In addition, the hormones epinephrine and norepinephrine, secreted into the blood by the adrenal glands, also stimulate the heart. When a person is frightened, for example, the heart pumps faster and stronger due to both nervous and hormonal stimulation.

MP3 Cardiac Cycle

The Electrocardiogram. An **electrocardiogram (ECG)** is a recording of the electrical changes that occur in the myocardium during a cardiac cycle. Body fluids contain ions that conduct electrical currents, and therefore these electrical changes can be detected on the body surface. During an ECG procedure, these changes pass from electrodes placed on the skin through wires to an instrument, generating "waves" that can be traced onto paper. Figure 32.9b depicts the pattern that results from a normal cardiac cycle.

When the SA node triggers an impulse, the atrial fibers produce an electrical change called the P wave. The P wave indicates that the atria are about to contract. After that, the QRS complex signals that the ventricles are about to contract and the atria are relaxing. The electrical changes that occur as the ventricular muscle fibers recover produce the T wave.

Animation Cardiac Cycle

Various types of abnormalities can be detected by an electrocardiogram. One of these, called ventricular fibrillation, is

a.

b. Normal ECG

c. Ventricular fibrillation

d. Recording of an ECG

Figure 32.9 Conduction system of the heart. **a.** The SA node sends out a stimulus (black arrows), which causes the atria to contract. When this stimulus reaches the AV node, it signals the ventricles to contract. Impulses pass down the two branches of the atrioventricular bundle to the Purkinje fibers, and thereafter the ventricles contract. **b.** A normal ECG usually indicates that the heart is functioning properly. The P wave occurs just prior to atrial contraction; the QRS complex occurs just prior to ventricular contraction; and the T wave occurs when the ventricles are recovering from contraction. **c.** Ventricular fibrillation produces an irregular electrocardiogram due to irregular stimulation of the ventricles. **d.** The recording of an ECG.

caused by uncoordinated contraction of the ventricles (Fig. 32.9c). Ventricular fibrillation is of special interest because it can be caused by an injury or drug overdose. It is the most common cause of sudden cardiac death in a seemingly healthy person. When the ventricles are fibrillating, they can be defibrillated by applying a strong electric current for a short period of time. Then the SA node may be able to reestablish a coordinated beat. Many public places, and even private homes, have automatic external defibrillators. These are small devices that can be used to determine whether a person is suffering from ventricular fibrillation. If so, the AED administers an appropriate electrical shock to the chest.

Comparison of Circulatory Circuits

As mentioned, the human cardiovascular system includes two major circular pathways, the pulmonary circuit and the systemic circuit (Fig. 32.10).

The Pulmonary Circuit

In the pulmonary circuit, the path of blood can be traced as follows: oxygen-poor blood from all regions of the body collects in the right atrium and then passes into the right ventricle, which pumps it into the pulmonary trunk. The pulmonary trunk divides into the right and left pulmonary arteries, which carry blood to the lungs. As blood passes through pulmonary capillaries, carbon dioxide is given off and oxygen is picked up. Oxygen-rich blood returns to the left atrium of the heart, through pulmonary venules that join to form pulmonary veins.

The Systemic Circuit

The **aorta** [L. *aorte*, great artery] and the **venae cavae** (sing., vena cava) [L. *vena*, blood vessel, and *cavus*, hollow] are the major blood vessels in the systemic circuit. To trace the path of blood to any organ in the body, you need only start with the left ventricle, mention the aorta, the proper branch of the aorta, the organ, and the vein returning blood to the vena cava, which enters the right atrium. In the systemic circuit, arteries contain oxygen-rich blood and have a bright red color, but veins contain oxygen-poor blood and appear dull red or, when viewed through the skin, blue.

The coronary arteries are extremely important because they supply oxygen and nutrients to the heart muscle itself (see Fig. 32.6). The coronary arteries arise from the aorta just above the aortic semilunar valve. They lie on the exterior surface of the heart, where they branch into arterioles and then capillaries. In the capillary beds, nutrients, wastes, and gases are exchanged between the blood and the tissues. The capillary beds enter venules, which join to form the cardiac veins, and these empty into the right atrium.

A **portal system** [L. *porto*, carry, transport] is a structure in which blood from capillaries travels through veins to reach another set of capillaries, without first traveling through the heart. The hepatic portal system takes blood from the intestines directly to the liver. The liver then performs such functions as metabolizing nutrients and removing toxins (liver functions are explored further in Chapter 34). Blood leaves the liver by way of the hepatic vein, which enters the inferior vena cava.

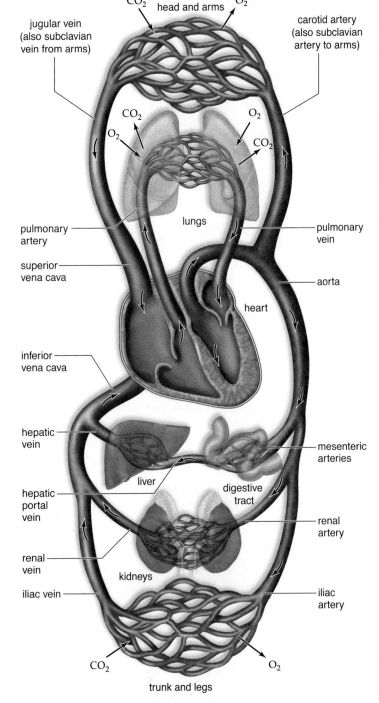

Figure 32.10 Path of blood. When tracing blood from the right to the left side of the heart in the pulmonary circuit, you must mention the pulmonary vessels. When tracing blood from the digestive tract to the right atrium in the systemic circuit, you must mention the hepatic portal vein, the hepatic vein, and the inferior vena cava. The blue-colored vessels carry oxygen-poor blood, and the red-colored vessels carry oxygen-rich blood; the arrows indicate the flow of blood.

Tracing the Path of Blood. Branches from the aorta go to the organs and major body regions. For example, this is the path of blood to and from the lower legs:

left ventricle—aorta—common iliac artery—femoral artery—lower leg capillaries—femoral vein—common iliac vein—inferior vena cava—right atrium

In most instances, the artery and the vein that serve the same region are given the same name. For example, iliac and femoral are names applied to both arteries and veins. What happens in between the artery and the vein? Arterioles from the artery branch into capillaries, where exchange takes place, and then venules join to form the vein that enters a vena cava. An exception occurs between the digestive tract and the liver, where blood must pass through two sets of capillaries because of the hepatic portal system.

Blood Pressure

When the left ventricle contracts, blood is forced into the aorta and then other systemic arteries under pressure. Systolic pressure results from blood being forced into the arteries during ventricular systole, and diastolic pressure is the pressure in the arteries during ventricular diastole. Human **blood pressure** can be measured with a *sphygmomanometer*, which has a pressure cuff that determines the amount of pressure required to stop the flow of blood through an artery.

Blood pressure is normally measured on the brachial artery, an artery in the upper arm. Today, digital manometers are often used to take one's blood pressure instead of the older type with a dial. Blood pressure is given in millimeters of mercury (mm Hg). A blood pressure reading consists of two numbers—for example, 120/80—that represent systolic and diastolic pressures, respectively.

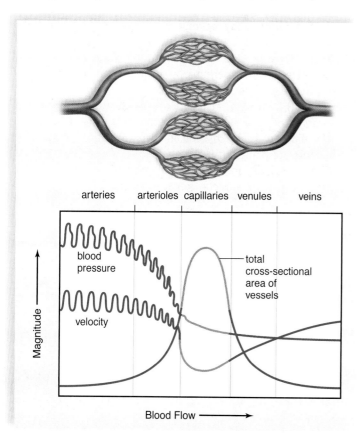

Figure 32.11 Velocity and blood pressure related to vascular cross-sectional area. In capillaries, blood is under minimal pressure and has the least velocity. Blood pressure and velocity drop off because capillaries have a greater total cross-sectional area than arterioles.

a. Contracted skeletal muscle pushes blood past open valve.

b. Closed valve prevents backward flow of blood.

Figure 32.12 Cross section of a valve in a vein. **a.** Pressure on the walls of a vein, exerted by skeletal muscles, increases blood pressure within the vein and forces a valve open. **b.** When external pressure is no longer applied to the vein, blood pressure decreases, and back pressure forces the valve closed. Closure of the valves prevents the blood from flowing in the opposite direction.

As blood flows from the aorta into the various arteries and arterioles, blood pressure falls. Also, the difference between systolic and diastolic pressure gradually diminishes. In the capillaries, there is a slow, fairly even flow of blood. This may be related to the very high total cross-sectional area of the capillaries (Fig. 32.11). It has been calculated that if all the blood vessels in a human body were connected end to end, the total distance would reach around the Earth at the equator two times! Most of this distance would be due to the large number of capillaries.

Blood pressure in the veins is low and is insufficient for moving blood back to the heart, especially from the limbs of the body. Venous return is dependent on three factors:

- Skeletal muscles near veins put pressure on the collapsible walls of the veins, and therefore on the blood contained in these vessels, when they contract.
- Valves in the veins prevent the backward flow of blood, and therefore pressure from muscle contraction moves blood toward the heart (Fig. 32.12). Varicose veins, abnormal dilations in superficial veins, develop when the valves of the veins become weak and ineffective due to a backward pressure of the blood.
- Variations in pressure in the chest cavity during breathing, also known as the *respiratory pump*, cause blood to flow from areas of higher pressure (such as the abdominal cavity) to lower pressure (in the thoracic cavity) during each inhalation.

MP3
Blood Flow and
Blood Pressure

Cardiovascular Disease

Cardiovascular disease (CVD) is the leading cause of death in most Western countries. According to the American Heart Association, CVD has been the most common cause of death in the United States every year since 1900. The only exception to this statistic was 1918, the worst year of a global influenza pandemic. In 2010, nearly 2,300 Americans died of CVD each day, an average of 1 death every 38 seconds. The Nature of Science feature "New Information About Preventing Cardiovascular Disease" emphasizes the possible prevention of CVD.

Hypertension

It is estimated that about 30% of Americans suffer from **hypertension**, which is high blood pressure. Another 30% are thought to have a condition called prehypertension, which can lead to hypertension. Under age 45, a reading above 130/90 is hypertensive, and beyond age 45, a reading above 140/95 is hypertensive.

Hypertension is most often caused by a narrowing of arteries due to atherosclerosis (described next). This narrowing causes the heart to work harder to supply the required amount of blood. The resulting increase in blood pressure can damage the heart, arteries, and other organs. Other risk factors that can contribute to hypertension include obesity, smoking, chronic stress, and a high dietary salt intake (which causes retention of fluid). Only about two-thirds of people with hypertension seek medical help for their condition, and it is likely that many people with high blood pressure are unaware of it.

Atherosclerosis

Atherosclerosis is an accumulation of soft masses of fatty materials, particularly cholesterol, beneath the inner linings of arteries (see Fig. 32A). Such deposits are called plaque. As deposits occur, plaque tends to protrude into the lumen of the vessel, interfering with the flow of blood. Plaque can also cause a clot to form on the irregular arterial wall. As long as the clot remains stationary, it is called a *thrombus*, but when and if it dislodges and moves along with the blood, it is called an *embolus*. If thromboembolism is not treated, complications can arise (see the following section).

Atherosclerosis often begins in early adulthood and develops progressively through middle age, but symptoms may not appear until an individual is 50 or older. See the Nature of Science feature "New Information About Preventing Cardiovascular Disease" for some recent recommendations on reducing risk.

Stroke and Heart Attack

Strokes and heart attacks are associated with hypertension and atherosclerosis. A **stroke,** or disruption of blood supply to the brain, often results when a small cranial arteriole bursts or is blocked by an embolus. A lack of oxygen causes a portion of the brain to die, and paralysis or death can result. A person is sometimes forewarned of a stroke by a feeling of numbness in

a. Artery is blocked.   b. Stent is placed.   c. Balloon is inflated.

Figure 32.13 Angioplasty with stent placement.   **a.** A plastic tube (catheter) is inserted into the coronary artery until it reaches the clogged area. **b.** A metal stent with a balloon inside it is pushed out the end of the plastic tube into the clogged area. **c.** When the balloon is inflated, the vessel opens, and the stent is left in place to keep the vessel open.

the hands or the face, difficulty in speaking, or temporary blindness in one eye.

If a coronary artery becomes partially blocked, the individual may suffer from **angina pectoris,** characterized as a squeezing sensation or a flash of burning. If a coronary artery is completely blocked, perhaps by a thromboembolism, a portion of the heart muscle dies due to a lack of oxygen. This is a myocardial infarction, also called a **heart attack.** It may be necessary to place a stent, or self-expanding wire mesh tube, inside a blocked artery to keep it open. About 1.3 million of these stents are placed in U.S. patients every year (Fig. 32.13). If this approach is unsuccessful, a coronary bypass may be required, in which a surgeon replaces one or more blocked coronary arteries with an artery taken from elsewhere in the patient's body. In 2009, about 450,000 of these procedures were performed in the United States.

Video
Cardiac Repair

Video
Heart Stem Cells

Check Your Progress   32.3

1. Name each blood vessel and heart chamber that blood passes through on its way from the venae cavae to the aorta, and identify which artery carries oxygen-poor blood.
2. Explain what specifically causes the sounds of the heartbeat.
3. Discuss why systolic blood pressure is higher than diastolic.
4. Predict what type of conditions might occur as a result of chronic hypertension and plaque.

THEME Nature of Science

New Information About Preventing Cardiovascular Disease

For decades several factors have been associated with an increased risk of cardiovascular disease (CVD), especially atherosclerosis (Fig. 32A). Some of these cannot be avoided, such as increasing age, male gender, family history of heart disease, and belonging to certain races, including African American, Mexican American, and American Indian. Other risk factors—smoking, obesity, high cholesterol, hypertension, diabetes, physical inactivity—can be avoided or at least affected by changing one's behavior or taking medications. In recent years however, other factors have been under consideration; we discuss a few of them below.

- **Alcohol.** Alcohol abuse can destroy just about every organ in the body, the heart included. But recent research suggests that a moderate level of alcohol intake can improve cardiovascular health by improving the blood cholesterol profile, decreasing unwanted clot formation, increasing blood flow in the heart, and reducing blood pressure. According to the American Heart Association, people who consume one or two drinks per day have a 30% to 50% reduction in cardiovascular disease compared to nondrinkers.

  Please note, however, that the maximum protective effect is achieved with only one or two drinks per day—con-

suming more than that increases the risk of many alcohol-related problems. The American Heart Assocation does *not* recommend that nondrinkers start using alcohol, or that drinkers increase their consumption, based on these findings.

- **Resvertrol.** The "red wine effect" or "French paradox" refers to the observation that levels of CVD in France are relatively low, despite the consumption of a high fat diet. One possible explanation is that wine is frequently consumed with meals.

  In addition to its alcohol content, red wine contains especially high levels of antioxidants, including resvertrol. Resvertrol is mainly produced in the skin of grapes, so it is also found in grape juice. Resvertrol supplements are also available at health food stores.

  The benefits of resvertrol alone are questionable, however, and most controlled studies to date have demonstrated no beneficial effects. The lower incidence of CVD in the French may be due to multiple factors, including lifestyle and genetic differences.

- **Omega-3 Fatty Acids.** The influence that diet has on blood cholesterol levels has been well studied. It is generally beneficial to minimize our intake of foods high in saturated fat (red meat, cream, and butter) and trans-fats

(most margarines, commercially baked goods, and deep-fried foods). Replacing these harmful fats with healthier ones, such as monounsaturated fats (olive and canola oils) and polyunsaturated fats (corn, safflower, and soybean oils), is beneficial.

In addition, the American Heart Association now recommends eating at least two servings of fish a week, especially fish like salmon, mackerel, herring, lake trout, sardines, and albacore tuna, which are are high in omega-3 fatty acids. These essential fatty acids can decrease triglyceride levels, slow the growth rate of atherosclerotic plaque, and lower blood pressure.

However, children and pregnant women are advised to limit their fish consumption because of the high levels of mercury contamination in some fishes. For middle-aged and older men and postmenopausal women, the benefits of fish consumption far outweigh the potential risks.

Questions to Consider

1. Would you be helping your health if you decided to eat mackerel every day and drink two glasses of red wine with it? Why or why not?
2. What what would be some difficulties in trying to determine the true cause of the "French paradox"?

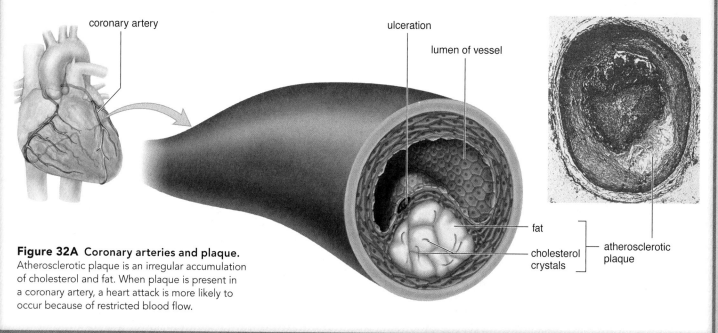

Figure 32A Coronary arteries and plaque.
Atherosclerotic plaque is an irregular accumulation of cholesterol and fat. When plaque is present in a coronary artery, a heart attack is more likely to occur because of restricted blood flow.

32.4 Blood

As discussed in Chapter 31, blood is considered to be a connective tissue with a fluid matrix. In contrast to the hemolymph found in open circulatory systems, blood is normally contained within blood vessels. The blood of mammals has a number of functions that help maintain homeostasis, including:

- transporting gases, nutrients, waste products, and hormones throughout the body;
- combating pathogenic microorganisms;
- helping to maintain water balance and pH;
- regulating body temperature; and
- carrying platelets and factors that ensure clotting to prevent blood loss.

Blood has two main portions: a liquid portion, called plasma, and the formed elements, consisting of cells and platelets (Fig. 32.14).

Plasma

Plasma [Gk. *plasma*, something molded] contains many types of molecules, including nutrients, wastes, salts, and hundreds of different types of proteins. Some of these proteins are involved in buffering the blood, effectively keeping the pH near 7.4. They also maintain the blood's osmotic pressure so that water has an automatic tendency to enter blood capillaries. Several plasma proteins are involved in blood clotting, and others transport large organic molecules in the blood.

Albumin, the most plentiful of the plasma proteins, transports bilirubin, a breakdown product of hemoglobin, and various types of lipoproteins transport cholesterol. Another very significant group of plasma proteins are the **antibodies,** which are proteins produced by the immune system in response to specific pathogens and other foreign materials (see Chapter 33).

Formed Elements

The **formed elements** are of three types: red blood cells, or erythrocytes [Gk. *erythros*, red, and *kytos*, cell]; white blood cells, or leukocytes [Gk. *leukos*, white]; and platelets, or thrombocytes [Gk. *thrombos*, blood clot].

Red Blood Cells

Red blood cells (RBCs) are small, biconcave disks that at maturity lack a nucleus and contain the respiratory pigment hemoglobin. The average adult human has five to six million RBCs per cubic millimeter (mm³) of whole blood, and each one of these cells contains about 250 million hemoglobin molecules. **Hemoglobin** [Gk. *haima*, blood; L. *globus*, ball] contains four globin protein chains, each associated with heme, an iron-containing group.

Figure 32.14 Composition of blood.

Iron combines loosely with oxygen, and in this way oxygen is carried in the blood. If the number of RBCs is insufficient, or if the cells do not have enough hemoglobin, the individual suffers from anemia and has a tired, run-down feeling.

In adults, RBCs are manufactured in the red bone marrow of the skull, the ribs, the vertebrae, and the ends of the long bones. The hormone erythropoietin, produced by the kidneys, stimulates RBC production. Now available as a drug, erythropoietin is helpful to persons with anemia and is also sometimes abused by athletes who want to enhance the oxygen-carrying capacity of their blood.

Before they are released from the bone marrow into blood, RBCs synthesize hemoglobin and lose their nuclei. After living about 120 days, they are destroyed chiefly in the liver and the spleen, where they are engulfed by large phagocytic cells. When RBCs are destroyed, hemoglobin is released. The iron is recovered and returned to the red bone marrow for reuse. The heme portions of the molecules undergo chemical degradation and are excreted by the liver as bile pigments in the bile. The bile pigments are primarily responsible for the color of feces.

MP3
General Functions and
Composition of Blood

Blood Types

The earliest attempts at blood transfusions resulted in illness and even death of some recipients. Eventually, it was discovered that only certain transfusion donors and recipients are compatible because red blood cell membranes carry specific proteins or carbohydrates that are antigens to blood recipients. An **antigen** [Gk. *anti,* against; L. *genitus,* forming, causing] is a molecule, usually a protein or carbohydrate, that can trigger a specific immune response. Several groups of RBC antigens exist, the most significant being the ABO and Rh systems. Clinically, it is very important that the blood groups be properly cross-matched to avoid a potentially deadly transfusion reaction.

ABO System

In the ABO system, the presence or absence of type A and type B antigens on RBCs determines a person's blood type. For example, if a person has type A blood, the A antigen is on his or her RBCs. Because it is considered by the immune system to be "self," this molecule is not recognized as an antigen by this individual, although it can be an antigen to a recipient who does not have type A blood.

In the ABO system, there are four blood types: A, B, AB, and O. Because the A and B antigens are also commonly found on microorganisms present in and on our bodies, a person's plasma usually contains antibodies to the A or B antigens not present on his or her RBCs. These antibodies are called anti-A and anti-B. This chart explains what antibodies are present in the plasma of each blood type:

Blood Type	Antigen on Red Blood Cells	Antibody in Plasma
A	A	Anti-B
B	B	Anti-A
AB	A, B	None
O	None	Anti-A and anti-B

Because type A blood has anti-B and not anti-A antibodies in the plasma, a donor with type A blood can give blood to a recipient with type A blood (Fig. 32.15). However, if type A blood is given to a type B recipient, **agglutination** (Fig. 32.16), the clumping of RBCs, can cause blood to stop circulating in small blood vessels, leading to organ damage.

Theoretically, a person with which blood type could donate to all recipients? The answer is that type O RBCs have no A or B antigens, and this is sometimes called the universal donor type. A person with which blood type could receive blood from any donor? Type AB blood has no anti-A or anti-B antibodies, and thus it is sometimes called the universal recipient. In practice, however, it is not safe to rely solely on the ABO system when matching blood. Instead, samples of the two types of blood are physically mixed, and the result is microscopically examined for agglutination before blood transfusions are done.

An equally important concern when transfusing blood is to make sure that the donor is free from transmissible infectious agents, such as the microbes that cause AIDS, hepatitis, and syphilis.

Rh System

Another important antigen on RBCs is the Rh factor. Eighty-five percent of the U.S. population have this particular antigen on their RBCs and are Rh positive. Fifteen percent do not have the

Figure 32.15 Matched blood transfusion. No agglutination occurs when the donor and recipient have the same type blood.

Figure 32.16 Mismatched blood transfusion. Agglutination occurs because blood type B has anti-A antibodies in the plasma.

antigen and are Rh negative. The designation of blood type usually includes whether the person has or does not have the Rh factor on the RBCs, e.g., type A-positive (A+). Unlike the case with the A and B antigens, Rh-negative individuals normally do not have antibodies to the Rh factor, but they may make them when exposed to the Rh factor.

During pregnancy, if the mother is Rh negative and the father is Rh positive, the child may be Rh positive. If the Rh-positive fetal RBCs leak across the placenta, the mother may produce anti-Rh antibodies. In this or a subsequent pregnancy with another Rh-positive baby, these antibodies may cross the placenta and destroy the child's RBCs. This condition, called hemolytic disease of the newborn (HDN), can be fatal without an immediate blood transfusion after birth.

The problem of Rh incompatibility can be prevented by giving Rh-negative women an Rh immunoglobulin injection toward the end of pregnancy and within 72 hours of giving birth to an Rh-positive child. This treatment contains a relatively low level of anti-Rh antibodies that help destroy any Rh-positive blood cells in the mother's blood before her immune system produces high levels of anti-Rh antibodies.

MP3
Blood Groupings

White Blood Cells

Because they are a critical component of the immune system, the functions of white blood cells are discussed in detail in Chapter 33 and only briefly here. **White blood cells (WBCs)**, or **leukocytes**, differ from RBCs in that they are usually larger, have a nucleus, lack hemoglobin, and without staining appear translucent. With staining, WBCs appear light blue unless they have granules that bind with certain stains (see Fig. 32.14). There are far fewer WBCs than RBCs in the blood, with approximately 5,000–11,000 WBCs per mm^3 in humans.

On the basis of their structure, WBCs can be divided into granular and agranular leukocytes. Within these two categories, five main types of WBCs can be identified.

Granular Leukocytes. The cytoplasm of **granular leukocytes** (neutrophils, eosinophils, and basophils) contains spherical vesicles, or granules, filled with enzymes and proteins that these cells use to help defend the body against invading microbes and other parasites.

Neutrophils [Gk. *neuter*, neither, and *phileo*, love] have a multilobed nucleus, resulting in their other name, polymorphonuclear cells. They are the most abundant of the WBCs and are able to squeeze through capillary walls and enter the tissues, where they phagocytize and digest bacteria. The thick, yellowish fluid called *pus* that develops in some bacterial infections contains mainly dead neutrophils that have fought the infection. **Basophil** granules stain a deep blue and contain inflammatory chemicals such as histamine. The prominent granules of **eosinophils** stain a deep red, and these WBCs are involved in fighting parasitic worms, among other actions.

Agranular Leukocytes. The **agranular leukocytes**, which are also called mononuclear cells, lack obvious granules and include the monocytes and the lymphocytes.

Monocytes are the largest of the WBCs, and they tend to migrate into tissues in response to chronic, ongoing infections, where they differentiate into large phagocytic **macrophages** [Gk. *makros*, long, and *phagein*, to eat]. These long-lived cells not only fight infections directly, but they also release growth factors that increase the production of different types of WBCs by the bone marrow. Some of these factors are available for medicinal use and may be helpful to people with low immunity, such as AIDS patients or people on chemotherapy for cancer. A third function of macrophages is to interact with lymphocytes to help initiate the adaptive immune response (see Chapter 33).

Lymphocytes [L. *lympha*, clear water; Gk. *kytos*, cell] are the second most common type of WBC in the blood. The two major types of lymphocytes, T cells and B cells, each play a distinct role in adaptive immune responses to specific antigens. One type of T cell, the helper T cell, initiates and influences most of the other cell types involved in adaptive immunity. The other type, the cytotoxic T cell, attacks infected cells that contain viruses. In contrast, the main function of B cells is to produce antibodies. Each B cell produces just one type of antibody, which is specific for one type of antigen. As mentioned earlier in this section, an antigen is a molecule that causes a specific immune response because the immune system recognizes it as "foreign." When antibodies combine with antigens, the complex is often phagocytized by a macrophage. The activities of lymphocytes, along with other aspects of animal immune systems, are discussed in more detail in Chapter 33.

Platelets and Blood Clotting

Platelets (thrombocytes) result from fragmentation of large cells, called *megakaryocytes*, in the red bone marrow. Platelets are produced at a rate of 200 billion a day, and the blood contains 150,000–300,000 per mm^3. These formed elements are involved in blood **clotting**, or coagulation.

When a blood vessel in the body is damaged, platelets clump at the site of the puncture and partially seal the leak. Platelets and the injured tissues release a clotting factor called prothrombin activator that converts prothrombin in the plasma to thrombin. This reaction requires calcium ions (Ca^{2+}). *Thrombin*, in turn, acts as an enzyme that severs two short amino acid chains from a *fibrinogen* molecule, one of the proteins in plasma. These activated fragments then join end to end, forming long threads of *fibrin*.

Fibrin threads wind around the platelet plug in the damaged area of the blood vessel and provide the framework for the clot. Red blood cells also are trapped within the fibrin threads; these cells make a clot appear red (Fig. 32.17). A fibrin clot is present only temporarily. As soon as blood vessel repair is initiated, an enzyme called *plasmin* destroys the fibrin network and restores the fluidity of plasma.

The Nature of Science feature "How Horseshoe Crabs Save Human Lives" on page 622 describes how a clotting reaction in these arthropods can help identify bacterial contamination.

Figure 32.17 Blood clotting.   A number of plasma proteins participate in a series of enzymatic reactions that lead to the formation of fibrin threads.

1. Blood vessel is punctured.

2. Platelets congregate and form a plug.

3. Fibrin threads form and trap red blood cells.

Capillary Exchange

Figure 32.18 illustrates capillary exchange between a systemic capillary and tissue fluid, the fluid between the body's cells. Blood that enters a capillary at the arterial end is rich in oxygen and nutrients, and it is under pressure created by the pumping of the heart. Two forces primarily control movement of fluid through the capillary wall: (1) osmotic pressure, which tends to cause water to move from tissue fluid into blood, and (2) blood pressure, which tends to cause water to move in the opposite direction. At the arterial end of a capillary, the osmotic pressure of blood (21 mm Hg) is lower than the blood pressure (30 mm Hg). Osmotic pressure is created by the presence of salts and the plasma proteins. Because osmotic pressure is lower than blood pressure at the arterial end of a capillary, water exits a capillary at this end.

Midway along the capillary, where blood pressure is lower, the two forces essentially cancel each other, and there is no net movement of water. Solutes now diffuse according to their concentration gradient: Oxygen and nutrients (glucose and amino acids) diffuse out of the capillary; carbon dioxide and wastes diffuse into the capillary. Red blood cells and almost all plasma proteins remain in the capillaries.

The substances that leave a capillary contribute to **tissue fluid,** the fluid between the body's cells. Because plasma proteins are too large to readily pass out of the capillary, tissue fluid tends to contain all components of plasma but has much lower amounts of protein.

At the venule end of a capillary, where blood pressure has fallen even more, osmotic pressure is greater than blood pressure, and water tends to move into the capillary. Almost the same amount of fluid that left the capillary returns to it, although some

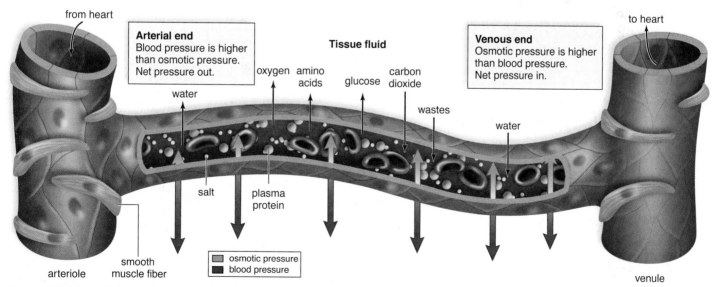

Figure 32.18 Capillary exchange.   A capillary, illustrating the exchanges that take place and the forces that aid the process. At the arterial end of a capillary, the blood pressure is higher than the osmotic pressure; therefore, water (H_2O) tends to leave the bloodstream. In the midsection, molecules, including oxygen (O_2) and carbon dioxide (CO_2), follow their concentration gradients. At the venous end of a capillary, the osmotic pressure is higher than the blood pressure; therefore, water tends to enter the bloodstream. Notice that the red blood cells and the plasma proteins are too large to exit a capillary.

THEME Nature of Science

How Horseshoe Crabs Save Human Lives

Take a walk along a beach on the northeastern U.S. coast, and you are likely to see horseshoe crabs (*Limulus polyphemus*) (Fig. 32B). Although not truly "crabs," they are classified in the phylum Arthropoda, along with insects, arachnids, and crustaceans. Because of their prehistoric appearance, horseshoe crabs are sometimes called "living fossils," and in fact they were living on Earth before the dinosaurs. They have an open circulatory system, with an elongated heart that pumps hemolymph between the gills and the body, without returning to the heart in between.

Instead of hemoglobin, the hemolymph of horseshoe crabs contains hemocyanin, which binds to oxygen using copper instead of iron, giving the blood a light blue color. The blood also contains amebocytes, cells that are analogous to the neutrophils or macrophages of higher animals, which serve a similar role in protecting against bacterial infections. Oddly enough, these amebocytes turned out to be the key to developing a method for detecting potentially fatal bacterial contamination of medical products such as IV solutions, vaccines, and injectable medications.

In the summer of 1950, a scientist named Frederick Bang was working at the Marine Biological Laboratory in Woods Hole, Massachusetts. Bang was interested in the immune system of primitive organisms, and so he chose to inject various types of bacteria into horseshoe crabs to study their immune response. What he found was that injection of any bacteria of the Gram-negative type, or an extract of their cell walls, caused the horseshoe crabs to quickly die, not from the infection, but from a massive coagulation of their circulatory fluid.

After many experiments and collaborations with other scientists, Bang developed a test using an extract of the amebocytes, which could be mixed with any sample to determine if that sample contained any contamination by Gram-negative bacteria. If so, the material would clot within 45 minutes. This LAL test, as it is now called, replaced the existing pyrogen test, which required that materials be injected into rabbits, took more time, and was less sensitive to low levels of contamination.

The only drawback of the LAL test is that it requires the removal of hemolymph from the horseshoe crabs. To do this, biomedical companies hire trawlers to catch adult horseshoe crabs. These are brought to a laboratory, washed, and about 30% of the animal's hemolymph removed from the animal's heart with a large gauge needle. The hemolymph is then centrifuged to separate the amebocytes, distilled water is added to lyse the cells, and the proteins responsible for the clotting reaction are separated and processed into the product used for the LAL test.

The horseshoe crabs are usually returned to the ocean within 72 hours of bleeding, and studies suggest that most of them survive, perhaps to be caught and bled again. Because one quart of hemolymph is worth about $15,000, the companies have good reason to preserve this ancient, fascinating species.

Questions to Consider

1. Compared to hemoglobin, hemocyanins are much larger, free-floating molecules. Why might hemocyanins work better with an open circulatory system, compared to hemoglobin?
2. The amebocytes of horseshoe crabs cause the animal's hemolymph to clot in response to certain bacteria. How could this response be beneficial to the animal?

Figure 32B Horseshoe crabs. Horseshoe crabs have lived on the Earth for an estimated 450 million years.

---

excess tissue fluid is always collected by the lymphatic capillaries (Fig. 32.19). Tissue fluid contained within lymphatic vessels is called **lymph.** Lymph is returned to the systemic venous blood when the major lymphatic vessels enter the subclavian veins in the shoulder region. See Chapter 33 for more information about the lymphatic system.

Figure 32.19 Capillary bed. A lymphatic capillary bed lies near a blood capillary bed. When lymphatic capillaries take up excess tissue fluid, it becomes lymph. Precapillary sphincters can shut down a blood capillary, and blood then flows through the shunt.

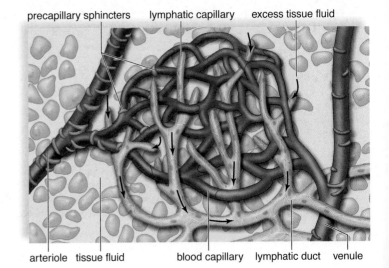

precapillary sphincters   lymphatic capillary   excess tissue fluid

arteriole   tissue fluid   blood capillary   lymphatic duct   venule

Not all capillary beds are open at the same time. When the precapillary sphincters (circular muscles) shown in Figure 32.4 are relaxed, the capillary bed is open and blood flows through the capillaries. When precapillary sphincters are contracted, blood flows through a shunt that carries blood directly from an arteriole to a venule.

In addition to nutrients and wastes, the blood distributes heat to body parts. When you are warm, many capillaries that serve the skin are open, and your face is flushed. This helps rid the body of excess heat. When you are cold, skin capillaries close, conserving heat, and your skin takes on a bluish tinge.

 MP3
Capillary Exchange and Bulk Flow

Animation
Fluid Exchange Across the Walls of Capillaries

Check Your Progress   32.4

1. List the major components of blood and the functions of each.
2. Name the major events, in chronological order, that result in a blood clot.
3. Explain why Rh incompatibility is a problem only when a fetus is Rh-positive and the mother is Rh-negative, but not vice-versa.
4. Describe the major factors that affect the rate of capillary exchange.

CONNECTING the CONCEPTS with the THEMES

Evolution

- Some animals have had no adaptive need to develop a circulatory system because their structure allows each cell to directly exchange nutrients and wastes with the environment.
- The open circulatory system most likely evolved first. As demands for oxygen and efficient exchange increased with a terrestrial lifestyle, natural selection favored the development of closed systems.
- Within closed systems, the heart evolved from the one atrium–one ventricle heart seen in most fish, to the four-chambered heart seen in crocodilians, birds, and mammals.

Nature of Science

- Because the circulatory system's function is so critical, a major research effort has been devoted to understanding and treating cardiovascular diseases.
- Recent advances in cardiovascular disease prevention and treatment range from lifestyle changes to drug therapies and surgical interventions.

Biological Systems

- The cardiovascular system's function is linked with the functions of several other systems: the respiratory system (gas exchange); the urinary system (waste excretion); the digestive system (providing nutrients); and the immune system (body defenses).
- In more complex animals, circulatory systems also transport many substances such as hormones, bilirubin, and cholesterol; protect against microbial invaders; and participate in temperature regulation.

Media Study Tools

www.mhhe.com/maderbiology11

Enhance your study of this chapter with study tools and practice tests. Also ask your instructor about the resources available through ConnectPlus, including the media-rich eBook, interactive learning tools, and animations.

Summarize

32.1 Transport in Invertebrates

Some invertebrates do not have a transport system. The presence of a gastrovascular cavity allows diffusion alone to supply the needs of cells in cnidarians and flatworms. Roundworms make use of their pseudocoelom in the same way that echinoderms use their coelom to circulate materials.

Other invertebrates do have a transport system. Insects have an open circulatory system, and earthworms have a closed one.

32.2 Transport in Vertebrates

Vertebrates have a closed system in which arteries carry blood away from the heart to capillaries, where exchange takes place, and veins carry blood to the heart.

Fishes have a one-circuit circulatory pathway because the heart, with the single atrium and ventricle, pumps blood to the gills and then to the body, without a second pass through the heart. The other vertebrates have both pulmonary and systemic circuits. Amphibians have two atria but a single ventricle. Crocodilians, birds, and mammals, including humans, have a heart with two atria and two ventricles, in which oxygen-rich blood is always separate from oxygen-poor blood.

32.3 The Human Cardiovascular System

The heartbeat in humans begins when the SA (sinoatrial) node (pacemaker) causes the two atria to contract, and blood moves through the atrioventricular valves to the two ventricles. The SA node also stimulates the AV (atrioventricular) node, which in turn causes the two ventricles to contract. Ventricular contraction sends blood through the semilunar valves to the pulmonary trunk and the aorta. Now all chambers rest. The heart sounds, lub-dub, are caused by the closing of the valves.

In the pulmonary circuit, blood travels to and from the lungs. In the systemic circuit, the aorta divides into blood vessels that serve the body's cells. The venae cavae return oxygen-poor blood to the heart.

Blood pressure created by the pumping of the heart accounts for the flow of blood in the arteries, but skeletal muscle contraction is largely responsible for the flow of blood in the veins, which have valves preventing a backward flow.

Hypertension and atherosclerosis are two circulatory disorders that can lead to heart attack and to stroke. Following a heart-healthy diet, getting regular exercise, maintaining a proper weight, and not smoking cigarettes can help protect against the development of these conditions.

32.4 Blood

Blood has two main parts: plasma and formed elements. Plasma is mostly water (90–92%), but also contains proteins (7–8%), nutrients, and wastes.

The formed elements include red blood cells, white blood cells, and platelets. Red blood cells contain hemoglobin, which functions in oxygen transport.

White blood cells, which include granulocytes and agranulo-cytes, defend the body against infections. Three types of granulo-cytes are the neutrophils, which are phagocytes; basophils, which are involved in inflammation; and eosinophils, which are important in parasitic infections.

The two types of agranulocytes are the lymphocytes, which carry out adaptive (specific) immunity to disease; and monocytes, which enter tissues to become phagocytic macrophages.

The platelets and two plasma proteins, prothrombin and fibrino-gen, function in blood clotting, an enzymatic process that results in fibrin threads. Blood clotting includes three major events: (1) Platelets and injured tissue release prothrombin activator, which (2) enzymati-cally changes prothrombin to thrombin, which is an enzyme that (3) causes fibrinogen to be converted to fibrin threads.

The ABO blood typing system is based on the presence or absence of A and B antigens on the red blood cells (A and B). If a mismatched transfusion is given, antibodies in the recipient's blood may react to these antigens. A second type of red blood cell antigen is the Rh factor. If an Rh-negative woman becomes pregnant with an Rh-positive fetus, she may produce anti-Rh antibodies that could damage any Rh-positive fetus she carries.

When blood reaches a capillary, water moves out at the arterial end due to blood pressure. At the venous end, water moves in due to osmotic pressure. In between, nutrients diffuse out of, and wastes diffuse into, the capillary according to concentration gradients.

Key Terms

agglutination 619
agranular leukocyte 620
angina pectoris 616
antibody 618
antigen 619
aorta 614
arteriole 608
artery 608
atherosclerosis 616
atrioventricular valve 611
atrium 610
basophil 620
blood 606
blood pressure 615
capillary 608
cardiac cycle 612
cardiac output 612
circulatory (or cardiovascular) system 606, 608

closed circulatory system 607
clotting 620
diastole 612
electrocardiogram (ECG) 613
eosinophil 620
formed elements 618
granular leukocyte 620
heart 610
heart attack 616
hemoglobin 618
hemolymph 606
hypertension 616
leukocyte 620
lymph 622
lymphocyte 620
macrophage 620
monocyte 620
neutrophil 620

open circulatory system 606
pacemaker 613
plasma 618
platelet 620
portal system 614
pulmonary circuit 609
pulse 613
red blood cell 618
semilunar valve 611
septum 610

stroke 616
systemic circuit 609
systole 612
tissue fluid 621
vein 608
vena cava 614
ventricle 611
venule 608
white blood cell 620

Assess

Reviewing This Chapter

1. Describe transport in invertebrates that have no circulatory system; in those that have an open circulatory system; and in those that have a closed circulatory system. 606–7
2. Compare the circulatory systems of a fish, an amphibian, and a mammal. 608–9
3. Trace the path of blood in humans from the right ventricle to the left atrium; from the left ventricle to the kidneys and to the right atrium; from the left ventricle to the small intestine and to the right atrium. 611
4. Describe the mechanism of a heartbeat, mentioning all the factors that account for this repetitive process. Describe how the heartbeat affects blood flow. What other factors are involved in blood flow? 612–13
5. Define these terms: pulmonary circuit, systemic circuit, and portal system. 614
6. Discuss the life cycle and function of red blood cells. 618–19
7. Explain the ABO and Rh systems of typing blood. 619–20
8. How are white blood cells classified? What are the functions of neutrophils, monocytes, and lymphocytes? 620
9. Name the steps that take place when blood clots. Which substances are present in blood at all times, and which appear during the clotting process? 620
10. What forces facilitate exchange of molecules across the capillary wall? 621–23

Testing Yourself

Choose the best answer for each question.

1. Which one of these would you expect to be part of a closed, but not an open, circulatory system?
   a. ostia
   b. capillary beds
   c. hemocoel
   d. heart
   e. All of these are correct.

2. In which animal does aortic blood have less oxygen than blood in the pulmonary vein?
   a. frog
   b. chicken
   c. monkey
   d. fish
   e. All of these are correct.

3. In humans, blood returning to the heart from the lungs returns to
   a. the right ventricle.
   b. the right atrium.
   c. the left ventricle.
   d. the left atrium.
   e. both the right and left sides of the heart.

4. Systole refers to the contraction of the
   a. major arteries.
   b. SA node.
   c. atria and ventricles.
   d. major veins.
   e. All of these are correct.

5. Which of these is an incorrect association?
   a. white blood cells—infection fighting
   b. red blood cells—blood clotting
   c. plasma—water, nutrients, and wastes
   d. red blood cells—hemoglobin
   e. platelets—blood clotting

6. Water enters capillaries on the venous end as a result of
   a. active transport from tissue fluid.
   b. an osmotic pressure gradient.
   c. higher blood pressure on the venous end.
   d. higher blood pressure on the arterial side.
   e. higher red blood cell concentration on the venous end.

7. Macrophages are derived from
   a. basophils.   d. lymphocytes.
   b. eosinophils.   e. monocytes.
   c. neutrophils.

8. Which of the following is not a formed element of blood?
   a. leukocyte   c. fibrinogen
   b. eosinophil   d. platelet

9. Which of these is an incorrect statement concerning the heartbeat?
   a. The atria contract at the same time.
   b. The ventricles relax at the same time.
   c. The atrioventricular valves open at the same time.
   d. The semilunar valves open at the same time.
   e. First, the right side contracts, and then the left side contracts.

10. All arteries in the body contain O_2-rich blood, with the exception of the
    a. aorta.   c. renal arteries.
    b. pulmonary arteries. d. coronary arteries.

11. The "lub," the first heart sound, is produced by the closing of
    a. the aortic semilunar valve.
    b. the pulmonary semilunar valve.
    c. the right (atrioventricular) tricuspid valve.
    d. the left (atrioventricular) bicuspid valve, or mitral valve.
    e. both atrioventricular valves.

12. Label this diagram of the heart.

a. _____
b. _____
c. _____
d. _____
e. _____
f. _____
g. _____
h. _____
i. _____
j. _____
k. _____
l. _____
m. _____
n. _____
o. _____
p. _____
q. _____

Engage

Virtual Labs
Virtual Frog Dissection
Earthworm Dissection

The Virtual Labs "Virtual Frog Dissection" and "Earthworm Dissection" provide an interactive look at the circulatory systems of vertebrate and invertebrate animals.

Thinking Scientifically

1. For several years, researchers have attempted to produce an artificial blood for transfusions. Artificial blood would most likely be safer and more readily available than human blood. While artificial blood might not have all the characteristics of human blood, it would be useful on the battlefield and in emergency situations. Which characteristics of normal blood must artificial blood have to be useful, and which would probably be too difficult to reproduce?

2. You have to stand in front of the class to give a report. You are nervous, and your heart is pounding. What is the specific mechanism behind this reaction? How would your ECG appear?

Bioethical Issue
A Healthy Lifestyle

Many deaths a year could be prevented if people adopted the healthy lifestyle described in the Nature of Science feature "New Information About Preventing Cardiovascular Disease." Tobacco, lack of exercise, and a high-fat diet probably cost the nation about $200 billion per year in health-care costs. To what lengths should we go to prevent these deaths and reduce health-care costs?

E. A. Miller, a meat-packing subsidiary of ConAgra in Hyrum, Utah, charges extra for medical coverage of employees who smoke. Eric Falk, Miller's director of human resources, says, "We want to teach employees to be responsible for their behavior." Anthem Blue Cross–Blue Shield of Cincinnati, Ohio, takes a more positive approach. They give insurance plan participants $240 a year in extra benefits, such as additional vacation days, if they get good scores in five out of seven health-related categories. The University of Alabama, Birmingham, School of Nursing has a health-and-wellness program that counsels employees about how to get into shape in order to keep their insurance coverage. Audrey Brantley, who is in the program, has mixed feelings. She says, "It seems like they are trying to control us, but then, on the other hand, I know of folks who found out they had high blood pressure or were borderline diabetics and didn't know it."

Does it really work? Turner Broadcasting System in Atlanta has a policy that affects all employees hired after 1986. They will be fired if caught smoking—whether at work or at home—but some admit they still manage to sneak a smoke. What steps do you think are ethical to encourage people to adopt a healthy lifestyle?

33

The Lymphatic and Immune Systems

David Vetter, who suffered from severe combined immune deficiency and had to be kept in an isolated environment.

CHAPTER OUTLINE

BEFORE YOU BEGIN

Before beginning this chapter, take a few moments to review the following discussions.

Figure 5.3 Which of the major protein functions are most important in the immune system?

Figure 21.21 In what ways do the amoeboid protists resemble macrophages of the mammalian immune system?

Section 31.2 What life processes are carried out by the lymphatic and immune systems?

The opening story for Chapter 31 noted how an astronaut walking in space needs a protective suit to provide his or her body with the oxygen, warmth, and other factors needed for internal homeostasis. Equally important is our ability to keep a variety of microbial and other threats from damaging our body. The many and varied molecules, cells, and tissues that carry out this task are collectively known as the immune system.

Unfortunately not everyone inherits a healthy immune system. Without treatment, most children born with a severe immunodeficiency disorder die at a few months of age. In the 1970s, almost everyone in the U.S. was familiar with the case of David Vetter, better known as "The Boy in the Plastic Bubble." Born with a faulty immune system, David spent most of his life inside a series of sterile plastic enclosures. Because of the high risk of infection, he was never allowed to hug his family or walk barefoot in the grass (as was his dream), although at age six he was able to briefly explore the outside world in a special suit produced for him by NASA. David died at age 12 after a failed bone marrow transplant. His sad and controversial story has inspired many articles, songs, TV episodes, and at least two movies. It can also serve to remind us of the critical role of our immune system in protecting us against a vast array of viruses, bacteria, fungi, parasites, and toxins in our environment. In this chapter we explore that system, along with the lymphatic system that helps to produce and distribute the cells of the immune system.

As you read through the chapter, think about the following questions:

1. What are the most essential components of the immune system?
2. How do the lymphatic and immune systems work together?
3. We no longer hear much about keeping severely immunodeficient patients in plastic bubbles today, so how do you suppose they are treated?

FOLLOWING *the* THEMES

CHAPTER 33 THE LYMPHATIC AND IMMUNE SYSTEMS

UNIT 7 COMPARATIVE ANIMAL BIOLOGY		
	Evolution	Even the simplest of multicellular organisms have developed cells that specialize in immune defenses, which provides clues about how more complex immunity may have evolved.
	Nature of Science	Because the immune system is essential to our health, studies of patients with immune system disorders such as AIDS have improved our basic understanding of how the immune system functions.
	Biological Systems	The lymphatic and immune systems are both essential to homeostasis, with the lymphatic system serving some additional functions unrelated to immunity.

33.1 Evolution of Immune Systems

Learning Outcomes

Upon completion of this section, you should be able to

1. Summarize the evidence suggesting that cellular slime molds can form a rudimentary "immune system."
2. Define PAMPs and explain how they enable many animals to identify the presence of harmful microbes.
3. Compare the types of antigens recognized by the innate versus the adaptive immune system.

Our **immune system** protects us from all sorts of harmful invaders, including bacterial and viral pathogens, various toxins, and perhaps even cancerous cells that occasionally arise. It is a very intricate system made up of many components that work together, perhaps rivaling the nervous system in its complexity. But how did such a complicated system first evolve? And which components developed first? Scientists are beginning to answer those questions.

Immunity in Cellular Slime Molds

In August 2007, researchers at Baylor College of Medicine in Houston, Texas, discovered that very simple creatures called cellular slime molds can exhibit signs of a rudimentary immune system. These organisms are commonly known as "social amoebas" because of their unique life cycle. When food is plentiful, these protists live as separate amoeboid cells (Figure 33.1a), ingesting bacteria through phagocytosis and reproducing by binary fission (dividing into identical copies). As the food supply dwindles, many thousands of these amoebas can join together to form a slug two to four millimeters long (Figure 33.1b). The slug migrates toward light as a single, multicellular body, then differentiates into a reproductive structure that releases spores, many of which disperse to become new amoebas.

For several years biologists have known that individual cells within the slug can become specialized to perform various functions, but the Baylor group discovered a new type of cell within the slug that they named *sentinel cells.* These cells circulate throughout the slug, engulfing bacteria and toxins. Eventually the sentinel cells are sloughed from the body of the slug, thereby "sacrificing themselves" for the good of the organism. Some scientists believe that phagocytic white blood cells in the human body, such as neutrophils and macrophages, may have evolved from these types of cells.

Immunity in *Drosophila*

Although social amoebas may provide an example of how phagocytic cells first became specialized to protect multicellular organisms, the immune system is far more developed in invertebrates such as the fruit fly, *Drosophila melanogaster.* It was in this well-studied insect that scientists discovered the existence of a group of cellular receptors that could recognize common components found in many pathogenic microbes, but not in the insect's own cells. When these receptors bind to these

a.   b.

Figure 33.1 Social amoebas (*Dictyostelium discoideum*)
a. The single-celled form, shown here at a high magnification. **b.** Under certain conditions thousands of amoebas can form a multicellular slug, in which some cells develop protective functions.

pathogen-associated molecular patterns, or *PAMPs*, they trigger an immune reaction, increasing the odds that the pathogen can be eliminated from the fly.

Examples of PAMPs found on pathogenic microbes include the double-stranded RNA that is produced during the replication cycle of many viruses, and certain arrangements of carbohydrates, lipids, or proteins found only on bacterial cell walls. Receptors for PAMPs have been found in organisms as diverse as fruit flies, plants, and humans, suggesting that they were one of the earliest, and most successful, types of cellular receptors that evolved for the recognition of pathogens.

The Rise of Adaptive Immunity

As you will see later in Section 33.3, these first two examples illustrate a type of host defense known as **innate immunity,** which can recognize common microbial invaders very quickly, but shows no signs of an increased response upon repeated exposure to the same invader. Most vertebrate animals also exhibit **adaptive immunity,** characterized by the production of a very large number of diverse receptors that are found on the surface of specialized white blood cells (such as B and T lymphocytes in humans). These receptors bind very specifically to molecules called **antigens,** much as a key fits a lock. This binding stimulates lymphocytes to divide and become much more numerous, resulting in characteristic features of adaptive immunity, such as greatly increased responses to specific antigens and immunological memory after the initial exposure to an antigen.

The generation of such a diverse array of antigen receptors depends on a rearrangement of the DNA that codes for these receptors, somewhat like choosing different combinations of cards from a deck. Scientists have now discovered that this process developed quite suddenly in an ancestor that gave rise to the jawed vertebrates—including the cartilaginous fishes (sharks and rays), bony fishes, amphibians, reptiles, birds, and mammals.

The precise mechanism by which this "explosion" of adaptive immunity occurred is still incompletely understood, although it now seems quite likely that it involved the insertion of a small piece of DNA (a transposon, or "jumping gene"; see Section 14.4) into a gene coding for a more primitive, less variable antigen receptor—perhaps similar to the receptors for

PAMPs mentioned earlier here. Note that in contrast to the relatively "fixed" receptors for PAMPs recognized by the innate immune system, the generation of antigen receptors by gene rearrangement allows the adaptive immune system to be able to respond to new antigens that evolve, for example, in emerging infectious agents. In other words, the vertebrate immune system has evolved an ability to respond to the continuing evolution of pathogenic microbes and other threats to our health.

Check Your Progress   33.1

1. Describe the function of sentinel cells found in cellular slime molds.
2. List three specific types of PAMPs found on microbes.
3. Describe three ways that the evolution of receptors for specific antigens increased the effectiveness of the immune system.

33.2 The Lymphatic System

Learning Outcomes

Upon completion of this section, you should be able to

1. Describe three major functions of the lymphatic system.
2. Distinguish between the roles of primary and secondary lymphoid tissues, and list examples of each.

The **lymphatic system,** which is closely associated with the cardiovascular and immune systems, includes the lymphatic vessels and the lymphoid organs. It has three main functions that contribute to homeostasis:

🎵 **MP3** Lymphatic System

- Lymphatic capillaries absorb excess tissue fluid and return it to the bloodstream.
- In the small intestine, lymphatic capillaries called lacteals absorb fats in the form of lipoproteins and transport them to the bloodstream.
- The lymphoid organs and lymphatic vessels are sites of production and distribution of lymphocytes, which help defend the body against pathogens.

Lymphatic Vessels

Lymphatic vessels form a one-way system that begins with lymphatic capillaries (Fig. 33.2). Most regions of the body are

Figure 33.2 Lymphatic system. Lymphatic vessels drain excess fluid from the tissues and return it to the cardiovascular system. The enlargement shows that lymphatic vessels, like cardiovascular veins, have valves to prevent backward flow. The lymph nodes, spleen, thymus, and red bone marrow are the main lymphoid organs that assist immunity.

Right lymphatic duct: empties lymph into the right subclavian vein

Right subclavian vein: transports blood away from the right arm and the right ventral chest wall toward the heart

Axillary lymph nodes: located in the underarm region

Thoracic duct: empties lymph into the left subclavian vein

Inguinal lymph nodes: located in the groin region

Tonsils: aggregates of lymphoid tissue that respond to pathogens in the pharynx

Left subclavian vein: transports blood away from the left arm and the left ventral chest wall toward the heart

Red bone marrow: site for the origin of all types of blood cells

Thymus: lymphoid organ where T cells mature

Spleen: resident T cells and B cells respond to the presence of antigen in blood

tissue fluid

lymphatic capillary

tissue cell

blood capillary

valve

Figure 33.3 The lymphatic organs. a. Blood cells, including lymphocytes, are produced in red bone marrow. B cells mature in the bone marrow, but (**b**) T cells mature in the thymus. **c.** Lymph is cleansed in lymph nodes, while (**d**) blood is cleansed in the spleen.

richly supplied with **lymphatic capillaries**—tiny, closed-ended vessels. Lymphatic capillaries take up excess tissue fluid. The fluid inside lymphatic capillaries is called **lymph.**

The lymphatic capillaries join to form lymphatic vessels that merge before entering either the thoracic duct or the right lymphatic duct. The larger thoracic duct returns lymph to the left subclavian vein. The right lymphatic duct returns lymph to the right subclavian vein.

The construction of the larger lymphatic vessels is similar to that of cardiovascular veins. Skeletal muscle contraction forces lymph through lymphatic vessels, and it is prevented from flowing backward by one-way valves.

A number of diseases may result in an increased amount of fluid leaving the blood capillaries, or an insufficient return of fluid to the blood via the lymphatic vessels. In either case, a localized accumulation of tissue fluid called *edema* may result, illustrating the importance of this aspect of lymphatic system function.

Animation
Lymphatic System

Lymphoid Organs

The **lymphoid (lymphatic) organs** are reviewed in Figures 33.2 and 33.3. Lymphocytes develop and mature in **primary lymphoid organs** such as bone marrow and the thymus; **secondary lymphoid organs** are sites where some lymphocytes are activated by antigens.

A major primary lymphoid organ is the **red bone marrow**, a spongy, semisolid red tissue where hematopoietic stem cells divide and produce all the types of blood cells, including lymphocytes (Fig. 33.3*a*). In a child, most of the bones have red bone marrow, but in an adult, it is present only in the bones of the skull, the sternum (breastbone), the ribs, the clavicle (collarbone), the pelvic bones, the vertebral column, and the proximal heads of the femur and humerus.

There are two main types of lymphocytes: B lymphocytes (B cells) and T lymphocytes (T cells). Although both types begin their development in the red bone marrow, **B cells** remain there until they are mature. In contrast, immature **T cells** migrate from

the bone marrow via the bloodstream to the thymus, where they mature.

The soft, bilobed **thymus** is a primary lymphoid organ located in the thoracic cavity between the trachea and the sternum ventral to the heart (see Fig. 33.2). It is in the thymus that T cells learn to recognize the combinations of self-molecules and foreign molecules; this recognition characterizes mature T-cell responses (see Section 33.4). The thymus varies in size, but it is largest in children and shrinks as we get older. When well developed, it contains many lobules (Fig. 33.3*b*).

Once lymphocytes are mature, they enter the bloodstream. From there they frequently migrate into secondary lymphoid organs, such as the lymph nodes and spleen. Here lymphocytes may encounter foreign molecules or cells, and in response they proliferate and become activated. Activated lymphocytes then reenter the bloodstream, searching for signs of infection or inflammation, like a squadron of highly trained military personnel seeking to destroy a specific enemy.

Lymph nodes are small (about 1–25 mm in diameter) ovoid structures occurring along lymphatic vessels. They are a major type of secondary lymphoid organ. As lymph percolates through the cortex and medulla of a lymph node (Fig. 33.3*c*), resident phagocytic cells engulf any foreign debris and pathogens. These phagocytes can then "present" these foreign materials to T cells in the lymph node (see Section 33.4).

Sometimes incorrectly called "lymph glands," lymph nodes are named for their location. For example, inguinal lymph nodes are in the groin, and axillary lymph nodes are in the armpits. Physicians often feel for the presence of swollen, tender lymph nodes as evidence that the body is fighting an infection. Unfortunately, cancer cells sometimes enter lymphatic vessels and congregate in lymph nodes. Therefore, when a person undergoes surgery for cancer, it is a common procedure to remove some lymph nodes and examine them to determine whether the cancer has spread to other regions of the body.

The **spleen,** an oval secondary lymphoid organ with a dull purplish color, is located in the upper left side of the abdominal cavity posterior to the stomach. Most of the spleen contains red pulp that filters and cleanses the blood. Red pulp consists of blood vessels and sinuses, where macrophages remove old and defective blood cells. The spleen also has white pulp that consists of small areas of secondary lymphoid tissue (Fig. 33.3*d*). Much as the lymph nodes serve as sites for lymphocytes to respond to foreign material from the tissues, the spleen serves a similar role for the blood.

The spleen's outer capsule is relatively thin, and an infection or trauma can cause the spleen to burst, necessitating surgical removal. Although some of the spleen's functions can be largely replaced by other organs, an asplenic individual is more susceptible to certain types of infections and may require antibiotic therapy indefinitely.

Patches of lymphatic tissue in the body include the *tonsils*, located in the pharynx; *Peyer's patches*, located in the intestinal wall; and the *vermiform appendix*, attached to the cecum. These structures encounter pathogens and antigens that enter the body by way of the mouth.

Check Your Progress   33.2

1. Write a brief description of the lymphatic system.
2. Summarize the functions of the lymphatic system.
3. Describe the general appearance, location, and function of the lymphatic organs.

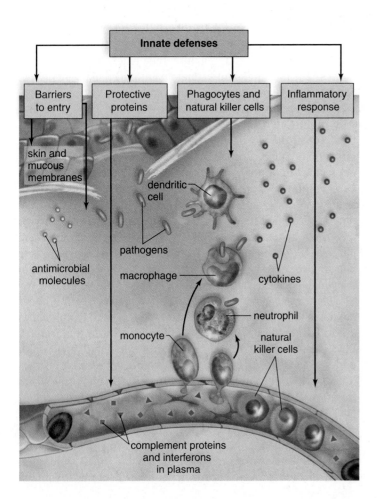

33.3 Innate Immune Defenses

Learning Outcomes

Upon completion of this section, you should be able to

1. Define innate immunity.
2. Describe four mechanisms of innate immunity, and the major tissues, molecules, and/or cells involved.
3. Explain some specific ways that the innate immune system interacts with and influences the adaptive immune system.

We are constantly exposed to microbes such as viruses, bacteria, and fungi in our environment. **Immunity** is the capability of removing or killing foreign substances, pathogens, and cancer cells from the body. Mechanisms of *innate immunity* are fully functional without previous exposure to these invaders, while *adaptive immunity* (see Section 33.4) is initiated and amplified by exposure.

As summarized in Figure 33.4, innate immune defenses include:

- physical and chemical barriers,
- the inflammatory response,
- phagocytes and natural killer cells, and
- protective proteins such as complement and interferons.

Innate defenses occur immediately or very shortly after an infection occurs. With innate immunity, there is no recognition that an intruder has attacked before, and therefore no immunological "memory" is present for the attacker.

Physical and Chemical Barriers

Physical barriers to various types of invaders include the skin as well as the mucous membranes lining the respiratory, digestive, and urinary tracts. As you saw in Chapter 31, the outer layers of our skin are composed of dead, keratinized cells that form a relatively impermeable barrier. But when the skin has been injured, one of the first concerns is the possibility of an infection.

The mucus produced by mucous membranes physically ensnares microbes. The upper respiratory tract is lined by ciliated cells that sweep mucus and trapped particles up into the throat, where they can be swallowed or expectorated (coughed out). In addition, various bacteria that normally reside in the intestine and in other areas, such as the vagina, take up nutrients and block binding sites that potentially could be exploited by pathogens.

The secretions of oil glands found in human skin also contain chemicals that weaken or kill certain bacteria; saliva, tears, milk, and mucus contain lysozyme, an enzyme that can lyse bacteria; and the stomach has an acidic pH, which inhibits or kills many microbes.

Figure 33.4 Overview of innate immune defenses. Most innate defenses act rapidly to detect and respond to various, highly conserved molecules expressed by pathogens.

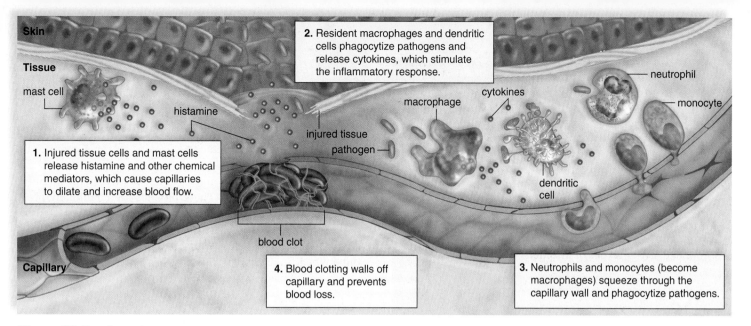

Figure 33.5 Inflammatory response. Due to capillary changes in a damaged area and the release of chemical mediators, such as histamine by mast cells, an inflamed area exhibits redness, heat, swelling, and pain. The inflammatory response can be accompanied by other reactions to the injury. Macrophages and dendritic cells, present in the tissues, phagocytize pathogens, as do neutrophils, which squeeze through capillary walls from the blood. Macrophages and dendritic cells release cytokines, which stimulate the inflammatory and other immune responses. A blood clot can form to seal a break in a blood vessel.

Inflammatory Response

When tissues are damaged by a variety of causes, including pathogens, a series of events known as the **inflammatory response** occurs. An inflamed area has at least four common signs: redness, heat, swelling, and pain. Most of these signs are due to capillary changes in the damaged area, as illustrated in Figure 33.5. Chemical mediators released by damaged cells, including **histamine** that is mainly secreted by tissue-dwelling cells of the innate immune system called **mast cells,** cause capillaries to dilate and become more permeable. Increased blood flow to the area causes the skin to redden and become warm. Increased permeability of the capillaries allows proteins and fluids to escape into the tissues, resulting in swelling. Various chemicals released by damaged cells stimulate free nerve endings, causing the sensation of pain.

Inflammation also causes various types of white blood cells to migrate from the bloodstream into damaged tissues. Once in the tissues, monocytes can differentiate into dendritic cells and macrophages, both of which are able to devour many pathogens and still survive (Fig. 33.6). Macrophages also release colony-stimulating factors, namely cytokines, which pass by way of the blood to the red bone marrow where they stimulate the production and release of white blood cells.

Animation
Inflammatory Response

Sometimes an inflammation persists, and the result is chronic inflammation that can itself become damaging to tissues. Examples include the chronic responses to the bacterium that causes tuberculosis, or to asbestos fibers that, once inhaled into the lungs, cannot be removed. Some cases of chronic inflammation are treated by administering anti-inflammatory drugs such as aspirin, ibuprofen, or cortisone. These medications inhibit the responses to inflammatory chemicals being released in the damaged area.

From the site of their production in damaged tissues, various inflammatory mediators are absorbed into the bloodstream, where they can affect several other organs. Although it is not normally thought of as a part of the immune system, the liver responds to these chemicals by increasing production of various *acute phase proteins,* some of which can coat microbial invaders, making them easier for phagocytes to engulf. One type of acute phase protein, called C-reactive protein, is frequently measured to assess levels of inflammation in patients suffering from certain diseases.

Inflammatory chemicals in the blood may also act on the brain to initiate an elevated body temperature or *fever.* Although the exact function of the body's fever response is unknown, many speculate that certain bacteria or viruses may not survive as well at higher temperatures, or that certain immune mechanisms work better at higher body temperatures. Experimental data have been collected that support both hypotheses, and in fact, both may be true. In either case, because mild to moderate fever appears to help the body fight off invaders more effectively, the wisdom of using drugs to treat mild fevers can be questioned. However, body temperatures above 103°F can be fatal, especially in children, so obviously this situation must be treated as an emergency.

Inflammatory responses are accompanied by other responses to the injury. The clotting system can be activated to seal a break in a blood vessel. Antigens, chemical mediators, dendritic cells, and macrophages move from the damaged tissue via the lymph to the lymph nodes. There, these phagocytes interact with T cells and B cells to activate a specific, adaptive response to the infection (see Section 33.4). Finally, inflammation also initiates the healing response, in which macrophages play an essential role.

Phagocytes and Natural Killer Cells

Several types of white blood cells are phagocytic, meaning that they can engulf and digest relatively large particles such as viruses and bacteria. **Neutrophils** are able to leave the bloodstream and phagocytize bacteria in tissues. They have multiple

Figure 33.6 Macrophage engulfing bacteria. Monocyte-derived macrophages are the body's scavengers. They engulf microbes and debris in the body's fluids and tissues, as illustrated in this colorized scanning electron micrograph.

ways of killing bacteria. The cytoplasm of a neutrophil is packed with granules that contain antimicrobial peptides, as well as enzymes that can digest bacteria. Other enzymes inside neutrophil granules generate highly reactive free radicals such as superoxide and hydrogen peroxide, all of which participate in killing engulfed bacteria.

As the infection is being overcome, some neutrophils die. These—along with dead tissue cells, dead bacteria, and living white blood cells—may form pus, a whitish material. The presence of pus usually indicates that the body is trying to overcome a bacterial infection.

Eosinophils can be phagocytic, but they are better known for mounting an attack against animal parasites such as tapeworms that are too large to be phagocytized.

As mentioned, the two longer-lived types of phagocytic white blood cells are **macrophages** (see Fig. 33.6) and **dendritic cells.** Macrophages are found in all sorts of tissues, whereas dendritic cells are especially prevalent in the skin. Both cell types engulf pathogens, which are then digested and broken down into smaller molecular components. They then travel to lymph nodes, where they stimulate T cells, which are responsible for initiating adaptive immune responses.

Natural killer (NK) cells are large, granular lymphocytes that kill virus-infected cells and cancer cells by cell-to-cell contact. NK cells do their work while adaptive defenses are still mobilizing, and they produce cytokines that promote adaptive immunity.

What makes NK cells attack and kill a cell? NK cells seek out cells that lack a particular type of "self" molecule, called MHC-I (major histocompatibility complex I), on their surface. Because some virus-infected and cancer cells may lack these MHC-I molecules, they may be recognized by NK cells, which kill these cells by inducing them to undergo cellular suicide (apoptosis). Because NK cells do not recognize specific viral

or tumor antigens, and do not proliferate when exposed to a particular antigen, their numbers do not increase after stimulation.

Protective Proteins

Complement is composed of a number of blood plasma proteins, produced mainly by the liver, that "complement" certain immune responses. These proteins are continually present in the blood plasma but must be activated by pathogens to exert their effects. The complement system helps destroy pathogens in three ways:

1. *Enhanced inflammation.* Complement proteins are involved in and amplify the inflammatory response because certain ones can bind to mast cells and trigger histamine release, and others can attract phagocytes to the scene.
2. *Increased phagocytosis.* Some complement proteins bind to the surface of pathogens, increasing the odds that the pathogens will be phagocytized by a neutrophil or macrophage.
3. *Membrane attack complexes.* Certain other complement proteins join to form a membrane attack complex that produces holes in the surface of some bacteria and viruses. Fluids and salts then enter the bacterial cell or virus to the point that it bursts (Fig. 33.7).

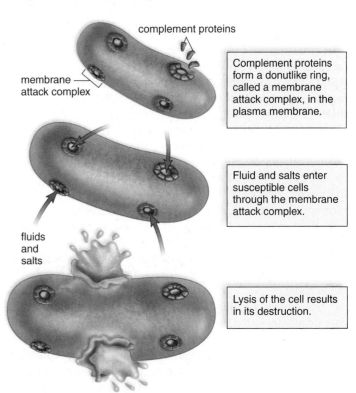

Figure 33.7 Action of the complement system against a bacterium. When complement proteins in the blood plasma are activated by an immune response, they form a membrane attack complex that makes holes in bacterial cell walls and plasma membranes, allowing fluids and salts to enter until the cell eventually bursts.

Interferons come in several different types, but all are **cytokines,** soluble proteins that affect the behavior of other cells. Most interferons are made by virus-infected cells. They bind to the receptors of noninfected cells, causing them to produce substances that slow cellular metabolism and interfere with viral replication. Interferons are used to treat certain cancers and viral infections such as hepatitis C.

 Animation
Antiviral Activity
of Interferon

Check Your Progress   33.3

1. List three physical and three chemical barriers.
2. Describe the four cardinal signs associated with an inflammatory response. How is this response beneficial?
3. Name five cell types involved in innate immunity, and the major functions of each.
4. Summarize three specific functions of the complement system.

33.4 Adaptive Immune Defenses

Learning Outcomes

Upon completion of this section, you should be able to

1. Compare and contrast the activities of B cells and T cells.
2. Describe the basic structure of an antibody molecule, explain the different functions of IgG, IgA, IgM, and IgE.
3. Define monoclonal antibodies, and list some specific applications of this technology.
4. Discuss active and passive immune responses, giving specific examples of each.

Even while innate defenses are trying to fight an infection, adaptive defenses also begin to respond. Because these defenses do not normally react to our own cells or molecules, it is said that the adaptive immune system can distinguish "self" from "nonself." Adaptive defenses usually take from five to seven days to become activated, but they may last for years. This explains why, once we recover from some infectious diseases, we usually do not get the same disease a second time. Because we are not born with these defenses, some prefer the term *acquired immunity* to describe this type of immunity.

Adaptive defenses depend primarily on the activities of B cells and T cells (Fig. 33.8). Both B cells and T cells are manufactured in the red bone marrow. As mentioned earlier, B cells mature there, but T cells mature in the thymus. Both cell types are capable of binding to and thus "recognizing" specific antigens because they have **antigen receptors** on their plasma membrane. Pathogens, cancer cells, and transplanted tissues and organs bear antigens the immune system usually recognizes as nonself.

During our lifetime, we need a diversity of B cells and T cells to recognize these antigens and protect us against them. Remarkably, diversification occurs during the lymphocyte

maturation process to so great an extent that there are specific B cells and/or T cells for almost every possible antigen. Because B and T cells defend us from disease by specifically reacting to antigens, they can be likened to special forces that can attack selected targets without harming nearby residents (uninfected cells).

B Cells and Antibody-Mediated Immunity

The receptor for antigen on the surface of a B cell is called a **B-cell receptor (BCR).** B cells are usually activated in a lymph node or the spleen, after their BCRs bind to a specific antigen. Subsequently, the B cell divides by mitosis many times, making many copies (clones) of itself. The **clonal selection theory** states that the antigen receptor of each B cell or T cell binds to only a single type of antigen.

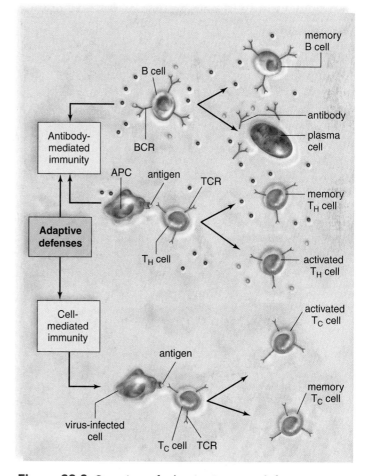

Figure 33.8 Overview of adaptive immune defenses. B cells, helper T (T$_H$) cells, and cytotoxic T (T$_C$) cells respond to specific antigens by dividing and differentiating. The BCRs of B cells bind to whole, intact antigens, while the TCRs of T$_H$ and T$_C$ cells only bind to antigens that are processed and presented by MHC proteins on the surface of other cells. When activated by antigens, B cells differentiate into antibody-secreting plasma cells, T$_H$ cells become cytokine-secreting cells, and T$_C$ cells are able to destroy virus-infected or cancer cells. Each cell type also produces memory cells that can respond more quickly to a subsequent exposure to the same antigen.

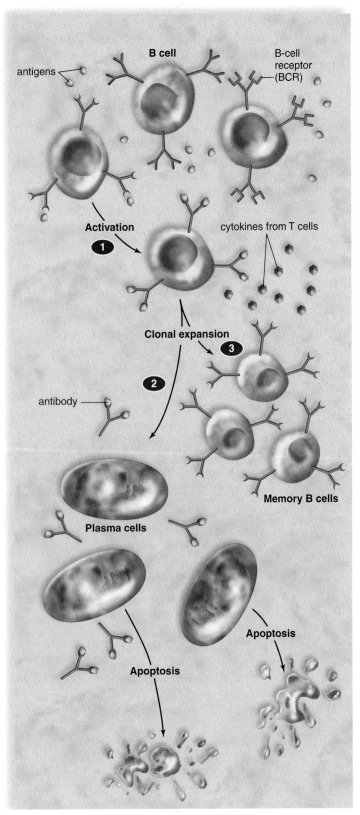

Figure 33.9 Clonal selection theory as it applies to B cells.
Each B cell has a B-cell receptor (BCR) designated by shape that will
combine with a specific antigen. Activation of a B cell occurs when its
BCR can combine with an antigen (colored green). In the presence of
cytokines, the B cell undergoes clonal expansion, producing many plasma
cells and memory B cells. These plasma cells secrete antibodies specific
to the antigen, and memory B cells immediately recognize the antigen
in the future. After the infection passes, plasma cells undergo apoptosis,
also called programmed cell death.

As illustrated in Fig. 33.9, ❶ many B cells are present, but only those that have BCRs that can combine with the specific antigen(s) present go on to divide and produce many new cells. Therefore, the antigen is said to "select" the B cells that will begin dividing. At the same time, cytokines secreted by helper T cells stimulate B cells to differentiate. ❷ Many of these B cells become **plasma cells**, which are specialized for secretion of antibodies. Plasma cells are larger than regular B cells because they have extensive rough endoplasmic reticulum for the mass production and secretion of antibodies that bind to a specific antigen. Antibodies are the secreted form of the BCR of an activated B cell, and these antibodies react to the same antigen as the original B cell. Once the threat of an infection has passed, the development of new plasma cells ceases, and those present undergo apoptosis. ❸ Other progeny of the dividing B cells become **memory B cells**, so named because these cells always "remember" a particular antigen and make us immune to a particular illness, but not to any other illness.

Defense of the body by B cells is known as **antibody-mediated immunity** (see Fig. 33.8, *top*). It is also called humoral immunity because these antibodies are present in blood and lymph. (Historically, the term *humor* referred to any fluid normally occurring in the body.)

Structure of Antibodies

The basic unit of antibody structure is a Y-shaped protein molecule with two arms. Each arm has a "heavy" (long) polypeptide chain and a "light" (short) polypeptide chain (Fig. 33.10). These chains have constant (C) regions, located at the trunk of the Y, where the sequence of amino acids is set. The variable (V) regions at the tips of the Y form two antigen-binding sites, and their shape is specific to a particular antigen. The antigen combines with the antibody at the antigen-binding site in a lock-and-key manner.

The binding of antibodies to an antigen can have several outcomes. Often, the reaction produces a clump of antigens combined with antibodies, termed an *immune complex*. The antibodies in an immune complex are like a beacon that attracts white blood cells that move in for the kill. For example, immune complexes may be engulfed by neutrophils or macrophages, or they may activate NK cells to destroy a cell coated with antibodies. Immune complexes may also activate the complement system. Antibodies may also "neutralize" viruses or toxins by preventing them from binding to specific receptors on cells.

There are several types, or classes, of antibodies, also called **immunoglobulins (Ig).** The class of antibody is determined by the structure of the antibody's constant region. The major class of antibody found in the blood, called *IgG*, is a single Y-shaped molecule (see Fig. 33.10). IgG antibodies are the major type that can cross the placenta from a mother to her fetus, to provide some temporary protection to the newborn. IgG is also found in breast milk, along wth a type called IgA. *IgA* is also the main class secreted in milk, tears, saliva, and at mucous membranes. Antibodies of the *IgM* class are pentamers—that is, clusters of

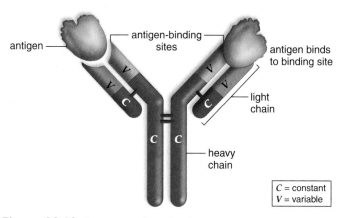

Figure 33.10 Structure of antibodies. An antibody contains two heavy (long) polypeptide chains and two light (short) chains arranged so there are two variable regions, where a particular antigen is capable of binding with the antibody. The shape of the antigen fits the shape of the binding site.

five Y-shaped molecules linked together. IgM antibodies are the first antibodies produced during most B-cell responses. As such, their presence is often interpreted as indicating a recent infection. The other major type of antibody is *IgE*, which is mainly found bound to receptors on eosinophils and on mast cells in the tissues.

Monoclonal Antibodies

As has been noted, every plasma cell derived from a single B cell secretes antibodies that bind to a single antigen. This discovery, along with the development of techniques for growing cells in the laboratory, led to the production of **monoclonal antibodies**. Niels Jerne, George Köhler, and César Milstein were awarded the Nobel Prize in 1984 for their development of this technology.

Monoclonal antibodies are produced by cells derived from a single plasma cell, thus all these antibodies have identical specificity for one antigen. Monoclonal antibodies are typically produced by first immunizing an animal (usually a mouse) with the antigen of interest. The animal is then killed, its spleen removed, and the spleen cells (including a large number of B cells) are fused with mouse myeloma cells (malignant plasma cells that live and divide indefinitely). The fused cells are called *hybridomas*: *hybrid-* because they result from the fusion of two different cells, and *-oma* because one of the cells is a cancer cell. The hybridomas are then isolated as individual cells and screened to select only those that are producing the desired monoclonal antibody.

Research Uses for Monoclonal Antibodies. The ability to quickly produce monoclonal antibodies in the laboratory has made them an important tool for academic research. Monoclonal antibodies are very useful because of their extreme specificity for only a particular molecule. A monoclonal antibody can be used to select out a specific molecule among many others, much like

finding needles in a haystack. Now the target molecule can be purified from all the others that are also present in a sample. In this way, monoclonal antibodies have simplified formerly tedious laboratory tasks.

Animation
Monoclonal Antibody Production

Medical Uses for Monoclonal Antibodies. Monoclonal antibodies also have many applications in medicine. In one application, they can be used to make quick and certain diagnoses of infections and other conditions. For example, a particular hormone called hCG is present in the urine of a woman only if she is pregnant. An anti-hCG monoclonal antibody can be used to detect this hormone. Thanks to this technology, pregnancy tests that once required a visit to a doctor's office and the use of expensive laboratory equipment can now be performed at home, and at minimal expense.

Monoclonal antibodies can be used not only to diagnose infections and illnesses but also to fight them. RSV, a common virus that causes serious respiratory tract infections in very young children, is now being successfully treated with a monoclonal antibody drug. The antibody recognizes a protein on the viral surface, and when it binds very tightly to the surface of the virus, the patient's own immune system can easily recognize the virus and destroy it before it has a chance to cause serious illness.

Because monoclonal antibodies can distinguish some cancer cells from normal tissue cells, they may also be used to identify cancers at very early stages when treatment can be most effective. Herceptin (trastuzumab) is a monoclonal antibody used to treat breast cancer. Given intravenously, it binds to a protein receptor found on some breast cancer cells and prevents them from dividing so quickly.

Since the first therapeutic monoclonal antibody was approved by the FDA in 1986, over 20 are now available, and hundreds more are currently being tested.

T Cells and Cell-Mediated Immunity

After a T cell completes its development in the thymus, it has a unique **T-cell receptor (TCR)** similar to the BCR on B cells. Unlike B cells however, T cells are unable to recognize an antigen without help. The antigen must be displayed, or "presented," to the TCR by an **MHC (major histocompatibility complex) protein** on the surface of another cell.

There are two major types of T cells: **helper T cells,** (T$_H$ cells) which regulate adaptive immunity, and **cytotoxic T cells** (T$_C$ cells, or CTLs), which attack and kill virus-infected cells and cancer cells. Each type of T cell has a TCR that can recognize an antigen fragment in combination with an MHC molecule. A major difference, however, is that the T$_H$ cells only recognize and respond to antigens presented by specialized **antigen-presenting cells (APCs)** with MHC class II proteins on their surface, while T$_C$ cells only recognize and respond to antigens presented by various cell types with MHC class I proteins on their surface.

Figure 33.11 Clonal selection theory as it applies to T_C cells. Each T cell has a T-cell receptor (TCR) designated by a shape that will combine only with a specific antigen. Activation of a T cell occurs when its TCR can combine with an antigen. A dendritic cell presents the antigen (colored green) in the groove of an MHC class I (MHC-I) molecule. Thereafter, the T_C cell undergoes clonal expansion, and many copies of the same type of T cell are produced. After the immune response has been successful, the majority of T cells undergo apoptosis, but a small number are memory T cells. Memory T cells provide protection should the same antigen enter the body again at a future time.

Figure 33.11 illustrates the important role that APCs such as macrophages and dendritic cells play in stimulating T_H cells. After phagocytizing a pathogen, APCs travel to a lymph node or the spleen, where T_H cells, T_C cells, and B cells also congregate. In the meantime, the APC has broken the pathogen apart in a lysosome. A fragment of the pathogen is then displayed in association with an MHC class II protein on the cell's surface ❶ which can bind to and select any T_H cell that has a TCR capable of combining with a particular antigen/MHC combination. This interaction stimulates the T_H cell to divide, thereby cloning itself. ❷ Some of these proliferating T_H cells secrete various cytokines that influence B cells, T_C cells, and other cell types. ❸ Many other cloned T_H cells become **memory T cells.** Like memory B cells, memory T cells are long-lived, and their number is far greater than the original number of T cells that could recognize a specific antigen. Therefore, when the same antigen enters the body later on, the immune response may occur so rapidly that no detectable illness occurs. As the illness disappears, the immune response wanes, and activated T cells become susceptible to apoptosis, ❹ just as plasma cells do during a B-cell response.

By releasing a variety of cytokines, activated helper T cells are largely responsible for **cell-mediated immunity** (see Fig. 33.8, *middle*), which refers to the destruction or elimination of pathogens and other threats by T_C cells, macrophages, natural killer cells, or other cells. For example, certain cytokines cause T_C cells to proliferate (see Fig. 33.8, *bottom*), while others activate macrophages to more actively seek, engulf, and destroy pathogens. Other cytokines released by T_H cells influence B-cell activities, even though B cells are responsible for antibody-mediated immunity. Cytokines are also used for immunotherapy purposes, as discussed in the next section.

Functions of Cytotoxic T Cells

A major difference in recognition of an antigen by helper T cells and cytotoxic T cells is that helper T cells recognize an antigen only in combination with MHC class II proteins, while T_C cells recognize an antigen only in combination with MHC class I proteins, which are found on almost all types of cells. The outcome of this recognition is also very different—activated T_H cells secrete a variety of cytokines that "help" other cells, but activated T_C cells specialize in killing other cells.

The cytoplasm of a T_C cell contains storage vacuoles that are filled with a chemical called *perforin*, as well as enzymes called *granzymes* (Fig. 33.12). After a T_C cell is activated, it travels via the bloodstream to areas of inflammation in the body. Upon migrating into the tissues, if the T_C cell recognizes its unique target combination of antigen plus MHC-I protein on a virus-infected cell or a cancer cell, it releases perforin molecules, which perforate the plasma membrane, forming a pore. Granzymes then use the pore to enter the abnormal cell, causing it to undergo apoptosis and die. Once T_C cells have released the perforins and granzymes, they move on to the next target cell. Because of this ability, some have referred to T_C cells as the "serial killers" of the immune system. As with B cells and T_H cells, most activated T_C cells are short-lived, while others become long-lived memory T_C cells, ever ready to defend against the same virus or kill the same type of cancer cell again.

Video T Lymphocyte

Animation Cytotoxic T-Cell Activity Against Target Cells

a.

b.   SEM 1,250×

Figure 33.12 Cell-mediated immunity. **a.** How a T cell destroys a virus-infected cell or cancer cell. **b.** The scanning electron micrograph shows cytotoxic T cells attacking and destroying a cancer cell (target cell).

HIV Infections

By the end of 2009, an estimated 33.3 million people worldwide were infected with **HIV (human immunodeficiency virus),** and more than 25 million people have died of AIDS since 1981. Helper T cells are the major host cell for HIV, but macrophages and dendritic cells can also be infected.

After HIV enters a host cell, it reproduces as was illustrated in Figure 20.4, inserting itself into the host cell DNA, where it will remain for the life of the cell. Perhaps years later, this hidden viral DNA will begin producing more HIV particles, which go on to infect and destroy more and more helper T cells. (Figure 33A in the Biological Systems feature, on page 638, details some key features of the progression of an HIV infection over time.)

At first the immune system is able to control the virus, probably through a combination of antibodies and cell-mediated immunity. But gradually the virus mutates so that it is no longer recognized by the immune system, and as the HIV count rises, the helper T-cell count drops to way below normal. As noted in the Biological Systems feature, the HIV-infected person begins to develop opportunistic infections—infections that would be unable to take hold in a person with a healthy immune system. Now the individual has AIDS (acquired immunodeficiency syndrome).

Animation
How the HIV Infection Cycle Works

Fortunately, antiretroviral drugs have been developed that have made HIV a manageable infection in most treated individuals, although the drugs have many side effects. Unfortunately, there is still a shortage of these expensive drugs in many developing countries.

Animation
Treatment of HIV

Cytokines as Therapeutic Agents

Cytokines are produced by T cells, macrophages, and many other cells. Because they affect white blood cell formation and/or function, some cytokines are approved for use as therapy for cancer and certain other conditions. As mentioned, interferon-alpha is used to treat hepatitis C and certain cancers, and it may also slow the progression of multiple sclerosis. The T-cell activating cytokine interleukin-2 is used to treat some forms of melanoma and kidney cancer.

In some cases it may be desirable to inhibit the activity of certain cytokines, especially those involved in promoting chronic inflammatory diseases. For example, tumor necrosis factor (TNF) is a major cytokine produced by macrophages that has the ability to promote the inflammatory response. Several treatments that inhibit the TNF response, including anti-TNF monoclonal antibodies, are currently being tested as potential treatments for inflammatory diseases such as rheumatoid arthritis, Crohn's disease, and asthma. As would be expected however, these medications may also inhibit some of the beneficial effects of inflammation, and patients taking them may be more prone to infections.

Active Versus Passive Immunity

In general, adaptive immune responses can be induced actively or passively. **Active immunity** occurs when an individual produces their own immune response against an antigen. For example, when you catch a cold, you recover because your body

THEME Biological Systems

AIDS and Opportunistic Infections

AIDS (acquired immunodeficiency syndrome) is caused by HIV, the human immunodeficiency virus. An HIV infection leads to the eventual destruction of helper T (T$_H$) cells. HIV kills T$_H$ cells by directly infecting them, and it also causes many uninfected T$_H$ cells to die by a variety of mechanisms. Many HIV-infected T$_H$ cells are also killed by the person's own immune system.

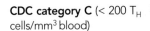
AIDS victim: Kaposi sarcoma is evident

A healthy individual typically has 800–1,000 T$_H$ cells per mm^3 of blood (Fig. 33A). After an initial HIV infection, it may take several years for an individual's T$_H$-cell numbers to drop below 500 cells per mm^3 of blood, at which point the HIV-infected individual usually begins to suffer from many unusual types of infections that would not cause disease in a person with a healthy immune system. Such infections are known as "opportunistic infections" (OIs). The U.S. Centers for Disease Control and Prevention (CDC) have defined three categories of HIV infection, based mainly on the types of OIs seen in the patient. These OIs also tend to be associated with a decreasing number of T$_H$ cells in the blood, as indicated below:

CDC category A (>500 T$_H$ cells/mm^3 blood)

- typically no OIs seen; may have persistently enlarged lymph nodes

CDC category B (200-499 T$_H$ cells/mm^3 blood)

- Shingles, a painful infection with varicella zoster (chickenpox) virus.
- Candidiasis, or thrush, a fungal infection of the mouth, throat, or vagina.

Shingles

Candidiasis

CDC category C (< 200 T$_H$ cells/mm^3 blood)

- Pneumocystis pneumonia, a fungal infection causing the lungs to become useless as they fill with fluid and debris.
- Kaposi's sarcoma, a cancer of blood vessels due to human herpesvirus 8 gives rise to reddish purple, coin-sized spots and lesions on the skin.
- Toxoplasmic encephalitis, a protozoan infection characterized by severe headaches, fever, seizures, and coma.

Pneumocystis pneumonia

- *Mycobacterium avium* complex (MAC), a bacterial infection resulting in persistent fever, night sweats, fatigue, weight loss, and anemia.
- Cytomegalovirus, a viral infection that leads to blindness, inflammation of the brain, and throat ulcerations.

Thanks to development of powerful drug therapies that inhibit the life cycle of HIV, people infected with HIV in the United States are suffering lower incidence of OIs than in the 1980s and 1990s.

Questions to Consider

1. Why has it been so difficult to develop an effective vaccine for HIV?
2. What are some possible differences between the types of OIs typically seen in category B and those seen in category C (i.e., why do shingles and candidiasis occur in B, but others more commonly in C)?
3. What, if any, obligation do relatively wealthy countries like the United States have in providing anti-HIV drugs to poorer countries?

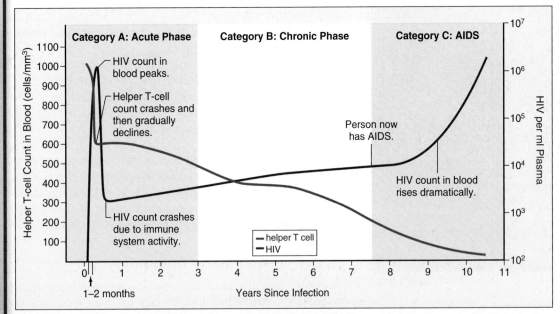

Figure 33A Progression of HIV infection during its three stages, called categories A, B, and C. In category A, the individual may have no symptoms or very mild symptoms associated with the infection. By category B, opportunistic infections have begun to occur, such as candidiasis, shingles, and diarrhea. Category C is characterized by more severe opportunistic infections and is clinically described as AIDS.

Figure 33.13 Antibody titers. During immunization, the primary response after the first injection of a vaccine is minimal, but the secondary response, which occurs after the second injection, shows a dramatic rise in the amount of antibody present in plasma.

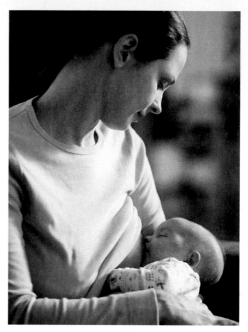

Figure 33.14 Passive immunity. Breast-feeding is believed to prolong the passive immunity an infant receives from the mother during pregnancy because antibodies are present in the mother's milk.

produces the T-cell and B-cell responses that eventually clear the offending viruses from your body. Active immunity can also be induced artificially when a person is well, to prevent infection in the future. **Immunization** involves the use of vaccines, substances that contain an antigen to which the immune system responds (Fig. 33.13). Traditionally, vaccines are the pathogens themselves, or their products, that have been treated so they are no longer virulent (able to cause disease). The use of vaccines has been effective in reducing the rates of bacterial diseases such as diphtheria, tetanus, and whooping cough, as well as viral diseases such as measles, mumps, and rubella. In fact, vaccination against smallpox was so successful that the disease was eradicated from the planet in 1977.

Today, it is possible to genetically engineer bacteria to mass-produce a protein from pathogens, and this protein can be used as a vaccine. This method was used to produce a vaccine against hepatitis B, a viral disease, and is being used to prepare a potential vaccine against malaria. The Nature of Science feature describes a recently FDA-approved type of cancer vaccine that boosts the immunity of prostate cancer patients by stimulating their own antigen-presenting cells.

Video Potato Vaccine

Animation Constructing Vaccines

After most vaccines are given, it is possible to determine the antigen-specific antibody titer (the amount of antibody present in a sample of plasma). After the first vaccination, a primary response occurs. For a period of several days, no antibodies are present; then the titer rises slowly, followed by first a plateau and then a gradual decline as the antibodies bind to the antigen or simply break down (see Fig. 33.13). After a second exposure, a secondary response occurs. The second exposure is called a "booster" because it boosts the immune response to a high level. The high levels of antigen-specific T cells and antibodies are expected to prevent disease symptoms if the individual is later exposed to the disease-causing agent. Even years later, if the antigen enters the body, memory B cells can quickly give rise to more plasma cells capable of producing the correct type of antibody.

Passive immunity occurs when an individual receives another person's antibodies or immune cells. The passive transfer of antibodies is a common natural process. For example, newborn infants are passively immune to some diseases because antibodies have crossed the placenta from the mother's blood. These antibodies soon disappear, however, so that within a few months, infants become more susceptible to infections as their own immune system must now protect them. Breast-feeding may prolong the natural passive immunity an infant receives from its mother because antibodies are present in the mother's milk (Fig. 33.14).

Even though passively administered antibodies last only a few weeks, they can sometimes be used to prevent illness in a patient who has been unexpectedly exposed to certain infectious agents or toxins. Examples of diseases that may be prevented or treated in this manner include rabies, tetanus, botulism, and snakebites. Individuals with certain types of genetic immunodeficiencies may also benefit greatly from regular, intravenous injections of human IgG, extracted from a large, diverse adult population.

Instead of antibodies, cells of the immune system can also be transferred into a patient. The best example is a bone marrow transplant, in which stem cells that produce blood cells are replenished after a cancer patients's own marrow has been intentionally destroyed by radiation or chemotherapy.

MP3 Specific Immunity

Check Your Progress 33.4

1. Describe the three types of blood cells that are mainly responsible for adaptive defenses, and explain the major function of each type.
2. List three possible outcomes of antigen complex formation in the body.
3. Explain the difference between active and passive immunity, and list three examples of each.

Cancer Vaccines: Becoming a Reality

Approximately 200 different types of human cancer have been identified, all of which involve an uncontrolled proliferation of cells. Some of these cancer cells express unusual molecules on their surface, which may allow the immune system to identify and destroy them. Unfortunately, many cancers cells grow unchecked in the body, apparently avoiding the immune system's many weapons.

Vaccines against infectious disease are an essential component of modern medicine. Most vaccines are administered before a person is exposed to an infection, but in a few cases (e.g., rabies, tetanus) vaccines can be used therapeutically, after exposure to a pathogen. Medical researchers are now developing vaccines to treat certain types of cancer, and in April, 2010, the U.S. Food and Drug Administration approved the first therapeutic cancer vaccine for use in humans.

Prostate cancer is the second most common type of cancer among men in the United States (behind skin cancer); about 27,000 men died from the disease in 2009. Provenge (sipuleucel-T) can now be used to treat certain types of advanced prostate cancer.

Provenge is prepared in a very different manner than a typical vaccine (Fig. 33B). First, the patient undergoes a procedure called leukapheresis, in which a catheter is inserted into a large vein, and blood flows into a machine that removes some of the white blood cells. Another catheter returns the plasma and red blood cells to the patient. Within the white blood cells are the antigen-presenting cells, such as dendritic cells. These cells are exposed to a protein called PAP that is commonly expressed on prostate cancer cells. The APCs can take up the PAP molecule, and present it on MHC molecules. These APCs are also activated using a cytokine called granulocyte-macrophage-CSF. Three days later, the cells are shipped back and infused into the patient. Typically three doses of Provenge are administered, each containing a minimum of 50 million stimulated cells, at a cost of about $31,000 per dose.

Once inside the patient, the APCs are able to activate a cytotoxic T-cell response that targets prostate cancer cells for destruction. In a 2010 trial of 512 men with advanced prostate cancer, the median survival for patients receiving Provenge was 25.8 months, compared to 21.7 months for those who received a placebo.

Although this approach to cancer therapy is a significant advance, there are also drawbacks, including the fact that a separate vaccine must be prepared for each patient. Other cancer vaccines are currently in clinical testing. Another 2010 study showed that prostate cancer patients who received Prostvac, a vaccine containing harmless viruses that express prostate specific antigen (PSA), lived an average of 8.5 months longer than patients who received a placebo injection.[1] Researchers are also making progress on therapeutic vaccines for cancers of the lung, breast, prostate, colon, and skin.

Questions to Consider

1. In what ways is this approach to vaccination similar to vaccination for infectious diseases? In what ways is it different?
2. Do you see any ethical issues with the cost of this cancer vaccine? Even if a prostate cancer patient lives only an additional four months, is it ever reasonable to place a monetary value on human life?

---

1 Kantoff, Philip W., Schuetz, Thomas J., et al. 2010. Overall survival analysis of a Phase II randomized controlled trial of a poxviral-based PSA-targeted immunotherapy in metastatic castration-resistant prostate cancer. *Journal of Clinical Oncology* 28: 1099–1105.

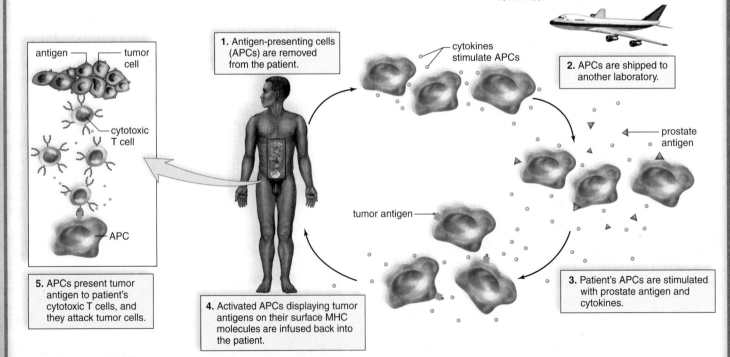

1. Antigen-presenting cells (APCs) are removed from the patient.

cytokines stimulate APCs

2. APCs are shipped to another laboratory.

prostate antigen

antigen — tumor cell

cytotoxic T cell

APC

tumor antigen

3. Patient's APCs are stimulated with prostate antigen and cytokines.

5. APCs present tumor antigen to patient's cytotoxic T cells, and they attack tumor cells.

4. Activated APCs displaying tumor antigens on their surface MHC molecules are infused back into the patient.

Figure 33B Prostate cancer vaccine. The first therapeutic vaccine for a human cancer involves a complex procedure in which the patient's own antigen-presenting cells (APCs) are removed, shipped to another laboratory, stimulated with cytokines and prostate antigen, then returned to be injected back into the patient.

33.5 Immune System Disorders and Adverse Reactions

Learning Outcomes

Upon completion of this section, you should be able to

1. Describe the two main types of immunodeficiency disorders, and provide examples of each.
2. Discuss the most common immunological mechanisms responsible for allergies, and how these may be treated.
3. Define autoimmune disease, and list several specific examples of these diseases.
4. Explain the types of precautions that must be taken when transplanting organs.

The immune system can be thought of as a "double-edged sword." It is essential for our health and survival, as demonstrated by the diseases, some of them fatal, that occur in people who are immunodeficient. In other instances, the immune system may work against the best interests of the body, as occurs in allergies, autoimmune disorders, and rejection of transplanted organs.

Immunodeficiencies

A number of immunodeficiency disorders are known, but all result in some degree of increased susceptibility to infections. Primary immunodeficiencies are genetic in nature, meaning they are passed from parents to offspring. In **severe combined immunodeficiency (SCID),** both T cells and B cells are either lacking completely or not functioning well enough to protect the body from a variety of infections that aren't a problem for most people. SCID only occurs in about one in 500,000 births.

A variety of faulty genes can cause SCID, but in most cases, by about three months of age (when most of the antibodies obtained from the mother have been degraded), untreated infants usually die. Possible treatments include a bone marrow transplant to replace the stem cells that form all of our white blood cells, or gene therapy to replace the faulty DNA. As was seen in the chapter-opening story of David Vetter, if these treatments are unsuccessful, the outcome is usually poor.

Another primary immunodeficiency is X-linked agammaglobulinemia (XLA), which is due to a mutated gene on the X-chromosome that is needed for proper development of B cells. XLA affects only males, because their cells only have one X chromosome. A female with a normal gene on at least one of her two X chromosomes does not develop the disease. Because their T cells are unaffected, boys with XLA can live relatively normal lives as long as they receive regular injections of human IgG. About 1 in 50,000 males has XLA.

We have already seen that HIV infection causes AIDS, which is an example of a secondary immunodeficiency. These disorders are not genetic, but instead are acquired after birth. Besides infections, other potential causes of secondary immunodeficiencies include malnutrition, irradiation, certain drugs and toxins, and certain cancers. Some of these can be cured by addressing the initiating cause.

Allergies

Allergies are hypersensitivities to substances such as pollen, food, or animal hair, that ordinarily would do no harm to the body. The response to these antigens, called allergens, usually includes some degree of tissue damage.

An **immediate allergic response** can occur within seconds of contact with an allergen. The response is caused by antibodies of the IgE class (Table 33.1). IgE antibodies are attached to receptors on the plasma membrane of mast cells in the tissues, and also to basophils and eosinophils in the blood. When an allergen attaches to these IgE antibodies, the cells release histamine and other substances that bring about the symptoms of an allergy (Fig. 33.15). When an allergen such as pollen is inhaled, histamine stimulates the inflammatory response in the mucous membranes of the nose and eyes typical of *hay fever.* If a person has **asthma,** the airways leading to the lungs constrict, resulting in difficult breathing accompanied by wheezing. When an allergen is in food, nausea, vomiting, and diarrhea typically occur.

Anaphylactic shock is an immediate allergic response that occurs after an allergen has entered the bloodstream. Bee stings, foods, various medications, and latex rubber are all known to cause this reaction in some individuals. Anaphylactic shock is characterized by a sudden and life-threatening drop in blood

Figure 33.15 An allergic reaction. An allergen attaches to IgE antibodies, which then cause mast cells to release histamine and other chemicals that are responsible for the allergic reaction.

Table 33.1 Comparison of Immediate and Delayed Allergic Responses

	Immediate Response	Delayed Response
Onset of Symptoms	Takes several minutes	Takes 1 to 3 days
Lymphocytes Involved	B cells	T cells
Immune Reaction	IgE antibodies	Cell-mediated immunity
Type of Symptoms	Hay fever, asthma, and many other allergic responses	Contact dermatitis (e.g., poison ivy)
Therapy	Antihistamine and epinephrine	Cortisone

pressure, due to an increased dilation of the capillaries by histamine throughout the body. The smooth muscle lining the bronchi may also be strongly stimulated to constrict, resulting in an inability to breathe. Injecting epinephrine can counteract this reaction until medical help is available, and some people carry an epinephrine-containing spring-loaded syringe (sometimes called an EpiPen) for this purpose.

Mild to moderate allergies are usually treated with antihistamines, which compete with histamine for binding to histamine receptors. In more serious cases, injections of the allergen can be given in an effort to stimulate the immune system to produce high quantities of IgG against the allergen. The hope is that these IgG antibodies will combine with the allergen molecules before they have a chance to reach the IgE antibodies. A monoclonal antibody called Xolair is also available, which blocks the binding of IgE to its receptor on inflammatory cells.

A **delayed allergic response** is initiated by memory T cells at the site of allergen contact in the body. The allergic response is regulated by the cytokines secreted by these "sensitized" T cells at the site. A classic example of a delayed allergic response is the skin test for tuberculosis (TB). When the test result is positive, the tissue where the antigen was injected becomes red and hardened. This indicates prior exposure to *Mycobacterium tuberculosis*, the bacterium that causes TB. Contact dermatitis, which occurs when a person's skin reacts to poison ivy, jewelry, cosmetics, or many other substances that touch the skin, is another example of a delayed allergic response.

Autoimmune Diseases

When a person has an **autoimmune disease,** their immune system mistakenly attacks their body's own cells or molecules. Exactly what causes autoimmune diseases is not known. In some cases, there appears to be a genetic tendency to develop autoimmune diseases. Many autoimmune diseases also seem to occur after an individual has recovered from an infection. It is also known that certain antigens of microbial pathogens can resemble antigens found in their host, a phenomenon known as molecular mimicry. A good example of this is rheumatic fever, which sometimes follows an infection with bacteria of the genus *Streptococcus*. Certain proteins in the cell wall of these bacteria are known to resemble proteins in the heart, and as a result antibodies formed against the bacterial proteins may cause inflammation of the heart that can continue even after the bacteria are cleared from the body.

Some autoimmune diseases affect only specific tissues. Rheumatoid arthritis is a common autoimmune disorder that causes recurring inflammation in synovial joints (Fig. 33.16). Complement proteins, T cells, and B cells all participate in the destruction of the joints, which eventually become immobile. In myasthenia gravis, antibodies interfere with the functioning of neuromuscular junctions, causing muscular weakness. In multiple sclerosis, T cells attack the myelin sheath of nerve fibers, causing a variety of symptoms related to the defective transmission of messages by nerves.

Systemic lupus erythematosus (lupus) is a chronic autoimmune disorder that affects multiple tissues and organs. It is characterized by the production of antibodies that react with the DNA contained in almost every cell of the body. The symptoms vary somewhat, but most patients experience a characteristic skin rash (Fig. 33.17), joint pain, and kidney damage, which may be life-threatening. About 500,000 to 1.5 million people in the United States have lupus, 90 percent of whom are women of childbearing age. Because little is known about the origin of autoimmune disorders, no cures are currently available. The symptoms can sometimes be controlled using immunosuppressive drugs such as cortisone, but these drugs can have serious side effects.

**Figure 33.16
Rheumatoid arthritis.**
Rheumatoid arthritis is due to recurring inflammation in skeletal joints, due to immune system attack.

**Figure 33.17
Systemic lupus.** A butterfly-shaped rash appears on the face.

Transplant Rejection

Certain organs, such as skin, the heart, and the kidneys, could be transplanted relatively easily from one person to another if the body did not attempt to reject them. Unfortunately, like the immune system itself, MHC proteins are a double-edged sword. In addition to their beneficial role in presenting antigens to T cells, MHC proteins are major targets of the immune response during rejection of a transplanted organ.

The MHC proteins of different individuals differ by the sequence of their amino acids, and the immune system will attack any foreign tissue that bears MHC antigens different from those of the individual. Ideally, a transplant donor would have exactly the same type of MHC proteins as those of the recipient, but because it is difficult to find a perfect MHC match, the odds of organ rejection can be reduced by administering immunosuppressive drugs. Two commonly used drugs, cyclosporine and tacrolimus, act by inhibiting the production of certain cytokines by T cells.

Xenotransplantation, the transplantation of animal tissues and organs into human beings, is a potential way to solve the shortage of organs from human donors. The pig is the most popular choice as an organ source, because pig organs are generally the right size, and pigs are a common meat source and are thus readily available. Genetic engineering can make pig organs less antigenic by removing the MHC antigens. The ultimate goal is to make pig organs as widely accepted as type O blood cells.

Other researchers hope that tissue engineering, including the production of human organs from stem cells, will one day do away with the problem of rejection. Scientists have recently grown new heart valves in the laboratory using stem cells gathered from amniotic fluid following amniocentesis, and surgeons have sucessfully used lab-grown urinary bladder tissue to rebuild defective bladders in human patients.

Check Your Progress 33.5

1. Explain the general type of abnormality that causes most primary immunodeficiencies.
2. Describe the treatments for autoimmune diseases.
3. Define xenotransplantation.

CONNECTING *the* CONCEPTS *with the* THEMES

Evolution

- Cells specialized for phagocytizing pathogens can be found in some of the most primitive multicellular organisms.
- Insects such as *Drosophila melanogaster* have a relatively advanced innate immune system, including the ability to recognize pathogens by their expression of pathogen-associated molecular patterns.
- Although the origins of the adaptive immune system are not completely understood, the ability to generate specific antigen receptors occurred early in vertebrate history.

Nature of Science

- Research targeted toward the development of new medical treatments for infectious disease has also resulted in an increased understanding of basic immunological mechanisms.
- Medical investigators hope that cancer vaccines will help trigger the body's adaptive immune response to target cancer cells that otherwise may go undetected.

Biological Systems

- Immune systems found in animals can range from a loose association of phagocytic cells to the vastly complicated interactions seen in the mammalian immune system.
- The innate and adaptive immune systems interact with and influence each other in a number of ways to provide both short-term and long-term protection.

Media Study Tools

www.mhhe.com/maderbiology11

Enhance your study of this chapter with study tools and practice tests. Also ask your instructor about the resources available through ConnectPlus, including the media-rich eBook, interactive learning tools, and animations.

Summarize

33.1 Evolution of Immune Systems

From the available evidence, it appears that innate immunity is much older than adaptive immunity, because aspects of innate immunity are present in relatively simple multicellular animals. Innate immunity is quite well developed in insects and often involves recognition of pathogen-associated molecular patterns (PAMPs). Available evidence indicates that the ability to generate a diverse array of antigen receptors first appeared in an ancestor of the jawed vertebrates.

33.2 The Lymphatic System

The lymphatic system consists of lymphatic vessels and lymphoid organs. The lymphatic system (1) removes excess tissue fluid collected by lymphatic capillaries; (2) absorbs fats from the small intestine; and (3) produces and distributes lymphocytes.

Lymphocytes are produced in the primary lymphoid organs (red bone marrow and thymus) and lymphocytes respond to antigens in secondary lymphoid organs (lymph nodes, spleen, etc.) T lymphocytes mature in the thymus, while B lymphocytes mature in the red bone marrow.

33.3 Innate Immune Defenses

Innate defenses are always present, or occur very soon after exposure to an infection. These include barriers to entry, the inflammatory response, phagocytes and natural killer cells, and protective proteins.

33.4 Adaptive Immune Defenses

Adaptive defenses (also called acquired immunity) involve B lymphocytes and T lymphocytes, also called B cells and T cells. After exposure to specific antigen, both types of lymphocytes undergo clonal selection. Upon binding of their B-cell receptor with a specific antigen, B cells divide and differentiate into plasma cells and memory B cells. Plasma cells secrete antibodies and are responsible for antibody-mediated immunity.

Antibodies are Y-shaped molecules that have at least two binding sites for a specific antigen. Monoclonal antibodies, which are produced by cells derived from a single plasma cell fused to a myeloma cancer cell, have various uses, from detecting infections to treating cancer.

The two main types of T cells are helper T (T_H) cells and cytotoxic T (T_C) cells. For a T_H cell to recognize an antigen, the antigen must be presented by MHC (major histocompatibility complex) class II proteins on the surface of an antigen-presenting cell (APC). Types of APCs include dendritic cells and macrophages. Thereafter, the activated T cell undergoes clonal expansion forming activated T_H cells and memory T_H cells. Activated T_H cells produce cytokines that affect many other immune cells. HIV infection induces an immunodeficiency by infecting and reducing the numbers of T_H cells.

T_C cells recognize antigens presented by MHC class I proteins on the surface of virus-infected or cancer cells. They then kill these cells by releasing perforin and granzymes, inducing apoptosis.

Active immunity occurs as a response to an illness or the administration of vaccines. Passive immunity is needed when an individual is in immediate danger of succumbing to an infectious disease. Passive immunity can occur naturally (as in the case of transfer of antibodies from mother to infant) or may be used as a medical treatment.

33.5 Immune System Disorders and Adverse Reactions

Immunodeficiencies can be primary (genetic) or secondary (due to some other cause). Allergic responses occur when the immune system reacts to substances not normally recognized as dangerous. Autoimmune diseases occur when the immune system attacks the body's own cells or tissues. In a transplant rejection, the immune system is usually responding to unmatched MHC proteins found on the cells of a donated organ.

Key Terms

active immunity   637
adaptive immunity   627
allergy   641
anaphylactic shock   641
antibody-mediated
   immunity   634
antigen   627
antigen-presenting cell
   (APC)   635
antigen receptor   633
asthma   641
autoimmune disease   642
B cell   629
B cell receptor (BCR)   633
cell-mediated immunity   636
clonal selection theory   633
complement   632
cytokine   633
cytotoxic T cell   635
delayed allergic response   642
dendritic cell   632
eosinophil   632
helper T cell   635
histamine   631
human immunodeficiency virus
   (HIV)   637
immediate allergic
   response   641
immune system   627
immunity   630
immunization   639
immunoglobulin (Ig)   634
inflammatory response   631
innate immunity   627
interferon   633
lymph   629
lymphatic capillary   629
lymphatic system   628
lymphatic vessel   628
lymph node   629
lymphoid (lymphatic) organ 629
macrophage   632
mast cell   631
memory B cell   634
memory T cell   636
MHC (major histocompatibility
   complex) protein   635
monoclonal antibody   635
natural killer (NK) cell   632
neutrophil   631
passive immunity   639
plasma cell   634
primary lymphoid organ   629
red bone marrow   629
secondary lymphoid organ   629
severe combined
   immunodeficiency (SCID)
   641
spleen   629
T cell   629
T-cell receptor (TCR)   635
thymus   629

Assess

Reviewing This Chapter

1. Which functions of the lymphatic system are not assisted by another system? Explain.   628
2. Describe the microscopic structure and the function of lymph nodes, the spleen, the thymus, and red bone marrow.   629–30
3. Discuss the body's innate defense mechanisms.   630–33
4. Describe the inflammatory response, and give a role for each type of cell and molecule that participates in the response.   630–33
5. Describe the clonal selection theory as it applies to B cells. B cells are responsible for which type of immunity?   633–34
6. How is active immunity artificially achieved? How is passive immunity achieved?   637, 639
7. Describe the structure of an antibody, and define the terms variable regions and constant regions.   634
8. How are monoclonal antibodies produced, and what are their applications?   635
9. Discuss the clonal selection theory as it applies to T cells.   635–36
10. Name the two main types of T cells and state their functions.   635–36
11. What are cytokines, and how are they used in immunotherapy?   636–37
12. Discuss autoimmune diseases and allergies as they relate to the immune system.   641–42

Testing Yourself

Choose the best answer for each question.

1. Both veins and lymphatic vessels
   a. have thick walls of smooth muscle.
   b. contain valves for one-way flow of fluids.
   c. empty directly into the heart.
   d. are fed fluids from arterioles.

2. Complement
   a. is an innate defense mechanism.
   b. is involved in the inflammatory response.
   c. is a series of proteins present in the plasma.
   d. plays a role in destroying bacteria.
   e. All of these are correct.

3. Which of these pertain(s) to T cells?
   a. have specific receptors
   b. recognize antigen presented by MHC proteins
   c. are responsible for cell-mediated immunity
   d. stimulate antibody production by B cells
   e. All of these are correct.

4. Which one of these does not pertain to B cells?
   a. have passed through the thymus
   b. have specific receptors
   c. are responsible for antibody-mediated immunity
   d. become plasma cells that synthesize and release antibodies

5. The clonal selection model says that
   a. an antigen selects certain B cells and suppresses them.
   b. an antigen stimulates the multiplication of B cells that produce antibodies against it.
   c. T cells select those B cells that should produce antibodies, regardless of antigens present.
   d. T cells suppress all B cells except the ones that should multiply and divide.
   e. Both b and c are correct.

6. Plasma cells are
   a. the same as memory cells.
   b. formed from blood plasma.
   c. B cells that are actively secreting antibody.
   d. inactive T cells carried in the plasma.
   e. a type of red blood cell.

7. Which of these pairs is incorrectly matched?
   a. cytotoxic T cells—help complement react
   b. cytotoxic T cells—active in tissue rejection
   c. macrophages—activate T cells
   d. memory T cells—long-living T cells
   e. T cells—mature in thymus

8. Vaccines are
   a. the same as monoclonal antibodies.
   b. treated bacteria or viruses, or one of their proteins.
   c. short-lived.
   d. MHC proteins.
   e. All of these are correct.

9. Which is an innate defense against pathogens?
   a. skin   d. interferons
   b. gastric juice   e. All of these are correct.
   c. complement

10. Which cell is not a phagocyte?
    a. neutrophil   c. dendritic cell
    b. lymphocyte   d. macrophage

11. B cells mature within
    a. the lymph nodes. c. the thymus.
    b. the spleen.   d. the bone marrow.

12. Plasma cells secrete
    a. antibodies.   d. histamine.
    b. perforins.   e. lymphokines.
    c. lysosomal enzymes.

13. Immediate hypersensitivity occurs after an allergen combines with
    a. IgG antibodies.   c. IgM antibodies.
    b. IgE antibodies.   d. IgA antibodies.

14. After a second exposure to a vaccine,
    a. antibodies are made quickly and in greater amounts.
    b. immunity lasts longer than after the first exposure.
    c. antibodies of the IgG class are produced.
    d. plasma cells are active.
    e. All of these are correct.

15. Active immunity may be produced by
    a. having a disease.
    b. receiving a vaccine.
    c. receiving gamma globulin injections.
    d. Both a and b are correct.
    e. Both b and c are correct.

Engage

Thinking Scientifically

1. The transplantation of organs from one person to another was impossible until the discovery of immunosuppressant drugs. Now, with the use of drugs such as cyclosporine, organs can be transplanted without rejection. Transplant patients must take immunosuppressant drugs for the remainder of their lives. What is a major expected side effect of this lifelong therapy?

2. Laboratory mice are immunized with a measles vaccine. When the mice are challenged with measles virus to test the strength of their immunity, the memory cells do not completely prevent replication of the measles virus. The virus undergoes a few rounds of replication before the immune response is observed. You have developed a strain of mice with a much faster response to a viral challenge, but these mice often develop an autoimmune disease. Speculate on the connection between speed of response and an autoimmune disease.

Bioethical Issue

Cost of Drugs to Treat AIDS

As noted in this chapter, an estimated 33.3 million people worldwide were living with HIV infection at the end of 2009. Most of these people will develop AIDS if their HIV infection is not treated. Drug companies typically charge a high price for anti-HIV medications because people in developed countries and their insurance companies can afford to pay for them. However, these prices are out of reach in many countries, such as those in Africa, where AIDS is a widespread problem.

Some people argue that drug companies should use the profits from other drugs (such as those for heart disease, depression, and impotence) to make AIDS drugs affordable to those who need them. This has not happened yet. In some countries, governments have allowed companies to infringe on foreign patents held by major drug companies so that affordable AIDS drugs can be produced. Do drug companies have a moral obligation to provide low-cost AIDS drugs, even if they have to do so at a loss of revenue? Is it right for governments to ignore patent laws in order to provide their citizens with affordable drugs?

34

Digestive Systems and Nutrition

Cattle, like sheep, goats, and other ruminants, are able to digest the cellulose found in grasses because of their highly specialized digestive system.

CHAPTER OUTLINE

BEFORE YOU BEGIN

Before beginning this chapter, take a few moments to review the following discussions.

Chapter 3 What are some structural differences between carbohydrates, lipids, proteins, and nucleic acids?

Figure 6.1 How does energy flow from the Sun, into chemical energy, to be ultimately dissipated as heat?

Figure 8.11 How do components of the human diet enter common metabolic pathways?

Humans first domesticated cattle around 8,000 years ago. Cattle are part of a large group of mammals called ruminants, which use a process of digestion that begins when plant material is swallowed and enters a large chamber called the rumen. Here, a rich population of bacteria and other microbes break down the cellulose present in plant material. During this process some solid material is also regurgitated as the cud, which is chewed slowly to break down the plant fibers into a more digestible size.

This ability of ruminants to utilize the cellulose present in grasses and other plants is the main advantage of using these animals as a source of meat for human consumption. Rangeland that is not suitable for growing other kinds of crops can be used to raise cattle (although most beef cattle in the United States are fed grain). However, due largely to the growing human population and high demand for meat in some countries, the total number of domesticated cattle on Earth has more than doubled in the last 40 years to an estimated 1.5 billion in 2009. Estimates vary, but ruminants account for about 15–20% of the global production of methane, an important contributor to climate change. Most medical experts also believe a diet containing too much red meat is an important factor in major diseases like atherosclerosis, diabetes, and many cancers. As you will see in this chapter, eating a well-balanced diet is one of the most important things we can do to maintain good health.

As you read through the chapter, think about the following questions:

1. What different types of strategies have animals evolved to efficiently obtain nutrients?

2. In what ways do the types of diets that humans choose to consume play a role in our health, as well as in the quality of our environment?

FOLLOWING *the* THEMES

UNIT 7 COMPARATIVE ANIMAL BIOLOGY	**Evolution**	Animals have evolved a wide variety of strategies to acquire nutrients from their environment.
	Nature of Science	With the incidence of obesity rising in developed countries, medical researchers seek to learn more about the condition to develop new treatments.
	Biological Systems	Like all living organisms, animals require a source of energy and the molecular building blocks needed to construct their components.

CHAPTER 34 DIGESTIVE SYSTEMS AND NUTRITION

34.1 Digestive Tracts

Learning Outcomes

Upon completion of this section, you should be able to

1. Compare the structural features of incomplete versus complete digestive tracts.
2. Describe several examples of animals that are either continuous or discontinuous feeders.
3. Discuss some specific adaptations that are seen in omnivores, herbivores, and carnivores.

A digestive system includes all the organs, tissues, and cells involved in ingesting food and breaking it down into smaller components. Digestion contributes to homeostasis by providing the body with the nutrients needed to sustain the life of cells. A digestive system:

1. ingests food,
2. breaks food down into small molecules that can cross plasma membranes,
3. absorbs these nutrient molecules, and
4. eliminates undigestible remains.

A digestive tract, or *gut*, is typically defined as a long tube through which food passes as it is being digested. The majority of animals have some sort of digestive tract, but some, like sponges, have no digestive tract at all. Instead, as water from the aqueous environment flows through the sponge (see Fig. 28.6), food particles are removed by cells that make up the inner lining of the organism. Cells in the sponge called *archaeocytes* may also ingest and distribute food to the rest of the organism.

Incomplete Versus Complete Tracts

An **incomplete digestive tract** has a single opening, usually called a mouth; however, the single opening is used both as an entrance for food and an exit for wastes. Planarians, which are flatworms, have an incomplete tract (Fig. 34.1). It begins with a mouth and muscular pharynx, and then the tract, a gastrovascular cavity, branches throughout the body.

Planarians are primarily carnivorous and feed largely on smaller aquatic animals, as well as bits of organic debris. When a planarian is feeding, the pharynx actually extends beyond the mouth. The body is wrapped about the prey and the pharynx sucks up small quantities at a time. Digestive enzymes present in the tract allow some extracellular digestion to occur. Digestion is finished intracellularly by the cells that line the tract. No cell in the body is far from the digestive tract; therefore, diffusion alone is sufficient to distribute nutrient molecules.

The digestive tract of a planarian is notable for its lack of specialized parts. It is saclike because the pharynx serves not only as an entrance for food but also as an exit for undigestible material. This use of the same body parts for more than one function tends to minimize the evolution of more specialized parts, such as those seen in complete tracts.

Planarians have some modified parasitic relatives. Tapeworms, which are parasitic flatworms, lack a digestive system.

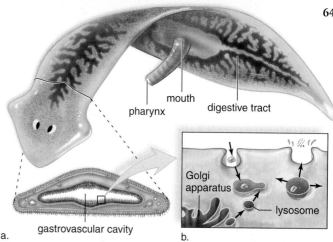

Figure 34.1 Incomplete digestive tract of a planarian.
a. Planarians, which are flatworms, have a gastrovascular cavity with a single opening that acts as both an entrance and an exit. Like hydras, planarians rely on intracellular digestion to complete the digestive process. **b.** Phagocytosis produces a vacuole, which joins with an enzyme-containing lysosome. The digested products pass from the vacuole into the cytoplasm before any undigestible material is eliminated at the plasma membrane.

Nutrient molecules are absorbed by the tapeworm from the intestinal juices of the host, which surround the tapeworm's body. The integument and body wall of the tapeworm are highly modified for this purpose. They have millions of microscopic, fingerlike projections that increase the surface area for absorption.

In contrast to planarians, earthworms, which are annelids, have a **complete digestive tract,** meaning that the tract has a mouth and an anus (Fig. 34.2). Earthworms feed mainly on the decayed organic matter found in soil. The muscular pharynx draws in a large amount of soil with a sucking action. Soil then enters the crop, which is a storage area with thin, expansive walls. From there, it goes to the gizzard, where thick, muscular walls crush the food and ingested sand grinds it. Digestion is extracellular within the intestine. The surface area of digestive tracts is often increased for absorption of nutrient molecules, and in earthworms, this is accomplished by an intestinal fold called the *typhlosole*. Undigested remains pass out of the body at the

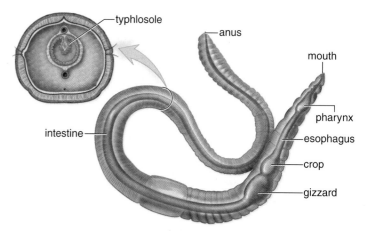

Figure 34.2 Complete digestive tract of an earthworm.
Complete digestive tracts have both a mouth and an anus and can have many specialized parts, such as those labeled in this drawing. Also in earthworms, which are annelids, the absorptive surface of the intestine is increased by an internal fold called the typhlosole.

Figure 34.3 Nutritional mode of a clam compared to a squid. Clams and squids are molluscs. A clam burrows in the sand or mud, where it filter feeds, whereas a squid swims freely in open waters and captures prey. In keeping with their lifestyles, a clam **(a)** is a continuous feeder and a squid **(b)** is a discontinuous feeder. Digestive system labels are shaded green.

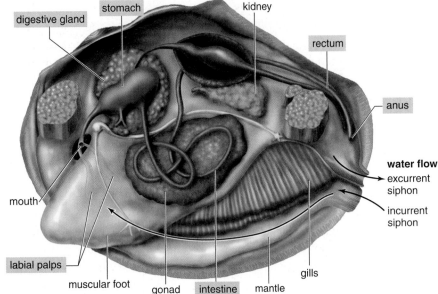

a. Digestive system (green) of clam

b. Digestive system (green) of squid

anus. Specialization of parts is obvious in the earthworm because the pharynx, the crop, the gizzard, and the intestine have particular functions as food passes through the digestive tract.

Continuous Versus Discontinuous Feeders

Some aquatic animals acquire their nutrients by continuously passing water through some type of apparatus that captures food. Clams, which are molluscs, are filter feeders (Fig. 34.3a). Water is always moving into the mantle cavity by way of the incurrent siphon (slitlike opening) and depositing particles, including algae, protozoans, and minute invertebrates, on the gills. The size of the incurrent siphon permits the entrance of only small particles, which adhere to the gills. Ciliary action moves suitably sized particles to the labial palps, which force them through the mouth into the stomach. Digestive enzymes are secreted by a large digestive gland, but amoeboid cells present throughout the tract are believed to complete the digestive process by intracellular digestion.

Not all filter feeders are relatively small invertebrates. A baleen whale, such as the blue whale, is an active filter feeder. Baleen, a keratinized curtainlike fringe, hangs from the roof of the mouth and filters small shrimp called krill from the water. A baleen whale filters up to a ton of krill every few minutes.

Discontinuous feeders have evolved the ability to store food temporarily while it is being digested, enabling them to spend

less time feeding and more time engaging in other activites. Discontinuous feeding requires a storage area for food, which can be a crop, where no digestion occurs, or a stomach, where digestion begins.

Squids, which are molluscs, are discontinuous feeders (Fig. 34.3b). The body of a squid is streamlined, and the animal moves rapidly through the water using jet propulsion (forceful expulsion of water from a tubular funnel). The head of a squid is surrounded by ten arms, two of which have developed into long, slender tentacles whose suckers have toothed, horny rings. These tentacles seize prey (fishes, shrimps, and worms) and bring it to the squid's beaklike jaws, which bite off pieces pulled into the mouth by the action of a *radula*, a tonguelike structure. An esophagus leads to a stomach and a cecum (blind sac), where digestion occurs. The stomach, supplemented by the cecum, retains food until digestion is complete.

Adaptations to Diet

Beyond the general categories of continuous versus discontinuous feeders, some animals have further adapted to more specialized diets. Some animals are omnivores; they eat both plants and animals. Others are strict herbivores; they feed only on plants. Still others are strict carnivores; they eat only other animals. Among invertebrates, filter feeders such as clams and tube worms are omnivores. Land snails, which are terrestrial

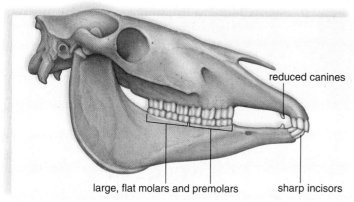

a. Horses are herbivores.

reduced canines

large, flat molars and premolars

sharp incisors

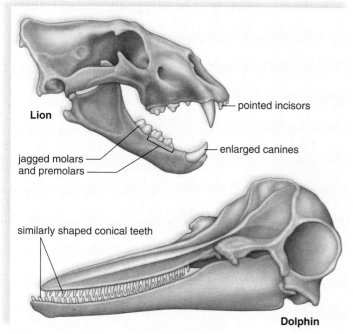

Lion

pointed incisors

enlarged canines

jagged molars
and premolars

similarly shaped conical teeth

Dolphin

b. Lions and dolphins are carnivores.

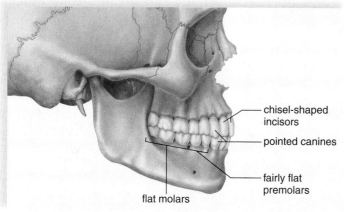

chisel-shaped
incisors

pointed canines

fairly flat
premolars

flat molars

c. Humans are omnivores.

Figure 34.4 Dentition among mammals. **a.** Horses are
herbivores and have teeth suitable to clipping and chewing grass.
b. Lions and dolphins are carnivores. Dentition in a lion is suitable for
killing large animals such as zebras and wildebeests and tearing apart
their flesh. Dentition in a dolphin is suitable to grasping small animals like
fishes, which are swallowed whole. **c.** Humans are omnivores and have
teeth suitable to a mixed diet of vegetables and meat.

molluscs, and some insects, such as grasshoppers and locusts,
are herbivores. Spiders (arthropods) are carnivores, as are sea
stars (echinoderms), which feed on clams. A sea star positions
itself above a clam and uses its tube feet to pull the valves of
the shell apart (see Fig. 28.29). Then, it everts a part of its
stomach to start the digestive process, even while the clam is
trying to close its shell. Some invertebrates are cannibalistic. A
female praying mantis (an insect), if starved, will feed on her
mate as the reproductive act is taking place!

Mammals have also adapted to consume a variety of different food sources. Among herbivores, the koala of Australia is
famous for its diet of only eucalyptus leaves, and likewise many
other mammals are browsers, feeding on bushes and trees.
Grazers, like the horse, feed off grasses. The horse has sharp,
even incisors for neatly clipping off blades of grass and large,
flat premolars and molars for grinding and crushing the grass
(Fig. 34.4a). Extensive grinding and crushing disrupts plant cell
walls, allowing bacteria located in a part of the digestive tract
called the cecum to digest cellulose.

As mentioned in the chapter-opening story, ruminants such
as cattle, sheep, and deer have a large, four-chambered stomach.
In contrast to horses, they graze quickly and swallow partially
chewed grasses into the **rumen,** which is the first chamber.
The rumen serves as a fermentation vat where microorganisms
break down material such as cellulose that the animal could
not otherwise digest. Later on, when the ruminant is no longer
feeding, undigested solid material called cud is regurgitated and
chewed again to facilitate more complete digestion.

Many mammals, including dogs, lions, toothed whales, and
dolphins, are carnivores. Lions use pointed canine teeth for
killing, short incisors for scraping bones, and pointed molars
for slicing flesh (Fig. 34.4b, *top*). Dolphins and toothed whales
swallow food whole without chewing it first; they are equipped
with many identical, conical teeth that are used to catch and
grasp their slippery prey before swallowing (Fig. 34.4b, *bottom*).
Meat is rich in protein and fat and is easier to digest than plant
material. The intestine of a rabbit, a herbivore, is much longer
than that of a similarly sized cat, a carnivore.

Humans, like pigs, raccoons, mice, and most bears, are
omnivores. Therefore, the dentition has a variety of specializa-
tions to accommodate both a vegetable diet and a meat diet.
An adult human has 32 teeth. One-half of each jaw has teeth
of four different types: two chisel-shaped incisors for shearing;
one pointed canine (cuspid) for tearing; two fairly flat premolars (bicuspids) for grinding; and three molars, well flattened
for crushing (Fig. 34.4c). Omnivores are generally better able
to adapt to different food sources, which can vary in different
locations and seasons.

Check Your Progress   34.1

1. Compare the digestive tract of a planarian with that of an
   earthworm.
2. Describe some of the limitations of an incomplete
   digestive tract.
3. Compare the teeth of carnivores to those of herbivores.

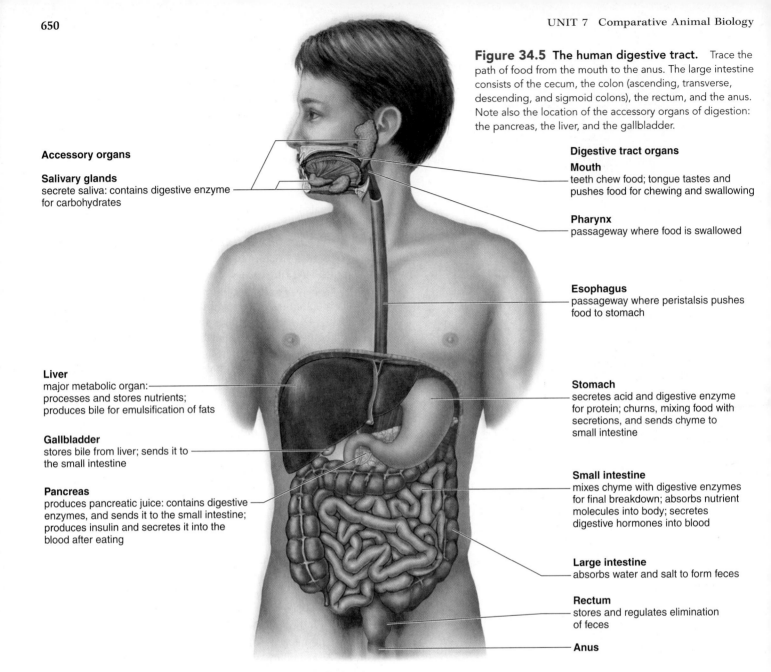

Figure 34.5 The human digestive tract. Trace the path of food from the mouth to the anus. The large intestine consists of the cecum, the colon (ascending, transverse, descending, and sigmoid colons), the rectum, and the anus. Note also the location of the accessory organs of digestion: the pancreas, the liver, and the gallbladder.

Accessory organs

Salivary glands
secrete saliva: contains digestive enzyme for carbohydrates

Liver
major metabolic organ: processes and stores nutrients; produces bile for emulsification of fats

Gallbladder
stores bile from liver; sends it to the small intestine

Pancreas
produces pancreatic juice: contains digestive enzymes, and sends it to the small intestine; produces insulin and secretes it into the blood after eating

Digestive tract organs

Mouth
teeth chew food; tongue tastes and pushes food for chewing and swallowing

Pharynx
passageway where food is swallowed

Esophagus
passageway where peristalsis pushes food to stomach

Stomach
secretes acid and digestive enzyme for protein; churns, mixing food with secretions, and sends chyme to small intestine

Small intestine
mixes chyme with digestive enzymes for final breakdown; absorbs nutrient molecules into body; secretes digestive hormones into blood

Large intestine
absorbs water and salt to form feces

Rectum
stores and regulates elimination of feces

Anus

34.2 The Human Digestive System

Learning Outcomes

Upon completion of this section, you should be able to

1. List all the major components of the human digestive tract, from the mouth to the anus.
2. Compare and contrast the structural features of the small intestine vs. large intestine.
3. Discuss the major functions of the pancreas, liver, and gallbladder.

Humans have a complete digestive tract, which begins with a mouth and ends in an anus. The major structures of the human digestive tract are illustrated in Figure 34.5. The pancreas, liver, and gallbladder are accessory organs that aid digestion.

MP3
An Overview of the Digestive System

Animation
Organs of Digestion

The digestion of food in humans is an extracellular event and requires a cooperative effort between different parts of the body. Digestion consists of two major stages: mechanical digestion and chemical digestion.

Mechanical digestion involves the physical breakdown of food into smaller particles. This task is accomplished through the chewing of food in the mouth and the physical churning and mixing of food in the stomach and small intestine. Chemical digestion requires enzymes that are secreted by the digestive tract or by accessory glands that lie nearby. Specific enzymes break down particular macromolecules into smaller molecules that can be absorbed.

Mouth

The **mouth,** or oral cavity, serves as the beginning of the digestive tract. The *palate,* or roof of the mouth, separates the oral cavity from the nasal cavity. It consists of the anterior hard palate and the posterior soft palate. The fleshy *uvula* is the posterior

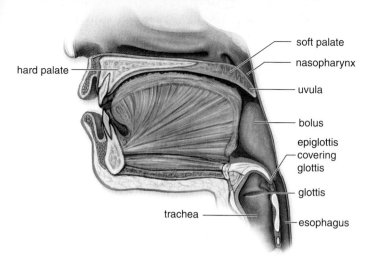

Figure 34.6 Swallowing. Respiratory and digestive passages converge and diverge in the pharynx. When food is swallowed, the soft palate closes off the nasopharynx, and the epiglottis covers the glottis, forcing the bolus to pass down the esophagus. Therefore, a person does not breathe when swallowing.

extension of the soft palate (Fig. 34.6). The cheeks and lips retain food while it is chewed by the teeth and mixed with saliva.

Three major pairs of **salivary glands** send their juices by way of ducts into the mouth. Saliva contains the enzyme **salivary amylase,** which begins to digest the starch that is present in many foods of plant origin. The disaccharide maltose is a typical end product of salivary amylase digestion (see Section 34.3).

While in the mouth, food is manipulated by a muscular tongue, which has touch and pressure receptors similar to those in the skin. Taste buds, sensory receptors that are stimulated by the chemical composition of food, are also found primarily on the tongue as well as on the surface of the mouth. The tongue, which is composed of striated muscle and an outer layer of mucous membrane, mixes the chewed food with saliva. It then forms this mixture into a mass called a *bolus* in preparation for swallowing.

MP3 Oral Cavity, Esophagus, and the Swallowing Reflex

The Pharynx and the Esophagus

The digestive and respiratory passages come together in the **pharynx** and then separate. The **esophagus** [Gk. *eso,* within, and *phagein,* eat] is a tubular structure, of about 25 cm in length, that takes food to the stomach. *Sphincters* are muscles that encircle tubes and act as valves; tubes close when sphincters contract, and they open when sphincters relax. The lower gastroesophageal sphincter is located where the esophagus enters the stomach. When food enters the stomach, the sphincter relaxes for a few seconds and then it closes again. Heartburn occurs due to acid reflux, when some of the stomach's contents escape into the esophagus. When vomiting occurs, the abdominal muscles and the diaphragm, a muscle that separates the thoracic and abdominal cavities, contract.

When food is swallowed, the soft palate, the rear portion of the mouth's roof, moves back to close off the nasopharynx. A flap of tissue called the epiglottis covers the glottis, or opening into the trachea. Now the bolus must move through the pharynx into the esophagus because the air passages are blocked (see Fig. 34.6).

The central space of the digestive tract, through which food passes as it is digested, is called the **lumen** (Fig. 34.7). From the esophagus to the large intestine, the wall of the digestive tract is composed of four layers. The innermost layer next to the lumen is called the **mucosa**. The mucosa is a type of mucous membrane and therefore it produces mucus, which protects the wall from the digestive enzymes inside the lumen.

The second layer in the digestive wall is called the **submucosa**. The submucosal layer is a broad band of loose connective tissue that contains blood vessels, lymphatic vessels, and nerves. Lymph nodules, called Peyer's patches, are also in the submucosa. Like other secondary lymphoid tissues, they are sites of lymphocyte responses to antigens (see Chapter 33).

The third layer is termed the **muscularis**, and it contains two layers of smooth muscle. The inner, circular layer encircles the tract; the outer, longitudinal layer lies in the same direction as the tract. The contraction of these muscles, which are under involuntary nervous control, accounts for the movement of the gut contents from the esophagus to the rectum by **peristalsis** [Gk. *peri,* around, and *stalsis,* compression], a rhythmic contraction that serves to move the contents along in various tubular organs. (Fig. 34.8).

The fourth layer of the wall is the **serosa**, which secretes a watery fluid that lubricates the outer surfaces of the digestive tract and reduces friction as various parts rub against each

Figure 34.7 Wall of the digestive tract. The esophagus, stomach, small intestine, and large intestine all have a lumen and walls composed of similar layers.

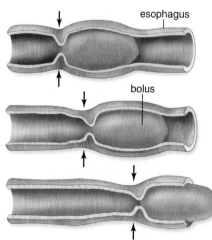

Figure 34.8 Peristalsis in the digestive tract. These three drawings show how a peristaltic wave moves through a single section of the esophagus over time. The arrows point to areas of contraction.

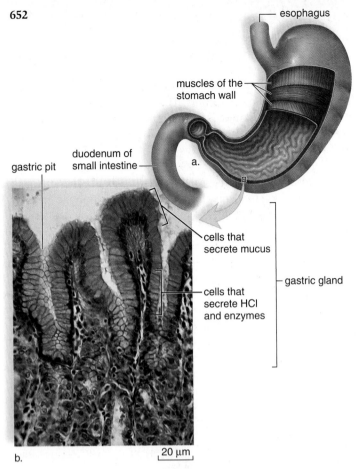

Figure 34.9 **Anatomy of the stomach.** **a.** The stomach, which has thick walls, expands as it fills with food. **b.** The mucous membrane layer of its walls secretes mucus and contains gastric glands, which secrete a gastric juice active in the digestion of protein.

The epithelial lining of the stomach has millions of *gastric pits,* which lead into *gastric glands* (see Fig. 34.9). The gastric glands produce gastric juice. So much hydrochloric acid is secreted by the gastric glands that the stomach routinely has a pH of about 2.0. Such a high acidity usually is sufficient to kill bacteria and other microorganisms that might be in food. This low pH also stops the activity of salivary amylase, which functions optimally at the near-neutral pH of saliva.

As with the rest of the digestive tract, a thick layer of mucus protects the wall of the stomach from enzymatic action. Still, some individuals develop ulcers, which are areas where the protective epithelial layer has been damaged. Gastric ulcers can be caused by an acid-resistant bacterium, *Helicobacter pylori,* which is able to attach to the epithelial lining. Wherever the bacterium attaches, the lining stops producing mucus, and the area becomes damaged by acid and digestive enzymes. If promptly diagnosed, antibiotic treatment is usually curative.

Eventually, food mixing with gastric juice in the stomach contents becomes **chyme,** which has a thick, creamy consistency. At the base of the stomach is a narrow opening controlled by a sphincter. Whenever the sphincter relaxes, a small quantity of chyme passes through the opening into the small intestine. When chyme enters the small intestine, it sets off a neural reflex that causes the muscles of the sphincter to contract vigorously and to close the opening temporarily. Then the sphincter relaxes again and allows more chyme to enter. The slow manner in which chyme enters the small intestine allows for thorough digestion.

MP3
Stomach

Animation
Three Phases of
Gastric Secretion

The Small Intestine

The **small intestine** is named for its small diameter (compared to that of the large intestine), but perhaps it should be called the long intestine. The small intestine averages about 6 m in length, compared to the large intestine, which is about 1.5 m in length.

The first 25 cm of the small intestine is called the **duodenum.** A duct brings bile from the liver and gallbladder, and pancreatic juice from the pancreas, into the small intestine (see Fig. 34.12*a*). **Bile** emulsifies fat—emulsification causes fat droplets to disperse in water. The intestine has a slightly basic pH because pancreatic juice contains sodium bicarbonate ($NaHCO_3$), which neutralizes chyme. The enzymes in pancreatic juice and enzymes produced by the intestinal wall complete the process of food digestion.

It has been estimated that the surface area of the small intestine is approximately that of a tennis court. What factors contribute to increasing its surface area? First, the wall of the small intestine contains fingerlike projections called villi (sing., **villus**), which give the intestinal wall a soft, velvety appearance (Fig. 34.10). Second, a villus has an outer layer of columnar epithelial cells, and each of these cells has thousands of microscopic extensions called microvilli. Collectively, in electron micrographs, microvilli give the villi a fuzzy border, known as a "brush border." Because the microvilli bear the intestinal enzymes, these enzymes are called brush-border enzymes. The

other and other organs. The serosa is actually a part of the *peritoneum,* the internal lining of the abdominal cavity.

Stomach

The **stomach** (Fig. 34.9) is a thick-walled, J-shaped organ that lies on the left side of the body beneath the diaphragm. The wall of the stomach has deep folds (rugae) that disappear as the stomach fills to its capacity (approximately 1 liter in humans). Therefore, many animals can periodically eat relatively large meals and spend the rest of their time at other activities.

The stomach is much more than a storage organ, as was discovered by William Beaumont (1785–1853) in the mid-nineteenth century. Beaumont, an American doctor, had a French Canadian patient who had been shot in the stomach, and when the wound healed, he was left with a fistula, or opening, that allowed Beaumont to look inside the stomach and to collect gastric (stomach) juices produced by gastric glands. Beaumont was able to determine that the muscular walls of the stomach contract vigorously and mix food with juices that are secreted whenever food enters the stomach. He found that gastric juice contains hydrochloric acid (HCl) and a substance, now called pepsin, that is active in digestion. Beaumont's work, which was carefully and painstakingly done, pioneered the study of digestive physiology. For similar reasons, modern animal scientists can surgically create fistulas into the rumen of cattle in order to study ruminant nutrition.

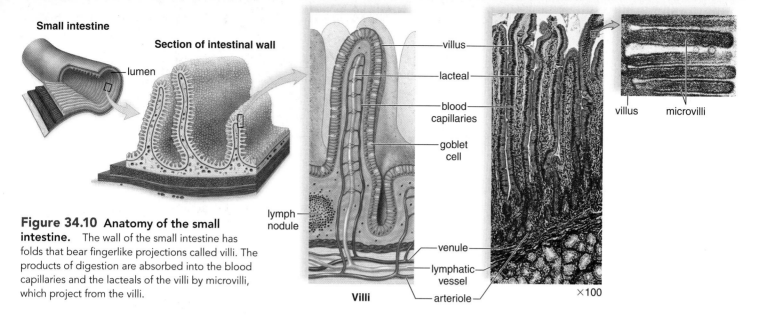

Figure 34.10 Anatomy of the small intestine. The wall of the small intestine has folds that bear fingerlike projections called villi. The products of digestion are absorbed into the blood capillaries and the lacteals of the villi by microvilli, which project from the villi.

microvilli greatly increase the surface area of the villus for the absorption of nutrients.

Nutrients are absorbed into the vessels of a villus, which contains blood capillaries and a lymphatic capillary, called a **lacteal.** Sugars (digested from carbohydrates) and amino acids (digested from proteins) enter the blood capillaries of a villus. Glycerol and fatty acids (digested from fats) enter the epithelial cells of the villi, and within these cells they are joined and packaged as lipoprotein droplets, which enter a lacteal. After nutrients are absorbed, they are eventually carried to all the cells of the body by the bloodstream.

MP3
Absorption of Nutrients and Water

Animation
Enzymatic Action and the Hydrolysis of Sucrose

Large Intestine

The **large intestine,** which includes the cecum, the colon, the rectum, and the anus, is larger in diameter (6.5 cm) but shorter in length (1.5 m) than the small intestine. The large intestine absorbs water, salts, and some vitamins. It also stores undigestible material until it is eliminated as feces.

The cecum, which lies below the junction with the small intestine, is the blind end of the large intestine. The cecum has a small projection called the vermiform **appendix** [L. *verm,* worm, and *form,* shape; and *append,* an addition] (Fig. 34.11). The function of the human appendix is unclear, although many experts suggest it may serve as a reservoir for the "good bacteria" that help to maintain our intestinal health. In the case of appendicitis, the appendix becomes infected and so filled with fluid that it may burst. If an infected appendix bursts before it can be removed, it can lead to a serious, generalized infection of the abdominal lining called peritonitis.

The colon joins the rectum, the last 20 cm of the large intestine. About 1.5 liters of water enters the digestive tract daily as a result of eating and drinking. An additional 8.5 liters enter the digestive tract each day carrying the various substances secreted by the digestive glands. About 95% of this water is absorbed by the small intestine, and much of the remaining portion is absorbed by the colon. If this water is not reabsorbed, **diarrhea,** the passing of watery feces, can lead to serious dehydration and ion loss, especially in children.

The large intestine has a large population of bacteria, including *Escherichia coli* and perhaps 400 other species. By taking up space and nutrients, these bacteria provide protection against more pathogenic species. They also produce some vitamins, such as vitamin K, which is necessary to blood clotting. Digestive wastes, or feces, eventually leave the body through the **anus,** the opening of the anal canal.

Feces are normally about 75% water and 25% solid matter. Almost one-third of this solid matter is made up of intestinal bacteria. In fact, there are about 100 billion bacteria per gram of feces! The rest of the solids are undigested plant material, fats, waste products (such as bile pigments), inorganic material, mucus, and dead cells from the intestinal lining. The color of feces is the result of bilirubin breakdown and the presence of oxidized iron. The foul odor is the result of bacterial action.

Video
Fat Microbes

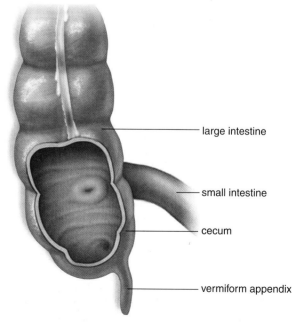

Figure 34.11 Junction of the small intestine and the large intestine.

The colon is subject to the development of **polyps,** which are small growths arising from the mucosa. Polyps, whether they are benign or cancerous, can be removed surgically. Some investigators believe that dietary fat increases the likelihood of colon cancer. Dietary fat causes an increase in bile secretion, and it could be that intestinal bacteria convert bile salts to substances that promote the development of colon cancer. Dietary fiber absorbs water and adds bulk, thereby diluting the concentration of bile salts and facilitating the movement of substances through the intestine. Regular elimination reduces the time that the colon wall is exposed to any cancer-promoting agents in feces.

Three Accessory Organs

The pancreas, liver, and gallbladder are accessory digestive organs. Figure 34.12*a* shows how the pancreatic duct from the pancreas and the common bile duct from the liver and gallbladder enter the duodenum.

The Pancreas

The **pancreas** lies deep in the abdominal cavity, resting on the posterior abdominal wall. It is an elongated and somewhat flattened organ that has both an endocrine and an exocrine function. As an endocrine gland, it secretes insulin and glucagon, hormones that help keep the blood glucose level within normal limits (see Chapter 40). In this chapter, however, we are interested in its exocrine function. Most pancreatic cells produce pancreatic juice, which contains sodium bicarbonate ($NaHCO_3$) and digestive enzymes for all types of food. Sodium bicarbonate neutralizes acid chyme from the stomach. Pancreatic amylase digests starch, trypsin digests protein, and lipase digests fat.

The Liver

The **liver,** which is the largest gland in the body, lies mainly in the upper right section of the abdominal cavity, under the diaphragm (see Fig. 34.5). The liver contains approximately 100,000 lobules that serve as its structural and functional units (Fig. 34.12*b*). Triads, located between the lobules, consist of a bile duct, which takes bile away from the liver; a branch of the hepatic artery, which brings oxygen-rich blood to the liver; and a branch of the hepatic portal vein, which transports nutrients to the liver from the intestines (see Fig. 34.10). The central veins of lobules enter a hepatic vein. Blood moves from the intestines to the liver via the hepatic portal vein and from the liver to the inferior vena cava via the hepatic veins.

In some ways, the liver acts as the gatekeeper to the blood. As blood in the hepatic portal vein passes through the liver, it removes many toxic substances and metabolizes them. The liver also removes and stores iron and the vitamins A, B_{12}, D, E, and K. The liver makes many of the proteins found in blood plasma and helps regulate the quantity of cholesterol in the blood.

The liver maintains the blood glucose level at about 100 mg/100 mL (0.1%), even though a person eats intermittently. When insulin is present, any excess glucose present in blood is removed and stored by the liver as glycogen. Between meals, glycogen is broken down to glucose, which enters the hepatic veins, and in this way, the blood glucose level remains constant.

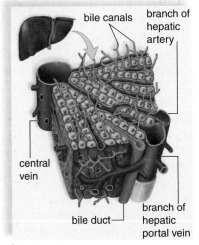

Figure 34.12 Liver, gallbladder, and pancreas. **a.** The liver makes bile, which is stored in the gallbladder and sent (black arrow) to the small intestine by way of the common bile duct. The pancreas produces digestive enzymes that are sent (black arrows) to the small intestine by way of the pancreatic duct. **b.** The liver contains over 100,000 lobules. Each lobule contains many cells that perform the various functions of the liver. They remove and add materials to the blood and deposit bile in a duct.

If the supply of glycogen is depleted, the liver converts glycerol (from fats) and amino acids to glucose molecules. The conversion of amino acids to glucose necessitates deamination, the removal of amino groups. By a complex metabolic pathway, the liver then combines ammonia with carbon dioxide to form urea. Urea is the usual nitrogenous waste product from amino acid breakdown in humans.

The liver produces bile, which is stored in the gallbladder. Bile has a yellowish green color because it contains the bile pigment *bilirubin,* derived from the breakdown of hemoglobin, the red pigment of red blood cells. Bile also contains bile salts. Bile salts are derived from cholesterol, and they emulsify fat in the small intestine. When fat is emulsified, it breaks up into droplets, providing a much larger surface area, which can be acted upon by a digestive enzyme from the pancreas.

Liver Disorders.   Because the liver performs so many vital functions, serious disorders of the liver can be life-threatening. When a person has a liver ailment, a yellowing of the skin and the sclera of the eyes called **jaundice** may occur. Jaundice results when the liver is not helping the body excrete excess bilirubin, which is then deposited in the tissues.

Regardless of the cause, inflammation of the liver is called **hepatitis.** The most common causes of hepatitis are viruses. Hepatitis A virus is usually acquired from food or water that has been contaminated with feces. Hepatitis B, which is usually spread by

THEME Nature of Science

New Approaches to Treating Obesity

Diet and exercise. We all know that the most critical factor in weight gain is consuming more calories than we need for our level of physical activity. But considering the rising rates of obesity in developed countries, and the many associated health risks, researchers are investigating factors and approaches that might help some people to reduce their weight:

Adequate Sleep

According to the National Sleep Foundation's annual poll in 2009, Americans got an average of 6.7 hours of sleep on weekdays, down from 7 hours in 2001. Whatever the reasons for this decline, an increasing amount of scientific evidence points to a link between declining sleep and increasing obesity rates.

Even a modest amount of sleep deprivation can cause alterations in hormones that control appetite and regulate metabolism. In a 2004 study, 12 healthy college-age males were divided into two groups: one that slept ten hours a night, and a second that slept only four hours. After two days, the sleep-deprived subjects averaged an 18% decrease in serum leptin (a hormone that normally suppresses appetite) and a 28% increase in ghrelin (an appetite stimulator). Those with the greatest hormonal differences also reported greater increases in hunger, especially for high-carb foods.[1] Other, larger studies have mostly confirmed these findings, suggesting that adequate sleep may be a significant factor in avoiding obesity.

Anti-Obesity Drugs

In general, two types of drugs are available for the treatment of obesity: fat absorption inhibitors and appetite suppressants. Xenical (Orlistat), taken three times a day with meals, interferes with fat digestion by inhibiting pancreatic lipase. Various studies have shown that Xenical is more effective than dietary management alone in promoting weight loss, although the typical patient may lose only a few pounds. Because an increased amount of fat is passing undigested through the digestive tract, some people experience side effects such as abdominal

pain, increased frequency of bowel movements, or even fecal incontinence (inability to control fecal release).

Although several appetite suppressor drugs are available, some have been removed from the market due to safety concerns. Research is continuing on identifying strategies to control hunger using drugs that effect various appetite control mechanisms.

Surgical Procedures

Despite advances in understanding the factors behind obesity, many individuals still struggle with this problem. The number of bariatric (weight loss) surgeries performed per year in the United States has increased from about 16,000 in the early 1990s to an estimated 220,000 in 2008. Many different types of procedures are performed, but all are intended to reduce the size of the stomach, to decrease the absorption of nutrients, or both. When successful, any procedure that reduces the weight of an obese person to a value closer to normal can lead to a significant reduction in the risk of other health problems. However, as with any major surgery, there is also a substantial risk of harm, including death.

Traditionally, bariatric surgery has been recommended only for people who are morbidly obese (BMI greater than 40), or a BMI greater than 35 but with weight-related med-

ical problems. Many of these procedures require removal of stomach tissue, or bypassing the stomach altogether. However, less invasive procedures are being developed, and in December 2010 a panel of FDA advisors recommended that a product called Lap-Band be approved for use in patients whose BMI is as low as 30. As shown in Figure 34A, the Lap-Band is an adjustable plastic strip that is inserted into the abdomen and over the top of the stomach via a small incision. Advantages of this procedure over more traditional surgeries are that the tension can be adjusted for greater or less restriction of stomach volume, and it can be removed. Many experts seem to believe that gastric banding procedures are not as effective as other types of bariatric surgery, however.

Questions to Consider

1. From an evolutionary perspective, why are humans predisposed to gain weight when food supplies are readily available?
2. Besides diet, exercise, and lack of sleep, what are some some other factors that could cause some people to be more prone to obesity?
3. The average cost for various bariatric surgeries is $18,000 to $35,000. With limited health care dollars to go around, do you think this is a justifiable expense, either practically or ethically?

1 Spiegel, K., et al. 2004. Sleep Curtailment in Healthy Young Men. . . . Ann. Internal Medicine 141: 846–50.

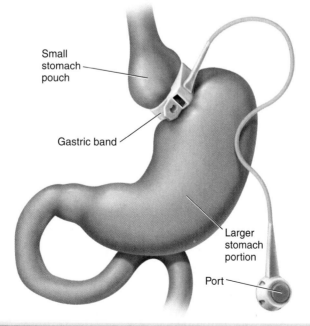

Small stomach pouch

Gastric band

Larger stomach portion

Port

Figure 34A The Lap-Band. The Lap-Band is an inflatable loop that is surgically placed around the upper part of the stomach to reduce the amount of food that can enter. It is approved for use only in obese people for whom other weight loss therapies have failed.

sexual contact, can also be spread by blood transfusions or contaminated needles. The hepatitis B virus is more contagious than the AIDS virus, which is spread in the same way. A vaccine is now available for hepatitis B, however. Hepatitis C, which is usually acquired by contact with infected blood and for which no vaccine is available, can lead to chronic hepatitis, liver cancer, and death.

Video
Halting Hepatitis

Cirrhosis is another chronic disease of the liver. First, the organ becomes fatty, and then liver tissue is replaced by inactive fibrous scar tissue. Cirrhosis of the liver is often seen in alcoholics, due to malnutrition and to the excessive amounts of alcohol (a toxin) the liver is forced to break down.

The liver has amazing regenerative powers and can recover if the rate of regeneration exceeds the rate of damage. During liver failure, however, there may not be enough time to let the liver heal itself. Liver transplantation is usually the preferred treatment for liver failure, but currently an estimated 4,000 people in the United States alone are waiting for a liver transplant.

Because the liver serves so many functions, artificial livers have been difficult to develop. One type is a cartridge that contains cultured liver cells (either human or pig). Like kidney dialysis, the patient's blood is passed outside of the body and through an apparatus containing the liver cells, which perform their normal functions, and the blood is returned to the patient.

Progress is also being made in the area of transplanting a smaller number of liver cells, as opposed to the entire organ. These cells can either be grown from stem cells, or may be derived from the livers of donors who have died, but whose livers as entire organs are not suitable for transplantation.

The Gallbladder

The **gallbladder** is a pear-shaped, muscular sac attached to the surface of the liver (see Fig. 34.5). About 1,000 mL of bile is produced by the liver each day, and any excess is stored in the gallbladder. Water is reabsorbed by the gallbladder so that bile becomes a thick, mucuslike material. When bile is needed, the gallbladder contracts, releasing bile into the duodenum via the common bile duct (see Fig. 34.12).

The cholesterol content of bile can come out of solution and form crystals called gallstones. These stones can be as small as a grain of sand or as large as a golf ball. The passage of the stones from the gallbladder may block the common bile duct, causing pain as well as possible damage to the liver or pancreas. Then, the gallbladder must be removed.

Check Your Progress   34.2

1. Trace the path of food from the mouth to the large intestine.
2. Describe the likely selective pressures that resulted in the evolution of taste buds.
3. Explain how the stomach, small intestine, and large intestine are each adapted to perform their particular functions.
4. Discuss how each accessory organ contributes to the digestion of food.

34.3 Digestive Enzymes

Learning Outcomes

Upon completion of this section, you should be able to

1. Describe the overall characteristics and functions of digestive enzymes.
2. Compare the specific types of nutrients that are digested in the mouth, stomach, and small intestine.

The various digestive enzymes present in the digestive juices, mentioned earlier, help break down carbohydrates, proteins, nucleic acids, and fats, the major nutritional components of food. Starch is a polysaccharide, and its digestion begins in the mouth. Saliva from the salivary glands has a neutral pH and contains **salivary amylase**, the first enzyme to act on starch.

$$\text{starch} + \text{H}_2\text{O} \xrightarrow{\text{salivary amylase}} \text{maltose}$$

Maltose molecules cannot be absorbed by the intestine; additional digestive action in the small intestine converts maltose to glucose, which can be absorbed.

Protein digestion begins in the stomach. Gastric juice secreted by gastric glands has a very low pH—about 2.0—because it contains hydrochloric acid (HCl). Pepsinogen, a precursor that is converted to **pepsin** when exposed to HCl, is also present in gastric juice. Pepsin acts on protein to produce peptides.

$$\text{protein} + \text{H}_2\text{O} \xrightarrow{\text{pepsin}} \text{peptides}$$

Peptides are usually too large to be absorbed by the intestinal lining, but later they are broken down to amino acids in the small intestine.

Starch, proteins, nucleic acids, and fats are all enzymatically broken down in the small intestine. Pancreatic juice, which enters the duodenum, has a basic pH because it contains sodium bicarbonate (NaHCO$_3$). One pancreatic enzyme, **pancreatic amylase**, digests starch (Fig. 34.13a).

$$\text{starch} + \text{H}_2\text{O} \xrightarrow{\text{pancreatic amylase}} \text{maltose}$$

Another pancreatic enzyme, **trypsin**, digests protein (Fig. 34.13b).

$$\text{protein} + \text{H}_2\text{O} \xrightarrow{\text{trypsin}} \text{peptides}$$

Trypsin is secreted as trypsinogen, which is converted to trypsin in the duodenum.

Maltase and peptidases, enzymes produced by the small intestine, complete the digestion of starch to glucose and protein to amino acids, respectively. Glucose and amino acids are small molecules that cross into the cells of the villi and enter the blood (Fig. 34.13a, b).

Maltose, a disaccharide that results from the first step in starch digestion, is digested to glucose by **maltase.**

$$\text{maltose} + \text{H}_2\text{O} \xrightarrow{\text{maltase}} \text{glucose} + \text{glucose}$$

The brush border of the small intestine produces other enzymes for digestion of specific disaccharides. The absence of any one of these enzymes can cause illness. For example, approximately 75% of the world's adult human population is estimated to be lactose intolerant, because of a decreased expression of the enzyme lactase beyond the age of childhood. When such a person ingests milk or other products containing lactose, the undigested sugar is fermented by intestinal bacteria, resulting in a variety of unpleasant intestinal symptoms.

Peptides, which result from the first step in protein digestion, are digested to amino acids by **peptidases.**

$$\text{peptides} + H_2O \xrightarrow{\text{peptidases}} \text{amino acids}$$

Lipase, a third pancreatic enzyme, digests fat molecules in fat droplets after they have been emulsified by bile salts.

$$\text{fat} \xrightarrow{\text{bile salts}} \text{fat droplets}$$

$$\text{fat droplets} + H_2O \xrightarrow{\text{lipase}} \text{glycerol} + 3 \text{ fatty acids}$$

Specifically, the end products of lipase digestion are monoglycerides (glycerol + one fatty acid) and fatty acids. These enter the cells of the villi, and within these cells, they are rejoined and packaged as lipoprotein droplets, called chylomicrons. Chylomicrons enter the lacteals (Fig. 34.13c).

MP3 Chemical Digestion in the Small Intestine

Check Your Progress   34.3

1. Describe the location(s) in the digestive tract where each of the major types of nutrients is broken down.
2. Explain what final molecule (monomer) results from the digestion of carbohydrates, proteins, and fats.

34.4 Nutrition and Human Health

Learning Outcomes

Upon completion of this section, you should be able to

1. List the major types of nutrients, and provide examples of foods that are a good source of each.
2. Describe the connection between a person's diet and the likely development of obesity, type 2 diabetes, and cardiovascular disease.
3. Distinguish between vitamins, coenzymes, and minerals.

This section of the chapter discusses the components of a balanced human diet, as well as some problems that may arise from consuming a poor diet.

Carbohydrates

Carbohydrates are present in food in the form of sugars, starch, and fiber. Fruits, vegetables, milk, and honey are natural sources of sugars. Glucose and fructose are monosaccharide sugars, and lactose (milk sugar) and sucrose (table sugar) are disaccharides. Disaccharides are broken down in the small intestine, and monosaccharides are absorbed into the bloodstream and delivered to cells. Once inside animal cells, monosaccharides are converted to glucose, much of which is used for the production of ATP by cellular respiration (see Section 8.1).

Plants store glucose as starch, and animals store glucose as glycogen. Good sources of starch are beans, peas, cereal grains, and potatoes. Starch is digested to glucose in the digestive tract, and excess glucose is stored as glycogen. The human liver and muscles can only store a total of about 600 g of glucose in the form of glycogen; excess glucose is converted into fat and stored in adipose tissues.

Although other animals likewise store glucose as glycogen in liver or muscle tissue (meat), little is left by the time an animal is eaten for food. Except for honey and milk, which contain sugars, animal foods do not contain high levels of carbohydrates.

Fiber includes various undigestible carbohydrates derived from plants. Food sources rich in fiber include beans, peas,

Figure 34.13 Digestion and absorption of nutrients. **a.** Starch is digested to glucose, which is actively transported into the epithelial cells of intestinal villi. From there, glucose moves into the bloodstream. **b.** Proteins are digested to amino acids, which are actively transported into the epithelial cells of intestinal villi. From there, amino acids move into the bloodstream. **c.** Fats are emulsified by bile and digested to monoglycerides and fatty acids. These diffuse into epithelial cells, where they recombine and join with proteins to form lipoproteins, called chylomicrons. Chylomicrons enter a lacteal.

a. Carbohydrate digestion

b. Protein digestion

c. Fat digestion

nuts, fruits, and vegetables. Whole-grain products are also a good source of fiber, and are therefore more nutritious than food products made from refined grains. During *refinement*, fiber and also vitamins and minerals are removed from grains, so that primarily starch remains. For example, a slice of bread made from whole-wheat flour contains 3 g of fiber; a slice of bread made from refined wheat flour contains less than 1 g of fiber.

Technically, fiber is not a nutrient for humans because it cannot be digested to small molecules that enter the bloodstream. Insoluble fiber, however, adds bulk to fecal material, which stimulates movement in the large intestine, preventing constipation. Soluble fiber combines with bile acids and cholesterol in the small intestine and prevents them from being absorbed. In this way, high-fiber diets may protect against heart disease. The typical American consumes only about 15 g of fiber each day; the recommended daily intake of fiber is 25 g for women and 38 g for men. To increase your fiber intake, eat whole-grain foods, snack on fresh fruits and raw vegetables, and include nuts and beans in your diet (Fig. 34.14).

If you, or someone you know, has lost weight by following low carbohydrate diets, you may think "carbs" are unhealthy and should be avoided. According to the American Dietetic Association, however, some low-carbohydrate, high-fat diets are potentially hazardous and have no benefits over well-balanced diets that include the same number of calories. In fact, a recent study of over 4,400 Canadian adults found the lowest risk of obesity in people who consumed about half of their calories from carbohydrates.[1] Evidence also suggests that many Americans are not eating the right kind of carbohydrates. In some countries, the traditional diet is 60–70% high-fiber carbohydrates, and these people have a low incidence of the diseases that plague Americans.

A current controversy in human nutrition is the relative risk of consuming high levels of high fructose corn syrup (HFCS), compared to other sweeteners. HFCS, or corn sugar, is now the most commonly used sweetening agent, found in soft drinks and a huge variety of foods that end up on our plates. Many websites and a few research studies have suggested that HFCS is a major factor responsible for the rising epidemic of obesity and related diseases, but many nutritionists contend that the *type* of sugar consumed is not as important as the *amount*. As an example, the typical American obtains about one-sixth of his or her daily caloric intake from HFCS and other sugars. It is likely that consuming such a high percentage of "empty calories" in the form of simple sugars is contributing to the increasing incidence of obesity in the United States.

Lipids

Like carbohydrates, *triglycerides* (fats and oils) supply energy for cells, but *fat* is also stored for the long term in the body. Dietary experts generally recommend that people include unsaturated, rather than saturated, fats in their diets (see Fig. 3.10 to review these structures). Two unsaturated fatty acids, alpha-linolenic and linoleic acids (also called omega-3 fatty acids), are *essential* in the diet, meaning that we cannot synthesize them. Delayed

1 Merchant, A. T., et al. 2009. Carbohydrate intake and overweight-obesity among healthy adults. *J. Am. Dietetic Assn.* 109: 1165–72.

Figure 34.14 Fiber-rich foods. Plants provide a good source of carbohydrates. They also provide a good source of vitamins, minerals, and fiber when they are not processed (refined).

growth and skin problems can develop in people who consume an insufficient amount of these essential unsaturated fatty acids, which are found in high amounts in certain fish and in plant oils like canola and soybean oils.

Another type of lipid, *cholesterol*, is a necessary component of the plasma membrane of all animal cells. It is also a precursor for synthesis of various compounds, including bile, steroid hormones, and vitamin D. Plant foods do not contain cholesterol, but animal foods such as cheese, egg yolks, liver, and certain shellfish (shrimp and lobster) are rich in cholesterol. Elevated blood cholesterol levels are associated with an increased risk of cardiovascular disease, the number one cause of disease-related death in the U.S. (described later on).

Animal-derived foods, such as butter, red meat, whole milk, and cheeses, contain saturated fats, which are also associated with cardiovascular disease. Statistical studies suggest that trans-fatty acids (trans-fats) are even more harmful than saturated fatty acids. Trans-fatty acids arise when unsaturated oils are hydrogenated to produce a solid fat, as in shortening and some margarines. Trans-fats may reduce the function of the plasma membrane receptors that clear cholesterol from the bloodstream. Trans-fats are found in commercially packaged foods, such as cookies and crackers; in commercially fried foods, such as french fries; and in packaged snacks.

Proteins

Dietary *proteins* are digested to amino acids, which cells use to synthesize thousands of different cellular proteins. Of the 20 different amino acids, eight are *essential amino acids* that normal adult humans cannot synthesize and thus must be present in the diet. Animal products like beef, pork, poultry, eggs, and dairy products contain all these essential amino acids and are considered "complete" or "high-quality" protein sources.

Most foods derived from plants do not have as much protein per serving as those derived from animals, and some types of plant foods lack one or more of the essential amino acids. For example, the proteins found in corn have a low content of the essential amino acid lysine (although high-lysine corn has been produced through genetic engineering technology). Approximately 3% of Americans (and millions of people in other countries) are either vegetarians, who avoid eating animal flesh, or vegans, who avoid consuming any products derived from animals. Neither group needs to rely on animal sources of protein.

To meet their protein needs, vegetarians and vegans can eat grains, beans, and nuts in various combinations. Also, tofu, soymilk, and other foods made from processed soybeans are complete protein sources. A 2009 report from the American Dietetic Association states that "Well-planned vegetarian diets are appropriate for individuals during all stages of the life cycle, including pregnancy, lactation, infancy, childhood, and adolescence, and for athletes."[2]

Although a severe deficiency in dietary protein intake can be life-threatening, most Americans probably consume too much protein. Even further, some health food stores are full of protein supplements, aimed mainly at athletes who are trying to build muscle mass. However, both the American and Canadian Dietetic Associations recommend that even athletes should consume only 1 to 1.5 grams of protein per kilogram of body weight per day, which is just slightly higher than the 0.8 grams per kilogram recommended for sedentary people. This means an inactive 150 pound person would need to consume only about 60 grams of protein per day, which is about the amount contained in two cheeseburgers.

When amino acids are broken down, the liver removes the nitrogen portion (*deamination*) and uses it to form urea, which is excreted in urine. The water needed for excretion of urea can cause dehydration when a person is exercising and losing water by sweating. High-protein diets can also increase calcium loss in the urine and encourage the formation of kidney stones. Furthermore, high-protein foods derived from animals often contain a high amount of fat.

Diet and Obesity

As mentioned, the consumption of an excess amount of calories (relative to calories expended) from any source causes storage of these calories in the form of body fat. Obesity can be defined in several ways, including: 1) a condition in which excess body fat has an adverse effect on normal activity and health; 2) weighing over 20% more than the ideal for your height and body build, and 3) having a body mass index (BMI) over 30. A person's BMI can be calculated by dividing weight in kilograms by height in meters squared, or by using an online BMI calculator. As of 2009, most estimates indicate that about 30% of Americans are obese. Obesity raises the risk of many medical conditions, including type 2 diabetes and cardiovascular disease. The seriousness of obesity as a health care problem is evidenced by increasing popularity of surgical procedures designed to reduce food consumption (see the Nature of Science feature).

Type 2 Diabetes

Diabetes mellitus occurs when the hormone insulin is not functioning properly, resulting in abnormally high levels of glucose in the blood. This may occur due to a deficiency of insulin secretion by the pancreas, as in type 1 diabetes, or to an inability of cells to respond to insulin (also called insulin resistance), defined as type 2 diabetes. In both types, the excess blood glucose spills over into the urine, leading to increased urination, thirst, and weight loss. Over time, the high levels of blood glucose, and

Figure 34.15 Exercising for good health. Regular exercise helps prevent and control type 2 diabetes.

lack of other insulin functions, can lead to damage to blood vessels, nerves, eyes, kidneys, and even to death. Type 1 diabetes can usually be successfully managed with insulin injections, but type 2 diabetes can be much more resistant to treatment.

In a 2010 report published in the Journal of the American Medical Association, 4,193 adults were studied for an average of 12.4 years, during which 339, or 8.1%, developed diabetes. Among the key findings, people who gained 20 pounds or more after age 50 had three times the risk of developing diabetes, and the risk was four times greater for those with the biggest waist circumferences and highest BMIs. Because we tend to lose muscle and gain fat as we age, the study authors noted the importance of exercise, as opposed to weight loss alone, in maintaining good health (Fig. 34.15).

Animation
Blood Sugar Regulation in Diabetics

Cardiovascular Disease

Cardiovascular disease is the leading cause of death in the United States. Heart attacks and strokes often occur when arteries become blocked by plaque, which contains saturated fats and cholesterol. Cholesterol is carried in the blood by two types of lipoproteins: low-density lipoprotein (LDL) and high-density lipoprotein (HDL). LDL molecules are considered "bad" because they are like delivery trucks that carry cholesterol from the liver to the cells and to the arterial walls. HDL molecules are considered "good" because they are like garbage trucks that dispose of cholesterol. HDL transports cholesterol from the cells to the liver, which converts it to bile salts that enter the small intestine.

According to the American Heart Association, diets high in saturated fats, trans-fats, and/or cholesterol tend to raise LDL cholesterol levels, while eating unsaturated fats may actually lower LDL cholesterol levels. Furthermore, coldwater fish (e.g., herring, sardines, tuna, and salmon) contain polyunsaturated fatty acids and especially omega-3 fatty acids, which are believed to reduce the risk of cardiovascular disease. However, taking fish oil supplements to obtain omega-3s is not recommended without a physician's approval, because too much of these fatty acids can interfere with normal blood clotting.

The American Heart Association also recommends limiting total cholesterol intake to 300 mg per day. This requires careful selection of the foods we include in our daily diets. For example, an egg yolk contains about 210 mg of cholesterol, which would be two-thirds of the recommended daily intake. Still, this doesn't mean eggs should be eliminated from a healthy diet, because the proteins in them are very nutritious; in fact, most healthy people can eat a couple of whole eggs each week without experiencing an increase in their blood cholesterol levels.

A physician can determine whether blood lipid levels are normal. If a person's cholesterol and triglyceride levels are elevated, modifying the fat content of the diet, losing excess

2 Craig, W. J., and Mangels, A. R., 2009. Position of the American Dietetic Association: Vegetarian diets. *J. Am. Dietetic Assn.* 109: 1266–82.

body fat, and exercising regularly can reduce them. If lifestyle changes do not lower blood lipid levels enough to reduce the risk of cardiovascular disease, a physician may prescribe cholesterol-lowering medications.

Video
A Burger a Day

Vitamins and Minerals

Vitamins are organic compounds other than carbohydrates, fats, and proteins that regulate various metabolic activities and must be present in the diet. Many vitamins are part of coenzymes; for example, niacin is the name for a portion of the coenzyme NAD^+, and riboflavin is a part of FAD. Coenzymes are needed in small amounts because they are used over and over again in cells. Not all vitamins are coenzymes, however; vitamin A, for example, is a precursor for the pigment that prevents night blindness.

It has been known for some time that the absence of a vitamin can be associated with a particular disorder. Vitamins are especially abundant in fruits and vegetables, and so it is suggested that we eat about $4\frac{1}{2}$ cups of fruits and vegetables per day. Although many foods are now enriched or fortified with vitamins, some individuals are still at risk for vitamin deficiencies, generally as a result of poor food choices.

Animation
B Vitamins

The body also needs about 20 elements called *minerals* for various physiological functions, including regulation of biochemical reactions, maintenance of fluid balance, and incorporation into certain structures and compounds. Occasionally individuals (especially women) do not receive enough iron, calcium, magnesium, or zinc in their diets. Adult females need more iron in the diet than males (18 mg compared to 10 mg) if they are menstruating each month. Many people take calcium supplements, as directed by a physician, to counteract osteoporosis, a degenerative bone disease that especially affects older men and women. Many people consume too much sodium, even double the amount needed. Excess sodium can cause water retention and contribute to hypertension.

Animation
Osteoporosis

Check Your Progress   34.4

1. Review several reasons why a diet that includes plenty of vegetables is generally better for you than a diet that includes excess protein.
2. Discuss the relationship between blood cholesterol, saturated fat intake, and cardiovascular disease.
3. Define vitamin.

CONNECTING *the* CONCEPTS *with the* THEMES

Evolution

- An incomplete digestive tract fulfills the nutritional needs of some relatively simple animals. The evolution of a complete digestive tract has allowed specialization of function and efficient food processing.
- Discontinuous feeders have developed the ability to store food temporarily while it is being digested, enabling them to spend less time feeding and more time engaging in other activities.
- Many features of animal body structure—including type of dentition, ability to catch prey, and structure of the digestive tract—have evolved as adaptations to a particular diet: herbivore, carnivore, or omnivore.

Nature of Science

- Observational studies of the digestive systems of animals, ranging from the simplest to the most complex, have greatly aided our understanding of digestion and nutrition.
- Basic research on the digestive system has resulted in screenings and treatments for diseases such as ulcers, hepatitis, gallstones, and colon cancer.
- Through research on the causes of obesity, medical scientists are attempting to develop new strategies and medications to help reduce weight.

Biological Systems

- Some animals are simple enough, with no cell located far from their aqueous environment, that their cells can obtain nutrients with no need for a digestive system.
- The human digestive system is a good example of the complexity and specialization of the digestive system of an omnivorous mammal.
- Humans in modern societies have access to types and quantities of food that were unknown to our ancestors, and this may account for the rise of obesity.

Media Study Tools

www.mhhe.com/maderbiology11

Enhance your study of this chapter with study tools and practice tests. Also ask your instructor about the resources available through ConnectPlus, including the media-rich eBook, interactive learning tools, and animations.

Summarize

34.1 Digestive Tracts

A few animals (e.g., sponges) lack a digestive tract; others, such as planarians, have an incomplete digestive tract that has only one opening. An incomplete tract has little specialization. Many other animals, such as earthworms, have a complete digestive tract that has both a mouth and an anus. A complete tract tends to have specialized regions.

Some animals are continuous feeders (e.g., clams, which are filter feeders); others are discontinuous feeders (e.g., squid). Discontinuous feeders need a storage organ for food.

Most mammals have teeth. Herbivores need teeth that can clip off plant material and grind it up. Also, the herbivore's stomach contains bacteria that can digest cellulose. Carnivores need teeth that can tear and rip animal flesh into pieces. Meat is easier to digest than plant material, so the digestive system of carnivores has fewer specialized regions and the intestine is shorter than that of herbivores.

34.2 The Human Digestive System

In the human digestive system, both mechanical and chemical digestion begins in the mouth, where food is chewed and mixed with saliva. Saliva contains salivary amylase, which begins carbohydrate digestion.

Food then passes to the pharynx and down the esophagus by peristalsis to the stomach. The stomach stores and mixes food with mucus and gastric juices to produce chyme. Pepsin begins protein digestion in the stomach.

Chyme passes into the small intestine. The duodenum of the small intestine receives bile from the liver and pancreatic juice from the pancreas. Bile emulsifies fat and readies it for digestion by pancreatic lipase. The pancreas also produces amylase and proteases. These and other intestinal enzymes finish the process of chemical digestion.

The walls of the small intestine have fingerlike projections called villi where small nutrient molecules are absorbed. Amino acids and glucose enter the blood vessels of a villus. Glycerol and fatty acids are joined and packaged as lipoproteins before entering lymphatic vessels called lacteals in a villus.

The large intestine consists of the cecum, the colon, and the rectum, which ends at the anus. The cecum, a blind pouch at the junction of the small and large intestine, has a small projection called the appendix, which sometimes becomes infected and inflamed, necessitating its removal. The large intestine does not produce digestive enzymes; it does absorb water, salts, and some vitamins. Reduced water absorption results in diarrhea. The intake of water and fiber help prevent constipation.

Three accessory organs of digestion—the pancreas, liver, and gallbladder—send secretions to the duodenum via ducts. The pancreas produces pancreatic juice, which contains digestive enzymes for carbohydrates, protein, and fat.

The liver produces bile, which is stored in the gallbladder. The liver receives blood from the small intestine by way of the hepatic portal vein. It has numerous important functions, and any malfunction of the liver is a matter of considerable concern.

34.3 Digestive Enzymes

Digestive enzymes are present in digestive juices and break down food into the nutrient molecules glucose, amino acids, fatty acids, and glycerol. Salivary amylase and pancreatic amylase begin the digestion of starch. Pepsin and trypsin digest protein to peptides. Following emulsification by bile, lipase digests fat to glycerol and fatty acids. Intestinal enzymes finish the digestion of starch and protein.

Each digestive enzyme is present in a particular part of the digestive tract. Salivary amylase functions in the mouth; pepsin functions in the stomach; trypsin, lipase, and pancreatic amylase occur in the intestine along with the various enzymes that digest disaccharides and peptides.

34.4 Nutrition and Human Health

The nutrients released by the digestive process should provide us with an adequate amount of major nutrients, essential amino acids and fatty acids, and all necessary vitamins and minerals.

Carbohydrates are necessary in the diet, but simple sugars and refined starches are not as healthy because they provide calories but little or no fiber, vitamins, or minerals. Proteins supply us with essential amino acids, but many Americans may consume more protein than is healthy. It is also wise to restrict one's intake of meats that are fatty because animal fats are saturated fats. Unsaturated fatty acids, particularly the omega-3 fatty acids, are protective against cardio-

vascular disease, whereas saturated fatty acids may lead to plaque formation, which blocks blood vessels.

Obesity is becoming an increasingly serious problem, especially because it is associated with the development of type 2 diabetes and cardiovascular disease.

Key Terms

anus 653	mouth 650
appendix (vermiform appendix) 653	mucosa 651
	muscularis 651
bile 652	pancreas 654
chyme 652	pancreatic amylase 656
cirrhosis 656	pepsin 656
complete digestive tract 647	peptidase 657
diarrhea 653	peristalsis 651
duodenum 652	pharynx 651
esophagus 651	polyp 654
gallbladder 656	rumen 649
hepatitis 654	salivary amylase 651, 656
incomplete digestive tract 647	salivary gland 651
jaundice 654	serosa 651
lacteal 653	small intestine 652
large intestine 653	stomach 652
lipase 657	submucosa 651
liver 654	trypsin 656
lumen 651	villus 652
maltase 656	

Assess

Reviewing This Chapter

1. Contrast the incomplete digestive tract with the complete digestive tract, using the planarian and earthworm as examples. 647–48
2. Contrast a continuous feeder with a discontinuous feeder, using the clam and squid as examples. 648
3. Contrast the dentition of the mammalian herbivore with that of the mammalian carnivore, using the horse and lion as examples. 649
4. List the parts of the human digestive tract, anatomically describe them, and state the contribution of each to the digestive process. 650–54, 656
5. Discuss the absorption of the products of digestion into the lymphatic and cardiovascular systems. 652–53
6. Describe the structure and function of the large intestine. Name several medical conditions associated with the large intestine. 653–54
7. State the location and describe the functions of the pancreas, the liver, and the gallbladder. 654, 656
8. Name and discuss two serious illnesses of the liver. 654, 656
9. Assume that you have just eaten a ham sandwich. Discuss the digestion of the contents of the sandwich. Mention all the necessary enzymes. 656–57
10. Explain why good nutrition is important to human health. Explain why obesity can lead to type 2 diabetes and cardiovascular disease. 657–60

Testing Yourself

Choose the best answer for each question.

1. Animals that feed discontinuously
   a. have digestive tracts that permit storage.
   b. are always filter feeders.
   c. exhibit extremely rapid digestion.
   d. have a nonspecialized digestive tract.
   e. usually eat only meat.

2. Archaeocytes are associated with
   a. digestion in bacteria.
   b. the digestive tracts of sponges.
   c. the filter organs of continuous feeders.
   d. the human appendix.
   e. ingestion and distribution of food in sponges.

3. The typhlosole within the gut of an earthworm compares best to which of these organs in humans?
   a. teeth in the mouth
   b. esophagus in the thoracic cavity
   c. folds in the stomach
   d. villi in the small intestine
   e. the large intestine because it absorbs water

4. Which of these animals is a continuous feeder with a complete digestive tract?
   a. planarian   d. lion
   b. clam   e. human
   c. squid

5. Tracing the path of food in humans, which step is out of order first?
   a. mouth   c. esophagus   e. stomach
   b. pharynx   d. small intestine f. large intestine

6. The products of digestion are
   a. large macromolecules needed by the body.
   b. enzymes needed to digest food.
   c. small nutrient molecules that can be absorbed.
   d. regulatory hormones of various kinds.
   e. the foods we eat.

7. Why can a person not swallow food and talk at the same time?
   a. To swallow, the epiglottis must close off the trachea.
   b. The brain cannot control two activities at once.
   c. To speak, air must come through the larynx to form sounds.
   d. A swallowing reflex is only initiated when the mouth is closed.
   e. Both a and c are correct.

8. Which of these could be absorbed directly without need of digestion?
   a. glucose   d. nucleic acid
   b. fat   e. All of these are correct.
   c. protein

9. Which association is incorrect?
   a. protein—trypsin   d. starch—amylase
   b. fat—lipase   e. protein—pepsin
   c. maltose—pepsin

10. Most of the absorption of the products of digestion takes place in humans across
    a. the squamous epithelium of the esophagus.
    b. the convoluted walls of the stomach.
    c. the fingerlike villi of the small intestine.
    d. the smooth wall of the large intestine.
    e. the lacteals of the lymphatic system.

11. The hepatic portal vein is located between
    a. the hepatic vein and the vena cava.
    b. two capillary beds.
    c. the pancreas and the small intestine.
    d. the small intestine and the liver.
    e. Both b and d are correct.

12. Bile in humans
    a. is an important enzyme for the digestion of fats.
    b. is made by the gallbladder.
    c. emulsifies fat.
    d. must be activated during the first few weeks of life.
    e. All of these are correct.

13. Which of these is not a function of the liver in adults?
    a. produces bile
    b. stores glucose
    c. produces urea
    d. makes red blood cells
    e. produces proteins needed for blood clotting

14. The large intestine in humans
    a. digests all types of food.
    b. is the longest part of the intestinal tract.
    c. absorbs water.
    d. is connected to the stomach.
    e. All of these are correct.

15. The appendix connects to the
    a. cecum.   d. large intestine.
    b. small intestine.   e. liver.
    c. esophagus.   f. All of these are correct.

16. Which association is incorrect?
    a. mouth—starch digestion
    b. esophagus—protein digestion
    c. small intestine—starch, lipid, protein digestion
    d. stomach—food storage
    e. liver—production of bile

17. Predict and explain the expected digestive results per test tube for this experiment.

Incubator

Engage

Virtual Labs
Earthworm Dissection
Virtual Frog Dissection
Nutrition

The virtual labs "Earthworm Dissection" and "Virtual Frog Dissection" provide you with a more detailed look at digestive systems. The virtual lab "Nutrition" allows you to input your personal information to assess the health of your diet.

Thinking Scientifically

1. A drug for leukemia is not broken down in the stomach and is well absorbed by the intestine. However, the molecular form of the drug collected from the blood is not the same as the form that was swallowed by the patient. What explanation is most likely?

2. Snakes often swallow whole animals, a process that takes a long time. Then snakes spend some time digesting their food. What structural modifications would allow slow swallowing and storage of a whole animal to occur? What chemical modifications would be necessary to digest a whole animal?

David Blaine displays an amazing ability to hold his breath while under water, which he has learned through training. Mammals living in aquatic environments have gained this ability through adaptation.

Respiratory Systems

BEFORE YOU BEGIN

Before beginning this chapter, take a few moments to review the following discussions.

Figure 7.4 During which specific parts of photosynthesis do plants produce oxygen, and use carbon dioxide?

Section 8.4 At what point is carbon dioxide produced inside mitochondria, and why is oxygen required?

Figure 32.5 What path does blood travel from the heart to the site of gas exchange in fish, amphibians, and birds?

On April 30, 2008, magician David Blaine set a world record by holding his breath for 17 minutes, 4 seconds, while submerged in a glass globe filled with cold water. While this was an amazing feat, Blaine may have been aided by an ancient evolutionary adaptation called the "diving response"—simply immerse your face in cold water, and your heart rate decreases, your spleen may contract (to release stored red blood cells), and blood vessels in your extremities constrict. Taken to the extreme, however, this response—along with decreasing oxygen levels—can lead to painful muscle cramping, and even tissue damage.

Despite efforts to push the limits of human physiology, the true breath-holding champions are aquatic mammals such as the elephant seal, which can dive almost a mile deep and hold its breath for up to two hours. These animals benefit from various evolutionary adaptations: They have more red blood cells per body weight than we do; their muscles contain more oxygen-storing proteins; and they have a particularly effective diving response. Research indicates that elephant seals also tolerate exceptionally low levels of oxygen in their blood. Wherever they live, animals have evolved an amazing variety of strategies for delivering oxygen to their cells and removing carbon dioxide.

As you read through the chapter, think about the following questions:

1. What are some possible evolutionary pressures that might explain why a strictly terrestrial species, such as humans, would have a diving response?

2. Considering the adaptations that are required, what kinds of physiological limitations prevent elephant seals from being able to hold their breath for even longer?

FOLLOWING *the* THEMES

CHAPTER 35 RESPIRATORY SYSTEMS		
UNIT 7 COMPARATIVE ANIMAL BIOLOGY	**Evolution**	Strategies have evolved in virtually all multicellular animals that allow them to efficiently extract oxygen from their environment, and eliminate carbon dioxide.
	Nature of Science	Research studies into respiration are providing the basic biological framework needed for treating respiratory disease and building functioning lung tissues in the laboratory.
	Biological Systems	Animal respiratory systems are responsive to changing demands for oxygen. Because of the respiratory system's direct contact with the environment, it is also susceptible to a number of serious diseases.

35.1 Gas Exchange Surfaces

Learning Outcomes

Upon completion of this section, you should be able to

1. Distinguish between ventilation, external respiration, and internal respiration.
2. Compare and contrast the gas-exchange mechanisms of hydras, earthworms, insects, aquatic vertebrates, and terrestrial vertebrates.
3. Trace the path of a molecule of oxygen as it passes from the human nose to an alveolus.

Respiration is the sequence of events that results in gas exchange between the body's cells and the environment. In terrestrial vertebrates, respiration includes these steps:

- **Ventilation** (i.e., breathing) includes inspiration (entrance of air into the lungs) and expiration (exit of air from the lungs).
- **External respiration** is gas exchange between the air and the blood within the lungs. Blood then transports oxygen from the lungs to the tissues.
- **Internal respiration** is gas exchange between the blood and the tissue fluid. (The body's cells exchange gases with the tissue fluid.) The blood then transports carbon dioxide to the lungs.

External Respiration

lungs

CO_2 O_2

CO_2 O_2

tissue cells

Internal Respiration

Gas exchange takes place by the physical process of diffusion (see Section 5.2). For external respiration to be effective, the gas-exchange region must be (1) moist, (2) thin, and (3) large in relation to the size of the body.

Some animals are small and shaped in a way that allows the surface of the animal to be the gas-exchange surface. Most complex animals have evolved specialized tissues for external respiration, such as gills in aquatic animals and lungs in terrestrial animals. The effectiveness of diffusion is enhanced by vascularization (the presence of many capillaries), and delivery of oxygen to the cells is promoted when the blood contains a respiratory pigment, such as hemoglobin.

Regardless of the particular external respiration surface and the manner in which gases are delivered to the cells, in the end, oxygen enters mitochondria, where cellular respiration takes place (see Section 8.1). A rare exception to this was discovered in April 2010, when a team of Italian and Danish deep-sea divers discovered a new species of tiny jellyfish-like animals called loriciferans living in sediment more than 10,000 feet below the surface of the Mediterranean Sea that contains almost no oxygen. This discovery represents the first known multicellular animals that do not appear to require oxygen! Subsequent studies have indicated that the cells of these animals may lack mitochondria, but instead contain structures that resemble those used by anaerobic bacteria to undergo cellular respiration in the absence of oxygen. For most animals however, if internal respiration does not occur, ATP production declines dramatically, and life ceases.

Overview of Gas-Exchange Surfaces

It is more difficult for animals to obtain oxygen from water than from air. Water fully saturated with air contains only a fraction of the amount of oxygen that is present in the same volume of air. Also, water is more dense than air. Therefore, aquatic animals expend more energy carrying out gas exchange than do terrestrial animals. Fishes use as much as 25% of their energy output to respire, while terrestrial mammals use only 1–2% of their energy output for that purpose.

Hydras, which are cnidarians, and planarians, which are flatworms, have a large surface area in comparison to their size. This makes it possible for most of their cells to exchange gases directly with the environment. In hydras, the outer layer of cells is in contact with the external environment, and the inner layer can exchange gases with the water in the gastrovascular cavity (Fig. 35.1).

The earthworm is an example of a terrestrial invertebrate that is able to use its body surface for respiration because the capillaries come close to the surface (Fig. 35.2). An earthworm keeps its body surface moist by secreting mucus and by releasing fluids from excretory pores. Further, the worm is behaviorally adapted to remain in damp soil during the day, when the air is driest.

Aquatic invertebrates (e.g., clams and crayfish) and aquatic vertebrates (e.g., fish and tadpoles) have gills that extract oxygen from a watery environment. **Gills** are finely divided, vascularized outgrowths of the body surface or the pharynx (Fig. 35.3a). Various mechanisms are used to pump water across the gills, depending on the organism.

Insects have a system of air tubes called **tracheae** through which oxygen is delivered directly to the cells without entering the blood (Fig. 35.3b). Air sacs located near the wings, legs,

Figure 35.1 Hydra. Some small aquatic animals, such as a hydra, use their body surface for gas exchange. This works because the body surface is large compared to the size of the animal.

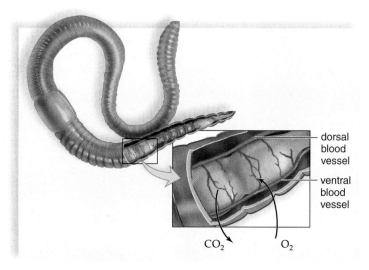

Figure 35.2 Earthworm. An earthworm's entire external surface functions in external respiration.

a.

b.

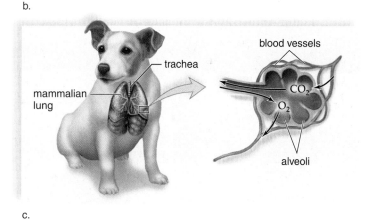

c.

Figure 35.3 Respiratory organs. a. Fish have gills to assist external respiration. **b.** Insects have a tracheal system that delivers oxygen directly to their cells. **c.** Vertebrates have lungs with a large total external respiration surface.

and abdomen act as bellows to help move the air into the tubes through external openings.

Terrestrial vertebrates usually have **lungs,** which are vascularized outgrowths from the lower pharyngeal region. The tadpoles of frogs live in the water and have gills as external respiratory organs, but adult amphibians possess simple, saclike lungs. Most amphibians respire to some extent through the skin, and some salamanders depend entirely on the skin, which is kept moist by mucus produced by numerous glands on the surface of the body.

The lungs of birds and mammals are elaborately subdivided into small passageways and spaces (Fig. 35.3c). It has been estimated that human lungs have a total surface area of about 70 square meters, which is about 50 times the skin's surface area. Air is a rich source of oxygen compared to water; however, it does have a drying effect on external respiratory surfaces. A human loses about 350 mL of water per day through respiration when the air has a relative humidity of only 50%. To keep the lungs from drying out, air is moistened as it moves in through the passageways leading to the lungs.

The Gills of a Fish

Animals with gills use various means of ventilation. Among molluscs, such as clams or squids, water is drawn into the mantle cavity, where it passes through the gills. In crustaceans like crabs and shrimp, the gills are located in thoracic chambers covered by the exoskeleton. The action of specialized appendages located near the mouth keeps the water moving. In fish, ventilation is brought about by the combined action of the mouth and gill covers, or opercula (sing., operculum; L. *operculum,* small lid). When the mouth is open, the opercula are closed and water is drawn in. Then the mouth closes, and the opercula open, drawing the water from the pharynx through the gill slits located between the gill arches.

As mentioned, the gills of bony fishes are outward extensions of the pharynx (Fig. 35.4). On the outside of the gill arches, the gills are composed of filaments that are folded into platelike lamellae. Fish use **countercurrent exchange** to transfer oxygen from the surrounding water into their blood. *Concurrent* flow would mean that oxygen (O_2)-rich water passing over the gills would flow in the same direction as oxygen-poor blood in the blood vessels. This arrangement results in an equilibrium point, at which only half the oxygen in the water would be captured. *Counter*current flow, in contrast, means that the two fluids flow in opposite directions. With countercurrent flow, as blood gains oxygen, it always encounters water having an even higher oxygen content. A countercurrent mechanism prevents an equilibrium point from being reached, and about 80–90% of the initial dissolved oxygen in water is extracted.

The Tracheal System of Insects

Arthropods are coelomate animals, but the coelom is reduced and the internal organs lie within a cavity called the hemocoel because it contains hemolymph, a mixture of blood and lymph (see Chapter 32). Hemolymph flows freely through the hemocoel, making circulation in arthropods inefficient. Many insects are adapted for flight, and their flight muscles require a steady supply of oxygen.

Figure 35.4 Anatomy of gills in bony fishes. **a.** The operculum (folded back) covers and protects several layers of delicate gills. **b.** Each gill layer has two rows of gill filaments. **c.** Each filament is divided into a series of capillary laden lamellae, which are also shown in the scanning electron micrograph. Blood in the capillaries flows in the direction opposite that of the water. **d.** Gases are exchanged between the capillaries inside the lamellae and the water that flows between the lamellae. Blood takes up almost all of the oxygen in the water as a result of countercurrent flow.

operculum

lamellae

900×

a.

Water passes out of the pharynx and over the finely divided gills.

O_2-rich blood
O_2-poor blood

Direction of H_2O flow

gill arch

gill filaments

b.

Water passes by the gill lamellae in a direction opposite to blood flow.

Direction of H_2O flow

lamellae

blood flow

gill filament

c.

Oxygen content of water is always higher than the oxygen content of the blood.

O_2 movement

water flow

100%   70%   40%   15%

90%   60%   30%   5%

blood flow

lamella

d.

Figure 35.5 Tracheae of insects.
A system of air tubes extends throughout the body of an insect, and the tubes carry oxygen to the cells. Air enters the tracheae at openings called spiracles. From here, the air moves to the smaller tracheoles, which take it to the cells, where gas exchange takes place. The photomicrograph shows how the walls of the trachea are stiffened with bands of chitin.

Insects overcome the inefficiency of their blood flow by having a respiratory system that consists of *tracheae,* tiny air tubes that take oxygen directly to the cells (Fig. 35.5). The tracheae branch into even smaller tubules called tracheoles, which also branch and rebranch until finally the air tubes are only about 0.1 μm in diameter. There are so many fine tracheoles that almost every cell is near one. Also, the tracheoles indent the plasma membrane so that they terminate close to mitochondria. Therefore, O_2 can flow more directly from a tracheole to mitochondria, where cellular respiration occurs. The tracheae also dispose of CO_2.

The tracheoles are fluid-filled, but the larger tracheae contain air and open to the outside by way of spiracles (Fig. 35.5). Usually, the spiracle has some sort of closing device that reduces water loss, and this may be why insects have no trouble inhabiting drier climates. Scientists have determined that the tracheae can actually expand and contract, thereby drawing air into and out of the system. To improve the efficiency of the tracheal system, many larger insects also have air sacs, which are thin-walled and flexible, located near major muscles. Contraction of these muscles causes the air sacs to empty, and relaxation causes the air sacs to expand and draw in air. This method is comparable to the way that human lungs expand to draw air into them.

Even with all these adaptations, insects still lack the efficient circulatory system of birds and mammals that is able to pump oxygen-rich blood through arteries to all the cells of the body. This may be why insects have remained relatively small, despite the attempts of science-fiction movies to make us think otherwise.

A tracheal system is an adaptation to breathing air, and yet some insect larval stages, and even some adult insects, live in the water. In these instances, the tracheae do not receive air by way of spiracles. Instead, diffusion of oxygen across the body wall supplies the tracheae with oxygen. Mayfly and stonefly nymphs have thin extensions of the body wall called tracheal gills—the tracheae are particularly numerous in this area. This is an interesting adaptation because it dramatizes that tracheae function to deliver oxygen in the same manner as vertebrate blood vessels.

Some aquatic insects have developed a different strategy. Like most insects, water beetles breathe through spiracles. Because they live in water however, they capture a bubble of air from the surface, and carry it with them, exchanging the oxygen inside for CO_2. Water spiders even spin an underwater web, which they fill with air bubbles, forming what some scientists have called an "external lung."

The Lungs of Humans

The human respiratory system includes all of the structures that conduct air in a continuous pathway to and from the lungs (Fig. 35.6a). The lungs lie deep in the body, within the thoracic cavity, where they are protected from drying out. As air moves through the nose, the pharynx, the trachea, and the bronchi to the lungs, it is filtered so that it is free of debris, warmed, and humidified. By the time the air reaches the lungs, it is at body temperature and saturated with water.

In the nose, hairs and cilia act as a screening device. In the trachea and the bronchi, cilia beat upward, carrying mucus, dust, and occasional small bits of food that "went down the wrong way" back into the throat, where the accumulation may be swallowed or expectorated (Fig. 35.6*b*).

The hard and soft palates separate the nasal cavities from the mouth, but the air and food passages cross in the **pharynx.** This arrangement may seem inefficient, and there is danger of choking if food accidentally enters the trachea; however, it does have the advantage of letting you breathe through your mouth in case your nose is plugged up. In addition, it permits greater intake of air during heavy exercise, when greater gas exchange is required.

Air passes from the pharynx through the **glottis,** which is an opening into the **larynx,** or voice box. At the edges of the glottis are two folds of connective tissue covered by mucous membrane, called the **vocal cords.** These flexible and pliable bands vibrate against each other, producing sound when air is expelled past them through the glottis from the larynx.

The larynx and the trachea remain open to receive air at all times. The larynx is held open by a complex of nine cartilages, among them the Adam's apple. Easily seen in many men, the Adam's apple resembles a small, rounded apple just under the skin in the front of the neck. The **trachea** (windpipe) is held open by a series of C-shaped, cartilaginous rings that do not completely meet in the rear. When food is being swallowed, the larynx rises, and the glottis is covered by a flap of tissue called the **epiglottis.** A backward movement of the soft palate covers

the entrance of the nasal passages into the pharynx. The food then enters the esophagus, which lies behind the larynx.

The trachea divides into two primary **bronchi,** which enter the right and left lungs. Branching continues, eventually forming a great number of smaller passages called **bronchioles.** The two bronchi resemble the trachea in structure, but as the bronchial tubes divide and subdivide, their walls become thinner, and rings of cartilage are absent. Each bronchiole terminates in an elongated space enclosed by a multitude of air pockets, or sacs, called **alveoli,** which fill the internal region of the lungs (Fig. 35.6*c*). Internal gas exchange occurs between the air in the alveoli and the blood in the capillaries.

Check Your Progress   35.1

1. List some features common to animals like hydras, earthworms, and salamanders, which are able to exchange gases directly with their environment.
2. Explain why the countercurrent flow that occurs in the gills of fish is much more efficient than concurrent flow would be.
3. Describe the role of each of the following in insect respiration: hemolymph, tracheae, tracheoles, spiracles, air sacs, tracheal gills.

Figure 35.6 The human respiratory tract.   **a.** The respiratory tract extends from the nose to the lungs, which are composed of air sacs called alveoli. **b.** The lining of the trachea is a ciliated epithelium with mucus-producing goblet cells. The lining prevents inhaled particles from reaching the lungs: the mucus traps the particles, and the cilia help move the mucus toward the throat, where it can be swallowed or expectorated. **c.** Gas exchange occurs between air in the alveoli and blood within a capillary network that surrounds the alveoli.

35.2 Breathing and Transport of Gases

Learning Outcomes

Upon completion of this section, you should be able to

1. Compare the mechanisms used by amphibians, mammals, and birds to inflate their lungs.
2. Explain how the breathing rate in humans is influenced by both physical and chemical factors.
3. Describe how carbon dioxide (CO_2) is carried in the blood, and the effect that blood P_{CO_2} has on blood pH.

During breathing, the lungs are ventilated. Oxygen (O_2) moves into the blood, and carbon dioxide (CO_2) moves out of the blood into the lungs. Blood transports O_2 to the body's cells and CO_2 from the cells to the lungs.

Breathing

Terrestrial vertebrates ventilate their lungs by moving air into and out of the respiratory tract. Amphibians use positive pressure to force air into the respiratory tract. With the mouth and nostrils firmly shut, the floor of the mouth rises and pushes the air into the lungs. Reptiles, birds, and mammals use negative pressure to move air into the lungs and positive pressure to move it out. **Inspiration** (or inhalation) is the act of moving air into the lungs, and **expiration** (or exhalation) is the act of moving air out of the lungs.

Reptiles have jointed ribs that can be raised to expand the lungs, but mammals have both a rib cage and a diaphragm. The

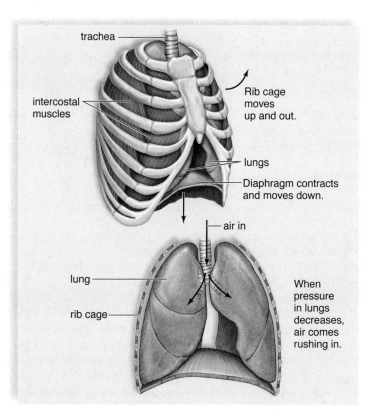

Figure 35.7 Inspiration. During inspiration, the thoracic cavity and lungs expand so that air is drawn in.

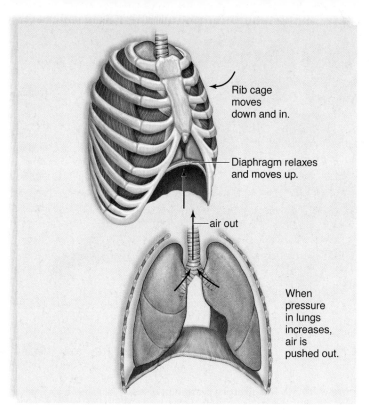

Figure 35.8 Expiration. During expiration, the thoracic cavity and lungs resume their original positions and pressures. Now, air is forced out.

diaphragm is a horizontal muscle that divides the thoracic cavity (above) from the abdominal cavity (below). During inspiration in mammals, the rib cage moves up and out, and the diaphragm contracts and moves down (Fig. 35.7). As the thoracic (chest) cavity expands and lung volume increases, air flows into the lungs due to decreased air pressure in the thoracic cavity and lungs. Also, inspiration is the active phase of breathing in reptiles and mammals.

During expiration in mammals, the rib cage moves down, and the diaphragm relaxes and moves up to its former position (Fig. 35.8). No muscle contraction is required, thus expiration is the passive phase of breathing in reptiles and mammals. During expiration, air flows out as a result of increased pressure in the thoracic cavity and lungs.

We can compare ventilation in reptiles and mammals to the way a bellows, used to fan a fire, functions (Fig. 35.9). First, the handles of the bellows are pulled apart, decreasing the air pressure inside the bellows. This causes air to automatically flow into the bellows, just as air automatically enters the lungs

Figure 35.9 Bellows. Lungs function much as bellows do.

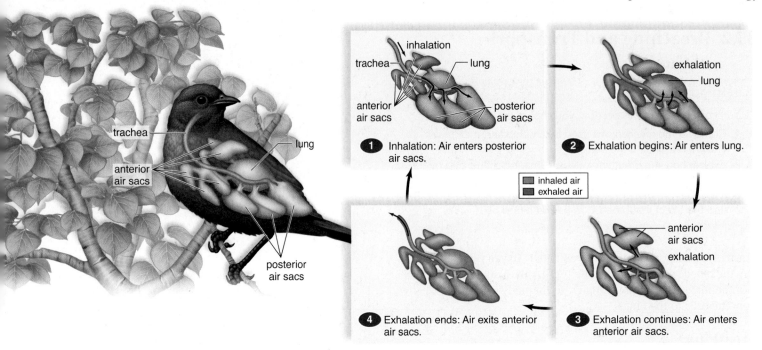

Figure 35.10 Respiratory system in birds. Air sacs are attached to the lungs of birds. These allow birds to have a one-way mechanism of ventilating their lungs.

because the rib cage moves up and out during inspiration. Then, when the handles of the bellows are pushed together, air automatically flows out because the air pressure increases inside the bellows. Similarly, air automatically exits the lungs when the rib cage moves down and in during expiration. The analogy is not exact, however, because no force is required for the rib cage to move down, and inspiration is the only active phase of breathing. Forced expiration can occur if we so desire, however.

All terrestrial vertebrates, except birds, use a *tidal ventilation mechanism,* so called because the air moves in and out by the same route. This means that the lungs of amphibians, reptiles, and mammals are not completely emptied and refilled during each breathing cycle. Because of this, the air entering mixes with used air remaining in the lungs. Although this does help conserve water, it also decreases gas-exchange efficiency. In contrast, birds use a *one-way ventilation mechanism* (Fig. 35.10). Incoming air is carried past the lungs by a trachea, which takes it to a set of posterior air sacs. The air then passes forward through the lungs into a set of anterior air sacs. From here, it is finally expelled. Notice that fresh air never mixes with used air in the lungs of birds, thereby greatly improving gas-exchange efficiency.

Modifications of Breathing in Humans

Normally, adults have a breathing rate of 12 to 20 ventilations per minute. The rhythm of ventilation is controlled by a **respiratory center** in the medulla oblongata of the brain. The respiratory center automatically sends out impulses by way of a spinal nerve to the diaphragm (phrenic nerve) and intercostal nerves to the intercostal muscles of the rib cage (Fig. 35.11). Now inspiration occurs. Then, when the respiratory center stops sending neuronal signals to the diaphragm and the rib cage, expiration occurs.

Although the respiratory center automatically controls the rate and depth of breathing, its activity can also be influenced by nervous input and chemical input. Following forced inhalation, stretch receptors in the alveolar walls initiate inhibitory nerve impulses

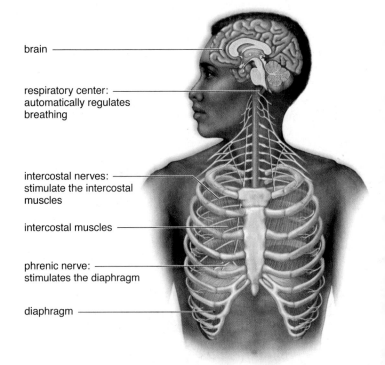

Figure 35.11 Nervous control of breathing. The breathing rate can be modified by nervous stimulation of the intercostal muscles and diaphragm.

that travel from the inflated lungs to the respiratory center. This stops the respiratory center from sending out nerve impulses.

The respiratory center is directly sensitive to the levels of hydrogen ions (H^+). However, when carbon dioxide enters the blood, it reacts with water and releases hydrogen ions. In this way, CO_2 participates in regulating the breathing rate. When hydrogen ions rise in the blood and the pH decreases, the respiratory center increases the rate and depth of breathing. The

Figure 35.12 External and internal respiration. During external respiration (*top*) in the lungs, carbon dioxide (CO_2) leaves blood, and oxygen (O_2) enters blood. During internal respiration (*bottom*) in the tissues, oxygen leaves blood, and carbon dioxide enters blood.

chemoreceptors in the **carotid bodies,** located in the carotid arteries, and in the **aortic bodies,** located in the aorta, stimulate the respiratory center during intense exercise due to a reduction in pH, and also if and when arterial oxygen decreases to 50% of normal.

MP3
Control of Respiration

Gas Exchange and Transport

Respiration includes the exchange of gases in our lungs, called external respiration, as well as the exchange of gases in the tissues, called internal respiration (Fig. 35.12). The principles of diffusion largely govern the movement of gases into and out of blood vessels in the lungs and in the tissues. Gases exert pressure, and the amount of pressure each gas exerts is called the

partial pressure, symbolized as P_{O_2} and P_{CO_2}. If the partial pressure of oxygen differs across a membrane, oxygen will diffuse from the higher to the lower pressure. Similarly, carbon dioxide diffuses from the higher to the lower partial pressure.

Ventilation causes the alveoli of the lungs to have a higher P_{O_2} and a lower P_{CO_2} than the blood in pulmonary capillaries, and this accounts for the exchange of gases in the lungs. When blood reaches the tissues, cellular respiration in cells causes the tissue fluid to have a lower P_{O_2} and a higher P_{CO_2} than the blood in the systemic capillaries, and this accounts for the exchange of gases in the tissues.

MP3
Gas Exchange

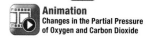
Animation
Changes in the Partial Pressure of Oxygen and Carbon Dioxide

Transport of Oxygen and Carbon Dioxide

The transport of O_2 and CO_2 is somewhat different in external respiration than in internal inspiration, although the driving forces of diffusion are the same.

External Respiration. As blood enters the lungs, a small amount of CO_2 is being carried by hemoglobin with the formula $HbCO_2$. Also, some hemoglobin is carrying hydrogen ions with the formula HbH^+. Most of the CO_2 in the pulmonary capillaries is carried as bicarbonate ions (HCO_3^-) in the plasma. As the free CO_2 from the following equation begins to diffuse out, this reaction is driven to the right:

$$H^+ \quad + \quad HCO_3^- \quad \rightarrow \quad H_2CO_3 \quad \rightarrow \quad H_2O \quad + \quad CO_2$$

hydrogen   bicarbonate   carbonic   water   carbon
  ion   ion   acid   dioxide

The reaction occurs in red blood cells, where the enzyme **carbonic anhydrase** speeds the breakdown of carbonic acid (see Fig. 35.12, *top left*). Pushing this equation to the far right by breathing fast can cause you to stop breathing for a time; pushing this equation to the left by not breathing is even more temporary because breathing will soon resume due to the rise in H^+.

Most oxygen entering the pulmonary capillaries from the alveoli of the lungs combines with **hemoglobin (Hb)** in red blood cells (RBCs) to form **oxyhemoglobin** (Fig. 35.12, *top right*):

$$Hb \quad + \quad O_2 \quad \rightarrow \quad HbO_2$$

deoxyhemoglobin   oxygen   oxyhemoglobin

At the normal P_{O_2} in the lungs, hemoglobin is practically saturated with oxygen. Each hemoglobin molecule contains four polypeptide chains, and each chain is folded around an iron-containing group called **heme** (Fig. 35.13). The iron forms a loose association with oxygen. Because there are about 250 million hemoglobin molecules in each red blood cell, each red blood cell is capable of carrying at least one billion molecules of oxygen.

Carbon monoxide (CO) is an air pollutant that is produced by the incomplete combustion of natural gas, gasoline, kerosene, and even wood and charcoal. Because CO is a colorless, odorless gas, people can be unaware that they are breathing it. But once CO is in the bloodstream, it combines with the iron of hemoglobin 200 times more tightly than oxygen, and the result can be death. This is the reason that homes are equipped with CO detectors.

Internal Respiration. Blood entering the systemic capillaries is a bright red color because RBCs contain oxyhemoglobin. Because the temperature in the tissues is higher and the pH is lower than in the lungs, oxyhemoglobin has a tendency to give up oxygen:

$$HbO_2 \rightarrow Hb + O_2$$

Oxygen diffuses out of the blood into the tissues because the P_{O_2} of tissue fluid is lower than that of blood (see Fig. 35.12, *bottom right*). The lower P_{O_2} is due to cells continuously using up oxygen in cellular respiration. After oxyhemoglobin gives up O_2, this oxygen leaves the blood and enters tissue fluid, where it is taken up by cells.

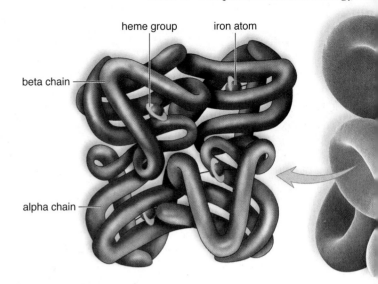

Figure 35.13 Hemoglobin. Hemoglobin consists of four polypeptide chains, two alpha (*red*) and two beta (*purple*), each associated with a heme group. Each heme group contains an iron atom, which can bind to O_2.

Carbon dioxide, in contrast, enters blood from the tissues because the P_{CO_2} of tissue fluid is higher than that of blood. Carbon dioxide, produced continuously by cells, collects in tissue fluid. After CO_2 diffuses into the blood, it enters the red blood cells, where a small amount combines with the protein portion of hemoglobin to form **carbaminohemoglobin** ($HbCO_2$). Most of the CO_2, however, is transported in the form of the **bicarbonate ion** (HCO_3^-). First, CO_2 combines with water, forming carbonic acid, and then this dissociates to a hydrogen ion (H^+) and HCO_3^-:

$$CO_2 \quad + \quad H_2O \quad \rightarrow \quad H_2CO_3 \quad \rightarrow \quad H^+ \quad + \quad HCO_3^-$$

carbon   water   carbonic   hydrogen   bicarbonate
dioxide   acid   ion   ion

Carbonic anhydrase also speeds this reaction. The HCO_3^- diffuses out of the red blood cells to be carried in the plasma (see Fig. 35.12, *bottom left*).

The release of H^+ from this reaction could drastically change the pH of the blood, which is highly undesirable because cells require a normal pH in order to remain healthy. However, the H^+ is absorbed by the globin portions of hemoglobin. Hemoglobin that has combined with H^+ is called reduced hemoglobin and has the formula HbH^+. HbH^+ plays a vital role in maintaining the normal pH of the blood. Blood that leaves the systemic capillaries is a dark maroon color because red blood cells contain reduced hemoglobin.

 Video
Gas Transport

 Animation
Gas Exchange During Respiration

Check Your Progress   35.2

1. Compare the mechanism of ventilation in reptiles and mammals as being similar to the operation of a bellows.
2. Explain how the carotid bodies and aortic bodies affect the rate of respiration.
3. Define the role of oxyhemoglobin, reduced hemoglobin, and carbaminohemoglobin in homeostasis.

35.3 Respiration and Human Health

Learning Outcomes

Upon completion of this section, you should be able to

1. Describe several common disorders that mainly affect the upper respiratory tract, and several that affect the lower respiratory tract.
2. Classify several common respiratory disorders according to whether they are mainly caused by allergies, infections, a genetic defect, or toxin exposure.

The human respiratory tract is constantly exposed to environmental air that may contain infectious agents, allergens, tobacco smoke, or other toxins. This results in the respiratory tract being susceptible to a number of diseases. Some of the most important of these are summarized here.

Disorders of the Upper Respiratory Tract

The upper respiratory tract consists of the nasal cavities, sinuses, pharynx, and larynx. Because the upper part of the respiratory tract filters out many pathogens and other materials that may be present in the air, it is commonly affected by a variety of infections, which may also spread to the middle ear or the sinuses.

The Common Cold

Most "colds" are relatively mild viral infections of the upper respiratory tract characterized by sneezing, rhinitis (runny nose), and perhaps a mild fever. Most colds last a few days, after which the immune response is able to eliminate the inciting virus. However, since colds are caused by several different viruses, and by several hundred strains of these viruses, we usually have no immunity to the next strain that "goes around," and vaccines are very difficult to develop. As with all viral infections, antibiotics like penicillin are useless in treating colds.

Figure 35.14 Strep throat. Pharyngitis caused by the bacterium *Streptococcus pyogenes* can cause swollen tonsils, as shown here. The whitish patches are areas of pus formation, indicating that white blood cells are fighting the infection.

Strep Throat

Most cases of **pharyngitis**, or inflammation of the pharynx, are caused by viruses, but strep throat is an acute pharyngitis caused by the bacterium *Streptococcus pyogenes*. Typical symptoms include severe sore throat, high fever, and white patches in the tonsillar area (Fig. 35.14). Adults experience about half as many sore throats as do children, who average about five upper respiratory infections per year, and about one strep throat infection every four years. Many untreated strep infections probably resolve on their own, but some can lead to more serious conditions like scarlet fever or rheumatic fever. Fortunately, infection with *S. pyogenes* can be easily and quickly diagnosed with specific laboratory tests, and is usually curable with antibiotics.

Disorders of the Lower Respiratory Tract

Several common disorders affecting the lower respiratory tract are summarized in Figure 35.15.

Disorders Affecting the Trachea and Bronchi

One of the most obvious and life-threatening disorders that can affect the trachea is choking. The best way for a person without extensive medical training to help someone who is choking is to perform the Heimlich maneuver, which involves grabbing the choking person around the waist from behind, and forcefully pulling both hands into their upper abdomen to expel whatever is lodged. If this fails, trained medical personnel may be able to quickly insert a breathing tube through an incision made in the trachea. This procedure is called a tracheotomy, and the opening is a *tracheostomy*.

If infections of the upper respiratory tract spread into the lower respiratory tract, *acute bronchitis*, or inflammation of the bronchi, often results. Other causes of acute bronchitis include allergic reactions and damage from environmental toxins, such as those present in cigarette smoke. It is estimated that approximately 5% of the U.S. population suffers from a bout of acute bronchitis in any given year. Symptoms include fever and a cough that produces phlem or pus, and chest pain. Depending on the cause, acute bronchitis maybe be treatable with antibiotics, or may resolve with time or progress to more serious conditions.

If the inciting cause (such as smoking) persists, acute bronchitis can develop into *chronic bronchitis* (Fig. 35.15), in which the airways are inflamed and filled with mucus. Over time, the bronchi undergo degenerative changes, including the loss of cilia and their normal cleansing action. Under these conditions, infections are more likely to occur. Smoking and exposure to other airborne toxins are the most frequent causes of chronic bronchitis. Along with emphysema, chronic bronchitis is a major component of *chronic obstructive pulmonary disease*, the fourth leading cause of death in the U.S.

Asthma is a disease of the bronchi and bronchioles marked by coughing, wheezing, and breathlessness. The airways are unusually sensitive to various irritants, which can include allergens such as pollen, animal dander, dust, and/or cigarette smoke. Even cold air or exercise can be an irritant.

An asthmatic attack results from inflammation in the airways and contraction of smooth muscle lining their walls,

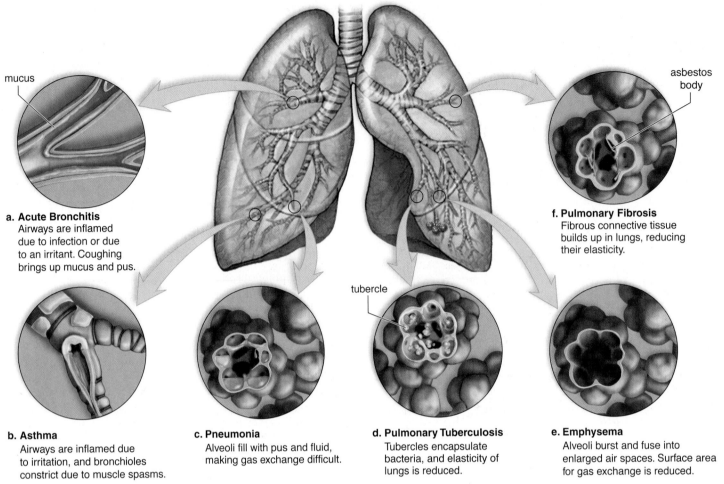

a. Acute Bronchitis
Airways are inflamed due to infection or due to an irritant. Coughing brings up mucus and pus.

mucus

asbestos body

f. Pulmonary Fibrosis
Fibrous connective tissue builds up in lungs, reducing their elasticity.

tubercle

b. Asthma
Airways are inflamed due to irritation, and bronchioles constrict due to muscle spasms.

c. Pneumonia
Alveoli fill with pus and fluid, making gas exchange difficult.

d. Pulmonary Tuberculosis
Tubercles encapsulate bacteria, and elasticity of lungs is reduced.

e. Emphysema
Alveoli burst and fuse into enlarged air spaces. Surface area for gas exchange is reduced.

Figure 35.15 Common bronchial and pulmonary diseases. Exposure to infectious pathogens and/or polluted air, including tobacco smoke, causes the diseases and disorders shown here.

resulting in a narrowing of the diameter of the airways (Fig. 35.15). All estimates indicate that the incidence of asthma in American children has been increasing steadily since the early 1980s. Possible explanations for this include a more sedentary lifestyle, with more exposure to indoor toxins, and less frequent exposure to beneficial microbes. Asthma is not curable, but it is treatable. Drugs administered by inhalers can help to prevent the inflammation and dilate the bronchi.

Disorders Affecting the Lungs

Combined together, various diseases of the lung cause about 400,000 deaths per year in the United States, and affect hundreds of millions of people worldwide. Depending on the cause, treatments for lung disease may include antibiotics, supplemental oxygen, and administration of anti-inflammatory drugs. For patients with serious lung conditions who have exhausted all other treatment options, a lung transplant may be the best option, but there aren't enough donor lungs to meet the need. The Nature of Science feature on page 676 describes some recent advances in artificial-lung technology.

Pneumonia is a viral, bacterial, or fungal infection of the lungs in which bronchi and alveoli fill with a discharge, such as pus and fluid (Fig. 35.15). Along with coughing and difficulty breathing, people suffering from pneumonia often have a high fever, sharp chest pain, and a cough that produces thick phlem or even pus. Several bacteria can cause pneumonia, as can the influenza virus, especially in the very young, very old, or people with a suppressed immune system. AIDS patients are subject to a particularly rare form of pneumonia caused by a fungus of the genus *Pneumocystis*, but they suffer from many other types of pneumonias as well.

Pulmonary tuberculosis is caused by the bacterium *Mycobacterium tuberculosis*. Tuberculosis (TB) was a major killer in the United States before the middle of the twentieth century, after which antibiotic therapy brought it largely under control. However, the incidence of TB is rising in certain areas of the world, especially where HIV infection (which reduces immunity to *M. tuberculosis*) is common, and treatments are not widely available. According to the Centers for Disease Control, in 2007 approximately one-third of the world's population were infected with *M. tuberculosis*, and TB was the actual cause of death for as many as half of all persons with AIDS.

When tubercle bacilli invade the lung tissue, the cells build a protective capsule about the organisms, isolating them from the rest of the body. This tiny capsule is called a tubercle (Fig. 35.15). If the resistance of the body is high, the imprisoned organisms die, but if the resistance is low, the organisms can escape and spread.

It is possible to tell if a person has ever been exposed to *M. tuberculosis* with a TB skin test, in which a highly diluted extract of the bacteria is injected into the skin of the patient. A person who has never been exposed to the bacterium shows no reaction, but one who has previously been infected develops an area of inflammation that peaks in about 48 hours.

Inhaling particles such as silica (sand), coal dust, or asbestos can lead to **pulmonary fibrosis**, a condition in which fibrous connective tissue builds up in the lungs. The lungs cannot inflate properly and are always tending toward deflation (Fig. 35.15). Breathing asbestos is also associated with the development of cancer, including a type called mesothelioma. In the U.S., the use of asbestos as a fireproofing and insulating agent has been limited since the 1970s; however, many thousands of lawsuits are filed each year by patients suffering from asbestos-related illnesses.

Emphysema is a chronic and incurable lung disorder in which the alveoli are distended and their walls damaged so that the surface area available for gas exchange is reduced (Fig. 35.15). Emphysema is often preceded by chronic bronchitis. Air trapped in the lungs leads to alveolar damage and a noticeable ballooning of the chest. The elastic recoil of the lungs is reduced, so not only are the airways narrowed, but the driving force behind expiration is also reduced. The patient is breathless and may have a cough. Because the surface area for gas exchange is reduced, less oxygen reaches the heart and brain, leaving the person feeling depressed, sluggish, and irritable. Exercise, drug therapy, and supplemental oxygen, along with giving up smoking, may relieve the symptoms and possibly slow the progression of emphysema. Upon death, the lungs are decidedly abnormal (Fig. 35.16*b*).

Lung cancer is the leading cause of cancer-related death in the U.S. and worldwide. It is slightly more common in men than women, but that gap has been narrowing in recent years as lung cancer rates in women have increased, due to an increasing number of women who smoke. Lung cancer rates remain low until about age 40, when they gradually start to rise, peaking at around age 70. Symptoms may include coughing, shortness of breath, blood in the sputum, and chest pain. Many other symptoms can occur if the cancer spreads to other parts of the body, which is common.

The only treatment that offers a possibility of cure is to remove a lobe or the whole lung before metastasis has had time to occur. Chemotherapy and radiation may also be used. Even with treatment, lung cancer is highly lethal—five-year survival rates range from 15% in the United States to 8% in less developed countries. About 150,000 people in the United States die of lung cancer each year (Fig. 35.16*c*). The American Cancer Society links over 85% of these deaths to smoking. Smoking is also associated with bronchitis, emphysema, heart disease, and other types of cancer. Considering that the nicotine in cigarette smoke is addictive, it is better never to start smoking than to try quitting later on.

Cystic fibrosis (CF) is an example of a lung disease that is genetic rather than infectious, although infections also play a role in the disease. One in 31 Americans carries the defective gene, but a child must inherit two copies of the gene to have the disease. Still, CF is the most common genetic disease in the U.S. white population.

The gene that is defective in CF codes for cystic fibrosis transmembrane regulator (CFTR), a protein needed for proper transport of chloride (Cl^-) ions out of the epithelial cells of the lung. Because this also reduces the amount of water transported out of lung cells, the mucus secretions become very sticky and can form plugs that interfere with breathing.

Symptoms of CF include coughing and shortness of breath; part of the treatment involves clearing mucus from the airways by vigorously slapping the patient on the back as well as by administering mucus-thinning drugs. None of these treatments is curative, however, and because the lungs can be severely affected, the median survival age for people with CF is only 30 years. Researchers are attempting to develop gene therapy strategies to replace the faulty CFTR gene.

Video Good Poison

Check Your Progress   35.3

1. Explain why antibiotic drugs such as penicillin are ineffective at treating the common cold.
2. Name two disorders of the lower respiratory tract that mainly cause a narrowing of the airways, and two that restrict the lungs' ability to expand.
3. List six illnesses associated with smoking cigarettes.

Figure 35.16 Smoking and lung disorders.
Smoking causes almost 90% of all lung cancers and is also a major cause of emphysema. **a.** Normal lungs. **b.** The lungs of a person who died from emphysema are shrunken and blackened from trapped smoke. **c.** The lungs of a person who died from lung cancer are blackened from smoke except for the presence of the tumor, which is a mass of malformed soft tissue.

a. Normal lungs

b. Emphysema

tumor

c. Lung cancer

THEME Nature of Science

Artificial Lung Technology

Some organs, such as the kidneys, are relatively easy to transplant from one well-matched individual to another, with a high rate of success. Lungs are more difficult to transplant, however, with a ten-year survival rate of only 10 to 20 percent. Some very recent research is showing how one day it may be possible to replace diseased lungs with laboratory-grown versions.

In early 2010, a group of scientists at Yale University anesthetized a group of adult rats, surgically removed their left lungs, and replaced them with tissue-engineered lungs that had been produced in the laboratory. For periods of up to two hours, the implanted lung tissue exchanged oxygen and carbon dioxide at similar rates as the natural lungs.[1]

In order to build the artificial rat lungs, the Yale researchers began by removing lungs from adult rats, and treating the organs to remove most of the cellular components, while preserving the airways and supporting connective tissue matrix. Next, they placed these decellularized structures, along with various types of cultured cells, into a sterile container designed to mimic some aspects of the fetal environment in which the lungs normally first develop. The scientists found that the cells were able to form much of the lung tissues as well as the blood vessels needed to supply the tissue with blood and transport gases.

Although these results are an important early step toward growing replacement lungs in the lab, there is a long way to go before anyone will contemplate implanting engineered lungs into humans.

In a separate study published on the same day as the Yale study, a Harvard group announced that they had developed a pea-sized device that mimics human lung tissues. Made of human lung cells, a permeable membrane, plus blood capillary cells, all mounted on a microchip (Fig. 35A), the device is able to mimic the function of alveoli. When the researchers placed bacteria on the alveolar side of the device, and white blood cells on the capillary side, the blood cells crossed the membrane, mimicking an immune response.[2] At a minimum, the researchers hope that their "lung-on-a-chip" device can be used for testing certain drugs or the effects of various toxins on the lungs, which might replace much of the animal testing that is currently performed.

Questions to Consider

1. With regard to producing tissue-engineered human lungs, what is the major drawback in the procedure developed by the Yale group?
2. What are some of the aspects of lung structure that make it a more difficult organ to grow in the lab than, for example, a urinary bladder?
3. Besides increased availability, what are two other potential advantages of laboratory-grown lungs (or other tissues) compared to regular donor tissues?

1 Petersen, T. H., et al. 2010. Tissue-engineered lungs for in vivo implantation. *Science* 329: 538–41.

2 Huh, D., et al. 2010. Reconstituting organ-level lung functions on a chip. *Science* 328: 1662–68.

lung cells

membrane

capillary blood vessel cells

Side chambers

Figure 35A Lung on a chip developed by Harvard researchers.   About the size of a credit card, the device consists of a semipermeable membrane with lung cells on one side and blood vessel cells on the other. Liquid medium flows in a channel on the blood cell side, while air flows in and out on the lung cell side.

CONNECTING *the* CONCEPTS *with the* THEMES

Evolution

- Animals that are small and have sufficient body surface area may exchange gases directly with the environment. The evolution of respiratory systems allowed a more efficient exchange of gases.
- Gills evolved in many aquatic animals as an effective way to obtain sufficient oxygen from water.
- A wide variety of respiratory structures have evolved in terrestrial animals, including tracheoles in insects and lungs in some amphibians, reptiles, birds, and mammals.

Nature of Science

- Studies of respiratory systems have provided us with extensive knowledge that has been applied to respiratory diseases.
- Medical researchers are working to develop new strategies for treating respiratory diseases, including the possibility of replacing diseased lungs with laboratory-engineered lung tissue.

Biological Systems

- The respiratory and cardiovascular systems work together to provide animal tissues with oxygen and to remove carbon dioxide and other wastes.
- Respiration is regulated to adjust to changing needs. In humans, the carotid bodies and aortic bodies detect lowering of blood pH and oxygen content and increase respiration accordingly.

Media Study Tools

www.mhhe.com/maderbiology11

Enhance your study of this chapter with study tools and practice tests. Also ask your instructor about the resources available through ConnectPlus, including the media-rich eBook, interactive learning tools, and animations.

Summarize

35.1 Gas Exchange Surfaces

Some aquatic animals, such as hydras, earthworms, and some amphibians, use their entire body surface for gas exchange.

Most animals have a specialized gas-exchange area. Large aquatic animals usually pass water through gills. In bony fishes, blood in the capillaries flows in the direction opposite that of the water. Blood takes up almost all of the oxygen in the water as a result of this countercurrent flow.

On land, insects use tracheal systems, and vertebrates have lungs. In insects, air enters the tracheae at openings called spiracles. From there, the air moves to ever smaller tracheoles until gas exchange takes place at the cells themselves. Lungs are found inside the body, where water loss is reduced. To ventilate the lungs, some vertebrates use positive pressure, but most inhale, using muscular contraction to produce a negative pressure that causes air to rush into the lungs. When the breathing muscles relax, air is exhaled.

Birds have a series of air sacs attached to the lungs. When a bird inhales, air enters the posterior air sacs, and when a bird exhales, air moves through the lungs to the anterior air sacs before exiting the respiratory tract. The one-way flow of air through the lungs allows more fresh air to be present in the lungs with each breath, and this leads to greater uptake of oxygen from one breath of air. Mammals have two-way or tidal airflow in and out of the lungs, and as a result some mixing is always occurring between fresh air and previously inhaled air, with less uptake of oxygen than in birds.

35.2 Breathing and Transport of Gases

During inspiration, air enters the body at nasal cavities and then passes from the pharynx through the glottis, larynx, trachea, bronchi, and bronchioles to the alveoli of the lungs, where exchange occurs; during expiration, air passes in the opposite direction. Humans breathe by negative pressure, as do other mammals. During inspiration, the rib cage goes up and out, and the diaphragm lowers. The lungs expand and air comes rushing in. During expiration, the rib cage goes down and in, and the diaphragm rises. Therefore, air rushes out.

The rate of breathing increases when the amount of H^+ and carbon dioxide in the blood rises, as detected by chemoreceptors such as the aortic and carotid bodies.

Gas exchange in the lungs and tissues is brought about by diffusion. Hemoglobin transports oxygen in the blood; carbon dioxide is mainly transported in plasma as the bicarbonate ion. Excess hydrogen ions are transported by hemoglobin. The enzyme carbonic anhydrase found in red blood cells speeds the formation of the bicarbonate ion.

35.3 Respiration and Human Health

The respiratory tract is susceptible to a wide variety of infections and other disease conditions. Infections of the upper respiratory tract include the common cold, caused by several different viruses, and strep throat, caused by a bacterium. In the lower tract, bronchitis is an inflammation of the bronchi, usually due to infections, whereas in asthma the inflammation and smooth muscle contraction in the bronchi and bronchioles is due to sensitivity to various irritants. Many important diseases affect the lungs, including pneumonia, tuberculosis, pulmonary fibrosis, emphysema, lung cancer, and cystic fibrosis.

Key Terms

alveolus (pl., alveoli) 668	carotid body 671
aortic body 671	countercurrent exchange 666
asthma 673	cystic fibrosis (CF) 675
bicarbonate ion 672	diaphragm 669
bronchiole 668	emphysema 675
bronchus (pl., bronchi) 668	epiglottis 668
carbaminohemoglobin 672	expiration 669
carbonic anhydrase 672	external respiration 664

Assess

Reviewing This Chapter

1. Compare the respiratory organs of aquatic animals to those of terrestrial animals. 664–67
2. Why is it beneficial for the body wall of earthworms to be moist? Why don't insects require circulatory system involvement in air transport? 664
3. How does the countercurrent flow of blood within gill capillaries and water passing across the gills assist respiration in fishes? 666
4. Name the parts of the human respiratory system, and list a function for each part. How is air reaching the lungs cleansed? 669–70
5. Explain the phrase "breathing by using negative pressure." 669
6. Contrast the tidal ventilation mechanism in humans with the one-way ventilation mechanism in birds, and explain the benefits of the ventilation mechanism in birds. 670
7. The concentration of what substances in blood controls the breathing rate in humans? Explain. 670–71
8. How are oxygen and carbon dioxide transported in blood? What does carbonic anhydrase do? 671–72
9. Which conditions depicted in Figure 35.15 are due to infection? Which are due to behavioral or environmental factors? Explain. 673–75

Testing Yourself

Choose the best answer for each question.

1. Label the following diagram depicting respiration.

a.

lungs

b.   g.

c.   f.

d.

e.

2. Birds have more efficient lungs than humans because the flow of air in birds
   a. is the same during both inspiration and expiration.
   b. travels in only one direction through the lungs.
   c. follows a tidal ventilation pattern.
   d. is not hindered by a larynx.
   e. enters their bones.
3. Which animal breathes by positive pressure?
   a. fish
   b. human
   c. bird
   d. frog
   e. planarian
4. Which of these is a true statement?
   a. In lung capillaries, carbon dioxide combines with water to produce carbonic acid.
   b. In tissue capillaries, carbonic acid breaks down to carbon dioxide and water.
   c. In lung capillaries, carbonic acid breaks down to carbon dioxide and water.
   d. In tissue capillaries, carbonic acid combines with hydrogen ions to form the carbonate ion.
   e. All of these statements are true.
5. Air enters the human lungs because
   a. atmospheric pressure is less than the pressure inside the lungs.
   b. atmospheric pressure is greater than the pressure inside the lungs.
   c. although the pressures are the same inside and outside, the partial pressure of oxygen is lower within the lungs.
   d. the residual air in the lungs causes the partial pressure of oxygen to be less than it is outside.
   e. the process of breathing pushes air into the lungs.
6. If the digestive and respiratory tracts were completely separate in humans, there would be no need for
   a. swallowing.
   b. a nose.
   c. an epiglottis.
   d. a diaphragm.
   e. All of these are correct.
7. In humans, the respiratory control center
   a. is stimulated by carbon dioxide.
   b. is located in the medulla oblongata.
   c. controls the rate of breathing.
   d. is stimulated by hydrogen ion concentration.
   e. All of these are correct.
8. Carbon dioxide is carried in the plasma
   a. in combination with hemoglobin.
   b. as the bicarbonate ion.
   c. combined with carbonic anhydrase.
   d. only as a part of tissue fluid.
   e. All of these are correct.
9. Which of these is anatomically incorrect?
   a. The nose has two nasal cavities.
   b. The pharynx connects the nasal and oral cavities to the larynx.
   c. The larynx contains the vocal cords.
   d. The trachea enters the lungs.
   e. The lungs contain many alveoli.

10. The chemical reaction that converts carbon dioxide to a bicarbonate ion takes place in
    a. the blood plasma.
    b. red blood cells.
    c. the alveolus.
    d. the hemoglobin molecule.

11. Which of these is incorrect concerning inspiration?
    a. Rib cage moves up and out.
    b. Diaphragm contracts and moves down.
    c. Pressure in lungs decreases, and air comes rushing in.
    d. The lungs expand because air comes rushing in.

12. Asthma
    a. mainly affects the upper respiratory tract.
    b. is usually caused by an infection.
    c. is considered to be a genetic disorder.
    d. is usually curable.
    e. None of these statements are true.

13. Label this diagram of the human respiratory system.

a.
b.
c.
d.
e.
f.
g.
h.
i.

Engage

Thinking Scientifically

1. You are a physician who witnessed Christopher Reeve's riding accident. Why might you immediately use mouth to mouth resuscitation until mechanical ventilation becomes available?

2. Fetal hemoglobin picks up oxygen from the maternal blood. If the oxygen-binding characteristics of hemoglobin in the fetus were identical to the hemoglobin of the mother, oxygen could never be transferred at the placenta to fetal circulation. What hypothesis about the oxygen-binding characteristics of fetal hemoglobin would explain how fetuses get the oxygen they need?

Bioethical Issue

Antibiotic Therapy

Antibiotics can cure many respiratory infections, but problems are associated with antibiotic therapy. Aside from a possible allergic reaction, antibiotics not only kill off disease-causing bacteria, but they also reduce the number of beneficial bacteria in the intestinal tract and other locations. These beneficial bacteria hold in check the growth of other pathogens that now begin to flourish. Diarrhea can result, as can yeast infections.

Especially alarming is the occurrence of bacterial resistance. Resistance takes place when vulnerable bacteria are killed off by an antibiotic, while resistant bacteria continue to live and thus become more prevalent. Many bacteria that cause ear, nose, and throat infections as well as scarlet fever and pneumonia have developed resistant populations because we have not been using antibiotics properly. Moreover, new strains of the bacterium that causes tuberculosis are resistant to the usual combined antibiotic therapy. As mentioned in Chapter 20, methicillin resistant *Staphylococcus aureus* (MRSA) infection has become a major concern in hospitals and other institutions; infection with this bacterium can be deadly.

Every citizen needs to be aware of the serious problem of antibiotic resistance. Stuart Levy, a Tufts University School of Medicine microbiologist, says that we should do what is ethical for society and ourselves. Antibiotics kill bacteria, not viruses—therefore, we shouldn't take antibiotics unless we know for sure we have a bacterial infection. And we shouldn't take them prophylactically—that is, just in case we might need one. If antibiotics are taken in low dosages and intermittently, resistant strains are more likely to arise. Many experts advocate that the use of antibiotics in animals produced for food should be pared down, and household disinfectants should no longer be spiked with antibacterial agents such as triclosan, often found in hand soaps. Perhaps then, Levy says, vulnerable bacteria will begin to supplant the resistant ones in the population.[1]

Body Fluid Regulation and Excretory Systems

Marine organisms rid the body of excess salt; fishes extrude salt at their gills, and turtles do so near their eyes.

CHAPTER OUTLINE

BEFORE YOU BEGIN

Before beginning this chapter, take a few moments to review the following discussions.

Figure 5.8 What occurs when a cell is surrounded by a solution having a greater or lesser solute concentration than that inside the cell?

Section 8.5 What process results in the production of urea in humans?

Section 34.4 What happens to excess nutrients and minerals that cannot be stored?

If the salt concentration in body fluids is too high, cells shrivel and die. If it is too low, cells swell and rupture. Yet animals are found in all sorts of environments, including marine environments that are too salty, freshwater environments that don't have enough salt, and even terrestrial environments that are simply too dry. Animals clearly spend a lot of energy regulating the composition of their body fluids, and chief among the organs that help are the kidneys of the urinary system. Sometimes animals such as marine birds and reptiles get some assistance from accessory glands. Sea turtles have salt glands located above their eye that, true to their name, rid the body of salt. When the glands excrete a salty solution collected from body fluids, sea turtles appear to cry. Humans lack salt glands and cannot survive after drinking too much salt water because the kidneys alone can't handle all the salt.

In this chapter, you'll learn how animals maintain their normal water-salt balance while excreting various metabolic wastes and regulating their pH. All these functions are of primary importance to homeostasis and continued good health.

As you read through the chapter, think about the following questions:

1. Besides salt glands, what other types of strategies have animals developed to either conserve or excrete excess salt?

2. If you were stranded on a desert island with plenty of food but only seawater to drink, how long do you think you could survive?

3. By what mechanisms is the human kidney able to regulate the salt concentration of urine it produces?

FOLLOWING *the* THEMES

UNIT 7 COMPARATIVE ANIMAL BIOLOGY	CHAPTER 36 BODY FLUID REGULATION AND EXCRETORY SYSTEMS	
	Evolution	Many different mechanisms for maintaining water-salt balance and excreting metabolic wastes have evolved, molded by the environments in which animals live.
	Nature of Science	By studying many different animals in a variety of environments, scientists have learned how animal excretory systems regulate water-salt balance, excrete metabolic wastes, and maintain a healthy pH.
	Biological Systems	The urinary system of most vertebrates includes the kidneys, organs that have a microscopic anatomy that is specialized for the production of urine.

36.1 Animal Excretory Systems

Learning Outcomes

Upon completion of this section, you should be able to

1. Describe the overall, specific functions of animal excretion systems.
2. List the costs and benefits of the excretion of ammonia, urea, or uric acid as nitrogenous waste products.
3. Compare and contrast the excretory organs of earthworms, arthropods, aquatic vertebrates, and terrestrial vertebrates.

An important part of maintaining homeostasis in animals involves **osmoregulation**, or balancing the levels of water and salts in the body. Often the osmoregulatory system of an animal also removes metabolic wastes from the body, a process called **excretion**.

Nitrogenous Waste Products

The breakdown of nitrogen-containing molecules, such as amino acids and nucleic acids, results in excess nitrogen that must be excreted. When amino acids are broken down by the body to generate energy, or are converted to fats or carbohydrates, the amino ($-NH_2$) groups must be removed because they are not needed, and they may be toxic at high levels. Depending on the species, this excess nitrogen may be excreted in the form of ammonia, urea, or uric acid. Removal of amino groups from amino acids requires a fairly constant amount of energy; however, the amount of energy required to convert amino groups to ammonia, urea, or uric acid differs, as indicated in Figure 36.1.

Ammonia

Amino groups removed from amino acids immediately form **ammonia** (NH_3) by the addition of a third hydrogen ion (H^+). This reaction requires little or no energy. Ammonia is quite toxic, but it can be a nitrogenous excretory product if sufficient water is available to wash it from the body. Ammonia is excreted by most fishes and other aquatic animals whose gills and/or body surfaces are in direct contact with the water of the environment.

Urea

Sharks, adult amphibians, and mammals usually excrete **urea** as their main nitrogenous waste. Urea is much less toxic than ammonia and can be excreted in a moderately concentrated solution. This elimination strategy allows body water to be conserved, an important advantage for terrestrial animals with limited access to water. Production of urea requires the expenditure of energy, however, because it is produced in the liver by a set of energy-requiring enzymatic reactions, known as the urea cycle. In this cycle, carrier molecules take up carbon dioxide and two molecules of ammonia, finally releasing urea.

Uric Acid

Uric acid is synthesized by a long, complex series of enzymatic reactions that requires expenditure of even more energy than does urea synthesis. Uric acid is not very toxic, and it is poorly soluble in water. Poor solubility is an advantage if water conser-

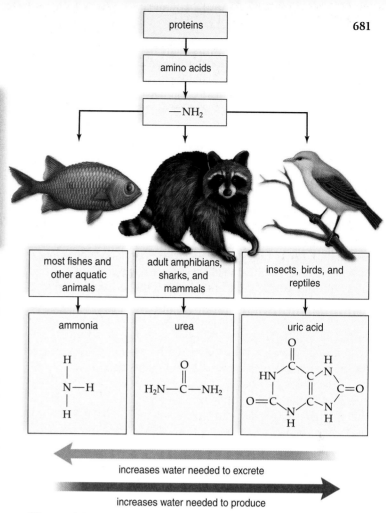

Figure 36.1 Nitrogenous wastes. Proteins are hydrolyzed to amino acids, whose breakdown results in carbon chains and amino groups ($-NH_2$). The carbon chains can be used as an energy source, but the amino groups must be excreted as ammonia, urea, or uric acid.

vation is needed, because uric acid can be concentrated even more readily than can urea.

Uric acid is routinely excreted by insects, reptiles, and birds. In reptiles and birds, a dilute solution of uric acid passes from the kidneys to the *cloaca*, a common reservoir for the products of the digestive, urinary, and reproductive systems. The cloacal contents are refluxed into the large intestine, where water is reabsorbed. The white substance in bird feces is uric acid.

Embryos of reptiles and birds develop inside completely enclosed shelled eggs. The production of insoluble, relatively nontoxic uric acid is advantageous for shelled embryos because all nitrogenous wastes are stored inside the shell until hatching takes place. For all these reasons, the evolutionary advantages of uric acid production have outweighed the disadvantage of energy expenditure needed for its synthesis.

Humans have retained the ability to produce uric acid, mainly from the breakdown of excess purine and pyrimidine nucleic acids in the diet. Although the exact causes are unknown, in some individuals uric acid builds up in the blood and can precipitate in and around the joints, producing a painful ailment called *gout*.

Excretory Organs Among Invertebrates

Most invertebrates have tubular excretory organs that regulate the water-salt balance of the body and excrete metabolic wastes into the environment.

The planarians, flatworms that live in fresh water, have two strands of branching excretory tubules that open to the outside of the body through excretory pores (Fig. 36.2*a*). Located along the tubules are bulblike *flame cells,* each of which contains a cluster of beating cilia that looks like a flickering flame under the microscope. The beating of flame-cell cilia propels fluid through the excretory tubules and out of the body. The system is believed to function in ridding the body of excess water and in excreting wastes.

The body of an earthworm is divided into segments, and nearly every body segment has a pair of excretory structures called *nephridia.* Each nephridium is a tubule with a ciliated opening and an excretory pore (Fig. 36.2*b*). As fluid from the coelom is propelled through the tubule by beating cilia, its composition is modified. For example, nutrient substances are reabsorbed and carried away by a network of capillaries surrounding the tubule. **Urine** is a liquid that contains metabolic wastes, excreted salts, and water; the urine of an earthworm is passed out of the body via the excretory pore. Although the earthworm is considered a terrestrial animal, it excretes a very dilute urine. Each day, an earthworm may produce a volume of urine equal to 60% of its body weight.

Insects have a unique excretory system consisting of long, thin *Malpighian tubules* attached to the gut. Uric acid is actively transported from the surrounding hemolymph into these tubules, and water follows a salt gradient established by active transport of K^+. Water and other useful substances are reabsorbed at the rectum, but the uric acid leaves the body through the anus. Insects that live in water, or eat large quantities of moist food, reabsorb little water. But insects in dry environments reabsorb most of the water and excrete a dry, semisolid mass of uric acid.

The excretory organs of other arthropods are given different names, although they function similarly. In aquatic crustaceans (e.g., crabs, crayfish), nitrogenous wastes are generally removed by diffusion across the gills. Some crustaceans also possess excretory organs called *green glands* located in the ventral portion of the head region. Fluid collects within the tubules from the surrounding blood of the hemocoel, but this fluid is modified by the time it leaves the tubules. The secretion of salts into the tubule regulates the amount of urine excreted.

In shrimp and pillbugs, the excretory organs are located in the maxillary segments and are called *maxillary glands.* Spiders, scorpions, and other arachnids possess *coxal glands,* which are located near one or more appendages and used for excretion. Coxal glands are spherical sacs resembling annelid nephridia. Wastes are collected from the surrounding blood of the hemocoel and discharged through pores at one to several pairs of appendages.

Osmoregulation by Aquatic Vertebrates

In most vertebrates the kidneys are the most important organs involved in osmoregulation. As described later in this chapter, the kidneys perform several functions critical to homeostasis, including maintaining the balance between water and several types of salts. This is a necessity because ions such as Na^+, Ca^{2+}, K^+, and PO^{4-} greatly affect the workings of the body systems, such as the skeletal, nervous, and muscular systems.

The kidneys produce urine, a liquid that contains a number of different metabolic wastes. The concentration of urine produced by an animal varies depending on its environment, as well as on factors like water and salt intake.

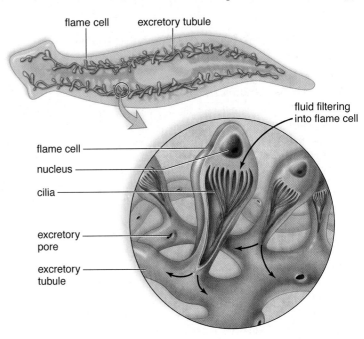

a.   **Flame-cell excretory system in planarians**

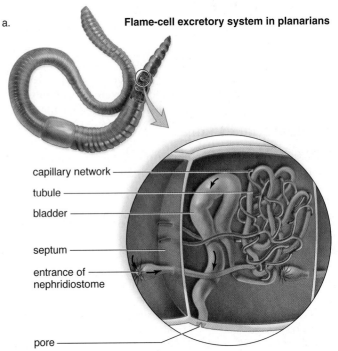

b.   **Earthworm nephridium**

Figure 36.2 Excretory organs in animals. **a.** Two or more tracts of branching tubules run the length of the body and open to the outside by pores. At the ends of side branches are small bulblike cells called flame cells. **b.** The nephridium has a ciliated opening, the nephridiostome, that leads to a coiled tubule surrounded by a capillary network. Urine can be temporarily stored in the bladder before being released to the outside via a pore termed a nephridiopore.

Cartilaginous Fishes

The total concentration of the various ions in the blood of sharks, rays, and skates is less than that in seawater. Their blood plasma is nearly isotonic to seawater because they pump it full of urea, and this molecule gives their blood the same tonicity as seawater. Excess salts are secreted by the kidneys and by a special excretory organ, the rectal gland.

Marine Bony Fishes

The marine environment, which is high in salts, is hypertonic to the blood plasma of bony fishes. Apparently, the common ancestor of marine fishes evolved in fresh water, and only later did some groups invade the sea. Therefore, marine bony fishes must avoid the tendency to become dehydrated (Fig. 36.3*a*).

As the sea washes over their gills, marine bony fishes lose water by osmosis. To counteract this, they drink seawater almost constantly. On the average, marine bony fishes swallow an amount of water equal to 1% of their body weight every hour. This is equivalent to a human drinking about 700 mL of water every hour around the clock. But while they get water by drinking, this habit also causes these fishes to acquire salt. To rid the body of excess salt, they actively transport it into the surrounding seawater at the gills. The kidneys conserve water, and marine bony fishes produce a scant amount of isotonic urine.

Freshwater Bony Fishes

The osmotic problems of freshwater bony fishes and the response to their environment are exactly opposite those of marine bony fishes (Fig. 36.3*b*). Freshwater fishes tend to gain water by osmosis across the gills and the body surface. As a consequence, these fishes never drink water. They actively transport salts into the blood across the membranes of their gills. They eliminate excess water by producing large quantities of dilute (hypotonic) urine. They discharge a quantity of urine equal to one-third their body weight each day.

Osmoregulation by Terrestrial Vertebrates

An important evolutionary adaptation that allowed animals to survive on land was the development of a kidney that could produce a concentrated (hypertonic) urine. The need for water conservation is particularly well illustrated in desert mammals such as the kangaroo rat, as well as in animals that drink seawater.

Kangaroo Rat

Dehydration threatens all terrestrial animals, especially those that live in a desert, like the kangaroo rat. During daylight hours, these animals remain in a cool burrow, a behavioral adaptation to conserve water. In addition, the kangaroo rat's nasal passages have a highly convoluted mucous membrane surface that captures condensed water from exhaled air. Exhaled air is usually full of moisture, which is why you can see it on cold winter mornings—the moisture in exhaled air is condensing.

A major adaptation that allows the kangaroo rat to conserve water is the ability to form a very hypertonic urine—20 times more concentrated than its blood plasma. The kidneys of a kangaroo rat are able to accomplish this feat because the structure in their kidneys that is largely responsible for producing concentrated urine, called the loop of the nephron (see Fig. 36.8) is much longer and more efficient than that in most other animals. Also, kangaroo rats produce fecal material that is almost completely dry.

Most terrestrial animals need to drink water at least occasionally to make up for the water lost from the skin and respiratory passages and through urination. However, the kangaroo rat is so adapted to conserving water that it can survive by using metabolic water derived from cellular respiration, and it never drinks water (Fig. 36.4).

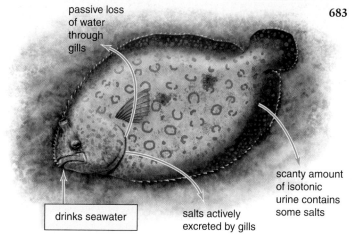

passive loss of water through gills

drinks seawater

salts actively excreted by gills

scanty amount of isotonic urine contains some salts

a. Marine bony fish (a flounder)

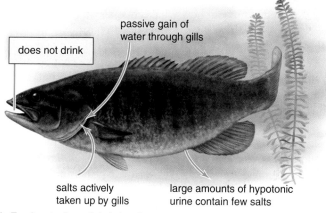

passive gain of water through gills

does not drink

salts actively taken up by gills

large amounts of hypotonic urine contain few salts

b. Freshwater bony fish (a trout)

Figure 36.3 Body fluid regulation in bony fishes. Marine bony fishes **(a)** employ different mechanisms compared to freshwater fishes **(b)** in order to osmoregulate their body fluids.

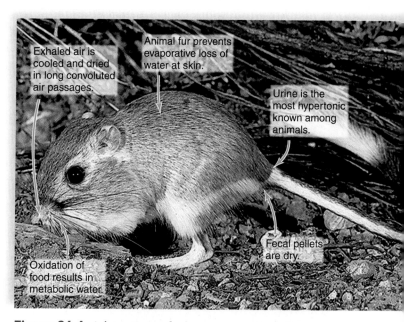

Exhaled air is cooled and dried in long convoluted air passages.

Animal fur prevents evaporative loss of water at skin.

Urine is the most hypertonic known among animals.

Oxidation of food results in metabolic water.

Fecal pellets are dry.

Figure 36.4 Adaptations of a kangaroo rat to a dry environment. The ways that a kangaroo rat minimizes water loss.

Seagulls, Reptiles, and Mammals

Birds, reptiles, and mammals evolved on land, and their kidneys are especially good at conserving water. However, some of these vertebrates have become secondarily adapted to living in or near the sea. They can drink seawater and still manage to survive. If

Figure 36.5 Adaptations of marine birds to a high salt environment. Many marine birds and reptiles have glands that pump salt out of the body.

salt solution exits here

salt solution runs down beak here

36.2 The Human Urinary System

Learning Outcomes

Upon completion of this section, you should be able to

1. Trace the anatomical path taken by urine from the glomeruli to its exit from the body.
2. Discuss the contributions of glomerular filtration, tubular reabsorption, and tubular secretion to the formation of urine.
3. Summarize the four major functions of human kidneys in maintaining homeostasis.

humans drink seawater, we lose more water than we take in just ridding the body of all that salt!

Little is known about how whales manage to get rid of extra salt, but we know that their kidneys are enormous. In some marine animals, however, the kidneys are not efficient enough to secrete all of the excess salt. As mentioned in the chapter opening story, some animals living in high salt environments have developed specialized glands for excreting these salts. These glands work by actively transporting salt from the blood into the gland, where it can be excreted as a concentrated solution.

In sea birds, salt-excreting glands are located near the eyes. The glands produce a salty solution that is excreted through the nostrils and moves down grooves on their beaks until it drips off (Fig. 36.5). In marine turtles, the salt gland is a modified tear (lacrimal) gland, and in sea snakes, a salivary sublingual gland beneath the tongue gets rid of excess salt. The work of these glands is regulated by the nervous system. Osmoreceptors, perhaps located near the heart, are thought to stimulate the brain, which then directs the gland to excrete salt until the salt concentration in the blood decreases to a tolerable level.

The major excretory organs of humans, as with most other vertebrates, are the kidneys (Fig. 36.6). The kidneys are the ultimate regulators of blood composition because they can remove various unwanted products from the body.

Human **kidneys** are bean-shaped, reddish-brown organs, each about the size of a fist. They are located on each side of the vertebral column just below the diaphragm, in the lower back, where they are partially protected by the lower rib cage. The right kidney is slightly lower than the left kidney.

Urine made by the kidneys is conducted from the body by the other organs in the urinary system. Each kidney is connected to a **ureter**, a duct that takes urine from the kidney to the **urinary bladder**, where it is stored until it is voided from the body through the single **urethra**. In males, the urethra passes through the penis, and in females, the opening of the urethra is ventral to that of the vagina. No connection exists between the genital (reproductive) and urinary systems in females, but in males, the urethra also carries sperm during ejaculation.

Check Your Progress   36.1

1. Distinguish between osmoregulation and excretion.
2. Describe two advantages of excreting urea instead of ammonia or uric acid.
3. List five strategies used by kangaroo rats to conserve water.

Figure 36.6 The human urinary system. **a.** The kidneys are well supplied with blood, as shown in the angiogram. **b.** Urine is found only within the kidneys, the ureters, the urinary bladder, and the urethra.

renal artery
renal vein
aorta
inferior vena cava

1. Kidneys produce urine.

2. Ureters transpor urine.

3. Urinary bladder stores urine.

4. Urethra passes urine to outside.

a.   b.

Kidneys

If a kidney is sectioned longitudinally, three major parts can be distinguished (Fig. 36.7). The *renal cortex,* which is the outer region of a kidney, has a somewhat granular appearance. The *renal medulla* consists of six to ten cone-shaped renal pyramids that lie on the inner side of the renal cortex. The innermost part of the kidney is a hollow chamber called the *renal pelvis.* Urine collects in the renal pelvis and then is carried to the bladder by a ureter.

Nephrons

Microscopically, each kidney is composed of over 1 million tiny tubules called **nephrons** [Gk. *nephros,* kidney]. The nephrons of a kidney produce urine. Some nephrons are located primarily in the renal cortex, but others dip down into the renal medulla, as shown in Figure 36.7b. Each nephron is made of several parts (Fig. 36.8). The blind end of a nephron is pushed in on itself to form a cuplike structure called the **glomerular capsule** [L. *glomeris,* ball] (also known as Bowman's capsule). The outer layer of the glomerular capsule is composed of squamous epithelial

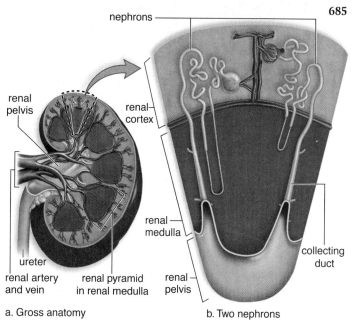

a. Gross anatomy

b. Two nephrons

Figure 36.7 Macroscopic and microscopic anatomy of the kidney. a. Longitudinal section of a kidney, showing the location of the renal cortex, the renal medulla, and the renal pelvis. **b.** An enlargement of one renal lobe, showing the placement of nephrons.

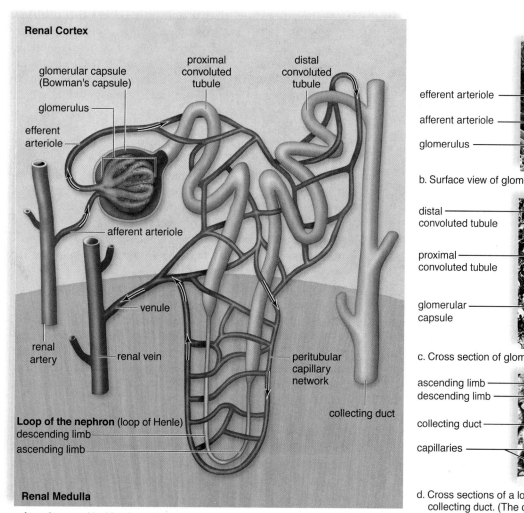

a. A nephron and its blood supply

b. Surface view of glomerulus and its blood supply

c. Cross section of glomerulus and convoluted tubules   50×

d. Cross sections of a loop of nephron limbs and collecting duct. (The other cross sections are those of capillaries.)   100×

Figure 36.8 Nephron anatomy. a. You can trace the path of blood about a nephron by following the arrows. A nephron is made up of a glomerular capsule, the proximal convoluted tubule, the loop of the nephron, the distal convoluted tubule, and the collecting duct. The micrographs in **(b)**, **(c)**, and **(d)** show these structures.

cells; the inner layer is composed of specialized cells that allow easy passage of molecules.

Leading from the glomerular capsule is a portion of the nephron known as the **proximal convoluted tubule** [L. *proximus,* nearest], which is lined by cells with many mitochondria and tightly packed microvilli. Then, simple squamous epithelium appears in the **loop of the nephron** (loop of Henle), which has a descending limb and an ascending limb. This is followed by the **distal convoluted tubule** [L. *distantia,* far]. Several distal convoluted tubules enter one **collecting duct.** The collecting duct transports urine down through the renal medulla and deliver it to the renal pelvis.

Each nephron has its own blood supply (Fig. 36.8). The renal artery branches into numerous small arteries, which branch into arterioles, one for each nephron. Each arteriole, called an afferent arteriole, divides to form a capillary bed, the **glomerulus** [L. *glomeris,* ball], which is surrounded by the glomerular capsule. The glomerulus drains into an efferent arteriole, which subsequently branches into a second capillary bed around the tubular parts of the nephron. These capillaries, called peritubular capillaries, lead to venules that join to form veins leading to the renal vein, a vessel that enters the inferior vena cava.

Urine Formation

An average human produces between 1 and 2 liters of urine daily. The fundamental process of urine formation involves initially filtering a large amount of water and a collection of solutes out of the blood, then reabsorbing much of the water, along with other material the body needs to conserve.

Urine production requires three distinct processes (see Fig. 36.9a), and, as you can see, the entire tubule portion of a nephron participates in the last two steps in urine formation:

1. glomerular filtration at the glomerular capsule;
2. tubular reabsorption at the convoluted tubules; and
3. tubular secretion at the convoluted tubules.

 MP3
An Overview of
Urine Formation

Glomerular Filtration

Glomerular filtration (Fig. 36.9a) is the movement of small molecules across the glomerular wall into the glomerular capsule as a result of blood pressure. When blood enters the glomerulus, blood pressure is sufficient to cause small molecules, such as water, nutrients, salts, and wastes, to move from the glomerulus to the inside of the glomerular capsule, especially since the glomerular walls are 100 times more permeable than the walls of most capillaries elsewhere in the body. The molecules that leave the blood and enter the glomerular capsule are called the *glomerular filtrate.* Plasma proteins and blood cells are too large to be part of this filtrate, so they remain in the blood as it flows into the efferent arteriole.

Glomerular filtrate is essentially protein free, but otherwise it has the same composition as blood plasma. If this composition were not altered in other parts of the nephron, death from starvation (loss of nutrients) and dehydration (loss of water) would quickly follow. The total blood volume averages about 5 liters, and this amount of fluid is filtered every 40 minutes.

Thus 180 liters of filtrate is produced daily, some 60 times the amount of blood plasma in the body. Most of the filtered water is obviously quickly returned to the blood, or a person would actually die from urination. Tubular reabsorption prevents this from happening.

Tubular Reabsorption

Tubular reabsorption (Fig. 36.9a) takes place when substances move across the walls of the tubules into the associated peritubular capillary network (Fig. 36.9a, b). Here, osmosis comes into play. You may remember that *osmosis* is the diffusion of water down its concentration gradient across a membrane (see Section 5.2). *Osmolarity* is a measure of the potential for osmosis; water tends to move from a solution with low osmolarity into a solution with high osmolarity.

The osmolarity of the blood is essentially the same as that of the filtrate within the glomerular capsule, and therefore osmosis of water from the filtrate into the blood cannot yet occur. However, sodium ions (Na^+) are actively pumped into the peritubular capillary, and then chloride ions (Cl^-) follow passively. Now the osmolarity of the blood is such that water moves passively from the tubule into the blood. About 60–70% of salt and water are reabsorbed at the proximal convoluted tubule.

Nutrients such as glucose and amino acids also return to the blood at the proximal convoluted tubule. This is a selective process, because only molecules recognized by carrier proteins in plasma membranes are actively reabsorbed. The cells of the proximal convoluted tubule have numerous microvilli, which increase the surface area, and numerous mitochondria, which supply the energy needed for active transport (Fig. 36.9b).

Glucose is an example of a molecule that ordinarily is reabsorbed completely because the supply of carrier molecules for it is plentiful. However, if the filtrate contains more glucose than there are carriers to handle it, glucose exceeds its renal threshold, or transport maximum. When this happens, the excess glucose in the filtrate appears in the urine. In diabetes mellitus, an abnormally large amount of glucose is present in the filtrate because the liver cannot store all of the excess glucose as glycogen. The presence of glucose in the filtrate results in less water being absorbed; the increased thirst and frequent urination in untreated diabetics are a result of less water being reabsorbed into the peritubular capillary network.

Urea is an example of a substance that is passively reabsorbed from the filtrate. At first, the concentration of urea within the filtrate is the same as that in blood plasma. But after water is reabsorbed, the urea concentration is greater than that of peritubular plasma. In the end, about 50% of the filtered urea is reabsorbed.

Tubular Secretion

Tubular secretion is the second way substances are removed from blood and added to tubular fluid (Fig. 36.9a). Substances such as uric acid, hydrogen ions, ammonia, creatinine, histamine, and penicillin are eliminated by tubular secretion. The process of tubular secretion may be viewed as helping to rid the body of potentially harmful compounds that were not filtered into the glomerulus.   **Animation**
Kidney Function

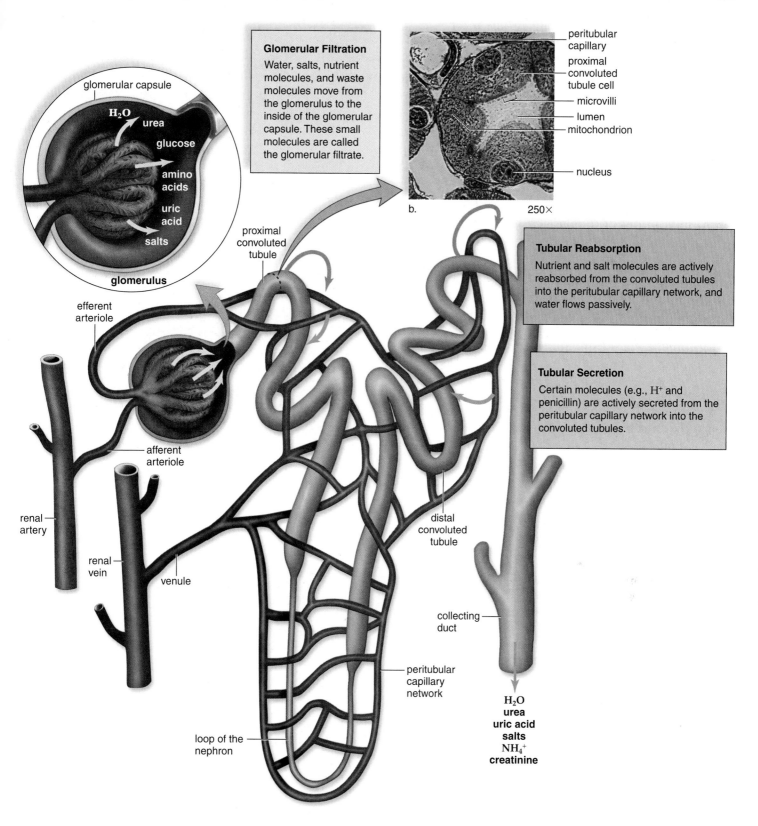

Glomerular Filtration

Water, salts, nutrient molecules, and waste molecules move from the glomerulus to the inside of the glomerular capsule. These small molecules are called the glomerular filtrate.

Tubular Reabsorption

Nutrient and salt molecules are actively reabsorbed from the convoluted tubules into the peritubular capillary network, and water flows passively.

Tubular Secretion

Certain molecules (e.g., H^+ and penicillin) are actively secreted from the peritubular capillary network into the convoluted tubules.

Figure 36.9 Processes in urine formation. **a.** The three main processes in urine formation are described in boxes and color coded to arrows that show the movement of molecules into or out of the nephron at specific locations. In the end, urine is composed of the substances within the collecting duct (see blue arrow). **b.** This photomicrograph shows that the cells lining the proximal convoluted tubule have a brush border composed of microvilli, which greatly increases the surface area exposed to the lumen. The peritubular capillary adjoins the cells.

The Kidneys and Homeostasis

The kidneys are organs of homeostasis for four main reasons:

1. The kidneys *excrete metabolic wastes* such as urea, which is the primary nitrogenous waste of humans.
2. They *maintain the water-salt balance,* which in turn affects blood volume and blood pressure.
3. Kidneys *maintain the acid-base balance,* and therefore, the pH balance.
4. They *secrete hormones.*

One hormone secreted by the kidneys, called **erythropoietin,** stimulates the stem cells in the bone marrow to produce more red blood cells. The Nature of Science feature examines the potential abuse of this hormone by endurance athletes. Another substance produced by the kidneys, called renin, is discussed later in this section.

Maintaining the Water-Salt Balance

Most of the water and salt (NaCl) present in the filtrate is reabsorbed across the wall of the proximal convoluted tubule. The excretion of a hypertonic urine (one that is more concentrated than blood) is dependent on the reabsorption of water from the loop of the nephron and the collecting duct. During the process of reabsorption, water passes through water channels called **aquaporins,** which were discovered in 1992.

Loop of the Nephron.   A long loop of the nephron, which typically penetrates deep into the renal medulla, is made up of a descending (downward) limb and an ascending (upward) limb. Salt (NaCl) passively diffuses out of the lower portion of the ascending limb, but the upper, thick portion of the limb actively extrudes salt out into the tissue of the outer renal medulla (Fig. 36.10). Less and less salt is available for transport as fluid moves up the thick portion of the ascending limb. Because of these circumstances, an osmotic gradient is created within the tissues of the renal medulla: The concentration of salt is greater in the direction of the inner medulla. (Note that water cannot leave the ascending limb because this limb is impermeable to water.)

The innermost portion of the inner medulla has the highest concentration of solutes. This cannot be due to salt because active transport of salt does not start until fluid reaches the thick portion of the ascending limb. Urea is believed to leak from the lower portion of the collecting duct, and it is this molecule that contributes to the high solute concentration of the inner medulla.

Because of the osmotic gradient within the renal medulla, water leaves the descending limb along its entire length. This is a countercurrent mechanism: As water diffuses out of the descending limb, the remaining fluid within the limb encounters an even greater osmotic concentration of solute; therefore, water continues to leave the descending limb from the top to the bottom. Filtrate within the collecting duct also encounters the same osmotic gradient mentioned earlier (Fig. 36.10). Therefore, water diffuses out of the collecting duct into the renal medulla, and the urine within the collecting duct becomes hypertonic to blood plasma.

Antidiuretic hormone (ADH) [Gk. *anti,* against; L. *ouresis,* urination] is released by the posterior lobe of the pituitary in response to an increased concentration of salts in the blood. To

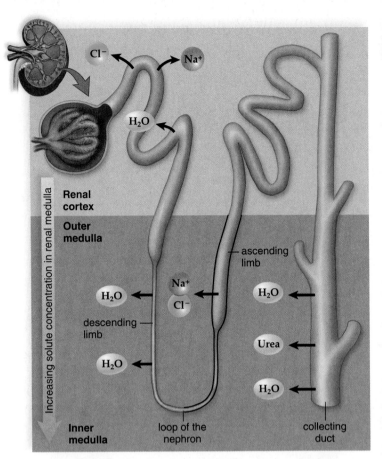

Figure 36.10 Reabsorption of salt and water.   Salt (NaCl) diffuses and is actively transported out of the ascending limb of the loop of the nephron into the renal medulla; also, urea leaks from the collecting duct and enters the tissues of the renal medulla. These actions create a hypertonic environment, which draws water out of the descending limb and the collecting duct. This water is returned to the cardiovascular system.

understand the action of this hormone, consider its name. *Diuresis* means increased amount of urine, and *antidiuresis* means decreased amount of urine. When ADH is present, more water is reabsorbed (blood volume and pressure rise), and a decreased amount of more concentrated urine is produced. One way by which ADH accomplishes this change is by causing the insertion of additional aquaporin water channels into the epithelial cells of the distal tubule and collecting duct, allowing more water to be reabsorbed.

In practical terms, if an individual does not drink much water on a certain day, the posterior lobe of the pituitary releases ADH, causing more water to be reabsorbed and less urine to form. On the other hand, if an individual drinks a large amount of water and does not perspire much, ADH is not released. Now more water is excreted, and more urine forms. Diuretics, such as caffeine and alcohol, increase the flow of urine by interfering with the action of ADH. ADH production also decreases at night, an adaptation that allows longer periods of sleep without the need to wake up to urinate.

Hormones Control the Reabsorption of Salt.   Usually, more than 99% of Na^+ filtered at the glomerulus is returned to the blood. Most sodium (67%) is reabsorbed at the proximal

THEME   Nature of Science

Misuse of Erythropoietin in Sports

Lance Armstrong is a hero to many sports fans (Fig. 36A). He is a seven-time winner of the Tour de France cycling event, a survivor of testicular cancer, and a sponsor of many charitable causes. On May 22, 2011, the TV news program 60 Minutes aired a segment in which Tyler Hamilton, a former teammate of Armstrong's, said he witnessed Armstrong using performance enhancing drugs on several occasions. Armstrong has denied these charges, noting that he tested negative nearly 500 times during his 20-year career.

The substance that Armstrong is most often accused of abusing is erythropoietin (EPO), a hormone secreted by the kidney in response to low blood oxygen levels. EPO binds to a specific cellular receptor, found mainly on bone marrow cells that produce red blood cells (RBCs). The gene coding for EPO was isolated in 1985, and since 1989, the use of recombinant human EPO (rHuEPO) has been approved for medical purposes, such as treating the anemia that is often associated with kidney failure. However, rHuEPO use can have serious side effects, including increased blood clotting, high blood pressure, and even sudden death.

In addition to its legitimate medical uses, rHuEPO has been misused by athletes in several endurance sports. Research has generally verified that EPO is effective at increasing athletic performance. A small study published in 2007 showed a 13% increase in peak power output, and a 54% increase in time to exhaustion in cyclists who used rHuEPO (Fig. 36B). Because this is an unfair advantage, rHuEPO use has been banned by the Tour de France, the Olympics, and other sports organizations.

To determine whether an athlete is using rHuEPO, an accurate test is needed. One method of testing athletes for any treatment designed to increase the RBC count (including collecting one's own blood, storing it, and transfusing it back into the athlete soon before an event) is to monitor the *hematocrit*; the percentage of the blood that is comprised of cells. Since 1997, sports cycling governing bodies have decreed that any athlete whose hematocrit is over 50% may be suspended from competition. However, normal hematocrit values for men can vary widely, from 40% to 54%. This means an athlete with a naturally high hematocrit could be unfairly accused of cheating.

A better approach would be to directly measure levels of rHuEPO in an athlete's body. Unfortunately, these tests have limitations as well. Part of the problem is that when rHuEPO is injected, it may persist in the body for as little as 24 hours, but its effect continues for as long as two weeks. Unless a test is conducted during the short time that rHuEPO is present, even the most accurate test may miss it. A second issue is that rHuEPO must be distinguished from the EPO produced by an athlete's own kidneys. rHuEPO is produced in cultured hamster ovary cells, which process the protein differently, attaching different sugar molecules to the amino acids. This should result in slight differences in the movement of rHuEPO versus EPO through a gel material that is subjected to an electrical field (i.e., electrophoresis).

Unfortunately, direct testing for rHuEPO may also be unreliable. In a 2008 study, eight adult male volunteers received weekly rHuEPO injections, and identical samples of their urine were submitted to two labs that were approved for rHuEPO testing. "Lab A" found that 6 of 16 samples were positive, but "Lab B" concluded that all samples were negative.[1]

Because of these issues, the question of whether Armstrong abused rHuEPO may never be resolved. It will also be difficult to eliminate the misuse of rHuEPO in endurance sports, especially in participants whose motivation to win overpowers their concern about the risks of abusing rHuEPO.

Questions to Consider

1. Certain kidney tumors secrete large amounts of EPO. What types of symptoms might this cause?
2. Some medical conditions, e.g., bacterial infections, cause the numbers of WBCs to increase, perhaps even to twice the normal levels. Why does this have very little effect on the hematocrit?

---

1 Lundby, C., et al. 2008. Testing for recombinant human erythropoietin in urine: problems associated with current anti-doping testing. *J. Applied Physiology* 105: 417–19.

Figure 36A Lance Armstrong and Tyler Hamilton.   Hamilton (*green and white helmet*) says he observed Armstrong (*red, white, and blue helmet*) using performance enhancing drugs, including rHuEPO.

Figure 36B Use of rHuEPO improves athletic performance.   Four weeks of rHuEPO treatments increased the peak power output and prolonged the time that relatively fit cyclists were able to ride (at 80% of their maximum exertion level).

Figure 36.11 The renin-angiotensin-aldosterone system. The liver secretes angiotensinogen into the bloodstream. Renin from the kidneys initiates the chain of events that results in angiotensin II. Angiotensin II acts on the adrenal cortex to secrete aldosterone, which causes reabsorption of sodium ions by the kidneys and a subsequent rise in blood pressure.

convoluted tubule, and a sizable amount (25%) is extruded by the ascending limb of the loop of the nephron. The rest is reabsorbed from the distal convoluted tubule and collecting duct.

Blood volume and pressure is, in part, regulated by salt reabsorption. When blood volume, and therefore blood pressure, is not sufficient to promote glomerular filtration, a cluster of cells near the glomerulus called the *juxtaglomerular apparatus* secretes renin. **Renin** is an enzyme that changes angiotensinogen (a large plasma protein produced by the liver) into angiotensin I. Later, angiotensin I is converted to **angiotensin II,** a powerful vasoconstrictor that also stimulates the adrenal glands, which lie on top of the kidneys, to release aldosterone (Fig. 36.11). **Aldosterone** is a hormone that promotes the excretion of potassium ions (K^+) and the reabsorption of sodium ions (Na^+) at the distal convoluted tubule. The reabsorption of sodium ions is followed by the reabsorption of water. Therefore, blood volume and blood pressure increase.

Atrial natriuretic hormone (ANH) is a hormone secreted by the atria of the heart when cardiac cells are stretched due to increased blood volume. ANH inhibits the secretion of renin by the juxtaglomerular apparatus and the secretion of aldosterone by the adrenal cortex. Its effect, therefore, is to promote the excretion of Na^+—that is, natriuresis. When Na^+ is excreted, so is water, and therefore blood volume and blood pressure decrease.

These examples show that the kidneys regulate the water balance in blood by controlling the excretion and the reabsorption of ions. Sodium is an important ion in plasma that must be regulated, but the kidneys also excrete or reabsorb other ions, such as potassium ions (K^+), bicarbonate ions (HCO_3^-), and magnesium ions (Mg^{2+}), as needed.

MP3
Water Conservation

Maintaining the Acid-Base Balance

The functions of cells are influenced by pH. Therefore regulation of pH is extremely important to good health. The *bicarbonate (HCO_3^-) buffer system* and breathing work together to help maintain the pH of the blood. Central to the mechanism is this reaction, which you have seen before:

$$H^+ + HCO_3^- \rightleftharpoons H_2CO_3 \rightleftharpoons H_2O + CO_2$$

The *excretion of carbon dioxide (CO_2) by the lungs* helps keep the pH within normal limits, because when carbon dioxide is exhaled, this reaction is pushed to the right, and hydrogen ions are tied up in water. As you learned in the preceding chapter, when blood pH

decreases, chemoreceptors in the carotid bodies (in the carotid arteries) and in aortic bodies (in the aorta) stimulate the respiratory control center, and the rate and depth of breathing increase. And, when blood pH begins to rise, the respiratory control center is depressed, and the amount of bicarbonate ion increases in the blood.

As powerful as this system is, only the kidneys can rid the body of a wide range of acidic and basic substances. The kidneys are slower acting than the buffer/breathing mechanism, but they have a more powerful effect on pH. For the sake of simplicity, we can think of the kidneys as reabsorbing bicarbonate ions and excreting hydrogen ions as needed to maintain the normal pH of the blood:

If the blood is acidic, hydrogen ions are excreted and bicarbonate ions are reabsorbed. If the blood is basic, hydrogen ions are not excreted and bicarbonate ions are not reabsorbed. The fact that urine is typically acidic (pH about 6) shows that usually an excess of hydrogen ions are excreted. Ammonia (NH_3) provides a means for buffering these hydrogen ions in urine: ($NH_3 + H^+ \longrightarrow NH_4^+$). Ammonia is produced in tubule cells by the deamination of amino acids. Phosphate provides another means of buffering hydrogen ions in urine.

MP3
Acid-Base Balance

Check Your Progress   36.2

1. Describe which of the four major functions of the human urinary system are accomplished solely by the kidneys, and which are shared with other body systems.
2. Explain the effect of the renin-angiotensin-aldosterone system on water-salt balance.
3. Describe how the kidneys contribute to the maintenance of normal blood pH.

CONNECTING *the* CONCEPTS *with the* THEMES

Evolution

- Proper salt balance has a critical effect on cellular functions, and many adaptations have evolved to maintain it.
- Animals that live in wet or watery environments tend to secrete nitrogenous wastes as ammonia; those in drier environments secrete urea or uric acid, which require more energy to produce.
- A variety of excretory organs have evolved in animals, from relatively simple tubular structures in invertebrates, to extremely efficient kidneys found in the kangaroo rat.

Nature of Science

- By studying the excretory systems of many different animals, scientists have come to understand the great variety of evolutionary strategies and mechanisms that regulate the composition of body fluids.
- The production of the recombinant hormone erythropoietin is an example of a discovery that has tremendous benefits, but also the potential for misuse.

Biological Systems

- Without removal of wastes and excess salts, an animal would die. In most animals the kidneys are the main regulators of the internal environment.
- Human kidneys excrete nitrogenous waste (mainly as urea), maintain the salt balance, work with the respiratory system to maintain pH, and secrete hormones that affect water reabsorption, blood volume and blood pressure, and red blood cell production.

Media Study Tools

www.mhhe.com/maderbiology11

Enhance your study of this chapter with study tools and practice tests. Also ask your instructor about the resources available through ConnectPlus, including the media-rich eBook, interactive learning tools, and animations.

Summarize

36.1 Animal Excretory Systems

Animals excrete nitrogenous wastes. Aquatic animals usually excrete ammonia (requires little energy but much water to excrete), and land animals excrete either urea or uric acid (requires much energy to produce).

Most animals have specialized excretory organs. The flame cells of planarians rid the body of excess water. Earthworm nephridia exchange molecules with the blood in a manner similar to that of vertebrate kidneys. Malpighian tubules in insects take up metabolic wastes and water from the hemolymph. Later, the water is absorbed by the gut.

Osmotic regulation is important to animals. Most must balance their water and salt intake and excretion to maintain normal solute and water concentration in body fluids. Marine fishes constantly drink water, excrete salts at the gills, and pass an isotonic urine. Freshwater fishes never drink water; they take in salts at the gills and excrete a hypotonic urine.

Some terrestrial animals have adapted to extreme environments. For example, the desert kangaroo rat can survive on metabolic water; marine birds and reptiles have glands that extrude salt.

36.2 The Human Urinary System

The human urinary system includes the kidneys, ureters, urinary bladder, and urethra. The kidneys serve four basic homeostatic functions: excretion of metabolic waste; maintenance of water-salt balance; maintenance of pH balance; and production of hormones, such as erythropoietin.

Kidneys are made up of nephrons, each of which has several parts. Urine formation by a nephron requires three steps: glomerular filtration, during which nutrients, water, and wastes enter the nephron's glomerular capsule; tubular reabsorption, when nutrients and most water are reabsorbed into the peritubular capillary network; and tubular secretion, during which additional wastes are added to the convoluted tubules.

In order to excrete a hypertonic urine, the ascending limb of the loop of the nephron extrudes salt so that the renal medulla is increasingly hypertonic. Since urea leaks from the lower end of the collecting duct, the inner renal medulla has the highest concentration of solute. Therefore, a countercurrent mechanism ensures that water diffuses out of the descending limb and the collecting duct.

Three hormones are involved in maintaining the water-salt balance of the blood. ADH (antidiuretic hormone), which makes the collecting duct more permeable to water, is secreted by the posterior pituitary in response to an increase in the osmotic pressure of the blood. Aldosterone is secreted by the adrenal cortex after low blood pressure has caused the kidneys to release renin. The presence of renin leads to the formation of angiotensin II, which causes the adrenal cortex to release aldosterone. Aldosterone causes the kidneys to retain Na^+; therefore, water is reabsorbed and blood pressure rises. Atrial natriuretic hormone, in contrast, prevents the secretion of renin and aldosterone.

The kidneys also keep blood pH within normal limits. They reabsorb HCO_3^- and excrete H^+ as needed to maintain the pH at about 7.4.

Key Terms

aldosterone 690	kidneys 684
ammonia 681	loop of the nephron 686
angiotensin II 690	nephron 685
antidiuretic hormone (ADH) 688	osmoregulation 681
aquaporin 688	proximal convoluted tubule 686
atrial natriuretic hormone (ANH) 690	renin 690
collecting duct 686	tubular reabsorption 686
distal convoluted tubule 686	tubular secretion 686
erythropoietin 688	urea 681
excretion 681	ureter 684
glomerular capsule 685	urethra 684
glomerular filtration 686	uric acid 681
glomerulus 686	urinary bladder 684
	urine 682

Assess

Reviewing This Chapter

1. Relate the three primary nitrogenous wastes to the habitat of animals.   681
2. Describe how the excretory organs of the earthworm and the insect function.   682
3. Give examples of how other types of animals regulate their water and salt balance.   682–84
4. Contrast the osmotic regulation of a marine bony fish with that of a freshwater bony fish.   683
5. Describe the path of urine in humans, and give a function for each structure mentioned.   684
6. Describe the macroscopic anatomy of a human kidney, and relate it to the placement of nephrons.   685
7. List the parts of a nephron, and give a function for each structure mentioned.   685–86
8. Describe how urine is made by outlining what happens at each part of the nephron.   686–87
9. Describe the reabsorption of water and salt along the length of the nephron. Include the contribution of the loop of the nephron.   688, 690
10. Name and describe the action of antidiuretic hormone (ADH), the renin-aldosterone connection, and the atrial natriuretic hormone (ANH).   688, 690
11. How does the nephron regulate the pH of the blood?   690

Testing Yourself

Choose the best answer for each question.

1. Which of these pairs is mismatched?
   a. insects—excrete uric acid
   b. humans—excrete urea
   c. fishes—excrete ammonia
   d. birds—excrete ammonia
   e. All of these are correct.
2. One advantage of excretion of urea instead of uric acid is that urea
   a. requires less energy than uric acid to produce.
   b. can be concentrated to a greater extent.
   c. is not a toxic substance.
   d. requires no water to excrete.
   e. is a larger molecule.
3. Freshwater bony fishes maintain water balance by
   a. excreting salt across their gills.
   b. periodically drinking small amounts of water.
   c. excreting a hypotonic urine.
   d. excreting wastes in the form of uric acid.
   e. Both a and c are correct.
4. Animals with which of these are most likely to excrete a semisolid nitrogenous waste?
   a. nephridia
   b. Malpighian tubules
   c. flame cells
   d. All of these are correct.
5. Excretion of a hypertonic urine in humans is associated best with
   a. the glomerular capsule.
   b. the proximal convoluted tubule.
   c. the loop of the nephron.
   d. the collecting duct.
   e. Both c and d are correct.
6. ADH (antidiuretic hormone) causes an individual to excrete
   a. less salt.
   b. less water.
   c. more water.
   d. Both a and c are correct.
7. Which of these causes blood pressure to decrease?
   a. aldosterone
   b. antidiuretic hormone (ADH)
   c. renin
   d. atrial natriuretic hormone (ANH)

8. Which of these materials is not filtered from the blood at the glomerulus?
   a. water
   b. urea
   c. protein
   d. glucose
9. By what process are most molecules secreted from the blood into the convoluted tubules?
   a. osmosis
   b. diffusion
   c. active transport
   d. facilitated diffusion
10. Which of these is not correct?
    a. Uric acid is produced from the breakdown of nucleic acids.
    b. Urea is produced from the breakdown of proteins.
    c. Ammonia results from the deamination of amino acids.
    d. All of these are correct.
11. When tracing the path of blood, the blood vessel that follows the renal artery is the
    a. peritubular capillary.
    b. efferent arteriole.
    c. afferent arteriole.
    d. renal vein.
12. Label this diagram of a nephron.

Engage

Virtual Labs
Earthworm Dissection
Virtual Frog Dissection

The Virtual Labs "Earthworm Dissection" and "Virtual Frog Dissection" allow you to explore the excretory systems of invertebrate and vertebrate animals.

Thinking Scientifically

1. High blood pressure often is accompanied by kidney damage. In some people, the kidney damage is subsequent to the high blood pressure, but in others the kidney damage is what caused the high blood pressure. Explain how a low-salt diet would enable you to determine whether the high blood pressure or the kidney damage came first?

2. The renin-angiotensin-aldosterone system can be inhibited in order to reduce high blood pressure. Usually, the angiotensin-converting enzyme, which converts angiotensin I to angiotensin II, is inhibited by drug therapy. Why would this enzyme be an effective point to disrupt the system?

Muhammad Ali, nicknamed "The Greatest," in the prime of his boxing career.

37

Neurons and Nervous Systems

BEFORE YOU BEGIN

Before beginning this chapter, take a few moments to review the following discussions.

Figure 5.10 How does the sodium-potassium pump function?

Section 29.1 From what embryonic structures are the brain, spinal cord, and (in vertebrates) vertebral column derived?

Section 30.1 How has the evolution of a large, complex brain allowed humans to become the most dominant species on the planet?

M uhammad Ali was perhaps the greatest heavyweight boxer of all time. A three-time world champion, Ali ruled boxing during the early to mid-1970s. Although he was 6 feet 3 inches tall and fought at a weight of about 220 pounds, Ali was incredibly fast, often pummeling opponents with flurries of punches while gliding around the ring with a style that became known as "float like a butterfly, sting like a bee."

To watch a professional athlete like Ali display his skills is to watch the nervous system performing at a high level. No computer has yet been invented that could coordinate the complex muscular movements involved not only in delivering punches but also avoiding the aggression of one's opponent. Sadly, in 1984 Ali was diagnosed with a form of Parkinson disease (PD), a nervous system disorder that affects his ability to speak or control his muscles. Although his thought processes remain intact, Ali's speech is slow and slurred, and his muscles tremble when he attempts to move. It is unknown whether the years of trauma to Ali's brain caused his condition, especially since the great majority of PD patients have suffered no apparent brain trauma. Later on in the chapter you can learn more about one method scientists are using to investigate the cause of PD.

As you read through the chapter, think about the following questions:

1. How did the evolution of the nervous system provide advantages to animals?
2. What specific types of processes occur uniquely in nervous tissues?
3. Why are diseases of the human nervous system generally difficult to treat?

FOLLOWING *the* THEMES

CHAPTER 37 NEURONS AND NERVOUS SYSTEMS		
UNIT 7 COMPARATIVE ANIMAL BIOLOGY	**Evolution**	Nervous systems have evolved in all types of animals except the simplest multicellular animals and range from relatively simple nerve nets to the highly complex human brain.
	Nature of Science	Scientific studies have revealed much (but not all) about how the nervous system functions, leading to new treatments for some neurological diseases.
	Biological Systems	Although animal nervous systems vary greatly, all are involved in controlling and coordinating body functions and activities.

37.1 Evolution of the Nervous System

The nervous system is vitally important in complex animals, enabling them to seek food and mates and avoid danger. It ceaselessly monitors internal and external conditions and makes appropriate changes to maintain homeostasis. A comparative study of animal nervous systems shows the evolutionary trends that led to the nervous system of mammals.

Invertebrate Nervous-System Organization

The simplest multicellular animals, such as sponges, lack neurons (nerve cells), and therefore have no nervous system. However, their cells can respond to their environment and can communicate with each other, perhaps by releasing calcium or other ions; the most common example is closure of the osculum (central opening) in response to various stimuli.

Hydras, which are cnidarians with the tissue level of organization and radial symmetry, have a **nerve net** that is composed of neurons in contact with one another and with contractile cells in the body wall (Fig. 37.1a). They can contract and extend their bodies, move their tentacles to capture prey, and even turn somersaults. Sea anemones and jellyfish, which are also cnidarians, seem to have two nerve nets: A fast-acting one allows major responses, particularly in times of danger; and the slower one coordinates slower and more delicate movements.

Planarians (flatworms) have a nervous organization that reflects their bilateral symmetry. They have a ladderlike nervous system, with two ventrally located lateral or longitudinal nerve cords (bundles of nerves) that extend from the cerebral ganglia to the posterior end of their body. Transverse nerves connect the nerve cords, as well as the cerebral ganglia, to the eyespots. **Cephalization**, or concentration of nervous tissue in the anterior or head region, has occurred. A cluster of neuron cell bodies is called a **ganglion** (pl., ganglia), and the anterior cerebral ganglia of flatworms receive sensory information from photoreceptors in the eyespots and sensory cells in the auricles (Fig. 37.1b). The two lateral nerve cords allow a rapid transfer of information from the cerebral ganglia to the posterior end, and the transverse nerves between the nerve cords keep the movement of the two sides coordinated. Bilateral symmetry plus cephalization are two significant trends in the development of a nervous organization that is adaptive for an active way of life.

Annelids (e.g., earthworm, Fig. 37.1c) and arthropods (e.g., crab, Fig. 37.1d), are complex animals with the typical invertebrate nervous system. A brain is present, and a ventral nerve cord has a ganglion in each segment. The brain, which normally receives sensory information, controls the activity of the ganglia

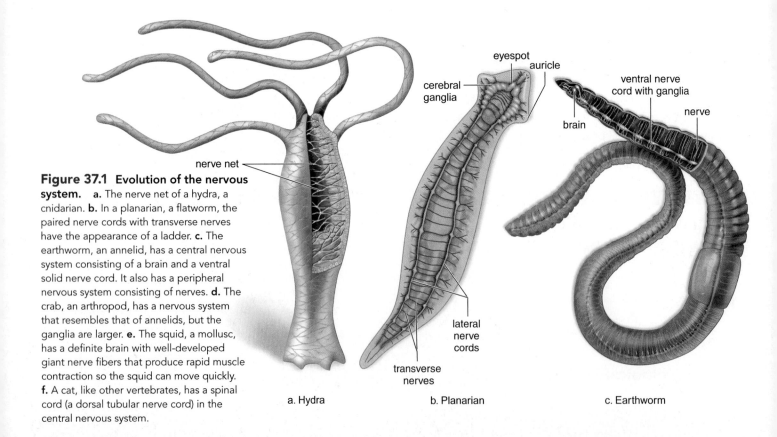

Figure 37.1 Evolution of the nervous system. a. The nerve net of a hydra, a cnidarian. **b.** In a planarian, a flatworm, the paired nerve cords with transverse nerves have the appearance of a ladder. **c.** The earthworm, an annelid, has a central nervous system consisting of a brain and a ventral solid nerve cord. It also has a peripheral nervous system consisting of nerves. **d.** The crab, an arthropod, has a nervous system that resembles that of annelids, but the ganglia are larger. **e.** The squid, a mollusc, has a definite brain with well-developed giant nerve fibers that produce rapid muscle contraction so the squid can move quickly. **f.** A cat, like other vertebrates, has a spinal cord (a dorsal tubular nerve cord) in the central nervous system.

a. Hydra

b. Planarian

c. Earthworm

and assorted nerves so that the muscle activity of the entire animal is coordinated.

A group of molluscs called cephalopods (e.g. squid, Fig. 37.1*e*) show marked cephalization—the anterior end has a well-defined brain, and well-developed sense organs, such as eyes, are present. The cephalopods are widely regarded as the most intelligent invertebrates; many are highly social creatures and some, such as the octopus, have been observed to collect, transport, and assemble coconut shells for later use as a shelter.

Vertebrate Nervous-System Organization

Vertebrates have many more neurons than do invertebrates. For example, an insect's entire nervous system contains a total of about 1 million neurons, while a cat's nervous system may contain many thousand times that number (Fig. 37.1*f*). The human cerebral cortex alone contains an estimated 11 billion neurons; some whales have even more.

All vertebrates have a brain that controls the nervous system. It is customary to divide the vertebrate brain into the hindbrain, midbrain, and forebrain (Fig. 37.2), although the relative sizes of the parts vary greatly among species. The hindbrain is the most ancient part of the brain, which regulates motor activity below the level of consciousness. For example, the lungs and heart function even when an animal is sleeping. The medulla oblongata contains control centers for breathing and heart rate. Coordination of motor activity associated with limb movement, posture, and balance eventually became centered in the cerebellum.

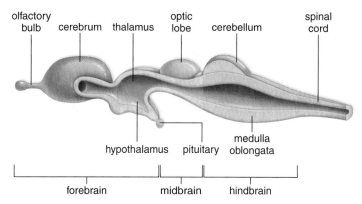

Figure 37.2 Organization of the vertebrate brain. The vertebrate brain is divided into the forebrain, the midbrain, and the hindbrain.

Several types of paired sensory receptors, including the eyes, ears, and olfactory structures, allow the animal to gather information from the environment. These sense organs are generally located at the anterior end of the animal, because this end is usually the first to enter new environments. The optic lobes are part of the midbrain, which was originally a center for coordinating reflexes involving the eyes and ears. In early vertebrate evolution, the forebrain was concerned mainly with the sense of smell. Beginning with the amphibians and continuing in the other vertebrates, the forebrain processes sensory information. Later, the thalamus evolved to receive sensory input from the midbrain and the hindbrain and to pass it on to the cerebrum,

d. Crab   e. Squid   f. Cat the anterior part of the forebrain in vertebrates. In the forebrain, the hypothalamus is particularly concerned with homeostasis, and in this capacity, the hypothalamus communicates with the medulla oblongata and the pituitary gland.

The **central nervous system (CNS)** consists of the brain and spinal cord (Fig. 37.3). The **peripheral nervous system (PNS)** [Gk. *periphereia,* circumference] consists of all the nerves and ganglia that lie outside the central nervous system. The CNS and PNS are considered in more detail in sections 37.3 and 37.4.

The Mammalian Nervous System

The hindbrain and midbrain of mammals are similar to those of other vertebrates. However, the forebrain of mammals is greatly enlarged, due to the addition of an outermost layer called the *neocortex*, which is seen only in mammals. It functions in higher mental processes such as spatial reasoning, conscious thought, and language.

Although all mammals have a neocortex, all neocortexes are not the same. Large variation has been observed in the number of crevices and folds, which can greatly increase the surface area and numbers of connections between regions. The frontal lobes (see Section 37.3) are especially large and complex in primates, and in humans other parts of the cortex are also enlarged and form very complex connections with other parts of the brain. It is likely that this greatly increased brain capacity allowed mammals, and especially humans, to become increasingly adept at higher mental activities such as manipulating the environment, complex learning, and anticipating the future, all of which have provided tremendous evolutionary advantages.

Check Your Progress   37.1

1. Define nerve net, ganglion, and brain.
2. Describe the major functions of the hindbrain, midbrain, and forebrain.
3. Identify the specific location of the more recently evolved parts of the brain, compared to the older parts.

Figure 37.3 Organization of the nervous system in humans.
a. The central nervous system (CNS) is composed of brain and spinal cord; the peripheral nervous system (PNS) consists of nerves. **b.** In the somatic system of the PNS, nerves conduct impulses from sensory receptors located in the skin and internal organs to the CNS and motor impulses from the CNS to the skeletal muscles. In the autonomic system, consisting of the sympathetic and parasympathetic divisions, motor impulses travel to smooth muscle, cardiac muscle, and glands.

brain
cranial nerves
cervical nerves
thoracic nerves
spinal cord
lumbar nerves
radial nerve
median nerve
ulnar nerve
sacral nerves
sciatic nerve
tibial nerve
common fibular nerve

a.

b.

37.2 Nervous Tissue

Learning Outcomes

Upon completion of this section, you should be able to

1. Describe the basic structure of a neuron, and compare the functions of the three types of neurons.
2. Discuss the changes in ion concentrations inside and outside of a neuron that result in an action potential.
3. Summarize the role of various neurotransmitters in propagating nerve impulses.

Although complex, nervous tissue is composed of just two principal types of cells. **Neurons,** also known as nerve cells, are the functional units of the nervous system. They receive sensory information, convey the information to an integration center such as the brain, and conduct signals from the integration center to effector structures such as the glands and muscles. **Neuroglia** serve as supporting cells, providing support and nourishment to the neurons.

Neurons and Neuroglia

Neurons vary in appearance depending on their function and location. They consist of three major parts: a cell body, dendrites, and an axon (Fig. 37.4). The **cell body** contains a nucleus and a variety of organelles. The **dendrites** [Gk. *dendron*, tree] are short, highly branched processes that receive signals from the sensory receptors or other neurons and transmit them to the cell body. The **axon** [Gk. *axon*, axis] is the portion of the neuron that conveys information to another neuron or to other cells. Axons can be bundled together to form nerves. For this reason, axons are often called **nerve fibers.** Many axons are covered by a white insulating layer called the **myelin sheath** [Gk. *myelos*, spinal cord].

Neuroglia, or glial cells (see Section 3.1), greatly outnumber neurons in the brain. There are several different types of neuroglia in the CNS, each with specific functions. **Microglia** are phagocytic cells that help remove bacteria and debris, while **astrocytes** (astrocytes) provide metabolic and structural support directly to the neurons. The myelin sheath is formed from the membranes of tightly spiraled neuroglia. In the PNS, **Schwann cells** perform this function, leaving gaps called **nodes of Ranvier.** In the CNS, neuroglial cells called **oligodendrocytes** form the myelin sheath.

MP3
Cells of the Nervous System

Types of Neurons

Neurons can be described in terms of their function and shape. **Motor (efferent) neurons** take nerve impulses from the CNS to muscles or glands. Motor neurons are said to have a *multipolar* shape because they have many dendrites and a single axon (Fig. 37.4*a*). Motor neurons cause muscle fibers to contract or glands to secrete, and therefore they are said to innervate these structures.

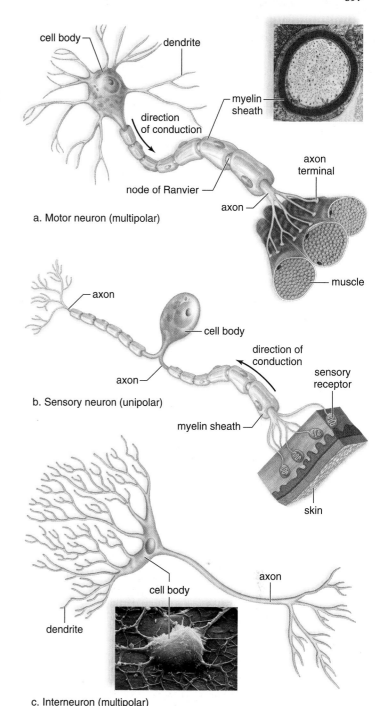

Figure 37.4 Neuron anatomy.   a. Motor neuron. Note the branched dendrites and the single, long axon, which branches only near its tip. **b.** Sensory neuron with dendritelike structures projecting from the peripheral end of the axon. **c.** Interneuron (from the cortex of the cerebellum) with very highly branched dendrites.

Sensory (afferent) neurons take nerve impulses from sensory receptors to the CNS. The sensory receptor, which is the distal end of the long axon of a sensory neuron, may be as simple as a naked nerve ending (a pain receptor), or may be built into a highly complex organ, such as the eye or ear. Almost all sensory neurons have a structure that is termed *unipolar* (Fig. 37.4*b*). In unipolar neurons, the process that extends from the cell body divides into a branch that extends to the periphery and another that extends to the CNS.

Interneurons [L. *inter*, between] occur entirely within the CNS. Interneurons, which are typically multipolar in shape (Fig. 37.4c), convey nerve impulses between various parts of the CNS. Some lie between sensory neurons and motor neurons; some take messages from one side of the spinal cord to the other or from the brain to the cord, and vice versa. They also form complex pathways in the brain, leading to higher mental functions like thinking, memory, and language.

Video Making Brain Cells

Transmission of Nerve Impulses

In the early 1900s, scientists first hypothesized that the nerve impulse is an electrochemical phenomenon involving the movement of unequally distributed ions on either side of an axonal membrane, the plasma membrane of an axon. It was not until the 1960s, however, that experimental techniques were developed to test this hypothesis. Investigators were able to insert a tiny electrode into the giant axon of the squid *Loligo*. This internal electrode was then connected to a voltmeter, an instrument with a screen that shows voltage differences over time

(Fig. 37.5). Voltage is a measure of the electrical potential difference between two points, which in this case is the difference between the electrode placed inside and another placed outside the axon. An electrical potential difference across a membrane is called the *membrane potential*.

Resting Potential

When the axon is not conducting an impulse, the voltmeter records a membrane potential equal to about −70 mV (millivolts), indicating that the inside of the neuron is more negative than the outside (Fig. 37.5a). This is called the **resting potential** because the axon is not conducting an impulse.

The existence of this polarity can be correlated with a difference in ion distribution on either side of the axonal membrane. As Figure 37.5a shows, there is a higher concentration of sodium ions (Na^+) outside the axon and a higher concentration of potassium ions (K^+) inside the axon.

The unequal distribution of these ions is in part due to the activity of the *sodium-potassium pump* (described in Section 5.3; see Figure 5.10). This pump is an active transport system in the plasma membrane that pumps three sodium ions out of the axon and two potassium ions into the axon. The pump is always working because the membrane is somewhat permeable

Figure 37.5 Resting and action potential of the axonal membrane. **a.** Resting potential. A voltmeter that records voltage changes indicates the axonal membrane has a resting potential of −70 mV. There is a preponderance of Na^+ outside the axon and a preponderance of K^+ inside the axon. The permeability of the membrane to K^+ compared to Na^+, and the presence of large, negatively charged proteins (not shown) within the axon, causes the inside to be negative compared to the outside. **b.** Action potential. Depolarization occurs when Na^+ gates open and Na^+ moves inside the axon, and **(c)** repolarization occurs when K^+ gates open and K^+ moves outside the axon. **d.** Graph of the action potential.

a. Resting potential: more Na^+ outside the axon and more K^+ inside the axon causes polarization.

b. Action potential begins: depolarization occurs when Na^+ gates open and Na^+ moves to inside the axon.

to these ions, and they tend to diffuse toward areas of lesser concentration. Because the membrane is more permeable to potassium than to sodium, there are always more positive ions outside the membrane than inside; this accounts for some of the membrane potential recorded by the voltmeter. The axon cytoplasm also contains large, negatively charged proteins. Altogether, then, the voltmeter records that the resting potential is −70 mV inside the cell.

Animation
How the Sodium-Potassium Pump Works

Action Potential

An **action potential** is a rapid change in polarity across a portion of an axonal membrane as the nerve impulse occurs. An action potential involves two types of gated ion channels in the axonal membrane, one that allows passage of Na⁺, and another that allows passage of K⁺. In contrast to ungated ion channels, which constantly allow ions across the membrane, gated ion channels open and close in response to a stimulus, such as a signal from another neuron.

The *threshold* is the minimum change in polarity across the axonal membrane that is required to generate an action potential. Therefore, the action potential is an all-or-none event. During *depolarization,* the inside of a neuron becomes positive because of the sudden entrance of sodium ions. If threshold is reached, many more sodium channels open, and the action potential begins. As sodium ions rapidly move across

the membrane to the inside of the axon, the action potential swings up from −70 mV to +40 mV (Fig. 37.5*b*). This reversal in polarity causes the sodium channels to close and the potassium channels to open. As potassium ions leave the axon, the membrane potential swings down from +40 mV to −70 mV. In other words, a *repolarization* occurs (Fig. 37.5*c*). An action potential only takes 2 msec (milliseconds). To visualize such rapid fluctuations in voltage across the axonal membrane, researchers generally find it useful to plot the voltage changes over time (Fig. 37.5*d*).

Animation
Nerve Impulse

Propagation of Action Potentials

In nonmyelinated axons (such as sensory receptors in the skin), the action potential travels down an axon one small section at a time, at a speed of about 1 m/sec (meter per second). In myelinated axons, the gated ion channels that produce an action potential are concentrated at the nodes of Ranvier. *Saltar* in Spanish means "to jump," and so this mode of conduction, called **saltatory conduction,** means that the action potential "jumps" from node to node:

c. Action potential ends: repolarization occurs when K⁺ gates open and K⁺ moves to outside the axon.

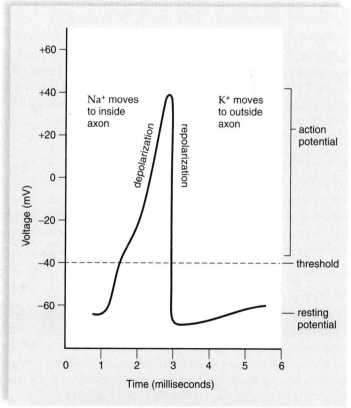

d. An action potential can be visualized if voltage changes are graphed over time.

Speeds of 200 m/sec (about 450 miles per hour) have been recorded. As you can see, this speed is considerably greater than the rate of travel in nonmyelinated axons and allows what seems to be an instantaneous response.

As soon as an action potential has moved on, the previous section undergoes a **refractory period,** during which the Na$^+$ gates are unable to open. Notice, therefore, that the action potential cannot move backward and instead always moves down an axon toward its terminals. The intensity of a signal traveling down a nerve fiber is determined by how many nerve impulses are generated within a given time span.

Transmission Across a Synapse

Every axon branches into many fine endings, each tipped by a small swelling, called an axon terminal (Fig. 37.6). Each terminal lies very close to the dendrite (or the cell body) of another neuron. This region of close proximity is called a **synapse.** At a synapse, the membrane of the first neuron is called the *pre*synaptic membrane, and the membrane of the next neuron is called the *post*synaptic membrane. The small gap between the neurons is called the **synaptic cleft.**

A nerve impulse cannot cross a synaptic cleft. Transmission across a synapse is carried out by molecules called **neurotransmitters,** which are stored in synaptic vesicles. When nerve impulses traveling along an axon reach an axon terminal, gated channels for calcium ions (Ca^{2+}) open, and calcium enters the terminal. This sudden rise in Ca^{2+} stimulates synaptic vesicles to merge with the presynaptic membrane, and neurotransmitter molecules are released into the synaptic cleft. They diffuse across the cleft to the postsynaptic membrane, where they bind with specific receptor proteins.

Depending on the type of neurotransmitter and/or the type of receptor, the response of the postsynaptic neuron can be toward excitation or toward inhibition. Excitatory neurotransmitters that use gated ion channels are fast acting. Other neurotransmitters affect the metabolism of the postsynaptic cell and therefore are slower acting.

Animation
Action Potential Propagation

Neurotransmitters

More than 100 substances are known or suspected to be neurotransmitters in both the CNS and PNS. Many of these can have opposing effects on different tissues. *Acetylcholine (ACh)* excites skeletal muscle but inhibits cardiac muscle. It has either an excitatory or inhibitory effect on smooth muscle or glands, depending on their location. In the CNS, *norepinephrine* is important to dreaming, waking, and mood. *Dopamine* is involved in emotions, learning, and attention, and *serotonin* is involved in

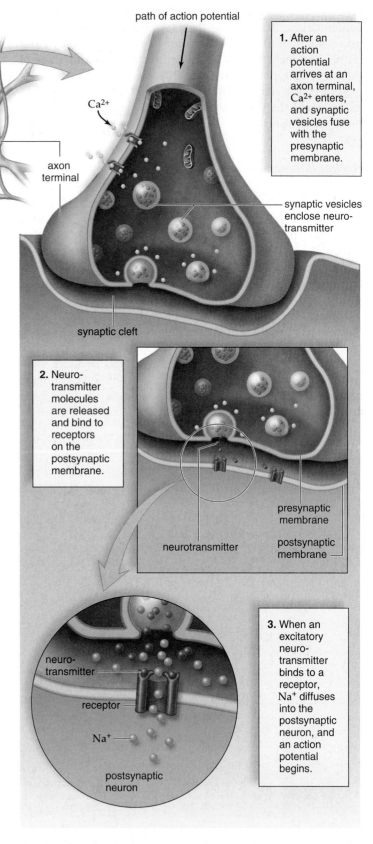

path of action potential

Ca^{2+}

axon terminal

cell body of postsynaptic neuron

synaptic vesicles enclose neurotransmitter

1. After an action potential arrives at an axon terminal, Ca^{2+} enters, and synaptic vesicles fuse with the presynaptic membrane.

synaptic cleft

2. Neurotransmitter molecules are released and bind to receptors on the postsynaptic membrane.

presynaptic membrane

neurotransmitter

postsynaptic membrane

3. When an excitatory neurotransmitter binds to a receptor, Na$^+$ diffuses into the postsynaptic neuron, and an action potential begins.

neurotransmitter

receptor

Na$^+$

postsynaptic neuron

Figure 37.6 Synapse structure and function.   Transmission across a synapse from one neuron to another occurs when a neurotransmitter is released at the presynaptic membrane, diffuses across a synaptic cleft, and binds to a receptor in the postsynaptic membrane. An action potential may begin.

a.

cell body of the neuron   axon terminals

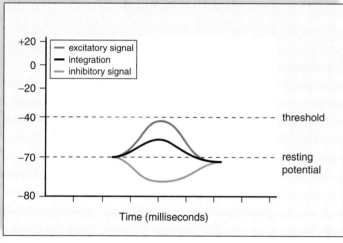

b.

Figure 37.7 Synaptic integration. **a.** Many neurons synapse with a cell body. **b.** Both inhibitory signals (blue) and excitatory signals (red) are summed up in the dendrite and cell body of the postsynaptic neuron. Only if the combined signals cause the membrane potential to rise above threshold does an action potential occur. In this example, threshold was not reached.

thermoregulation, sleeping, emotions, and perception. *Endorphins* are neurotransmitters that bind to natural opioid receptors in the brain. They are associated with the "runner's high" of exercisers because they also produce a feeling of tranquility. Endorphins are produced by the brain not only when there is physical stress but also when emotional stress is present.

After a neurotransmitter has been released into a synaptic cleft and has initiated a response, it is removed from the cleft. In some synapses, the postsynaptic membrane contains enzymes that rapidly inactivate the neurotransmitter. For example, the enzyme *acetylcholinesterase (AChE)* breaks down acetylcholine. In other synapses, the presynaptic cell is responsible for reuptake, a process in which it rapidly reabsorbs the

neurotransmitter, possibly for repackaging in synaptic vesicles or for molecular breakdown. The short existence of neurotransmitters at a synapse prevents continuous stimulation (or inhibition) of postsynaptic membranes.

Animation
Chemical Synapse

It is of interest to note here that many drugs affecting the nervous system act by interfering with or potentiating the action of neurotransmitters. Such drugs can enhance or block the release of a neurotransmitter, mimic the action of a neurotransmitter or block the receptor, or interfere with the removal of a neurotransmitter from a synaptic cleft. Depression, a common mood disorder, appears to involve imbalances in norepinephrine and serotonin. Some antidepressant drugs, such as fluoxetine (Prozac®), prevent the reuptake of serotonin, and others, including bupropion hydrochloride (Wellbutrin®), prevent the reuptake of both serotonin and norepinephrine. Blocking reuptake prolongs the effects of these two neurotransmitters in networks of neurons within the brain that are involved in the emotional state.

Drugs that affect neurotransmitter activity are often abused for "recreational" purposes, with often unfortunate and sometimes deadly results. The Biological Systems feature on page 710 describes a number of these dangerous drugs.

Synaptic Integration

A single neuron has many dendrites plus the cell body, and both can have synapses with many other neurons. One thousand to 10,000 synapses per single neuron is not uncommon. Therefore, a neuron is on the receiving end of many excitatory and inhibitory signals. An excitatory signal produces a potential change that causes the neuron to become less polarized, or closer to triggering an action potential. An inhibitory signal causes the neuron to become hyperpolarized, or farther from an action potential.

Neurons integrate these incoming signals, and do so specifically at the area of the neuron cell body where the axon emerges, called the *axon hillock.* **Integration** is the summing up of excitatory and inhibitory signals (Fig. 37.7). If a neuron receives many excitatory signals (either from different synapses or at a rapid rate from one synapse), chances are the axon will transmit a nerve impulse. In Fig. 37.7, the inhbitory signals (shown in blue) are cancelling out the excitatory signals, resulting in no nerve impulse.

MP3
Synapses

Check Your Progress 37.2

1. Explain why a nerve impulse travels more quickly down a myelinated axon as compared with an unmyelinated axon.
2. Describe the movement of specific ions during the generation of a nerve impulse.
3. Analyze how the bite of a black widow spider, which contains a powerful AChE inhibitor, might cause each of these common symptoms: muscle cramps, salivation, fast heart rate, high blood pressure.

37.3 The Central Nervous System

Learning Outcomes

Upon completion of this section, you should be able to

1. Describe the anatomy of the spinal cord and spinal nerves.
2. List the major regions of the human brain and describe some major functions of each.
3. Compare the causes and types of symptoms seen in some common CNS disorders.

The central nervous system (CNS) consists of the spinal cord and the brain. It has three specific functions:

1. *Receives sensory input*—sensory receptors in skin and other organs respond to external and internal stimuli by generating nerve impulses that travel to the CNS.
2. *Performs integration*—the CNS sums up the input it receives from all over the body.
3. *Generates motor output*—nerve impulses from the CNS go to the muscles and glands. Muscle contractions and gland secretions are responses to stimuli received by sensory receptors.

As an example of the operation of the CNS, consider the events that occur as a person raises a glass to the lips. Continuous sensory input to the CNS from the eyes and hand informs the CNS of the position of the glass, and the CNS continually sums up the incoming data before commanding the hand to proceed. At any time, integration with other sensory data might cause the CNS to command a different motion instead. The lips detect the

arrival of the glass, passing this information to the CNS, which then directs the actions of drinking.

MP3
Organization of the
Nervous System

The spinal cord and the brain are both protected by bone; the spinal cord is surrounded by vertebrae, and the brain is enclosed by the skull. Both the spinal cord and the brain are wrapped in three protective membranes known as **meninges** (see Fig. 37.8). The spaces between the meninges are filled with **cerebrospinal fluid,** which cushions and protects the CNS. Cerebrospinal fluid, produced by a type of glial cell, is contained in the central canal of the spinal cord and within the **ventricles** of the brain, which are interconnecting spaces that produce and serve as reservoirs for cerebrospinal fluid. **Meningitis** (inflammation of the meninges) is a serious disorder caused by a number of bacteria or viruses that can invade the meninges.

The Spinal Cord

The **spinal cord** is a bundle of nervous tissue enclosed in the vertebral column (see Fig. 37.12); it extends from the base of the brain to the vertebrae just below the rib cage. The spinal cord has two main functions: (1) it is the center for many **reflex actions,** which are automatic responses to external stimuli, and (2) it provides a means of communication between the brain and the spinal nerves, which leave the spinal cord.

A cross section of the spinal cord reveals that it is composed of a central portion of gray matter and a peripheral region of white matter. The **gray matter** consists of cell bodies and unmyelinated fibers. In cross section it is shaped like a butterfly, or the letter H, with two dorsal (posterior) horns and two ventral (anterior) horns surrounding a central canal. The gray

Cerebrum
(telencephalon)

skull

meninges

corpus
callosum

pituitary gland

Brain stem

midbrain

pons

medulla
oblongata

a. Parts of brain

opening to lateral
ventricle

third ventricle

Diencephalon

thalamus
(surrounds the
third ventricle)

hypothalamus

pineal gland

fourth ventricle

Cerebellum

spinal cord

Figure 37.8 The human brain. a. The right cerebral hemisphere is shown here, along with other, closely associated structures. The hemispheres are connected by the corpus callosum. **b.** The cerebrum is divided into the right and left cerebral hemispheres.

b. Cerebral hemispheres

matter contains portions of sensory neurons and motor neurons, as well as short interneurons that connect sensory and motor neurons.

Myelinated long fibers of interneurons that run together in bundles called **tracts** give **white matter** its color. These tracts connect the spinal cord to the brain. These tracts are like a busy superhighway, by which information continuously passes between the brain and the rest of the body. In the dorsal part of the cord the tracts are primarily ascending, taking information *to* the brain. Ventrally, the tracts are primarily descending, carrying information *from* the brain. Because the tracts cross over at one point, the left side of the brain controls the right side of the body, and the right side of the brain controls the left side of the body. Researchers estimate that there are about 100,000 miles of myelinated nerve fibers in the adult human brain.

If the spinal cord is damaged as the result of an injury, paralysis may result. If the injury occurs in the cervical (neck) region, all four limbs are usually paralyzed, a condition known as quadriplegia. If the injury occurs in the thoracic region, the lower body may be paralyzed, a condition called paraplegia.

Other disease processes can cause paralysis. In **amyotrophic lateral sclerosis (ALS)**, or Lou Gehrig's disease, motor neurons in the brain and spinal cord degenerate and die, leaving patients weakened, then paralyzed, then unable to breathe properly. Although there is no cure, some drugs slow the disease, and others are currently in clinical trials.

The Brain

Nerve impulses are the same in all neurons, so how is it that stimulation of our eyes causes us to see, and stimulation of our ears causes us to hear? Essentially, the central nervous system carries out the function of integrating incoming data. The **brain** allows us to perceive our environment, reason, and remember. The exact processes by which the brain generates these higher functions remain largely mysterious.

The Cerebrum

The **cerebrum** is the largest, outermost portion of the brain in humans (Fig. 37.8a). The cerebrum is the last center to receive sensory input and carry out integration before commanding voluntary motor responses. It communicates with and coordinates the activities of the other parts of the brain. The cerebrum also contains the two lateral ventricles; the third ventricle is surrounded by the diencephalon, and the fourth ventricle lies between the cerebellum and the pons.

Cerebral Hemispheres. The cerebrum is divided into two halves, called **cerebral hemispheres** (see Fig. 37.8b). A deep groove called the *longitudinal fissure* divides the cerebrum into the right and left hemispheres. Each hemisphere receives information from and controls the opposite side of the body. Although the hemispheres appear the same, the right hemisphere is associated with artistic and musical ability, emotion, spatial relationships, and pattern recognition. The left hemisphere is more adept at mathematics, language, and analytical reasoning. The two cerebral hemispheres are connected by a bridge of tracts within the *corpus callosum*.

Shallow grooves called *sulci* (sing., *sulcus*) divide each hemisphere into paired lobes (Fig. 37.9). The *frontal lobes* lie toward the front of the hemispheres and are associated with

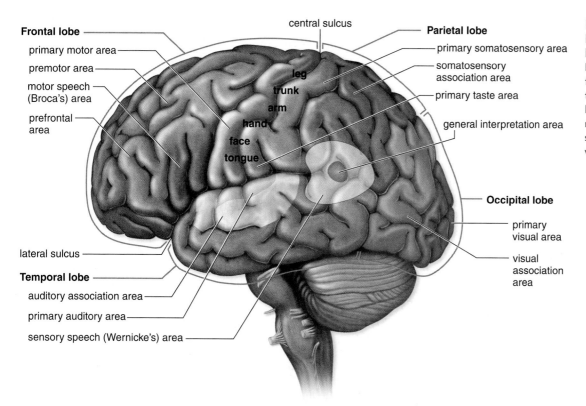

Figure 37.9 The lobes of a cerebral hemisphere. Each cerebral hemisphere is divided into four lobes: frontal, parietal, temporal, and occipital. These lobes contain centers for reasoning and movement, somatic sensing, hearing, and vision, respectively.

Frontal lobe
primary motor area
premotor area
motor speech (Broca's) area
prefrontal area
leg
trunk
arm
hand
face
tongue
central sulcus
Parietal lobe
primary somatosensory area
somatosensory association area
primary taste area
general interpretation area
Occipital lobe
primary visual area
visual association area
lateral sulcus
Temporal lobe
auditory association area
primary auditory area
sensory speech (Wernicke's) area

motor control, memory, reasoning, and judgment. For example, if a fire occurs, the frontal lobes enable you to decide whether to exit via the stairs or the window, or if it is winter, how to dress if the temperature plummets to subzero. The left frontal lobe contains *Broca's area*, which organizes motor commands to produce speech.

The *parietal lobes* lie posterior to the frontal lobe and are concerned with sensory reception and integration, as well as taste. A *primary taste area* in the parietal lobe accounts for taste sensations.

The *temporal lobes* are located laterally. A primary auditory area in each temporal lobe receives information from our ears. The *occipital lobes* are the most posterior lobes. A *primary visual area* in each occipital lobe receives information from the eyes.

MP3
The Cerebrum

The Cerebral Cortex.

The **cerebral cortex** is a thin (less than 5 mm thick), but highly convoluted, outer layer of gray matter that covers the cerebral hemispheres. The convolutions increase the surface area of the cerebral cortex. The cerebral cortex contains tens of billions of neurons and is the region of the brain that accounts for sensation, voluntary movement, and all the thought processes required for learning, memory, language, and speech.

Two regions of the cerebral cortex are of particular interest. The *primary motor area* is in the frontal lobe just ventral to (before) the central sulcus. Voluntary commands to skeletal muscles begin in the primary motor area, and each part of the body is controlled by a certain section. The size of the section indicates the precision of motor control. For example, controlling the muscles of the face and hands takes up a much larger portion of the primary motor area than controlling the entire trunk. The *primary somatosensory area* is just dorsal to the central sulcus in the parietal lobe. Sensory information from the skin and skeletal muscles arrives here.

Video
Brain Surgery

When the blood supply to any area of the brain is disrupted, a **stroke** results. Stroke is the third leading cause of death in the United States. The most common type is *ischemic* stroke, in which there is a sudden loss of blood supply to an area of the brain, usually due to arterial blockage or clot formation. The area(s) of the brain affected by a stroke will determine what type of symptoms arise. For example, a stroke that affects only the motor areas of the cerebral cortex might paralyze one side of the body, while a stroke involving Broca's area might render a stroke victim unable to speak.

Although strokes are most common in older people, a study released in 2011 noted a 51 percent increase in strokes in young men aged 15 through 34, and a 17 percent increase in women the same age. Because many of the risk factors for stroke are similar to those for cardiovascular disease, see the Nature of Science feature, "New Information About Preventing Cardiovascular Disease," in Chapter 32 to learn how to reduce your risk.

Video
Brain Healing

Basal Nuclei.

Although the bulk of the cerebrum is composed of white matter (i.e., tracts), masses of gray matter are located deep within the white matter. These so-called **basal nuclei** (basal ganglia) integrate motor commands, ensuring that proper muscle groups are activated or inhibited. As mentioned in the chapter opening essay about Muhammad Ali, **Parkinson disease (PD),** is a brain disorder characterized by tremors, speech difficulties, and difficulty standing and walking. PD results from a loss of cells in the basal nuclei that normally produce the neurotransmitter dopamine. See the Nature of Science feature on page 706 to learn about the somewhat strange history of research into PD, as well as some treatments for this disease.

MP3
The Brain

Other Parts of the Brain

The hypothalamus and the thalamus are in the *diencephalon*, a region that encircles the third ventricle. The **hypothalamus** forms the floor of the third ventricle. It is an integrating center that helps maintain homeostasis by regulating hunger, sleep, thirst, body temperature, and water balance. The hypothalamus controls the pituitary gland and, thereby, serves as a link between the nervous and endocrine systems (see Chapter 40).

The **thalamus** consists of two masses of gray matter located in the sides and roof of the third ventricle. It receives all sensory input except smell. The thalamus integrates this information and sends it on to the appropriate portions of the cerebrum. For this reason, the thalamus is often referred to as the "gatekeeper" for sensory information en route to the cerebral cortex. The thalamus also participates in higher mental functions such as memory and emotions.

The **pineal gland,** which secretes the hormone melatonin, is also located in the diencephalon. *Melatonin* is a hormone that is involved in maintaining our normal sleep-wake cycle. It is sometimes recommended for people suffering from insomnia, but many side effects can occur. Relatively high levels of melatonin are a key ingredient in "relaxation brownies" that are sold at convenience stores as well as online; many states are banning their sale, however.

Video
Winter Mood

The **cerebellum** lies under the occipital lobe of the cerebrum and is separated from the brain stem by the fourth ventricle. It is the largest part of the hindbrain. The cerebellum receives sensory input from the eyes, ears, joints, and muscles about the present position of body parts, and it also receives motor output from the cerebral cortex about where these parts should be located. After integrating this information, the cerebellum sends motor impulses by way of the brain stem to the skeletal muscles. In this way, the cerebellum maintains posture and balance. It also ensures that all of the muscles work together to produce smooth, coordinated voluntary movements, such as playing the piano or hitting a baseball.

The **brain stem** contains the midbrain, the pons, and the medulla oblongata (see Fig. 37.8). The **midbrain** acts as a relay station for tracts passing between the cerebrum and the spinal cord or cerebellum. The tracts cross in the brain stem so that the right side of the body is controlled by the left portion of the brain, and the left side of the body is controlled by the right portion of the brain.

The **pons** [L. *pons*, bridge] contains bundles of axons that form a "bridge," traveling between the cerebellum and the rest of the CNS. The pons also works with the medulla oblongata to regulate many basic body functions.

The **medulla oblongata** lies just superior to the spinal cord, and it contains tracts that ascend or descend between the spinal cord and higher brain centers. It regulates heartbeat, breathing, swallowing, and blood pressure. It also contains reflex centers for vomiting, coughing, sneezing, hiccuping, and swallowing.

The most common neurological disease of young adults is **multiple sclerosis (MS)**. This disease typically affects myelinated nerves in the cerebellum, brain stem, basal ganglia, and optic nerve. MS is considered an autoimmune disease, in which the patient's own white blood cells attack the myelin, oligodendrocytes, and eventually, neurons in the CNS. The word sclerosis refers to the multiple scars, or plaques, that can be seen using various types of scans. The damage to myelin affects transmission of nerve impulses, resulting in the most common symptoms like fatigue, vision problems, weakness, numbness, and tingling. Nearly 350,000 people in the United States have MS, and about 10,000 new cases are diagnosed each year, mainly in young adults.

The Reticular Activating System.

The **reticular activating system (RAS)** contains the reticular formation, a complex network of nuclei and nerve fibers that extend the length of the brain stem (Fig. 37.10). The reticular formation receives sensory signals that it sends up to higher centers, and motor signals that it sends to the spinal cord.

The RAS arouses the cerebrum via the thalamus and causes a person to be alert. Apparently, the RAS can filter out unnecessary sensory stimuli, explaining why you can study with the TV on. If you want to awaken the RAS, surprise it with a sudden stimulus, like splashing your face with cold water; if you want to deactivate it, remove visual and auditory stimuli. A severe injury to the RAS can cause a person to be comatose, from which recovery may be impossible.

The Limbic System

The **limbic system** is a complex network of tracts and nuclei that incorporates medial portions of the cerebral lobes, the basal

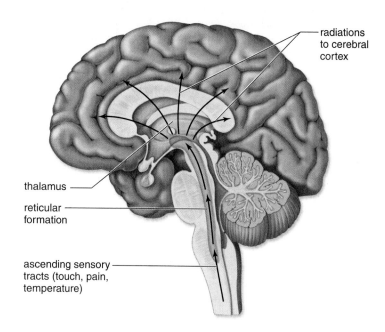

Figure 37.10 The reticular activating system. The reticular formation receives and sends on motor and sensory information to various parts of the CNS. One portion, the reticular activating system (RAS; see arrows), arouses the cerebrum and, in this way, controls alertness versus sleep.

nuclei, and the diencephalon (Fig. 37.11). The limbic system blends higher mental functions and primitive emotions into a united whole. It accounts for why activities like sexual behavior and eating seem pleasurable, and also why, as an example, mental stress can cause high blood pressure.

Two significant structures within the limbic system are the hippocampus and the amygdala, which are essential for learning and memory. The **hippocampus**, a seahorse-shaped structure that lies deep in the temporal lobe, is well situated in the brain to make the prefrontal area aware of past experiences

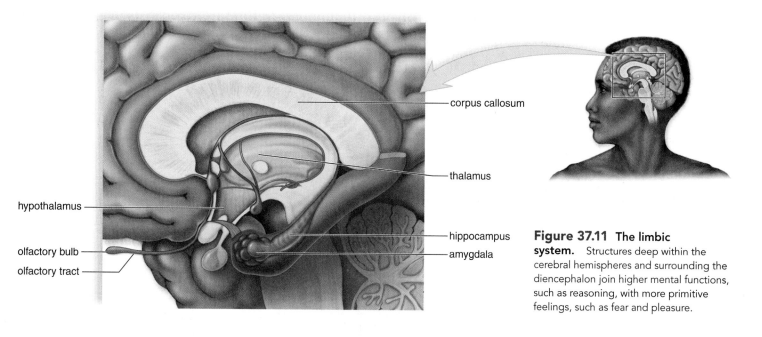

Figure 37.11 The limbic system. Structures deep within the cerebral hemispheres and surrounding the diencephalon join higher mental functions, such as reasoning, with more primitive feelings, such as fear and pleasure.

THEME Nature of Science

An Accidental Experimental Model for Parkinson Disease

Parkinson disease (PD) was first described as the "Shaking Palsy" in 1817 by English surgeon James Parkinson, for whom the disease was later named. It affects about 1.5 million people in the United States, and over six million worldwide. PD is most common in people over 60 and rarely affects those under 40. The symptoms of PD include bradykinesis (slow movements), tremors, rigidity of the limbs and trunk, and impaired speech, balance, and coordination. PD is caused by injury to or death of dopamine-producing neurons in the basal ganglia (specifically the substantia nigra), deep in the forebrain, that normally help control voluntary movement. The initial event(s) that cause the neuron damage aren't well understood, and there is no cure.

Frozen Junkies

In 1976, Barry Kidston, a graduate student in chemistry at the University of Maryland, wanted to experiment with hard drugs and decided to synthesize a narcotic he had read about in a 1947 scientific paper. The drug, called MPPP, was said to be less addictive than morphine, and was technically not illegal (although it is now). Kidston was successful at first, and was apparently able to achieve a satisfactory "high" by intravenously injecting the compound, which he synthesized in a makeshift lab he set up in his parent's basement. His luck ran out, however, when he accidently produced a related compound called MPTP instead of MPPP. Soon after injecting the MPTP, Kidston's speech became slurred, he had trouble walking, and within three days he could hardly move.

Kidston's doctors were baffled, but after a neurologist noted that his symptoms resembled Parkinson disease, he was treated with anti-PD drugs, and he dramatically improved. For two years he was able to function well on medication, but then he died, somewhat ironically, from a cocaine overdose. His autopsy revealed a substantial loss of dopamine-producing cells in the substantia nigra, which is a hallmark of PD (Fig. 37A).

Kidston's case was published in a medical journal, but it was barely noticed until 1981, when six IV drug users turned up at various emergency rooms in the San Francisco area, all showing very similar symptoms, as if they had "turned to stone." Some quick investigative work turned up the fact that all had tried some new heroin that had become available on the street.

When some of this material was sent in for analysis, one of the lab toxicologists remembered seeing the article about Kidston a few years earlier, and quickly determined that the drug all the new patients had injected indeed contained MPTP.[1]

New Treatments

As news that PD could be induced by MPTP in humans reached the biomedical research community, scientists were quickly able to demonstrate that MPTP could also induce PD in animals such as monkeys and mice. Since the mid-1980s, animals with MPTP-induced PD have been used in hundreds of studies that have advanced our understanding of how PD develops, and have been instrumental in the development of new therapies, such as:

- Drugs that increase dopamine. These vary from L-Dopa, which is converted into dopamine in the brain, and is still the most effective drug therapy, to newer drugs like Entacapone that inhibit the normal breakdown of dopamine.
- Surgical treatments. The most common of these is deep brain stimulation,

in which an electrode is inserted into an area of the brain called the subthalamic nucleus, which seems to be overactive in PD. Coincidentally, one of the original "frozen addicts," still serving time in prison, had this procedure done and has had very significant improvement in his condition.
- Stem cell transplants. The use of fetal stem cells to replace diseased or dying neurons in PD remains controversial in many countries. However, results from animal models continue to be encouraging, and private groups such as the Michael J. Fox Foundation for Parkinson Disease Research continue to support stem cells as the most likely approach that may result in a cure for PD.

Questions to Consider

1. What are some other instances where accidental findings have resulted in scientific discoveries?
2. Should the families of people like Kidston, who accidentally benefit medicine, be compensated financially?
3. Why is it so difficult to determine the specific causes of PD and other brain diseases?

---

1 Further details about these cases can be read in Langston, J. W., and Palfreman, J. 1995. *The Case of The Frozen Addicts* (Pantheon, NY). A PBS video of the same name is also available.

Cut section of the midbrain where a portion of the substantia nigra is visible

Substantia nigra

Diminished substantia nigra as seen in Parkinson disease

Figure 37A Parkinson Disease.   Neurons in the substantia nigra of the brain appear dark due to a high melanin content. In PD, this area appears lighter due to a loss of these neurons.

stored in sensory association areas. The **amygdala**, in particular, can cause these experiences to have emotional overtones. For example, the smell of smoke may serve as an alarm to search for fire in the house. The inclusion of the frontal lobe in the limbic system gives us the capability of restraining ourselves from acting out on strong feelings by using reason.

Learning and Memory. **Memory** is the ability to hold a thought in mind or recall events from the past, ranging from a word we learned only yesterday to an early emotional experience that has shaped our lives. Learning takes place when we retain and use past memories.

The prefrontal area in the frontal lobe is active during short-term memory as when we temporarily recall a telephone number. Some telephone numbers go into long-term memory. Think of a telephone number you know by heart, and see if you can bring it to mind without also thinking about the place or person associated with that number. Most likely you cannot, because typically long-term memory is a mixture of what is called semantic memory (numbers, words, etc.) and episodic memory (persons, events, etc.). Skill memory is a type of memory that can exist independently of episodic memory. Skill memory is being able to perform motor activities like riding a bike or playing ice hockey.

What parts of the brain are functioning when you remember something from long ago? The hippocampus gathers our long-term memories, which are stored in bits and pieces throughout the sensory association areas, and makes them available to the frontal lobe. Why are some memories so emotionally charged? The amygdala is responsible for fear conditioning and associating danger with sensory information received from the thalamus and the cortical sensory areas.

Several diseases of the brain can affect memory. **Alzheimer disease (AD)** is the most common cause of dementia, or a loss of reasoning, memory, and other higher brain functions, especially in people over age 65. AD patients have abnormal neurons throughout the brain, but especially in the hippocampus and amygdala. These neurons have two abnormalities: 1) plaques, containing a protein called beta amyloid, accumulate around the axons, and 2) neurofibrillary tangles (bundles of fibrous protein) surround the nucleus. The cause of these protein abnormalites is unknown, although several genes that predispose a person to develop AD have been identified. Although no cure is available, most of the drugs that are currently approved to treat symptoms of AD are cholinesterase inhibitors, which effectively increase the levels of acetylcholine in the AD patient's brain. This in turn can improve learning and memory, at least temporarily.

Check Your Progress 37.3

1. Trace the path of a nerve impulse from a stimulus in an internal organ (such as food in the intestine stimulating peristalsis) to the brain and back.
2. Name the four major lobes of the human brain.
3. List at least two common diseases of the CNS and describe their symptoms and causes.

37.4 The Peripheral Nervous System

Learning Outcomes

Upon completion of this section, you should be able to

1. Describe the overall anatomy of the PNS, including the cranial nerves and spinal nerves.
2. Explain how the somatic system differs from the autonomic system.
3. Contrast the functions of the sympathetic and parasympathetic divisions of the autonomic nervous system.

The peripheral nervous system (PNS) lies outside the central nervous system and contains **nerves,** which are bundles of axons. Axons that occur in nerves are also called *nerve fibers.* The cell bodies of neurons are found in the CNS and in ganglia, collections of cell bodies outside the CNS.

MP3
Organization of the Nervous System

nerve

bundle of nerve fibers

myelin sheath

single nerve fiber (axon)

The paired cranial and spinal nerves are part of the PNS. In the PNS, the somatic nervous system has sensory and motor functions that control the skeletal muscles. Ascending tracts carry sensory information to the brain, and descending tracts carry motor commands to the neurons in the spinal cord that control the muscles. The autonomic nervous system controls smooth muscle, cardiac muscle, and the glands. It is further divided into the sympathetic and parasympathetic divisions.

Humans have 12 pairs of **cranial nerves** attached to the brain (Fig. 37.12*a*). Some of these are sensory nerves; that is, they contain only sensory nerve fibers. Some are motor nerves that contain only motor fibers, and others are mixed nerves that contain both sensory and motor fibers. Cranial nerves are largely concerned with the head, neck, and facial regions of the body. However, the vagus nerve has branches not only to the pharynx and larynx but also to most of the internal organs.

Humans also have 31 pairs of **spinal nerves** (Figs. 37.12*b* and 37.13) that emerge from the spinal cord via two short branches, or roots. The dorsal roots contain axons of sensory neurons, which conduct impulses to the spinal cord from sensory receptors. The cell body of a sensory neuron is in the **dorsal root ganglion.** The ventral roots contain axons of motor neurons, which conduct impulses away from the spinal cord to effectors. These two roots join to form a spinal nerve. All spinal nerves are mixed nerves that contain many sensory and motor fibers.

Somatic System

The PNS has two divisions—somatic and autonomic. The nerves in the **somatic system** serve the skin, joints, and skeletal muscles. Therefore, the somatic system includes nerves that

- take sensory information from external sensory receptors in the skin and joints to the CNS, and
- carry motor commands away from the CNS to the skeletal muscles.

The neurotransmitter acetylcholine (ACh) is active in the somatic system.

Voluntary control of skeletal muscles always originates in the brain. Involuntary responses to stimuli, called reflex actions, can involve only the spinal cord. Reflexes enable the body to react swiftly to stimuli that could disrupt homeostasis. Flying objects cause our eyes to blink, and sharp pins cause our hands to jerk away, even without our having to think about it.

The Reflex Arc. Figure 37.13 illustrates the path of a reflex that involves only the spinal cord. If your hand touches a sharp pin, **sensory receptors** generate nerve impulses that move along sensory axons through a dorsal root ganglion toward the spinal cord. Sensory neurons that enter the cord dorsally pass signals on to many interneurons in the gray matter of the spinal cord. Some of these interneurons synapse with motor neurons. The short dendrites and the cell bodies of motor neurons are also in the spinal cord, but their axons leave the cord ventrally. Nerve

impulses travel along motor axons to an **effector,** which brings about a response to the stimulus. In this case, a muscle contracts so that you withdraw your hand from the pin. (Sometimes an effector is a gland.)

Various other reactions are possible—you will most likely look at the pin, wince, and cry out in pain. This whole series of responses is explained by the fact that some of the interneurons in the white matter of the cord carry nerve impulses in tracts to the brain. The brain makes you aware of the stimulus and directs subsequent reactions to the situation. You don't feel pain until the brain receives the information and interprets it! Visual information received directly by way of a cranial nerve may make you aware that your finger is bleeding. Then you might decide to look for a Band-Aid.

Autonomic System

The **autonomic system** of the PNS regulates the activity of cardiac and smooth muscle and glands. It carries out its duties without our awareness or intent. The system is divided into the sympathetic and parasympathetic divisions (see Table 37.1 and Fig. 37.14). Both of these divisions

- function automatically and usually in an involuntary manner,
- innervate all internal organs, and
- use two neurons and one ganglion for each impulse.

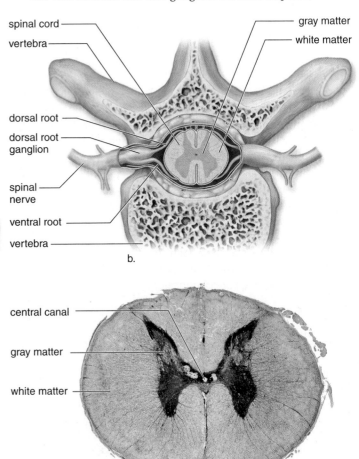

Figure 37.12 Cranial and spinal nerves. **a.** Ventral surface of the brain, showing the attachment of the cranial nerves. **b.** Cross section of the vertebral column and spinal cord, showing a spinal nerve. Each spinal nerve has a dorsal root and a ventral root attached to the spinal cord. **c.** Photomicrograph of spinal cord cross section.

Labels for figure a: frontal lobe, olfactory bulb, olfactory tract, optic nerve, optic chiasma, temporal lobe, cerebellum, medulla

Labels for figure b: spinal cord, vertebra, dorsal root, dorsal root ganglion, spinal nerve, ventral root, vertebra, gray matter, white matter

Labels for figure c: central canal, gray matter, white matter

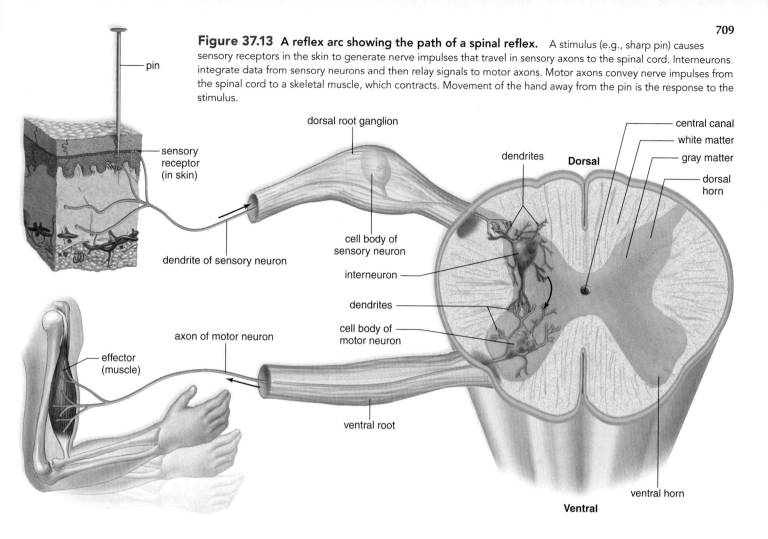

Figure 37.13 A reflex arc showing the path of a spinal reflex. A stimulus (e.g., sharp pin) causes sensory receptors in the skin to generate nerve impulses that travel in sensory axons to the spinal cord. Interneurons integrate data from sensory neurons and then relay signals to motor axons. Motor axons convey nerve impulses from the spinal cord to a skeletal muscle, which contracts. Movement of the hand away from the pin is the response to the stimulus.

The first neuron has a cell body within the CNS and a preganglionic fiber. The second neuron has a cell body within the ganglion and a postganglionic fiber.

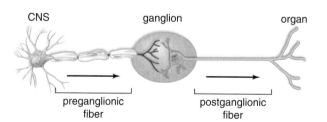

Reflex actions, such as those that regulate blood pressure and breathing rate, are especially important to the maintenance of homeostasis. These reflexes begin when the sensory neurons in contact with internal organs send information to the CNS. They are completed by motor neurons within the autonomic system.

Sympathetic Division

Most preganglionic fibers of the **sympathetic division** arise from the middle, or thoracolumbar, portion of the spinal cord and almost immediately terminate in ganglia that lie near the cord. Therefore, in this division, the preganglionic fiber is short, but the postganglionic fiber that makes contact with an organ is long.

Table 37.1 Comparison of Somatic Motor and Autonomic Motor Pathways

	Somatic Motor Pathway	Autonomic Motor Pathways	
		Sympathetic	Parasympathetic
Type of control	Voluntary/involuntary	Involuntary	Involuntary
Number of neurons per message	One	Two (preganglionic shorter than postganglionic)	Two (preganglionic longer than postganglionic)
Location of motor fiber	Most cranial nerves and all spinal nerves	Thoracolumbar spinal nerves	Cranial (e.g., vagus) and sacral spinal nerves
Neurotransmitter	Acetylcholine	Norepinephrine	Acetylcholine
Effectors	Skeletal muscles	Smooth and cardiac muscle, glands	Smooth and cardiac muscle, glands

THEME Biological Systems

Drugs of Abuse

Drug abuse is apparent when a person takes a drug at a dose level and under circumstances that increase the potential for a harmful outcome. Addiction is present when more of the drug is needed to get the same effect, and withdrawal symptoms occur when the user stops taking the drug. This is true not only for teenagers and adults, but also for newborn babies of mothers who abuse and are addicted to drugs.

Alcohol

With the exception of caffeine, alcohol (ethanol) consumption is the most socially accepted form of drug use in the United States. According to a 2006 survey, nearly one-third of all U.S. high school students reported hazardous drinking (five or more drinks in one setting) during the 30 days preceding the survey. Notably, 80% of college-age young adults drink. According to a U.S. government study, drinking in college contributes to an estimated 1,400 student deaths, 500,000 injuries, and 70,000 cases of sexual assault or date rape each year.

Alcohol acts as a *depressant* on many parts of the brain by increasing the action of GABA, an inhibitory neurotransmitter. Depending on the amount consumed, the effects of alcohol on the brain can lead to a feeling of relaxation, lowered inhibitions, impaired concentration and coordination, slurred speech, and vomiting. If the blood level of alcohol becomes too high, coma or death can occur.

Beginning in about 2005, several manufacturers began selling alcoholic energy drinks. With names like Four Loco, Joose, and Sparks, these drinks combine fairly high levels of alcohol with caffeine and other ingredients. Although interactions between drugs can be complex, the stimulant effects of caffeine can counteract some of the depressant effects of alcohol, so that users feel able to drink more. Because caffeine does not reduce the intoxicating effects of alcohol, many state legislatures are banning these products, and in November 2010, the U.S. Food and Drug Administration warned several manufacturers that they would no longer be allowed to mix caffeine with alcohol in their products.

Nicotine

About 23% of U.S. high school students, and 8% of middle school students, reported smoking cigarettes in 2006. Young adults between age 18 and 25 reported the highest tobacco usage of any age group, at 45%. When tobacco is smoked or chewed, nicotine is rapidly delivered throughout the body. It causes a release of epinephrine from the adrenal glands, increasing blood sugar and causing the initial feeling of stimulation. As blood sugar falls, depression and fatigue set in, causing the user to seek more nicotine. In the CNS, nicotine stimulates neurons to release dopamine, a neurotransmitter that promotes a temporary sense of pleasure, and reinforces dependence on the drug. About 70% of people who try smoking become addicted.

As mentioned in earlier chapters, smoking is strongly associated with serious diseases of the cardiovascular and respiratory systems. Once addicted, however, only 10% to 20% of smokers are able to quit. Most medical approaches to quitting smoking involve the administration of nicotine in safer forms, like skin patches, gum, or a newly developed nicotine inhaler, so that withdrawal symptoms can be minimized while dependence is gradually reduced. As of 2010, an anti-nicotine vaccine called NicVAX was showing promise in early clinical trials. The vaccine stimulates the production of antibodies that prevent nicotine from entering the brain.

Club and Date Rape Drugs

Methamphetamine and Ecstasy are considered club or party drugs. Methamphetamine (commonly called meth or crank) is a powerful CNS stimulant. Meth is often produced in makeshift home laboratories, usually starting with ephedrine or pseudoephedrine, common ingredients in many cold and asthma medicines. As a result, many states have passed laws making these medications more difficult to purchase. The number of toxic chemicals used to prepare the drug makes a former meth lab site hazardous to humans and to the environment. Over 9 million people in the United States have used methamphetamine at least once in their lifetime. It is available as a powder that can be snorted, or as crystals (crystal meth or ice) that can be smoked.

The structure of methamphetamine is similar to that of dopamine, and the most immediate effect of taking meth is a rush of euphoria, energy, alertness, and elevated mood. However, this is typically followed by a state of agitation that, in some individuals, leads to violent behavior. Chronic use can result in what is called an amphetamine psychosis, characterized by paranoia, hallucinations, irritability, and aggressive, erratic behavior.

Video
Meth and the Brain

Ecstasy is the street name for MDMA (methylenedioxymethamphetamine), which is chemically similar to methamphetamine. Many users say that "X," taken as a pill that looks like an aspirin or candy, increases their feelings of well-being and love for other people. However, it has many of the same side effects as other stimulants, plus it can interfere with temperature regulation, leading to hyperthermia, high blood pressure, and seizures. In June 2010, a 15-year-old girl died from Ecstasy-related causes after attending a large rave party in Los Angeles.

Drugs with sedative effects, known as date rape or predatory drugs, include Rohypnol (roofies), gamma-hydroxybutyric acid (GHB), and ketamine (special K). Ketamine is actually a drug that veterinarians sometimes use to perform surgery on animals. Any of these drugs can be given to an unsuspecting person, who may fall into a dreamlike state where they are unable to move, and thus are vulnerable to sexual assault.

Cocaine and Crack

Cocaine is an alkaloid derived from the shrub *Erythroxylon coca*. Approximately 35 million Americans have used cocaine by sniffing/snorting, injecting, or smoking. Cocaine is a powerful *stimulant* in the CNS that interferes with the reuptake of dopamine at synapses, increasing overall brain activity (Fig. 37B). The result is a rush of well-being that lasts from 5 to 30 minutes.

"Crack" is the street name given to cocaine that is processed to a free base form for smoking. The term *crack* refers to the crackling sound heard when the drug is smoked. Smoking allows high doses of the drug to reach the brain rapidly, providing an intense and immediate high, or "rush." Approximately 8 million Americans use crack.

A cocaine binge is a period in which a user takes the drug at ever-higher doses. The user is hyperactive, with little desire for food or sleep but an increased sex drive. This is followed by a crash period, characterized by fatigue, depression, irritability, and lack of interest in sex. In fact, men who use cocaine often become impotent.

Cocaine is highly addictive; with continued use, the brain makes less dopamine to compensate for a seemingly endless supply. The user experiences withdrawal symptoms and an intense craving for cocaine. Overdosing on cocaine can cause cardiac and/or respiratory arrest.

Heroin

Heroin is derived from the resin or sap of the opium poppy plant, which is widely grown—from Turkey to Southeast Asia and in parts of Latin America. Drugs derived from opium are called opiates, a class that also includes morphine and codeine. After heroin is injected, snorted, or smoked, a feeling of euphoria, along with relief of any pain, occurs within a few minutes. It is estimated that 4 million Americans have used heroin some time in their lives, and over 300,000 people use heroin annually.

As with other drugs of abuse, addiction is common. Heroin binds to receptors meant for the endorphins, naturally occurring neurotransmitters that kill pain and produce feelings of tranquility. With repeated heroin use, the body's production of endorphins decreases. Tolerance develops so that the user needs to take more of the drug just to prevent withdrawal symptoms (tremors, restlessness, cramps, vomiting), and the original euphoria is no longer felt. Long-term users commonly acquire hepatitis, HIV/AIDS, and various bacterial infections due to the use of shared needles, and heavy users may experience convulsions and death by respiratory arrest.

Heroin addiction can be treated with synthetic opiate compounds, such as methadone or suboxone, that decrease withdrawal symptoms and block heroin's effects. However, methadone itself can be addictive, and methadone-related deaths are on the rise.

Marijuana and K2

The dried flowering tops, leaves, and stems of the marijuana plant, *Cannabis sativa*, contain and are covered by a resin that is rich in THC (tetrahydrocannabinol). The names *cannabis* and *marijuana* apply to either the plant or THC. Marijuana can be ingested, but usually it is smoked in a cigarette called a "joint." Although the drug was banned in the United States in 1937, an estimated 22 million Americans use marijuana, making it the most commonly used illegal drug in the U.S. Beginning with California in 1996, several states have legalized its use for medical purposes, such as treating cancer, AIDS, or glaucoma. In 2005 however, the Supreme Court ruled that patients prescribed medical marijuana can still be prosecuted by federal agencies.

Researchers have found that THC binds to a receptor for anandamide, a naturally occurring neurotransmitter that is important for short-term memory processing, and perhaps for feelings of contentment. The occasional marijuana user experiences mild euphoria, along with alterations in vision and judgment. Heavy use can cause hallucinations, anxiety, depression, paranoia, and psychotic symptoms. Some researchers believe that long-term marijuana use leads to brain impariment.

In recent years, awareness is increasing about a synthetic compound called K2 or Spice. Originally synthesized by an organic chemist at Clemson University, K2 is about ten times as potent as THC. The chemical is typically sprayed onto a mixture of other herbal products, and smoked. However, because there is no regulation of how it is produced, the amount of K2 itself, or contaminants, can vary greatly. This may account for the several reports of serious medical problems and even deaths in K2 users.

Questions to Consider

1. Suppose a form of heroin could be synthesized that had only the desired effects (euphoria and pain relief) with no side effects. Should such a drug be legal?
2. Should medical marijuana be legal for use in all states? If so, how should it be regulated?
3. In November 2010, the U.S. Drug Enforcement Agency banned the sale of five chemicals used to make K2. Is this an overreaction?

brain activity ⟶

Before cocaine use, brain is less active.

After cocaine use, brain is more active.

Figure 37B Drug use. Brain activity before and after the use of cocaine.

Figure 37.14 Autonomic system structure and function. Sympathetic preganglionic fibers (*left*) arise from the cervical, thoracic, and lumbar portions of the spinal cord; parasympathetic preganglionic fibers (*right*) arise from the cranial and sacral portions of the spinal cord. Each system innervates the same organs but has contrary effects.

The sympathetic division is especially important during emergency situations and is associated with "fight or flight" (Fig. 37.14). If you need to fend off a foe or flee from danger, active muscles require a ready supply of glucose and oxygen. The sympathetic division accelerates the heartbeat and dilates the bronchi. At the same time, the sympathetic division inhibits the digestive tract, because digestion is not an immediate necessity if you are under attack. The neurotransmitter released by the postganglionic axon is primarily norepinephrine (NE). Structurally, NE resembles epinephrine (adrenaline), an adrenal medulla hormone that usually increases heart rate and contraction (see Chapter 40).

Parasympathetic Division

The **parasympathetic division** includes a few cranial nerves (e.g., the vagus nerve) and also fibers that arise from the sacral (bottom) portion of the spinal cord. Therefore, this division often is referred to as the craniosacral portion of the autonomic system. In the parasympathetic division, the preganglionic fiber is long, and the postganglionic fiber is short because the ganglia lie near or within the organ.

The parasympathetic division, sometimes called the "housekeeper" or "rest and digest division," promotes all the internal responses we associate with a relaxed state; for example, it causes the pupil of the eye to contract, promotes digestion of food, and slows the heartbeat. The neurotransmitter used by the parasympathetic division is acetylcholine (ACh).

Check Your Progress   37.4

1. Review the neurological explanation for the observation that, after you touch a hot stove, you withdraw your hand before you feel any pain.
2. Apply your knowledge of the autonomic nervous system to explain why, if you eat a big lunch, then go out for a jog, your stomach may ache.
3. Describe the shift in autonomic system activity that occurs when you go from quietly reading to having ice dumped down the back of your shirt.

CONNECTING *the* CONCEPTS *with the* THEMES

Evolution

- The simplest type of nervous system is the nerve net found in cnidarians, which is a network of neurons in contact with each other and with contractile cells.
- Most invertebrates have a brain and ventral nerve cord with a ganglion in each body segment.
- Vertebrates have a great increase in total number of neurons that make up their nervous system, as well as a well-developed brain and, in the case of mammals, a cerebral cortex.

Nature of Science

- Research studies of the electrical charges that develop across the cell membrane of the giant axon of squids first helped scientists understand the action potentials generated by neurons.
- The discovery that Parkinson disease could be induced by a potent toxin accidently synthesized in a home lab led to useful animal models for studying PD and developing new treatments.
- Brain imaging techniques are useful in examining the effects of illicit drugs, as well as other brain conditions.

Biological Systems

- Nervous tissue is made up of cells called neurons, which transmit nerve impulses, and supporting cells called neuroglia. Transmission of impulses between neurons is usually accomplished by means of chemical neurotransmitters.
- The central nervous system includes the brain and spinal cord; the peripheral nervous system is divided into a somatic system that controls skeletal muscles, and an autonomic system that regulates the activity of the heart, smooth muscle, and glands.

Media Study Tools

www.mhhe.com/maderbiology11

Enhance your study of this chapter with study tools and practice tests. Also ask your instructor about the resources available through ConnectPlus, including the media-rich eBook, interactive learning tools, and animations.

Summarize

37.1 Evolution of the Nervous System

A comparative study of the invertebrates shows a gradual increase in the complexity of the nervous system. Vertebrate nervous systems are much more complex, and the mammalian nervous system is the most complex of all.

37.2 Nervous Tissue

The anatomical unit of the nervous system is the neuron, of which there are three types: sensory neuron, motor neuron, and interneuron. Each of these is made up of a cell body, an axon, and dendrites.

When an axon is not conducting an action potential (nerve impulse), the resting potential indicates that the inside of the fiber is negative compared to the outside. The sodium-potassium pump helps maintain this resting potential. When the axon is conducting a nerve impulse, an action potential (i.e., a change in membrane potential) travels along the fiber. Depolarization occurs (inside becomes positive) due to the movement of Na^+ to the inside, and then repolarization occurs (inside becomes negative again) due to the movement of K^+ to the outside of the fiber.

Transmission of the nerve impulse from one neuron to another takes place across a synapse. Synaptic vesicles usually release a chemical, known as a neurotransmitter, into the synaptic cleft. The binding of neurotransmitters to receptors in the postsynaptic membrane can either increase the chance of an action potential (stimulation) or decrease the chance of an action potential (inhibition) in the next neuron. A neuron may transmit several nerve impulses, one after the other.

37.3 The Central Nervous System

The CNS consists of the spinal cord and brain, which are both protected by bone. The CNS receives and integrates sensory input and formulates motor output. The gray matter of the spinal cord contains neuron cell bodies; the white matter consists of myelinated axons that occur in bundles called tracts. The spinal cord sends sensory information to the brain, receives motor output from the brain, and carries out reflexes.

In the brain, the cerebrum has two cerebral hemispheres connected by the corpus callosum. Sensation, reasoning, learning and memory, and language and speech take place in the cerebrum. The cerebral cortex is a thin layer of gray matter covering the cerebrum.

The cerebral cortex of each cerebral hemisphere has four lobes: a frontal, parietal, occipital, and temporal lobe. The primary motor area in the frontal lobe sends out motor commands to lower brain centers, which pass them on to motor neurons. The primary somatosensory area in the parietal lobe receives sensory information from lower brain centers in communication with sensory neurons. Association areas for vision are in the occipital lobe, and those for hearing are in the temporal lobe.

The brain has a number of other regions. The hypothalamus controls homeostasis, and the thalamus specializes in sending sensory input on to the cerebrum. The cerebellum primarily coordinates skeletal muscle contractions. The medulla oblongata and the pons have centers for vital functions such as breathing and the heartbeat.

A number of important diseases affect the human nervous system. In amyotrophic lateral sclerosis (ALS), motor neurons in the brain and spinal cord degenerate and die. Strokes can affect any area of the brain, often due to a blockage in the blood supply. Multiple sclerosis (MS) is an autoimmune disease that affects the myelin sheaths, disrupting nerve transmission. Parkinson disease and Alzheimer disease are brain disorders that mainly affect older individuals.

37.4 The Peripheral Nervous System

The PNS contains the somatic system and the autonomic system. Reflexes are automatic, and some do not require involvement of the brain. A simple reflex utilizes neurons that make up a reflex arc. In the somatic system, a sensory neuron conducts nerve impulses from a sensory receptor to an interneuron, which in turn transmits impulses to a motor neuron, which stimulates an effector to react.

The motor portion of the somatic system of the PNS controls skeletal muscle; in contrast, the motor portion of the autonomic system controls smooth muscle of the internal organs and glands. The sympathetic division, which is often associated with reactions that occur during times of stress, and the parasympathetic division, which is often associated with activities that occur during times of relaxation, are both parts of the autonomic system.

Key Terms

action potential 699
Alzheimer disease 707
amygdala 707
amyotrophic lateral sclerosis
    (ALS) 703
astrocyte 697
autonomic system 708
axon 697

basal nuclei 704
brain 703
brain stem 704
cell body 697
central nervous system
    (CNS) 696
cephalization 694
cerebellum 704

cerebral cortex 704
cerebral hemisphere 703
cerebrospinal fluid 702
cerebrum 703
cranial nerve 707
dendrite 697
dorsal root ganglion 707
effector 708
ganglion 694
gray matter 702
hippocampus 705
hypothalamus 704
integration 701
interneuron 698
limbic system 705
medulla oblongata 705
memory 707
meninges 702
meningitis 702
microglia 697
midbrain 704
motor (efferent) neuron 697
multiple sclerosis 705
myelin sheath 697
nerve 707
nerve fiber 697
nerve net 694
neuroglia 697
neuron 697

neurotransmitter 700
nodes of Ranvier 697
oligodendrocyte 697
parasympathetic division 713
Parkinson disease (PD) 704
peripheral nervous system
    (PNS) 696
pineal gland 704
pons 704
reflex action 702
refractory period 700
resting potential 698
reticular activating system
    (RAS) 705
saltatory conduction 699
Schwann cell 697
sensory (afferent) neuron 697
sensory receptor 708
somatic system 708
spinal cord 702
spinal nerve 707
stroke 704
sympathetic division 709
synapse 700
synaptic cleft 700
thalamus 704
tract 703
ventricle 702
white matter 703

▮▮ Assess

Reviewing This Chapter

1. Trace the evolution of the nervous system by contrasting its organization in hydras, planarians, earthworms, and mammals. 694–96
2. Describe the structure of a neuron, and give a function for each part mentioned. Name three types of neurons, and give a function for each. 697–98
3. What are the major events of an action potential, and what ion changes are associated with each event? 699–700
4. Describe the mode of action of a neurotransmitter at a synapse, including how it is stored and how it is destroyed. 700–1
5. Name the major parts of the human brain, and give a principal function for each part. 702–4
6. Describe the limbic system, and discuss its possible involvement in learning and memory. 705, 707
7. Discuss the structure and function of the peripheral nervous system. 707–9, 712–13
8. Trace the path of a spinal reflex. 708–9
9. Contrast the sympathetic and parasympathetic divisions of the autonomic system. 708–9, 712–13

Testing Yourself

Choose the best answer for each question.

1. Which of these are the first and last elements in a spinal reflex?
   a. axon and dendrite
   b. sense organ and muscle effector
   c. ventral horn and dorsal horn
   d. motor neuron and sensory neuron
   e. sensory receptor and the brain

2. A spinal nerve takes nerve impulses
   a. to the CNS.
   b. away from the CNS.
   c. both to and away from the CNS.
   d. only inside the CNS.
   e. only from the cerebrum.

3. Which of these correctly describes the distribution of ions on either side of an axon when it is not conducting a nerve impulse?
   a. more sodium ions (Na^+) outside and fewer potassium ions (K^+) inside
   b. K^+ outside and Na^+ inside
   c. charged proteins outside; Na^+ and K^+ inside
   d. charged proteins inside
   e. Both a and d are correct.

4. When the action potential begins, sodium gates open, allowing Na^+ to cross the membrane. Now the polarity changes to
   a. negative outside and positive inside.
   b. positive outside and negative inside.
   c. There is no difference in charge between outside and inside.
   d. Any one of these could be correct.

5. Transmission of the nerve impulse across a synapse is accomplished by
   a. the release of Na^+ at the presynaptic membrane.
   b. the release of neurotransmitters at the postsynaptic membrane.
   c. the reception of neurotransmitters at the postsynaptic membrane.
   d. Only a and c are correct.

6. The autonomic system has two divisions, called the
   a. CNS and PNS.
   b. somatic and skeletal systems.
   c. efferent and afferent systems.
   d. sympathetic and parasympathetic divisions.

7. Synaptic vesicles are
   a. at the ends of dendrites and axons.
   b. at the ends of axons only.
   c. along the length of all long fibers.
   d. at the ends of interneurons only.
   e. Both b and d are correct.

8. Which of these pairs is mismatched?
   a. cerebrum—thinking and memory
   b. thalamus—motor and sensory centers
   c. hypothalamus—internal environment regulator
   d. cerebellum—motor coordination
   e. medulla oblongata—fourth ventricle

9. Repolarization of an axon during an action potential is produced by
   a. inward diffusion of Na^+.
   b. active extrusion of K^+.
   c. outward diffusion of K^+.
   d. inward active transport of Na^+.

10. Which two parts of the brain are least likely to work directly together?
    a. thalamus and cerebrum
    b. cerebrum and cerebellum
    c. hypothalamus and medulla oblongata
    d. cerebellum and medulla oblongata

11. Which of the following is not part of the spinal cord?
    a. central canal   d. tracts
    b. dorsal horn   e. ventral horn
    c. association areas

12. A drug that inactivates acetylcholinesterase
    a. stops the release of ACh from presynaptic endings.
    b. prevents the attachment of ACh to its receptor.
    c. increases the ability of ACh to stimulate postsynaptic cells.
    d. All of these are correct.

13. Which of these statements about autonomic neurons is correct?
    a. They are motor neurons.
    b. Preganglionic neurons have cell bodies in the CNS.
    c. Postganglionic neurons innervate smooth muscles, cardiac muscle, and glands.
    d. All of these are correct.

14. Which of these fibers release norepinephrine?
    a. preganglionic sympathetic axons
    b. postganglionic sympathetic axons
    c. preganglionic parasympathetic axons
    d. postganglionic parasympathetic axons

15. Sympathetic nerve stimulation does not cause
    a. the liver to release glycogen.
    b. dilation of bronchioles.
    c. the gastrointestinal tract to digest food.
    d. an increase in the heart rate.

16. The limbic system
    a. involves portions of the cerebral lobes, basal nuclei, and the diencephalon.
    b. is responsible for our deepest emotions, including pleasure, rage, and fear.
    c. is not responsible for reason and self-control.
    d. All of these are correct.

17. Label this diagram of a reflex arc.

Engage

Thinking Scientifically

1. In individuals with panic disorder, the fight-or-flight response is activated by inappropriate stimuli. How might it be possible to directly control this response in order to treat panic disorder? Why is such control often impractical?

2. A man who lost his leg several years ago continues to experience pain as though it were coming from the missing limb. What hypothesis could explain the neurological basis of this pain?

38

Sense Organs

BEFORE YOU BEGIN

Before beginning this chapter, take a few moments to review the following discussions.

Sections 37.3 and 37.4 What are the roles of the central and peripheral nervous systems in an animal's responses to its environment?

Figure 37.9 How is the cerebral cortex involved in the processing of sensory information?

Figure 37.13 How do sensory receptors in the skin stimulate a spinal reflex?

Certain snakes can detect infrared energy emitted by their prey. In this infrared image, the red-orange areas are the warmest, and the blue-black areas are the coldest.

Visible light is made up of waves of electromagnetic energy with different wavelengths. As you'll see in this chapter, sensory receptors in the human eye contain pigments that undergo a chemical change when exposed to electromagnetic energy at these various wavelengths, which is then perceived by the brain as vision. Electromagnetic energy with a wavelength at the shortest end of the visible spectrum is perceived as violet; that with a wavelength at the highest end is perceived as red, with other colors in between.

A few types of animals have evolved the ability to detect electromagnetic energy with longer wavelengths, known as the infrared spectrum. Just about any source of heat—the Sun, a fire, or a warm body—emits energy in the infrared spectrum. Certain kinds of snakes, such as the pit vipers, have evolved specialized infrared sensory organs. Located in a pit below each eye, these organs are very sensitive to infrared waves emitted by their warm-blooded prey; the photo above, taken using an infrared-sensitive camera, shows how a mouse might "appear" to a snake. Even when placed in total darkness, snakes with this ability can track and find such prey quickly. Although the ability to detect infrared energy with such precision is unusual, all animals rely upon many types of sensory systems to maintain homeostasis.

As you read through the chapter, think about the following questions:

1. How does the ability to detect infrared energy provide snakes with a competitive advantage over predators lacking this ability?

2. Of the types of sensory receptors described in this chapter—chemoreceptors, photoreceptors, mechanoreceptors, or thermoreceptors—which is the most necessary for an animal to survive?

FOLLOWING *the* THEMES

CHAPTER 38 SENSE ORGANS		
UNIT 7 COMPARATIVE ANIMAL BIOLOGY	**Evolution**	The sense organs that have evolved in animals are essential to their ability to maintain homeostasis, avoid danger, find food, and locate mates.
	Nature of Science	Biomedical scientists are using the knowledge of transmission of sensory information to restore the ability of deaf people to hear, and blind people to see.
	Biological Systems	Four types of sensory receptors—chemoreceptors, photoreceptors, mechanoreceptors, and thermoreceptors—provide animals with information about their internal and external environments.

38.1 Sensory Receptors

Learning Outcomes

Upon completion of this section, you should be able to

1. Explain the differences between sensory receptors, sensory transduction, and perception.
2. Describe four types of sensory receptors, and list examples of each.

In order to survive, animals must be able to maintain homeostasis as well as locate required nutrients, avoid dangers, and learn from previous experiences. These kinds of selective pressures have resulted in the evolution of the many different types of **sensory receptors,** which are specialized cells capable of detecting changes in internal or external conditions, and of communicating that information to the central nervous system.

A sensory receptor is able to convert some type of event, or *stimulus*, occurring in the environment into a nerve impulse. This process is known as **sensory transduction.** Some sensory receptors are modified neurons, and others are specialized cells closely associated with neurons.

The plasma membrane of a sensory receptor contains proteins that react to a stimulus. For example, these membrane proteins might be sensitive to temperature, or react with a certain chemical. When this happens, ion channels open, and ions flow across the plasma membrane. If the stimulus is sufficient, nerve impulses begin and are carried by a sensory nerve fiber within the PNS to the CNS.

Note that there is no difference between the nerve impulses carried by the different types of sensory nerves. All these impulses are simply the action potentials discussed in the preceding chapter, regardless of whether they arise in the eyes, ears, nose, mouth, skin, or internal organs. The interpretation of

these nerve impulses by the brain brings about a response that is appropriate for the particular type of stimulus. That is why artificial stimulation of the nerves that normally carry impulses generated in the ear or the eye are interpreted by the brain as sound or light, respectively (see the Nature of Science feature on page 725).

What's more, not all of these sensory impulses are received at the conscious levels of the brain—for example, we are not aware of the constant adjustments that are occurring in response to various internal stimuli. Any sensory stimuli of which humans, and perhaps other animals, become conscious are known as *perceptions*.

Although the extent to which nonhuman animals have perceptions is largely unknown, it is likely that some of them perceive their world in very different ways. As noted in the opening essay, some snakes can detect infrared energy that is completely invisible to humans. Bats, dolphins, and whales are capable of *echolocation*, meaning they can produce very high frequency sounds, and then learn about objects in their environment by listening for echoes. Some whales can also hear very low frequency sounds emitted by other whales hundreds of miles away. Dogs have a sense of smell that is many times more sensitive than that of humans, and they can be trained to detect drugs, human remains, blood, and even bedbugs. Several scientific studies have confirmed that dogs can detect some types of human cancer just by sniffing the appropriate samples. Clearly the sensory systems are a subject of much fascination to biologists, and they are the systems that literally determine how we experience our world. Video Sex and the Senses

An animal's ability to detect information in its environment is dependent on just a few types of sensory receptors. **Chemoreceptors** [Gk. *chemo*, pertaining to chemicals; L. *receptor*, receiver] can respond to a diverse range of chemical substances, from oxygen levels in the blood, to molecules of food in the mouth or nasal passages. **Photoreceptors** [Gk. *photos*, light], such as those found in the human retina, respond to light energy. **Mechanoreceptors** are stimulated by mechanical forces, usually pressure of some sort. Mechanoreceptors are responsible for detecting changes that are perceived as sound or touch, as well as for maintaining our equilibrium, balance, and proper tone in muscles and joints. **Thermoreceptors,** located in the hypothalamus and skin, are stimulated by changes in temperature. MP3 Sensations and Receptors

Check Your Progress 38.1

1. Define sensory transduction.
2. List three examples of sensory capabilities found in animals that are lacking in humans.

38.2 Chemical Senses

Learning Outcomes

Upon completion of this section, you should be able to

1. Discuss the locations of chemoreceptors in arthropods, crustaceans, and vertebrates.
2. Describe the types and locations of taste receptors in humans.
3. Compare and contrast how the brain receives information about taste versus smell.

Chemoreception is found almost universally in animals and is therefore believed to be the most primitive sense. Chemoreceptors sensitive to certain chemical substances can be important in locating food, finding a mate, and detecting potentially dangerous chemicals in the environment.

The location and sensitivity of chemoreceptors vary throughout the animal kingdom. Although chemoreceptors are present throughout the body of planarians, they are concentrated in the auricles located on the sides of the head. Many insects have taste receptors on their mouthparts, but in the housefly, chemoreceptors are located primarily on the feet. Insects also detect airborne *pheromones*, which are chemical messages passed between individuals.

Video Sexy Bugs

In crustaceans such as lobsters and crabs, chemoreceptors are widely distributed on their appendages and antennae. Many fish have chemoreceptors scattered over the surface of their skin. Snakes possess *Jacobson's organs*, a pair of sensory pitlike organs located in the roof of the mouth. When a snake flicks its forked tongue, scent molecules are carried to the Jacobson's organs and sensory information is transmitted to the brain for interpretation.

Sense of Taste in Humans

In adult humans, approximately 3,000 **taste buds** are located primarily on the tongue (Fig. 38.1). Many taste buds lie along the walls of the papillae, the small elevations on the tongue that are visible to the unaided eye. Isolated taste buds are also present on the hard palate, the pharynx, and the epiglottis.

Taste buds on the tongue open at a taste pore. Taste buds have supporting cells and a number of elongated taste cells that end in microvilli. The microvilli, which project into the taste pore, bear receptor proteins for certain molecules. When molecules bind to receptor proteins, nerve impulses are generated in associated sensory nerve fibers. These nerve impulses travel to the brain, where they are interpreted as tastes.

Animation Taste

Humans have five main types of taste receptors: sweet, sour, salty, bitter, and umami (Japanese: savory, delicious). Foods rich in certain amino acids, such as the common seasoning monosodium glutamate (MSG), as well as certain flavors of cheese, beef broth, and some seafood, produce the taste of umami. Taste buds for each of these tastes are located throughout the tongue, although certain regions may be slightly more sensitive to particular tastes. A food can stimulate more than one of these types of taste buds. The brain appears to survey the overall pattern of incoming sensory impulses and to take a "weighted average" of their taste messages as the perceived taste.

In 2010, researchers at the University of Maryland found chemoreceptors in the human lung that are sensitive only to chemicals that normally taste bitter. These receptors are not clustered in buds, and they do not send taste signals to the brain. Stimulation of these receptors causes the airways to dilate, leading the researchers to speculate about implications for new medications to treat diseases like asthma.

Figure 38.1 Taste buds in humans. **a.** Papillae on the tongue contain taste buds that are sensitive to sweet, sour, salty, bitter, and umami. **b.** Photomicrograph and enlargement of papillae. **c.** Taste buds occur along the walls of the papillae. **d.** Taste cells end in microvilli that bear receptor proteins for certain molecules. When molecules bind to the receptor proteins, nerve impulses are generated and go to the brain, where the sensation of taste occurs.

Sense of Smell in Humans

In humans, the sense of smell, or olfaction, is dependent on between 10 and 20 million **olfactory cells.** These structures are located within olfactory epithelium high in the roof of the nasal cavity (Fig. 38.2). Olfactory cells are modified neurons. Each cell ends in a tuft of about five olfactory cilia that bear receptor proteins for odor molecules. Each olfactory cell has only 1 out of 1,000 different types of receptor proteins. Nerve fibers from similar olfactory cells lead to the same neuron in the olfactory bulb, an extension of the brain.

An odor contains many odor molecules that activate a characteristic combination of receptor proteins. A rose might stimulate certain olfactory cells, designated by blue and green in Figure 38.2, whereas a gardenia might stimulate a different combination. When the neurons communicate this information via the olfactory tract to the olfactory areas of the cerebral cortex, we perceive that we have smelled a rose or a gardenia.

Have you ever noticed that a certain aroma vividly brings to mind a certain person or place? A whiff of perfume may remind you of someone you knew, or the smell of boxwood may remind you of your grandfather's farm. The olfactory bulbs have direct connections with the limbic system and its centers for emotions and memory. One study found that participants with previous negative experiences of visiting the dentist rated the smell of a chemical often encountered in dentist's offices as unpleasant, while those lacking such negative experiences rated it as pleasant.

The number of olfactory cells declines with age, and the remaining population of receptors becomes less sensitive. Thus, older people may tend to apply excessive amounts of perfume or aftershave. The ability to smell can also be lost as the result of head trauma, respiratory infection, or brain disease. This condition can become dangerous if these individuals cannot smell spoiled food, smoke, or a gas leak.

Usually, the sense of taste and the sense of smell work together to create a combined effect when interpreted by the cerebral cortex. For example, when you have a cold, you may think food has lost its taste, but most likely you have lost the ability to detect its smell. This method works in reverse also. When you smell something, some of the molecules move from the nose down into the mouth region and stimulate the taste buds there. Therefore, part of what we refer to as smell may in fact be taste.

MP3
Taste and Smell

Video
Mosquitoes and Sweat

Check Your Progress   38.2

1. Compare and contrast the senses of smell and taste.
2. List the five types of taste receptors in humans.
3. Discuss what could account for nerve impulses, which are all action potentials, being interpreted as arising from different sense organs.

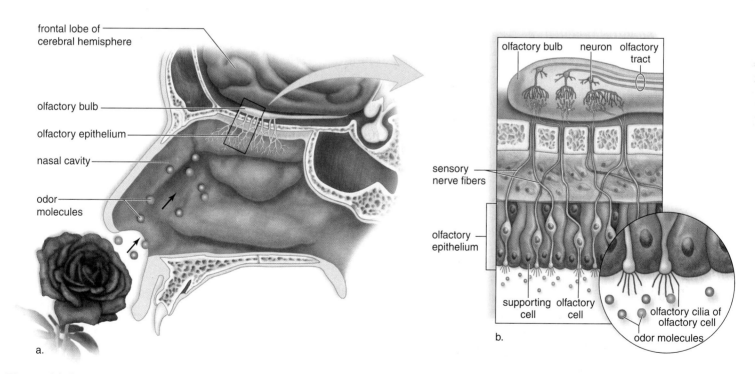

Figure 38.2 Olfactory cell location and anatomy.   a. The olfactory epithelium in humans is located high in the nasal cavity. **b.** Olfactory cells end in cilia that bear receptor proteins for specific odor molecules. The cilia of each olfactory cell can bind to only one type of odor molecule (signified here by color). For example, if a rose causes olfactory cells sensitive to "blue" and "green" odor molecules to be stimulated, then neurons designated by blue and green in the olfactory bulb are activated. The primary olfactory area of the cerebral cortex interprets the pattern of stimulation as the scent of a rose.

38.3 Sense of Vision

Learning Outcomes

Upon completion of this section, you should be able to

1. Compare the structure of the compound eyes of arthropods with the camera-type eyes of vertebrates.
2. List all tissues or cell layers through which light passes from when it enters the eye until it is converted to a nerve impulse.
3. Discuss the distinct roles of rod cells, cone cells, and rhodopsin in converting a light stimulus into a nerve impulse.
4. Describe several common disorders affecting vision.

Vision is an important capability for many, but not all, animals. Like the senses of smell and hearing, vision allows us to perceive the environment at a distance, which can have survival value. In this section we review how animals detect light and how the human eye accomplishes vision.

How Animals Detect Light

Photoreceptors are sensory receptors that are sensitive to light. Some animals lack photoreceptors and depend on senses such as smell and hearing instead; other animals have photoreceptors but live in environments that do not require them. For example, moles live underground and use their senses of smell and touch rather than eyesight.

Not all photoreceptors form images. The "eyespots" of planarians allow these animals to sense and move away from light. Image-forming eyes are found among four invertebrate groups: cnidarians, annelids, molluscs, and arthropods. Arthropods have **compound eyes** composed of many independent visual units called ommatidia [Gk. *ommation,* dim. of *omma,* eye], each possessing all the elements needed for light reception (Fig. 38.3). Both the cornea and crystalline cone function as lenses to direct light rays toward the photoreceptors. The photoreceptors generate nerve impulses, which pass to the brain by way of optic nerve fibers. The outer pigment cells absorb stray light rays so that the rays do not pass from one visual unit to the other.

Figure 38.4 Nectar guides. Evening primrose, *Oenothera,* as seen by humans (*left*) and insects (*right*). Humans see no markings, but insects see distinct lines and central blotches because their eyes respond to ultraviolet rays. These types of markings, known as nectar guides, often highlight the reproductive parts of flowers, where insects feed on nectar and pick up pollen at the same time.

Flies and mosquitoes can only see a few millimeters in front of them, but dragonflies can see small prey insects several meters away. Research has shown that foraging bees use their sense of vision as a sort of "odometer" to estimate how far they have flown from their hive.

Most insects have color vision, but they see a limited number of colors compared to humans. However, many insects can also see some ultraviolet rays, and this enables them to locate the particular parts of flowers, such as nectar guides, that have ultraviolet patterns (Fig. 38.4). Some fishes, all reptiles, and most birds are believed to have color vision, but among mammals, only humans and other primates have color vision. It would seem, then, that this trait was adaptive for a diurnal habit (active during the day), which accounts for its retention in only a few mammals.

Vertebrates (including humans) and certain molluscs, such as the squid and the octopus, have a **camera-type eye.** Because molluscs and vertebrates are not closely related, this similarity is an example of convergent evolution. A single lens focuses an image of the visual field on photoreceptors, which are closely packed together. In vertebrates, the lens changes shape to aid focusing, but in molluscs the lens moves back and forth. All of

Figure 38.3 Compound eye.

Each visual unit of a compound eye has a cornea and a lens that focus light onto photoreceptors. The photoreceptors generate nerve impulses that are transmitted to the brain, where interpretation produces a mosaic image.

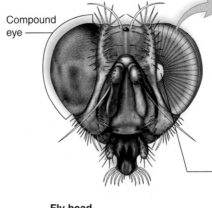

Compound eye

cornea
crystalline cone
photoreceptor cells
pigment cells
optic nerve fibers

Fly head

Ommatidium

sclera
choroid
retina

retinal blood vessels

optic nerve

fovea centralis

posterior compartment filled with vitreous humor

retina
choroid
sclera

ciliary body

lens

iris

pupil

cornea

anterior compartment filled with aqueous humor

suspensory ligament

Figure 38.5 Anatomy of the human eye. Notice that the sclera, the outer layer of the eye, becomes the cornea and that the choroid, the middle layer, is continuous with the ciliary body and the iris. The retina, the inner layer, contains the photoreceptors for vision. The fovea centralis is the region where vision is most acute.

the photoreceptors taken together can be compared to a piece of film in a camera. The human eye is more complex than a camera, however, as you will see.

Animals with two eyes facing forward have three-dimensional vision, or **stereoscopic vision.** The visual fields overlap, and each eye is able to view an object from a different angle. Predators tend to have stereoscopic vision and so do humans. Animals with eyes facing sideways, such as rabbits, don't have stereoscopic vision, but they do have **panoramic vision,** meaning that the visual field is very wide. Panoramic vision is useful to prey animals because it makes it more difficult for a predator to sneak up on them.

Many vertebrates have a membrane in the back of their eye called a *tapetum lucidum,* which reflects light back into the photoreceptor cells of the retina to increase sensitivity to light. This explains the eerie glowing appearance of some animals' eyes at night.

The Human Eye

The human eye, which is an elongated sphere about 2.5 cm in diameter, has three layers: the sclera, the choroid, and the retina (Fig. 38.5). The outer **sclera** [Gk. *skleros,* hard], is an opaque, white, fibrous layer that covers most of the eye; in front of the eye, the sclera becomes the transparent **cornea,** the window of the eye. A thin layer of epithelial cells forms a mucous membrane called the **conjunctiva** that covers the surface of the sclera and keeps the eyes moist.

The middle, thin, dark-brown **choroid** [Gk. *chorion,* membrane] layer contains many blood vessels and a brown pigment that absorbs stray light rays. Toward the front of the eye, the

choroid thickens and forms the ring-shaped ciliary body and a thin, circular, muscular diaphragm, the iris. The **iris** is the colored portion of the eye and regulates the size of an opening called the pupil. The **pupil,** like the aperture of a camera lens, regulates light entering the eye. The **lens,** which is attached to the ciliary body by ligaments, divides the cavity of the eye into two portions and helps form images. A basic, watery solution called aqueous humor fills the anterior compartment between the cornea and the lens. The aqueous humor provides a fluid cushion and nutrient and waste transport for the eye.

The inner layer of the eye, the **retina** [L. *rete,* net], is located in the posterior compartment. The retina contains photoreceptors called **rod cells** and **cone cells.** The rods are very sensitive to light, but they do not respond to colors; therefore, at night or in a darkened room, we see only shades of gray. Rods are distributed in the peripheral regions of the retina. The cones, which require bright light, are sensitive to different wavelengths of light, and therefore, humans have the ability to distinguish colors. The retina has a central region called the **fovea centralis,** where cone cells are densely packed. Light is normally focused on the fovea when we look directly at an object. This is helpful because vision is most acute in the fovea centralis.

Sensory fibers form the optic nerve, which takes nerve impulses to the brain. No rods or cones are present where the optic nerve exits the retina (see Fig. 38.9). Therefore, no vision is possible in this area, and it is termed the **blind spot.** You can detect your own blind spot by putting a dot to the right of center on a piece of paper. Use your right hand to move the paper slowly toward your right eye while you look straight ahead. The dot will disappear at one point—this is your blind spot.

Video
Artificial Eye

Focusing of the Eye

When we look directly at something, such as the printed letters on this page, light rays pass through the pupil and are focused on the retina. The image produced is much smaller than the object because light rays are bent (refracted) when they are brought into focus. The image on the retina is also upside down and is reversed from left to right. When information from the retina reaches the brain, it is processed so that we perceive our surroundings in the correct orientation.

Focusing starts at the cornea and continues as the rays pass through the lens. The lens provides additional focusing power as **visual accommodation** occurs for close vision. The shape of the lens is controlled by the **ciliary muscle** within the ciliary body. When we view a distant object, the ciliary muscle is relaxed, causing the suspensory ligaments attached to the ciliary body to be taut; therefore, the lens remains relatively flat (Fig. 38.6a). When we view a near object, the ciliary muscle contracts, releasing the tension on the suspensory ligaments, and the lens becomes more round due to its natural elasticity (Fig. 38.6b). Because close work requires contraction of the ciliary muscle, it very often causes muscle fatigue known as eyestrain. With normal aging, the lens loses its ability to accommodate for near objects (Fig. 38.6b); therefore, people frequently need reading glasses once they reach middle age.

Photoreceptors of the Eye

Sensory transduction occurs once light has been focused on the photoreceptors in the retina. Figure 38.7 illustrates the structure of these rod cells and cone cells. Both rods and cones have an outer segment joined to an inner segment by a stalk. Pigment molecules that react to light are embedded in the membrane of the many disks present in the outer segment. Synaptic vesicles are located at the synaptic endings of the inner segment.

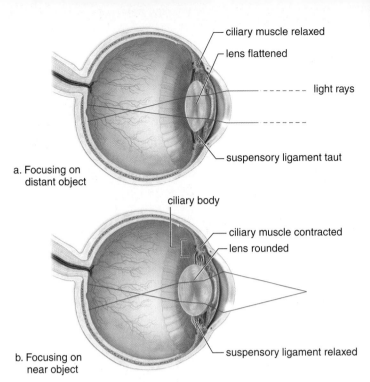

a. Focusing on distant object

b. Focusing on near object

Figure 38.6 Focusing of the human eye. Light rays from each point on an object are bent by the cornea and the lens in such a way that an inverted and reversed image of the object forms on the retina. **a.** When focusing on a distant object, the lens is flat because the ciliary muscle is relaxed and the suspensory ligament is taut. **b.** When focusing on a near object, the lens accommodates; that is, it becomes rounded because the ciliary muscle contracts, causing the suspensory ligament to relax.

The visual pigment in rods is called rhodopsin. **Rhodopsin** is a complex molecule made up of the protein opsin and a light-absorbing molecule called *retinal*, which is a derivative of vitamin A. When a rod absorbs light, rhodopsin splits into opsin and retinal, leading to a cascade of reactions and the closure of ion channels in the rod cell's plasma membrane. The release of

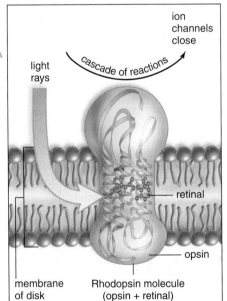

Figure 38.7 Photoreceptors in the eye. The outer segment of rods and cones contains stacks of membranous disks, which contain visual pigments. In rods, the membrane of each disk contains rhodopsin, a complex molecule containing the protein opsin and the pigment retinal. When rhodopsin absorbs light energy, it splits, releasing opsin, which sets in motion a cascade of reactions that cause ion channels in the plasma membrane to close. Thereafter, nerve impulses go to the brain.

inhibitory transmitter molecules from the rod's synaptic vesicles ceases. Thereafter, nerve impulses go to the visual areas of the cerebral cortex. Rods are very sensitive to light and, therefore, are suited to night vision. Carrots and other brightly-colored vegetables are rich in *carotenoids*, some of which can be easily converted to vitamin A in the body, so eating these foods may improve your night vision. Rod cells are plentiful in the peripheral region of the retina; therefore, they also provide us with peripheral vision and perception of motion.

The cones, by contrast, are located primarily in the fovea centralis and are activated by bright light. They allow us to detect the fine detail and the color of an object. Color vision depends on three different kinds of cones, which contain pigments called the B (blue), G (green), and R (red) pigments. Each pigment is made up of retinal and opsin, but a slight difference is present in the opsin structure of each, which accounts for their individual absorption patterns. Various combinations of cones are believed to be stimulated by in-between shades of color. For example, the color yellow is perceived when green cones are highly stimulated, red cones are partially stimulated, and blue cones are not stimulated. In color blindness, an individual lacks certain visual pigments. As indicated in Chapter 11, color blindness is often a sex-linked hereditary disorder; however, the Nature of Science feature, "Inbreeding in Populations," in Chapter 16 describes a case of non-sex-linked color blindness.

Integration of Visual Signals in the Retina

The retina has three layers of neurons (Fig. 38.8). The layer closest to the choroid contains the rod cells and cone cells; the middle layer contains bipolar cells; and the innermost layer contains ganglion cells, whose sensory fibers become the optic nerve. Only the rod cells and the cone cells are sensitive to light, and therefore light must penetrate to the back of the retina before they are stimulated.

The rod cells and the cone cells synapse with the bipolar cells, which in turn synapse with ganglion cells that initiate nerve impulses. Notice in Figure 38.8 that there are many more rod cells and cone cells than ganglion cells. In fact, the human retina has about 150 million rod cells and 6 million cone cells, but only 1 million ganglion cells.

The sensitivity of cones versus rods is mirrored by how directly they connect to ganglion cells. As many as 150 rods may excite the same ganglion cell, meaning that each ganglion cell receives signals from rod cells covering about 1 mm^2 of retina (about the size of a thumbtack hole). Therefore, stimulation of rods results in vision that is blurred and indistinct. In contrast, some cone cells in the fovea centralis excite only one ganglion cell. This explains why cones provide us with a sharper, more detailed image of an object.

Animation
Vision

MP3
Sense of Vision

Figure 38.8 Structure and function of the retina.

a. The retina is the inner layer of the eyeball. Rod cells and cone cells, located at the back of the retina nearest the choroid, synapse with bipolar cells, which synapse with ganglion cells. Further, notice that many rod cells share one bipolar cell, but cone cells do not. Certain cone cells synapse with only one ganglion cell. Cone cells, in general, distinguish more detail than do rod cells. **b.** Micrograph of retina.

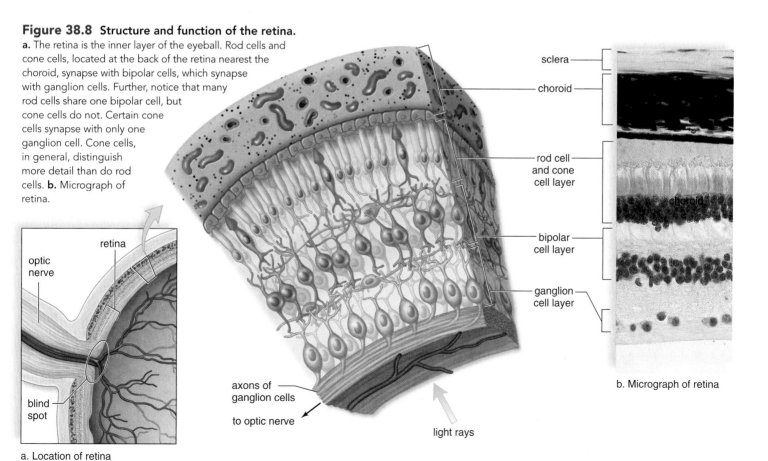

sclera
choroid
rod cell and cone cell layer
bipolar cell layer
ganglion cell layer

b. Micrograph of retina

optic nerve
retina
blind spot

a. Location of retina

axons of ganglion cells

to optic nerve

light rays

Disorders of Vision

Disorders of vision include diseases of the retina, glaucoma and cataracts, and problems with visual focus.

Diseases of the Retina

Diseases of the retina are the most common cause of blindness in adults. These include **diabetic retinopathy,** in which capillaries to the retina become damaged secondary to diabetes. In **macular degeneration,** the leading cause of blindness for people in the U.S. under the age of 65, capillaries supplying the retinas become damaged, and hemorrhages and blocked vessels can occur. Smokers are 20 times more likely to acquire this disorder than are nonsmokers. If diagnosed early, both of these retinal diseases can be treated, using drugs that are injected directly into the vitreous humor. With **retinal detachment,** the retina peels away from the supportive choroid layer, due to eye trauma or other diseases. A detached retina can often be reattached using a laser. As noted in the Nature of Science feature, artificial retina technology is becoming an option for some blind people whose visual pathways remain intact.

Glaucoma and Cataracts

Glaucoma is the second most common cause of blindness in the United States. Glaucoma occurs when the drainage system of the eyes fails, so that aqueous humor builds up and increases intraocular pressure. In the early stages, this pressure tends to destroy nerve fibers responsible for peripheral vision, but untreated glaucoma can result in total blindness. Eye doctors always check intraocular pressure, but the disorder can come on quickly, and any nerve damage is permanent. Treatment usually involves drugs that increase the outflow of aqueous humor, but surgery may be required.

With aging, the eye is increasingly subject to **cataracts,** in which the lens can become opaque and therefore incapable of transmitting light rays. Cataracts occur in 50% of people between the ages of 65 and 74, and in 70% of those ages 75 or older. In most cases, vision can be restored by surgical removal of the unhealthy lens and replacement with a clear plastic artificial lens. Cataract surgery is the most frequently performed surgery in the United States. Surgeons may be able to replace cataracts with multifocal lenses that allow the eye to focus, eliminating the need for glasses in some patients.

Visual Focus Disorders

People who can read what are designated as size 20 letters on an optometrist's chart 20 ft away are said to have 20/20 vision. Those who cannot read these letters but can focus on close objects are said to be **nearsighted (myopic)**. These individuals often have an elongated eyeball, and when they attempt to look at a distant object, the image is brought to focus in front of the retina. Concave lenses, which diverge the light rays so that the image can be focused on the retina, usually correct this problem (Fig. 38.9a).

Those who can easily read the optometrist's chart but cannot easily focus on near objects are said to be **farsighted (hyperopic).** They often have a shortened eyeball, and when they try to view near objects, the image is focused behind the

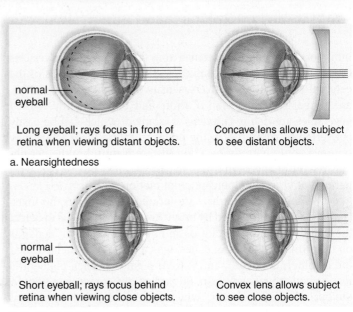

Long eyeball; rays focus in front of retina when viewing distant objects. / normal eyeball

Concave lens allows subject to see distant objects.

a. Nearsightedness

Short eyeball; rays focus behind retina when viewing close objects. / normal eyeball

Convex lens allows subject to see close objects.

b. Farsightedness

Uneven cornea; rays do not focus evenly.

Uneven lens allows subject to see objects clearly.

c. Astigmatism

Figure 38.9 Common abnormalities of the eye with possible corrective lenses. **a.** A concave lens in nearsighted persons focuses light rays on the retina. **b.** A convex lens in farsighted persons focuses light rays on the retina. **c.** An uneven lens in persons with astigmatism focuses light rays on the retina.

retina. Convex lenses that increase the bending of light rays allow the image to be focused on the retina (Fig. 38.9b).

When the cornea or lens is uneven, the image appears fuzzy. This condition, called **astigmatism,** can sometimes be corrected by an unevenly ground lens to compensate for the uneven cornea (Fig. 38.9c).

Rather than wear glasses or contact lenses, many people with visual focus problems are now choosing to undergo laser-assisted in situ keratomileusis, or LASIK. First, specialists determine how much the cornea needs to be flattened to achieve optimum vision. Controlled by a computer, the laser then removes this amount of the cornea. Various surveys indicate that about 95% of people who have the LASIK procedure are satisfied with the results.

Check Your Progress   38.3

1. Compare rods and cones in terms of main functions, light sensitivity, and excitation of ganglion cells.
2. List the three layers of cells in the human retina. Why do you think this arrangement is sometimes described as "backwards"?
3. Summarize how the shape of the eyeball can result in nearsightedness or farsightedness. Also, describe the cause of astigmatism.

THEME Nature of Science

Artificial Retinas Come into Focus

Over 25 million people worldwide are blind due to diseases of the retinas. In most cases, there are no cures and few effective treatments. However, after years of work, medical researchers have now developed artificial retina technology that is restoring some vision for people who were completely blind.

Retinal diseases like macular degeneration cause the rods and cones to die but leave the ganglion cells and neurons intact. In 1988, researchers first demonstrated that a blind person could see light if the nerve cells behind the retina were stimulated with an electrical current. Since then, scientists have been working on developing technological approaches that could take the place of the diseased photoreceptors. In March 2011, a California company received approval in Europe to sell the Argus II, a retinal prosthesis designed for implantation in blind patients who still have intact connections between their retinas and brain.

Priced at about $115,000, the device includes a tiny digital camera embedded in a pair of glasses that are worn by the patient. Images from the camera are translated into electrical signals representing patterns of light and dark. These signals are transmitted wirelessly to a receiver implanted above the ear or near the eye. This receiver in turn sends signals via a tiny wire that attaches to a 1 mm × 1 mm microchip that has been surgically implanted under the retina (Fig. 38A). The chip contains 60 electrodes that can stimulate the ganglion cells, producing electrical impulses that travel via the optic nerve to the brain, where they are interpreted as vision.

Although it takes time for patients to learn to interpret the patterns of light and dark transmitted by the device, some formerly blind patients have been able to recognize simple objects, see people in front of them and follow their movement, and even read large print slowly. The Argus II device may be approved for use in patients in the United States by 2012. Moreover, researchers are already working on upgraded models that incorporate up to 1,500 electrodes, to increase the resolution of the image produced. This is anticipated to be the threshold of information that will be required for formerly blind patients to recognize faces. Other groups are working on artificial retinas that can be implanted inside the eye itself.

Although the amount of information that is transmitted by an artificial retina device is important, other scientists are focusing on the type of information that is transmitted. A 2010 study conducted at Weill Cornell Medical College in New York by investigators Shiela Nirenberg and Chethan Pandarinath demonstrated that a different approach could restore normal vision in blind mice. First, these scientists focused on deciphering the patterns by which the ganglion cells normally transmit information from the photoreceptors to the brain. Next, they tested these codes in blind mice that had been genetically altered so that their ganglion cells express a protein called channelrhodopsin, which initiates a nerve impulse when it is exposed to light. That way the investigators didn't have to implant artificial retinas in the mice, but instead exposed the mice to different patterns of flashing light. The results of these experiments showed that the mice receiving light information using the proper code appeared to be able to see at nearly normal levels (Fig. 38A).

While eliminating the need for surgery is a major advantage of this approach, it is impossible (or at least unethical) to genetically engineer humans to express certain genes. The solution to this problem may lie in gene therapy, in which the ganglion cells of blind patients would be treated so that they express the *channelrhodopsin* gene. If that approach is successful, patients would again wear a pair of glasses with an embedded camera, only this time the camera would emit light that had been translated into the patterns that the brain can understand.

Questions to Consider

1. Although this technology is very exciting, it is also expensive. Do you believe that health insurance companies should pay the $115,000 cost of an artificial retina?

2. Suppose this technology advances to the point where vision can not only be restored, but also greatly enhanced. Should it then be legally available to anyone who can afford it, for example, highly paid professional baseball players? What about for children who want to be professional athletes?

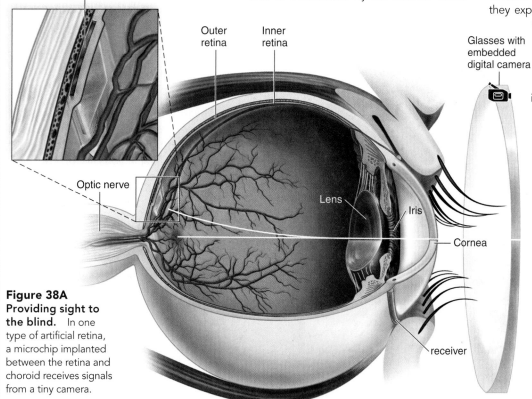

Figure 38A
Providing sight to the blind. In one type of artificial retina, a microchip implanted between the retina and choroid receives signals from a tiny camera.

38.4 Senses of Hearing and Balance

Learning Outcomes

Upon completion of this section, you should be able to

1. Compare several strategies that different types of animals use to hear sounds.
2. Distinguish the parts of the human ear that make up the outer, middle, and inner ear.
3. Review the differences between rotational and gravitational equilibrium, and how each is accomplished.
4. Describe several common disorders affecting hearing and/or equilibrium.

Mechanoreception is sensing physical contact on the surface of the skin or movement of the surrounding environment (such as sound waves in air or water). The simplest mechanoreceptors are free nerve endings found in the skin. At the other end of the spectrum, the most complex mechanoreception occurs in the middle and inner ear of vertebrates.

The evolutionary advantage of hearing is that it allows animals to receive information at a distance, and from any direction. Hearing plays an important role in avoiding danger, detecting prey, finding mates, and communication. In the most basic sense, hearing is caused by the vibration in a surrounding medium to resonate some part of an animal's body. This resonance is converted into electrical signals through some means that can then be interpreted by the animal's brain.

How Animals Detect Sound Waves

Many insects can detect sounds. A common structure involved in insect hearing is a thin membrane, or tympanum, that stretches across an air space of some sort, such as the tracheae that also function in insect respiration (see Chapter 35). Tympanal organs are also located on the thorax (chest) of grasshoppers, and on the front

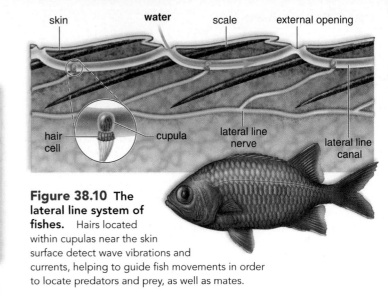

Figure 38.10 The lateral line system of fishes. Hairs located within cupulas near the skin surface detect wave vibrations and currents, helping to guide fish movements in order to locate predators and prey, as well as mates.

legs of crickets. Similar to a mammalian eardrum, the membrane is stimulated to vibrate by sound waves, but in insects, this directly activates nerve impulses in attached receptor cells.

The **lateral line** system of fishes (Fig. 38.10) guides them in their movements and in locating other fishes, including predators, prey, and mates. Usually running along both sides of a fish from the gills to the tail, the system detects water currents and pressure waves from nearby objects in a similar manner as the sensory receptors in the human ear. Water from the environment enters tiny canals that contain hair cells with cilia embedded in a gelatinous cupula. When the cupula bends due to pressure waves, the hair cells initiate nerve impulses.

Most terrestrial vertebrates can hear sound traveling in air, but some, like amphibians and snakes, are also sensitive to vibrations from the ground, which travel to their inner ear via various parts of their skeleton. A middle ear with an eardrum that transmits sound waves to the inner ear via three small bones is unique to mammals.

The Human Ear

The ear has two sensory functions: hearing and balance (equilibrium). The mechanoreceptors for both of these are located in the inner ear, and each consists of *hair cells* with stereocilia (long microvilli) that are sensitive to mechanical stimulation.

MP3
The Sense of Hearing and Equilibrium

The ear has three distinct divisions: the outer, inner, and middle ear (Fig. 38.11). The **outer ear** consists of

Figure 38.11 Anatomy of the human ear. In the middle ear, the malleus (hammer), the incus (anvil), and the stapes (stirrup) amplify sound waves. In the inner ear, the mechanoreceptors for equilibrium are in the semicircular canals and the vestibule, and the mechanoreceptors for hearing are in the cochlea.

the pinna (external "ear") and the auditory canal. The opening of the auditory canal is lined with fine hairs and glands. Glands that secrete earwax, or cerumen, are located in the upper wall of the auditory canal. Earwax helps guard the ear against the entrance of foreign materials, such as air pollutants and microorganisms.

The **middle ear** begins at the **tympanic membrane** (eardrum) and ends at a bony wall containing two small openings covered by membranes. These openings are called the *oval window* and the *round window*. Three small bones are found between the tympanic membrane and the oval window. Collectively called the **ossicles,** individually they are the *malleus* (hammer), the *incus* (anvil), and the *stapes* (stirrup) because their shapes resemble these objects. The malleus adheres to the tympanic membrane, and the stapes touches the oval window.

An **auditory tube** (eustachian tube), which extends from each middle ear to the nasopharynx, permits equalization of air pressure. Chewing gum, yawning, and swallowing in elevators and airplanes help move air through the auditory tubes upon ascent and descent. As this occurs, we often hear the ears "pop."

Whereas the outer ear and the middle ear contain air, the inner ear is filled with fluids. Anatomically speaking, the **inner ear** has three areas: the **semicircular canals** and the **vestibule** are both concerned with equilibrium; the **cochlea** is concerned with hearing. The cochlea resembles the shell of a snail because it spirals.

The Auditory Canal and Middle Ear

The process of hearing begins when sound waves enter the auditory canal. Just as ripples travel across the surface of a pond, sound waves travel by the successive vibrations of molecules. Ordinarily, sound waves do not carry much energy, but when a large number of waves strike the tympanic membrane, it moves back and forth (vibrates) ever so slightly. The malleus then takes the pressure from the inner surface of the tympanic membrane and passes it by means of the incus to the stapes in such a way that the pressure is multiplied about 20 times as it moves. The stapes strikes the membrane of the oval window, causing it to vibrate, and in this way, the pressure is passed to the fluid within the cochlea.

Inner Ear

When the snail-shaped cochlea is examined in cross section (Fig. 38.12), the vestibular canal, the cochlear canal, and the tympanic canal become apparent. The cochlear canal contains endolymph, which is similar in composition to tissue fluid. The vestibular and tympanic canals are filled with perilymph, which is continuous with the cerebrospinal fluid. Along the length of the basilar membrane, which forms the lower wall of the *cochlear canal*, are little hair cells whose stereocilia are embedded within a gelatinous material called the *tectorial membrane*. The hair cells of the cochlear canal, called the **organ of Corti,** or spiral organ, synapse with nerve fibers of the *cochlear nerve* (auditory nerve).

When the stapes strikes the membrane of the oval window, pressure waves move from the vestibular canal to the tympanic canal across the basilar membrane, and the round window membrane bulges. The basilar membrane moves up and down,

Cochlea cross section

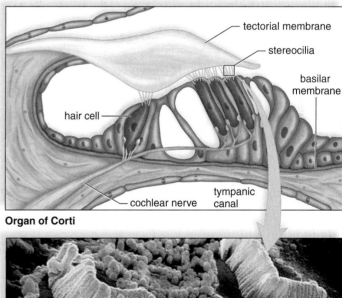

Organ of Corti

Stereocilia $2\ \mu m$

Figure 38.12 Mechanoreceptors for hearing. The organ of Corti is located within the cochlea. In the uncoiled cochlea, note that the organ consists of hair cells resting on the basilar membrane, with the tectorial membrane above. Pressure waves move from the vestibular canal to the tympanic canal, causing the basilar membrane to vibrate. This causes the stereocilia (or at least a portion of the more than 20,000 hair cells) embedded in the tectorial membrane to bend. Nerve impulses traveling in the cochlear nerve result in hearing.

and the stereocilia of the hair cells embedded in the tectorial membrane bend. Then nerve impulses begin in the cochlear nerve and travel to the brain stem. When they reach the auditory areas of the cerebral cortex, they are interpreted as a sound.

Each part of the organ of Corti is sensitive to different wave frequencies, or the pitch of sound. Near the tip, the organ of Corti responds to low pitches, such as a tuba, and near the base, it responds to higher pitches, such as a bell or a whistle. The nerve fibers from each region along the length of the organ of Corti lead to slightly different areas in the brain. The pitch sensation we experience depends on which region of the basilar membrane vibrates and which area of the brain is stimulated.

Volume is a function of the amplitude of sound waves. Loud noises cause the fluid within the vestibular canal to exert more pressure and the basilar membrane to vibrate to a greater extent. The resulting increased stimulation is interpreted by the brain as volume. It is believed that the brain interprets the tone of a sound based on the distribution of the hair cells stimulated.

Animation
Hearing

Animation
Effect of Sound Waves
on Cochlear Structures

Sense of Balance

Gravitational equilibrium organs, called statocysts (Fig. 38.13), are found in cnidarians, molluscs, and crustaceans, which are arthropods. When the head stops moving, a small particle called a statolith stimulates the cilia of the closest hair cells, and these cilia generate impulses that are interpreted as the position of the head.

In the human ear, mechanoreceptors in the semicircular canals detect rotational and/or angular movement of the head

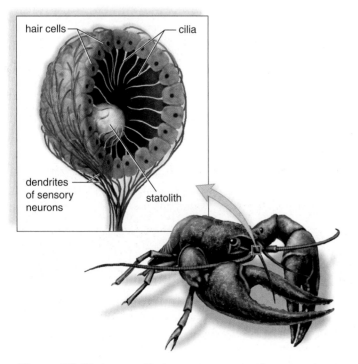

Figure 38.13 Sense of balance in an invertebrate.   Within a statocyst, a small particle (the statolith) comes to rest on hair cells and allows a crustacean to sense the position of its head.

(i.e., **rotational equilibrium**), while mechanoreceptors in the utricle and saccule detect straight-line movement of the head in any direction (i.e., **gravitational equilibrium**).

Rotational Equilibrium

Rotational equilibrium (Fig. 38.14*a*) involves the semicircular canals, which are arranged so that there is one in each dimension of space. The base of each of the three canals, called the ampulla, is slightly enlarged. Little hair cells, whose stereocilia are embedded within a gelatinous material called a cupula, are found within the ampullae. Because there are three semicircular canals, each ampulla responds to head movement in a different plane of space. As fluid (endolymph) within a semicircular canal flows over and displaces a cupula, the stereocilia of the hair cells bend, and the pattern of impulses carried by the vestibular nerve to the brain changes. The brain uses information from the semicircular canals to maintain equilibrium through appropriate motor output to various skeletal muscles that can right our position in space as need be.

Gravitational Equilibrium

Gravitational equilibrium (Fig. 38.14*b*) depends on the **utricle** and **saccule,** two membranous sacs located in the vestibule. Both of these sacs contain little hair cells, whose stereocilia are embedded within a gelatinous material called an otolithic membrane. Calcium carbonate ($CaCO_3$) granules, or **otoliths,** rest on this membrane. The utricle is especially sensitive to horizontal (back and forth) movements of the head, while the saccule responds best to vertical (up and down) movements.

When the head is still, the otoliths in the utricle and the saccule rest on the otolithic membrane above the hair cells. When the head moves in a straight line, the otoliths are displaced and the otolithic membrane sags, bending the stereocilia of the hair cells beneath. If the stereocilia move toward the largest stereocilium, called the kinocilium, nerve impulses increase in the vestibular nerve. If the stereocilia move away from the kinocilium, nerve impulses decrease in the vestibular nerve. If you are upside down, nerve impulses in the vestibular nerve cease. These data tell the brain the direction of the movement of the head.

Disorders of Hearing and Equilibrium

Hearing loss can develop gradually or suddenly and has many potential causes. Especially in children, the middle ear is subject to infections that, in severe cases, can lead to hearing impairment. Age-associated hearing loss usually develops gradually, beginning at around age 20. By age 60, about one in three people report significant hearing loss.

Most cases of hearing loss can be attributed to the effect of years of frequent (and preventable) exposure to loud noise that can damage the stereocilia of the spiral organ. Prolonged exposure to noise above a level of 80 decibels can damage the hair cells of the organ of Corti (Fig. 38.15). The first signs of noise-induced hearing loss are usually muffled hearing, pain or a "full" feeling in the ears, or tinnitus (ringing in the ears). If you have any of these symptoms, take steps immediately to prevent

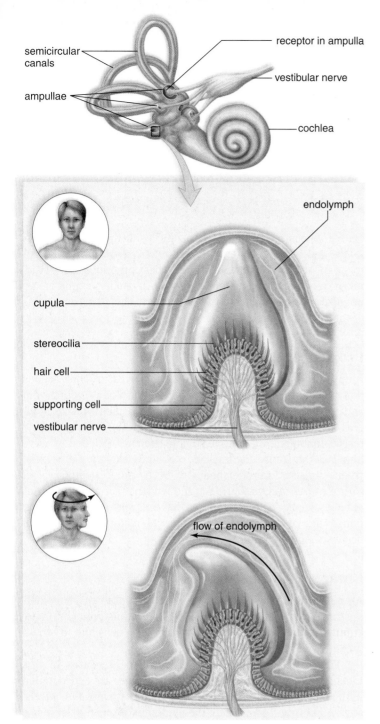

a. Rotational equilibrium: receptors in ampullae of semicircular canal

b. Gravitational equilibrium: receptors in utricle and saccule of vestibule

Figure 38.14 Mechanoreceptors for equilibrium.
a. Rotational equilibrium. The ampullae of the semicircular canals contain hair cells with stereocilia embedded in a cupula. When the head rotates, the cupula is displaced, bending the stereocilia. Thereafter, nerve impulses travel in the vestibular nerve to the brain. **b.** Gravitational equilibrium. The utricle and the saccule contain hair cells with stereocilia embedded in an otolithic membrane. When the head bends, otoliths are displaced, causing the membrane to sag and the stereocilia to bend. If the stereocilia bend toward the kinocilium, the longest of the stereocilia, nerve impulses increase in the vestibular nerve. If the stereocilia bend away from the kinocilium, nerve impulses decrease in the vestibular nerve. This difference tells the brain in which direction the head moved.

a.   b.

Figure 38.15 Studies of hearing loss. **a.** Microscopic view of normal hair cells in the organ of Corti of a guinea pig. **b.** Damage to these hair cells occurred after 24 hours of exposure to a noise level typical of a rock concert.

further damage. If exposure to loud noise is unavoidable, noise-reducing earmuffs or earplugs are available.

Some types of deafness can be present at birth. Several genetic disorders can interfere with the ability to hear, as can infections with German measles (rubella) or mumps virus when contracted by a woman during her pregnancy. For this reason, every girl should be vaccinated against these viruses before she reaches childbearing age.

People with certain types of deafness may be able to hear again with cochlear implants. A cochlear implant consists of an external device that sits behind the ear, and an internal device that is surgically implanted under the skin. The external part picks up sounds from the environment and converts them into electrical impulses, which are sent directly to different regions of the auditory nerve and then to the brain. As of 2010, about 22,000 adults and 15,000 children in the U.S. had received cochlear implants.

Disorders of equilibrium often manifest as **vertigo,** the feeling that a person or their environment is moving when no motion is occurring. It is possible to simulate a feeling of vertigo by spinning your body rapidly and then stopping suddenly. Vertigo can be caused by problems in the brain as well as the inner ear. An estimated 20% of those who experience these symptoms have benign positional vertigo (BPV), which may result from the formation of abnormal particles in the semicircular canals. When individuals with BPV move their head suddenly, especially when lying down, these particles shift like pebbles inside a tire. When the movement stops, the particles tumble down with gravity, stimulating the stereocilia and resulting in the sensation of movement.

Because the senses of hearing and equilibrium are anatomically linked, certain disorders can affect both. An example of this is Meniere's disease, which is usually characterized by vertigo, a feeling of fullness in the affected ear(s), tinnitus, and hearing loss. The disease usually strikes between the ages of 20 and 50, and only one ear is affected in about 80% of cases. The exact cause of this disease is unknown, but it seems related to an increased volume of fluid in the semicircular canals, vestibule, and/or cochlea. For this reason, it has been called "glaucoma of the ear." No cure is known for Meniere's disease, but the vertigo and feeling of pressure can often be managed by adhering to a low-salt diet, which is thought to decrease the amount of fluid present. Any hearing loss that occurs, however, is usually permanent.

Check Your Progress   38.4

1. Determine whether each of the following belongs to the outer, middle, or inner ear: **a.** ossicles, **b.** pinna, **c.** semicircular canals, **d.** cochlea, **e.** vestibule, **f.** auditory canal.
2. List, in order, the structures that must conduct a sound wave from the time it enters the auditory canal until it reaches the cochlea.
3. Identify which structures of the inner ear are responsible for gravitational equilibrium, and for rotational equilibrium.

38.5 Somatic Senses

Learning Outcomes

Upon completion of this section, you should be able to

1. Compare and contrast the functions of proprioceptors, cutaneous receptors, and pain receptors.
2. List specific types of cutaneous receptors that are sensitive to fine touch, pressure, pain, and temperature.

Senses whose receptors are associated with the skin, muscles, joints, and viscera are termed the *somatic senses.* These receptors can be categorized into three types: proprioceptors, cutaneous receptors, and pain receptors. All of these send nerve impulses via the spinal cord to the primary somatosensory areas of the cerebral cortex (see Fig. 37.9).

Proprioceptors

Proprioceptors are mechanoreceptors involved in reflex actions that maintain muscle tone, and thereby the body's equilibrium and posture. For example, proprioceptors called *muscle spindles* are embedded in muscle fibers (Fig. 38.16). If a muscle relaxes too much, the muscle spindle stretches, generating nerve impulses that cause the muscle to contract slightly. Conversely, when muscles are stretched too much, proprioceptors called *Golgi tendon organs*, buried in the tendons that attach muscles to bones, generate nerve impulses that cause the muscles to relax. Both types of receptors act together to maintain a functional degree of muscle tone.

Cutaneous Receptors

As noted in Chapter 31, the skin is composed of an epidermis and a dermis (see Fig. 31.8). The dermis contains many **cutaneous receptors**, which make the skin sensitive to touch, pressure, pain, and temperature.

Four types of cutaneous receptors are sensitive to fine touch. *Meissner corpuscles* and *Krause end bulbs* are concentrated in the fingertips, palms, lips, tongue, nipples, penis, and clitoris. *Merkel disks* are found where the epidermis meets the dermis. A free nerve ending called a *root hair plexus* winds around the base of a hair follicle and fires if a hair is touched.

Two types of cutaneous receptors are sensitive to pressure. *Pacinian corpuscles* are onion-shaped sensory receptors that lie deep inside the dermis. *Ruffini endings* are encapsulated by sheaths of connective tissue and contain lacy networks of nerve fibers.

At least two types of free nerve endings in the epidermis are thermoreceptors. Both cold and warm receptors contain ion channels with activities that are affected by temperature. Cold receptors generate nerve impulses at an increased frequency as the temperature drops; warm receptors increase activity as temperature rises. Some chemicals (e.g., menthol) can stimulate cold receptors.

Figure 38.16 Muscle spindles and Golgi tendon organs. ① When a muscle is stretched, muscle spindles send sensory nerve impulses to the spinal cord. ② Motor nerve impulses from the spinal cord cause slight muscle contraction. ③ When tendons are stretched excessively, Golgi tendon organs cause muscle relaxation.

muscle spindle
muscle fiber
quadriceps muscle
bundle of muscle fibers
③ sensory neuron to spinal cord
Golgi tendon organ
tendon

Pain Receptors

The skin and many internal organs and tissues have pain receptors, also called free nerve endings or *nociceptors*. Regardless of the cause, damaged cells release chemicals that cause nociceptors to generate nerve impulses that are interpreted by the brain as pain. Other types of nociceptors are sensitive to extreme temperatures, or excessive pressure.

Pain receptors have arisen in evolution because they alert us to potential danger. If you accidentally reach too close to a fire, for example, the reflex action of withdrawing your hand will help protect you from further tissue damage, while the unpleasant sensation perceived by your brain will help you to remember not to reach too close to a fire again.

Check Your Progress 38.5

1. Identify the likely problems that would occur if a person lacked muscle spindles, or nociceptors.
2. In evolutionary terms, assess why cutaneous receptors quickly become adapted to stimuli (i.e., we don't continue to feel a chair once we settle in), while the sense of pain seems to be much less adaptable (i.e., many people suffer from chronic pain).

CONNECTING *the* CONCEPTS *with the* THEMES

Evolution

- Through the evolutionary process, animals tend to rely on those stimuli and senses that are adaptive to their particular environment and way of life.
- In humans and perhaps other animals, impulses received from sensory receptors result in perception, or conscious awareness of events occurring in the external environment.
- Virtually all animals are capable of learning from their sensory experiences and to engage in behavior that helps them to avoid danger, locate food, and find potential mates.

Nature of Science

- Scientists now have a fairly thorough understanding of how sensory receptors function; however, the processes of sensory transduction and, in particular, perception remain considerably more mysterious.
- Researchers in biomedical science are developing new technologies to enable hearing in some cases of deafness and vision in some cases of blindness.

Biological Systems

- Sensory receptors convey information to the nervous system by converting environmental stimuli into nerve impulses (sensory transduction).
- Depending on the level of stimulus and its source, the nervous system may react by altering heart rate and breathing rate, releasing hormones from glands, and stimulating muscles to perform actions such as fight-or-flight, feeding, or mating behaviors.
- Our knowledge of the world around us is completely dependent upon functioning sensory receptors and interpretation of their signals.

Media Study Tools

www.mhhe.com/maderbiology11

Enhance your study of this chapter with study tools and practice tests. Also ask your instructor about the resources available through ConnectPlus, including the media-rich eBook, interactive learning tools, and animations.

Summarize

38.1 Sensory Receptors

Sensory receptors evolved to enable animals to receive and respond to information about their internal and external environments. Sensory receptors are specialized cells capable of detecting various stimuli, then performing sensory transduction, or conversion of those events into nerve impulses. Four types of sensory receptors are chemoreceptors, photoreceptors, proprioceptors, and thermoreceptors.

38.2 Chemical Senses

Chemoreception is found universally in animals and is, therefore, believed to be the most primitive sense. Chemoreceptors are present in a wide variety of locations in animals. Examples of chemoreceptors in humans include taste buds and olfactory cells.

38.3 Sense of Vision

Most animals have photoreceptors that are sensitive to light. Arthropods have compound eyes; vertebrates and some molluscs have a camera-type eye. In humans, vision is dependent on the eye, the optic nerves, and the visual areas of the cerebral cortex. The human eye has three layers. The sclera can be seen as the white of the eye; it also becomes the transparent bulge in the front of the eye called the cornea. The middle choroid layer contains blood vessels and pigment that absorbs stray light rays. The rod cells (sensory receptors for dim light) and the cone cells (sensory receptors for bright light and color) are located in the retina, the inner layer.

The cornea and lens focus light rays on the retina. The retina is composed of three layers of cells: the rod and cone layer, the bipolar cell layer, and the ganglion cell layer. When light strikes rhodopsin within the membranous disks of rod cells, rhodopsin splits into opsin and retinal, generating nerve impulses that are transmitted from the ganglion cells, via the optic nerve, to the brain. To see a close object, accommodation occurs as the lens rounds up.

Common causes of blindness include retinal disorders, glaucoma, and cataracts. Problems with visual focus are usually managed with corrective lenses.

38.4 Senses of Hearing and Balance

Animals use a variety of strategies to detect sounds or vibrations in their environment. Hearing in humans is dependent on the ear, the cochlear nerve, and the auditory areas of the cerebral cortex. The ear is divided into three parts. The outer ear consists of the pinna and the auditory canal, which direct sound waves to the middle ear. The middle ear begins with the tympanic membrane and contains the ossicles (malleus, incus, and stapes). The malleus is attached to the tympanic membrane, and the stapes is attached to the oval window, which is covered by membrane. The inner ear contains the cochlea and the semicircular canals, plus the utricle and saccule.

Hearing begins when the outer and middle portions of the ear convey and amplify the sound waves that strike the oval window. Its vibrations set up pressure waves within the cochlea, which contains the organ of Corti, consisting of hair cells whose stereocilia are embedded within the tectorial membrane. When the stereocilia of the hair cells bend, nerve impulses begin in the cochlear nerve and are carried to the brain.

The ear also contains receptors for our sense of equilibrium. Rotational equilibrium is dependent on the stimulation of hair cells within the ampullae of the semicircular canals. Gravitational equilibrium relies on the stimulation of hair cells within the utricle and the saccule. Disorders affecting hearing and balance include age-associated hearing loss, vertigo, and Meniere's disease.

38.5 Somatic Senses

The somatic sensory receptors include proprioceptors, sensory receptors, and pain receptors. Proprioceptors, such as muscle spindles and Golgi tendon organs, help maintain equilibrium and posture. Cutaneous receptors in the skin detect touch, pressure, pain, and temperature. Pain receptors are free nerve endings that respond to chemicals released by damaged cells.

Key Terms

astigmatism 724	olfactory cell 719
auditory tube 727	organ of Corti 727
blind spot 721	ossicle 727
camera-type eye 720	otolith 728
cataracts 724	outer ear 726
chemoreceptor 717	panoramic vision 721
choroid 721	photoreceptor 717, 720
ciliary muscle 722	proprioceptor 730
cochlea 727	pupil 721
compound eye 720	retina 721
cone cell 721	retinal detachment 724
conjunctiva 721	rhodopsin 722
cornea 721	rod cell 721
cutaneous receptor 730	rotational equilibrium 728
diabetic retinopathy 724	saccule 728
fovea centralis 721	sclera 721
glaucoma 724	semicircular canal 727
gravitational	sensory receptors 717
equilibrium 728	sensory transduction 717
farsighted (hyperopic) 724	stereoscopic vision 721
inner ear 727	taste bud 718
iris 721	thermoreceptor 717
lateral line 726	tympanic membrane 727
lens 721	utricle 728
macular degeneration 724	vertigo 730
mechanoreceptor 717	vestibule 727
middle ear 727	visual accommodation 722
nearsighted (myopic) 724	

Assess

Reviewing This Chapter

1. Discuss the structure and the function of human chemoreceptors. 718–19
2. In general, how does the eye in arthropods differ from that in humans? 720–21
3. Name the parts of the human eye, and give a function for each part. 721–23
4. Explain focusing and accommodation in terms of the anatomy of the human eye. 722
5. Contrast the location and the function of rod cells to those of cone cells. 722–23
6. Explain the process of integration in the retina and the brain. 723
7. Review some common disorders of the eye. 724
8. Describe some of the ways that animals detect sound waves. 726
9. Describe the structure of the human ear. 726–27
10. Describe how we hear. 727–28
11. Describe the role of the semicircular canals, utricle, and saccule in balance. 728
12. Discuss some common problems with hearing and equilibrium. 728–30
13. Distinguish between the functions of proprioceptors, cutaneous receptors, and pain receptors. 730–31

Testing Yourself

Choose the best answer for each question.

1. Which type of sensory receptor would be involved in detecting blood pressure?
   a. chemoreceptors
   b. mechanoreceptors
   c. photoreceptors
   d. thermoreceptors

2. Which of these gives the correct path for light rays entering the human eye?
   a. sclera, retina, choroid, lens, cornea
   b. fovea centralis, pupil, aqueous humor, lens
   c. cornea, pupil, lens, vitreous humor, retina
   d. optic nerve, sclera, choroid, retina, humors
   e. All of these are correct.

3. Which gives an incorrect function for the structure?
   a. lens—focusing
   b. iris—regulation of amount of light
   c. choroid—location of cones
   d. sclera—protection
   e. fovea centralis—acute vision

4. Retinal is
   a. a derivative of vitamin A.
   b. sensitive to light energy.
   c. a part of rhodopsin.
   d. found in rod cells.
   e. All of these are correct.

5. Which association is incorrect?
   a. taste buds—humans
   b. compound eye—arthropods
   c. camera-type eye—squid
   d. statocysts—sea stars
   e. chemoreceptors—planarians

6. Which one of these wouldn't you mention if you were tracing the path of sound vibrations?
   a. auditory canal
   b. tympanic membrane
   c. semicircular canals
   d. cochlea
   e. ossicles

7. Which one of these correctly describes the location of the organ of Corti?
   a. between the tympanic membrane and the oval window in the inner ear
   b. in the utricle and saccule within the vestibule
   c. between the tectorial membrane and the basilar membrane in the cochlear canal
   d. between the outer and inner ear within the semicircular canals

8. Which of these pairs is mismatched?
   a. semicircular canals—inner ear
   b. utricle and saccule—outer ear
   c. auditory canal—outer ear
   d. ossicles—middle ear
   e. cochlear nerve—inner ear

9. Both olfactory receptors and sound receptors have cilia, and they both
   a. are chemoreceptors.
   b. are a part of the brain.
   c. are mechanoreceptors.
   d. initiate nerve impulses.
   e. All of these are correct.

10. Stimulation of hair cells in the semicircular canals results from the movement of
    a. endolymph.
    b. aqueous humor.
    c. basilar membrane.
    d. otoliths.

11. To focus on objects that are close to the viewer,
    a. the suspensory ligaments must be pulled tight.
    b. the lens needs to become more rounded.
    c. the ciliary muscle will be relaxed.
    d. the image must focus on the area of the optic nerve.

12. Which abnormality of the eye is incorrectly matched?
    a. astigmatism—either the lens or cornea is not even
    b. farsightedness—eyeball is shorter than usual
    c. nearsightedness—image focuses behind the retina
    d. color blindness—genetic disorder in which certain types of cones may be missing

13. Which of these would allow you to know that you were upside down, even if you were in total darkness?
    a. utricle and saccule
    b. cochlea
    c. semicircular canals
    d. tectorial membrane

14. The thin, darkly pigmented layer that underlies most of the sclera is the
    a. conjunctiva.
    b. cornea.
    c. retina.
    d. choroid.

15. Adjustment of the lens to focus on objects close to the viewer is called
    a. convergence.
    b. accommodation.
    c. focusing.
    d. constriction.

16. Which of the following is/are not involved with detection of sound waves?
    a. tympanum of insects
    b. statocysts of crustaceans
    c. lateral line of fishes
    d. skeleton of amphibians and snakes

17. Label this diagram of the human eye. State a function for each structure labeled.

Engage

Thinking Scientifically

1. The density of taste buds on the tongue can vary. Some obese individuals have a lower density of taste buds than usual. Assume that taste perception is related to taste bud density. If so, what hypothesis would you test to see if there is a relationship between taste bud density and obesity?

2. A man who has spent many years serving on submarines complains of hearing loss, particularly the inability to hear high tones. When a submarine submerges, the inside air pressure intensifies. What hypothesis or hypotheses might explain hearing loss in this individual?

Bioethical Issue

Preventable Hearing Loss

The National Institute on Deafness and Other Communication Disorders (NIDCD) tells us that, of the approximately 28 million people in the United States with hearing loss, over one-third have been affected to some degree by noise exposure. Simple steps can be taken to prevent noise-induced hearing loss, such as wearing ear protection when engaged in loud activities such as mowing the lawn. Portable music devices are common culprits in hearing loss: If you can hear sound coming from someone's earbuds or headphones from a distance of 3 feet, that person is inflicting a damaging level of noise on him- or herself.

It's clear that for many of us, our own behavior contributes to the occurrence of hearing loss. Those with hearing loss may cope by using hearing aids, which can be costly and do not restore one's hearing to "normal." A device called a cochlear implant can compensate for damaged hair cells by directly stimulating the auditory nerve. However, the device must be surgically implanted, requires extensive postsurgical rehabilitation, does not replicate unassisted hearing, and is extremely expensive. Today, most health insurance provides at least partial assistance for hearing aids and cochlear implants. However, it is estimated that over the past 30 years, the number of people in the United States with hearing loss has doubled. Therefore, health insurance costs must rise in order to assist those with hearing loss.

What is your responsibility as an individual when it comes to protecting your own hearing? Does this responsibility change if you are in a group, say, taking a road trip in a car with the stereo turned all the way up? If you are aware that a friend is damaging his or her hearing in preventable ways, should you say anything? What is society's responsibility for educating its members about the importance of hearing protection? And does society have a responsibility to restrict sound levels at certain events, or to require that hearing protection be made available?

39

Locomotion and Support Systems

Gymnastics requires coordination between the nervous and support systems.

When Paul Hamm, a three-time Olympic medalist in gymnastics, does routines on rings, his muscular and skeletal systems are working together under the control of his nervous system. The same is true when eagles fly, fish swim, or when animals feed, escape prey, reproduce, or simply play. Although some animals lack muscles and bones, they all use contractile fibers to move about at some stage of their life. In many invertebrates, muscles push against body fluids located inside either a gastrovascular cavity or a coelom.

Only in vertebrates are muscles attached to a bony endoskeleton. Both the skeletal system and the muscular system contribute to homeostasis. Aside from giving the body shape and protecting internal organs, the skeleton serves as a storage area for inorganic calcium and produces blood cells. The skeleton also protects internal organs while supporting the body against the pull of gravity. While contributing to body movement, the skeletal muscles give off heat, which warms the body. This chapter compares locomotion in animals and reviews the musculoskeletal system of vertebrates.

As you read through the chapter, think about the following questions:

1. What advantages do animals with a skeletal system have over animals that completely lack such a system?
2. How does the nervous system specifically control the skeletal system?
3. How do the sensory systems exert influence over the nervous system, and therefore over the muscular and skeletal systems?

BEFORE YOU BEGIN

Before beginning this chapter, take a few moments to review the following discussions.

Figure 37.6 What is the function of acetylcholine in the transmission of a nerve impulse to skeletal muscle?

Sections 37.3 and 37.4 How does the primary motor area of the cerebral cortex generate commands to skeletal muscle, and how does the somatic division of the PNS control the muscles?

Chapter 38 How do the various types of sensory receptors provide information and feedback to the brain?

FOLLOWING *the* THEMES

CHAPTER 39 LOCOMOTION AND SUPPORT SYSTEMS

UNIT 7 COMPARATIVE ANIMAL BIOLOGY		
	Evolution	The need for protection, support, and mobility in different environments has led to the evolution of a number of different skeletal systems.
	Nature of Science	Investigations into bone and muscle functions have provided an understanding of how animals are adapted to their particular life styles, as well as having many applications to human health.
	Biological Systems	In humans, the skeletal system protects the internal organs, stores ions and contributes to homeostasis, produces blood cells for the circulatory system, and works together with the muscular system.

39.1 Diversity of Skeletons

Learning Outcomes

Upon completion of this section, you should be able to

1. Describe a typical hydrostatic skeleton, and list some examples of animals that possess one.
2. Discuss some advantages of having an endoskeleton versus an exoskeleton.
3. Provide several examples of how mammalian skeletons are adapted to particular forms of locomotion.

Skeletons serve as support systems for animals, providing rigidity, protection, and surfaces for muscle attachment. Several different kinds of skeletons occur in the animal kingdom. Cnidarians, flatworms, roundworms, and annelids have a hydrostatic skeleton. Typically, molluscs and arthropods have an exoskeleton (external skeleton) composed of calcium carbonate or chitin, respectively. Sponges, echinoderms, and vertebrates possess an endoskeleton (internal skeleton). In echinoderms, the endoskeleton is composed of calcareous plates and in vertebrates, the endoskeleton is comprised of cartilage, bone, or both.

Hydrostatic Skeleton

In animals that lack a hard skeleton, a fluid-filled gastrovascular cavity or a fluid-filled coelom can act as a hydrostatic skeleton. A **hydrostatic skeleton** utilizes fluid pressure to offer support and resistance to the contraction of muscles so that mobility results. As analogies, consider that a garden hose stiffens when filled with water, and that a water-filled balloon changes shape when squeezed at one end. Similarly, an animal with a hydrostatic skeleton can change shape and perform a variety of movements.

Hydras and planarians use their fluid-filled gastrovascular cavity as a hydrostatic skeleton. The tentacles of a hydra also have hydrostatic skeletons, allowing them to be extended to capture food. Roundworms have a fluid-filled pseudocoelom and move in a whiplike manner when their longitudinal muscles contract.

The coelom of annelids, such as earthworms, is segmented and has septa that divide it into compartments (Fig. 39.1). Each segment has its own set of longitudinal and circular muscles and its own nerve supply, so each segment or group of segments may function independently. When circular muscles contract, the segments become thinner and elongate. When longitudinal muscles contract, the segments become thicker and shorten. By alternating circular muscle contraction and longitudinal muscle contraction and by using its setae to hold its position during contractions, the animal moves forward.

Use of Muscular Hydrostats

Even animals that have an exoskeleton or an endoskeleton move selected body parts by means of *muscular hydrostats*, meaning that fluid contained within the individual cells that comprise a muscle assists with movement of that part. Muscular hydrostats are used by clams to extend their muscular foot and by sea stars to extend their tube feet. Spiders depend on them to move their legs, and moths depend on them to extend their proboscis. In vertebrates, movement of an elephant's trunk involves a muscular hydrostat that allows the animal to reach high into trees, pick up a morsel of food off the ground, or manipulate other objects.

Exoskeletons and Endoskeletons

Molluscs and arthropods have a rigid **exoskeleton,** an external covering composed of a stiff material. The strength of an exoskeleton can be improved by increasing its thickness and weight, but this leaves less room for internal organs.

In molluscs, such as snails and clams, a thick and nonmobile calcium carbonate shell is primarily used for protection against the environment and predators. A mollusc's shell can grow as the animal grows.

The exoskeleton of arthropods, such as insects and crustaceans, is composed of chitin, a strong, flexible nitrogenous polysaccharide. Their exoskeleton protects them against wear and tear, predators, and desiccation (drying out)—an important feature for arthropods that live on land. Working together with muscles, the jointed and movable appendages of arthropods allow them to crawl, fly, and/or swim. Because their exoskeleton is of fixed size, however, arthropods must *molt*, or shed their skeleton, in order to grow (Fig. 39.2).

a.

b.

circular muscles   longitudinal muscles   septa   fluid   setae

anterior

Figure 39.1 Locomotion in an earthworm.
a. The coelom is divided by septa, and each body segment is a separate locomotor unit. Both circular and longitudinal muscles are present. **b.** As circular muscles contract, a few segments extend. The worm is held in place by setae, needlelike chitinous structures on each segment of the body. Then, as longitudinal muscles contract, a portion of the body is brought forward. This series of events occurs down the length of the worm.

circular muscles contracted   longitudinal muscles contracted   circular muscles contract, and anterior end moves forward   longitudinal muscles contract, and segments catch up   circular muscles contract, and anterior end moves forward

Figure 39.2 Exoskeleton. Exoskeletons support muscle contraction and prevent drying out. The chitinous exoskeleton of an arthropod is shed as the animal molts; until the new skeleton dries and hardens, the animal is more vulnerable to predators, and muscle contractions may not translate into body movements. In this photo, a dog-day cicada, *Tibicen*, has just finished molting.

Both echinoderms and vertebrates have an **endoskeleton,** which is made up of rigid internal structures. The skeleton of echinoderms consists of spicules and plates of calcium carbonate embedded in the living tissue of the body wall. In contrast, the vertebrate endoskeleton is living tissue. Sharks and rays have skeletons composed only of cartilage. Other vertebrates, such as bony fishes, amphibians, reptiles, birds, and mammals, have endoskeletons composed of bone and cartilage.

The advantages of the jointed vertebrate endoskeleton are listed in Figure 39.3. An endoskeleton grows with the animal, thus molting is not required. It supports the weight of a large animal without limiting the space for internal organs. An endoskeleton also offers protection to vital internal organs, but it is protected by the soft tissues around it. Injuries to soft tissue are usually easier to repair than injuries to a hard skeleton. Compared to the relatively limited mobility of arthropod appendages, vertebrate limbs are generally more flexible and have different types of joints, allowing for even more complex movements.

The skeletons of mammals come in many sizes and shapes, which are often adapted to a particular mode of locomotion. Aquatic animals like seals, sea lions, whales, and dolphins have a streamlined, torpedo-shaped skeleton that facilitates movement through water. Many animals that jump, such as kangaroos and rabbits, have a compact skeleton with elongated hindlimbs that propel them forward. Carnivores, such as members of the cat family, walk on their toes, which is an adaptation to running and chasing prey. (Note that when humans run, we push off with our toes to move faster.) Hoofed mammals, such as horses or deer, have evolved long legs and run on the tips of elongated phalanges. The hoof of a horse is its third phalange only.

Humans are bipedal and walk on the soles of feet formed by the tarsal and metatarsal bones. This form of locomotion allows the hands to be free and may have evolved from the monkeys' and apes' habit of using only forelimbs as they swing through the branches of trees. Dexterity of hands and feet is actually the ancestral mammalian condition. In humans and apes, the bones of the hands and feet are not fused, and the wrist and ankle can rotate in three dimensions.

Check Your Progress 39.1

1. Identify the type of skeleton of each of the following animals: butterfly, crow, shrimp, oyster, and sea urchin.
2. Describe the type of support system that makes it possible to stick out your tongue.
3. Explain why an earthworm loses its cylindrical shape when it dies.

Advantages of Jointed Endoskeleton

Can grow with the animal

Supports the weight of large animal

Protects vital internal organs

Is protected by outer tissues

Allows flexible movements

Figure 39.3 The vertebrate endoskeleton. The jointed vertebrate endoskeleton has the advantages listed. In addition, an endoskeleton lends itself to adaptation to the environment. Vertebrates move in various ways (e.g., jumping, flying, swimming, running).

39.2 The Human Skeletal System

Learning Outcomes

Upon completion of this section, you should be able to

1. Review the five major functions of the skeletal system.
2. Describe the macroscopic and microscopic structure of bone.
3. List the major bones that comprise the human axial and appendicular skeletons.

The skeletal system has many functions that contribute to homeostasis:

- *Support of the body.* The rigid skeleton provides an internal framework that largely determines the body's shape.
- *Protection of vital internal organs,* such as the brain, heart, and lungs. The bones of the skull protect the brain; the rib cage protects the heart and lungs. The vertebrae protect the spinal cord.
- *Sites for muscle attachment.* The pull of muscles on the bones makes movement possible. Articulations (joints) occur between all the bones, but we associate body movement particularly with jointed appendages.
- *Storage reservoir for ions.* All bones have a matrix that contains calcium phosphate, a source of calcium ions and phosphate ions in the blood.
- *Production of blood cells.* Blood cells and other blood elements are produced within the red bone marrow of the skull, ribs, sternum, pelvis, and long bones.

In this section, we describe the characteristics of human bones, the components of various regions of the skeleton, and the different types and functions of joints.

Bone Growth and Renewal

During prenatal development, the structures that will form the bones of the human skeleton are composed of cartilage. Because these cartilaginous structures are shaped like the future bones, they provide "models" of these bones. The models are converted to bones as calcium salts are deposited in the matrix (nonliving material), first by the cartilage cells and later by bone-forming cells called **osteoblasts** [Gk. *osteon,* bone, and *blastos,* bud]. The conversion of cartilaginous models to bones is called endochondral ossification.

In some cases, ossification occurs without any previous cartilaginous model. This type of ossification occurs in the dermis and forms bones called dermal bones. Examples include the mandible (lower jaw), certain bones of the skull, and the clavicle (collarbone). During intramembranous ossification, fibrous connective tissue membranes give support as ossification begins.

Endochondral ossification of a long bone begins in a region called a primary ossification center, located in the middle of the cartilaginous model. In the primary ossification center, the cartilage is broken down and invaded by blood vessels, and cells in the area mature into bone-forming osteoblasts. Later, secondary ossification centers form at the ends of the model. A cartilaginous *growth plate* remains between the primary ossification

center and each secondary center. As long as these plates remain, growth is possible. The rate of growth is controlled by hormones, particularly growth hormone (GH) and the sex hormones. Eventually, the plates become ossified, causing the primary and secondary centers of ossification to fuse, and the bone stops growing.

Animation Bone Growth

Video Nano Bones

In the adult, bone is continually being broken down and built up again. Bone-absorbing cells called **osteoclasts** [Gk. *osteon,* bone, and *klastos,* broken in pieces] break down bone, remove worn cells, and deposit calcium in the blood. In this way, osteoclasts help maintain the blood calcium level and contribute to homeostasis.

Among many other functions, calcium ions play a major role in muscle contraction and nerve conduction. The blood calcium level is closely regulated by the antagonistic hormones parathyroid hormone (PTH) and calcitonin. PTH promotes the activity of osteoclasts, and calcitonin inhibits their activity to keep the blood calcium level within normal limits.

MP3 Calcium Homeostasis

Assuming that the blood calcium level is normal, bone destruction caused by the work of osteoclasts is repaired by osteoblasts. As they form bone, some of these osteoblasts get caught in the matrix (nonliving material) they secrete and are converted to **osteocytes** [Gk. *osteon,* bone, and *kytos,* cell]. These cells live within the lacunae of osteons, where they continue to affect the timing and location of bone remodeling.

While a child is growing, the rate of bone formation is greater than the rate of bone breakdown. The skeletal mass continues to increase until ages 20 to 30. After that, the rate of formation and rate of breakdown of bone mass are equal, until ages 40 to 50. Then, reabsorption begins to exceed formation, and the total bone mass slowly decreases.

As people age, an abnormal thinning of the bones called **osteoporosis** can lead to an increased risk of fractures, especially of the wrist, vertebrae, and pelvis. About ten million people in the United States have osteoporosis, which results in 1.5 million fractures each year.

Women are twice as likely as men to have an osteoporosis-related fracture in their lifetime, and about one in four women will experience such a fracture. This is partly due to the fact that women have about 30% less bone mass than men to begin with. Also, because sex hormones play an important role in maintaining bone strength, women typically lose about two percent of their bone mass each year after menopause. Estrogen replacement therapy has been shown to increase bone mass and reduce fractures, but it can also increase the risk of cardiovascular disease and certain types of cancer. Other strategies for decreasing osteoporosis risk include consuming 1,000-1,500 mg of calcium per day, obtaining sufficient vitamin D, and engaging in regular physical exercise.

Animation Osteoporosis

Video Bear Bones

Anatomy of a Long Bone

A long bone, such as the humerus, illustrates principles of bone anatomy. When the bone is split open, as in Figure 39.4, the longitudinal section shows that it is not solid but has a

Figure 39.4 Anatomy of a long bone. *Left:* A long bone is encased by fibrous membrane (periosteum) except where it is covered at the ends by hyaline cartilage (see micrograph). Spongy bone located beneath the cartilage may contain red bone marrow. The central shaft contains yellow bone marrow and is bordered by compact bone, which is shown in the enlargement and micrograph (*right*).

cavity called the medullary cavity bounded at the sides by compact bone and at the ends by spongy bone. Beyond the spongy bone, there is a thin shell of compact bone and finally a layer of hyaline cartilage. The cavity of an adult long bone usually contains yellow bone marrow, which is a fat-storage tissue.

Compact bone contains many osteons (also called Haversian systems), where osteocytes lie in tiny chambers called lacunae. The lacunae are arranged in concentric circles around central canals that contain blood vessels and nerves. The lacunae are separated by a matrix of collagen fibers and mineral deposits, primarily calcium and phosphorus salts.

Spongy bone has numerous bony bars and plates separated by irregular spaces. Although lighter than compact bone, spongy bone is still designed for strength. Just as braces are used for support in buildings, the solid portions of spongy bone follow lines of stress. The spaces in spongy bone are often filled with **red bone marrow,** a specialized tissue that produces blood cells. This is an additional way the skeletal system assists homeostasis. As you know, red blood cells transport oxygen, and white blood cells are a part of the immune system, which fights infection.

MP3
Bone Structure

The Axial Skeleton

The **axial skeleton** [L. *axis,* axis, hinge; Gk. *skeleton,* dried body] lies in the midline of the body and consists of the skull, the vertebral column, the thoracic cage, the sacrum, and the coccyx (blue labels in Fig. 39.5). A total of 80 bones make up the axial skeleton.

The Skull

The skull, which protects the brain, is formed by the cranium and the facial bones (Fig. 39.6). In newborns, certain bones of the cranium are joined by membranous regions called *fontanels* (or "soft spots"), all of which usually close and become **sutures** by the age of two years. The bones of the cranium contain the sinuses [L. *sinus,* hollow], air spaces lined by mucous membrane that reduce the weight of the skull and give a resonant sound to the voice. Two sinuses, called the mastoid sinuses, drain into the middle ear. Mastoiditis, a condition that can lead to deafness, is an inflammation of these sinuses.

The major bones of the cranium have the same names as the lobes of the brain. On the top of the cranium, the frontal bone forms the forehead, and the parietal bones extend to the sides. Below the much larger parietal bones, each temporal bone has an opening that leads to the middle ear. In the rear of the skull, the occipital bone curves to form the base of the skull. At the base of the skull, the spinal cord passes upward through a large opening called the *foramen magnum* [L. *foramen,* hole, and *magnus,* great, large] and becomes the brain stem.

The temporal and frontal bones are cranial bones that contribute to the face. The sphenoid bones account for the flattened

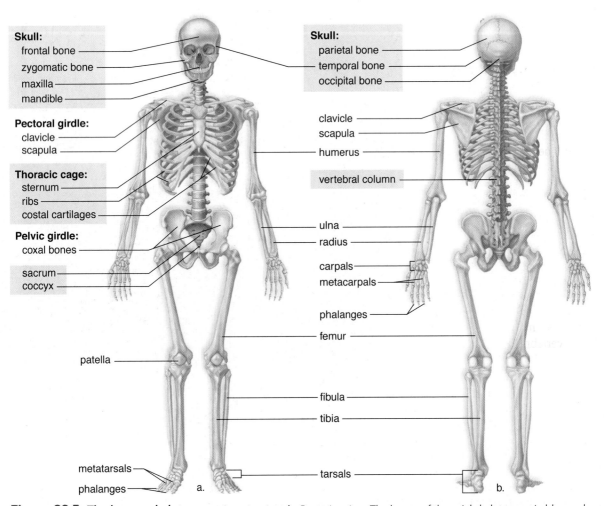

Figure 39.5 The human skeleton. **a.** Anterior view. **b.** Posterior view. The bones of the axial skeleton are in blue and the rest is the appendicular skeleton.

Lateral view

Frontal view

Figure 39.6
The skull.
The skull consists of the cranium and the facial bones. The frontal bone is the forehead; the zygomatic arches form the cheekbones, and the maxillae form the upper jaw. The mandible has a projection we call the chin.

areas on each side of the forehead, which we call the temples. The frontal bone not only forms the forehead, but it also has supraorbital ridges where the eyebrows are located. Glasses sit where the frontal bone joins the nasal bones.

The most prominent of the facial bones are the mandible [L. *mandibula*, jaw], the maxillae, the zygomatic bones, and the nasal bones. The mandible, or lower jaw, is the only freely movable portion of the skull (Fig. 39.6), and its action permits us to chew our food. It also forms the "chin." Tooth sockets are located in the mandible and on the maxillae, which form the upper jaw and a portion of the hard palate. The zygomatic bones are the cheekbone prominences, and the nasal bones form the bridge of the nose. Other bones make up the nasal septum, which divides the nose cavity into two regions.

Whereas the ears are formed only by cartilage and not by bone, the nose is a mixture of bones, cartilage, and connective tissues. The lips and cheeks have a core of skeletal muscle.

MP3
The Skull

The Vertebral Column and Rib Cage

The **vertebral column** [L. *vertebra*, bones of backbone] supports the head and trunk and protects the spinal cord and the roots of the spinal nerves. It is a longitudinal axis that serves either directly or indirectly as an anchor for all the other bones of the skeleton.

Twenty-four vertebrae make up the vertebral column. Seven cervical vertebrae are located in the neck; 12 thoracic vertebrae are in the thorax; five lumbar vertebrae are in the lower back; five fused sacral vertebrae form a single sacrum; and several fused vertebrae are in the coccyx, or tailbone. Normally, the vertebral column has four curvatures that provide more resilience and strength for an upright posture than could a straight column.

Intervertebral disks, composed of fibrocartilage between the vertebrae, provide padding. They prevent the vertebrae from grinding against one another and absorb shock caused by movements such as running, jumping, and even walking. The presence of the disks allows the vertebrae to move as we bend forward, backward, and from side to side. Unfortunately, these disks become weakened with age and can herniate and rupture. Pain results if a disk presses against the spinal cord

and/or spinal nerves. The body may heal itself, or the disk can be removed surgically. If the latter, the vertebrae can be fused together, but this limits the flexibility of the body.

The thoracic vertebrae are a part of the *rib cage*, sometimes also called the thoracic cage. The rib cage also contains the ribs, the costal cartilages, and the sternum, or breastbone (Fig. 39.7).

There are 12 pairs of ribs. The upper seven pairs are "true ribs" because they attach directly to the sternum. The lower five pairs do not connect directly to the sternum and are called the "false ribs." Three pairs of false ribs attach by means of a common cartilage, and two pairs are "floating ribs" because they do not attach to the sternum at all.

The rib cage demonstrates how the skeleton is protective but also flexible. The rib cage protects the heart and lungs; yet it swings outward and upward upon inspiration and then downward and inward upon expiration.

MP3
The Vertebral Column and Thoracic Cage

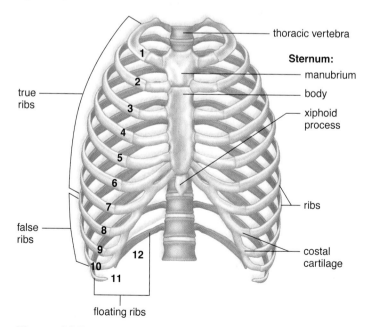

Figure 39.7 The rib cage. The rib cage consists of the thoracic vertebrae, the 12 pairs of ribs, the costal cartilages, and the sternum, or breastbone.

The Appendicular Skeleton

The **appendicular skeleton** [L. *appendicula*, dim. of *appendix*, appendage] consists of the bones within the pectoral and pelvic girdles and the attached limbs (see Fig. 39.5). The pectoral (shoulder) girdle and upper limbs are specialized for flexibility, but the pelvic girdle (hipbones) and lower limbs are specialized for strength. A total of 126 bones make up the appendicular skeleton.

MP3
The Appendicular Skeleton

The Pectoral Girdle and Upper Limb

The components of the **pectoral girdle** [Gk. *pechys*, forearm] are only loosely linked together by ligaments (Fig. 39.8). Each clavicle (collarbone) connects with the sternum and the scapula (shoulder blade), but the scapula is held in place only by muscles. This allows it to glide and rotate on the clavicle.

The single long bone in the arm, the humerus, has a smoothly rounded head that fits into a socket of the scapula. The socket, however, is very shallow and much smaller than the head. Although this means that the arm can move in almost any direction, the joint lacks stability. Therefore, this is the joint that is most apt to dislocate. The opposite end of the humerus meets the two bones of the lower arm, the ulna and the radius, at the

clavicle
head of humerus
scapula
humerus
head of radius
radius
ulna
carpals
metacarpals
phalanges

Figure 39.8 Bones of the pectoral girdle and upper limb. The humerus is known as the "funny bone" of the elbow. The sensation upon bumping it is due to the activation of a nerve that passes across its end.

elbow. (The prominent bone in the elbow is the topmost part of the ulna.) When the upper limb is held so that the palm is turned frontward, the radius and ulna are about parallel to one another. When the upper limb is turned so that the palm is next to the body, the radius crosses in front of the ulna, a feature that contributes to the easy twisting motion of the forearm.

The many bones of the hand increase its flexibility. The wrist has eight carpal bones, which look like small pebbles. From these, five metacarpal bones fan out to form a framework for the palm. The metacarpal bone that leads to the thumb is placed in such a way that the thumb can reach out and touch the other digits (digit is a term that refers to either fingers or toes). Beyond the metacarpals are the phalanges, the bones of the fingers and the thumb. The phalanges of the hand are long, slender, and lightweight.

The Pelvic Girdle and Lower Limb

The **pelvic girdle** [L. *pelvis*, basin] (Fig. 39.9) consists of two heavy, large coxal bones (hip bones). The coxal bones are anchored to the sacrum, and together these bones form a hollow cavity called the pelvic cavity. The wider pelvic cavity in females compared to that of males accommodates pregnancy and childbirth. The weight of the body is transmitted through the pelvis to the lower limbs and then onto the ground. The largest bone in the body is the femur, or thighbone.

In the leg, the larger of the two bones, the tibia, has a ridge we call the shin. Both of the bones of the leg have a prominence that contributes to the ankle—the tibia on the inside of the ankle and the fibula on the outside of the ankle.

Although there are seven tarsal bones in the ankle, only one receives the weight and passes it on to the heel and the ball of the foot. If you wear high-heeled shoes, the weight is thrown toward the front of your foot. The metatarsal bones participate in forming the arches of the foot. There is a longitudinal arch from the heel to the toes and a transverse arch across the foot. These provide a stable, springy base for the body. If the tissues that bind the metatarsals together become weakened, "flat feet" are apt to result. The bones of the toes are called phalanges, just as are those of the fingers, but in the foot the phalanges are stout and extremely sturdy.

Classification of Joints

Bones are connected at the **joints,** which are classified as fibrous, cartilaginous, and synovial. Most fibrous joints, such as the sutures that exist between the cranial bones, are immovable. Cartilaginous joints, such as those between the vertebrae, are slightly movable. The vertebrae are also separated by disks, which increase their flexibility. The two hipbones are slightly movable because they are ventrally joined by cartilage at the pubic symphysis. Owing to hormonal changes, this joint becomes more flexible during late pregnancy, allowing the pelvis to expand during childbirth.

In freely movable **synovial joints,** the two bones are separated by a cavity. **Ligaments,** composed of fibrous connective tissue, bind the two bones to each other, holding them in place

Figure 39.9 Bones of the pelvic girdle and lower limb. The femur is our strongest bone—it withstands a pressure of 540 kg per 2.5 cm³ when we walk.

Figure 39.10 Knee joint. The knee joint is an example of a synovial joint. The cavity between the bones is encased by ligaments and lined by synovial membrane. The patella (kneecap) serves to guide the quadriceps tendon over the joint when flexion or extension occurs.

as they form a capsule. In a "double-jointed" individual, the ligaments are unusually loose. The joint capsule is lined by synovial membrane, which produces synovial fluid, a lubricant for the joint.

The shoulders, elbows, hips, and knees are examples of synovial joints (Fig. 39.10). In the knee, as in other freely movable joints, the bones are capped by a layer of articular cartilage. In addition, crescent-shaped pieces of cartilage called menisci [Gk. *meniscus,* crescent] lie between the bones. These give added stability, helping to support the weight placed on the knee joint. Unfortunately, athletes often suffer injury of the meniscus, known as torn cartilage. Thirteen fluid-filled sacs called bursae (sing., bursa; L. *bursa,* purse) occur around the knee joint. Bursae ease friction between tendons and ligaments and between tendons and bones. Inflammation of the bursae is called bursitis. Tennis elbow is a form of bursitis.

Different types of synovial joints can be distinguished. The knee and elbow joints are *hinge joints* because, like a hinged door, they largely permit movement in one direction only. The joint between the first two cervical vertebrae, which permits side-to-side movement of the head, is an example of a *pivot joint,* which only allows rotation. More movable are the *ball-and-socket joints;* for example, the ball of the femur fits into a

socket on the hipbone. Ball-and-socket joints allow movement in all planes and even rotational movement.

All types of joints are subject to **arthritis,** or inflammation of the joints. The Arthritis Foundation estimates that nearly one in three adult Americans has some degree of chronic joint pain, and arthritis is secondary only to heart disease as a cause of work disability in the United States. The most common type of arthritis is osteoarthritis, which results from the deterioration of the cartilage in one or more synovial joints. The hands, hips, knees, lower back, and neck are most commonly affected. Rheumatoid arthritis is considered to be an autoimmune disease, in which the immune system attacks the joints for reasons that are not well understood.

Regardless of the cause, arthritis is most often treated by over-the-counter anti-inflammatory drugs such as aspirin and ibuprofen, or more powerful prescription drugs such as the corticosteroids. In severe cases, certain joints can be replaced with artificial versions made of ceramic, metal, and/or plastic. About 500,000 artificial knees and 200,000 artificial hips are installed in U.S. patients each year.

Check Your Progress   39.2

1. Describe the function of osteoblasts, osteoclasts, and osteocytes.
2. Distinguish between the structure and functions of spongy bone and compact bone.
3. Determine whether each of the following bones belongs to the axial or appendicular skeleton: sacrum, frontal bone, humerus, tibia, vertebra, coxal bone, temporal bone, scapula, and sternum.

39.3 The Muscular System

Muscles are composed of contractile tissue that is capable of changing its length by contracting and relaxing. Most animals rely on muscle tissue to produce movement—to swim, crawl, walk, run, jump, or fly. Clearly there are strong evolutionary advantages to be able to move into new environments, to flee from danger, to seek and/or capture food, and to find new mates. Only a few animals are nonmotile (also called sessile), and most of these live in water, where currents can bring a supply of food to them.

As discussed in Chapter 31, humans and other vertebrates have three distinct types of muscle tissue: smooth, cardiac, and skeletal. Most of the focus in this chapter is on skeletal muscle, or striated voluntary muscle, which is important in maintaining posture, providing support, and allowing for movement. The processes responsible for skeletal muscle contraction also release heat that is distributed throughout the body, helping to maintain a constant body temperature.

MP3 Muscle Tissue

Macroscopic Anatomy and Physiology

The nearly 700 skeletal muscles and their associated tissues make up approximately 40% of the weight of an average human. Muscle tissue is approximately 15% more dense than fat tissue, so that a pound of muscle takes up less space than does a pound of fat. However, even at rest, muscle tissue consumes about three times more energy than adipose tissue.

Several of the major human superficial muscles are illustrated in Figure 39.11. Skeletal muscles are attached to the skeleton by bands of fibrous connective tissue called **tendons** [L. *tendo,* stretch]. When muscles contract, they shorten. Therefore, muscles can only pull; they cannot push. Because of this, skeletal muscles must work in antagonistic pairs. One muscle of an antagonistic pair flexes the joint and bends the limb; the other one extends the joint and straightens the limb. Figure 39.12 illustrates this principle.

In the laboratory, if a muscle is given a rapid series of threshold stimuli (i.e., stimuli strong enough to bring about action potentials, as described on page 699), it can respond to the next stimulus without relaxing completely. In this way, muscle contraction builds, or summates, until maximal sustained contraction, called **tetany,** is achieved. Tetanic contractions ordinarily occur in the body's muscles whenever skeletal muscles are actively used.

Even when muscles appear to be at rest, they exhibit **tone,** in which some of their fibers are contracting. As you saw in the preceding chapter, sensory receptors called muscle spindles and

Figure 39.11 Human musculature. Anterior view of some of the major superficial skeletal muscles.

frontalis
orbicularis oculi
zygomaticus
trapezius
pectoralis major
latissimus dorsi
external oblique
flexor carpi group
sartorius
quadriceps femoris group
peroneus longus
tibialis anterior
extensor digitorum longus

orbicularis oris
masseter
sternocleidomastoid
deltoid
biceps brachii
triceps brachii
brachioradialis
rectus abdominis
iliopsoas
adductor longus
gracilis
gastrocnemius

Golgi tendon organs are partly responsible for maintaining tone. Muscle tone is particularly important in maintaining posture. If all the fibers within the muscles of the neck, trunk, and legs were to suddenly relax, the body would collapse.

Muscle tone has also been implicated in the formation of facial wrinkles. As described the Nature of Science feature, medical injections of Botox® interfere with muscle contraction, smoothing wrinkles.

Microscopic Anatomy and Physiology

A vertebrate skeletal muscle is composed of a number of muscle fibers in bundles. Each muscle fiber is a cell containing the usual cellular components, but some components have special features (Fig. 39.13).

The **sarcolemma,** or plasma membrane [Gk. *sarkos,* flesh, and *lemma,* sheath], forms a transverse system, or T system. The T tubules penetrate, or dip down, into the cell so that they come into contact—but do not fuse—with the **sarcoplasmic reticulum,** which consists of expanded portions of modified endoplasmic

Figure 39.12 Antagonistic muscles. Muscles can exert force only by shortening; therefore, they often work as antagonistic pairs. The biceps and triceps brachii exemplify an antagonistic pair of muscles that act opposite to one another. The biceps brachii flexes the elbow joint, and the triceps brachii extends the elbow joint.

reticulum (ER). These expanded portions serve as storage sites for calcium ions (Ca²⁺), which are essential for muscle contraction. The sarcoplasmic reticulum encases hundreds and sometimes even thousands of **myofibrils** [Gk. *myos*, muscle; L. *fibra*, thread], which are the contractile portions of a muscle fiber.

Myofibrils are cylindrical in shape and run the length of the muscle fiber. The light microscope shows that a myofibril has light and dark bands termed striations. These bands are responsible for skeletal muscle's striated appearance. The electron microscope reveals that the striations of myofibrils are formed by the placement of protein filaments within contractile units called **sarcomeres** [Gk. *sarkos*, flesh, and *meros*, part].

Examining sarcomeres when they are relaxed shows that a sarcomere extends between two dark lines called the Z lines (Fig. 39.13). There are two types of protein filaments: thick filaments made up of **myosin,** and thin filaments made up of **actin.** The I band is light colored because it contains only actin filaments attached to a Z line. The dark regions of the A band contain overlapping actin and myosin filaments, and its H zone has only myosin filaments.

MP3 Muscle Structure

Sliding Filament Model

Examining muscle fibers when they are contracted reveals that the sarcomeres within the myofibrils have shortened. When a sarcomere shortens, the actin (thin) filaments slide past the myosin (thick) filaments and approach one another. This causes the I band to shorten and the H zone to nearly or completely disappear.

The movement of actin filaments in relation to myosin filaments is called the **sliding filament model** of muscle

Figure 39.13 Skeletal muscle fiber structure and function. A muscle fiber contains many myofibrils, divided into sarcomeres, which are contractile. When the myofibrils of a muscle fiber contract, the sarcomeres shorten: the actin (thin) filaments slide past the myosin (thick) filaments toward the center so that the H zone gets smaller, to the point of disappearing.

The Accidental Discovery of Botox®

Several of the most important bacterial pathogens that cause human diseases—including cholera, diphtheria, tetanus, and botulism—do so by secreting potent toxins capable of sickening or killing their victims. The botulinum toxin, produced by the bacterium *Clostridium botulinum*, is one of the most lethal substances known. Less than a microgram of the purified toxin can kill an average size person, and four kilograms (8.8 pounds) would be enough to kill all humans on Earth! Given this scary fact, it seems that the scientists who discovered the lethal activity of this bacterial toxin nearly 200 years ago could never have anticipated that the intentional injection of a very dilute form of botulinum toxin (now known as Botox®) would become the most common non-surgical cosmetic procedure performed by many physicians.

As with many breakthroughs in science and medicine, the pathway from thinking about botulism as a deadly disease to using botulinum toxin as a beneficial treatment involved the hard work of many scientists, mixed with a considerable amount of luck.

In the 1820s, a German scientist, Justinus Kerner (1786–1862), was able to prove that the deaths of several people had been caused by their consumption of spoiled sausage (in fact, botulism is named for the Latin word for sausage, *botulus*). A few decades later a Belgian researcher named Emile Pierre van Ermengem (1851–1932) identified the specific bacterium responsible for producing the botulinum toxin, which could cause symptoms ranging from droopy eyelids to paralysis and respiratory failure.

By the 1920s, medical scientists at the University of California had obtained the toxin in pure form, which allowed them to determine that it acted by preventing nerves from communicating with muscles, specifically by interfering with the release of acetylcholine from the axon terminals of motor nerves (see Section 39.3).

Scientists soon began testing very dilute concentrations of the toxin as a treatment for conditions in which the muscles contract too much, such as crossed eyes or spasms of the facial muscles or vocal cords, and in 1989 the FDA first approved diluted botulinum toxin (Botox®) for treating specific eye conditions called blepharospasm (eyelid spasms) and strabismus (crossing of the eyes).

Right around this time, a lucky break occurred that eventually would open the medical community's eyes to the greater potential of the diluted toxin. A Canadian ophthalmologist, Jean Carruthers, had been using it to treat her patients' eye conditions when she noticed that some of their wrinkles had also subsided. One night at a family dinner, Dr. Carruthers shared this information with her husband, a dermatologist, who decided to investigate whether he could reduce the deep wrinkles of some of his

Figure 39A Treating wrinkles with diluted botulinum toxin.

patients by injecting the dilute toxin into their skin. The treatment worked well, and after trying it on several more patients, as well as on themselves (!), the Canadian doctors spent several years presenting their findings at scientific meetings and in research journals. Although they were initially considered "crazy," the Carruthers eventually were able to convince the scientific community that diluted botulinum toxin was effective in treating wrinkles; however, they never patented it for that use, so they missed out on much of the $1.3 billion in annual sales the drug now earns for the company that did patent it.

The uses of diluted botulinum toxin seem to be growing since it was FDA-approved for the treatment of frown lines in 2002 (Fig. 39A). In March 2010, it was approved for the treatment of muscle stiffness in people with upper limb spasticity, and the company is currently seeking approval for as many as 90 uses of diluted botulinum toxin, including treatment of migraine headaches.

Perhaps all of this would have eventually happened even without the observations of an alert eye doctor, but progress would have very likely been slower. As the French microbiologist Louis Pasteur observed in 1854, "Chance favors the prepared mind," meaning that many scientific discoveries involve many investigators, and years of work, mixed with a flash of inspiration.

Questions to Consider

1. Considering that botulism is caused by a preformed toxin, how do you suppose it can be treated?
2. Do you think companies should be allowed to patent a naturally occurring molecule like botulinum toxin? Why or why not?

---

contraction. During the sliding process, the sarcomere shortens, even though the filaments themselves remain the same length. When you play "tug of war," your hands grasp the rope, pull, let go, attach farther down the rope, and pull again. The myosin heads are like your hands—grasping, pulling, letting go, and then repeating the process.

Animation Sarcomere Contraction

The participants in muscle contraction have the functions listed in Table 39.1. ATP supplies the energy for muscle contraction. Although the actin filaments slide past the myosin filaments, it is the myosin filaments that do the work. Myosin filaments break down ATP and form cross-bridges that attach to and pull the actin filaments toward the center of the sarcomere.

Use of ATP in Contraction

ATP provides the energy for muscle contraction. Although muscle cells contain *myoglobin*, a molecule that stores oxygen, cellular respiration does not immediately supply all the ATP that is needed. In the meantime, muscle fibers rely on *creatine phosphate* (phosphocreatine), a storage form of high-energy phosphate. Creatine phosphate cannot directly participate in muscle contraction. Instead, it anaerobically regenerates ATP by the following reaction:

$$\text{creatine—P} + \text{ADP} \longrightarrow \text{ATP} + \text{creatine}$$

This reaction occurs in the midst of sliding filaments, and therefore, this method of supplying ATP is the speediest energy source available to muscles.

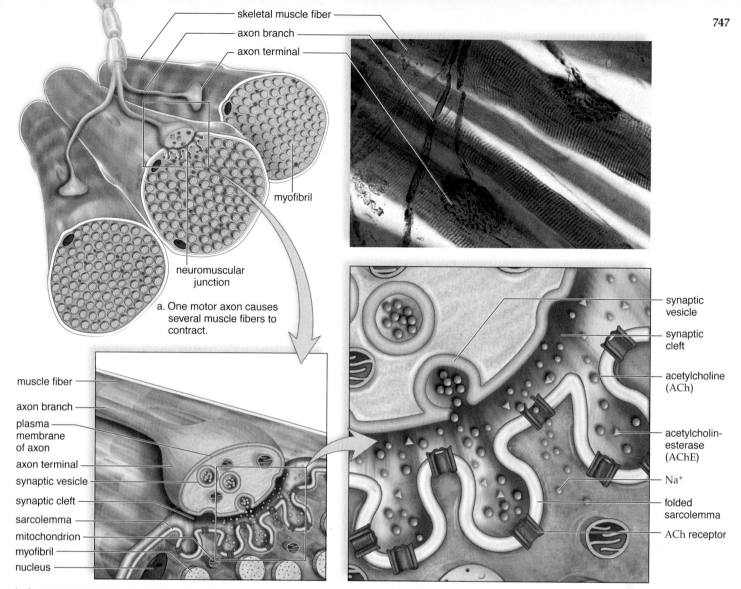

a. One motor axon causes several muscle fibers to contract.

skeletal muscle fiber
axon branch
axon terminal
myofibril
neuromuscular junction

b. A neuromuscular junction is the juxtaposition of an axon terminal and the sarcolemma of a muscle fiber.

muscle fiber
axon branch
plasma membrane of axon
axon terminal
synaptic vesicle
synaptic cleft
sarcolemma
mitochondrion
myofibril
nucleus

c. The release of a neurotransmitter (ACh) causes receptors to open and Na$^+$ to enter a muscle fiber.

synaptic vesicle
synaptic cleft
acetylcholine (ACh)
acetylcholin-esterase (AChE)
Na$^+$
folded sarcolemma
ACh receptor

Figure 39.14 Neuromuscular junction. The branch of a motor nerve fiber (a) ends in an axon terminal (b) that meets but does not touch a muscle fiber. A synaptic cleft separates the axon terminal from the sarcolemma of the muscle fiber. Nerve impulses traveling down a motor fiber cause synaptic vesicles (c) to discharge a neurotransmitter that diffuses across the synaptic cleft. When the neurotransmitter is received by the sarcolemma of a muscle fiber, impulses begin that lead to muscle fiber contraction.

Table 39.1 Muscle Contraction

Name	Function
Actin filaments	Slide past myosin, causing contraction
Ca^{2+}	Needed for myosin to bind to actin
Myosin filaments	Pull actin filaments by means of cross-bridges; are enzymatic and split ATP
ATP	Supplies energy for muscle contraction

When all of the creatine phosphate is depleted, mitochondria may by then be producing enough ATP for muscle contraction to continue. If not, fermentation is a second way for muscles to supply ATP without consuming oxygen. Fermentation, which is apt to occur when strenuous exercise first begins, supplies ATP for only a short time, and lactate builds up. Whether lactate causes muscle aches and fatigue upon exercising is now being questioned.

We all have had the experience of needing to continue deep breathing following strenuous exercise. This continued intake of oxygen, which is required to complete the metabolism of lactate and restore cells to their original energy state, offsets what is known as **oxygen debt.** The lactate is transported to the liver, where 20% of it is completely broken down to carbon dioxide (CO_2) and water (H_2O). The ATP gained by this respiration is then used to reconvert 80% of the lactate to glucose.

In persons who regularly exercise, such as athletes in training, the number of mitochondria increases, and muscles rely on them rather than on fermentation to produce ATP. Less lactate is produced, and there is less oxygen debt.

Muscle Innervation

Muscles are stimulated to contract by motor nerve fibers. Nerve fibers have several branches, each of which ends at an axon terminal that lies in close proximity to the sarcolemma of a muscle fiber. A small gap, called a synaptic cleft, separates the axon terminal from the sarcolemma. This entire region is called a **neuromuscular junction** (Fig. 39.14).

Axon terminals contain synaptic vesicles that are filled with the neurotransmitter acetylcholine (ACh). When nerve

a. Function of Ca²⁺

b. Function of myosin

Figure 39.15 The role of calcium and myosin in muscle contraction. **a.** Upon release, calcium binds to troponin, exposing myosin binding sites. **b.** After breaking down ATP **1**, myosin heads bind to an actin filament **2**, and later, a power stroke causes the actin filament to move **3**. When another ATP binds to myosin, the head detaches from actin **4**, and the cycle begins again. Although only one myosin head is featured, many heads are active at the same time.

impulses traveling down a motor neuron arrive at an axon terminal, the synaptic vesicles release ACh into the synaptic cleft. ACh quickly diffuses across the cleft and binds to receptors in the sarcolemma. Now the sarcolemma generates impulses that spread over the sarcolemma and down T tubules to the sarcoplasmic reticulum. The release of calcium from the sarcoplasmic reticulum causes the filaments within sarcomeres to slide past one another. Sarcomere contraction results in myofibril contraction, which in turn results in muscle fiber, and finally muscle, contraction.

Once a neurotransmitter has been released into a neuromuscular junction and has initiated a response, it is removed from the junction. When the enzyme acetylcholinesterase (AChE) breaks down acetylcholine, muscle contraction ceases due to reasons we discuss next.

Animation
Function of the
Neuromuscular
Junction

Role of Calcium in Muscle Contraction

Figure 39.15 illustrates the placement of two other proteins associated with a thin filament, which is composed of a double row of twisted actin molecules. Threads of tropomyosin wind about an actin filament, and troponin occurs at intervals along the threads. Calcium ions (Ca²⁺) that have been released from the sarcoplasmic reticulum combine with troponin. After binding occurs, the tropomyosin threads shift their position, and myosin binding sites are exposed.

Thick filaments are bundles of myosin molecules with double globular heads. Myosin heads function as ATPase enzymes, splitting ATP into ADP and ℗. This reaction activates the heads so that they can bind to actin. The ADP and ℗ remain on the myosin heads until the heads attach to actin, forming crossbridges. Now, ADP and ℗ are released, and this causes the cross-bridges to change their positions. This is the power stroke that pulls the thin filaments toward the middle of the sarcomere. When more ATP molecules bind to myosin heads, the crossbridges are broken as the heads detach from actin. The cycle begins again; the actin filaments move nearer the center of the sarcomere each time the cycle is repeated.

Contraction continues until nerve impulses cease and calcium ions are returned to their storage sites. The membranes of the sarcoplasmic reticulum contain active transport proteins that pump calcium ions back into the calcium storage sites, and muscle relaxation occurs. When a person or animal dies, ATP production ceases. Without ATP, the myosin heads cannot detach from actin, nor can calcium be pumped back into the sarcoplasmic reticulum. As a result, the muscles remain contracted, a phenomenon called *rigor mortis*.

MP3
Sliding Filament
Theory

Check Your Progress   **39.3**

1. Define an "antagonistic pair" of muscles.
2. Describe the microscopic levels of structure in a skeletal muscle.
3. Discuss the specific role of ATP in muscle contraction.

CONNECTING *the* CONCEPTS *with the* THEMES

Evolution

- Almost all animals have evolved some type of skeletal system to support the soft tissues of the body, provide protection, and provide surfaces for muscle attachment.
- The exoskeletons of arthropods and molluscs provide protection against enemies and prevents desiccation. It must be shed during molting, which can leave the animal vulnerable.
- Vertebrates, which have endoskeletons, have evolved limbs with many different types of joints, allowing for more complex movements.
- Muscles developed to facilitate locomotion, which can be critical to procuring food, escaping danger, finding mates, and/or moving into new environments.

Nature of Science

- Knowledge of the skeletal and muscular systems has come from studying a large variety of animals that have adapted to many environments on Earth.
- To understand the skeleton and muscles fully, we must be familiar with the nervous and sensory systems.
- The use of a very dilute form of botulinum toxin for treating many diseases, as well as for cosmetic purposes, provides an example of how basic scientific research can have unexpected practical applications.

Biological Systems

- Most animals have one of three types of skeletons: a hydrostatic skeleton, an exoskeleton, or an endoskeleton.
- The cartilaginous skeleton of the human fetus is converted into bones, which contain two types of bone tissue, compact bone and spongy bone.
- The human skeleton can be divided into an axial skeleton and an appendicular skeleton.
- Axon terminals of motor nerve fibers release acetylcholine at a neuromuscular junction, triggering muscle fiber contraction.
- Muscle fiber contraction is dependent on actin and myosin filaments, as well as a ready supply of ATP and calcium ions.

Media Study Tools

www.mhhe.com/maderbiology11

Enhance your study of this chapter with study tools and practice tests. Also ask your instructor about the resources available through ConnectPlus, including the media-rich eBook, interactive learning tools, and animations.

Summarize

39.1 Diversity of Skeletons

Three types of skeletons are found in the animal kingdom: hydrostatic skeleton (cnidarians, flatworms, and segmented worms); exoskeleton (certain molluscs and arthropods); and endoskeleton (sponges, echinoderms, and vertebrates). The rigid but jointed skeleton of arthropods and vertebrates helped them colonize the terrestrial environment. The overall shape of an animal's skeleton is adapted to its environment and the type(s) of locomotion it uses.

39.2 The Human Skeletal System

The human skeleton gives support to the body, helps protect internal organs, provides sites for muscle attachment, and is a storage area for calcium and phosphorus salts, as well as a site for blood cell formation.

Most bones are cartilaginous in the fetus but are converted to bone during development. A long bone undergoes endochondral ossification in which a cartilaginous growth plate remains between the primary ossification center in the middle and the secondary centers at the ends of the bones. Growth of the bone is possible as long as the growth plates are present, but eventually they too are converted to bone.

Bone is constantly being renewed; osteoclasts break down bone, and osteoblasts build new bone. Osteocytes are in the lacunae of osteons; a long bone has a shaft of compact bone and two ends that contain spongy bone. The shaft contains a medullary cavity with yellow marrow, and the ends contain red marrow. Osteoporosis, or loss of bone density, is a common disease in older adults.

The human skeleton is divided into two parts: (1) the axial skeleton, which is made up of the skull, the vertebral column, the sternum, and the ribs; and (2) the appendicular skeleton, which is composed of the girdles and their appendages.

Joints are classified as immovable, like those of the cranium; slightly movable, like those between the vertebrae; and freely movable (synovial joints), like those in the knee and hip. In synovial joints, ligaments bind the two bones together, forming a capsule containing synovial fluid.

39.3 The Muscular System

Whole skeletal muscles can only shorten when they contract; therefore, they work in antagonistic pairs. For example, if one muscle flexes the joint and brings the limb toward the body, the other muscle of the antagonistic pair extends the joint and straightens the limb. A muscle at rest exhibits tone, which is dependent on tetanic contractions.

A whole skeletal muscle is composed of muscle fibers. Each muscle fiber is a cell that contains myofibrils in addition to the usual cellular components. Longitudinally, myofibrils are divided into sarcomeres, which display the arrangement of actin and myosin filaments.

The sliding filament model of muscle contraction states that myosin filaments have cross-bridges, which attach to and detach from actin filaments, causing actin filaments to slide and the sarcomere to shorten. (The H zone disappears as actin filaments approach one another.) Myosin breaks down ATP, and this supplies the energy for muscle contraction. Anaerobic creatine phosphate breakdown and fermentation quickly generate ATP. Sustained exercise requires cellular respiration for the generation of ATP.

Nerves innervate muscles. Nerve impulses traveling down motor neurons to neuromuscular junctions cause the release of ACh, which binds to receptors on the sarcolemma (plasma membrane of a muscle fiber). Impulses begin and move down T tubules that approach the sarcoplasmic reticulum (endoplasmic reticulum of muscle fibers), where calcium is stored. Thereafter, calcium ions are released and bind to troponin. The troponin-Ca^{2+} complex causes tropomyosin threads winding around actin filaments to shift their position, revealing myosin binding sites. Myosin filaments are composed of many myosin molecules with double globular heads. When myosin heads break down ATP, they are ready to attach to actin. The release of ADP + $\textcircled{P}$ causes myosin heads to change their position. This is the power stroke that causes the actin filament to slide toward the center of a sarcomere. When more ATP molecules bind to myosin, the heads detach from actin, and the cycle begins again.

Key Terms

actin 745	osteoporosis 738
appendicular skeleton 742	oxygen debt 747
arthritis 743	pectoral girdle 742
axial skeleton 740	pelvic girdle 742
compact bone 739	red bone marrow 740
endoskeleton 737	sarcolemma 744
exoskeleton 736	sarcomere 745
hydrostatic skeleton 736	sarcoplasmic reticulum 744
joint 742	sliding filament model 745
ligament 742	spongy bone 740
myofibril 745	suture 740
myosin 745	synovial joint 742
neuromuscular junction 747	tendon 744
osteoblast 738	tetany 744
osteoclast 738	tone 744
osteocyte 738	vertebral column 741

Assess

Reviewing This Chapter

1. What are the three types of skeletons found in the animal kingdom and how do they differ? Cite animals that have these types of skeletons.   736–37
2. Give several functions of the skeletal system in humans. How does the skeletal system contribute to homeostasis?   738
3. Contrast compact bone with spongy bone. Explain how bone grows and is renewed.   738–40
4. Distinguish between the axial and appendicular skeletons.   740–42
5. List the bones that form the pectoral girdle and upper limb; the pelvic girdle and lower limb.   742
6. How are joints classified? Describe the anatomy of a freely movable joint.   742–43
7. Give several functions of the muscular system in humans. How does the muscular system contribute to homeostasis?   744
8. Describe how muscles are attached to bones. What is accomplished by muscles acting in antagonistic pairs?   744
9. Discuss the microscopic structural features of a muscle fiber and a sarcomere. What is the sliding filament model?   744–46
10. Discuss the availability and the specific role of ATP during muscle contraction. What is oxygen debt, and how is it repaid?   746–47
11. Describe the structure and function of a neuromuscular junction.   747–48
12. Describe the cyclical events as myosin pulls actin toward the center of a sarcomere.   748–49

Testing Yourself

Choose the best answer for each question.
For questions 1–4, match each bone to the location in the key.

KEY:

a. arm	d. pelvic girdle
b. forearm	e. thigh
c. pectoral girdle	f. leg

1. ulna

2. tibia

3. clavicle

4. femur

5. Spongy bone
   a. is a storage area for fat.
   b. contains red bone marrow, where blood cells are formed.
   c. lends strength to bones.
   d. Both b and c are correct.

6. The human skeletal system does not
   a. produce blood cells.
   b. store minerals.
   c. help produce movement.
   d. store fat.
   e. produce body heat.

7. All blood cells—red, white, and platelets—are produced by which of the following?
   a. yellow bone marrow
   b. red bone marrow
   c. periosteum
   d. medullary cavity

8. Which of the following is not a bone of the appendicular skeleton?
   a. the scapula
   b. a rib
   c. a metatarsal bone
   d. the patella
   e. the ulna

9. The vertebrae that articulate with the ribs are the
   a. lumbar vertebrae.
   b. sacral vertebrae.
   c. thoracic vertebrae.
   d. cervical vertebrae.
   e. coccyx.

10. In a muscle fiber,
    a. the sarcolemma is connective tissue holding the myofibrils together.
    b. the sarcoplasmic reticulum stores calcium.
    c. both myosin and actin filaments have cross-bridges.
    d. there is a T system but no endoplasmic reticulum.
    e. All of these are correct.

11. When muscles contract,
    a. sarcomeres shorten.
    b. myosin heads break down ATP.
    c. actin slides past myosin.
    d. the H zone disappears.
    e. All of these are correct.

12. Nervous stimulation of muscles
    a. occurs at a neuromuscular junction.
    b. involves the release of ACh.
    c. results in impulses that travel down the T system.
    d. causes calcium to be released from the sarcoplasmic reticulum.
    e. All of these are correct.

13. When calcium is released from the sarcoplasmic reticulum, it binds to
    a. myosin.
    b. actin.
    c. troponin.
    d. sarcomeres.
    e. Both b and d are correct.

14. Acetylcholine
    a. is active at somatic synapses but not at neuromuscular junctions.
    b. binds to receptors in the sarcolemma.
    c. precedes the buildup of ATP in mitochondria.
    d. is stored in the sarcoplasmic reticulum.
    e. Both b and d are correct.

15. Label this diagram of a muscle fiber, using these terms: myofibril, Z line, T tubule, sarcomere, sarcolemma, sarcoplasmic reticulum.

Engage

Virtual Lab
Muscle Stimulation

The virtual lab "Muscle Stimulation" allows you to visualize how the load on a muscle influences the structures of the muscle at the microscopic level.

Thinking Scientifically

1. It is observed that some motor neurons innervate only a few muscle fibers in the biceps brachii. Other motor neurons each innervate many muscle fibers. How might this observation correlate with our ability to pick up a pencil or a 2-liter soda bottle? On what basis would the brain bring about the correct level of contraction?

2. Some athletes believe that taking oral creatine will increase their endurance because it will increase the amount of phosphate available to their muscles for ATP synthesis. This statement can be regarded as two hypotheses: (a) oral creatine increases endurance, and (b) oral creatine increases the amount of creatine available in muscles for ATP synthesis. How could these two hypotheses be tested?

Bioethical Issue

Anabolic Steroids and Muscle Enhancement

A natural advantage does not bar an athlete from participating in and winning a medal in a particular sport at the Olympic Games. Nor are athletes restricted to a certain amount of practice or required to eliminate certain foods from their diets.

Athletes are, however, prevented from participating in the Olympic Games if they have taken certain performance-enhancing drugs. There is no doubt that regular use of drugs such as anabolic steroids leads to kidney disease, liver dysfunction, hypertension, increased aggression, and a myriad of other undesirable side effects (see Fig. 40.16). Even so, shouldn't the individual be allowed to take these drugs if he or she wants to? Anabolic steroids are synthetic forms of the male sex hormone testosterone. Taking large doses, along with strength training, leads to much larger muscles than otherwise. Extra strength and endurance can give an athlete an advantage in certain sports, such as racing, swimming, and weight lifting.

On what basis have anabolic steroids been banned by the Olympic Committee and other sports organizations? The basis can't be an unfair advantage, because some athletes naturally have an unfair advantage over other athletes. Should these drugs be outlawed because of long-term health effects? Excessive practice or a purposeful decrease or increase in weight to better perform in a sport can also be injurious to one's health. In other words, how can we justify allowing some behaviors that enhance performance and not others? (See also the Nature of Science feature, "Misuse of Erythropoietin in Sports," in Chapter 36, which described the controversy over use of erythropoietin in the Tour de France.)

40

Hormones and Endocrine Systems

The sphinx moth (*Manduca sexta*) begins life as a caterpillar. The caterpillar molts and undergoes metamorphosis, as orchestrated by hormones.

BEFORE YOU BEGIN

Before beginning this chapter, take a few moments to review the following discussions.

Section 3.3 What is the general structure and function of steroids?

Chapter 5 Nature of Science What are the general classifications of chemical signaling molecules?

Section 37.3 What is the location and function of the hypothalamus?

Hormones, chemical messengers of the endocrine system, regulate the metamorphosis of many insects from wormlike larval stages to their adult forms. One hormone, ecdysone, initiates shedding of the exoskeleton as the larva passes through a series of growth stages. A decline in the production of another hormone triggers the final metamorphosis into an adult, as shown in the inset above for the sphinx moth (adult form), also referred to as the tobacco hornworm (caterpillar form).

Along with the nervous system, the endocrine system coordinates the activities of the body's other organ systems and helps maintain homeostasis. In contrast to the nervous system, the endocrine system is not centralized, but consists of several organs scattered throughout the body. The hormones secreted by endocrine glands travel through the bloodstream and tissue fluid to reach their target tissues. The metabolism of a cell changes when it has a plasma membrane or nuclear receptor for that hormone. In this chapter, you'll learn how hormones exert their slow but powerful influences on the body. You'll see how the endocrine system maintains homeostasis when working properly, as well as some consequences of endocrine malfunction.

As you read through the chapter, think about the following questions:

1. Why do more complex animals, such as mammals, tend to use some of the same hormones that are present in more primitive invertebrates, instead of evolving completely new hormones?

2. What are some specific examples where the nervous system works with the endocrine system to control body functions?

3. What are some specific examples where the endocrine system works independently?

FOLLOWING *the* THEMES

CHAPTER 40 HORMONES AND ENDOCRINE SYSTEMS

UNIT 7 COMPARATIVE ANIMAL BIOLOGY

Evolution	Two major methods have evolved by which animals respond to changes in their internal and external environments: the nervous system, which is capable of rapid responses, and the endocrine system, which carries out slower, lasting responses.
Nature of Science	Advances in the understanding of how hormones function have led to effective treatments for many common disorders of the human endocrine system.
Biological Systems	A relatively limited number of peptide and steroid hormones are able to control a wide range of homeostatic processes in animals.

40.1 Animal Hormones

Learning Outcomes

Upon completion of this section, you should be able to

1. Distinguish between the mode of action of a neurotransmitter and that of a hormone.
2. Identify the major endocrine glands of the human body.
3. Compare the mechanisms of action of peptide and steroid hormones.

The nervous and endocrine systems work together to regulate the activities of the other organs. Both systems use chemical signals when they respond to changes that might threaten homeostasis. However, they have different means of delivering these signals (Fig. 40.1). As discussed in Chapters 37 and 38, sensory receptors detect changes in the internal and external environment and transmit that information to the CNS, which responds by stimulating muscles and glands. Communication depends on nerve signals, conducted in axons, and neurotransmitters, which cross synapses. Axon conduction occurs rapidly and so does diffusion of a neurotransmitter across the short distance of a synapse. In other words, the nervous system is organized to respond rapidly to stimuli. This is particularly useful if the stimulus is an external event that endangers our safety—we can move quickly to avoid being hurt.

The **endocrine system** functions differently. The endocrine system is largely composed of glands (Fig. 40.2). These glands secrete **hormones,** such as insulin, which are carried by the bloodstream to target cells throughout the body. It takes time to deliver hormones, and it takes time for cells to respond, but the effect is longer lasting. In other words, the endocrine system is organized for a slower but prolonged response.

Endocrine glands can be contrasted with exocrine glands. **Exocrine glands** secrete their products into ducts, which take them to the lumens of other organs or outside the body. For example, the salivary glands send saliva into the mouth by way of the salivary ducts. **Endocrine glands,** as stated, secrete their products into the bloodstream, which delivers them throughout the body.

Hormones influence almost every basic homeostatic function of an organism, including metabolism, growth, reproduction, osmoregulation, and digestion. Therefore, it is not surprising that hormones are produced by invertebrates as well as vertebrates. For example, the hormone insulin is a key regulator of metabolism in vertebrates, and insulin-related peptides have been identified in insects and molluscs, suggesting an early evolutionary origin of this hormone.

Hormones also control some processes that are unique to invertebrates. As mentioned in the chapter-opening story, hormones control insect *metamorphosis*, the dramatic transformation that some insects undergo between hatching from an egg as a wormlike larva, going through several molts where the

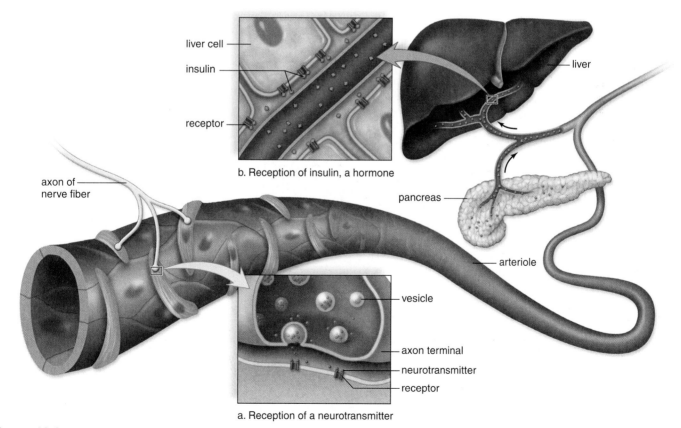

b. Reception of insulin, a hormone

a. Reception of a neurotransmitter

Figure 40.1 Modes of action of the nervous and endocrine systems. a. Nerve impulses passing along an axon cause the release of a neurotransmitter. The neurotransmitter, a chemical signal, binds to a receptor and causes the wall of an arteriole to constrict. **b.** The hormone insulin, a chemical signal, travels in the cardiovascular system from the pancreas to the liver, where it binds to a receptor and causes liver cells to store glucose as glycogen.

HYPOTHALAMUS

Releasing and inhibiting hormones: regulate the anterior pituitary

PITUITARY GLAND

Posterior Pituitary

Antidiuretic (ADH): water reabsorption by kidneys

Oxytocin: stimulates uterine contraction and milk letdown

Anterior Pituitary

Thyroid stimulating (TSH): stimulates thyroid

Adrenocorticotropic (ACTH): stimulates adrenal cortex

Gonadotropic (FSH, LH): egg and sperm production; sex hormone production

Prolactin (PL): milk production

Growth (GH): bone growth, protein synthesis, and cell division

THYROID

Thyroxine (T_4) and triiodothyronine (T_3): increase metabolic rate; regulates growth and development

Calcitonin: lowers blood calcium level

ADRENAL GLAND

Adrenal cortex

Glucocorticoids (cortisol): raises blood glucose level; stimulates breakdown of protein

Mineralocorticoids (aldosterone): reabsorption of sodium and excretion of potassium

Sex hormones: reproductive organs and bring about sex characteristics

Adrenal medulla

Epinephrine and norepinephrine: active in emergency situations; raise blood glucose level

Figure 40.2 Major glands of the human endocrine system. Major glands and the hormones they produce are depicted. Also, the endocrine system includes other organs such as the kidneys, gastrointestinal tract, and the heart, which also produce hormones but not as a primary function of these organs.

PINEAL GLAND

Melatonin: controls circadian and circannual rhythms

PARATHYROIDS

Parathyroid hormone (PTH): raises blood calcium level

parathyroid glands (posterior surface of thyroid)

THYMUS

Thymosins: production and maturation of T lymphocytes

PANCREAS

Insulin: lowers blood glucose level and promotes glycogen buildup

Glucagon: raises blood glucose level and promotes glycogen breakdown

testis (male)

ovary (female)

GONADS

Testes

Androgens (testosterone): male sex characteristics

Ovaries

Estrogens and progesterone: female sex characteristics

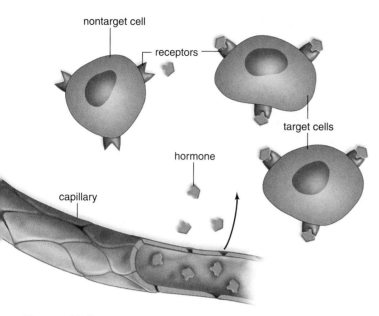

Figure 40.3 Target cell concept. Most hormones are distributed by the bloodstream to target cells. Target cells have receptors for the hormone, and the hormone combines with the receptor as a key fits a lock.

exoskeleton is shed, and maturing into adults. Several hormones have been identified that control this process.

Sometimes evolution produces new uses for the same hormones. In the freshwater snail *Lymnaea,* a peptide related to insulin is involved in body and shell growth as well as in energy metabolism. Variable hormone functions are seen in vertebrates as well. All vertebrates synthesize thyroid hormones, which generally increase metabolism, as you'll see later in this chapter. In amphibians, a surge of thyroid hormones also seems to promote metamorphosis from a tadpole into an adult. In contrast, the hormone prolactin inhibits metamorphosis in amphibians, stimulates skin pigmentation in reptiles, initiates incubation of eggs in birds, and stimulates milk production in mammals.

Hormones Are Chemical Signals

Like other **chemical signals,** hormones are a means of communication between cells, between body parts, and even between individuals. It must be stressed that only certain cells, called target cells, can respond to a specific hormone. A target cell for a particular hormone carries a receptor protein for that hormone (Fig. 40.3). The hormone and receptor protein bind together like a key fits a lock. The target cell then responds to that hormone. In a condition called *androgen insensitivity,* an individual has X and Y sex chromosomes, and the testes, which remain in the abdominal cavity, produce the sex hormone testosterone. However, the body cells lack receptors that are able to combine with testosterone, and the individual appears to be a normal female.

Chemical signals that influence the behavior of other individuals are called **pheromones.** Pheromones have been well documented in several animal species, although their influence

has been more difficult to prove in humans. Women who live in the same household tend to have synchronized menstrual cycles, perhaps because pheromones released by a woman who is menstruating affect the menstrual cycle of other women in the household. Studies also suggest that women prefer the smell of tee shirts worn by men who have a different MHC type from themselves. As noted in Chapter 33, MHC molecules are involved in immunity, and choosing a mate of a different MHC type could conceivably improve the health of offspring.

In a small study reported in 2011, men had lower testosterone levels in their saliva after they smelled a jar containing tears from women who were sad, as compared to saline droplets that were trickled down the women's cheeks. While the significance of these studies is unclear, they do suggest that humans may in fact be influenced by pheromones.

The Action of Hormones

Hormones exert a wide range of effects on cells. Some hormones induce target cells to increase their uptake of particular molecules, such as glucose, or ions, such as calcium. Others bring about an alteration of the target cell's structure in some way.

Most endocrine glands secrete **peptide hormones.** These hormones are peptides, proteins, glycoproteins, and modified amino acids. **Steroid hormones,** in contrast, all have the same molecular complex of four carbon rings because they are all derived from cholesterol (see Fig. 3.12).

The Action of Peptide Hormones. The actions of peptide hormones can vary, and as an example here, we concentrate on what happens in muscle cells after the hormone epinephrine binds to a receptor in the plasma membrane (Fig. 40.4). In muscle cells, the reception of epinephrine leads to the breakdown of glycogen to glucose, which provides energy for ATP production.

The immediate result of epinephrine binding is the formation of **cyclic adenosine monophosphate (cAMP).** Cyclic AMP contains one phosphate group attached to adenosine at two locations. Therefore, the molecule is cyclic. Cyclic AMP activates a protein kinase enzyme in the cell, and this enzyme, in turn, activates another enzyme, and so forth. The series of enzymatic reactions that follows cAMP formation is called an enzyme cascade (or signaling cascade). Because each enzyme can be used over and over again, more enzymes become involved at every step of the cascade. Finally, many molecules of glycogen are broken down to glucose, which enters the bloodstream.

Animation
Peptide Hormone
Action

Typical of a peptide hormone, epinephrine never enters the cell. Therefore, the hormone is called the **first messenger,** whereas cAMP, which sets the metabolic machinery in motion, is called the **second messenger.** To explain this terminology, let's imagine that the adrenal medulla, which produces epinephrine, is like the home office that sends out a courier (i.e., the hormone epinephrine—the first messenger) to a factory (the cell). The courier doesn't have a pass to enter the factory, but tells a supervisor through the screen door that the home office wants the factory to produce a particular product. The supervisor (i.e., cAMP—the second messenger) walks over and flips a

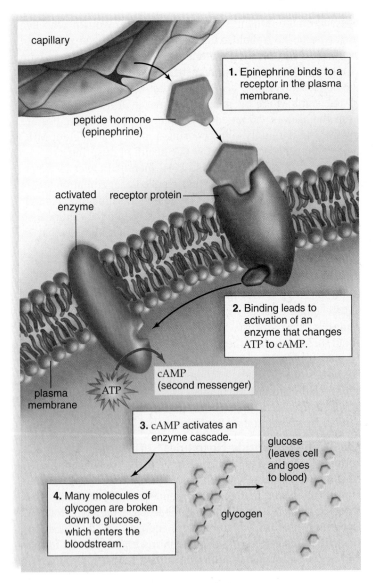

Figure 40.4 Epinephrine, a peptide hormone. Peptide hormones (epinephrine in this example) act as first messengers, binding to specific receptors in the plasma membrane. First messengers activate second messengers (cAMP in this case) that influence various cellular processes.

Figure 40.5 Steroid hormone. A steroid hormone passes directly through the target cell's plasma membrane before binding to a receptor in the nucleus or cytoplasm. The hormone-receptor complex binds to DNA and gene expression follows.

switch that starts the machinery (the enzymatic pathway), and a product is made.

The Action of Steroid Hormones. Only the adrenal cortex, the ovaries, and the testes produce steroid hormones. Steroid hormones do not bind to plasma membrane receptors; instead they are able to enter the cell because they are lipids (Fig. 40.5). Once inside, a steroid hormone binds to an internal receptor, usually in the nucleus but sometimes in the cytoplasm. Inside the nucleus, the hormone-receptor complex binds with DNA and activates certain genes. Messenger RNA (mRNA) moves to the ribosomes in the cytoplasm and protein synthesis (e.g., an enzyme) follows. To continue the analogy, a steroid hormone is like a courier that has a pass to enter the factory (the cell). Once inside, the courier makes contact with the plant manager

Animation
Second
Messengers

(DNA), who sees to it that the factory (cell) is ready to produce a product.

Steroids act more slowly than peptides because it takes more time to synthesize new proteins than to activate enzymes already present in cells. Their action lasts longer, however.

Animation
Mechanism of Steroid
Hormone Action

Check Your Progress   40.1

1. Compare and contrast the nervous and endocrine systems with regard to function and the types of signals used.
2. Compare the location of the receptors for peptide and steroid hormones.
3. Explain why second messengers are needed for most peptide hormones.

40.2 Hypothalamus and Pituitary Gland

Learning Outcomes

Upon completion of this section, you should be able to

1. Describe the relationship between the hypothalamus and the pituitary gland.
2. List and describe the functions of the hormones released by the anterior and posterior pituitary gland.
3. Explain how some hormones are regulated by negative feedback, and some by positive feedback; give an example of each.

The **hypothalamus** helps to regulate the internal environment of the body in two ways. Through the autonomic nervous system, it influences the heartbeat, blood pressure, appetite, body temperature, and water balance. It also controls the glandular secretions of the **pituitary gland** (hypophysis), a small gland about 1 cm in diameter that is connected to the hypothalamus by a stalklike structure. The pituitary has two portions: the posterior pituitary and the anterior pituitary.

 MP3 Endocrine System

Posterior Pituitary

Neurons in the hypothalamus called neurosecretory cells produce the hormones **antidiuretic hormone (ADH)** [Gk. *anti,* against, and *ouresis,* urination] and oxytocin (Fig. 40.6, *left*). These hormones pass through axons into the **posterior pituitary,** where they are stored in axon terminals. Certain neurons in the hypothalamus are sensitive to the water-salt balance of the blood. When these cells determine that the blood is too concentrated, ADH is released from the posterior pituitary. Upon reaching the kidneys, ADH causes water to be reabsorbed. As the blood becomes dilute, ADH is no longer released. This is an example of control by **negative feedback** because the *effect* of the hormone (to dilute blood) acts to shut down the *release* of the hormone. Negative feedback maintains stable conditions and homeostasis.

Animation Hormonal Communication

If too little ADH is secreted, or if the kidneys become unresponsive to ADH, a condition known as *diabetes insipidus* results. Patients with this condition are usually very thirsty; they produce copious amounts of urine and can become severely dehydrated if the condition is untreated.

The consumption of alcohol inhibits ADH release. This effect helps to explain the frequent urination associated with drinking alcohol.

Oxytocin [Gk. *oxys,* quick, and *tokos,* birth], the other hormone made in the hypothalamus, causes uterine contractions during childbirth and milk letdown when a baby is nursing. The more the uterus contracts during labor, the more nerve impulses reach the hypothalamus, causing oxytocin to be released. Similarly, the more a baby suckles, the more oxytocin is released. In both instances, the release of oxytocin from the posterior pituitary is controlled by **positive feedback**—that is, the stimulus continues to bring about an effect that ever increases in intensity. Oxytocin may also play a role in the propulsion of semen through the male reproductive tract and may affect feelings of sexual satisfaction and emotional bonding.

Anterior Pituitary

A portal system, which consists of two capillary networks connected by a vein, lies between the hypothalamus and the anterior pituitary (Fig. 40.6, *right*). The hypothalamus controls the anterior pituitary by producing **hypothalamic-releasing hormones** and in some instances **hypothalamic-inhibiting hormones.** For example, one hypothalamic-releasing hormone stimulates the anterior pituitary to secrete a thyroid-stimulating hormone, and a particular hypothalamic-inhibiting hormone prevents the anterior pituitary from secreting prolactin.

Anterior Pituitary Hormones Affecting Other Glands

Some of the hormones produced by the **anterior pituitary** affect other glands. **Gonadotropic hormones** stimulate the gonads—the testes in males and the ovaries in females—to produce gametes and sex hormones. **Adrenocorticotropic hormone (ACTH)** stimulates the adrenal cortex to produce cortisol. **Thyroid-stimulating hormone (TSH)** stimulates the thyroid to produce thyroxine (T_4) and triiodothyronine (T_3). In each instance, the blood level of the last hormone in the sequence exerts negative feedback control over the secretion of the first two hormones. This is how it works for TSH:

hypothalamus

releasing hormone (hormone 1)

anterior pituitary

stimulating hormone (TSH, hormone 2)

target gland

target gland hormone (T_3/T_4, hormone 3)

feedback inhibits release of hormone 1

feedback inhibits release of hormone 2

Anterior Pituitary Hormones Not Affecting Other Glands

Three hormones produced by the anterior pituitary do not affect other endocrine glands. **Prolactin (PRL)** [L. *pro,* before, and *lactis,* milk] is produced in quantity only after childbirth. It causes the mammary glands in the breasts to develop and produce milk. It also plays a role in carbohydrate and fat metabolism.

Melanocyte-stimulating hormone (MSH) [Gk. *melanos,* black, and *kytos,* cell] causes skin-color changes in many fishes, amphibians, and reptiles having melanophores, special skin cells that produce color variations. The concentration of this hormone in humans is very low.

Growth hormone (GH), or somatotropic hormone, promotes skeletal and muscular growth (Fig. 40.6, *right*). It increases the rate at which amino acids enter cells and protein synthesis occurs. It also promotes fat metabolism as opposed to glucose metabolism. The amount of GH produced is greatest during childhood and adolescence.

If too little GH is produced during childhood, the individual has *pituitary dwarfism,* characterized by normal proportions but small stature. Such children also have problems with low blood sugar (hypoglycemia), because GH normally helps oppose the effect of insulin on glucose uptake. Through the administration of GH, growth patterns can be restored and blood sugar problems alleviated. If too much GH is secreted

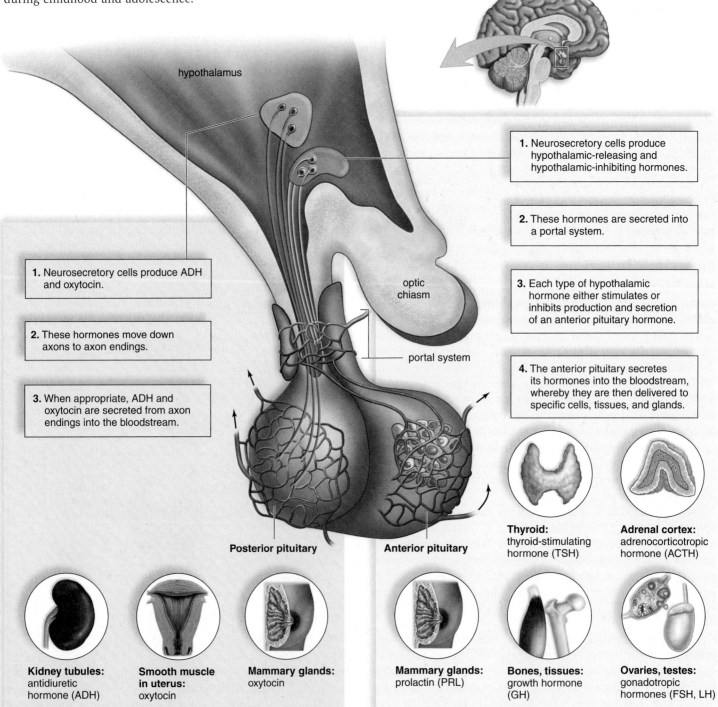

1. Neurosecretory cells produce hypothalamic-releasing and hypothalamic-inhibiting hormones.

2. These hormones are secreted into a portal system.

3. Each type of hypothalamic hormone either stimulates or inhibits production and secretion of an anterior pituitary hormone.

4. The anterior pituitary secretes its hormones into the bloodstream, whereby they are then delivered to specific cells, tissues, and glands.

1. Neurosecretory cells produce ADH and oxytocin.

2. These hormones move down axons to axon endings.

3. When appropriate, ADH and oxytocin are secreted from axon endings into the bloodstream.

hypothalamus

optic chiasm

portal system

Posterior pituitary

Anterior pituitary

Thyroid: thyroid-stimulating hormone (TSH)

Adrenal cortex: adrenocorticotropic hormone (ACTH)

Kidney tubules: antidiuretic hormone (ADH)

Smooth muscle in uterus: oxytocin

Mammary glands: oxytocin

Mammary glands: prolactin (PRL)

Bones, tissues: growth hormone (GH)

Ovaries, testes: gonadotropic hormones (FSH, LH)

Figure 40.6 Hypothalamus and the pituitary.   In this diagram, the name of the hormone is given below its target organ, which is depicted in the circle. *Left:* The hypothalamus produces two hormones, ADH and oxytocin, which are stored and secreted by the posterior pituitary. *Right:* The hypothalamus controls the secretions of the anterior pituitary, and the anterior pituitary controls the secretions of the thyroid, adrenal cortex, and gonads, which are also endocrine glands.

a.

b.

Figure 40.7
Effect of growth hormone.
a. The amount of growth hormone produced by the anterior pituitary during childhood affects the height of an individual. Plentiful growth hormone produces very tall basketball players.
b. Too much growth hormone can lead to giantism, while an insufficient amount results in limited stature and even pituitary dwarfism.

during childhood, the person may become a giant (Fig. 40.7*b*). Giants usually have poor health, primarily because elevated GH cancels out the effects of insulin, promoting diabetes mellitus (see the discussion in Section 40.3).

On occasion, GH is overproduced in the adult, and a condition called *acromegaly* results. Because long bone growth is no longer possible in adults, only the feet, hands, and face (particularly the chin, nose, and eyebrow ridges) can respond, and these portions of the body become overly large (Fig. 40.8).

A quick internet search reveals that many websites offer human growth hormone for sale as a "fountain of youth" that can help adults lose weight, add muscle, and reduce the effects of aging. Indeed, several professional actors and athletes have admitted to using human GH to build muscle and reduce body fat. (Note that GH is not a "steroid," which refers to testosterone or related hormones.) However, using human GH in this manner can have many undesired side effects, such as joint and muscle pain, high blood pressure, and diabetes mellitus.

MP3
Hormonal Secretion Action

Check Your Progress   **40.2**

1. Explain how the hypothalamus communicates with the endocrine system.
2. List the hormones produced by the posterior pituitary and provide a function for each.
3. List the hormones produced by the anterior pituitary and provide a function for each.

Age 9   Age 16   Age 33   Age 52

Figure 40.8
Acromegaly.
Acromegaly is caused by overproduction of GH in the adult. It is characterized by enlargement of the bones in the face, the fingers, and the toes as a person ages.

40.3 Other Endocrine Glands and Hormones

Learning Outcomes

Upon completion of this section, you should be able to

1. Distinguish between the functions of T_3, T_4, calcitonin, and parathyroid hormone.
2. Compare and contrast the mineralocorticoids and glucocorticoids.
3. Identify the cause and major symptoms of the major conditions associated with the endocrine system.

In this section we discuss the thyroid and parathyroid glands, adrenal glands, pancreas, pineal gland, thymus, and other tissues that produce hormones secondarily. All the hormone products of these glands and tissues play a role in health and homeostasis.

Thyroid and Parathyroid Glands

The **thyroid gland** [Gk. *thyreos*, large, door-shaped shield] is attached to the trachea just below the larynx (see Fig. 40.2). Weighing approximately 20 grams, the thyroid gland is composed of a large number of follicles, each a small spherical structure made of thyroid cells that produce the hormones triiodothyronine (T_3), which contains three iodine atoms, and **thyroxine (T_4)**, which contains four iodine atoms. Cells of a different type in the thyroid gland produce the hormone calcitonin. The parathyroid glands, which produce parathyroid hormone, are embedded in the posterior surface of the thyroid gland.

Effects of T_3 and T_4

Both of these thyroid hormones increase the overall metabolic rate. They do not have a single target organ; instead, they stimulate most the cells of the body to metabolize at a faster rate.

More glucose is broken down, and more energy is used. Interestingly, even though T_3 and T_4 are peptide hormones because they are derived from the amino acid tyrosine, their receptor is actually located inside cells, more like a steroid hormone receptor.

Animation
Mechanism of Thyroxine Action

To produce T_3 and T_4, the thyroid gland actively acquires iodine. The concentration of iodine in the thyroid gland is approximately 25 times that found in the blood. If a person consumes an insufficient amount of iodine, the thyroid gland is unable to produce the required amount of T_3 and T_4. This results in constant stimulation of the thyroid by TSH released by the anterior pituitary. The thyroid gland enlarges, resulting in a *simple goiter* (Fig. 40.9a). In the 1920s, scientists discovered that the use of iodized salt allows the thyroid to produce thyroid hormones and therefore helps prevent simple goiter. However, iodine deficiency is still extremely common in some parts of the world, with an estimated two billion people (one-third of the world's population) still suffering from some degree of iodine deficiency.

An insufficiency of T_3 and T_4 in the newborn is called *congenital hypothyroidism* (cretinism) (Fig. 40.9b). Babies with this condition are short and stocky, and are often mentally retarded. The causes vary from iodine deficiency in the mother during her pregnancy, to genetic defects affecting the production of TSH, T_3, T_4, or the receptor for any of these hormones. Once detected, iodine deficiency is easily treated by insuring appropriate levels of iodine consumption. However, according to the American Thyroid Association, congenital hypothyroidism due to iodine deficiency remains the most common preventable cause of mental retardation in the world.

Even mild iodine deficiency during pregnancy, which may be present in some women in the United States, may be associated with low intelligence in children. In cases due to problems with the thyroid gland itself, thyroxine therapy is curative, but must begin as early as possible to avoid permanently stunted growth and mental retardation.

a. Simple goiter

b. Congenital hypothyroidism

affected eye

c. Exophthalmic goiter

Figure 40.9 Abnormalities of the thyroid.   **a.** An enlarged thyroid gland is often caused by a lack of iodine in the diet. Without iodine, the thyroid is unable to produce its hormones and continued anterior pituitary stimulation causes the gland to enlarge. **b.** Individuals who develop hypothyroidism during infancy or childhood do not grow and develop as others do. Unless medical treatment is begun, the body is short and stocky; mental retardation is also likely. **c.** In exophthalmic goiter, a goiter is due to an overactive thyroid, and the eye protrudes because of edema in eye socket tissue.

Hypothyroidism can also occur in adults, most often when the immune system produces antibodies that destroy the thyroid gland. Untreated hypothyroidism in adults results in *myxedema,* which is characterized by lethargy, weight gain, loss of hair, slower heart rate, lowered body temperature, and thickness and puffiness of the skin. The administration of thyroxine usually restores normal body functions and appearance.

Hyperthyroidism results from the oversecretion of T_3 or T_4. In Graves disease, antibodies are produced that react with the TSH receptor on thyroid follicular cells, mimicking the effect of TSH and causing the overproduction of T_3 and T_4. One typical sign of Graves disease is **exophthalmos** (exophthalmia) or excessive protrusion of the eyes due to edema in eye socket tissues and inflammation of the muscles that move the eyes (Fig. 40.9c). The patient usually becomes hyperactive, nervous, and irritable and suffers from insomnia. Graves disease is the most common cause of hyperthyroidism in children and adolescents, and is five to ten times more common in females. Available treatments include drugs that block iodine uptake by the thyroid gland, surgical removal of part or all of the gland, or administration of radioactive iodine to destroy the overactive tissue.

Hyperthyroidism can also be caused by thyroid cancer, the most common cancer of the endocrine system, which is usually detected as a lump during physical examination. Again, the treatment is surgery in combination with administration of radioactive iodine. The prognosis for most patients is excellent.

Effects of Calcitonin

Calcium (Ca^{2+}) plays a significant role in both nervous conduction and muscle contraction. It is also necessary for blood clotting and the maintenance of healthy bones and teeth. The blood calcium level is regulated in part by **calcitonin,** a hormone secreted by the thyroid gland when the blood calcium level rises. The primary effect of calcitonin is to bring about the deposit of calcium in the bones (Fig. 40.10, *top*). It does this by temporarily reducing the activity and number of osteoclasts. When the blood calcium lowers to normal, the release of calcitonin by the thyroid is inhibited.

While calcitonin appears to play a very important role in regulating calcium homeostasis in fish and a few other animals, it appears to be less significant in humans. As evidence for this, a deficiency of calcitonin (as occurs when the thyroid glands are removed) is not linked with any specific disorder. However, because of its bone-building effects, calcitonin is an FDA-approved drug for reducing bone loss in osteoporosis.

Parathyroid Glands

Parathyroid hormone (PTH), produced by the **parathyroid glands,** causes the blood calcium level to increase, and the blood phosphate (HPO_4^{2-}) level to decrease. Low blood calcium stimulates the release of PTH, which promotes the activity of osteoclasts, releasing calcium from the bones. PTH also promotes the reabsorption of calcium by the kidneys, lessening its excretion. In the kidneys, PTH also brings about activation of vitamin D. Vitamin D, in turn, stimulates the absorption of calcium from the intestine (Fig. 40.10, *bottom*). These effects bring the blood calcium level back to the normal range, and PTH secretion stops.

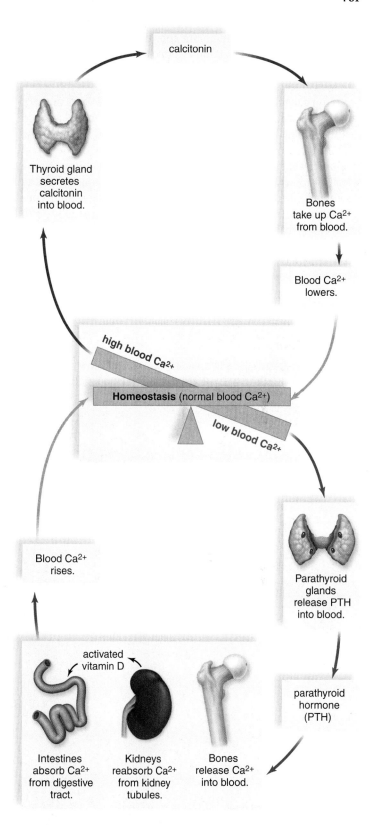

Figure 40.10 Regulation of blood calcium level. *Top:* When the blood calcium (Ca^{2+}) level is high, the thyroid gland secretes calcitonin. Calcitonin promotes the uptake of Ca^{2+} by the bones, and therefore the blood Ca^{2+} level returns to normal. *Bottom:* When the blood Ca^{2+} level is low, the parathyroid glands release parathyroid hormone (PTH). PTH causes the bones to release Ca^{2+} and the kidneys to reabsorb Ca^{2+} and activate vitamin D; thereafter, the intestines absorb Ca^{2+}. Therefore, the blood Ca^{2+} level returns to normal.

Calcitonin and PTH are therefore considered to be *antagonistic hormones* because their action is opposite to one another, and both hormones work together to regulate the blood calcium level.

Many years ago, the four parathyroid glands were sometimes mistakenly removed during thyroid surgery because of their small size and hidden location. Gland removal caused insufficient parathyroid hormone production or *hypoparathyroidism*. This condition leads to a dramatic drop in the blood calcium level, followed by excessive nerve excitability. Nerve signals happen spontaneously and without rest, causing a phenomenon called tetany. In *tetany*, the body shakes from continuous muscle contraction. Without treatment (usually with intravenous calcium), severe hypoparathyroidism causes seizures, heart failure, and death.

Untreated *hyperparathyroidism*, (oversecretion of PTH) can result in osteoporosis because of continuous calcium release from the bones. Hyperparathyroidism can also cause the formation of calcium kidney stones.

MP3
Calcium Homeostasis

Adrenal Glands

The **adrenal glands** [L. *ad,* toward, and *renis,* kidney] sit atop the kidneys (see Fig. 40.2). Each adrenal gland is about 5 cm long and 3 cm wide, weighs about 5 g, and consists of an inner portion called the **adrenal medulla** and an outer portion called the **adrenal cortex.** These portions, like the anterior and posterior pituitary, are two functionally distinct endocrine glands. Stress of all types, including both emotional and physical trauma, prompts the hypothalamus to stimulate both portions of the adrenal glands. The adrenal cortex is also involved in regulating the salt and water balance, and secreting a small amount of male and female sex hormones.

Adrenal Medulla

As noted in Chapter 37, during emergency situations that call for a "fight or flight" reaction, the hypothalamus sends nerve impulses by way of sympathetic nerve fibers to many organs, including the adrenal medulla (see Fig. 37.14). This neurological response to danger quickly dilates the pupils, speeds the heart, dilates the air passages, and inhibits many nonessential bodily functions. Meanwhile, the adrenal medulla secretes **epinephrine** (adrenaline) and **norepinephrine** (noradrenaline) into the bloodstream (Fig. 40.11). These hormones continue the response to stress throughout the body, for example by accelerating the breakdown of glucose to form ATP, triggering

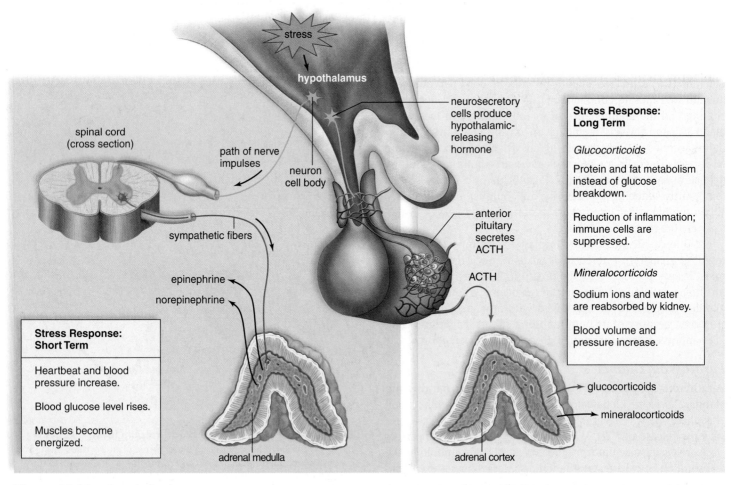

Figure 40.11 Adrenal glands.   Both the adrenal cortex and the adrenal medulla are under the control of the hypothalamus when they help us respond to stress. *Left:* Nervous stimulation causes the adrenal medulla to provide a rapid, but short-term, stress response. *Right:* ACTH from the anterior pituitary causes the adrenal cortex to release glucocorticoids. Independently, the adrenal cortex releases mineralocorticoids. The adrenal cortex provides a slower, but long-term, stress response.

the mobilization of glycogen reserves in skeletal muscle, and increasing the cardiac rate and force of contraction. These effects are usually short-lived however, as these two hormones are rapidly metabolized by the liver.

Adrenal Cortex

In contrast to the rapid response of the sympathetic nervous system and adrenal medulla, the hypothalamus produces a longer-term response to stress by stimulating the anterior pituitary to produce ACTH, which in turn causes the adrenal cortex to secrete glucocorticoids.

Glucocorticoids.   **Cortisol** is the most important **glucocorticoid** produced by the human adrenal cortex. Cortisol raises the blood glucose level in at least two ways:

1. It promotes the breakdown of muscle proteins to amino acids, which are taken up by the liver from the bloodstream and converted into glucose.
2. It promotes the catabolism of fatty acids rather than carbohydrates, and this spares glucose. The rise in blood glucose is beneficial to an animal under stress because glucose is the preferred energy source for neurons.

Glucocorticoids also counteract the inflammatory response, including the type of reaction that leads to the pain and swelling of joints in arthritis and bursitis. Cortisone, a glucocorticoid, is often used to treat these conditions because it reduces inflammation. However, very high levels of glucocorticoids in the blood can suppress the body's defense system, rendering an individual more susceptible to injury and infection.

Animation
Action of Glucocorticoid

Mineralocorticoids.   **Mineralocorticoids** produced by the adrenal cortex regulate salt and water balance, leading to increases in blood volume and blood pressure. **Aldosterone** is the most important of the mineralocorticoids. Aldosterone primarily targets the kidneys, where it promotes renal absorption of sodium (Na^+) and renal excretion of potassium (K^+), and thereby helps regulate blood volume and blood pressure.

The secretion of mineralocorticoids is not controlled by the anterior pituitary. In Chapter 36 we noted that when the atria of the heart are stretched due to increased blood volume, cardiac cells release a hormone called **atrial natriuretic hormone (ANH),** which inhibits the secretion of aldosterone from the adrenal cortex. (Note that the heart is one of several organs in the body that release a hormone but are not considered among the major endocrine organs.) The effect of ANH is to cause *natriuresis,* the excretion of sodium ions (Na^+). When sodium is excreted, so is water, and therefore blood pressure lowers to normal (Fig. 40.12, *top*).

We also noted in Chapter 36 that when the blood sodium (Na^+) level, and therefore blood pressure, is low, the kidneys secrete **renin** (Fig. 40.12, *bottom*). Renin is an enzyme that converts the plasma protein angiotensinogen to angiotensin I, which is changed to angiotensin II by an enzyme in lung capillaries. Angiotensin II stimulates the adrenal cortex to release aldosterone. The effect of this process, called the renin-angiotensin-aldosterone system, is to raise blood pressure in two ways:

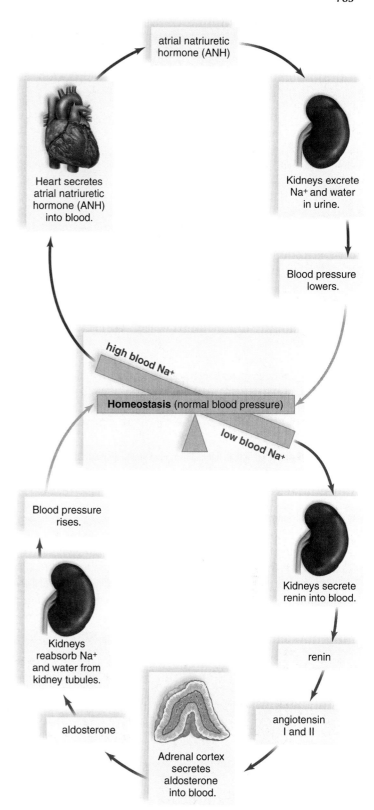

Figure 40.12 Regulation of blood pressure and volume. *Top:* When the blood Na^+ is high, a high blood volume causes the heart to secrete atrial natriuretic hormone (ANH). ANH causes the kidneys to excrete Na^+, and water follows. The blood volume and pressure return to normal. *Bottom:* When the blood sodium (Na^+) level is low, a low blood pressure causes the kidneys to secrete renin. Renin leads to the secretion of aldosterone from the adrenal cortex. Aldosterone causes the kidneys to reabsorb Na^+, and water follows, so that blood volume and pressure return to normal.

a.

b.

Figure 40.13 Addison disease.   Addison disease is characterized by a peculiar bronzing of the skin, particularly noticeable in light-skinned individuals. Note the color of the face **(a)** and the hands **(b)** compared to the hand of an individual without the disease.

(1) angiotensin II constricts the arterioles, and (2) aldosterone causes the kidneys to reabsorb sodium. When the blood sodium level rises, water is reabsorbed, in part because the hypothalamus secretes ADH (see Section 40.2). Then blood pressure rises to normal.

Malfunctions of the Adrenal Cortex.   Insufficient secretion of hormones by the adrenal cortex, also known as *Addison disease*, is relatively rare. The most common cause is an inappropriate attack on the adrenal cortex by the immune system. Because the disease affects the secretion of both glucocorticoids and mineralocorticoids, a variety of symptoms may occur, such as dehydration, weakness, weight loss, and hypotension (low blood pressure). The presence of excessive but ineffective ACTH often causes increased pigmentation of the skin because ACTH, like MSH, can stimulate melanocytes to produce melanin

(Fig. 40.13). Treatment involves replacement of the missing hormones. Left untreated, Addison disease can be fatal.

Excessive levels of glucocorticoids results in *Cushing syndrome*. This disorder can be caused by tumors that affect either the pituitary gland, resulting in excess ACTH secretion, or the adrenal cortex itself. The most common cause, however, is the administration of glucocorticoids to treat other conditions (e.g., to suppress chronic inflammation). Regardless of the source, excess glucocorticoids cause muscle protein to be metabolized and subcutaneous fat to be deposited in the midsection (Fig. 40.14). Excess production of adrenal male sex hormones in women may result in masculinization, including an increase in body hair, deepening of the voice, and beard growth. Depending on the cause, treatment of Cushing syndrome may involve a careful reduction in the amount of cortisone being taken, the use of cortisol-inhibiting drugs, or surgery to remove any existing pituitary or adrenal tumor.

Figure 40.14 Cushing syndrome.   This 40-year-old woman was diagnosed with a small tumor in her pituitary gland, which secreted large amounts of ACTH. The high ACTH levels stimulated the adrenal glands to produce excessive amounts of cortisol. *Left:* Patient at the time of surgery to remove her pituitary tumor. *Right:* Patient's appearance one year later.

Pancreas

The **pancreas** (see Fig. 40.2) is a slender, fish-shaped organ that stretches across the abdomen behind the stomach and near the duodenum of the small intestine. Approximately six inches long and weighing about 80 grams, the pancreas is composed of two types of tissue. Exocrine tissue produces and secretes digestive juices that go by way of ducts to the small intestine. Endocrine tissue, called the **pancreatic islets** (islets of Langerhans), produces and secretes the hormones insulin and glucagon directly into the blood. The Nature of Science feature on page 766 describes the discovery of insulin.

The pancreas is not under pituitary control. **Insulin** is secreted when there is a high blood glucose level, which usually occurs just after eating (Fig. 40.15, *top*). Insulin stimulates the uptake of glucose by cells, especially liver cells, muscle cells, and adipose tissue cells. In liver and muscle cells, glucose is then stored as glycogen, and in fat cells the breakdown of glucose supplies glycerol for the formation of fat. In these ways, insulin lowers the blood glucose level.

Glucagon is secreted from the pancreas, usually in between meals, when blood glucose is low (Fig. 40.15, *bottom*). The major target tissues of glucagon are the liver and adipose tissue. Glucagon stimulates the liver to break down glycogen to glucose and to use fat and protein in preference to glucose as energy sources. Adipose tissue cells break down fat to glycerol and fatty acids. The liver takes these up and uses them as substrates for glucose formation. In these ways, glucagon raises the blood glucose level. Insulin and glucagon are another example of antagonistic hormones, which work together to maintain the blood glucose level.

Diabetes Mellitus

In 2011, the National Diabetes Information Clearinghouse estimated that 25.8 million Americans (8.3% of the population) have *diabetes mellitus*, often referred to simply as diabetes. Of these, an estimated 7.0 million are undiagnosed. Diabetes is characterized by an inability of the body's cells, especially liver and muscle cells, to take up glucose as they should. This causes blood glucose to be higher than normal, and cells rely on other "fuels" like fatty acids for energy. Therefore, cellular famine exists in the midst of plenty. As the blood glucose level rises, glucose, along with water, is excreted in the urine (*mellitus*, from Greek, refers to "honey" or "sweetness"). This results in frequent urination and causes the diabetic to be extremely thirsty.

Other symptoms of diabetes include fatigue, constant hunger, and weight loss. Diabetics often experience vision problems due to diabetic retinopathy (see Section 38.2) and swelling in the lens of the eye due to the high blood sugar levels. If untreated, diabetics often develop serious and even fatal complications. Sores that don't heal develop into severe infections. Blood vessel damage causes kidney failure, nerve destruction, heart attack, or stroke.

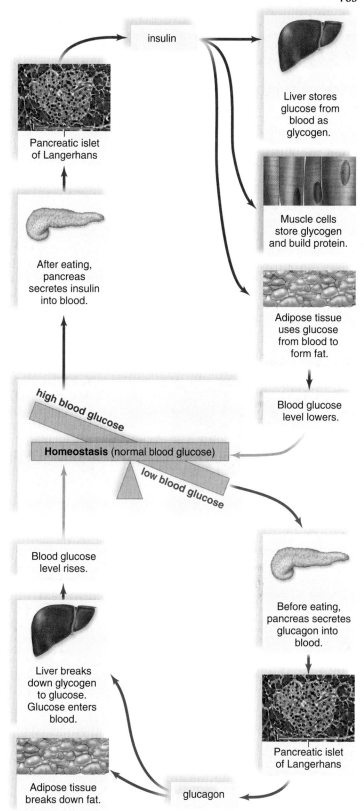

Figure 40.15 Regulation of blood glucose level. *Top:* When the blood glucose level is high, the pancreas secretes insulin. Insulin promotes the storage of glucose as glycogen and the synthesis of proteins and fats (as opposed to their use as energy sources). Therefore, insulin lowers the blood glucose level to normal. *Bottom:* When the blood glucose level is low, the pancreas secretes glucagon. Glucagon acts opposite to insulin; therefore, glucagon raises the blood glucose level to normal.

Identifying Insulin as a Chemical Messenger

The pancreas is both an exocrine gland and an endocrine gland. It sends digestive juices to the duodenum by way of the pancreatic duct, and it secretes the hormones insulin and glucagon into the bloodstream.

In 1920, physician Frederick Banting (1891–1941) decided to try to isolate insulin in order to identify it as a chemical messenger. Previous investigators had been unable to do this because the enzymes in the digestive juices destroyed insulin (a protein) during the isolation procedure. Banting hit upon the idea of ligating (tying

off) the pancreatic duct, which he knew from previous research would lead to the degeneration only of the cells that produce digestive juices and not of the pancreatic islets (of Langerhans), where insulin is made. His professor, J. J. Macleod, made a laboratory available to him at the University of Toronto and also assigned a graduate student, Charles Best (1899–1978), to assist him.

Banting and Best (Fig. 40A) had limited funds and spent that summer working, sleeping, and eating in the lab. By the end of the summer, they had obtained pancreatic extracts that did lower the blood glucose level in diabetic dogs. Macleod then brought in biochemists, who purified the extract. Insulin therapy for the first human patient began in 1922, and large-scale production of purified insulin from pigs and cattle followed. Banting and Macleod received a Nobel Prize for their work in 1923.

The amino acid sequence of insulin was determined in 1953. Insulin is now synthesized using recombinant DNA technology, using the bacterium *E. coli* to produce the hormone. Banting and Best performed the required steps (given in the chart below) to identify a chemical messenger.

Questions to Consider

1. What type of disease or symptoms would you expect to occur after ligating the pancreatic ducts of dogs?
2. What are some advantages, and potential disadvantages, of producing a medicine destined to be injected in humans (such as insulin) in a bacterium like *E. coli*?
3. Some people oppose the use of animals for medical research. Do you think that insulin would have eventually been discovered without animal experimentation? Why or why not?

Figure 40A Early insulin experiments. Charles H. Best and Sir Frederick Banting in 1921 with the first dog to be kept alive by insulin.

Steps to Identify a Chemical Messenger as Used by Banting and Best

1. Identify the source of the chemical	Pancreatic islets are source
2. Identify the effect to be studied	Presence of pancreas in body lowers blood glucose
3. Isolate the chemical	Insulin isolated from pancreatic secretions
4. Show that the chemical has the desired effect	Insulin lowers blood glucose

Two types of diabetes have been identified; these are termed type 1 diabetes, sometimes called juvenile diabetes, and type 2 diabetes, or adult-onset diabetes; however, both diseases may occur in children or adults.

Type 1 Diabetes. In *type 1 diabetes*, the pancreas is not producing enough insulin. This condition is believed to be brought on by exposure to an environmental agent, most likely a virus, whose presence causes cytotoxic T cells to destroy the pancreatic islets. The body turns to the metabolism of fat, which leads to the buildup of ketones in the blood, called ketoacidosis, which increases acidity of the blood and can lead to coma and death.

Individuals with type 1 diabetes must have daily insulin injections. These injections control the diabetic symptoms but still can cause inconveniences because the blood sugar level may swing between hypoglycemia (low blood glucose) and

hyperglycemia (high blood glucose). Without testing the blood glucose level, it is difficult to be certain which of these is present because the symptoms can be similar. These symptoms include perspiration, pale skin, shallow breathing, and anxiety. Whenever these symptoms appear, immediate attention is required to bring the blood glucose back within the normal range. If the problem is hypoglycemia, the treatment is one or two glucose tablets, hard candy, or orange juice. If the problem is hyperglycemia, the treatment is insulin. Better control of blood glucose levels can often be achieved with an insulin pump, a small device worn outside the body that is connected to a plastic catheter inserted under the skin.

Because diabetes is such a common problem, many researchers are working to develop more effective methods for treating diabetes. The most desirable would be an artificial pancreas, defined as an automated system that would provide insulin based on real-time changes in blood sugar levels. It is also possible to transplant a working pancreas, or even fetal pancreatic islet cells, into patients with type 1 diabetes. Another possibility is *xenotransplantation,* in which insulin-producing islet cells of another species, such as pigs, are placed inside a capsule that allows insulin to exit but prevents the immune system from attacking the foreign cells. Finally, researchers are close to testing a vaccine that could block the immune system's attack on the islet cells, perhaps by inducing T cells capable of suppressing these responses.

 Animation
Blood Sugar Regulation in Diabetics

Type 2 Diabetes.   Most adult diabetics have *type 2 diabetes.* Often, the patient is overweight or obese, and adipose tissue produces a substance that impairs insulin receptor function. However, complex genetic factors can be involved, as shown by the tendency for type 2 diabetes to occur more often in certain families, or even ethnic groups. For example, the condition is 77% more common in African Americans than in non-Hispanic whites.

Normally, the binding of insulin to its plasma membrane receptor causes the number of protein carriers for glucose to increase, causing more glucose to enter the cell. In the type 2 diabetic, insulin still binds to its receptor, but the number of glucose carriers does not increase. Therefore, the cell is said to be insulin resistant.

It is possible to prevent or at least control type 2 diabetes by adhering to a low-fat, low-sugar diet and exercising regularly. If this fails, oral drugs are available that stimulate the pancreas to secrete more insulin and enhance the metabolism of glucose in the liver and muscle cells. Millions of Americans may have type 2 diabetes without being aware of it; yet, the effects of untreated type 2 diabetes are as serious as those of type 1 diabetes.

Testes and Ovaries

The activity of the testes and ovaries is controlled by the hypothalamus and pituitary. The **testes** are located in the scrotum, and the **ovaries** are located in the pelvic cavity. The testes produce **androgens** (e.g., **testosterone**), the male sex hormones. The ovaries produce **estrogens** and **progesterone,** the female sex hormones. These hormones provide feedback that controls the hypothalamic secretion of gonadotropin-releasing hormone (GnRH). The pituitary gland secretion of follicle-stimulating hormone (FSH) and luteinizing hormone (LH), the gonadotropic hormones, is controlled by feedback from the sex hormones, too. The activities of FSH and LH are discussed in Chapter 41.

Under the influence of the gonadotropic hormones, the testes release an increased amount of testosterone at the time of puberty, which stimulates growth of the penis and the testes. Testosterone also brings about and maintains the male secondary sex characteristics that develop during puberty. These include the growth of facial, axillary (underarm), and pubic hair. It prompts the larynx and the vocal cords to enlarge, causing the voice to lower. Testosterone also stimulates the activity of oil and sweat glands in the skin. Another side effect of testosterone is baldness. Genes for baldness are inherited by both sexes, but baldness is seen more often in males because of the presence of testosterone.

Testosterone is partially responsible for the muscular strength of males, and this is the reason some athletes take supplemental amounts of **anabolic steroids,** which are either testosterone or related chemicals. The dangerous side effects of taking anabolic steroids are listed in Figure 40.16.

The female sex hormones, estrogens (often referred to in the singular) and progesterone, have many effects on the body. In

balding in men and women; hair on face and chest in women

deepening of voice in women

breast enlargement in men and breast reduction in women

liver dysfunction and cancer

kidney disease and retention of fluids, called "steroid bloat"

reduced testicular size, low sperm count, and impotency

'roid rage—
delusions and hallucinations; depression upon withdrawal; violent or aggressive behavior

severe acne

high blood cholesterol and atherosclerosis; high blood pressure and damage to heart

in women, increased size of ovaries; cessation of ovulation and menstruation

stunted growth in adolescents by prematurely halting fusion of the growth plates

Figure 40.16 The effects of anabolic steroid use.

particular, estrogen [Gk. *oistros,* sexual heat; L. *genitus,* producing] secreted at the time of puberty stimulates the growth of the uterus and the vagina. Estrogen is necessary for egg maturation and is largely responsible for the secondary sex characteristics in females, including female body hair and fat distribution. In general, females have a more rounded appearance than males because of a greater accumulation of fat beneath the skin. Also, the pelvic girdle is wider in females than in males, resulting in a larger pelvic cavity. Both estrogen and progesterone are required for breast development and regulation of the uterine cycle. This includes monthly menstruation (discharge of blood and mucosal tissues from the uterus).

Pineal Gland

The **pineal gland** (epiphysis), located deep in the human brain (see Fig. 40.2), produces the hormone **melatonin,** primarily at night. Melatonin is involved in our daily sleep-wake cycle; normally we grow sleepy at night when melatonin levels increase and awaken once daylight returns and melatonin levels are low (Fig. 40.17). Daily 24-hour cycles such as this are called **circadian rhythms** [L. *circum,* around, and *dies,* day], and circadian rhythms are controlled by an internal timing mechanism called a biological clock.

Video Winter Moods

Instead of being buried deep in the brain, the pineal gland of some vertebrates is located on top of the brain, and in certain fossilized reptiles and even some primitive extant reptiles and amphibians, an additional opening in the skull is present, covered only by a thin layer of skin. This, along with the presence of light-sensing cells in the pineal gland, has led some investigators to conclude that this gland functioned as a "third eye" at some point in evolution. The exact function(s) of this structure are not completely understood, although it may have aided in determining the position of the Sun, or in establishing circadian rhythms.

Figure 40.17 Melatonin production. Melatonin production is greatest at night when we are sleeping. Light suppresses melatonin production **(a),** so its duration is longer in the winter **(b)** than in the summer **(c).**

Animal research suggests that melatonin also regulates sexual development. In keeping with these findings, it has been noted that children whose pineal glands have been destroyed due to a brain tumor experience early puberty.

Thymus Gland

The lobular **thymus gland** lies just beneath the sternum (see Fig. 40.2). This organ reaches its largest size and is most active during childhood. With aging, the thymus gets smaller and becomes fatty. Lymphocytes that originate in the bone marrow and then pass through the thymus become T lymphocytes. The lobules of the thymus are lined by epithelial cells that secrete hormones called thymosins. These hormones aid in the differentiation of T lymphocytes packed inside the lobules.

Hormones from Other Organs or Tissues

Some organs not usually considered as endocrine glands do secrete hormones. Two examples already mentioned in this chapter are the excretion of renin by the kidneys, and atrial natriuretic hormone by the heart. A number of other tissues produce hormones.

Leptin

Leptin is a peptide hormone produced by adipose tissue throughout the body. Leptin acts on the hypothalamus, where it signals satiety or fullness. After leptin was discovered in the 1990s, researchers hoped that it could be used to control obesity in humans. Unfortunately, the trials have not yielded satisfactory results. In fact, the blood of obese individuals may be rich in leptin. It is possible that the leptin they produce is ineffective because of a genetic mutation or because their hypothalamic cells lack a suitable number of receptors for leptin.

Erythropoietin

As previously mentioned in Chapter 36, the kidneys secrete erythropoietin (EPO) in response to a low blood oxygen level. EPO stimulates the production of red blood cells in the red bone marrow. People with anemia, which is common in kidney disease, cancer, and AIDS, may be effectively treated with injections of recombinant EPO. In recent years, some athletes have practiced blood doping, in which EPO is used to improve performance by increasing the oxygen-carrying capacity of the blood. The potential dangers of blood doping far outweigh the temporary advantages. Because EPO increases the number of red blood cells, the blood becomes thicker, blood pressure can become elevated, and the athlete is at increased risk of heart attack or stroke.

Prostaglandins

Prostaglandins are potent chemical signals produced within cells from arachidonate, a fatty acid. Prostaglandins are not distributed in the blood. They act locally, quite close to where they were produced. In the uterus, prostaglandins cause muscles to contract; therefore, they are implicated in the pain and discomfort of menstruation in some women. Also, prostaglandins mediate the effects of *pyrogens,* chemicals believed to reset the temperature regulatory center in the brain. Aspirin reduces body temperature and controls pain because it prevents the synthesis of prostaglandins.

Certain prostaglandins increase the secretion of protective mucus in the stomach and thus are used to prevent gastric ulcers. Others lower blood pressure and have been used to treat hypertension. Still others inhibit platelet aggregation and have been used to prevent thrombosis. Because prostaglandins can affect various tissues however, unwanted side effects can be a problem. For example, Misoprostol, a prostaglandin commonly used to prevent stomach ulcers, should not be taken by pregnant women, as it may also cause uterine contractions, resulting in miscarriage or premature labor.

Check Your Progress   40.3

1. Explain how the renin-angiotensin-aldosterone system raises blood pressure.
2. List the endocrine gland that secretes each of the following hormones: aldosterone, melatonin, epinephrine, EPO, leptin, glucagon, ANH, cortisol, and calcitonin.
3. Name one hormone that stimulates the activity of osteoclasts, and one that inhibits them.

CONNECTING *the* CONCEPTS *with the* THEMES

Evolution

- The cells of even the simplest multicellular animals have evolved the ability to communicate with each other using chemical signals.
- The nervous and endocrine systems have evolved together, so that the two systems are structurally and functionally related.
- The nervous system has developed to be able to bring about a rapid response to stimuli, while the endocrine system provides a slower, longer-lasting response.

Nature of Science

- Through scientific research, we now have a better understanding of the structures and functions of the endocrine system.
- A relatively large number of disorders affect the human endocrine system, but many of these, such as diabetes and thyroid disorders, are treatable because of our understanding of how hormones work.

Biological Systems

- Invertebrates use hormones to control some unique processes, such as the metamorphosis of larvae to form adults.
- In vertebrates, the hypothalamus controls the function of the pituitary gland, which in turn controls several other endocrine glands.
- Hormones exhibit control and influence over a wide range of body systems and functions, including salt balance, growth, metabolism, sexual development, and responses to stimuli.
- Some tissues and organs having other main functions also produce hormones, and certain cells produce locally acting hormones.

Media Study Tools

www.mhhe.com/maderbiology11

Enhance your study of this chapter with study tools and practice tests. Also ask your instructor about the resources available through ConnectPlus, including the media-rich eBook, interactive learning tools, and animations.

Summarize

40.1 Animal Hormones

The nervous and endocrine systems both use chemical signals. Endocrine glands secrete hormones into the bloodstream, and from there they are distributed to target organs or tissues.

Hormones are a type of chemical signal that usually act at a distance between body parts. Hormones are either peptides or steroids. Reception of a peptide hormone at the plasma membrane activates an enzyme cascade inside the cell. Steroid hormones combine with a receptor inside the cell, and the complex attaches to and activates DNA. Protein synthesis follows.

40.2 Hypothalamus and Pituitary Gland

Neurosecretory cells in the hypothalamus produce antidiuretic hormone (ADH) and oxytocin, which are stored in axon endings in the posterior pituitary until they are released.

The hypothalamus produces hypothalamic-releasing and hypothalamic-inhibiting hormones, which pass to the anterior pituitary by way of a portal system. The anterior pituitary produces several types of hormones, and some of these stimulate other endocrine glands to secrete hormones.

40.3 Other Endocrine Glands and Hormones

The thyroid gland, controlled by TSH, requires iodine to produce thyroxine (T_4) and triiodothyronine (T_3), which increase the metabolic rate. Depending on the age of an individual, a deficiency of T_3 and T_4 may result in congenital hypothyroidism, simple goiter, or myxedema. Hyperthyroidism may be the result of Graves disease or thyroid cancer. The thyroid gland also produces calcitonin, which helps lower the blood calcium level.

The parathyroid glands secrete parathyroid hormone, which raises the blood calcium and decreases the blood phosphate levels.

The adrenal glands respond to stress: Immediately, the adrenal medulla secretes epinephrine and norepinephrine, which bring about responses we associate with emergency situations. On a long-term basis, the adrenal cortex, controlled by ACTH, produces the gluco-corticoids (e.g., cortisol) and the mineralocorticoids (e.g., aldoste-rone). Cortisol stimulates hydrolysis of proteins to amino acids that are converted to glucose; in this way, it raises the blood glucose level. Aldosterone causes the kidneys to reabsorb sodium ions (Na^+) and to excrete potassium ions (K^+). Addison disease develops when the adrenal cortex is underactive, and Cushing syndrome develops when the adrenal cortex is overactive.

The pancreatic islets secrete insulin, which lowers the blood glucose level, and glucagon, which has the opposite effect. The most common illness caused by hormonal imbalance is diabetes mellitus, which is due to the failure of the pancreas to produce insulin or the failure of the cells to take it up.

The gonads, controlled by gonadotropic hormones, produce the sex hormones; the pineal gland produces melatonin, which may be involved in circadian rhythms and the development of the repro-ductive organs; and the thymus secretes thymosins, which stimulate T-lymphocyte production and maturation.

Tissue and organs having other functions also produce hor-mones. Leptin is a newly described hormone that regulates appetite, and erythropoietin stimulates the production of red blood cells. Pros-taglandins are produced and act locally, with a variety of effects on different tissues.

Key Terms

Assess

Reviewing This Chapter

1. In what ways are the nervous and endocrine systems alike, and how are they different?   753
2. Explain how steroid hormones and peptide hormones affect the metabolism of the cell.   755–56
3. Explain the relationship of the hypothalamus to the posterior pituitary gland and to the anterior pituitary gland. List the hormones secreted by the posterior and anterior pituitary.   757–59
4. Give an example of the negative feedback relationship involving the hypothalamus, the anterior pituitary, and other endocrine glands.   757
5. Discuss the effect of too much or too little growth hormone when a young person is growing. What is the result if the anterior pituitary overproduces growth hormone in an adult?   758–59
6. What types of diseases are associated with a malfunctioning thyroid? Explain each type.   760–61
7. How do the thyroid and the parathyroid work together to control the blood calcium level?   761–62
8. How do the adrenal glands respond to stress? What hormones are secreted by the adrenal medulla, and what effects do these hormones have?   762–64
9. Name the most significant glucocorticoid and mineralocorticoid, and discuss the function of each. Explain the symptoms of Addison disease and Cushing syndrome.   763–64
10. Draw a diagram to explain how insulin and glucagon maintain the blood glucose level. Use your diagram to explain three major symptoms of type 1 diabetes mellitus.   765–67
11. Name the other endocrine glands cited in this chapter, and discuss the functions of the hormones they secrete. Also, discuss the hormones not produced by endocrine glands.   767–69

Testing Yourself

Choose the best answer for each question.
For questions 1–5, match each hormone to a gland in the key.

KEY:
   a. pancreas
   b. anterior pituitary
   c. posterior pituitary
   d. thyroid
   e. adrenal medulla
   f. adrenal cortex

1. cortisol

2. growth hormone (GH)

3. oxytocin storage

4. insulin

5. epinephrine

6. The anterior pituitary controls the secretion(s) of both
   a. the adrenal medulla and the adrenal cortex.
   b. the thyroid and the adrenal cortex.
   c. the ovaries and the testes.
   d. Both b and c are correct.

7. Diabetes mellitus is associated with
   a. too much insulin in the blood.
   b. too much glucose in the blood.
   c. blood that is too dilute.
   d. Both b and c are correct.

8. Which of these is not a pair of antagonistic hormones?
   a. insulin—glucagon
   b. calcitonin—parathyroid hormone
   c. aldosterone—atrial natriuretic hormone (ANH)
   d. thyroxine—growth hormone

9. Which hormone and condition are mismatched?
   a. cortisol—myxedema
   b. growth hormone—acromegaly
   c. thyroxine—goiter
   d. parathyroid hormone—tetany
   e. insulin—diabetes

10. The difference between type 1 and type 2 diabetes is that
    a. for type 2 diabetes, insulin is produced but not used; type 1 results from lack of insulin production.
    b. treatment for type 2 involves insulin injections, while type 1 can be controlled, usually by diet.
    c. only type 1 can result in complications such as kidney disease, reduced circulation, or stroke.
    d. type 1 can be a result of lifestyle, and type 2 is thought to be caused by a virus or other agent.

11. Which of the following hormones is/are found in females?
    a. estrogen
    b. testosterone
    c. follicle-stimulating hormone
    d. Both a and c are correct.
    e. All of these are correct.

12. Parathyroid hormone causes
    a. the kidneys to excrete more calcium ions.
    b. bone tissue to break down and release calcium into the bloodstream.
    c. fewer calcium ions to be absorbed by the intestines.
    d. more calcium ions to be deposited in bone tissue.

For questions 13–18, match the function to a hormone in the key. Choose more than one answer if correct. Answers may be used more than once.

KEY:
   a. antidiuretic hormone
   b. oxytocin
   c. glucocorticoids
   d. glucagon
   e. parathyroid hormone

13. raises blood glucose level

14. stimulates uterine muscle contraction

15. stimulates water reabsorption by kidneys

16. stimulates release of milk by mammary glands

17. raises blood glucose and stimulates breakdown of protein

18. raises blood calcium level

19. Steroid hormones are secreted by
    a. the adrenal cortex.
    b. the gonads.
    c. the thyroid.
    d. Both a and b are correct.
    e. Both b and c are correct.

20. Which one of the following statements about the pituitary gland is incorrect?
    a. The pituitary lies inferior to the hypothalamus.
    b. Growth hormone and prolactin are secreted by the anterior pituitary.
    c. The anterior pituitary and posterior pituitary communicate with each other.
    d. Axons run between the hypothalamus and the posterior pituitary.

Engage

Thinking Scientifically

1. Caffeine inhibits the breakdown of cAMP in the cell. Referring to Figure 40.4, how would this influence a stress response brought about by epinephrine?

2. Both males and females can develop secondary sex characteristics of the opposite sex if they take enough of the appropriate sex hormone. Hypothesize the mechanism that would make this possible after reviewing Figure 40.4.

Bioethical Issue
Growth Hormone

Untreated GH deficiency in childhood results in pituitary dwarfism. If young children with GH deficiency receive daily GH injections through adolescence, most will attain normal stature. Few would argue that treatment of pituitary dwarfism is not justified. But is it justified to use GH therapy to make a child of normal height taller?

GH levels naturally decline with age, and there is evidence that treating older adults with GH boosts muscle mass and reduces body fat. Pills do not work, and GH injections are by prescription only and very expensive, being around $1,000 a month. Furthermore, GH therapy can result in undesirable side effects, such as elevated blood sugar, fluid retention, and joint pain. Nevertheless, there is keen interest in GH therapy—not only from those who wish to delay or avoid the effects of aging, but also from athletes in search of performance-enhancing substances. Thus far, like anabolic steroids and erythropoietin (EPO), GH is banned by most competitive sports authorities, including the U.S. and International Olympic Committees.

The existence of GH therapy raises questions about medical treatment for disease versus enhancement of an already healthy body. Under what circumstances is it suitable to increase a child's growth? Should the physical decline of aging be accepted, or should we try to maintain a youthful build using GH? If an athlete wants to make himself or herself more competitive using GH, and is willing to accept the risks, should therapy be permitted? Who decides?

41

Reproductive Systems

CHAPTER OUTLINE

BEFORE YOU BEGIN

Before beginning this chapter, take a few moments to review the following discussions.

Chapter 10 How does meiosis halve the chromosome number to produce haploid cells?

Section 16.2 What influences does sexual selection have on mating patterns in animals?

Figure 40.6 What is the relationship between the hypothalamus/pituitary and the reproductive systems of males and females?

Male potbelly seahorses have a brood pouch that can hold 150–300 developing embryos.

Seahorses are fishes with an unusual style of sexual reproduction: The males become pregnant and give birth to the young. When seahorses mate, the female uses a tiny structure called an ovipositor to insert her unfertilized eggs into a brood pouch on the male's abdomen, where they are fertilized by his sperm. Tissues of the pouch then grow around the eggs, forming a placenta-like structure that provides oxygen and nutrition to the developing offspring. After about a month, the pouch opens and he gives birth.

Although the evolutionary benefit conferred by male pregnancy in seahorses is unclear, researchers are learning how this phenomenon can affect sexual selection. One finding is that the typical sex roles are often reversed—for example, because the males invest more resources into producing the offspring, they tend to be choosier about selecting mates, whereas females sometimes mate with multiple males during a breeding season.

In this chapter we focus on the more common strategies of asexual and sexual reproduction. Most of the chapter is devoted to the human male and female reproductive systems, methods that are available to help prevent unwanted pregnancies, and sexually transmitted infections that can have a detrimental effect on human reproduction.

As you read through the chapter, think about the following questions:

1. Considering this description of seahorse reproduction, define the terms "male," "female," "sex," and "pregnant."

2. List some common examples of secondary sex characteristics that develop in male animals in order to attract female mates.

FOLLOWING *the* THEMES

CHAPTER 41 REPRODUCTIVE SYSTEMS

UNIT 7 COMPARATIVE ANIMAL BIOLOGY		
	Evolution	Animals have evolved a large number of strategies, both sexual and asexual, for producing offspring.
	Nature of Science	Knowledge about human reproduction has led to the development of efficient methods of birth control, techniques for helping infertile couples, and better prevention and treatment of sexually transmitted diseases.
	Biological Systems	Animals reproducing asexually produce identical copies of themselves, whereas animals reproducing sexually have gonads that produce gametes, and accessory organs for the storage and/or passage of gametes into or out of the body.

41.1 How Animals Reproduce

Learning Outcomes

Upon completion of this section, you should be able to

1. Compare and contrast asexual and sexual reproduction, and list several animals that undergo each.
2. Describe some advantages of each of the following life histories: oviparous, ovoviviparous, viviparous.

For an animal species to survive, individuals must reproduce. As was discussed in Chapter 10, sexual reproduction involves a reshuffling of genetic material during *meiosis*. In animals, this process forms the sex cells, or gametes, which subsequently unite to form genetically unique offspring. The tremendous amount of genetic variation that is generated during meiosis can be advantageous to the survival of a species, especially during times when the environment is changing.

In asexual reproduction, a single parent gives rise to offspring that are identical to the parent, unless mutations have occurred. The adaptive advantage of asexual reproduction is that organisms can reproduce rapidly and colonize favorable environments quickly. Although the majority of animals reproduce sexually, a few groups of animals are also capable of asexual reproduction.

Asexual Reproduction

Several types of invertebrates, such as sponges, cnidarians, flatworms, annelids, and echinoderms, can reproduce asexually. In cnidarians, such as hydras, new individuals may arise asexually as an outgrowth (bud) of the parent (Fig. 41.1). Some species of hydras can also reproduce sexually.

Many flatworms can reproduce asexually by splitting in half, generating two identical individuals. In the laboratory, a planarian can be cut into as many as ten pieces, each of which will grow into a new planarian. To varying degrees, many other animals, including sponges, annelids, and echinoderms, also have the ability to regenerate from fragments. Scientists are studying the ability of some animals to regenerate, with the hope of learning how to regenerate certain human tissues (see the Nature of Science feature, "Regenerative Medicine," in Chapter 31).

Sexual Reproduction

The majority of animals are *dioecious*, which means having separate sexes. Usually during sexual reproduction, the egg of one parent is fertilized by the sperm of another. *Monoecious*, or **hermaphroditic,** animals have both male and female sex organs in a single body. Some hermaphroditic organisms, like tapeworms, are capable of self-fertilization, but the majority, such as earthworms, practice cross-fertilization with other individuals. Sequential hermaphroditism, or sex reversal, also occurs. In coral reef fishes called wrasses, a male has a harem of several females. If the male dies, the largest female becomes a male.

Animals usually produce gametes in specialized organs called **gonads.** Sponges are an exception to this rule because the collar cells lining the central cavity of a sponge give rise to sperm and eggs. Hydras and other cnidarians produce only temporary gonads in the fall, when sexual reproduction occurs. Animals in other phyla have permanent reproductive organs.

The gonads are **testes,** which produce sperm, and **ovaries,** which produce eggs. Eggs or sperm are derived from **germ cells,** which become specialized for this purpose during early development. Other cells present in a gonad support and nourish the developing gametes or produce hormones necessary to the reproductive process. The reproductive system also usually has a number of accessory structures, such as ducts and storage areas, that aid in bringing the gametes together.

Several types of flatworms, roundworms, crustaceans, annelids, insects, fishes, lizards, and even some turkeys have the ability to reproduce parthenogenetically. **Parthenogenesis** is a modification of sexual reproduction in which an unfertilized egg develops into a complete individual. In honeybees, the queen bee makes and stores sperm she uses to selectively fertilize eggs. Any unfertilized eggs become haploid males.

Many aquatic animals practice *external fertilization*, in which the gametes are released and unite outside the bodies of the reproducing animals. Among fishes, methods of fertilization and care of the developing embryos vary greatly. Some species simply scatter large numbers of eggs and sperm in the environment, and may even eat some of their eggs or offspring. Mouthbrooders scoop up their eggs or newly hatched young into their mouths, protecting them from predators. Other fish species build elaborate nests for their eggs, made from plant debris and saliva-coated bubbles.

An invertebrate aquatic species called palolo worms, which inhabit coral reefs in the South Pacific, exhibit a unique fertilization strategy. Always at the same time of year and during a particular phase of the moon, the worms break in half. During

budding of
new polyp

parental
polyp

Figure 41.1 Reproduction in *Hydra*. Hydras reproduce asexually and sexually. During asexual reproduction, a new polyp buds from the parental polyp. During sexual reproduction, temporary gonads develop in the body wall.

a period of just a few hours, hundreds of thousands of tail sections, containing the gonads, swim to the surface, releasing eggs and sperm. Meanwhile, local human populations take to the sea, using nets to scoop up large numbers of the half-worms, which are eaten raw or saved in buckets to be baked or fried, and consumed at an annual feast.

Copulation is sexual union to facilitate the reception of sperm, resulting in *internal fertilization*. In terrestrial vertebrates, males typically have a penis for depositing sperm into the vagina of females. But not so in birds, which lack a penis and vagina. They have a cloaca, a chamber that receives products from the digestive, urinary, and reproductive tracts. A male transfers sperm to a female after placing his cloacal opening against hers. In damselflies, the female curls her abdomen forward to receive sperm previously deposited in a pouch by the male, and copulation in the usual sense doesn't occur (Fig. 41.2).

Video
Frog Reproduction

Life History Strategies

Any animal that deposits an egg in the external environment is **oviparous.** Many oviparous animals have a larval stage, an immature form capable of feeding. Because the larva has a different lifestyle, it is able to use a different food source than the adult. Other animals, like crayfish, do not have a larval stage; the egg hatches into a tiny juvenile with the same form as the adult.

Some aquatic animals are **ovoviviparous,** meaning they retain their eggs in some way and release young able to fend for themselves. For example, oysters, which are molluscs, retain their eggs in the mantle cavity. As mentioned in the chapter-opening story, male seahorses have a brood pouch in which fertilized eggs develop.

Usually, reptiles (e.g., turtles and crocodiles) lay a leathery-shelled egg that contains **extraembryonic membranes** to serve

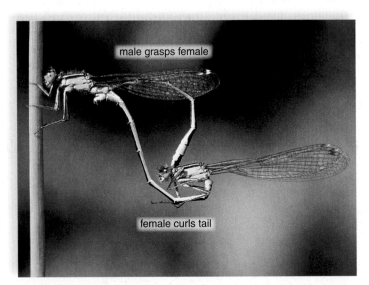

Figure 41.2 Damselflies mating on land.   On land, animals have various means to ensure that the gametes do not dry out. Here, a female damselfly receives sperm from the male.

Figure 41.3 Parenting in birds.   Birds, such as the American goldfinch, *Carduelis tristis,* are oviparous and lay hard-shelled eggs. They are well known for incubating their eggs and caring for their offspring after they hatch.

the needs of the embryo and prevent drying out. One membrane surrounds an abundant supply of **yolk,** which is a nutrient-rich material. The shelled egg with its internal extraembryonic membranes is a significant adaptation to the terrestrial environment. Birds lay and care for hard-shelled eggs; the newly hatched birds usually have to be fed before they are able to fly away and seek food for themselves (Fig. 41.3). Complex hormonal and neural regulation are involved in the reproductive behavior of parental birds.

Among mammals, the duckbill platypus and spiny anteater lay shelled eggs. Marsupials and placental mammals do not lay eggs. In marsupials, the yolk sac membrane functions briefly to supply the unborn embryo with nutrients acquired internally from the mother. Immature young finish their development within a pouch where they are nourished on milk.

The placental mammals are termed **viviparous,** because they do not lay eggs and development occurs inside the female's body until offspring can live independently. Their **placenta** is a complex structure derived, in part, from the chorion, another of the reptilian extraembryonic membranes. The evolution of this type of placenta allowed the developing young to internally exchange materials with the mother until they are able to function on their own. Viviparity represents the ultimate in caring for the unborn, and in placental mammals, the mother continues to supply milk to nourish her offspring after birth.

In the sections that follow, we take an in-depth look at the reproductive systems of humans and the issues of birth control and health.

Check Your Progress   41.1

1. List one advantage of asexual reproduction, and one advantage of sexual reproduction.
2. Distinguish between oviparous, ovoviviparous, and viviparous.
3. Explain how a shelled egg allows reproduction on land.

41.2 Human Male Reproductive System

Learning Outcomes

Upon completion of this section, you should be able to

1. Identify the structures of the human male reproductive system and provide a function for each.
2. Describe the location and stages of spermatogenesis.
3. Summarize how hormones regulate the male reproductive system.

Table 41.1 Male Reproductive System

Organ	Function
Testes	Produce sperm and sex hormones
Epididymides	Sites of maturation and some storage of sperm
Vasa deferentia	Conduct and store sperm
Seminal vesicles	Contribute fluid to semen
Prostate gland	Contributes fluid to semen
Urethra	Conducts sperm (and urine)
Bulbourethral glands	Contribute fluid to semen
Penis	Organ of copulation

The human male reproductive system includes the organs pictured in Figure 41.4 and listed in Table 41.1. The primary sex organs, or gonads, of males are the paired **testes** (sing., testis), which are suspended within the sacs of the scrotum.

The Testes

The testes produce sperm and the male sex hormones. They begin their development inside the abdominal cavity, but descend into the scrotal sacs during the last two months of fetal development. If the testes fail to descend—and the male does not receive hormone therapy or undergo surgery to place the testes in the scrotum—male infertility may result. The reason is that undescended testes developing in the body cavity are subject to

higher body temperatures than testes that have descended into the scrotum. The scrotum helps regulate testicular temperature by holding them closer or farther away from the body. In fact, any activity that increases testicular temperature, such as taking hot baths, can decrease sperm production. However, despite the frequently held belief that wearing boxer-style underwear favors higher sperm production compared to briefs, this assumption is unsupported by research.

Sperm produced in the testes mature within the **epididymis** (pl., epididymides), a tightly coiled duct lying just outside each testis. Maturation seems to be required for sperm to swim to the egg. Once the sperm have matured, they enter the **vas deferens** (pl., vasa deferentia), also called the ductus deferens. Sperm may be stored for a time in the vasa deferentia. Each

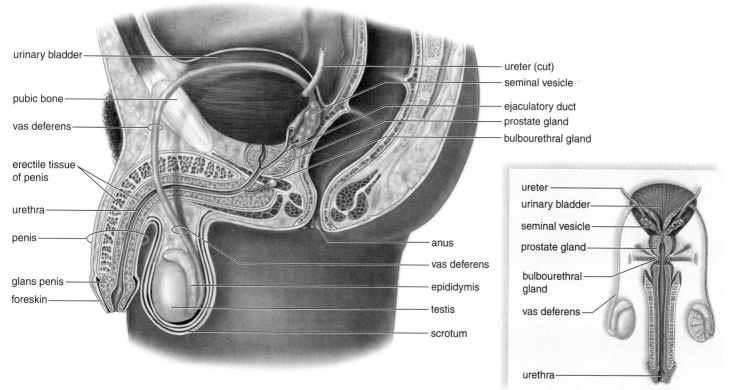

Figure 41.4 The male reproductive system. The testes produce sperm. The seminal vesicles, the prostate gland, and the bulbourethral glands provide a fluid medium for the sperm, which move from the vas deferens through the ejaculatory duct to the urethra in the penis. The foreskin (prepuce) is removed when a penis is circumcised.

Figure 41.5 Testis and sperm.   a. The lobules of a testis contain seminiferous tubules. **b.** Light micrograph of a cross section of the seminiferous tubules, where spermatogenesis occurs. Note the location of interstitial cells in clumps among the seminiferous tubules. **c.** Diagrammatic representation of spermatogenesis, which occurs in wall of tubules. **d.** A sperm has a head, a middle piece, and a tail. The nucleus is in the head, which is capped by the enzyme-containing acrosome.

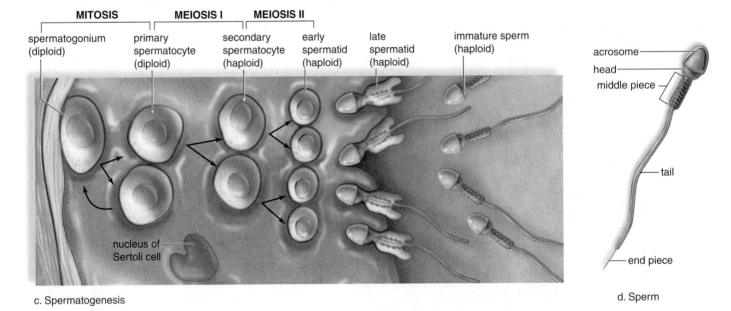

interstitial cells   immature sperm   Sertoli cell

b. Seminiferous tubules

100 µm

vas deferens

epididymis

uncoiled seminiferous tubule

lobule

testis

scrotal sac

a. Testis, cut to show lobules

MITOSIS   **MEIOSIS I**   **MEIOSIS II**

spermatogonium (diploid)   primary spermatocyte (diploid)   secondary spermatocyte (haploid)   early spermatid (haploid)   late spermatid (haploid)   immature sperm (haploid)

nucleus of Sertoli cell

c. Spermatogenesis

acrosome
head
middle piece

tail

end piece

d. Sperm

vas deferens passes into the abdominal cavity, where it curves around the bladder and empties into an ejaculatory duct. The vasa deferentia are severed or blocked in a surgical form of birth control called a *vasectomy*. Sperm are then unable to complete their journey through the male reproductive tract, and are phagocytized and destroyed by macrophages.

Testicular cancer is the most common type of cancer in young men between the ages of 15 and 34. The cure rate is high if early treatment is received. All men should perform regular self-exams to detect unusual lumps or swellings of the testes, and report any changes to their doctors.

Production of Sperm

A longitudinal section of a testis shows that it is composed of compartments called lobules, each of which contains one to three tightly coiled **seminiferous tubules** (Fig. 41.5a). Altogether, these tubules have a combined length of approximately 250 meters (over two and a half football fields). This provides a large amount of surface area for sperm development. A microscopic cross section of a seminiferous tubule shows that it is packed with cells undergoing *spermatogenesis* (Fig. 41.5b), the production of sperm.

During spermatogenesis, spermatogonia divide to produce primary spermatocytes (which have the 2n number of chromosomes).

Primary spermatocytes move away from the outer wall, increase in size, and undergo meiosis I to produce secondary spermatocytes. Each secondary spermatocyte has only 23 chromosomes (Fig. 41.5c). Secondary spermatocytes (n) undergo meiosis II to produce four spermatids, each of which also has 23 chromosomes. Spermatids then differentiate into sperm (Fig. 41.5d). Note the presence of *Sertoli cells* (purple in Fig. 41.5c), which support and nourish the developing sperm, and regulate spermatogenesis. It takes approximately 74 days for a spermatogonium to develop into sperm. **Animation** Spermatogenesis

Mature **sperm,** or *spermatozoa*, have three distinct parts: a head, a middle piece, and a tail (Fig. 41.5d). Mitochondria in the middle piece provide energy for the movement of the tail, which is a flagellum. Like other eukaryotic flagella and cilia, microtubules in the sperm tail form the characteristic 9 + 2 pattern (see Fig. 4.20). The head contains a nucleus covered by a cap called the *acrosome* [Gk. *akros*, at the tip, and *soma*, body], which stores enzymes needed to penetrate the thick membrane surrounding the egg. **Video** Human Sperm

The Penis and Male Orgasm

The **penis** (Fig. 41.6) is the male organ of sexual intercourse. The penis has a long shaft and an enlarged tip called the glans penis. The glans penis is normally covered by a layer of skin called the *foreskin*. Male *circumcision*, the surgical removal of the foreskin, is performed on more than 50% of newborn males in the United States, often for cultural, religious, or health reasons. Research shows that circumcised males are 25–35% less likely to acquire certain STDs, including AIDS.

Three cylindrical columns of spongy, erectile tissue containing distensible blood spaces extend through the shaft of the penis. During sexual arousal, autonomic nerves release nitric oxide (NO). This stimulus leads to the production of cGMP (cycline guanosine monophosphate), a type of second messenger similar to cAMP (see Section 40.1). The cGMP causes the smooth muscle of the incoming arterial walls to relax and the erectile tissue to fill with blood. The veins that normally take blood away from the penis are compressed, and the penis becomes erect.

Semen (seminal fluid) [L. *semen*, seed] is a thick, whitish fluid that contains sperm and secretions from three glands (Fig. 41.4 and Table 41.1). The paired **seminal vesicles** lie at the base of the bladder, and each has a duct that joins with a vas deferens. As sperm pass from the vasa deferentia into the ejaculatory ducts, the seminal vesicles secrete a thick, viscous fluid containing nutrients (fructose) for possible use by the sperm. The fluid also contains prostaglandins that stimulate smooth muscle contraction along the male and female reproductive tracts.

The **prostate gland** is a single, doughnut-shaped gland that surrounds the upper portion of the urethra just below the bladder. The prostate gland secretes a milky alkaline fluid believed to activate or increase the motility of sperm. By age 50, over half of all men experience a benign enlargement (hypertrophy) of the prostate gland (BPH). Because of its location, BPH can result in an increased frequency of urination, and a weak urinary stream. Also, after skin cancer, prostate cancer is the most common type of cancer among men in the United States. Based on current rates, 13–16% of men born today can expect to be diagnosed with prostate cancer during their lifetime.

Bulbourethral glands are pea-sized organs that lie posterior to the prostate on either side of the urethra. They produce a clear, viscous secretion known as *pre-ejaculate*. Secretions from the bulbourethral glands are the first to enter the urethra, where they may function to cleanse the urethra of acidic residue from urine. Since this fluid can also pick up sperm that remain in the urethra from previous ejaculations, it is possible for sperm to enter the genital tract of a female during sexual intercourse, even when ejaculation has not yet occurred.

As sexual stimulation intensifies, *ejaculation* may occur. During the first phase of ejaculation, called emission, the spinal cord sends sympathetic nerve impulses to the epididymides and vasa deferentia. Their muscular walls contract, causing sperm to enter the ejaculatory duct, whereupon the seminal vesicles, prostate gland, and bulbourethral glands release their secretions.

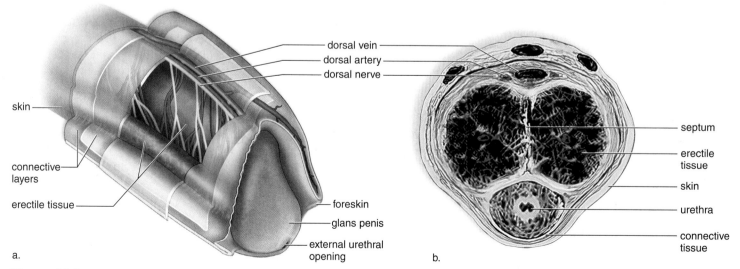

a.

dorsal vein
dorsal artery
dorsal nerve

skin

connective layers

erectile tissue

foreskin
glans penis
external urethral opening

b.

septum
erectile tissue
skin
urethra
connective tissue

Figure 41.6 Penis anatomy. **a.** Beneath the skin and the connective tissue lies the urethra, surrounded by erectile tissue. This tissue expands to form the glans penis, which in uncircumcised males is partially covered by the foreskin (prepuce). **b.** Micrograph of shaft in cross section showing location of erectile tissue. One column surrounds the urethra.

During the second phase of ejaculation, called expulsion, rhythmical contractions of muscles at the base of the penis and within the urethral wall expel semen in spurts from the opening of the urethra. During ejaculation, the urinary bladder sphincter normally contracts so that no semen can enter the bladder. (Note that the urethra carries either urine or semen at different times.)

The contractions that expel semen from the penis are a part of male *orgasm* [Gk. *orgasmos*, sexual excitement], the physiological and psychological sensations that occur at the climax of sexual stimulation. The physiological reactions of both male and female orgasm involve the genital (reproductive) organs and assocated muscles, as well as the entire body. Marked muscular tension is followed by contraction and relaxation. In the male, following ejaculation and/or loss of sexual arousal, the penis returns to its flaccid state. After ejaculating, males typically experience a period of time, called the *refractory period*, during which stimulation does not bring about an erection. The length of the refractory period increases with age.

An average male releases 2–5 mL of semen during orgasm. The ejaculated semen of a normal human male contains between 50 and 150 million sperm per mL, meaning there may be more than 400 million sperm released in one ejaculation. According to the World Health Organization, a low sperm concentration, or *oligozoospermia*, is defined as less than 15 million sperm per mL of ejaculate. Because only one sperm typically enters an egg, however, men with low sperm counts can still be fertile.

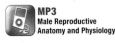
MP3
Male Reproductive Anatomy and Physiology

Erectile dysfunction (ED), formerly called impotency, is the inability to achieve or maintain an erection suitable for sexual intercourse. ED may have a number of causes, including any condition that affects blood flow, certain medications or illicit drugs, and psychological factors. Since 1998, medications have been available for the treatment of ED. All of these drugs—such as Viagra, Levitra, and Cialis—work by inhibiting an enzyme called PDE-5, found mainly in the penis, which normally breaks down cGMP. This extends the activity of cGMP, increasing the likelihood of achieving a full erection. Because the PDE-5 enzyme is also found in the retinas and certain other tissues, ED medications can cause vision problems and other undesirable side effects.

Hormonal Regulation in Males

The hypothalamus has ultimate control of the testes' sexual function because it secretes a hormone called gonadotropin-releasing hormone (GnRH). GnRH stimulates the anterior pituitary to produce the gonadotropic hormones, follicle-stimulating hormone (FSH) and luteinizing hormone (LH), which are present in both males and females. In males, FSH promotes spermatogenesis in the seminiferous tubules.

LH in males controls the production of the androgen testosterone by the interstitial cells (Leydig cells), which are scattered in the spaces between the seminiferous tubules (Fig. 41.5*b*). All these hormones, including inhibin, a hormone released by the seminiferous tubules, are involved in a negative feedback relationship that maintains the fairly constant production of sperm and testosterone (Fig. 41.7).

Testosterone is the main sex hormone in males. It is essential for the normal development and functioning of the organs

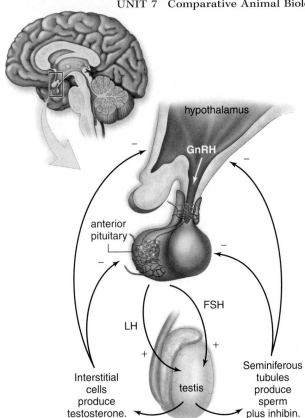

Figure 41.7 Hormonal control of the testes. GnRH (gonadotropin-releasing hormone) stimulates the anterior pituitary to produce FSH and LH. FSH stimulates the testes to produce sperm, and LH stimulates the testes to produce testosterone. Testosterone from interstitial cells and inhibin from the seminiferous tubules exert negative feedback control over the hypothalamus and the anterior pituitary, and this ultimately regulates the level of testosterone in the blood.

listed in Table 41.1. Testosterone also brings about and maintains the male *secondary sex characteristics* that develop at the time of puberty. Males are generally taller than females and have broader shoulders and longer legs relative to trunk length. The deeper voice of males compared to females is due to the development in males of a larger larynx with longer vocal cords. The "Adam's apple," which is a protrusion at the front of the larynx, is usually more prominent in males than in females. Testosterone causes males to develop noticeable hair on the face, chest, and occasionally other regions of the body, such as the back. A chemical called dihydrotestosterone (DHT) which is synthesized from testosterone in the hair follicles, leads to the receding hairline and male-pattern baldness in genetically susceptible individuals.

Testosterone is responsible for the greater muscular development in males. Knowing this, both males and females sometimes take anabolic steroids, either testosterone or related steroid hormones resembling testosterone, to build up their muscles. For more information about the risks of anabolic steroids, review Figure 40.16.

Check Your Progress   41.2

1. Trace the pathway a sperm must follow from its origin to its exit from the male reproductive tract.
2. List the glands that contribute fluids to the semen.
3. Describe the effects of FSH and LH in males.

41.3 Human Female Reproductive System

The human female reproductive system includes organs depicted in Figure 41.8 and listed in Table 41.2. The female gonads, or primary sex organs, are paired **ovaries** (sing., ovary), located on each side of the upper pelvic cavity.

The Ovaries, Uterus, and Vagina

The ovaries produce the female sex hormones and a secondary **oocyte** each month. The oviducts [L. *ovum*, egg, and *duco*, lead out], also called uterine or fallopian tubes, extend from the ovaries to the uterus; however, the oviducts are not attached to the ovaries. Instead, they have fingerlike projections called fimbriae (sing., fimbria) that sweep over the ovaries. When an oocyte bursts from an ovary during ovulation, it usually is swept into an oviduct by the combined action of the fimbriae and the beating of cilia that line the oviducts. Fertilization, if it occurs, normally takes place in an oviduct. The developing embryo is propelled slowly by ciliary movement and tubular muscle contraction to the uterus. Some women opt to permanently prevent pregnancy by having a surgery called *tubal ligation*, in which the oviducts are closed off so that sperm cannot reach the oocyte.

Normally, the ovaries alternate in producing one oocyte each month. For the sake of convenience, we will refer to the released oocyte as an **egg.** The ovaries also produce the female sex hormones; the **estrogens,** collectively called estrogen, and **progesterone,** during the ovarian cycle.

The **uterus** [L. *uterus*, womb] is a thick-walled muscular organ about the size and shape of an inverted pear. The narrow end of the uterus is called the **cervix.** The embryo completes its development after embedding itself in the uterine lining, called the **endometrium** [Gk. *endon*, within, and *metra*, womb]. If, by chance, the embryo should embed itself in another location, such as an oviduct, an *ectopic pregnancy* results.

A small opening in the cervix leads to the vaginal canal. The **vagina** [L. *vagina*, sheath] is a tube at a 45-degree angle to the small of the back. The mucosal lining of the vagina lies in folds and the vagina can be distended. This is especially important when the vagina serves as the birth canal, and it also can facilitate intercourse, when the vagina receives the penis during copulation. Several different types of bacteria normally reside in the vagina and create an acidic environment. This environment is protective against the possible growth of pathogenic bacteria, but sperm prefer the basic environment provided by semen.

Table 41.2 Female Reproductive Organs

Organ	Function
Ovaries	Produce egg and sex hormones
Oviducts (fallopian tubes)	Conduct egg; location of fertilization
Uterus (womb)	Houses developing embryo and fetus
Vagina	Receives penis during copulation and serves as birth canal

Figure 41.8 Female reproductive system. **a.** The ovaries produce one oocyte per month. Fertilization occurs in the oviduct, and development occurs in the uterus. The vagina is the birth canal and organ of sexual intercourse. **b.** Vulva. At birth, the opening of the vagina is partially occluded by a membrane called the hymen. Physical activities and sexual intercourse disrupt the hymen.

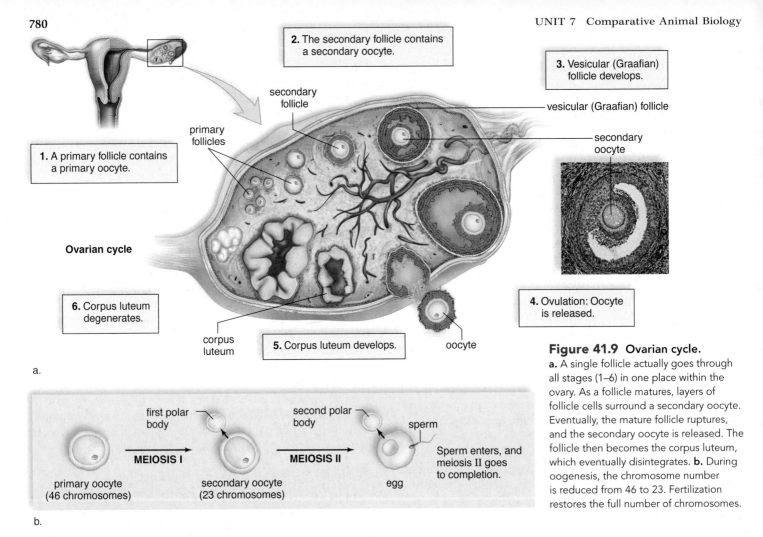

1. A primary follicle contains a primary oocyte.

2. The secondary follicle contains a secondary oocyte.

3. Vesicular (Graafian) follicle develops.

secondary follicle

primary follicles

vesicular (Graafian) follicle

secondary oocyte

Ovarian cycle

4. Ovulation: Oocyte is released.

6. Corpus luteum degenerates.

corpus luteum

5. Corpus luteum develops.

oocyte

a.

Figure 41.9 Ovarian cycle.
a. A single follicle actually goes through all stages (1–6) in one place within the ovary. As a follicle matures, layers of follicle cells surround a secondary oocyte. Eventually, the mature follicle ruptures, and the secondary oocyte is released. The follicle then becomes the corpus luteum, which eventually disintegrates. **b.** During oogenesis, the chromosome number is reduced from 46 to 23. Fertilization restores the full number of chromosomes.

first polar body

second polar body

sperm

MEIOSIS I

MEIOSIS II

Sperm enters, and meiosis II goes to completion.

primary oocyte (46 chromosomes)

secondary oocyte (23 chromosomes)

egg

b.

The Female Orgasm

The external genital organs of a female are known collectively as the vulva (Fig. 41.8b). The mons pubis and two folds of skin called labia minora and labia majora are on either side of the urethral and vaginal openings. Beneath the labia majora, pea-sized greater vestibular glands (Bartholin glands) open on either side of the vagina. They keep the vulva moist and lubricated during intercourse.

At the juncture of the labia minora is the *clitoris*, which is homologous to the penis in males. The clitoris has a shaft of erectile tissue and is capped by a pea-shaped glans. The many sensory receptors of the clitoris allow it to function as a sexually sensitive organ. The clitoris has twice as many nerve endings as the penis. As in males, female orgasm involves both psychological and physiological reactions. In the female there is also a release of neuromuscular tension in the muscles of the genital area, vagina, and uterus.

The Ovarian Cycle

The **ovarian cycle** occurs as a **follicle** [L. *folliculus*, little bag] changes from a primary, to a secondary, and finally to a vesicular (Graafian) follicle (Fig. 41.9a) under the influence of follicle-stimulating hormone (FSH) and luteinizing hormone (LH) from the anterior pituitary (Fig. 41.10). Epithelial cells of a primary follicle surround a primary oocyte. Pools of follicular fluid surround the oocyte in a secondary follicle. In a vesicular follicle, a fluid-filled cavity increases to the point that the follicle wall balloons out on the surface of the ovary.

Oogenesis and Ovulation

As a follicle matures, *oogenesis*, a form of meiosis depicted in Figure 41.9b, is initiated and continues. The primary oocyte divides, producing two haploid cells. One cell is a secondary oocyte, and the other is a polar body. The vesicular follicle bursts, releasing the secondary oocyte (egg) surrounded by a clear membrane. This process is referred to as **ovulation.** Once a vesicular follicle has lost the secondary oocyte, it develops into a **corpus luteum** [L. *corpus*, body, and *luteus*, yellow], a glandlike structure.

The secondary oocyte enters an oviduct. If fertilization occurs, a sperm enters the secondary oocyte and then the oocyte completes meiosis and becomes an egg. An egg with 23 chromosomes and a second polar body results. When the sperm nucleus unites with the egg nucleus, a zygote with 46 chromosomes is produced. If zygote formation and pregnancy do not occur, the corpus luteum begins to degenerate after about ten days.

Phases of the Ovarian Cycle

The ovarian cycle is controlled by the gonadotropic hormones, FSH and LH (Fig. 41.11). The gonadotropic hormones are not present in constant amounts and instead are secreted at different rates during the cycle. For simplicity's sake, it is convenient to emphasize that during the first half, or **follicular phase,** of the cycle, FSH promotes the development of a follicle that primarily secretes estrogen. As the estrogen level in the blood rises, it exerts negative feedback control over the anterior pituitary secretion of FSH so that the follicular phase comes to an end. At the same time that FSH along with LH release is being dampened by

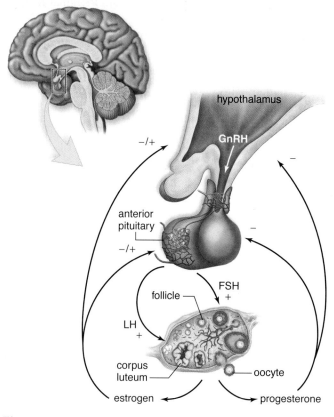

Figure 41.10 Hormonal control of ovaries. The hypothalamus produces GnRH (gonadotropic-releasing hormone). GnRH stimulates the anterior pituitary to produce FSH (follicle-stimulating hormone) and LH (luteinizing hormone). FSH stimulates the follicle to produce primarily estrogen, and LH stimulates the corpus luteum to produce primarily progesterone. Estrogen and progesterone maintain the sex organs (e.g., uterus) and the secondary sex characteristics, and they exert feedback control over the hypothalamus and the anterior pituitary. Feedback control regulates the relative amounts of estrogen and progesterone in the blood.

moderate amounts of estrogen, the synthesis of the gonadotropic hormones continues, and they build up in the anterior pituitary.

When the level of estrogen in the blood becomes very high, it exerts positive feedback on the hypothalamus and anterior pituitary. The hypothalamus is stimulated to suddenly secrete a large amount of GnRH. This leads to a surge of LH (and to a lesser degree, FSH) by the anterior pituitary and to ovulation at about the fourteenth day of a 28-day cycle (Fig. 41.11, *top*).

During the second half, or **luteal phase,** of the ovarian cycle, it is convenient to emphasize that LH promotes the development of the corpus luteum, which primarily secretes progesterone. As the blood level of progesterone rises, it exerts negative feedback control over anterior pituitary secretion of LH so that the corpus luteum begins to degenerate. As the luteal phase comes to an end, the low levels of progesterone and estrogen in the body cause menstruation to begin, as discussed next.

Animation
Maturation of the Follicle and Oocyte

The Uterine Cycle

The female sex hormones produced in the ovarian cycle (estrogen and progesterone) affect the endometrium of the uterus, causing the cyclical series of events known as the **uterine cycle** (Fig. 41.11, *bottom*). The twenty-eight-day cycle is divided into the three phases described next.

Phases of the Uterine Cycle

During *days 1–5,* there is a low level of female sex hormones in the body, causing the endometrium to disintegrate and its blood vessels to rupture. A flow of blood passes out of the vagina during **menstruation** [L. *menstrualis,* happening monthly], also known as the menstrual period. This is the *menstrual phase* of the uterine cycle.

During *days 6–13,* increased production of estrogen by an ovarian follicle causes the endometrium to thicken and to become vascular and glandular. This is called the *proliferative phase* of the uterine cycle.

Ovulation usually occurs on *day 14* of the 28-day cycle. During *days 15–28,* increased production of

Figure 41.11 Female hormone levels during the ovarian and uterine cycles. During the follicular phase of the ovarian cycle (*top*), FSH released by the anterior pituitary promotes the maturation of a follicle in the ovary. The ovarian follicle produces increasing levels of estrogen, which causes the endometrium to thicken during the proliferative phase of the uterine cycle (*bottom*). After ovulation and during the luteal phase of the ovarian cycle, LH promotes the development of the corpus luteum. This structure produces increasing levels of progesterone, which causes the endometrium to become secretory. Menstruation and the proliferative phase begin when progesterone production declines to a low level.

progesterone by the corpus luteum causes the endometrium to double in thickness and the uterine glands to mature, producing a thick mucoid secretion. This is called the *secretory phase* of the uterine cycle. The endometrium now is prepared to receive the developing embryo. If pregnancy does not occur, the corpus luteum degenerates, and the low level of sex hormones in the female body causes the endometrium to break down as menstruation occurs. Table 41.3 compares the stages of the uterine cycle with those of the ovarian cycle.

Menstruation

Seven to ten days before the start of menstruation, some women suffer from premenstrual syndrome (PMS). During this time a woman may exhibit breast enlargement and tenderness, achiness, headache, and irritability. The exact cause for PMS has yet to be discovered.

Animation
Female Reproductive System

During menstruation, arteries that supply the lining constrict and the capillaries weaken. Blood spilling from the damaged vessels detaches layers of the lining, not all at once but in random patches. Mucus, blood, and degenerating endometrium descend from the uterus, through the vagina, creating menstrual flow. Fibrinolysin, an enzyme released by dying cells, prevents the blood from clotting. Menstruation lasts from three to five days, as the uterus sloughs off the thick lining that was three weeks in the making.

The first menstrual period, called *menarche,* typically occurs between the ages of 11 and 13. Menarche signifies that the ovarian and uterine cycles have begun. If menarche does not occur by age 16, or if normal uterine cycles are interrupted for six months or more without pregnancy being the cause, the condition is termed amenorrhea. Primary amenorrhea is usually caused by nonfunctional ovaries or developmental abnormalities. Secondary amenorrhea may be caused by weight loss and/or excessive exercise.

Menopause, which usually occurs between ages 45 and 55, is the time in a woman's life when menstruation ceases because the ovaries are no longer functioning. Menopause is not complete until menstruation is absent for a year.

Fertilization and Pregnancy

If fertilization does occur, an embryo begins development even as it travels down the oviduct to the uterus. The endometrium is now prepared to receive the developing embryo, which becomes embedded in the lining several days following fertilization.

The placenta originates from both maternal and embryonic tissues. It is shaped like a large, thick pancake and is the site of the exchange of gases and nutrients between fetal and maternal blood, although the two rarely mix. At first, the placenta produces **human chorionic gonadotropin (HCG),** which maintains the corpus luteum until the placenta begins its own production of progesterone and estrogen. HCG is the hormone detected in pregnancy tests; it is present in the mother's blood and urine as soon as ten days after conception.

Progesterone and estrogen have two effects. They shut down the anterior pituitary so that no new follicles mature, and they maintain the lining of the uterus so that the corpus luteum is not needed. No menstruation occurs during pregnancy.

Estrogen and Progesterone

Estrogen in particular is essential for the normal development and functioning of the female reproductive organs listed in Table 41.2. Estrogen is also largely responsible for the secondary sex characteristics in females, including body hair and fat distribution. In general, females have a more rounded appearance than males because of a greater accumulation of fat beneath their skin. Also, the pelvic girdle enlarges so that females have wider hips than males, and the thighs converge at a greater angle toward the knees. Both estrogen and progesterone are required for breast development as well.

The Female Breast

A female breast contains between 15 and 24 lobules, each with its own mammary duct (Fig. 41.12). A duct begins at the nipple and divides into numerous other ducts that end in blind sacs called alveoli.

Lactation, the production of milk by the cells of the alveoli, is stimulated by the hormone prolactin. Milk is not produced during pregnancy because production of prolactin is suppressed by the feedback inhibition effect of estrogen and progesterone on the anterior pituitary. A couple of days after delivery of a baby, milk production begins. In the meantime, the breasts produce a watery, yellowish-white fluid called colostrum, which has a similar composition to milk but contains more protein and less fat. Colostrum is rich in antibodies that may provide some degree of immunity to the newborn. Milk contains water, proteins, amino acids, sugars, and lysozymes (enzymes with antibiotic properties). Human milk contains about 750 calories per liter, which is considerably higher than even whole cow's milk (about 500 calories per liter).

After skin cancer, breast cancer is the most common type of cancer among women in the United States. Based on current

Table 41.3 Ovarian and Uterine Cycles (Simplified)

Ovarian Cycle	Events	Uterine Cycle	Events
Follicular phase—Days 1–13	FSH	Menstrual phase—Days 1–5	Endometrium breaks down
	Follicle maturation	Proliferative phase—Days 6–13	Endometrium rebuilds
	Estrogen		
Ovulation—Day 14*	LH spike		
Luteal phase—Days 15–28	LH	Secretory phase—Days 15–28	Endometrium thickens and
	Corpus luteum		glands are secretory
	Progesterone		

*Assuming a 28-day cycle

lobule containing alveoli

mammary duct

nipple

areola

Figure 41.12 Anatomy of the breast. The female breast contains lobules consisting of ducts and alveoli. In the lactating breast, cells lining the alveoli have been stimulated to produce milk by the hormone prolactin.

rates, about 12% of women born today can expect to be diagnosed with cancer of the breast during their lifetime. Women should regularly check their breasts for lumps and other irregularities and have mammograms (X-ray photographs) taken as recommended by their physician. Although breast cancer genes have been described, most forms of breast cancer are nonhereditary. The number of treatment options for various types of breast cancer has expanded in recent years, resulting in increased survival rates. Currently, about 86% of women survive at least five years after their initial diagnosis.

Besides more traditional surgery, radiation, and chemotherapy, two newer types of breast cancer treatments are hormonal therapy and targeted therapy. Some breast cancers have receptors for estrogen, and they grow in response to increased estrogen levels. To treat these tumors, various drugs are available to either decrease estrogen synthesis, or to block the interaction of estrogen with its receptor. Targeted therapies usually involve the administration of a monoclonal antibody (see Chapter 33) that can react very specifically with antigens found on tumor cells. The best known example, called Herceptin, blocks a protein called HER2, expressed on 20–30% of breast cancer cells, where it is involved in stimulating uncontrolled cell growth. The routine use of this drug is somewhat controversial, however, partly because of its estimated cost of $100,000 per year.

Check Your Progress 41.3

1. Name the structures of the female reproductive system that (a) produce the egg, (b) transport the egg, (c) house a developing embryo, and (d) serve as the birth canal.
2. Explain the effects of FSH and LH on the ovarian cycle.
3. Summarize the roles of estrogen and progesterone in the ovarian and uterine cycles.

41.4 Control of Human Reproduction

Learning Outcomes

Upon completion of this section, you should be able to

1. List five commonly available methods of birth control that are designed to prevent conception.
2. Note which birth control methods are effective at preventing the spread of sexually transmitted diseases.
3. Describe several reproductive technologies that can help infertile couples to have children.

Several means are available to dampen or enhance the human reproductive potential. Contraceptives are medications and devices that reduce the chance of pregnancy.

Traditional Birth Control Methods

The most reliable method of birth control is abstinence—that is, not engaging in sexual intercourse. This form of birth control has the added advantage of preventing transmission of a sexually transmitted disease. The male and female condoms also offer some protection against sexually transmitted diseases in addition to helping prevent pregnancy. Some of the common means of birth control used in the United States are shown in Figure 41.13.

Morning-After Pills

The term "morning-after pill," or emergency contraception, refers to medications that can prevent pregnancy after unprotected intercourse. The expression "morning-after" is a misnomer, in that some treatments can be started up to five days after unprotected intercourse.

The first FDA-approved medication produced for emergency contraception was a kit called Preven. Preven includes four synthetic progesterone pills; two are taken up to 72 hours after unprotected intercourse, and two more are taken 12 hours later. The hormone upsets the normal uterine cycle, making it difficult for an embryo to implant in the endometrium. A recent study estimated that Preven was 85% effective in preventing unintended pregnancies. The Preven kit also includes a pregnancy test; women are instructed to take the test first before using the hormone, because the medication is not effective on an established pregnancy.

In 2006, the FDA approved another drug called Plan B, which is up to 89% effective in preventing pregnancy if taken within 72 hours after unprotected sex. It is available without a prescription to women age 17 and older. In August 2010, ulipristal acetate (also known as ella) was also approved for emergency contraception. It can be taken up to five days after unprotected sex, and studies indicate it is somewhat more effective than Plan B. Unlike Plan B, however, a prescription is required.

Mifepristone, also known as RU-486 or the "abortion pill," can cause the loss of an implanted embryo by blocking the progesterone receptors of endometrial cells. This causes the endometrium to slough off, carrying the embryo with it. When taken in conjunction with a prostaglandin to induce uterine

784

a. Intrauterine device placement

Intrauterine devices

uterus

cervix

female condom

b. Female condom placement

Female condom

c. Male condom placement

Male condom

Figure 41.13 Various birth control methods.   **a.** Intrauterine devices mechanically prevent implantation and can contain progesterone to prevent ovulation, prevent implantation, and thicken cervical mucus. **b.** Female condom that is fitted inside vagina prevents sperm entry and protects against STDs. **c.** Male condom that fits over penis prevents sperm from entering the vagina and protects against STDs.

contractions, RU-486 is 95% effective at inducing an abortion up to the 49th day of gestation. Because of its mechanism of action, the use of RU-486 is more controversial compared to other medications, and while it is currently available in the U.S. for early medical abortion, it is not approved for emergency contraception.

Vaccines

Contraceptive vaccines are now being developed. For example, a vaccine intended to immunize women against HCG, the hormone so necessary to maintaining the implantation of the embryo, was successful in a limited clinical trial. Because HCG is not normally present in the body, no autoimmune reaction is expected, but the immunization does wear off with time. Others believe that it would also be possible to develop a safe antisperm vaccine that could be used in women.

Male Hormonal Birth Control

A great deal of research is being devoted to developing safe and effective hormonal birth control for men. Implants, pills, patches, and injections are being explored as ways to deliver testosterone and/or progesterone at adequate levels to suppress sperm production. Even the most successful formulations are still in the experimental stage and are unlikely to be available outside of clinical trials for at least a few more years.

Reproductive Technologies

Infertility is the inability of a couple to achieve pregnancy after one year of regular, unprotected intercourse. The American Medical Association estimates that 15% of all couples are infertile. The cause of infertility can be attributed to the man (40%), the woman (40%), or both (20%).

Sometimes the causes of infertility may be corrected by medical intervention so that couples can have children. If no obstruction is apparent and body weight is normal, it is possible for women to take fertility drugs, which are gonadotropic hormones that stimulate the ovaries and bring about ovulation. Such hormone treatments may cause multiple ovulations and multiple births.

When reproduction does not occur in the usual manner, many couples adopt a child. Others sometimes try one of the assisted reproductive technologies (ARTs) developed to increase the chances of pregnancy. In these cases, sperm and/or oocytes are often retrieved from the testes and ovaries, and fertilization takes place in a clinical or laboratory setting.

Artificial Insemination by Donor (AID)

During artificial insemination, sperm from a donor are introduced into the woman's vagina by a physician. This technique is especially helpful if the male partner has a low sperm count, because the sperm can be collected over a period of time and concentrated so that the sperm count is sufficient to result in fertilization. Often, however, a woman is inseminated by sperm acquired from a different donor. At times, a combination of partner and donor sperm is used.

A variation of AID is *intrauterine insemination (IUI)*. In IUI, fertility drugs are given to stimulate the ovaries, and then the donor's sperm is placed into the uterus, rather than into the vagina.

If the prospective parents wish, sperm can be sorted into those believed to be X-bearing or Y-bearing, to increase the chances of having a child of the desired sex. First, the sperm are treated with a DNA-staining chemical. Because the X chromosome has slightly more DNA than the Y chromosome, it takes up more dye. When a laser beam shines on the sperm, the X-bearing sperm shine a little more brightly than the Y-bearing sperm. A machine sorts the sperm into two groups on this basis. Parents can expect about a 65% success rate when selecting for males and about 85% when selecting for females.

In Vitro Fertilization (IVF)

During IVF, fertilization occurs in laboratory glassware. Ultrasound machines can now spot follicles in the ovaries that hold immature oocytes; therefore, the latest method is to forgo the administration of fertility drugs and retrieve immature oocytes by using a needle. The immature oocytes are then brought to maturity in glassware before concentrated sperm are added. After about two to four days, the embryos are ready to be transferred to the uterus of the woman, who is now in the secretory phase of her uterine cycle. If desired, the embryos can be tested for a genetic disease, as discussed in the Nature of Science feature on page 786. If implantation is successful, development continues to term.

 Video One Healthy Baby

 Video In Vitro Fertilization

Gamete Intrafallopian Transfer (GIFT)

Recall that the term **gamete** refers to a sex cell, either a sperm or an oocyte. Gamete intrafallopian transfer was devised to overcome the low success rate (15–20%) of in vitro fertilization. The

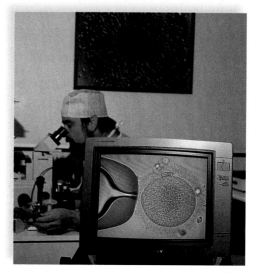

Figure 41.14 **Intracytoplasmic sperm injection (ICSI).** A microscope connected to a television screen is used to carry out in vitro fertilization. A pipette holds the oocyte steady while a needle (not visible) introduces the sperm into the oocyte.

method is exactly the same as for in vitro fertilization, except the oocytes and the sperm are placed in the oviducts immediately after they have been brought together. GIFT has the advantage of being a one-step procedure for the woman—the oocytes are removed and reintroduced all in the same time period. A variation on this procedure is to fertilize the eggs in the laboratory and then place the zygotes in the oviducts.

Surrogate Mothers

In some instances, women are contracted and paid to carry babies as *surrogate mothers.* The sperm and even the oocyte can be contributed by the contracting parents.

Intracytoplasmic Sperm Injection (ICSI)

In this highly sophisticated procedure, a single sperm is injected into an oocyte (Fig. 41.14). It is used effectively when a man has severe infertility problems.

If all the assisted reproductive technologies discussed were employed simultaneously, it would be possible for a baby to have five parents: (1) sperm donor, (2) oocyte donor, (3) surrogate mother, (4) contracting mother, and (5) contracting father. The legal definitions of "parent" can become a matter of contention in some cases.

Check Your Progress 41.4

1. Identify which of the birth control methods discussed in this section physically block sperm from entering the uterus.
2. Rank the following birth control methods regarding their effectiveness at preventing pregnancy: abstinence, female birth control pill, condoms, natural family planning, and vasectomy.
3. Briefly describe the following processes: artificial insemination by donor (AID), in vitro fertilization (IVF), gamete intrafallopian transfer (GIFT), and intracytoplasmic sperm injection (ICSI).

Preimplantation Genetic Diagnosis

If prospective parents are heterozygous for a genetic disorder, they may want the assurance that their offspring will be free of the disorder. Determining the genotype of an embryo can provide this assurance. For example, if both parents are *Aa* for a recessive disorder, the embryo will develop normally if it has the genotype *AA* or *Aa*. In contrast, if one of the parents is *Aa* for a dominant disorder, the embryo will develop normally only if it has the genotype *aa*.

Following in vitro fertilization (IVF), the zygote (fertilized egg) divides. When the embryo has six to eight cells (Fig. 41Aa), removal of one of these cells for testing purposes has no effect on normal development. Only embryos with a cell that tests negative for the genetic disorder of interest are placed in the uterus to continue developing.

So far, about 1,000 children with normal genotypes for genetic disorders that run in their families have been born worldwide following embryo testing. In the future, it's possible that embryos who test positive for a disorder could be treated by gene therapy, so that they, too, would be allowed to continue to term.

Testing the oocyte is possible if the condition of concern is recessive. Recall that meiosis in females results in a single egg and at least two polar bodies.[1] Polar bodies later disintegrate, and they receive very little cytoplasm, but they do receive a haploid number

---

1 Once meiosis is complete, the oocyte is termed an egg.

of chromosomes. When a woman is heterozygous for a recessive genetic disorder, about half the first polar bodies have received the genetic defect, and in these instances, the egg has received the normal allele. Therefore, if a polar body tests positive for a recessive defect, then the egg has received the normal dominant allele. Only normal eggs are then used for IVF. Even if the sperm should happen to carry the same mutant allele, the zygote will, at worst, be heterozygous. But the phenotype will appear normal (Fig. 41A*b*).

If, in the future, gene therapy becomes routine, it's possible that an egg could be given genes that control traits desired by the parents, such as musical or athletic ability, prior to IVF.

Questions to Consider

1. Some biomedical ethicists are concerned that embryo testing could lead to a form of eugenics, in which wealthier parents are able to afford improving their children's physical traits. Others argue that this technology should be developed as much as possible to reduce the occurrence of terrible diseases. Which argument is more compelling to you, and why?
2. Some experts feel that pre-implantation screening should be required for all embryos that are conceived by in vitro fertilization, to reduce the occurrence of disease. Do you agree or disagree?

Figure 41A Preimplantation genetic diagnosis. a. Following IVF and cleavage, genetic analysis is performed on one cell removed from an eight-celled embryo. If it is found to be free of the genetic defect of concern, the seven-celled embryo is implanted in the uterus and develops into a fetus. **b.** Chromosome and genetic analysis is performed on a polar body attached to an oocyte. If the oocyte is free of a genetic defect, the egg is used for IVF, and the embryo is implanted in the uterus for further development.

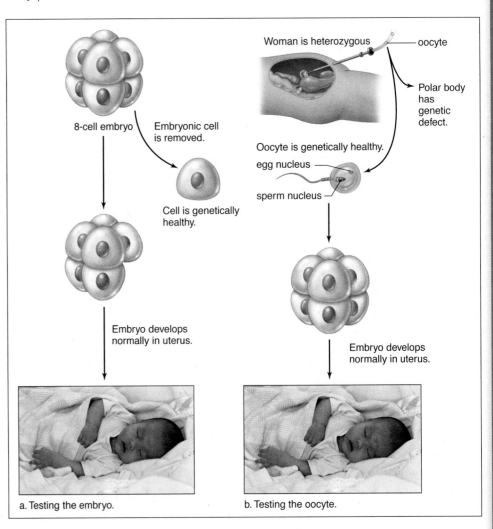

8-cell embryo   Embryonic cell is removed.

Cell is genetically healthy.

Embryo develops normally in uterus.

a. Testing the embryo.

Woman is heterozygous — oocyte

Polar body has genetic defect.

Oocyte is genetically healthy.
egg nucleus
sperm nucleus

Embryo develops normally in uterus.

b. Testing the oocyte.

41.5 Sexually Transmitted Diseases

Learning Outcomes

Upon completion of this section, you should be able to

1. List three STDs that are caused by viruses and three that are caused by bacteria.
2. Discuss how HIV affects the immune system and how this is related to the three categories of HIV infection.
3. Describe one STD that is currently preventable by vaccination.

According to a 2010 report, about 19 million new cases of sexually transmitted diseases (STDs) occur each year in the United States. Approximately 30 different STDs are caused by organisms ranging from viruses to arthropods; however, this discussion centers on the most prevalent and serious ones. In addition, the Biological Systems feature on page 789 describes methods to avoid transmission of STDs.

Viral STDs

AIDS, genital herpes, genital warts, and hepatitis A and B are STDs caused by viruses. Therefore, they do not respond to treatment with traditional antibiotics. Antiviral drugs have been developed to treat some of these viruses, but in many cases the infection persists for life.

AIDS

Acquired immunodeficiency syndrome (AIDS) is caused by the **human immunodeficiency virus (HIV).** An introduction to HIV and AIDS was provided in Chapter 33. As noted there, by the end of 2008, about 33.4 million people worldwide were infected with HIV, and more than 25 million people have died of AIDS since 1981. The great majority of these people live in underdeveloped countries; an estimated 68% of HIV-infected individuals in the world live in sub-Saharan Africa.

On a somewhat more positive note, total AIDS-related deaths have been decreasing worldwide since about 2004, mainly due to increased availability of antiretroviral therapy. In the United States, an estimated one million people are infected, and over 500,000 have died. Homosexual men make up the largest proportion of people living with HIV in the U.S., but the fastest rate of increase is now seen in heterosexuals. Over half of new HIV infections are now occurring in people under the age of 25.

Transmission. HIV is transmitted by sexual contact with an infected person, including vaginal or anal intercourse and oral-genital contact. Also, needle-sharing among intravenous drug users is a very efficient way to transmit HIV. Some of the earliest cases of AIDS resulted from transfusion of HIV-infected blood, but this is now extremely rare thanks to effective screening methods. Babies born to HIV-infected mothers may become infected before or during birth or through breast-feeding. Transmission through tears, saliva, or sweat is thought to be highly unlikely.

Cultural factors may also play an important role in transmission of HIV. For example, polygamy is common in many African countries, as are misconceptions about the effectiveness of condoms in preventing HIV transmission, and even about the fact that HIV causes AIDS. Such practices and beliefs may significantly increase the risk of HIV infection.

Stages and Symptoms of an HIV Infection. HIV infects helper T cells, macrophages, and other cells that have a molecule called CD4 on their surface (Fig. 41.15). As you may recall from Chapter 33, helper T cells control the activities of many other cells in the immune system. After HIV enters a host cell, it converts its viral RNA to DNA, which is then integrated into the host cell DNA.

In the early stages after an HIV infection, the person's blood contains a high amount of virus, even though the individual may experience only mild flulike symptoms, which soon disappear. Even if an HIV-infected person undergoes an HIV test at this time, it would probably be negative because this tests for the presence of anti-HIV antibodies, which are usually not detectable for an average of 25 days. However, the person can still be highly infectious at this stage.

 Animation How the HIV Infection Cycle Works

After the initial surge of HIV replication, the immune system temporarily reduces the virus levels in the blood. Over an average period of eight to ten years, the HIV that has been established in cells gradually produces increasing amounts of HIV, which infects and destroys more and more helper T cells. As the virus reproduces, it also mutates so that it is no longer recognized by the immune system.

Three categories of HIV infection are distinguished, based mainly on the type of disease seen in the patient. Within each category, the number of CD4 + T cells is also monitored. Patients in category A usually have greater than 500 CD4 + T cells per microliter of blood, and either lack symptoms completely or have persistently enlarged lymph nodes. Patients in category B have a CD4 + T-cell count between 200 and 499 per microliter, and begin to suffer from opportunistic infections (OIs)—infections that would be unable to take hold in a person with a healthy immune system. Once the CD4 + T-cell count falls below 200 per microliter, the patient is in category C, or true AIDS. The deficiency of helper T-cell functions in these patients results in their contracting one or more AIDS-defining OIs (see Chapter 33).

Figure 41.15 HIV, the AIDS virus. False-colored micrograph showing HIV particles budding from an infected helper T cell. These viruses can infect other helper T cells and also macrophages, which work with helper T cells to stem infection.

Figure 41.16 Genital warts. A photomicrograph of human papillomaviruses.

Treating or Preventing HIV Infection. Before the development of antiretroviral drugs, most HIV-infected individuals eventually progressed to category C AIDS, which was almost invariably fatal. There is still no cure for HIV infection, but a treatment called highly active antiretroviral therapy (HAART) is often able to stop HIV replication to such an extent that the viral load becomes undetectable.

HAART uses a combination of drugs that interfere with the life cycle of HIV. Entry inhibitors stop HIV from entering a cell by, for example, preventing the virus from binding to CD4. Reverse transcriptase inhibitors, such as AZT, interfere with the conversion of viral RNA into DNA. Integrase inhibitors prevent HIV from inserting its DNA into that of the host cells. Protease inhibitors prevent a viral enzyme from processing newly created polypeptides. By giving patients a combination of these drugs, the virus is less likely to become resistant to drug therapy, because several mutations would need to occur at once.

Throughout the world, more than 5 million people are now receiving HIV treatment. In 2009 alone, 1.2 million people received HIV antiretroviral therapy for the first time—a 30% increase in the number of people receiving treatment in a single year. This is largely due to the President's Emergency Plan for AIDS Relief, or PEPFAR program, which began as a commitment from the United States to provide $15 billion in antiretroviral drugs to resource-poor countries from 2003 to 2008. Since then, the program has been continued and expanded. A study published in 2009 showed the PEPFAR program had cut AIDS death rates by more than 10% in targeted countries in Africa, though it had no appreciable effect on prevalence of the disease in those nations.

An HIV-positive pregnant woman who takes reverse transcriptase inhibitors during her pregnancy reduces the chances of HIV transmission to her newborn. If possible, drug therapy should be delayed until the tenth to twelfth week of pregnancy to minimize any adverse effects of AZT on fetal development. If treatment begins at this time and delivery is by cesarean section, the chance of transmission from mother to infant is very slim (about 1%).

The general consensus is that control of the AIDS epidemic will not occur until a vaccine is available. Many different approaches have thus far been tried with limited success. The most encouraging news has been a large study in Thailand that concluded in 2009, showing that a combination of two different types of HIV vaccines reduced the risk of contracting the virus by nearly a third (31.2%).

Animation Treatment of HIV Infection

Genital Warts

An estimated 20 million Americans are currently infected with the human papillomavirus (HPV) (Fig. 41.16). There are over

Figure 41.17 Genital herpes. A photomicrograph of cells infected with the herpes simplex virus.

100 types of HPV. Most cause warts, and some specifically cause genital warts, which are an STD. Genital warts may appear as flat or raised lesions on the penis and foreskin of males, and on the vuvla, vagina, and cervix in females. Note that if warts are present only on the cervix, there may be no outward signs of the disease. Newborns can also be infected with HPV during passage through the birth canal.

Currently, there is no cure for an HPV infection, but the warts can be treated effectively by surgery, freezing, application of an acid, or laser burning. Even after treatment, however, the virus can sometimes be transmitted. Therefore, once someone has been diagnosed with genital warts, abstinence or the use of a condom is recommended.

About ten types of HPV can cause cancer of the cervix, as well as tumors of the vulva, vagina, anus, and penis. Cervical cancer is the second leading cause of cancer death in women in the United States (approximately 500,000 per year). Early detection of cervical cancer is possible by means of a *Pap smear*, in which a few cells are removed from the cervix for microscopic examination. If the cells are cancerous, a hysterectomy (removal of the uterus) may be recommended. According to a 2008 study, HPV now causes as many cancers of the mouth and throat in U.S. males as does tobacco, perhaps due to an increase in oral sex in combination with a decline in tobacco use.

A vaccine called Gardasil is available to prevent infection with the four most common types of HPV found in the U.S., including two types that cause the majority of cervical cancers. The vaccine was initially approved only for use in girls, and it is recommended that girls be vaccinated before they become sexually active. In late 2009, the Food and Drug Administration also approved Gardasil for use in boys ages 9 through 26.

Genital Herpes

Genital herpes is caused by the herpes simplex virus (Fig. 41.17), of which there are two types. Type 1 usually causes cold sores and fever blisters, while type 2 more often causes genital herpes. In the United States, it is estmated that approximately one in four women, and one in five men, have had a genital herpes infection, but about 20% of these never have symptoms. Even without symptoms, however, the virus can be transmitted.

After becoming infected, most people experience a tingling or itching sensation before blisters appear on the genitals within 2–20 days. Once the blisters rupture, they leave painful ulcers that take from five days to three weeks to heal. These symptoms may be accompanied by fever, pain on urination, swollen

THEME Biological Systems

Preventing Transmission of STDs

Being aware of how STDs are spread and then observing the following guidelines will greatly help prevent the transmission of STDs.

Sexual Activities Can Transmit STDs

Abstain from sexual intercourse or develop a long-term monogamous relationship (i.e., having only one sexual partner) with someone who is free of STDs (Fig. 41B).

Refrain from multiple sex partners or having relations with someone who has multiple sex partners. If you have sex with two other people and each of these has sex with two people and so forth, the number of people who can potentially be exposed to disease is quite large.

Remember that anyone can be at risk for HIV. The highest rate of increase in HIV infection is now occurring among heterosexuals.

Be aware that having sex with an intravenous drug user is risky because needle-sharing can lead to infection with hepatitis and HIV. Also, anyone who already has another STD is more susceptible to becoming infected with HIV.

Uncircumcised males are more likely to become infected with an STD than circum-cised males, at least partly because viruses and bacteria can remain under the foreskin for a long period of time.

Avoid anal-rectal intercourse (in which the penis is inserted into the rectum) because the lining of the rectum is thin and HIV can easily enter the body there.

Safer Sex Practices Can Help Prevent STD Transmission

Always use a latex condom during sexual intercourse if you do not know for certain that your partner is free of STDs. Be sure to follow the directions supplied by the manufacturer.

Avoid fellatio (kissing and insertion of the penis into a partner's mouth) *and cunnilingus* (kissing and insertion of the tongue into the vagina) because they may be a means of transmission. The mouth and gums often have cuts and sores that facilitate the entrance of infectious agents.

Be cautious about the use of alcohol or any drug that may prevent you from being able to control your behavior. Females have to be particularly aware of "date-rape" drugs like GHB (gamma-hydroxy-butyramine), that puts a person in an uninhibited state with no memory of what transpired. These drugs can easily be slipped into a beverage without the victim's knowledge.

Drug Use Transmits Hepatitis and HIV

Do not inject drugs. Be aware that hepatitis and HIV can be spread by blood-to-blood contact. If you are currently an IV drug user, stop immediately.

Always use a new, sterile needle for injection or one that has been cleaned in a bleach solution and then well rinsed if you are a drug user and cannot stop your behavior (Fig. 41C).

Questions to Consider

1. How can you be certain that a potential sexual partner doesn't have any STDs?
2. What does it mean if a person tells you he or she just had an HIV test, and it was negative?
3. Which methods of birth control are most effective at preventing transmission of STDs? Which are least effective or provide no protection?

Figure 41B Sexual activities can transmit STDs.   People of all sexual orientations need to be aware of STD dangers and use precautions.

Figure 41C Sharing needles transmits STDs.   Intravenous drug use with unclean, shared needles can transmit viral STDs.

lymph nodes in the groin, and in women, a watery vaginal discharge. At this time, the individual also has an increased risk of acquiring an HIV infection. Exposure to herpes during a vaginal delivery can cause an infection in the newborn, which can lead to neurological disorders and even death. Birth by cesarean section prevents this possibility.

After the blisters heal, the virus becomes latent (dormant). Blisters can recur repeatedly, at variable intervals and with milder symptoms. Sunlight, sexual intercourse, menstruation, and stress are associated with these recurrences. While the virus is latent, it resides in the ganglia of the sensory nerves associated with the infected skin. The ability of the virus to "hide" in this manner has made it difficult to develop an effective vaccine for herpes simplex viruses.

Viral Hepatitis

Several different viruses can cause *hepatitis*, or inflammation of the liver. Of these, hepatitis A and B viruses are the most important. Hepatitis A is usually acquired from sewage-contaminated drinking water, but this infection can also be sexually transmitted through oral-anal contact. Hepatitis B is spread through sexual contact and by blood-borne transmission (accidental needle-stick on the job, receiving a contaminated blood transfusion, sharing needles while injecting drugs, from mother to fetus, etc.). Simultaneous infection with hepatitis B virus and HIV is common, because both share the same routes of transmission. Fortunately, a combined vaccine is available for hepatitis A and B. It is recommended that all children receive the vaccine to prevent these infections.

Video
Halting Hepatitis

Bacterial STDs

Chlamydia, gonorrhea, and syphilis are major bacterial STDs that are usually curable with antibiotic therapy, if diagnosed early enough. If properly used, latex condoms can help prevent the spread of most STDs.

Chlamydia

Infection with the tiny bacterium *Chlamydia trachomatis*, simply known as chlamydia, is the most common STD in the United States today, with the highest rates of infection occurring in 15- to 19-year-olds. The rate of new chlamydial infections has increased steadily since 1987 (Fig. 41.18).

Chlamydial infections of the lower reproductive tract are usually mild or asymptomatic, especially in women. About 8–21 days after infection, men may experience a mild burning sensation on urination and a mucoid discharge. Women may have a vaginal discharge along with symptoms resembling a urinary tract infection. Chlamydia also causes cervical ulcerations, which increase the risk of aquiring HIV. If the infection is misdiagnosed or if a woman does not seek medical help, the infection may spread to the oviducts so that pelvic inflammatory disease (PID) results.

PID is characterized by inflamed oviducts that become partially or completely blocked by scar tissue. As a result, the woman can become infertile or at increased risk of ectopic pregnancy, which can be a medical emergency. If a baby comes in contact with chlamydia during delivery, pneumonia or eye infections can result.

Gonorrhea

Gonorrhea is caused by the bacterium *Neisseria gonorrhoeae* (Fig. 41.19). About 75% of reported cases occur in people between 15 and 29 years of age, and rates among African Americans are about 20 times greater than among Caucasians. Although as many as 20% of infected males are asymptomatic, usually they experience pain upon urination and a thick, greenish yellow urethral discharge.

Untreated gonorrhea can cause infertility in both males and females, by causing inflammation and scarring in either the vas deferens or the oviducts, respectively. If a baby is exposed

5000×

Figure 41.18 Chlamydial infection. Different stages of *Chlamydia trachomatis* are stained red, brown, and black, inside an infected cell.

during birth, an eye infection leading to blindness can result. All vaginally delivered newborns are treated with antibiotic eyedrops to prevent this possibility.

N. gonorrhoeae is also the most common cause of proctitis, an inflammation of the anus characterized by anal pain and blood or pus in the feces. Oral-genital contact can also cause infection of the mouth, throat, and tonsils. Gonorrhea can spread to internal parts of the body, causing heart damage or arthritis. If, by chance, the person touches infected genitals and then touches his or her eyes, a severe eye infection can result.

Gonorrhea is still considered to be curable by antibiotics. However, antibiotic-resistant strains of *N. gonorrhoeae* are becoming more common each year.

Syphilis

Syphilis is caused by the bacterium *Treponema pallidum* (Fig. 41.20). It is an STD of considerable historical importance that was first described hundreds of years ago. Untreated syphilis progresses through three stages, separated by latent periods during which the bacteria are not multiplying. In the primary stage, a hard chancre (ulcerated sore with hard edges) indicates the site of infection. During the secondary stage, the individual breaks out in a rash that does not itch, coinciding with the replication and spread of the bacteria all over the body.

Not all cases of syphilis progress to the tertiary stage, during which syphilis may affect the cardiovascular system, nervous system, or both. An infected person may become mentally disabled, become blind, walk with a shuffle, or show signs of insanity. Gummas, which are large, destructive ulcers, may develop on the skin or within the internal organs.

T. pallidum bacteria can cross the placenta, causing birth defects or a stillbirth. If diagnosed and treated in its early stages, syphilis is easy to cure with antibiotics.

Vaginal Infections

Vaginitis, meaning vaginal inflammation from any cause, is the most commonly diagnosed gynecologic condition. Bacterial vaginosis (BV), or overgrowth of certain bacteria inhabiting the vagina, accounts for 40–50% of vaginitis cases in American women. A common culprit is the bacterium *Gardnerella*

Figure 41.19 Gonorrhea. A photomicrograph of a urethral discharge from an infected male. Gonorrheal bacteria (*Neisseria gonorrhoeae*) occur in pairs; for this reason, they are called diplococci.

Figure 41.20 Syphilis. The syphilis-causing bacterium (*Treponema pallidum*) is a spirochete.

vaginalis. How women acquire this infection is not well understood. According to the Centers for Disease Control, BV is not considered an STD, but it is more common in women who are sexually active.

In addition to BV, the yeast *Candida albicans* can also cause vaginitis. Yeast is normally found living in the vagina; under certain circumstances, its growth increases above normal, causing vaginitis. For exmple, women taking birth control pills or antibiotics may be prone to yeast infections. Both can alter the normal balance of vaginal organisms, causing a yeast infection. Typical signs of a yeast infection include a thickish, white vaginal discharge and itching of the vulva and/or vagina. Antifungal medications inserted into the vagina are used to treat yeast infections.

The protozoan *Trichomonas vaginalis* can also infect the urethra of males and the vagina of females. Infected males are usually asymptomatic, but can pass the parasite to their partner through sexual intercourse. Symptoms of trichomoniasis in females are a foul-smelling, yellow-green exudate and itching of the vulva/vagina. Effective antiprotozoal drugs are available by prescription, but if one partner remains infected, reinfection will occur. For this reason, both people should be treated simultaneously.

Check Your Progress   41.5

1. Describe four classes of antiretroviral drugs, and the specific stage of the HIV reproduction cycle targeted by each class.
2. Describe the medical complications in women that are associated with HPV infection (genital warts).
3. Identify a serious condition that can occur in women due to both chlamydia and gonorrhea.

CONNECTING *the* CONCEPTS *with the* THEMES

Evolution

- The majority of animals have two separate sexes and undergo sexual reproduction, which generates genetic diversity that can be advantageous to species survival.
- The evolution of a hard-shelled egg with extraembryonic membranes to protect and nourish the developing embryo was a significant adaptation to living on land.

Nature of Science

- By understanding the details of human reproduction, scientists are developing more methods of birth control that will be more efficient and easier to use.
- The invention of new technologies for enhancing human replication has provided many infertile couples with the opportunity to have children, but has also raised many ethical concerns.
- Although many STDs are incurable, some effective treatments, and even vaccines, are becoming available.

Biological Systems

- Strategies used by animals that reproduce asexually include budding from the parent, or regeneration from animal parts.
- Sexually reproducing animals may be oviparous, ovoviviparous, or viviparous. Each of these has advantages in different environments.
- In marsupials and placental mammals, mothers produce milk to continue nourishing the offspring after birth. This maternal investment helps ensure offspring survival.

Media Study Tools

www.mhhe.com/maderbiology11

Enhance your study of this chapter with study tools and practice tests. Also ask your instructor about the resources available through ConnectPlus, including the media-rich eBook, interactive learning tools, and animations.

Summarize

41.1 How Animals Reproduce

Ordinarily, asexual reproduction may quickly produce a large number of offspring genetically identical to the parent. Sexual reproduction involves gametes and produces offspring that are genetically slightly different from the parents. The gonads are the primary sex organs. The accessory sex organs consist of storage areas for sperm and ducts that conduct the gametes. In males, they also contribute to formation of the semen.

The egg of oviparous animals contains yolk, and in terrestrial animals a shelled egg prevents drying out. The amount of yolk is dependent on whether there is a larval stage.

Eggs of reptiles have extraembryonic membranes that allow them to develop on land; these same membranes are modified for internal development in mammals. Ovoviviparous animals retain their eggs until the offspring have hatched, and viviparous animals retain the embryo and give birth. Placental mammals exemplify viviparous animals.

41.2 Human Male Reproductive System

In human males, sperm are produced in the testes, mature in the epididymides, and may be stored in the vasa deferentia before entering the urethra, along with seminal fluid (produced by seminal vesicles, the prostate gland, and bulbourethral glands). Sperm are ejaculated during male orgasm, when the penis is erect.

Spermatogenesis occurs in the seminiferous tubules of the testes, which also produce testosterone in interstitial cells. Testosterone brings about the maturation of the primary sex organs during puberty and promotes the secondary sex characteristics of males, such as low voice, facial hair, and increased muscle strength.

Follicle-stimulating hormone (FSH) from the anterior pituitary stimulates spermatogenesis, and luteinizing hormone (LH) stimulates testosterone production. A hypothalamic-releasing hormone, gonadotropin-releasing hormone (GnRH), controls anterior pituitary production and FSH and LH release. The level of testosterone in the blood controls the secretion of GnRH and the anterior pituitary hormones by a negative feedback system.

41.3 Human Female Reproductive System

In females, an oocyte produced by an ovary enters an oviduct, which leads to the uterus. The uterus opens into the vagina. The external genital area of women includes the vaginal opening, the clitoris, the labia minora, and the labia majora.

In either ovary, one follicle a month matures, produces a secondary oocyte, and becomes a corpus luteum. This process is called the ovarian cycle. The follicle and the corpus luteum produce estrogens, collectively called estrogen, and progesterone, the female sex hormones.

The uterine cycle occurs concurrently with the ovarian cycle. In the first half of these cycles (days 1–13, before ovulation), the anterior pituitary produces FSH and the follicle produces estrogen. Estrogen causes the endometrium to increase in thickness. In the second half of these cycles (days 15–28, after ovulation), the anterior pituitary produces LH and the follicle produces progesterone. Progesterone causes the endometrium to become secretory. Feedback control of the hypothalamus and anterior pituitary causes the levels of estrogen and progesterone to fluctuate. When they are at a low level, menstruation begins.

If fertilization occurs, a zygote is formed, and development begins. The resulting embryo travels down the oviduct and implants itself in the endometrium. A placenta, which is the region of exchange between the fetal blood and the mother's blood, forms. At first, the placenta produces HCG, which maintains the corpus luteum; later, it produces progesterone and estrogen.

The female sex hormones, estrogen and progesterone, also affect other traits of the body. Primarily, estrogen brings about the maturation of the primary sex organs during puberty and promotes the secondary sex characteristics of females, including body hair (usually less than in males), a wider pelvic girdle, a more rounded appearance, and development of breasts.

41.4 Control of Human Reproduction

Numerous birth control methods and devices, such as the birth control pill, diaphragm, and condom, are available for those who wish to prevent pregnancy. A "morning-after pill," RU-486, is now available.

Some couples are infertile, and if so, they may use assisted reproductive technologies to have a child. Artificial insemination and in vitro fertilization have been followed by more sophisticated techniques, such as intracytoplasmic sperm injection.

41.5 Sexually Transmitted Diseases

Important sexually transmitted diseases caused by viruses include AIDS, genital warts and cervical cancer, genital herpes, and hepatitis A and B. Major bacterial STDs include chlamydia and gonorrhea, which may cause pelvic inflammatory disease (PID), and syphilis, which has cardiovascular and neurological complications if untreated. Vaginal infections may have many causes; the most common are bacterial vaginosis (BV), yeast infection, and *Trichomonas* infection.

Key Terms

acquired immunodeficiency
  syndrome (AIDS) 787
bulbourethral glands 777
cervix 779
contraceptive vaccine 784
copulation 774
corpus luteum 780
egg 779
endometrium 779
epididymis 775
estrogen 779
extraembryonic
  membrane 774
follicle 780
follicular phase 780
gamete 785
germ cell 773
gonad 773
hermaphroditic 773

human chorionic gonadotropin
  (HCG) 782
human immunodeficiency virus
  (HIV) 787
infertility 784
lactation 782
luteal phase 781
menopause 782
menstruation 781
oocyte 779
ovarian cycle 780
ovary 773, 779
oviparous 774
ovoviviparous 774
ovulation 780
parthenogenesis 773
penis 777
placenta 774
progesterone 779

▮▮▮ Assess

Reviewing This Chapter

1. Contrast asexual reproduction with sexual reproduction, reproduction in water with reproduction on land, and the life history of an insect with that of a bird.   773–74
2. Discuss the anatomy and physiology of the testes. Describe the structure of sperm.   775–77
3. Trace the path of sperm in a human male. What glands contribute fluids to semen?   775–78
4. Name the endocrine glands involved in maintaining the sex characteristics of males and the hormones produced by each.   778
5. Trace the path of an oocyte in a human female. Where do fertilization and implantation occur? When does the oocyte become an egg?   779
6. Describe the external genital organs in females. Name two functions of the vagina.   779
7. Discuss the anatomy and physiology of the ovaries. Describe the ovarian cycle and ovulation.   780–81
8. Describe the uterine cycle, and relate it to the ovarian cycle. In what way is menstruation prevented if pregnancy occurs?   781–82
9. What events occur at fertilization? Name three functions of the female sex hormones, aside from their involvement in the uterine cycle.   782
10. Describe the anatomy and physiology of the breast.   782–83
11. Which means of birth control require surgery, use hormones, use barrier methods, or are dependent on none of these?   783–84
12. If couples are infertile, what assisted reproductive technologies are available?   784–85
13. List the cause, symptoms, and treatment for the most common types of sexually transmitted diseases.   787–91

Testing Yourself

Choose the best answer for each question.

1. Which of these is a requirement for sexual reproduction?
   a. male and female parents
   b. production of gametes
   c. optimal environmental conditions
   d. aquatic habitat
   e. All of these are correct.

2. Internal fertilization
   a. can prevent the drying out of gametes and zygotes.
   b. must take place on land.
   c. is practiced by humans.
   d. requires that males have a penis.
   e. Both a and c are correct.

3. Which of these pairs is mismatched?
   a. interstitial cells—testosterone
   b. seminiferous tubules—sperm production
   c. vasa deferentia—seminal fluid production
   d. urethra—conducts sperm
   e. Both c and d are mismatched.

4. Follicle-stimulating hormone (FSH)
   a. is secreted by females but not males.
   b. stimulates the seminiferous tubules to produce sperm.
   c. secretion is controlled by gonadotropin-releasing hormone (GnRH).
   d. is the same as luteinizing hormone.
   e. Both b and c are correct.

5. Which of these combinations is most likely to be present before ovulation occurs?
   a. FSH, corpus luteum, estrogen, secretory uterine lining
   b. luteinizing hormone (LH), follicle, progesterone, thick endometrium
   c. FSH, follicle, estrogen, endometrium becoming thick
   d. LH, corpus luteum, progesterone, secretory endometrium
   e. Both c and d are correct.

6. In tracing the path of sperm, you would mention vasa deferentia before
   a. testes.
   b. epididymides.
   c. urethra.
   d. seminiferous tubules.
   e. All of these are correct.

7. An oocyte is fertilized in
   a. the vagina.
   b. the uterus.
   c. the oviduct.
   d. the ovary.
   e. All of these are correct.

8. During pregnancy,
   a. the ovarian and uterine cycles occur more quickly than before.
   b. GnRH is produced at a higher level than before.
   c. the ovarian and uterine cycles do not occur.
   d. the female secondary sex characteristics are not maintained.
   e. Both b and c are correct.

9. Which means of birth control is most effective in preventing sexually transmitted diseases?
   a. condom
   b. pill
   c. diaphragm
   d. spermicidal jelly
   e. vasectomy

10. Which of these is a sexually transmitted disease caused by a bacterium?
    a. gonorrhea
    b. hepatitis B
    c. genital warts
    d. genital herpes
    e. HIV

11. The HIV virus has a preference for binding to
    a. B lymphocytes.
    b. cytotoxic T lymphocytes.
    c. helper T lymphocytes.
    d. All of these are correct.

For questions 12–14, match the descriptions with the sexually transmitted diseases in the key.

KEY:
   a. AIDS
   b. hepatitis B
   c. genital herpes
   d. genital warts
   e. gonorrhea
   f. chlamydia
   g. syphilis

12. blisters, ulcers, pain on urination, swollen lymph nodes

13. flulike symptoms, jaundice; eventual liver failure possible

14. males have a thick, greenish-yellow discharge; no symptoms in female; can lead to PID

15. Which of these is the primary sex organ of the male?
   a. penis
   b. scrotum
   c. testis
   d. prostate
   e. vasectomy

16. The luteal phase of the uterine cycle is characterized by
   a. high levels of LH and progesterone.
   b. low levels of estrogen and progesterone.
   c. increasing estrogen and little or no progesterone.
   d. high levels of LH only.

17. The secretory phase of the uterine cycle occurs during which ovarian phase?
   a. follicular phase
   b. ovulation
   c. luteal phase
   d. menstrual phase

18. Which of these is the correct path of an oocyte?
   a. oviduct, fimbriae, uterus, vagina
   b. ovary, fimbriae, oviduct, uterine cavity
   c. oviduct, fimbriae, abdominal cavity
   d. fimbriae, uterine tube, uterine cavity, ovary

19. Following ovulation, the corpus luteum develops under the influence of
   a. progesterone.
   b. FSH.
   c. LH.
   d. estradiol.

Engage

Virtual Lab
Virtual Frog Dissection

The Virtual Lab "Virtual Frog Dissection" provides an examination of the reproductive system of a vertebrate.

Thinking Scientifically

1. Female athletes who train intensively often stop menstruating. The important factor appears to be the reduction of body fat below a certain level. Give a possible evolutionary explanation for a relationship between body fat in females and reproductive cycles.

2. The average sperm count in males is now lower than it was several decades ago. The reasons for the lower sperm count usually seen today are not known. What data might be helpful in order to formulate a testable hypothesis?

Bioethical Issue
Fertility Drugs

Higher-order multiple births (triplets or more) in the United States increased 19% between 1980 and 1994. During these years, it became customary to use fertility drugs (gonadotropic hormones) to stimulate the ovaries. Although a variety of assisted reproductive technologies have become commonplace in recent years, fertility drugs are still routinely prescribed for women who are infertile due to ovulation disorders. However, fertility drugs frequently result in the release and subsequent fertilization of multiple oocytes.

The risks for premature delivery, low birth weight, and developmental abnormalities rise sharply for higher-order multiple births. In addition, the physical and emotional burden placed on the parents is extraordinary. They face endless everyday chores and find it difficult to maintain normal social relationships, if only because they get insufficient sleep. Finances are strained to provide for the children's needs, including housing and child-care assistance. About one-third report that they received no help from relatives, friends, or neighbors in the first year after the birth. Trips to the hospital for accidental injury are more frequent because parents often have difficulties keeping so many children safe at one time.

A higher-order multiple pregnancy can be terminated, or selective reduction can be done. During selective reduction, one or more of the fetuses is killed by an injection of potassium chloride. Selective reduction, however, could very well result in psychological and social complications for the mother and surviving children.

Many clinicians are now urging that all possible steps be taken to ensure that the chance of higher-order multiple births be reduced. For example, pre-ovulation oocytes may be obtained and subjected to in vitro fertilization (in which the eggs are fertilized in the lab), as shown in Figure 41A on page 786. Even this option poses an ethical dilemma: In vitro fertilization may be carried out with the intent that only one or two zygotes will be placed in the woman's womb. But then any "leftover" zygotes may never have an opportunity to continue development.

two days

three weeks

six weeks

five months

As development occurs, complexity increases.

42

Animal Development and Aging

Many of the fundamental processes that guide development, from fertilization onward, are shared throughout most of the animal kingdom. Whether the embryo will develop into a worm, insect, amphibian, bird, or mammal, it must first establish an anterior and a posterior end. As the embryo continues to grow, the body segments form and give rise to structures such as appendages. The coordination of these developmental events is quite intricate and is easily disrupted by harmful environmental factors such as chemicals and radiation. Interestingly, some of these same environmental factors are thought to cause cellular damage that, over time, contributes to the aging process.

Although the main focus of this chapter is on events that occur either at the beginning, or toward the end, of an animal's life span, we should note that once an animal has reached maturity, development does not cease. If an animal's body is injured, the wound must be repaired. Not surprisingly, many of the same genes involved in wound repair are those which were active during earlier stages in development. In this chapter, we examine the basic processes of early animal development, as well as human fetal development, and the consequences of aging.

As you read through the chapter, think about the following questions:

1. Why are so many similarities present in the early embryonic structures of animals as diverse as the lancelet, the frog, the chicken, and the human?

2. Why is the developing embryo of any species more susceptible to harmful environmental factors, compared to the mature animal?

3. What are some of the fundamental mechanisms by which cells can become specialized to form organs and tissues?

BEFORE YOU BEGIN

Before beginning this chapter, take a few moments to review the following discussions.

Figure 13.7 How do transcription factors control the expression of eukaryotic genes?

Figure 41.8 In the human female reproductive system, where are the oviducts located relative to the ovaries? To the uterus?

Section 41.3 What are the roles of estrogen and progesterone in the ovarian and uterine cycles?

FOLLOWING *the* THEMES

CHAPTER 42 ANIMAL DEVELOPMENT AND AGING

UNIT 7 COMPARATIVE ANIMAL BIOLOGY		
	Evolution	Similarities in the developmental stages of embryos from animals as diverse as the lancelet, frog, chicken, and human provide evidence for the evolutionary relatedness of all animals.
	Nature of Science	Research into the development of two model organisms, *Caenorhabditis elegans* (a roundworm) and *Drosophila melanogaster* (a fruit fly), have advanced the science of developmental biology and knowledge of the mechanisms of aging.
	Biological Systems	Animal development begins when egg and sperm nuclei unite, and it progresses through complex stages controlled by the differential expression of a common set of genes found in all cells of an animal's body.

42.1 Early Developmental Stages

Learning Outcomes

Upon completion of this section, you should be able to

1. Identify the structures of an egg and sperm that are directly involved in fertilization.
2. Compare and contrast the cellular, tissue, and organ stages of embryonic development.
3. Describe the major steps in the development of the central nervous system of vertebrates.

As noted in the preceding chapter, animals that reproduce sexually employ a wide variety of strategies to achieve **fertilization,** the union of a sperm and an egg to form a zygote. Figure 42.1 illustrates how fertilization occurs in mammals, including humans.

Details of Fertilization in Humans

Human sperm have three distinct parts: a tail, a middle piece, and a head. The head contains the sperm nucleus and is capped by a membrane-bounded *acrosome*. The egg of a mammal (actually the secondary oocyte) is surrounded by a few layers of adhering follicular cells, collectively called the *corona radiata*. These cells nourished the oocyte when it was in a follicle of the ovary. The oocyte also has an extracellular matrix termed the *zona pellucida* just outside the plasma membrane, but beneath the corona radiata.

Video Human Sperm

Fertilization requires a series of events that result in the diploid zygote. Although only one sperm actually fertilizes the oocyte, millions of sperm begin this journey, and perhaps a few hundred succeed in reaching the oocyte. The sperm cover the surface of the oocyte and secrete enzymes that help weaken the corona radiata. They squeeze through the corona radiata and bind to the zona pellucida. After a sperm head binds tightly to

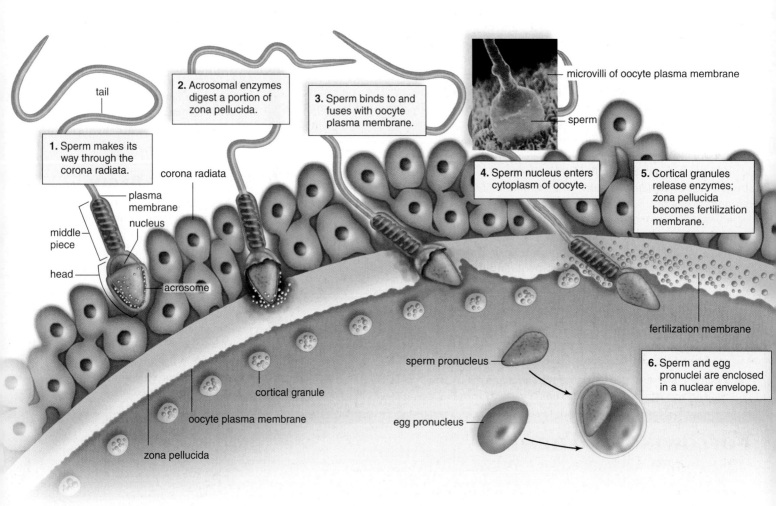

Figure 42.1 Fertilization. During fertilization, a single sperm is drawn into the oocyte by microvilli of its plasma membrane (micrograph). The head of a sperm has a membrane-bounded acrosome filled with enzymes. When released, these enzymes digest a pathway for the sperm through the zona pellucida. After a sperm binds to the plasma membrane of the oocyte, changes occur that prevent other sperm from entering the oocyte. The oocyte finishes the second meiotic division and is now an egg. Fertilization is complete when the sperm pronucleus and the egg pronucleus contribute chromosomes to the zygote.

the zona pellucida, the acrosome releases digestive enzymes that forge a pathway for the sperm through the zona pellucida to the oocyte plasma membrane.

When the first sperm binds to the oocyte plasma membrane, the next few events prevent *polyspermy* (entrance of more than one sperm). As soon as a sperm touches the plasma membrane of an oocyte, the oocyte's plasma membrane depolarizes, and this change in charge, known as the "fast block," serves to repel sperm only for a few seconds. Then vesicles in the oocyte called *cortical granules* secrete enzymes that turn the zona pellucida into an impenetrable *fertilization membrane.* The longer-lasting cortical reaction is known as the "slow block."

The last of the events includes formation of the diploid zygote. Microvilli extending from the plasma membrane of the oocyte (Fig. 42.1) bring the entire sperm into the oocyte. The sperm nucleus releases its chromatin, which re-forms into chromosomes enclosed within the sperm *pronucleus.* In the meantime, the secondary oocyte completes meiosis, becoming an egg whose chromosomes are also enclosed in a pronucleus. A single nuclear envelope soon surrounds both sperm and egg pronuclei. Cell division is imminent, and the centrosomes that give rise to a spindle apparatus are derived from the basal body of the sperm's flagellum. The two haploid sets of chromosomes share the first spindle apparatus of the newly formed zygote.

Embryonic Development

Development includes all the changes that occur during the life cycle of an organism. You first encountered the basics of animal development in Chapter 28. Although development is a continuous, complex process, it can be divided into three major stages: (1) cellular, (2) tissue, and (3) organ.

Cellular Stages of Development

During the early stages of development, an organism is called an **embryo.** The cellular stages of development are

1. cleavage, resulting in a multicellular embryo, and
2. formation of the blastula.

Cleavage is cell division without growth; DNA replication and mitotic cell division occur repeatedly, and the cells get smaller with each division.

As shown in Figure 42.2, cleavage in a primitive animal called a lancelet results in uniform cells that form a **morula** [L. *morula,* little mulberry], which is a solid ball of cells. The morula continues to divide, forming a **blastula** [Gk. *blastos,* bud; L. *-ula,* small], a hollow ball of cells having a fluid-filled cavity called a **blastocoel.** The blastocoel forms when the cells of the morula extrude Na^+ into extracellular spaces, and water follows by osmosis, collecting in the center.

All vertebrates have a blastula stage, but the appearance of the blastula can be different from that of a lancelet. Chickens lay a hard-shelled egg containing plentiful **yolk,** a dense nutrient material. Because yolk-filled cells do not participate in cleavage,

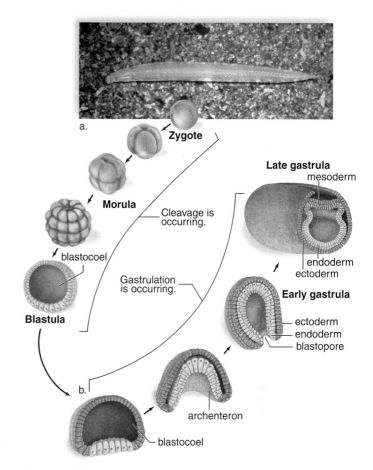

Figure 42.2 Lancelet early development.   a. A lancelet. **b.** The early stages of development are exemplified in the lancelet. Cleavage produces a number of cells that form a cavity, the blastocoel. Invagination during gastrulation produces the germ layers ectoderm and endoderm. Then the mesoderm arises.

the blastula is a layer of cells that spreads out over the yolk. The blastocoel then forms as a space that separates these cells from the yolk:

The zygotes of vertebrates, such as frogs, chickens, and humans, also undergo cleavage and form a morula. In frogs, cleavage is not equal because of the presence of the yolk. When yolk is present, the zygote and embryo exhibit polarity, and the embryo has an *animal pole* and a *vegetal pole.* The animal pole contains faster-growing, smaller cells that will eventually develop into the ectoderm and endoderm layers; the vegetal pole contains slower-growing, larger cells that develop into endoderm (see Fig. 42.3).

Tissue Stages of Development

The tissue stages of development involve **gastrulation,** the formation of a **gastrula** [Gk. *gaster,* belly; L. *-ula,* small] from the blastula. The two tissue stages are

(1) the early gastrula, and
(2) the late gastrula.

The early gastrula stage begins when certain cells begin to push, or invaginate, into the blastocoel, creating a double layer of cells (see Fig. 42.2). Cells migrate during this and other stages of development, sometimes traveling quite a distance before reaching a destination, where they continue developing. As cells migrate, they "feel their way" by changing their pattern of adhering to extracellular proteins.

An early gastrula has two layers of cells. The outer layer of cells is called the **ectoderm,** and the inner layer is called the **endoderm.** The endoderm borders the gut, but at this point, it is termed either the archenteron or the primitive gut. The pore, or hole, created by invagination (inward folding) is the **blastopore,** and in a lancelet, the blastopore eventually becomes the anus.

Gastrulation is not complete until three layers of cells that will develop into adult organs are produced. In addition to ectoderm and endoderm, the late gastrula has a middle layer of cells called the **mesoderm.**

Figure 42.2 illustrates gastrulation in a lancelet, and Figure 42.3 compares the lancelet, frog, and chicken late gastrula stages. In the lancelet, mesoderm formation begins as outpocketings from the primitive gut (Fig. 42.3). These outpocketings grow in size until they meet and fuse, forming two layers of mesoderm. The space between them is the coelom (see Section 28.1). The coelom is a body cavity lined by mesoderm that contains internal organs. In humans, the coelom becomes the thoracic and abdominal cavities of the body.

In the frog, the cells containing yolk do not participate in gastrulation and, therefore, they do not invaginate. Instead, a

slitlike blastopore is formed when the animal pole cells begin to invaginate from above, forming endoderm. Animal pole cells also move down over the yolk, to invaginate from below. Some yolk cells, which remain temporarily in the region of the blastopore, are called the yolk plug. Mesoderm forms when cells migrate between the ectoderm and endoderm. Later, a splitting of the mesoderm creates the coelom.

A chicken egg contains so much yolk that endoderm formation does not occur by invagination. Instead, an upper layer of cells becomes ectoderm, and a lower layer becomes endoderm. Mesoderm arises by an invagination of cells along the edges of a longitudinal furrow in the midline of the embryo. Because of its appearance, this furrow is called the *primitive streak.* Later, the newly formed mesoderm splits to produce a coelomic cavity.

Ectoderm, mesoderm, and endoderm are called the embryonic **germ layers.** No matter how gastrulation takes place, the result is the same: three germ layers are formed. It is possible to relate the development of future organs to these germ layers (Table 42.1).

Table 42.1 Embryonic Germ Layers

Embryonic Germ Layer	Vertebrate Adult Structures
Ectoderm (outer layer)	Nervous system; epidermis of skin and derivatives of the epidermis (hair, nails, glands); tooth enamel, dentin, and pulp; epithelial lining of oral cavity and rectum
Mesoderm (middle layer)	Musculoskeletal system; dermis of skin; cardiovascular system; urinary system; lymphatic system; reproductive system—including most epithelial linings; outer layers of respiratory and digestive systems
Endoderm (inner layer)	Epithelial lining of digestive tract and respiratory tract, associated glands of these systems; epithelial lining of urinary bladder; thyroid and parathyroid glands

Figure 42.3 Comparative development of mesoderm.
a. In the lancelet, mesoderm forms by an outpocketing of the archenteron. **b.** In the frog, mesoderm forms by migration of cells between the ectoderm and endoderm. **c.** In the chick, mesoderm also forms by invagination of cells.

a. Lancelet late gastrula

b. Frog late gastrula

c. Chick late gastrula

Figure 42.4 Development of neural tube and coelom in a frog embryo. **a.** Ectodermal cells that lie above the future notochord (called presumptive notochord) thicken to form a neural plate. **b.** The neural groove and folds are noticeable as the neural tube begins to form. **c.** A splitting of the mesoderm produces a coelom, which is completely lined by mesoderm. **d.** A neural tube and a coelom have now developed.

Organ Stages of Development

The organs of an animal's body develop from the three embryonic germ layers. Much study has been devoted to how the nervous system develops in chordates, so we summarize that process here.

The newly formed mesoderm cells lie along the main longitudinal axis of the animal and coalesce to form a dorsal supporting rod called the **notochord.** The notochord persists in lancelets, but in frogs, chickens, and humans, it is replaced later in development by the vertebral column, giving these animals the name vertebrates.

The nervous system develops from midline ectoderm located just above the notochord. At first, a thickening of cells, called the **neural plate,** is seen along the dorsal surface of the embryo. Then, neural folds develop on either side of a neural groove, which becomes the **neural tube** when these folds fuse. Figure 42.4 shows cross sections of frog development to illustrate the formation of the neural tube. At this point, the embryo is called a *neurula.* Later, the anterior end of the neural tube develops into the brain, and the rest becomes the spinal cord.

In addition, the *neural crest* is a band of cells that develops where the neural tube pinches off from the ectoderm. Neural crest cells migrate to various locations, where they contribute to formation of skin and muscles, in addition to the adrenal medulla and the ganglia of the peripheral nervous system.

Midline mesoderm cells that did not contribute to the formation of the notochord now become two longitudinal masses of tissue. These two masses become blocked off into *somites,* which are serially arranged along both sides along the length of the notochord. Somites give rise to muscles associated with the axial skeleton and to the vertebrae. The serial origin of axial muscles and the vertebrae illustrates that vertebrates (including humans) are segmented animals. Lateral to the somites, the mesoderm splits, forming the mesodermal lining of the coelom.

In development of other organs, a primitive gut tube is formed by endoderm as the body itself folds into a tube. The heart, too, begins as a simple tubular pump. Organ formation continues until the germ layers have given rise to the specific organs listed in Table 42.1. Figure 42.5 helps you relate the formation of vertebrate structures and organs to the three embryonic layers of cells: the ectoderm, the mesoderm, and the endoderm.

Check Your Progress   42.1

1. Describe the fast and slow blocks to polyspermy.
2. Name the germ layer of the gastrula that gives rise to each of the following: notochord, thyroid and parathyroid glands, nervous system, epidermis, skeletal muscles, kidneys, bones, and pancreas.
3. Identify the stage(s) of embryonic development in which cross sections of all chordate embryos closely resemble one another.

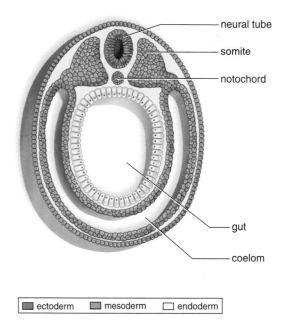

■ ectoderm   ■ mesoderm   □ endoderm

Figure 42.5 Vertebrate embryo, cross section. At the neurula stage, each of the germ layers, indicated by color (see key), can be associated with the later development of particular parts. The somites give rise to the muscles of each segment and to the vertebrae, which replace the notochord in vertebrates.

42.2 Developmental Processes

Learning Outcomes

Upon completion of this section, you should be able to

1. Distinguish between cellular differentiation and morphogenesis.
2. Define cytoplasmic segregation and induction, and explain how these phenomena contribute to cellular differentiation.
3. Describe the major steps of morphogenesis in *Drosophila melanogaster*.

Development requires three interconnected processes: growth, cellular differentiation, and morphogenesis. **Cellular differentiation** occurs when cells become specialized in structure and function; that is, a muscle cell looks different and acts differently than a nerve cell. **Morphogenesis** produces the shape and form of the body. One of the earliest indications of morphogenesis is cell movement. Later, morphogenesis includes **pattern formation,** which means how tissues and organs are arranged in the body. **Apoptosis,** or programmed cell death (see Fig. 9.2), is an important part of pattern formation.

Developmental genetics has benefited from research using the roundworm *Caenorhabditis elegans* and the fruit fly *Drosophila melanogaster*. These organisms are referred to as model organisms because the study of their development produced concepts that help us understand development in general.

Cellular Differentiation

At one time, investigators mistakenly believed that different cell types, e.g., human liver cells and brain cells, must inherit different DNA sequences from the original single-celled zygote. Perhaps, they speculated, the genes are parceled out as development occurs, and that is why cells of the body have a different structure and function. We now know that is not the case; rather, every cell in the body (except for the sperm and unfertilized egg) has a full complement of genes.

The zygote is **totipotent;** it has the ability to generate the entire organism and, therefore, must contain all the instructions needed by any other specialized cell in the body. For the first few days of cell division, all the embryonic cells are totipotent. When the embryonic cells begin to specialize and lose their totipotency, they do not lose genetic information. In fact, our ability today to clone mammals such as sheep, mice, and cats from specialized adult cells shows that every cell in an organism's body has the same collection of genes.

The answer to this puzzle becomes clear when we consider that only muscle cells produce the proteins myosin and actin; only red blood cells produce hemoglobin; and only skin cells produce keratin. In other words, we now know that specialization is not due to a parceling out of genes; rather, it is due to differential gene expression. Certain genes and not others are turned on (transcribed) in differentiated cells. In recent years, investigators have turned their attention to discovering the mechanisms that lead to differential gene expression. Two mechanisms—cytoplasmic segregation and induction—seem to be especially important.

Cytoplasmic Segregation

Differentiation must begin long before we can recognize specialized types of cells. Ectodermal, endodermal, and mesodermal cells in the gastrula look quite similar, but they must be different because they develop into different organs. The egg is now known to contain substances in the cytoplasm called **maternal determinants,** which influence the course of development. **Cytoplasmic segregation** is the parceling out of maternal determinants as mitosis occurs:

maternal determinants

Cytoplasmic segregation

An experiment conducted in 1935 showed that the cytoplasm of a frog's egg is not uniform. It is polar, having both an anterior/posterior axis and a dorsal/ventral axis, which can be correlated with the *gray crescent*, a gray area that appears after the sperm fertilizes the egg (Fig. 42.6*a*). If the gray crescent is divided equally by the first cleavage, each experimentally separated daughter cell develops into a complete embryo (Fig. 42.6*b*). However, if the zygote divides so that only one daughter cell receives the gray crescent, only that cell becomes a complete embryo (Fig. 42.6*c*). This experiment allowed scientists to speculate that the gray crescent must contain particular chemical signals that are needed for development to proceed normally.

Induction and Frog Experiments

As development proceeds, specialization of cells and formation of organs are influenced not only by maternal determinants but also by signals given off by neighboring cells. **Induction** [L. *in*, into, and *duco*, lead] is the ability of one embryonic tissue to influence the development of another tissue.

A frog embryo's gray crescent becomes the dorsal lip of the blastopore, where gastrulation begins. Because this region is necessary for complete development, the dorsal lip of the blastopore was termed the *primary organizer*. The cells closest to the primary organizer become endoderm, those farther away become mesoderm, and those farthest away become ectoderm. This suggests that a molecular concentration gradient may act as a chemical signal to induce germ layer differentiation.

The gray crescent in the zygote of a frog marks the dorsal side of the embryo where the mesoderm becomes notochord and ectoderm becomes nervous system. In a classic experiment researchers showed that presumptive (potential) notochord tissue induces the formation of the nervous system (Fig. 42.7). If presumptive nervous system tissue, located just above the presumptive notochord, is cut out and transplanted to the belly region of the embryo, it does not form a neural tube. But in contrast, if presumptive notochord tissue is cut out and transplanted beneath what would be belly ectoderm, this ectoderm does differentiate into neural tissue. Many other examples of induction are now known.

a. Zygote of a frog is polar and has axes.

b. Each cell receives a part of the gray crescent.

c. Only the cell on the left receives the gray crescent.

Figure 42.6
Cytoplasmic influence on development.   a. The zygote of a frog has anterior/posterior and dorsal/ventral axes that correlate with the position of the gray crescent. **b.** The first cleavage normally divides the gray crescent in half, and each daughter cell is capable of developing into a complete tadpole. **c.** But if only one daughter cell receives the gray crescent, then only that cell can become a complete embryo. This shows that maternal determinants are present in the cytoplasm of a frog's egg.

Presumptive nervous tissue is removed from a donor embryo.

Host embryo has undergone gastrulation.

After removal of host tissue, donor presumptive nervous tissue is transplanted to belly region of host embryo.

Host embryo undergoes neurulation.

Due to normal induction process, a host neural plate develops. But donated tissue is not induced to develop into a neural plate.

a.

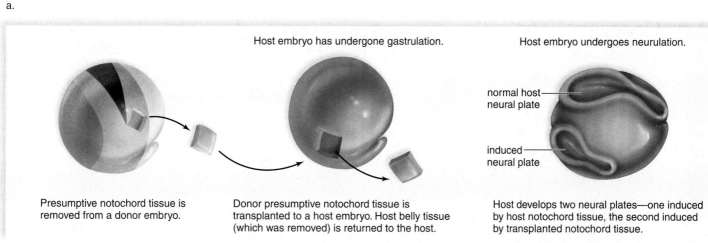

Presumptive notochord tissue is removed from a donor embryo.

Host embryo has undergone gastrulation.

Donor presumptive notochord tissue is transplanted to a host embryo. Host belly tissue (which was removed) is returned to the host.

Host embryo undergoes neurulation.

Host develops two neural plates—one induced by host notochord tissue, the second induced by transplanted notochord tissue.

b.

Figure 42.7   Control of nervous system development.   a. In this experiment, the presumptive nervous system (*blue*) does not develop into the neural plate if moved from its normal location. **b.** In this experiment, the presumptive notochord (*pink*) can cause even belly ectoderm to develop into the neural plate (*blue*). This shows that the notochord induces ectoderm to become a neural plate, most likely by sending out chemical signals.

Induction in Caenorhabditis elegans

The tiny nematode *Caenorhabditis elegans* is only 1 mm long, and vast numbers can be raised in the laboratory either in petri dishes or a liquid medium. The worm is hermaphroditic, and self-fertilization is the rule. Therefore, even though induced mutations may be recessive, the next generation will yield individuals that are homozygous recessive and show the mutation. Many modern genetic studies have been performed on *C. elegans,* and the entire genome has been sequenced. Individual genes have been altered and cloned and their products injected into cells or extracellular fluid.

As the result of genetic studies, much has been learned about *C. elegans.* Development of *C. elegans* takes only three days, and the adult worm contains only 959 cells. Investigators have been able to watch the process from beginning to end because the worm is transparent. *Fate maps* have been developed that show the destiny of each cell as it arises following successive cell divisions (Fig. 42.8).

Some investigators have studied in detail the development of the worm's vulva, a pore through which eggs are laid. A cell called the anchor cell induces the vulva to form. The cell closest to the anchor cell receives the most inducer and becomes the inner vulva. This cell in turn produces another inducer, which acts on its two neighboring cells, and they become the outer vulva. The inducers are growthlike factors that alter the metabolism of the receiving cell and activate particular genes. Work with *C. elegans* has shown that induction requires the transcriptional regulation of genes in a particular sequence.

Morphogenesis

An animal achieves its ordered and complex body form through morphogenesis, which requires that cells associate to form tissues, and tissues give rise to organs. Pattern formation is the process that enables morphogenesis. In pattern formation, cells of the embryo divide and differentiate, taking up orderly positions in tissues and organs.

Although animals display an amazingly diverse array of morphologies, or body forms, most share common sets of genes that direct pattern formation. When pattern formation has ensured that key cells are properly arranged, then morphogenesis, the construction of the ultimate body form, can take place.

Morphogenesis in Drosophila melanogaster

Much of the study of pattern formation and morphogenesis has been done using relatively simple models such as the fruit fly *Drosophila melanogaster.* A *Drosophila* egg is only about 0.5 mm long, and develops into an adult in about two weeks. The fly's genome is considerably smaller than that of humans or even mice (see Table 14.1). However, the genes that direct pattern formation appear to be highly conserved among animals with segmented body morphologies, including humans.

As pattern formation occurs in *Drosophila,* the embryonic cells begin to express genes differently in graded, periodic, and eventually striped arrangements. Boundaries between large body

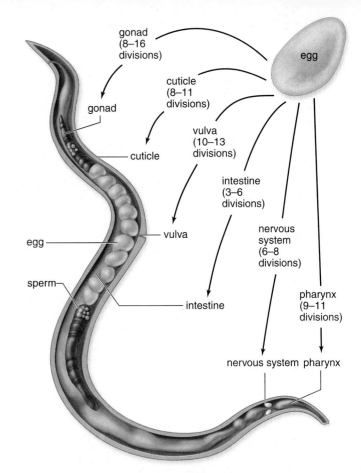

Figure 42.8 Development of *C. elegans*, a nematode. A fate map of the worm showing that as cells arise by cell division, they are destined to become particular structures.

regions are established first, before the refinement of smaller, subdivided parts can take place.

The Anterior/Posterior Axes. The first step in *Drosophila* pattern formation and morphogenesis begins with the establishment of anteroposterior polarity, meaning that the anterior (head) and posterior (abdomen) ends are different from one another. Such polarity is present in the egg before it is fertilized by a sperm.

Egg polarity results from maternal determinants, mRNAs that are deposited in specific positions within the egg while it is still in the ovary. The protein products of these genes diffuse away from the areas of their highest concentration in the embryo, forming gradients that influence patterns of tissue development. These proteins are also known as *morphogens* due to their crucial influence in morphogenesis. For example, the Bicoid protein is most concentrated anteriorly, where it prevents the formation of the posterior region. The Nanos protein is most concentrated posteriorly, and is required for abdomen formation.

The Segmentation Pattern. Once the anterior and posterior ends of the embryo have been established, a group of zygotic genes called *gap* genes come into play. The task of gap genes is to divide the anteroposterior axis into broad regions

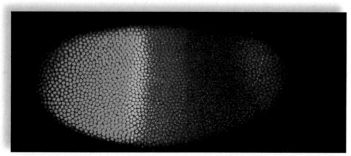

a. Protein products of gap genes

b. Protein products of pair-rule genes

c. Protein products of segment-polarity genes

Figure 42.9 Development in *Drosophila*, a fruit fly. a. The different colors show that two different gap gene proteins are present from the anterior to the posterior end of an embryo. **b.** The green stripes show that a pair-rule gene is being expressed as segmentation of the fly occurs. **c.** Now segment-polarity genes help bring about division of each segment into an anterior and posterior end.

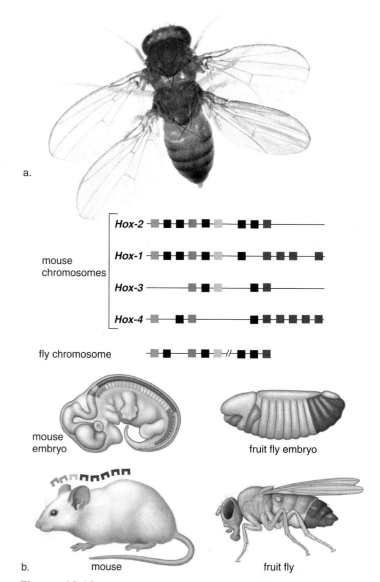

Figure 42.10 Pattern formation in *Drosophila*. Homeotic genes control pattern formation, an aspect of morphogenesis. **a.** If homeotic genes are activated at inappropriate times, abnormalities such as a fly with four wings occur. **b.** The green, blue, yellow, and red colors show that homologous homeotic genes occur on four mouse chromosomes and on a fly chromosome in the same order. These genes are color coded to the region of the embryo, and therefore the adult, where they regulate pattern formation. The black boxes are homeotic genes that are not identical between the two animals. In mammals, homeotic genes are called *Hox* genes.

(Fig. 42.9*a*). They are called gap genes because mutations in these genes result in gaps in the embryo, where large blocks of segments are missing. Gap genes are temporarily activated by the gradients of anterior and posterior morphogens, and in turn activate the *pair-rule* genes.

The pair-rule genes are expressed periodically, in alternating stripes (Fig. 42.9*b*). They serve to "rough out" a preliminary segmentation pattern along the anteroposterior axis. The products of pair-rule genes may stimulate or suppress the expression of other genes, particularly the *segment-polarity* genes. These genes ensure that each segment has boundaries, with distinct anterior and posterior halves. The segment-polarity genes are also expressed in a striped fashion, but with twice as many stripes as the pair-rule genes (Fig. 42.9*c*). Mutations in segment-polarity genes result in the loss of one part of each segment, and the duplication of another portion of the same segment.

Homeotic Genes. The **homeotic genes** are often referred to as *selector genes* because they select for segmental identity—in other words, they dictate which body parts arise from the segments. Mutations in homeotic genes may result in the development of body parts in inappropriate areas, such as legs instead of antennae, or wings instead of tiny balancing organs called halteres (Fig. 42.10*a*). Such alterations in morphology are known as *homeotic transformations.*

Interestingly, homeotic genes in *Drosophila* and other organisms have all been found to share a structural feature called a **homeobox.** (*Hox,* the term used for mammalian homeotic genes, is a shortened form of homeobox.) A homeobox is a sequence of nucleotides that encodes a 60-amino-acid sequence called a **homeodomain:**

variable DNA sequence | homeobox

homeotic gene

variable amino acid sequence | homeodomain

homeodomain protein

The homeodomain is a functionally important part of the protein encoded by a homeotic gene. Homeotic genes code for transcription factors, proteins that bind to regulatory regions of DNA and determine whether or not specific target genes are turned on. The homeodomain is the DNA-binding portion of the transcription factor, although the other, more variable sequences of a transcription factor determine which target genes are turned on. It is thought that the homeodomain proteins encoded by homeotic genes direct the activities of various target genes involved in morphogenesis, such as those involved in cell-to-cell adhesion. In the end, this orderly process determines the morphology of particular segments.

The importance of homeotic genes is underscored by the finding that the homeotic genes are highly conserved, being present in the genomes of many organisms, including mammals such as mice and even humans. Most homeotic genes have their loci on the same chromosome in *Drosophila,* while in mammals there are four clusters that reside on different chromosomes.

Notice that, in both flies and mammals, the position of the homeotic genes on the chromosome matches their anterior-to-posterior expression pattern in the body (Fig. 42.10*b*). The first gene clusters determine the final development of anterior segments, whereas those later in the sequence determine the final development of posterior segments of the animal's body.

Mutations in homeotic genes have similar effects in the mammalian body to the homeotic transformations observed in *Drosophila.* For instance, mutations in two adjacent *Hox* genes in the mouse result in shortened forelimbs that are missing the radius and ulna bones. In humans, mutations in a different *Hox* gene cause synpolydactyly, a rare condition in which there are extra digits (fingers and toes), some of which are fused to their neighbors.

Apoptosis. We have already discussed the importance of apoptosis (programmed cell death) in the normal day-to-day operation of the immune system and in preventing the occurrence of cancer. Apoptosis is also an important part of morphogenesis. During development of humans, we know that apoptosis is necessary to the shaping of the hands and feet; if it does not occur, the child is born with webbing between its fingers and toes.

The fate maps of *C. elegans* (see Fig. 42.8) indicate that apoptosis occurs in 131 cells as development takes place. When a cell-death signal is received, an inhibiting protein becomes inactive, allowing a cell-death cascade to proceed that ends in enzymes destroying the cell.

Check Your Progress   42.2

1. Name and define two mechanisms of cellular differentiation.
2. Define the term "morphogen."
3. Describe the function of the homeobox sequence in a homeotic gene.

42.3 Human Embryonic and Fetal Development

Learning Outcomes

Upon completion of this section, you should be able to

1. Name the membranes surrounding the human embryo, and list their functions.
2. Chronologically list the major events that occur during embryonic and fetal development.
3. Describe the structure and functions of the placenta.

In humans, the length of time from conception (fertilization followed by implantation in the endometrium) to birth (parturition) is approximately nine months. It is customary to calculate the time of birth by adding 280 days to the start of the last menstruation, because this date is usually known, whereas the day of fertilization is usually unknown. Because the time of birth is influenced by so many variables, only about 5% of babies actually arrive on the forecasted date.

Human development is often divided into embryonic development (months 1 and 2) and fetal development (months 3 through 9). During **embryonic development,** the major organs are formed, and during fetal development, these structures become larger and are refined.

Chick

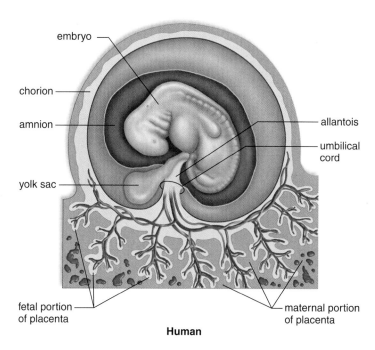

Human

Figure 42.11 Extraembryonic membranes. Extraembryonic membranes, which are not part of the embryo, are found during the development of chicks and humans. Each has a specific function.

Development can also be divided into *trimesters*. Each trimester can be characterized by specific developmental accomplishments. During the first trimester, embryonic and early fetal development occur. The second trimester is characterized by the development of organs and organ systems. By the end of the second trimester, the fetus appears distinctly human. In the third trimester, the fetus grows rapidly and the major organ systems become functional.

Extraembryonic Membranes

Before we consider human development chronologically, we must understand the placement of **extraembryonic membranes** [L. *extra,* on the outside]. Extraembryonic membranes are best understood by considering their function in reptiles and birds. In reptiles, these membranes made development on land first possible. If an embryo develops in the water, the water supplies oxygen for the embryo and takes away waste products. The surrounding water prevents desiccation, or drying out, and provides a protective cushion. For an embryo that develops on land, all these functions are performed by the extraembryonic membranes.

In the chick, the extraembryonic membranes develop from extensions of the germ layers, which spread out over the yolk. Figure 42.11 shows the chick surrounded by the membranes. The **chorion** [Gk. *chorion,* membrane] lies next to the shell and carries on gas exchange. The **amnion** [Gk. *amnion,* membrane around fetus] contains the protective amniotic fluid, which bathes the developing embryo. The **allantois** [Gk. *allantos,* sausage] collects nitrogenous wastes, and the **yolk sac** surrounds the remaining yolk, which provides nourishment.

The function of the extraembryonic membranes in humans has been modified to suit internal development. Their presence, however, shows that we are related to the reptiles.

The chorion develops into the fetal half of the placenta, the organ that provides the embryo/fetus with nourishment and oxygen, and takes away its wastes. Blood vessels within the chorionic villi are continuous with the umbilical blood vessels. The blood vessels of the allantois become the umbilical blood vessels, and the allantois accumulates the small amount of urine produced by the fetal kidneys and later gives rise to the urinary bladder. The yolk sac, which lacks yolk, is the first site of blood cell formation. The amnion contains fluid to cushion and protect the embryo, which develops into a fetus.

It is interesting to note that all chordate animals develop in water—either in bodies of water or surrounded by amniotic fluid within a shell or uterus.

Figure 42.12   Human development before implantation.   (1) At ovulation, the secondary oocyte leaves the ovary. A single sperm nucleus enters the oocyte, and (2) fertilization of the egg occurs in the oviduct. As the zygote moves along the oviduct, it undergoes (3) cleavage to produce (4) a morula. (5) The blastocyst forms and (6) implants itself in the uterine lining.

Embryonic Development

Embryonic development includes the first two months of development.

The First Week

Fertilization usually occurs in the upper third of the oviduct (Fig. 42.12). Cleavage begins 30 hours after fertilization and continues as the embryo passes through the oviduct to the uterus. By the time the embryo reaches the uterus on the third day, it is a morula. By about the fifth day, the morula has transformed into a blastula, and in mammals, a blastocyst then forms.

Video
Blastocyst
Formation

The **blastocyst** has a fluid-filled cavity, a single layer of outer cells called the **trophoblast** [Gk. *trophe,* food, and *blastos,*

bud], and an inner cell mass. The early function of the trophoblast is to provide nourishment for the embryo. Later, the trophoblast, reinforced by a layer of mesoderm, gives rise to the chorion, one of the extraembryonic membranes (see Fig. 42.11). The inner cell mass eventually becomes the embryo, which develops into a fetus.

The Second Week

At the end of the first week, the embryo begins the process of **implantation** in the wall of the uterus. The trophoblast secretes enzymes to digest away some of the tissue and blood vessels of the endometrium of the uterus (Fig. 42.12). The embryo is now about the size of the period at the end of this sentence. The trophoblast begins to secrete **human chorionic gonadotropin (HCG),** the hormone that is the basis for the pregnancy test and

THEME Biological Systems

Preventing and Testing for Birth Defects

Birth defects, or congenital disorders, are abnormal conditions that are present at birth. According to the Centers for Disease Control (CDC), about 1 in 33 babies born in the United States has a birth defect. Those due to genetics can sometimes be detected before birth by one of the methods shown in Figure 42A; however, these methods are not without risk.

Some birth defects are not serious, and not all can be prevented. But women can take steps to increase their chances of delivering a healthy baby.

Eat a Healthy Diet

Certain birth defects occur because the developing embryo does not receive sufficient nutrition. For example, women of childbearing age are urged to make sure they consume ad-

a. Amniocentesis

b. Chorionic villi sampling

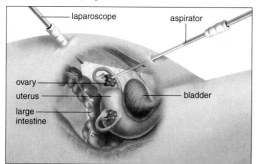

c. Preimplantation genetic diagnosis

equate amounts of the vitamin folic acid in order to prevent neural tube defects such as spina bifida and anencephaly. In spina bifida, part of the vertebral column fails to develop properly and cannot adequately protect the delicate spinal cord. With anencephaly, most of the fetal brain fails to develop. Anencephalic infants are stillborn or survive for only a few days after birth.

Fortunately, folic acid is plentiful in leafy green vegetables, nuts, and citrus fruits. It is also present in multivitamins, and many breads and cereals are fortified with it. The CDC recommends that all women of childbearing age get at least 400 micrograms of folic acid every day through supplements, in addition to eating a healthy, folic acid–rich diet. Unfortunately, neural tube birth defects can occur just a few weeks after conception, when many women are still unaware that they are pregnant—especially if the pregnancy is unplanned.

Avoid Alcohol, Smoking, and Drug Abuse

Alcohol consumption during pregnancy is a leading cause of birth defects. In severe instances, the baby is born with fetal alcohol syndrome (FAS), estimated to occur in 0.2 to 1.5 of every 1,000 live births in the United States. Children with FAS are frequently underweight, have an abnormally small head, abnormal facial development, and mental retardation. As they mature, children with FAS often exhibit short attention span, impulsiveness, and

Figure 42A Three methods for genetic defect testing before birth. About 20% of all birth defects are due to genetic or chromosomal abnormalities, which may be detected before birth. **a.** Amniocentesis is usually performed from the fifteenth to the seventeenth week of pregnancy. **b.** Chorionic villi sampling is usually performed from the eighth to the twelfth week of pregnancy. **c.** Preimplantation genetic diagnosis can be performed prior to in vitro fertilization, either on oocytes that have been collected from the woman, or on the early embryo.

poor judgment, as well as serious difficulties with learning and memory. Heavy alcohol use also reduces a woman's folic acid level, increasing the risk of the neural tube defects just described.

Cigarette smoking causes many birth defects. Babies born to smoking mothers typically have low birth weight, and are more likely to have defects of the face, heart, and brain than those born to nonsmokers.

Illegal drugs should also be avoided. For example, cocaine causes blood pressure fluctuations that deprive the fetus of oxygen. Cocaine-exposed babies may have problems with vision and coordination, and may be mentally retarded.

Alert Medical Personnel If You Are or May Be Pregnant

Several medications that are safe for healthy adults may pose a risk to a developing fetus. If pregnant women need to be immunized, they are usually given killed or inactivated forms of the vaccine, because live forms often present a danger to the fetus.

Because the rapidly dividing cells of a developing embryo or fetus are very susceptible to damage from radiation, pregnant women should avoid unnecessary X-rays. If a medical X-ray is unavoidable, the woman should notify the X-ray technician so that her fetus can be protected as much as possible, for example, by draping a lead apron over her abdomen if this area is not targeted for X-ray examination.

Avoid Infections That Cause Birth Defects

Certain pathogens such as the virus that causes rubella (German measles) can result in birth defects. In the past, this virus caused many birth defects, specifically mental retardation, deafness, blindness, and heart defects. Rubella is much less of a danger in developed countries today because most women have been vaccinated against rubella as children. Other infections that can cause birth defects include toxoplasmosis, herpes simplex, and cytomegalovirus.

Questions to Consider

1. Why is it likely that the actual rate of birth defects is higher than what is reported?
2. Besides tobacco, alcohol, and illegal drugs, what other potential risks should a pregnant woman avoid? Why?

a. 14 days

— amniotic cavity
— embryonic disk
— yolk sac
— blastocyst cavity
— trophoblast

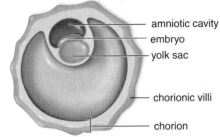

b. 18 days

— amniotic cavity
— embryo
— yolk sac
— chorionic villi
— chorion

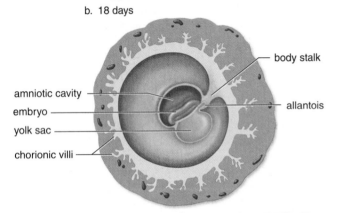

c. 21 days

amniotic cavity —
embryo —
yolk sac —
chorionic villi —
— body stalk
— allantois

that serves to maintain the corpus luteum past the time it normally disintegrates. (Recall that the corpus luteum is a yellow body formed in the ovary from a follicle that has discharged its secondary oocyte.) Because of this, the endometrium is maintained, and menstruation does not occur.

As the week progresses, the inner cell mass detaches itself from the trophoblast, and two more extraembryonic membranes form (Fig. 42.13a). The yolk sac, which forms below the embryonic disk, has no nutritive function as it does in chickens, but it is the first site of blood cell formation. However, the amnion and its cavity are where the embryo (and then the fetus) develops. In humans, amniotic fluid acts as an insulator against cold and heat and also absorbs shock, such as that caused by the mother exercising.

Gastrulation occurs during the second week. The inner cell mass now has flattened into the **embryonic disk,** composed of two layers of cells: ectoderm above and endoderm below. Once the embryonic disk elongates to form the primitive streak, the third germ layer, mesoderm, forms by invagination of cells along the streak. The trophoblast is reinforced by mesoderm and becomes the chorion (Fig. 42.13b). It is possible to relate the development of future organs to these germ layers (see Table 42.1).

The Third Week

Two important organ systems make their appearance during the third week. The nervous system is the first organ system to be visually evident. At first, a thickening appears along the entire

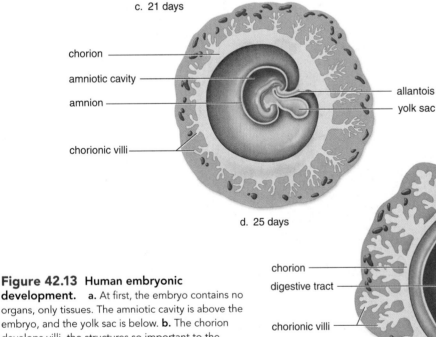

d. 25 days

chorion —
amniotic cavity —
amnion —
chorionic villi —
— allantois
— yolk sac

chorion —
digestive tract —
chorionic villi —
amnion —
— amniotic cavity
— umbilical cord

e. 35+ days

Figure 42.13 Human embryonic development.   a. At first, the embryo contains no organs, only tissues. The amniotic cavity is above the embryo, and the yolk sac is below. **b.** The chorion develops villi, the structures so important to the exchange between mother and child. **c., d.** The allantois and yolk sac, two more extraembryonic membranes, are positioned inside the body stalk as it becomes the umbilical cord. **e.** At 35+ days, the embryo has a head region and a tail region. The umbilical cord takes blood vessels between the embryo and the chorion (placenta).

Figure 42.14 Human embryo at beginning of fifth week. **a.** Scanning electron micrograph. **b.** The embryo is curled so that the head touches the heart, the two organs whose development is farther along than the rest of the body. The organs of the gastrointestinal tract are forming, and the arms and the legs develop from the bulges that are called limb buds. The tail is an evolutionary remnant; its bones regress and become those of the coccyx (tailbone). The pharyngeal arches become functioning gills only in fishes and amphibian larvae; in humans, the first pair of pharyngeal pouches becomes the auditory tubes. The second pair becomes the tonsils, while the third and fourth become the thymus gland and the parathyroid glands.

dorsal length of the embryo; then the neural folds appear. When the neural folds meet at the midline, the neural tube, which later develops into the brain and the nerve cord, is formed (see Fig. 42.4). After the notochord is replaced by the vertebral column, the nerve cord is called the spinal cord.

Development of the heart begins in the third week and continues into the fourth week. At first, there are right and left heart tubes; when these fuse, the heart begins pumping blood, even though the chambers of the heart are not fully formed. The veins enter posteriorly, and the arteries exit anteriorly from this largely tubular heart, but later the heart twists so that all major blood vessels are located anteriorly.

The Fourth and Fifth Weeks

At four weeks, the embryo is barely larger than the height of this print. A bridge of mesoderm called the body stalk connects the caudal (tail) end of the embryo with the chorion, which has tree-like projections called **chorionic villi** [Gk. *chorion*, membrane; L. *villus*, shaggy hair] (Fig. 42.13*c, d*). The fourth extraembryonic membrane, the allantois, is contained within this stalk, and its blood vessels become the umbilical blood vessels. These structures form the **umbilical cord** [L. *umbilicus*, navel], which connects the developing embryo to the placenta (Fig. 42.13*e*).

Little protrusions called *limb buds* appear (Fig. 42.14); later, the arms and the legs develop from the limb buds, and even the hands and the feet become apparent. At the same time—during the fifth week—the head enlarges, and the developing eyes, ears, and nose are discernable.

The Sixth through Eighth Weeks

During the sixth to eighth weeks of development, the embryo becomes easily recognizable as human. Concurrent with brain development, the head achieves its normal relationship with the body as a neck region develops. The nervous system is developed well enough to permit reflex actions, such as a startle response to touch. At the end of this period, the embryo is about 38 mm (1.5 in) long and weighs less than 1 g, even though all organ systems are established.

The Structure and Function of the Placenta

The **placenta** is a mammalian structure that functions in gas, nutrient, and waste exchange between embryonic (later fetal) and maternal cardiovascular systems. The placenta begins formation once the embryo is fully implanted. At first, the entire chorion has chorionic villi that project into endometrium. Later, these disappear in all areas except where the placenta develops. By the tenth week, the placenta (Fig. 42.15) is fully formed and is producing progesterone and estrogen. These hormones have two effects:

- They prevent any new follicles from maturing because of negative feedback control of the hypothalamus and anterior pituitary.
- They maintain the lining of the uterus, so now the corpus luteum is not needed. No menstruation occurs during pregnancy.

The placenta has a fetal side contributed by the chorion, and a maternal side consisting of uterine tissues. Notice in Figure 42.15 how the chorionic villi are surrounded by maternal blood; yet maternal and fetal blood do not mix under normal conditions because exchange always takes place across plasma membranes.

The umbilical cord is the lifeline of the fetus because it contains the umbilical arteries and vein, which transport waste

Placenta

Figure 42.15 Anatomy of the placenta in a fetus at six to seven months. The placenta is composed of both fetal and maternal tissues. Chorionic villi penetrate the uterine lining and are surrounded by maternal blood. Exchange of molecules between fetal and maternal blood takes place across the walls of the chorionic villi.

molecules (carbon dioxide and urea) to the placenta for disposal into the maternal blood and take oxygen and nutrient molecules from the placenta to the rest of the fetal circulatory system. If the placenta prematurely tears from the uterine wall, the lives of the fetus and the mother are endangered.

Late in fetal development, and peaking just before birth, maternal antibodies are transported across the placenta, into the fetal circulation. This helps to ensure that the newborn will be protected against common pathogens and other microbes to which the mother has been exposed, until the immune system of the newborn can mature and respond on its own. Harmful chemicals can also cross the placenta, as discussed in the Biological Systems feature on page 807.

Fetal Development and Birth

Fetal development (months 3–9) is marked by an extreme increase in size. Weight multiplies 600 times, going from less than 28 g to 3 kg. During this time, too, the fetus grows to about 50 cm in length. The genitalia appear in the third month, so it is possible to tell if the fetus is male or female.

Soon, hair, eyebrows, and eyelashes add finishing touches to the face and head. In the same way, fingernails and toenails complete the hands and feet. A fine, downy hair (lanugo) covers the limbs and trunk, only to later disappear. The fetus looks very old because the skin is growing so fast that it wrinkles. A waxy, almost cheeselike substance (vernix caseosa) [L. *vernix*, varnish, and *caseus*, cheese] protects the wrinkly skin from the watery amniotic fluid.

From about the fourth month on, the mother can feel movements of the fetal limbs. At about the same time, the fetal heartbeat can be heard through a stethoscope. Conversely, the fetus is able to hear and respond to sounds by about 18 weeks. A fetus born at 24 weeks has a chance of surviving, although the lungs are still immature and often cannot capture oxygen adequately. As a fetus rapidly grows during the third trimester, its chances of surviving being born a month or two prematurely increase dramatically.

The Stages of Birth

When the fetal brain is sufficiently mature, the fetal hypothalamus stimulates the pituitary to release ACTH, causing the adrenal cortex to release androgens into the bloodstream. These diffuse into the placenta, which uses androgens as a precursor for estrogens, hormones that stimulate the production of prostaglandins and oxytocin. All three of these molecules cause the uterus to contract and expel the fetus.

The process of birth (parturition) includes three stages. During the first stage, the cervix dilates to allow passage of the baby's head and body. The amnion usually bursts about this time, an event termed the mother's water breaking. During the second stage, the baby is born and the umbilical cord is cut. During the third stage, the placenta is delivered (Fig. 42.16).

Check Your Progress   42.3

1. Identify the location where fertilization usually occurs in the human female.
2. Name the extraembryonic membrane that gives rise to each of the following: umbilical blood vessels, the first blood cells, and the fetal half of the placenta.
3. Describe the major changes that occur in the human embryo between the third and fifth weeks of development.

a. First stage of birth: cervix dilates

ruptured amniotic sac

b. Second stage of birth: baby emerges

placenta

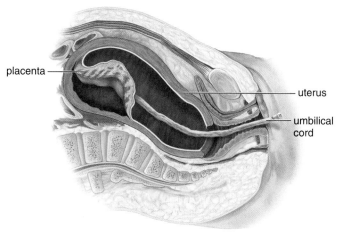

placenta

uterus

umbilical cord

c. Third stage of birth: expelling afterbirth

Figure 42.16 Three stages of parturition. **a.** Position of fetus just before birth begins. **b.** Dilation of cervix and birth of baby. **c.** Expulsion of afterbirth.

42.4 The Aging Process

Learning Outcomes

Upon completion of this section, you should be able to

1. Discuss the effects of aging on various body systems.
2. Compare and contrast the preprogrammed theories to the damage accumulation theories of aging.

Aging and death are as much a part of biology as are development and birth. If animals—and indeed, all forms of life—did not age and eventually die, their exponentially increasing numbers would presumably overwhelm the ability of the Earth to support life. Moreover, aging and death are a critical part of the evolutionary process, because animals that age and die are continuously replaced by individuals with new genetic combinations that can adapt to environmental changes that occur.

The Effects of Aging on Organ Systems

Today's human population is older on average than ever before. In the next half-century, the number of people over age 65 will increase by 147%. Before discussing some possible mechanisms behind the aging process, it seems appropriate to first consider the effects of aging on the various body systems.

Integumentary System

As aging occurs, the skin becomes thinner and less elastic because the number of elastic fibers decreases and the collagen fibers become increasingly cross-linked to each other, reducing their flexibility. There is also less adipose tissue in the subcutaneous layer; therefore, older people are more likely to feel cold. Together these changes typically result in sagging and wrinkling of the skin.

As people age, the sweat glands also become less active, resulting in decreased tolerance to high temperatures. There are fewer hair follicles, so the hair on the scalp and the limbs thins out. Older people also experience a decrease in the number of melanocytes, making their hair gray and their skin pale. In contrast, some of the remaining pigment cells are larger, and pigmented blotches ("age spots") appear on the skin.

Cardiovascular System

Common problems with cardiovascular function are usually related to diseases, especially atherosclerosis (see Chapter 32). However, even with normal aging, the heart muscle does weaken somewhat, and may increase slightly in size as it compensates for its decreasing strength. The maximum heart rate decreases even among the most fit older athlete, and it takes longer for the heart rate and blood pressure to return to normal resting levels following stress. Some part of this decrease in heart function may also be due to blood leaking back through heart valves that have become less flexible.

Aging also affects the blood vessels. The middle layer of arteries contains elastic fibers, which, like collagen fibers in the skin, become more cross-linked and rigid with time. These changes, plus a frequent decrease in the internal diameter of arteries due to atherosclerosis, contribute to a gradual increase in blood pressure with age. Indeed, nearly 50% of older adults have chronic hypertension. Such changes are common in individuals living in Western industrialized countries but not in agricultural societies. This indicates that a diet low in cholesterol and saturated fatty acids, along with a sensible exercise program, may help to prevent age-related cardiovascular disease.

Immune System

As people age, many of their immune system functions become compromised. Because a healthy immune system normally protects the entire body from infections, toxins, and at least some types of cancer, some investigators believe that losses in immune function can play a major role in the aging process.

As noted in Chapter 33, the thymus is an important site for T-cell maturation. Beginning in adolescence, the thymus begins to *involute,* gradually decreasing in size, and eventually becoming replaced by fat and connective tissue. The thymus of a 60-year-old adult is about 5% of the size of the thymus of a newborn, resulting in a decrease in the ability of older people to generate T-cell responses to new antigens.

The evolutionary rationale for this may be that the thymus is energetically expensive for an organism to maintain, and that compared to younger animals that must respond to a high number of new infections and other antigens, older animals have already responded to most of the antigens to which they will be exposed in their life.

Aging also affects other immune functions. Because most B-cell responses are dependent on T cells, antibody responses also begin to decline. This, in turn, may explain why the elderly do not respond as well to vaccinations as young people do. This presents challenges in protecting older people against diseases like influenza and pneumonia, which can otherwise be prevented by annual vaccination.

Not all immune functions decrease in older animals. The activity of natural killer cells, which are a part of the innate immune system, seems to change very little with age. Perhaps by investigating how these cells remain active throughout a normal human life span, researchers can learn to preserve other aspects of immunity in the elderly.

Digestive System

The digestive system is perhaps less affected by the aging process than other systems. Because secretion of saliva decreases, more bacteria tend to adhere to the teeth, causing more decay and periodontal disease. Blood flow to the liver is reduced, resulting in less efficient metabolism of drugs or toxins. This means that, as a person gets older, less medication is needed to maintain the same level in the bloodstream.

Respiratory System

Cardiovascular problems are often accompanied by respiratory disorders, and vice versa. Decreasing elasticity of lung tissues means that ventilation is reduced. Because we rarely use the entire vital capacity, these effects may not be noticed unless the demand for oxygen increases, such as during exercise.

Excretory System

Blood supply to the kidneys is also reduced. The kidneys become smaller and less efficient at filtering wastes. Salt and water balance are difficult to maintain, and the elderly dehydrate faster than young people. *Urinary incontinence* (lack of bladder control) increases with age, especially in women. In men, an enlarged prostate gland may reduce the diameter of the urethra, causing frequent or difficult urination.

Nervous System

Between the ages of 20 and 90, the brain loses about 20% of its weight and volume. Neurons are extremely sensitive to oxygen deficiency, and neuron death may be due not to aging itself but to reduced blood flow in narrowed blood vessels. However, contrary to previous scientific opinion, recent studies using advanced imaging techniques show that most age-related loss in brain function is not due to whatever loss of neurons is occurring. Instead, decreased function may occur due to alterations in complex chemical reactions, or increased inflammation in the brain. For example, an age-associated decline in levels of dopamine can affect brain regions involved in complex thinking.

Perhaps more important than the molecular details, recent studies have confirmed that lifestyle factors can affect the aging brain. For example, animals on restricted calorie diets developed fewer Alzheimer-like changes in their brains. Other positive factors that may help maintain a healthy brain include attending college (the "use it or lose it" idea), regular exercise, and sufficient sleep.

Sensory Systems

In general, with aging more stimulation is needed for taste, smell, and hearing receptors to function as before. A majority of people over age 80 have a significant decline in their sense of smell, and about 15% suffer from *anosmia*, or a total inability to smell. The latter condition can be a serious health hazard, due to the inability to detect smoke, gas leaks, or spoiled food. After age 50, most people gradually begin to lose the ability to hear tones at higher frequencies, and this can make it difficult to identify individual voices and to understand conversation in a group.

Starting at about age 40, the lens of the eye does not accommodate as well, resulting in *presbyopia*, or difficulty focusing on near objects, which causes many people to require reading glasses as they reach middle age. Finally, as noted in Chapter 38, cataracts and other eye disorders become much more common in the aged.

Musculoskeletal System

For the average person, muscle mass peaks between age 16–19 for females and 18–24 for males. Beginning in the 20s or 30s, but accelerating with increasing age, muscle mass generally decreases, due to decreases in both the size and number of muscle fibers. Most people who reach age 90 have 50% less muscle mass compared to when they were 20. Although some of this loss may be inevitable, regular exercise can slow this decline.

Like muscles, bones tend to shrink in size and density with age. Due to compression of the vertebrae, along with changes in posture, most of us lose height as we age. Those who reach age 80 will be about two inches shorter than they were in their 20s. Women lose bone mass more rapidly than men do, especially after menopause. As noted in Chapter 39, osteoporosis is a common disease in the elderly.

Although some decline in bone mass is a normal result of aging, certain extrinsic factors are also important. A proper diet and moderate exercise program has been found to slow the progressive loss of bone mass.

Endocrine System

As with the immune system, aging of the hormonal system can affect many different organs of the body. These changes are complex, however, with some hormone levels tending to decrease with age, while others increase. The activity of the thyroid gland generally declines, resulting in a lower basal metabolic rate. The production of insulin by the pancreas may remain stable, but cells become less sensitive to its effects, resulting in a rise in fasting glucose levels of about 10 mg/dL each decade after age 50.

Human growth hormone (HGH) levels also decline with age, but it is very unlikely that taking HGH injections will "cure" aging, despite internet claims. In fact, one study found that people with lower levels of HGH actually lived longer than those with higher levels.

Reproductive System

Testosterone levels are highest in men in their 20s. After age 30, testosterone levels decrease by about 1% per year. Extremely low testosterone levels have been linked to a decreased sex drive, excessive weight gain, loss of muscle mass, osteoporosis, general fatigue, and depression. However, the levels below which testosterone treatment should be initiated remain controversial. Testosterone replacement therapy, whether through injection, patches, or gels, is associated with side effects like enlargement of the prostate, acne or other skin reactions, and the production of too many red blood cells.

Menopause, the period in a woman's life during which the ovarian and uterine cycles cease, usually occurs between ages 45 and 55. The ovaries become unresponsive to the gonadotropic hormones produced by the anterior pituitary, and they no longer secrete estrogen or progesterone. At the onset of menopause, the uterine cycle becomes irregular, but as long as menstruation occurs, it is still possible for a woman to conceive. Therefore, a woman is usually not considered to have completed menopause (and thus be infertile) until menstruation has been absent for a year.

The hormonal changes during menopause often produce physical symptoms such as "hot flashes" (caused by circulatory irregularities), dizziness, headaches, insomnia, sleepiness, and depression. To ease these symptoms, female hormone replacement therapy (HRT) was routinely prescribed until 2002, when a large clinical study showed that in the long term, HRT caused more health problems than it prevented. For this reason, most doctors no longer recommend long-term HRT for the prevention of postmenopausal conditions.

It is also of interest that, as a group, females live longer than males. It is likely that estrogen offers women some protection against cardiovascular disorders when they are younger. Males suffer a marked increase in heart disease in their 40s, but an increase is not noted in females until after menopause, when women lead men in the incidence of stroke. Men remain more likely than women to have a heart attack at any age, however.

Hypotheses About Why We Age

Aging is a complex process, and multiple factors can affect the aging process. The many hypotheses about why aging occurs can be grouped into two major categories: (1) theories suggesting that aging is mainly due to preprogrammed genetic events and (2) theories that aging is mainly due to the accumulation of cellular damage.

Preprogrammed Theories

Most scientists who study *gerontology*, or the science of aging, believe that aging is partly genetically preprogrammed. This idea is supported by the observation that longevity runs in families, that is, the children of long-lived parents tend to live longer than those of short-lived parents. As would also be expected, studies show that identical twins have a more similar life span than nonidentical twins.

Many laboratory studies of aging have been performed in the nematode *C. elegans*, in which single-gene mutations have been shown to influence the life span. For example, mutations that decrease the activity of a hormone receptor similar to the insulin receptor more than double the life span of the worms, which also behave and look like much younger worms throughout their prolonged lives. Interestingly, small breed dogs like poodles or terriers, which may live 15–20 years, have lower levels of an analogous receptor, compared to large dog breeds that live 6–8 years.

Studies of the behavior of cells grown in the lab also suggest a genetic influence on aging. Most types of differentiated cells can only divide a limited number of times. One factor that may control the number of cell divisions is the length of the *telomeres*, sequences of DNA at the ends of chromosomes. As you learned in Section 12.2, telomeres protect the ends of chromosomes from deteriorating or fusing with other chromosomes. Each time a cell divides, the telomeres normally shorten, and cells with shorter telomeres tend to undergo fewer divisions. Perhaps as we grow older, more and more cells are unable to divide, and instead, they undergo degenerative changes and die.

However, if aging were mainly a function of genes, we would expect much less variation in life span to be observed among individuals of a given species than is actually seen. For this reason, experts have estimated that in most cases, genes account only for about 25% of what determines the length of life.

Damage Accumulation Theories

A second group of hypotheses postulate that aging involves the accumulation of damage over time. In 1900, the average human life expectancy was around 45 years. A baby born in the United States in 2009 is expected to live an average of about 78 years. Since human genes have presumably not changed much in such a short time, most of this gain in life span is due to better medical care, along with the application of scientific knowledge about how to prolong our lives.

There are two basic types of cellular damage that can accumulate over time. The first type can be thought of as agents that are unavoidable; for example, the accumulation of harmful DNA mutations, or the buildup of harmful metabolites. For some time medical researchers have known that proteins—such as the collagen fibers present in many support tissues—become increasingly cross-linked as people age. This cross-linking may account for the inability of such organs as the blood vessels, the heart, and the lungs to function as they once did. Some researchers have now found that glucose has the tendency to attach to any type of protein, which is the first step in a cross-linking process. They are currently experimenting with drugs that can prevent cross-linking.

Figure 42.17 Supercentenarians. The oldest verified human life span was that of Jeanne Calment (1875–1997), who lived 122 years and was documented by the Guinness Book of Records as the "World's Oldest Living Person."

Other sources of cellular damage, however, may be avoidable, such as a poor diet or exposure to the Sun. Recent work suggests that when an animal produces fewer free radicals, it lives longer. Free radicals are unstable molecules that have an unpaired electron. In order to stabilize themselves, free radicals react with another molecule, such as DNA or proteins (e.g., enzymes) or lipids found in plasma membranes. Eventually, these molecules are unable to function, and the cell is destroyed. By increasing one's consumption of natural antioxidants, such as those present in brightly colored and dark green vegetables, citrus fruits, nuts, fish, shellfish, and red wine, we can reduce our exposure to free radicals, and slow the aging process.

The longest-lived human whose age has been verified by modern methods was Jeanne Calment (Fig. 42.17), who lived in France her entire life, and died at the age of 122 years, 164 days (she had lived on her own until age 110, when she entered a nursing home). This is currently considered to be the longest potential human life span. However, our understanding of the aging process could be considered, ironically, to be in its infancy, and animal models and other studies suggest that it may be possible to extend human life far beyond that.

Check Your Progress   42.4

1. Describe how involution of the thymus can lead to decreased responses to vaccines in the elderly.
2. Define menopause, and explain why it occurs.
3. Distinguish between the two hypotheses regarding aging, and give examples of each.

CONNECTING *the* CONCEPTS *with the* THEMES

Evolution

- Many animals go through the same early embryonic stages, e.g., morula, blastula, and gastrula.
- Many of the genes involved in embryonic development—gap genes, pair-rule genes, and homeotic genes—are highly conserved throughout animal species, suggesting they arose very early in evolutionary history.
- Aging and eventual death of individuals is an evolutionary advantage; an infinite population of immortal animals would quickly use up all resources, leading to extinction.

Nature of Science

- The study of early developmental forms of diverse animals like the lancelet, frog, and chick have greatly advanced our understanding of development.
- Modern genetic techniques have allowed identification of key genes and molecules involved in developmental processes.
- Scientists are just beginning to understand the complex array of processes that result in the phenomenon of aging.

Biological Systems

- Animal development begins with fertilization. Early development can be divided into cellular, tissue, and organ stages.
- All cells of the body possess the same DNA sequences. Cellular differentiation involves the processes of cytoplasmic segregation and induction, by which transcription and translation of these sequences is controlled.
- The aging process likely involves a combination of preprogrammed genetic events, plus the accumulated damage from unavoidable events, such as DNA mutations and exposure to environmental agents.

Media Study Tools

Enhance your study of this chapter with study tools and practice tests. Also ask your instructor about the resources available through ConnectPlus, including the media-rich eBook, interactive learning tools, and animations.

Summarize

42.1 Early Developmental Stages

Development begins at fertilization. Only one sperm actually enters the oocyte. Both sperm and egg contribute chromosomes to the diploid zygote.

The early developmental stages in animals proceed from cellular stages to tissue stages to organ stages. During the cellular stage, cleavage (cell division) occurs, but there is no overall growth. The result is a morula, which becomes the blastula when an internal cavity (the blastocoel) appears.

During the tissue stage, gastrulation (invagination of cells into the blastocoel) results in formation of the germ layers: ectoderm, mesoderm, and endoderm. Both the cellular and tissue stages can be affected by the amount of yolk.

Organ formation can be related to germ layers. For example, during neurulation, the nervous system develops from midline ectoderm, just above the notochord. At this point, it is possible to draw a typical cross section of a vertebrate embryo in which the notochord has not been replaced by the vertebral column.

42.2 Developmental Processes

Cellular differentiation begins with cytoplasmic segregation in the egg. After the first cleavage of a frog embryo, only a daughter cell that receives a portion of the gray crescent is able to develop into a complete embryo.

Induction is also part of cellular differentiation. For example, the notochord induces the formation of the neural tube in frog embryos. In *C. elegans*, investigators have shown that induction is an ongoing process in which one type of tissue sequentially regulates the development of other types, through chemical signals coded for by particular genes.

Some morphogen genes determine the axes of the body, and others regulate the development of segments. An important concept has emerged: During development, sequential sets of master genes code for morphogen gradients that activate the next set of master genes in turn.

Homeotic genes control pattern formation such as the presence of antennae, wings, and limbs on the segments of *Drosophila*. Homeotic genes code for proteins that contain a homeodomain, a particular sequence of 60 amino acids. These proteins are also transcription factors, and the homeodomain is the portion of the protein that binds to DNA. Homologous homeotic genes have been found in a wide variety of organisms, and therefore they must have arisen early in the history of life and been conserved.

42.3 Human Embryonic and Fetal Development

Human development can be divided into embryonic development (months 1 and 2) and fetal development (months 3 through 9). Fertiliza-tion occurs in the oviduct, and cleavage occurs as the embryo moves toward the uterus. The morula becomes the blastocyst before implanting in the endometrium of the uterus. The extraembryonic membranes appear early in human development. The trophoblast of the blastocyst is the first sign of the chorion, which goes on to become the fetal part of the placenta.

Exchange occurs between fetal and maternal blood at the placenta. The amnion contains amniotic fluid, which cushions and protects the embryo. The yolk sac and allantois form the umbilical cord, which is a lifeline between the mother and the developing embryo and fetus.

Organ development begins with neural tube and heart formation. There follows a steady progression of organ formation during embryonic development. During fetal development, refinement of organ systems occurs, and the fetus adds weight.

42.4 The Aging Process

The aging process is an essential part of the biology and evolution of animals. Aging affects every organ system of the human body, in mostly predictable ways. Various hypotheses have been advanced to explain the aging process, which can be grouped into those suggesting that aging is genetically preprogrammed, and those emphasizing the accumulation of various types of cellular damage over time.

Key Terms

allantois 805	germ layer 798
amnion 805	homeobox 804
apoptosis 800	homeodomain 804
blastocoel 797	homeotic genes 803
blastocyst 806	human chorionic gonadotropin
blastopore 798	(HCG) 806
blastula 797	implantation 806
cellular differentiation 800	induction 800
chorion 805	maternal determinant 800
chorionic villus 809	menopause 813
cleavage 797	mesoderm 798
cytoplasmic segregation 800	morphogenesis 800
development 797	morula 797
ectoderm 798	neural plate 799
embryo 797	neural tube 799
embryonic development 805	notochord 799
embryonic disk 808	pattern formation 800
endoderm 798	placenta 809
extraembryonic	totipotent 800
membrane 805	trophoblast 806
fertilization 796	umbilical cord 809
gastrula 798	yolk 797
gastrulation 798	yolk sac 805

Assess

Reviewing This Chapter

1. Describe the events of fertilization that (a) allow the sperm to reach the plasma membrane of the secondary oocyte, (b) prevent polyspermy, and (c) result in a diploid zygote. 796–97
2. What happens during the cellular stages, the tissue stages, and the organ stages of early development in animals? 797–99
3. What are the germ layers, and which organs are derived from each of the germ layers? 798–99
4. Draw a cross section of a typical vertebrate embryo at the neurula stage, and label your drawing. 799

5. Describe two mechanisms that are known to be involved in the processes of cellular differentiation.   800–02
6. Describe the classic experiment suggesting that the notochord induces formation of the neural tube.   800–01
7. With regard to *C. elegans*, what is a fate map? How does induction occur?   802
8. With regard to *Drosophila*, what is a morphogen gradient, and what does such a gradient do to bring about morphogenesis?   802
9. What is the function of homeotic genes, and what is the significance of the homeobox within these genes?   803–04
10. List the human extraembryonic membranes, give a function for each, and compare their functions to those in the chick.   805
11. Explain where fertilization, cleavage, the morula stage, and the blastocyst stage occur in humans. What happens to the embryo in the third through fifth weeks?   806, 808–09
12. Describe the structure and the function of the placenta in humans.   809–10
13. List and describe the stages of birth.   810
14. Discuss the effects of aging on the organ systems.   811–13
15. Describe the two major categories of ideas about why we age.   813–14

Testing Yourself

Choose the best answer for each question.

1. Which of these stages is the first one out of sequence?
   a. cleavage
   b. blastula
   c. morula
   d. gastrula
   e. neurula
2. Which of these stages is mismatched?
   a. cleavage—cell division
   b. blastula—gut formation
   c. gastrula—three germ layers
   d. neurula—nervous system
   e. Both b and c are mismatched.
3. A cell that is capable of giving rise to a complete organism is said to be
   a. totipotent.
   b. homeotic.
   c. ectodermal.
   d. differentiated.
   e. induced.
4. Morphogenesis is associated with
   a. protein gradients.
   b. induction.
   c. transcription factors.
   d. homeotic genes.
   e. All of these are correct.
5. In humans, the placenta develops from the chorion. This indicates that human development
   a. resembles that of the chick.
   b. is dependent on extraembryonic membranes.
   c. cannot be compared to that of lower animals.
   d. begins only upon implantation.
   e. Both a and b are correct.

6. In humans, the fetus
   a. is surrounded by four extraembryonic membranes.
   b. has developed organs and is recognizably human.
   c. is dependent on the placenta for excretion of wastes and acquisition of nutrients.
   d. is embedded in the endometrium of the uterus.
   e. Both b and c are correct.
7. Developmental changes
   a. require growth, differentiation, and morphogenesis.
   b. stop occurring when one is grown.
   c. are dependent on a parceling out of genes into daughter cells.
   d. are dependent on activation of master genes in an orderly sequence.
   e. Both a and d are correct.
8. Which of these pairs is mismatched?
   a. brain—ectoderm
   b. gut—endoderm
   c. bone—mesoderm
   d. lens—endoderm
   e. heart—mesoderm
9. Label this diagram illustrating the placement of the extraembryonic membranes, and give a function for each membrane in humans.

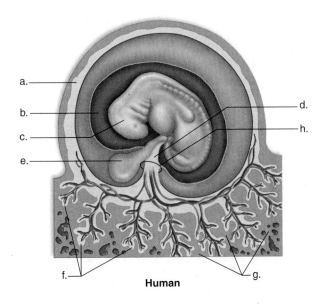

Human

For questions 10–13, match the statement with the terms in the key.

KEY:

   a. apoptosis
   b. homeotic genes
   c. fate maps
   d. morphogen gradients
   e. segment-polarity genes

10. have been developed that show the destiny of each cell that arises through cell division during the development of *C. elegans*
11. occurs when a cell-death cascade is activated
12. can have a range of effects, depending on its concentration in a particular portion of the embryo

13. genes that control pattern formation, the organization of differentiated cells into specific three-dimensional structures

14. The ability of one embryonic tissue to influence the growth and development of another tissue is termed
    a. morphogenesis.
    b. pattern formation.
    c. apoptosis.
    d. cellular differentiation.
    e. induction.

15. Which hormone is sometimes administered to stimulate parturition?
    a. estrogen
    b. oxytocin
    c. prolactin
    d. testosterone
    e. Both b and d are correct.

16. Only one sperm enters and fertilizes a human ovum because
    a. sperm have an acrosome.
    b. the corona radiata gets larger.
    c. the zona pellucida lifts up.
    d. the plasma membrane hardens.
    e. All of these are correct.

17. Which is a correct sequence in humans that ends with the stage that implants?
    a. morula, blastocyst, embryonic disk, gastrula
    b. ovulation, fertilization, cleavage, morula, early blastocyst
    c. embryonic disk, gastrula, primitive streak, neurula
    d. primitive streak, neurula, extraembryonic membranes, chorion
    e. cleavage, neurula, early blastocyst, morula

18. Which of the following is *not* an explanation for why the skin of older people tends to become wrinkled?
    a. increased subcutaneous fat deposition
    b. increased cross-linking of collagen fibers
    c. decreased sebaceous gland activity
    d. decreased number of elastic fibers

19. The onset of menopause is mainly due to
    a. a lack of ovarian follicles that are able to ovulate
    b. an involution of the uterus that begins around age 45
    c. an unresponsiveness of the ovaries to FSH and LH from the pituitary
    d. an increased production of male hormones

20. Possible causes of the cellular damage that can accumulate and contribute to aging include
    a. free radicals
    b. spontaneous DNA mutations
    c. cross-linked proteins
    d. uv radiation
    e. all of the above

Engage

Thinking Scientifically

1. *Drosophila* belongs to the insect order Diptera, in which one pair of wings is the norm. In *Drosophila*, *Ubx* mutation converts the halteres into an extra pair of wings located posterior to the normal pair (see Fig. 42.10a). Butterflies belong to the order Lepidoptera in which two pairs of wings

is normal. The ancestor of both flies and butterflies is thought to have possessed two pairs of wings. However, in butterflies, mutations in *Ubx* have been found to alter pigmentation, spot pattern, and scale morphology in the hindwings, but not the number of wing pairs. What does this tell us about the role of *Ubx* in insect wing development?

Bioethical Issue

Human Embryonic Stem Cell Research

Human embryonic stem cell lines (also called ES cell lines) are obtained by removing the inner cell mass from a blastocyst and growing the cells in a petri dish. The cells are valued by researchers because they are pluripotent, meaning they have the potential to differentiate into a wide range of different types of cells if properly stimulated. At this time, the federal government funds research on ES cell lines that were started before 2001, obtained from extra embryos left over from in vitro fertilization (IVF), and voluntarily donated for scientific study. However, funding for more new cell lines may be obtained from certain state or private sources, and researchers overseas are not subject to U.S. regulations.

Advocates of ES cell research say that such cells could be used to develop cures for conditions such as Parkinson disease, diabetes, heart disease, Alzheimer disease, cystic fibrosis, and spinal cord injuries. In addition, ES cells could be studied to help scientists understand the basic processes of human development and used to test new drugs.

ES cell research opponents say that it should be restricted because it requires the destruction of human life. Many believe that embryos, even those so early in development, should be considered human beings. If so, then producing an excess of them for IVF and then discarding them would be wrong. It might also be wrong to benefit from their destruction.

Stem cells may be obtained from other sources besides embryos. Some, known as embryonic germ cells, are harvested from aborted or miscarried fetuses, but this source is subject to the same sort of controversy as ES cells. Research using stem cells taken from the umbilical cord and placenta has yielded some very promising results; adult tissues such as bone marrow and parts of the brain are other stem cell sources. And as discussed in the Nature of Science feature, "Reproductive and Therapeutic Cloning," in Chapter 9, genetically modified fibroblasts can serve as stem cells. In fact, some of these nonembryonic cells have already been used to treat medical conditions, including blood disorders, spinal cord injury, and heart attack damage. Such stem cells are obtained without the use of embryos or fetuses. However, they appear to be more limited in their ability to differentiate than ES cells.

Should ES cell research continue to be permitted? If so, should it be supported by government funding? Do the origins of the ES cell lines make a difference? These are all decisions that have been faced by voters in recent years and will certainly continue to generate vigorous debate.

Behavior and Ecology

Ecology is the science that describes the interaction between the living and nonliving components of the environment, the role that species play within the environment, and the impact that humans have upon the Earth.

Ecologists have two statements that summarize these interactions: "Everything is affected by everything else" and "There is no free lunch." For example, when tall smokestacks were constructed in the Midwest, the pollutants didn't go away; instead, they caused acid rain in the Northeast. As is so often the case, the only way to solve an ecological problem is to stop the behavior or activity that caused the problem. It must be dealt with head-on.

Ecology describes the biosphere (the portions of the sea, land, and air that contain living things), but today ecology is also an experimental science. Ecologists use the scientific process to determine how ecosystems function and how they will likely respond to human impact. One of the main goals of conservation biology is to help preserve species and manage ecosystems for sustainable human welfare.

UNIT OUTLINE

UNIT LEARNING OUTCOMES

The learning outcomes for this unit focus on three major themes in the life sciences.

Evolution	Natural selection and coevolution have played a significant role in shaping the diversity found within ecosystems.
Nature of Science	Conservation biologists study many aspects of biology in order to determine how best to manage natural resources.
Biological Systems	Ecosystems consist of a complex web of interactions between individuals, species, communities and their environment.

worker

queen

nursing pups

worker

Among naked mole rats, *Heterocephalus glaber*, workers help the queen reproduce.

43

Behavioral Ecology

Naked mole rats spend almost their entire lives underground and are extremely social in the same manner as ants, which also have underground chambers. Like the ants, mole rats have a rigid social hierarchy. At the top is the queen, the only female who reproduces. At the bottom are workers of both sexes, who do not reproduce, but instead work tirelessly to excavate long intricate tunnels and to help the queen reproduce.

Behaviorists ask: Why are mole rats social? And they can give a two-part answer. Mole rats have to dig underground tunnels in order to obtain the roots and tubers that they rely on for food and moisture. Without efficient tunnel digging, a mole rat can't survive, and it takes several mole rats working together to efficiently dig a tunnel. The second part of the answer has to do with their common genes. The queen keeps a harem of very closely related males with whom she mates. The result of this inbreeding is that all members of the colony share about 80% of the same genes. Members of the group largely see to the propagation of their own genes when they help the queen reproduce.

Behavioral ecology, as discussed in this chapter, is dedicated to the principle that natural selection shapes behavior just as it does the anatomy and physiology of an animal.

As you read through the chapter, think about the following questions:

1. What are the benefits and drawbacks of living in a social group?
2. How do genetics and the environment work together to influence behavior?
3. Why are there so few mammal species that exhibit altruism?

BEFORE YOU BEGIN

Before beginning this chapter, take a few moments to review the following discussions.

Section 13.3 How can the environment influence gene expression?

Section 16.2 What role does sexual selection and male competition play in the evolution of the species?

Section 40.2 What role does the endocrine system play in controlling behavior?

FOLLOWING *the* THEMES

CHAPTER 43 BEHAVIORAL ECOLOGY

UNIT 8 BEHAVIOR AND ECOLOGY		
	Evolution	Natural selection has helped shape behavior by selecting the individuals with the most well-adapted traits.
	Nature of Science	Scientists have conducted experiments to show that both genetics and the environment help shape behavior.
	Biological Systems	Animal communication requires a sender and a receiver who can interpret chemical, auditory, visual, and tactile signals.

43.1 Inheritance Influences Behavior

Learning Outcomes

Upon completion of this section, you should be able to

1. Explain the key aspects of studies that suggest behavior has a genetic basis.
2. Describe the body systems that play a role in influencing behavior.

Behavior encompasses any action that can be observed and described. For example, in Chapter 1, Figure 1.15 described the aggressive behavior of male mountain bluebirds toward other males during mating. An investigator was able to center in on this behavior, observe it, and record it objectively. In the same manner, we wish to pose the question of whether genetics can determine the behavior an animal is capable of performing.

The "nature versus nurture" question asks to what extent our genes (nature) and the environment (nurture) influence behavior. We would expect that genes, which control the development of neural and hormonal mechanisms, also influence the behavior of an animal. The results of experiments done to discover the degree to which genetics controls behavior support the hypothesis that most behaviors have, at least in part, a genetic basis.

Experiments That Suggest Behavior Has a Genetic Basis

Among the many animal behavior studies, we summarize two that suggest that behavior has a genetic basis as well as a type of study in humans that attempts to evaluate nature versus nurture.

Nest-Building Behavior in Lovebirds

Lovebirds are small, green-and-pink African parrots that nest in tree hollows. Several closely related species of lovebirds in the genus *Agapornis* build their nests differently. Fischer's lovebirds cut large leaves (or in the laboratory, pieces of paper) into long strips with their bills. They use their bills to carry the strips (Fig. 43.1*a*) to the nest, where they weave them in with others to make a deep cup. In contrast, peach-faced lovebirds cut somewhat shorter strips and they carry them to the nest in a very unusual manner. They pick up the strips in their bills and then insert them into their feathers (Fig. 43.1*b*). In this way, they can carry several of these short strips with each trip to the nest, while Fischer lovebirds can carry only one of the longer strips at a time.

Researchers hypothesized that if the behavior for obtaining and carrying nesting material is inherited, then hybrids might show intermediate behavior. When the two species of birds were mated, the hybrid birds were observed to have difficulty carrying nesting materials. They cut strips of intermediate length and then attempted to tuck the strips into their rump feathers. They did not push the strips far enough into the feathers, however, and when they walked or flew, the strips always came out.

a. Fischer lovebird with nesting material in its beak.

b. Peach-faced lovebird with nesting material in its rump feathers.

Figure 43.1 Nest building behavior in lovebirds. **a.** Fischer lovebirds, *Agapornis fischeri*, carry strips of nesting material in the bill, as do most other birds. **b.** Peach-faced lovebirds, *Agapornis roseicollis,* tuck strips of nesting material into their rump feathers before flying back to the nest.

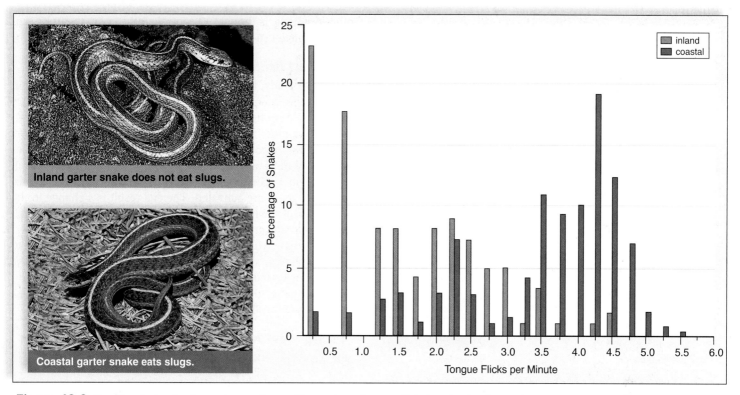

Figure 43.2 Feeding behavior in garter snakes. The number of tongue flicks by inland and coastal garter snakes, *Thamnophis elegans,* is measured in terms of their response to slug extract on cotton swabs. Coastal snakes tongue-flicked more than inland snakes.

Hybrid birds eventually learned, after about three years, to carry the cut strips in their beak, but they still briefly turned their head toward their rump before flying off. These studies support the hypothesis that behavior has a genetic basis.[1]

Food Choice in Garter Snakes

A variety of experiments have been conducted to determine if food preference in garter snakes has a genetic basis. There are two different types of garter snake populations in California. Inland populations are aquatic and commonly feed underwater on frogs and fish. Coastal populations are terrestrial and feed mainly on slugs. In the laboratory, inland adult snakes refused to eat slugs, while coastal snakes readily did so. The experimental results of matings between snakes from the two populations (inland and coastal) show their newborns have an overall intermediate incidence of slug acceptance.

Differences between slug acceptors and slug rejecters appear to be inherited, but what physiological difference is there between the two populations? A clever experiment answered this question. When snakes eat, their tongues carry chemicals to an odor receptor in the roof of the mouth. They use tongue flicks to recognize their prey. Even newborns will flick their tongues at cotton swabs dipped in fluids of their prey. Swabs were dipped in slug extract, and the number of tongue flicks were counted for newborn inland snakes and newborn coastal snakes. Coastal snakes had a higher number of tongue flicks than did inland snakes (Fig. 43.2).

Apparently, inland snakes do not eat slugs because they cannot detect their smell as easily as the coastal snakes. A genetic difference between the two populations of snakes results in a physiological difference in their nervous systems. Although hybrids showed a great deal of variation in the number of tongue flicks, they were generally intermediate, as predicted by the genetic hypothesis.[2]

Twin Studies in Humans

On occasion, human twins have been separated at birth and raised under different environmental conditions. Studies of these twins have shown that they have similar food preferences, activity patterns, and even select mates with similar characteristics. This type of study lends support to the hypothesis that at least certain behaviors are primarily influenced by nature (i.e., the genes).

Experiments That Demonstrate Behavior Has a Genetic Basis

The nervous and endocrine systems are both responsible for the overall coordination of body systems. Studies have shown that the endocrine system plays a role in determining behavior.

Egg-Laying Behavior in Marine Snails

The egg-laying behavior in the marine snail *Aplysia* involves a specific sequence of movements. Following copulation, the

1 Dilger, W. 1962. The behavior of lovebirds. *Scientific American* 206: 89–98.

2 Arnold, S. J. 1981. Behavioral variation in natural populations. I. *Evolution* 35: 489–509.

a.

b. *fosB* alleles present.

c. *fosB* alleles not present.

Figure 43.3 Maternal care in mice. **a.** A mother mouse with *fosB* alleles spends time retrieving and crouching over its young, whereas mice that lack these alleles do not display these maternal behaviors. **b.** This typical mother mouse retrieves her young and crouches over them. **c.** This mouse, lacking *fosB*, does not retrieve her young and does not crouch over them.

animal extrudes long strings of more than a million egg cases. The animal takes the egg case string in its mouth, covers it with mucus, waves its head back and forth to wind the string into an irregular mass, and attaches the mass to a solid object, such as a rock.

Several years ago, scientists isolated and analyzed an egg-laying hormone (ELH) that causes the snail to lay eggs, even if it has not mated. ELH was found to be a small protein of 36 amino acids that diffuses into the circulatory system and excites the smooth muscle cells of the reproductive duct, causing them to contract and expel the egg string. Using recombinant DNA techniques, the investigators isolated the ELH gene. The gene's product turned out to be a protein with 271 amino acids. The protein can be cleaved into as many as 11 possible products, and ELH is one of these. ELH alone, or in conjunction with these other products, is thought to control all the components of egg-laying behavior in *Aplysia*.[3]

Nurturing Behavior in Mice

In another study, investigators found that maternal behavior in mice was dependent on the presence of a gene called *fosB*. Normally, when mothers first inspect their newborn, various sensory information from their eyes, ears, nose, and touch receptors travel to the hypothalamus. This incoming information causes *fosB* alleles to be activated, and a particular protein is produced. The protein begins a process during which cellular enzymes and other genes are activated. The end result is a change in the neural circuitry within the hypothalamus, which manifests itself in maternal nurturing behavior toward the young.

Mice that do not engage in nurturing behavior were found to lack *fosB* alleles, and the hypothalamus fails to make any of the products or to activate any of the enzymes and other genes that lead to maternal nurturing behavior (Fig. 43.3).[4]

Video
Sex and the Senses

Check Your Progress 43.1

1. Identify several genes that have been linked to behavior.
2. Compare the studies that show how behavior has a genetic basis.

43.2 The Environment Influences Behavior

Learning Outcomes

Upon completion of this section, you should be able to

1. Choose the correct sequence of events required for classical and operant conditioning.
2. Identify examples of how the environment influences behavior.

Even though genetic inheritance serves as a basis for behavior, it is possible that environmental influences (nurture) also affect behavior. For example, behaviorists originally believed that some behaviors were **fixed action patterns (FAP),** that is, an unchanging behavioral response. An FAP is elicited by a **sign stimulus**—a particular trigger in the environment. For example, male stickleback fish aggressively defend a territory against other males. In laboratory studies, the male reacts more aggressively to any model that has a red belly like he has, rather than to a model that otherwise looks like a stickleback fish. In

3 Scheller, R. H., Jackson, J. F., et al. 1982. A family of genes that codes for ELH, a neuropeptide eliciting a stereotyped pattern of behavior in *Aplysia. Cell* 28: 707–19.

4 Brown, J. R., Ye, H., et al. 1996. A defect in nurturing in mice lacking the immediate early gene *fosB. Cell* 86: 297–309.

this instance, the color red is a sign stimulus that triggers the aggressive behavior.

male stickleback

Investigators discovered that many behaviors that were originally thought to be FAPs could improve with practice due to the organism's learning. In this context, **learning** is defined as a durable change in behavior brought about by experience. Habituation is a form of learning because, with experience, an animal no longer responds to a particular stimulus. Deer grazing on the side of a busy highway, ignoring traffic, is an example of habituation.

Instinct and Learning

Laughing gull chicks' begging behavior appears to be a FAP, because it is always performed the same way in response to the parent's red bill (the sign stimulus). A chick directs a pecking motion toward the parent's bill, grasps it, and strokes it downward (Fig. 43.4). Parents can bring about the begging behavior by swinging their bill gently from side to side. After the chick responds, the parent regurgitates food onto the floor of the nest. If need be, the parent then encourages the chick to eat. This interaction between the chicks and their parents suggests that the begging behavior involves learning.

To test this hypothesis, diagrammatic pictures of gull heads were painted on small cards, and then eggs were collected from nests in the field. The eggs were hatched in a dark incubator to eliminate visual stimuli before the test. On the day of hatching, each chick was allowed to make about a dozen pecks at the model. The chicks were returned to the nest, and then each was retested.

The tests showed that on average, only one-third of the pecks by a newly hatched chick strike the model. But one day after hatching, more than half of the pecks are accurate, and two days after hatching, the accuracy reaches a level of more than 75%. Investigators concluded that improvement in motor skills and learning can help improve the development of instinctive behaviors.[5]

Imprinting

Imprinting is considered a form of learning. Konrad Lorenz was one of the first individuals to study imprinting in birds. He observed chicks, ducklings, and goslings following the first moving object they saw after hatching. This object is ordinarily their mother. Imprinting in the wild has survival value and leads to reproductive success. This behavior enables an individual to recognize their own species and, therefore, eventually find an appropriate mate.

But in the laboratory, investigators found that birds can seemingly be imprinted on any object—a human or a red ball—if it is the first moving object they see during a sensitive period of two

5 Hailman, Jack P. 1967. The ontogeny of an instinct. *Behavior* (Suppl. 13). (E. J. Brill Academic Publishers, Leiden, Germany.)

Figure 43.4 Pecking behavior in laughing gulls. At about three days, a laughing gull chick grasps the red bill of a parent, stroking it downward, and the parent then regurgitates food. *Right:* The top diagrams show the accuracy of a chick when striking a test probe, painted red. The bottom diagram shows chick-pecking accuracy graphically. Note from these diagrams that a chick markedly improves its ability (within only two days) to peck a bill, a behavior that normally causes a parent to regurgitate food.

Pecking accuracy of newborn

Pecking accuracy of two-day old

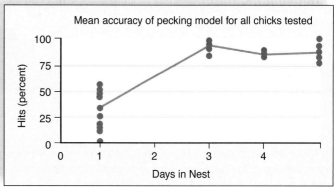

Mean accuracy of pecking model for all chicks tested

Hits (percent)

Days in Nest

to three days after hatching. The term *sensitive period* means the period of time in which a particular behavior develops. A chick imprinted on a red ball follows it around and chirps whenever the ball is moved out of sight.

Social interactions between parent and offspring during the sensitive period seem key to normal imprinting. For example, female mallards cluck during the entire time imprinting is occurring. It could be that vocalization before and after hatching is necessary to normal imprinting.

Goslings imprinted on an investigator

Social Interactions and Learning

White-crowned sparrows sing a species-specific song, but males of a particular region have their own dialect. Birds were caged in order to test the hypothesis that young white-crowned sparrows learn how to sing from older members of their species.

Three groups of birds were tested. Birds in the first group *heard no songs at all.* When grown, these birds sang a song that had a slight resemblance to the adult song. Birds in the second group *heard tapes of white-crowns singing.* When grown, they sang in that dialect, as long as the tapes had been played during a sensitive period from about age 10–50 days. White-crowned sparrows' dialects (or other species' songs) played before or after this sensitive period had no effect on the birds. Birds in a third group did not hear tapes and instead were *given an adult tutor.* No matter when the tutoring began these birds sang a song of a different species. Results like these show that social interactions apparently assist learning in birds.

Associative Learning

A change in behavior that involves an association between two events is termed **associative learning.** For example, birds that get sick after eating a monarch butterfly no longer prey on monarch butterflies, even though they may be readily available. Or the smell of fresh baked bread may entice you, even though you may have just eaten. If so, perhaps you associate the taste of bread with a pleasant memory, such as being at home. Both classical conditioning and operant conditioning are examples of associative learning.

Classical Conditioning

In **classical conditioning,** the paired presentation of two different types of stimuli (at the same time) causes an animal to form an association between them. The best-known laboratory example of classical conditioning is that of an experiment done by the Russian

psychologist Ivan Pavlov. First, Pavlov observed that dogs salivate when presented with food. Then, he rang a bell whenever the dogs were fed. Eventually, the dogs would salivate whenever the bell was rung, regardless of whether food was present (Fig. 43.5).

Classical conditioning suggests that an organism can be trained—that is, conditioned—to associate any response to any stimulus. Unconditioned responses are those that occur naturally, as when salivation follows the presentation of food. Conditioned responses are those that are learned, as when a dog learns to salivate when it hears a bell.

Advertisements attempt to use classical conditioning to sell products. Why do commercials pair attractive people with a product being advertised? The hope is that viewers will associate attractiveness with the product. This pleasant association may cause them to buy the product.

Some types of classical conditioning can be helpful. For example, it's been suggested that you hold a child on your lap when reading to them. Why? Because the child will associate a pleasant feeling with reading.

Operant Conditioning

During **operant conditioning,** a stimulus-response connection is strengthened. Most people know that it is helpful to give an animal a reward, such as food or affection, when teaching it a trick. When we go to an animal show, it is quite obvious that trainers use operant conditioning. They present a stimulus, say, a hoop, and then give a reward (food) for the proper response (jumping through the hoop). Sometimes the reward does not

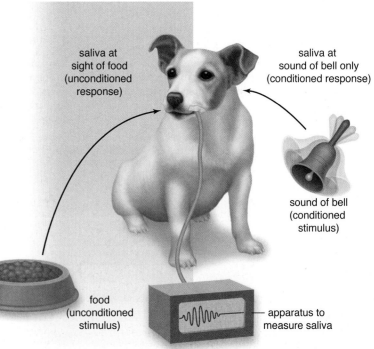

saliva at sight of food (unconditioned response)

saliva at sound of bell only (conditioned response)

sound of bell (conditioned stimulus)

food (unconditioned stimulus)

apparatus to measure saliva

Figure 43.5 Classical conditioning.   Ivan Pavlov discovered classical conditioning by performing this experiment with dogs. A bell is rung when a dog is given food. Salivation is measured. Eventually, the dog salivates when the bell is rung, even though no food is presented. Food is an unconditioned stimulus, and the sound of the bell is a conditioned stimulus that brings about the response—that is, salivation.

need to be immediate. In latent operant conditioning, an animal makes an association without the immediate reward, as when squirrels make a mental map of where they have hidden nuts.

B. F. Skinner was well known for studying this type of learning in the laboratory. In the simplest type of experiment performed by Skinner, a caged rat happens to press a lever and is rewarded with sugar pellets, which it avidly consumes. Thereafter, the rat regularly presses the lever whenever it wants a sugar pellet. In more sophisticated experiments, Skinner even taught pigeons to play Ping-Pong by reinforcing desired responses to stimuli.

In child rearing, it's been suggested that parents who give a positive reinforcement for good behavior will be more successful than parents who punish behaviors they believe are undesirable.

Orientation and Migratory Behavior

Migration is long-distance travel from one location to another. Loggerhead sea turtles hatch on a Florida beach and then travel across the Atlantic Ocean to the Mediterranean Sea, which offers an abundance of food. After several years, pregnant females return to the same beaches to lay their eggs. Every year, monarch butterflies fly from North America to Mexico where they overwinter, and then return in the spring to breed.

At the very least, migration requires **orientation,** the ability to travel in a particular direction, such as south in the winter and north in the spring. Most of the work regarding orientation has been done in birds. Many birds can use the Sun during the day or the stars at night to orient themselves. The Sun moves across the sky during the day, but the birds are able to compensate for this because they have a sense of time. They are presumed to have a biological clock that allows them to know where the Sun will be in relation to the direction they should be going any time of the day.

Experienced birds can also **navigate,** which is the ability to change direction in response to environmental clues. These clues are apt to come from the Earth's magnetic field. Figure 43.6 shows a study that was done with starlings, which typically migrate from the Baltics to Great Britain and return. Test starlings were captured in Holland and transported to Switzerland. Experienced birds corrected their flight pattern and still got to Great Britain. Young, inexperienced birds ended up in Spain instead of Great Britain! **Video Bird Radar**

Migratory behavior has a proximate cause and an ultimate cause. The proximate cause is due to environmental stimuli that tell the birds it is time to travel. The ultimate cause is due to the possibility of reaching a more favorable environment for survival and reproduction. Is the benefit worth the cost—the dangers of the journey? It must be, or else the behavior would not persist.

Cognitive Learning

In addition to the modes of learning already discussed, animals may learn through observation, imitation, and insight. For example, **Video Tool Use by Chimps**

Figure 43.6 Starling migratory experiment. Starlings, *Sturnus vulgaris,* on their way from the Baltics to Great Britain were captured and released in Switzerland. Inexperienced birds kept flying in the same direction and ended up in Spain. Experienced birds had learned to navigate, as witnessed by the fact that they still arrived in Great Britain.

Japanese macaques learn to wash sweet potatoes before eating them by imitating others.

Insight learning occurs when an animal suddenly solves a problem without any prior experience with the situation. The animal appears to call upon prior experience with other circumstances to solve the problem. For example, chimpanzees have been observed stacking boxes to reach bananas in laboratory settings.

Other animals too, aside from primates, seem to be able to reason things out. In one experiment, ravens were offered meat that was attached to string hanging from a branch in a confined aviary. The ravens were accustomed to eating meat, but had no knowledge of how strings work. It took several hours, but eventually one raven flew to the branch, reached down, grabbed

Ravens learn to retrieve food.

the string with its beak, and pulled the string up over and over again, each time securing the string with its foot. Eventually, the meat was within reach, and the raven was able to grab the meat with its beak. Other ravens were then also able to perform this behavior.

Can animals also plan ahead? It seems so. A sea otter saves a particular rock to act as a hard surface against which to bash open clams. A chimpanzee strips leaves off a twig, which it then uses to secure termites from a termite nest.

If animals can think, do they have emotions? This too is an unexplored area that is now an area of interest. The Nature of Science feature explores the possibility that animals have emotions.

Check Your Progress   43.2

1. Describe the type of learning that occurs when an animal no longer tries to eat bumblebees after being stung by one.
2. Give an example that shows how instinct and learning may interact as behavior develops.
3. Discuss evidence that shows that animals have cognitive abilities.

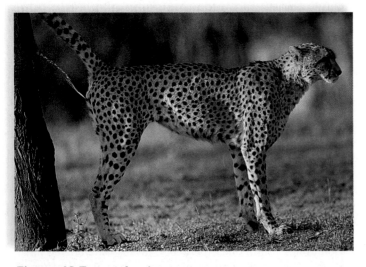

Figure 43.7 Use of a pheromone.   This male cheetah is spraying urine onto a tree to mark its territory.

43.3 Animal Communication

Learning Outcomes

Upon completion of this section, you should be able to

1. Recognize the various ways that animals can communicate.
2. Describe the advantages and disadvantages of chemical, auditory, visual, and tactile communication.

Animals exhibit a wide diversity of social behaviors. Some animals are largely solitary and join with a member of the opposite sex only for the purpose of reproduction. Others will find a mate and cooperate in raising offspring. Some form **societies** in which members of a species are organized in a cooperative manner, extending beyond sexual and parental behavior. We have already mentioned the social groups of naked mole rats, baboons, and red deer (see Chapter 16). Social behavior in these and other animals requires that they communicate with one another.

Communicative Behavior

Communication is an action by a sender that may influence the behavior of a receiver. The communication can be purposeful, but it does not have to be. Bats send out a series of sound pulses and listen for the corresponding echoes to find their way through dark caves and locate food at night. Some moths have an ability to hear these sound pulses, and they begin evasive tactics when they sense that a bat is near. Are the bats purposefully communicating with the moths? No, bat sounds are simply a cue to the moths that danger is near.

Chemical Communication

Chemical signals have the advantage of being effective both night and day. The term **pheromone** [Gk. *phero*, bear, carry, and *monos*, alone] designates a chemical signal in low concentration that is passed between members of the same species. Some animals are capable of secreting different pheromones, each with a different meaning. Female moths secrete chemicals from special abdominal glands, which are detected downwind by receptors on male antennae. The antennae are especially sensitive, and this ensures that only male moths of the correct species (and not predators) will be able to detect them.

Ants and termites mark their trails with pheromones. Cheetahs and other cats mark their territories by depositing urine, feces, and anal gland secretions at the boundaries (Fig. 43.7). Klipspringers (small antelope) use secretions from a gland below the eye to mark twigs and grasses of their territory. Pheromones are known to control the behavior of social insects, as when workers slavishly care for the offspring produced by a queen.

To what degree do pheromones, along with hormones, affect the behavior of animals? Are they responsible for determining whether the animal will carry out parental care, become aggressive, or engage in courtship behavior? Some researchers maintain that human behavior is influenced by pheromones

THEME Nature of Science

Do Animals Have Emotions?

In recent years, investigators have become interested in determining whether animals have emotions. The body language of animals can be interpreted to suggest that they have feelings. When wolves reunite, they wag their tails to and fro, whine, and jump up and down; elephants vocalize—emit their "greeting rumble"—flay their ears, and spin about. Many young animals play with one another or even by themselves, as when dogs chase their own tails. On the other end of the spectrum, upon the death of a friend or parent, chimps are apt to sulk, stop eating, and even die.

It seems reasonable to hypothesize that animals are "happy" when they reunite, "enjoy" themselves when they play, and are "depressed" over the loss of a close friend or relative. Even people who rarely observe animals usually agree about what an animal must be feeling when it exhibits certain behaviors (Fig. 43A).

In the past, scientists found it expedient to collect data only about observable behavior and to ignore the possible mental state of the animal. Why? Because emotions are personal, and no one can ever know exactly how another animal is feeling. B. F. Skinner, whose research method is described earlier in this chapter, regarded animals as robots that become conditioned to respond automatically to a particular stimulus. He and others never considered that animals might have feelings. But now, some scientists believe they have sufficient data to suggest that at least other vertebrates and/or mammals do have feelings, including fear, joy, embarrassment, jealousy, anger, love, sadness, and grief. And they believe that those who hypothesize otherwise should have to present the opposing data.

Perhaps it would be reasonable to consider the suggestion of Charles Darwin, who said that animals are different in degree rather than in kind. This means that animals can feel love but perhaps not to the degree that humans can.

Researcher Bendt Würsig watched the courtship of two baleen whales. They touched, caressed, rolled side-by-side, and eventually swam off together. He wondered if their behavior indicated they felt love for one another. When you think about it, it is unlikely that emotions first appeared in humans with no evolutionary homologies in animals.

Iguanas, but not fish and frogs, tend to stay where it is warm. Canadian biologist Michel Cabanac has found that warmth makes iguanas experience a rise in body temperature and an increase in heart rate. These are biological responses associated with emotions in humans. Perhaps the ability of animals to feel pleasure and displeasure is a mental state that rises to the level of consciousness.

Neurobiological data support the hypothesis that other animals, aside from humans, are capable of enjoying themselves when they perform an activity such as play. Researchers have found a high level of dopamine in the brain of rats when they play, and the dopamine level increases simply when rats anticipate the opportunity to play. Certainly even the staunchest critic is aware that many different species of animals have limbic systems and are capable of fight-or-flight responses to dangerous situations. Can we go further and suggest that animals feel fear even when no observable response has yet occurred?

Laboratory animals may be too stressed to provide convincing data on emotions; we have to consider that emotions evolved under an animal's normal environmental conditions. This makes field research more useful. It is possible to fit animals with devices that transmit information on heart rate, body temperature, and eye movements as they go about their daily routine. Such information would help researchers learn how animal emotions might correlate with their behavior, just as emotions influence human behavior. One possible definition describes emotion as a psychological phenomenon that helps animals direct and manage their behavior.

Marc Bekoff, who is prominent in the field of animal behavior, encourages us to be open to the possibility that animals have emotions. He states:

> By remaining open to the idea that many animals have rich emotional lives, even if we are wrong in some cases, little truly is lost. By closing the door on the possibility that many animals have rich emotional lives, even if they are very different from our own or from those of animals with whom we are most familiar, we will lose great opportunities to learn about the lives of animals with whom we share this wondrous planet.[1]

Questions to Consider

1. If it can be shown that animals have emotions, should animal testing be allowed to continue?
2. Do you think invertebrate animals have emotions? If so, what emotions might they experience?

---

1 Bekoff, M. 2000. Animal emotions: Exploring passionate natures. *Bioscience* 50: 869.

Is the snowshoe hare afraid?

Figure 43A Emotions in animals.

Is the young chimp comforted?

a.

b.

Figure 43.8 Auditory communication. **a.** Vervet monkeys, *Cercopithecus aethiops*, are responding to an alarm call. Vervet monkeys can give different alarm calls according to whether a troop member sights an eagle or a leopard, for example. **b.** The frequency per second of the sound differs for each type call.

wafting through the air—pheromones that are not perceived consciously. They have discovered that like the mouse, humans have an organ in the nose, called the vomeronasal organ (VNO), that can detect not only odors, but also pheromones. The neurons from this organ lead to the hypothalamus, the part of the brain that controls the release of many hormones in the body.

Video Bug Speak

Auditory Communication

Auditory communication (i.e., via sound) has some advantages over other kinds of communication. It is faster than chemical communication, and unlike visual communication, it is effective both night and day. Further, auditory communication can be modified not only by loudness but also by pattern, duration, and repetition. In an experiment with rats, a researcher discovered that an intruder can avoid attack by increasing the frequency with which it makes an appeasement sound.

Male crickets have calls, and male birds have songs for a number of different occasions. For example, birds may have one song for distress, another for courting, and still another for marking territories. Sailors have long heard the songs of humpback whales transmitted through the hull of a ship. But only recently has it been shown that the song has six basic themes, each with its own phrases, that can vary in length and be interspersed with sundry cries and chirps. The purpose of the song

Figure 43.9 Male baboon displaying full threat.

is probably sexual, serving to advertise the availability of the singer. Bottlenose dolphins are known to have one of the most complex languages in the animal kingdom.

Language is the ultimate auditory communication. Humans can produce a large number of different sounds and put them together in many different ways. Nonhuman primates have different vocalizations, each having a definite meaning, such as when vervet monkeys give alarm calls (Fig. 43.8). Although chimpanzees can be taught to use an artificial language, they do not progress beyond the capability level of a two-year-old human child. It has also been difficult to prove that chimps understand the concept of grammar or can use their language to reason. It still seems as though humans possess a communication ability greater than that of other animals.

Video Meerkat Warning Calls

Visual Communication

Visual signals are most often used by species that are active during the day. Contests between males often make use of threat postures that possibly prevent outright fighting. A male baboon displaying full threat is an awesome sight that establishes his dominance and keeps peace within the baboon troop (Fig. 43.9). Hippopotamuses perform territorial displays that include mouth opening.

Many animals use complex courtship behaviors and displays. The plumage of a male Raggiana Bird of Paradise allows him to put on a spectacular courtship dance to attract a female, giving her a basis on which to select a mate. Defense and courtship displays are exaggerated and always performed in the same way so that their meaning is clear. Fireflies use a flash pattern to signal females of the same species (Fig. 43.10).

Video Flirting Flies

Visual communication allows animals to signal others of their intentions without the need to provide any auditory or chemical messages. The body language of students during a lecture provides an example. Students who are leaning forward in their seats and making eye contact with the instructor appear interested and engaged with the material. Students who are leaning back in their chairs and gazing around the room or doodling are indicating that they have lost interest. Instructors can use students' body language to determine whether they are effectively presenting the material and make changes accordingly.

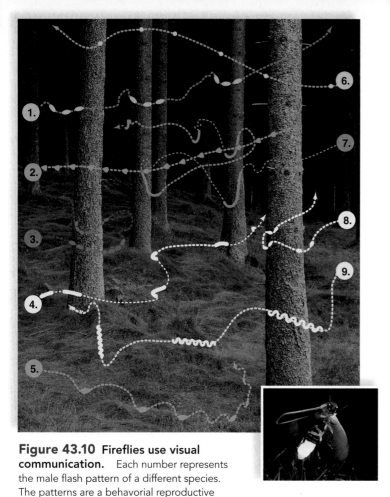

Figure 43.10 Fireflies use visual communication. Each number represents the male flash pattern of a different species. The patterns are a behavorial reproductive isolation mechanism.

The hairstyle and dress of a person, or the way he or she walks and talks, are also ways to send messages. Some studies have suggested that women tend to dress in a more sexually appealing manner when they are ovulating.[6] People who dress in black, move slowly, fail to make eye contact, and sit alone may be telling others that they are unhappy, or simply that they do not want to be socially engaged. Psychologists have long tried to understand how visual clues can be used to better understand human emotions and behavior. Similarly, body language in animals is being evaluated by researchers to determine whether they, as well as humans, have emotions.

Tactile Communication

Tactile communication occurs when one animal touches another. For example, laughing gull chicks peck at the parent's bill to induce the parent to feed them (see Fig. 43.4). A male leopard nuzzles the female's neck to calm her and to stimulate her willingness to mate. In primates, grooming—one animal cleaning the coat and skin of another—helps cement social bonds within a group.

Honeybees use a combination of communication methods, but especially tactile ones, to impart information about the environment. When a foraging bee returns to the hive, it performs a "waggle dance" that indicates the distance and the direction of a food source (Fig. 43.11). As the bee moves between the two

6 Haselton, M. G., et al. 2007. Ovulation and human female ornamentation: Near ovulation, women dress to impress. *Hormones and Behavior* 51: 41–5.

a.

Figure 43.11 Communication among bees. a. Honeybees do a waggle dance to indicate the direction of food. **b.** If the dance is done outside the hive on a horizontal surface, the straight run of the dance will point to the food source. If the dance is done inside the hive on a vertical surface, the angle of the straightaway to that of the direction of gravity is the same as the angle of the food source to the Sun.

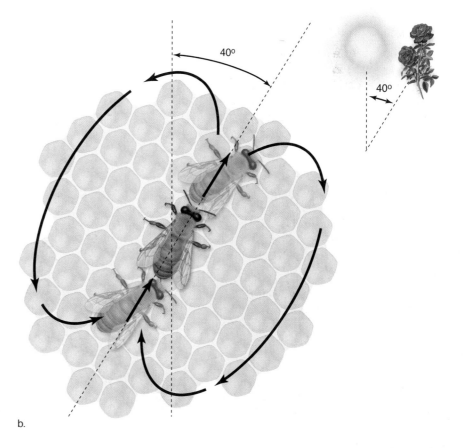

40°

40°

b.

loops of a figure 8, it buzzes noisily and shakes its entire body in so-called waggles. Outside the hive, the dance is done on a horizontal surface, and the straight run indicates the direction of the food. Inside the hive, the angle of the straight run to that of the direction of gravity is the same as the angle of the food source with the Sun. In other words, a 40° angle to the left of vertical means that food is 40° to the left of the Sun.

Bees can use the Sun as a compass to locate food because they have a biological clock, which allows them to compensate for the movement of the Sun in the sky. A biological clock is an internal means of telling time. Today, we know that the timing of the clock, in both insects and mammals (including humans), requires alterations in the expression of a gene called *period*.

Check Your Progress   43.3

1. Describe examples of how communication is meant to affect the behavior of the receiver.
2. Give an advantage and disadvantage to each type of communication discussed.
3. Identify the human receptor for each type of communication discussed.

Figure 43.12 Male and female gibbons. Siamang gibbons, *Hylobates syndactylus*, are monogamous, and they both share the task of raising offspring. They also share the task of marking their territory by singing. As is often the case in monogamous relationships, the sexes are similar in appearance. Male is above and female is below.

43.4 Behaviors That Increase Fitness

Learning Outcomes

Upon completion of this section, you should be able to

1. Describe how territoriality and the foraging techniques associated with it will increase fitness.
2. Recognize various strategies that will increase an individual's fitness.

Behavioral ecology begins with the assumption that behavior is subject to natural selection. It has been shown that behavior has a genetic basis, and investigators believe that certain behaviors lead to increased survival and production of offspring. Therefore, the behavior we can observe today in a species must have adaptive value. These types of behaviors in particular have been studied for their adaptive value: territoriality, reproductive strategies, social behaviors, and altruistic behaviors.

Territoriality and Fitness

In order to gather food, animals often have a particular home range where they carry out daily activities. The portion of the range that is defended for an animal's exclusive use, in which competing members of its species are not welcome, is called its **territory.** The behavior of defending one's territory is called **territoriality.** An animal's territory may have a good food source, and it may be the area in which the animal will reproduce.

As an example, gibbons live in the tropical rain forest of South and Southeast Asia. Normally, their home range can be covered in about 3–4 days, and they are also monogamous and territorial. Territories are maintained by loud singing (Fig. 43.12). Males sing just before sunrise, and mated pairs sing duets during the morning. Males, but not females, show evidence of fighting to defend their territory in the form of broken teeth and scars. Defense of a territory has a certain cost; it takes energy to sing and fight off others.

What is the adaptive value of being territorial? Chief among the benefits of territoriality are to ensure a source of food, to have breeding opportunities, and to have a place to rear young. The territory has to be the right size for the animal. Too large a territory cannot be defended, and too small a territory may not contain enough resources.

Cheetahs require a large territory in order to hunt for their prey. As a result, they need to mark their territory in a fashion that will last for awhile. As shown in Figure 43.7, cheetahs, like many dogs, use urine to mark their territory. Hummingbirds are known to defend a very small territory because they depend on only a small patch of flowers as their food source.

Territoriality is more likely to occur during times of reproduction. Seabirds have very large home ranges consisting of hundreds of kilometers of open ocean, but when they reproduce they become fiercely territorial. Each bird has a very small territory consisting of only a small patch of beach where they place their nest.

Video
Cichlid Territoriality

Foraging for Food

Food gathering is technically called foraging for food. An animal needs to acquire a food source that will provide more energy than the effort of acquiring the food. In one study, it was shown that shore crabs prefer to eat intermediate-sized mussels if they are given equal numbers of a variety of sizes. The net energy gain is greater than if the crabs eat larger-sized mussels; the large mussels take too much energy to open per the amount of energy they provide (Fig. 43.13). The **optimal foraging model** states that it is adaptive for foraging behavior to be as energetically efficient as possible.

Even though it can be demonstrated that animals that take in more energy during foraging are more likely to produce a greater number of offspring, other factors also come into play in survival. If an animal is killed and eaten, it has no chance of producing offspring—for example, if it forages in a way that puts it into danger. Animals often face trade-offs that lead to modification of their behavior toward maximizing their success.

Reproductive Strategies and Fitness

Many primate species are **polygamous,** meaning that a single male mates with multiple females. Because of gestation and lactation, females tend to invest more energy in their offspring than do males. Under these circumstances, it is adaptive for females to be concerned with a good food source. When food sources are clumped, females congregate in small groups around the food. Because only a few females are expected to be receptive at a time, males will likely be able to defend these few from other males. Males are expected to compete with other males for the limited number of receptive females available (Fig. 43.14).

A limited number of primates are **polyandrous,** meaning that a female mates with multiple males. Tamarins are squirrel-sized New World monkeys that live in Central or South America. Tamarins live together in groups of one or more families in which one female mates with more than one male. The female normally gives birth to twins of such a large size that the fathers, and not the mother, carry it about. This may be the reason these animals are polyandrous. Polyandry also occurs when the

Figure 43.14 Hamadryas baboons.   Among Hamadryas baboons, *Papio hamadryas*, a male, which is silver-white and twice the size of a female, keeps and guards a harem of females with whom he mates exclusively.

environment does not have sufficient resources to support several young at a time.

We have already mentioned the reproductive strategy of gibbons. They are **monogamous,** which means that they pair bond, and both male and female help with the rearing of the young. Males are active fathers, frequently grooming and handling infants. Monogamy is relatively rare in primates, which includes prosimians, monkeys, and apes (only about 18% are monogamous). In primates, monogamy occurs when males have limited mating opportunities, territoriality exists, and the male is fairly certain the offspring are his. In gibbons, females are evenly distributed in the environment, which can lead to an increase in aggression between females. Investigators note that females will attack an electronic speaker when it plays female sounds in their territory.

Sexual Selection

Sexual selection is a form of natural selection that favors features that increase an animal's chances of mating. In other words, these features are adaptive in the sense that they lead to increased fitness.

Sexual selection most often occurs due to female choice, which leads to male competition. Because most females produce a limited number of eggs relative to the number of sperm produced by the male, it is adaptive for females to be choosy about their mate. If they choose a mate that passes on features to a male offspring that will cause him to be chosen by females, the parents' fitness has increased.

Whether females actually choose features that are adaptive to the environment is in question. For example, peahens are likely to choose peacocks that have the most elaborate tails. Such a fancy tail could otherwise be detrimental to the male and make him more likely to be captured by a predator. In one study, an extra ornament was attached to a father zebra finch, and the daughters of this bird underwent the process of imprinting (see Section 43.2). Now, these females were more likely to choose a mate that also had the same artificial ornament.

While females can always be sure an offspring is theirs, males do not have this certainty. However, males produce a plentiful supply of sperm. The best strategy for males to increase their fitness, therefore, is to have as many offspring as possible. Competition may be required for them to gain access to females, and ornaments such as antlers can enhance a male's

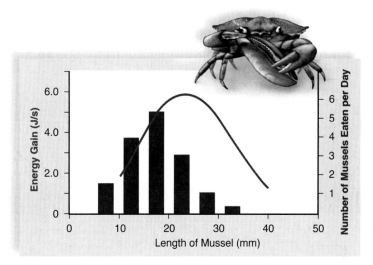

Figure 43.13 Foraging for food.   When offered a choice of an equal number of each size of mussel, the shore crab, *Carcinus maenas,* prefers the intermediate size. This size provides the highest rate of net energy return. Net energy is determined by the yield per time used in breaking open the shell.

THEME Evolution

Sexual Selection in Male Bowerbirds

At the start of the breeding season, male bowerbirds use small sticks and twigs to build elaborate display areas called bowers (Fig. 43B). They clear the space around the bower and decorate the area with items used to attract females. After the bower is complete, the male spends most of his time near his bower, calling to females, renewing his decorations, and guarding his work against possible raids by other males.

A female may approach, and then the male begins his display. He faces her, fluffs up his feathers, and flaps his wings to the beat of a call. If the female enters the bower, the two will mate. Some males mate with up to 25 females per year. Biologists discovered that females often chose males that had well-built bowers with well-decorated platforms.

Male bowerbirds are not gaudy in appearance, but their displays are highly intense and aggressive. Their courtship displays are similar to those used by males during aggressive encounters with other males. Males must display intensely to be attractive, but males that are too intense too soon can startle females. Females may benefit from mating with the most intensely displaying males, but if they are startled, they may not be able to efficiently assess male traits.

Communication between the two sexes might maximize the potential benefits of intense male courtship displays while minimizing the potential costs. Females make crouching motions, and the degree of crouching reflects the level of display intensity she will tolerate without being startled. By giving higher-intensity displays when females increase their crouching, males could increase their courtship success by displaying intensely enough to be attractive without threatening females.

The hypothesis tested was that males respond to female crouching signals by adjusting their intensity, and that a particular male's ability to respond to female signals is related to his success in courtship. A male's ability to modify his courtship display was difficult to measure in natural courtships, because it was not clear whether males were responding to females, or vice versa. To solve this problem, a robotic female bowerbird was used.

Using these "fembots," researchers were able to control female signals and measure male response in experimental courtships. Experiments showed that in general, male Satin Bowerbirds modulate their displays in response to robotic female crouching (Fig 43Ba). Video cameras were used to monitor behaviors at bowers, allowing each male's courtship/mating success to be measured. It was found that males who modulate their displays more effectively in response to robotic female signals startle real females less often in natural courtships, and are thus more successful in courting females (Fig. 43Bb).

The results suggest that females prefer intensely displaying males as mates, and that successful males modulate their intensity in response to female signals, thus producing displays attractive to females without threatening them.[1]

Male responsiveness to female signals may be an important part of successful courtship in many species. Sexual selection may favor the ability of males to read female signals and adjust courtship displays accordingly.

Questions to Consider

1. Why would it be more adaptable for a male bowerbird to be aggressive and have an intense courtship display instead of being gaudy?
2. How would an extremely intense male bowerbird mate?

1 Patricelli, G. L., Uy, J. A. C., Walsh, G., and Borgia, G. 2002. Sexual selection: Male displays adjusted to female's response. *Nature* 415: 279–80.

b.

c.

a.

Figure 43B Courtship success of males.   a. Among Satin Bowerbirds, *Ptilonorhynchus violaceus*, the male bowerbird prepares the bower and typically decorates its platform with blue objects. **b.** Some males are better able to vary the intensity of their courtship display depending on the crouch rate of a robotic female, and these males startle real females less often. **c.** Experimenters found that males who respond best under experimental conditions do startle live females less and do have better courtship success.

Figure 43.15 Competition. During the mating season, bull elk, *Cervus elaphus,* males may find it necessary to engage in antler wrestling in order to have sole access to females in a territory.

ability to fight (Fig. 43.15). When bull elk compete, they issue a number of loud screams that give way to a series of grunts. If a clear winner hasn't emerged, the two bulls walk in parallel to show each other their physique. If this doesn't convince one or the other to back off, the pair resorts to ramming each other with their antlers. The intent of the fight is for one male to gain dominance over the other, not to kill his rival—although these encounters may on occasion have fatal consequences due to injury or mishap.

Societies and Fitness

The principles of evolutionary biology can be applied to the study of social behavior in animals. Sociobiologists hypothesize that living in a society has a greater reproductive benefit than reproductive cost. A cost-benefit analysis can help determine whether this hypothesis is supported.

Group living does have its benefits. It can help an animal avoid predators, rear offspring, and find food. A group of impalas is more likely to hear an approaching predator than a solitary one. Many fish moving rapidly in many directions might distract a would-be predator. Weaver birds form giant colonies that help protect them from predators. The birds may also share information about food sources. Members of the same baboon troop signal to one another when they have found an especially bountiful fruit tree. Lions working together are able to capture large prey, such as zebra and buffalo.

Figure 43.16 Queen ant. A queen ant, *Solenopsis geminata,* has a large abdomen for egg production and is cared for by small ants, called nurses. The idea of inclusive fitness suggests that relatives, in addition to offspring, increase an individual's reproductive success. Therefore, sterile nurses are being altruistic when they help the queen produce offspring to whom they are closely related.

Group living also has its disadvantages. When animals are crowded together into a small area, disputes can arise over access to the best feeding places and sleeping sites. Dominance hierarchies are one way to apportion resources, but this puts subordinates at a disadvantage. Among red deer, sons are preferable because, as a harem master, sons will result in a greater number of grandchildren. However, sons, being larger than daughters, need to be nursed more frequently and for a longer period of time. Subordinate females do not have access to enough food resources to adequately nurse sons, and therefore tend to rear only daughters. Still, like the subordinate males in a baboon troop, subordinate females in a red deer harem may be better off in terms of fitness if they stay with a group, despite the cost involved.

Video Harris Hawks

Living in close quarters exposes individuals to illness and parasites that can easily pass from one animal to another. Social behavior helps to offset some of the proximity disadvantages. For example, baboons and other types of social primates invest a significant amount of time grooming one another. This most likely decreases their chances of contracting parasites. Humans use extensive medical care to help offset the health problems that arise from living in the densely populated cities of the world.

Altruism Versus Self-Interest

Altruism [L. *alter,* the other] is a behavior that has the potential to decrease the lifetime reproductive success of the altruist, while benefiting the reproductive success of another member of the society. In some insect societies, reproduction is limited to only one pair, the queen and her mate. For example, among army ants, the queen is inseminated only during her nuptial flight. The rest of her life is spent producing her offspring (Fig. 43.16).

The army-ant society has three different sizes of sterile female workers. The smallest workers (3 mm), called the nurses, take care of the queen and larvae, feeding them and keeping them clean. The intermediate-sized workers, constituting most of the population, go out on raids to collect food. The soldiers (14 mm), with huge heads and powerful jaws, run along the sides and rear of raiding parties and protect the column of ants from attack by intruders.

Although this type of society is rare in mammals, the introduction to this chapter describes how mole rats have a similar type of societal structure.

Can the altruistic behavior of sterile workers be explained in terms of fitness, which is judged by reproductive success? The answer is that genes are passed from one generation to the next in two quite different ways. The first way is direct: A parent can pass a gene directly to an offspring. The second way is indirect: A relative that reproduces can pass a shared gene to the next generation. *Direct selection* is adaptation to the environment due to the reproductive success of an individual. *Indirect selection,* called **kin selection,** is adaptation to the environment due to the reproductive success of the individual's relatives. The **inclusive fitness** of an individual includes personal reproductive success as well as the reproductive success of relatives.

Examples of Inclusive Fitness

Among social bees, social wasps, and ants, the queen is diploid (2n), but her mate is haploid (n). If the queen has had only one mate, sister workers are more closely related to each other. They share, on average, 75% of their genes because they inherit 100% of their father's alleles. Their potential offspring would share, on average, only 50% of their genes with the queen. Therefore, a worker can achieve a greater inclusive fitness by helping her mother (the queen) produce additional sisters than by directly reproducing. Under these circumstances a behavior that appears altruistic is more likely to evolve.

Indirect selection can also occur among animals whose offspring receive only a half set of genes from both parents. Consider that your brother or sister shares 50% of your genes, your niece or nephew shares 25%, and so on. Therefore, the survival of two nieces or nephews is worth the survival of one sibling, assuming they both go on to reproduce.

Among chimpanzees in Africa, a female in estrus frequently copulates with several members of the same group, and the males make no attempt to interfere with each other's matings. How can they be acting in their own self-interest? Genetic relatedness appears to underlie their apparent altruism. Members of a group share more than 50% of their genes in common because members never leave the territory in which they are born.

Reciprocal Altruism

In some bird species, offspring from a previous clutch of eggs may stay at the nest to help parents rear the next batch of offspring. In a study of Florida scrub jays, the number of fledglings produced by an adult pair doubled when they had helpers. Mammalian offspring are also observed to help their parents (Fig. 43.17). Among jackals in Africa, solitary pairs managed to rear an average of 1.4 pups, whereas pairs with helpers reared 3.6 pups.

What are the benefits of staying behind to help? First, a helper is contributing to the survival of its own kin. Therefore, the helper actually gains a fitness benefit. Second, a helper is more likely than a nonhelper to inherit a parental

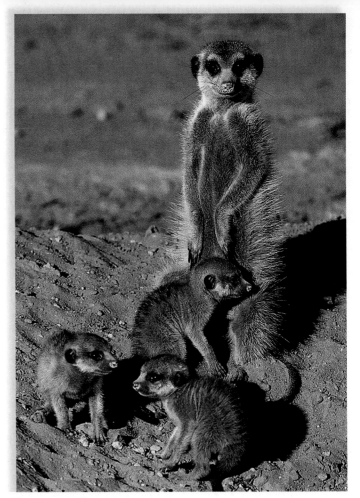

Figure 43.17 Inclusive fitness. A meerkat is acting as a babysitter for its young sisters and brothers while their mother is away. Researchers point out that the helpful behavior of the older meerkat can lead to increased inclusive fitness.

territory—including other helpers. Helping, then, involves making a short-term reproductive sacrifice in order to increase future reproductive potential. Therefore, helpers at the nest are also practicing a form of **reciprocal altruism.**

Reciprocal altruism also occurs in animals that are not necessarily closely related. In this event, an animal helps or cooperates with another animal with no immediate benefit. However, the animal that was helped repays the debt at some later time. Reciprocal altruism usually occurs in groups of animals that are mutually dependent. Cheaters in reciprocal altruism are recognized and are not reciprocated in future events.

An example of this type of reciprocal altruism occurs in vampire bats that live in the tropics. Bats returning to the roost after a feeding activity share their blood meal with other bats in the roost. If a bat fails to share blood with one that had previously shared blood with it, the cheater bat will be excluded from future blood sharing.

Check Your Progress 43.4

1. Explain how territoriality is related to foraging for food.
2. Compare and contrast reproductive strategies and forms of sexual selection.
3. Describe examples of how altruistic behavior is in the self-interest of the animal.

CONNECTING *the* CONCEPTS *with the* THEMES

Evolution

- Animal behavior, like other characteristics, can be acted upon by natural selection.
- For a behavior to persist for long periods of time, it cannot have negative consequences upon the population.
- Behaviors that increase fitness have a high probability of persisting in a population.

Nature of Science

- Research has shown that both nature and nurture—that is, genes and the environment—determine behavior.
- Behavior can be modified by experience (learning).

Biological Systems

- Animals possess a number of systems that enable them to respond to stimuli—primarily the nervous system and the endocrine system, which have far-reaching effects.
- Sexual selection has helped shape mating behaviors by helping to ensure that those with highest fitness reproduce the most.

Media Study Tools

www.mhhe.com/maderbiology11

Enhance your study of this chapter with study tools and practice tests. Also ask your instructor about the resources available through ConnectPlus, including the media-rich eBook, interactive learning tools, and animations.

Summarize

43.1 Inheritance Influences Behavior

Investigators have long been interested in the degree to which nature (genetics) or nurture (environment) influences behavior. Hybrid studies with lovebirds produce results consistent with the hypothesis that behavior has a genetic basis. Garter snake experiments indicate that the nervous system controls behavior. Studies of human twins have shown that certain types of behavior are apparently inherited. DNA studies of marine snails indicate that the endocrine system also controls behavior.

43.2 The Environment Influences Behavior

Even behaviors formerly thought to be fixed action patterns (FAPs), or otherwise inflexible, sometimes can be modified by learning. The red bill of laughing gulls initiates chick begging behavior. However, with experience, chick begging behavior improves and the chicks demonstrate an increased ability to recognize parents.

Other studies suggest that learning is involved in behaviors. Imprinting in birds, which occurs during a sensitive period, causes them to follow the first moving object they see. Song learning in birds involves various elements—including the existence of a sensitive period during which an animal is primed to learn—and the positive benefit of social interactions.

Associative learning includes classical conditioning and operant conditioning. In classical conditioning, the pairing of two different types of stimuli causes an animal to form an association between them. In this way, dogs will salivate at the sound of a bell. In operant conditioning, animals learn behaviors because they are rewarded when they perform them.

Orientation and migratory behavior occur in several groups of animals. Orientation is the ability to move in a certain direction, but migration can require navigation, and is a learned ability to change direction if need be. Animals use the Sun, stars, and the Earth's magnetic field in order to migrate.

Imitation and insight learning does occur in animals. Insight learning has occurred when an animal can solve a new and different problem without prior experience.

43.3 Animal Communication

Communication is an action by a sender that affects the behavior of a receiver. Chemical, auditory, visual, and tactile signals are forms of communication that foster cooperation that benefits both the sender and the receiver. Pheromones are chemical signals that are passed between members of the same species. Auditory communication includes language, which may occur between other types of animals and not just humans. Visual communication allows animals to signal others without the need of auditory or chemical messages. Tactile communication is often associated with sexual behavior.

43.4 Behaviors That Increase Fitness

Traits that promote reproductive success are expected to be advantageous overall, despite any possible disadvantage. Some animals are territorial and defend a territory where they have food resources and can reproduce. When animals choose those foods that return the most net energy, they have more energy left over for reproduction.

Reproductive strategies include monogamy, polygamy, and polyandry. Which strategy is employed depends on the animal and its environment. Sexual selection is a form of natural selection that selects for traits that increase an animal's fitness. Males produce many sperm and are expected to compete to inseminate females. Females produce few eggs and are expected to be selective about their mates.

Living in a social group can have its advantages (e.g., ability to avoid predators, raise young, and find food). It also has disadvantages (e.g., tension between members, spread of illness and parasites, and reduced reproductive potential). When animals live in groups, the benefits must outweigh the costs or the behavior would not exist.

In most instances, the individuals of a society act to increase their own fitness (ability to produce surviving offspring). In this context, it is necessary to consider inclusive fitness, which includes personal reproductive success and also the reproductive success of relatives. Sometimes animals perform altruistic acts, as when individuals help their parents rear siblings. Social insects help their mother reproduce, but this behavior seems reasonable when we consider that siblings share 75% of their genes. Among mammals, a parental helper may be likely to inherit the parent's territory. In reciprocal altruism, animals aid one another for future benefits.

Key Terms

Assess

Reviewing This Chapter

1. Describe two studies that suggest behavior has a genetic basis. 820–21
2. Describe two studies that show that behavior has a genetic basis. 821–22
3. How does an experiment with laughing gull chicks support the hypothesis that environment (nurture) influences behavior? 823
4. Describe two types of associative learning. 824–25
5. Give examples of the different types of communication among members of a social group. 826, 828–30
6. What is territoriality, and how might it increase fitness? 830
7. Name three types of reproductive strategies, and describe how they can be related to the environment. 831
8. What is sexual selection, and why does it foster female choice and male competition during mating? 831
9. Give examples of behaviors that appear to be altruistic but actually increase the inclusive fitness of an individual. 833–34

Testing Yourself

Choose the best answer for each question.
For questions 1–4, match the type of learning in the key with its description. Answers may be used more than once.

Key:

   a. classical conditioning
   b. insight learning
   c. imprinting
   d. migration

1. Ducks follow the first moving object they see after hatching.
2. A dog salivates when a bell is rung.
3. Starlings fly between the Balkins and Great Britain in the fall and spring.
4. Chimpanzees pile up boxes to reach bananas.
5. Behavior is
   a. any action that is learned.
   b. all responses to the environment.
   c. any action that can be observed and described.

   d. all activity that is controlled by hormones.
   e. unique to birds and humans.

6. Which one of the following is considered, by behaviorists, to control (in part or in whole) animal behavior?
   a. circulatory and respiratory systems
   b. respiratory and digestive systems
   c. digestive and nervous systems
   d. nervous and endocrine systems
   e. All systems of the body control behavior.

7. Which of the following is not an example of a genetically based behavior?
   a. Inland garter snakes do not eat slugs, while coastal populations do.
   b. One species of lovebird carries nesting strips one at a time, while another carries several.
   c. One species of warbler migrates, while another one does not.
   d. Snails lay eggs in response to egg-laying hormone.
   e. Wild foxes raised in captivity are not capable of hunting for food.

8. How would the following graph differ if pecking behavior in laughing gulls was a fixed action pattern?
   a. It would be a diagonal line with an upward incline.
   b. It would be a diagonal line with a downward incline.
   c. It would be a horizontal line.
   d. It would be a vertical line.
   e. None of these is correct.

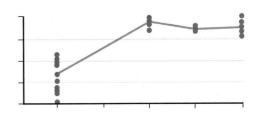

9. Using treats to train a dog to do a trick is an example of
   a. imprinting.
   b. tutoring.
   c. vocalization.
   d. operant conditioning.

10. The benefits of imprinting generally outweigh the costs because
   a. an animal that has been imprinted on the wrong object can be reimprinted on the mother.
   b. imprinting behavior never lasts more than a few months.
   c. animals in the wild rarely imprint on anything other than their mother.
   d. animals that imprint on the wrong object generally die before they pass their genes on.

11. In white-crowned sparrows, social experience exhibits a very strong influence over the development of singing patterns. What observation led to this conclusion?
   a. Birds only learned to sing when they were trained by other birds.
   b. The window in which birds learn from other birds is wider than that when birds learn from tape recordings.
   c. Birds can learn different dialects only from other birds.
   d. Birds that learned to sing from a tape recorder could change their song when they listened to another bird.

12. Which of the following best describes classical conditioning?
    a. The gradual strengthening of stimulus-response connections that seemingly are unrelated.
    b. A type of associative learning in which there is no contingency between response and reinforcer.
    c. The learning behavior in which an organism follows the first moving object it encounters.
    d. The learning behavior in which an organism exhibits a fixed action pattern from the time of birth.

13. The observation that male bowerbirds decorate their nests with blue objects favored by females can best be associated with
    a. insight learning.
    b. imprinting.
    c. sexual selection.
    d. altruism.

14. Migratory behavior
    a. has a higher cost than a benefit.
    b. affects the reproductive strategy.
    c. pertains only to birds.
    d. involves the ability to navigate.

For problems 15–19, match the type of communication in the key with its description. Answers may be used more than once.

Key:

    a. chemical communication
    b. auditory communication
    c. visual communication
    d. tactile communication

15. Aphids (insects) release an alarm pheromone when they sense they are in danger.

16. Male peacocks exhibit an elaborate display of feathers to attract females.

17. Ground squirrels give an alarm call to warn others of the approach of a predator.

18. Male silk moths are attracted to females by a sex attractant released by the female moth.

19. Sage grouses perform an elaborate courtship dance.

20. Bees that do a waggle dance are teaching other bees
    a. how to dance.
    b. where to find food.
    c. how to find and use the Sun for navigation.
    d. how to use auditory communication.

Engage

Virtual Lab
Mealworm Behavior

The virtual lab "Mealworm Behavior" provides an interactive method of studying the factors that influence behavior in animals.

Thinking Scientifically

1. Meerkats are said to exhibit altruistic behavior because certain members of a population act as sentries. How would you test the hypothesis that sentries are engaged in altruistic behavior?

2. You are testing the hypothesis that human infants instinctively respond to higher-pitched voices. Your design is to record head turns toward speakers when they play voices in different pitches. When you do the experiment using several different infants, your data support your hypothesis. However, prior learning by infants is still a serious criticism. What is the basis of this criticism?

Bioethical Issue
Putting Animals in Zoos

In light of the 2010 death of a Sea World trainer by a 5-ton orca whale, many people have questioned the ethical nature of keeping animals in captivity.

If we keep animals in zoos, are we depriving them of their freedom? Some point out that freedom is never absolute. Even an animal in the wild is restricted in various ways by its abiotic and biotic environment. Many modern zoos keep animals in habitats that nearly match their natural ones so that they have some freedom to roam and behave naturally—but is this really possible with an animal such as an orca?

Today, reputable zoos rarely go out and capture animals in the wild—they usually get their animals from other zoos. Most people feel it is not a good idea to take animals from the wild. Certainly, zoos should not be involved in the commercial and often illegal trade of wild animals that still goes on today. Many zoos today are involved in the conservation of animals, rather than just exploitation of animals for exhibit. They provide the best home possible while animals are recovering from injury or increasing their numbers until they can be released to the wild. Can we perhaps look at zoos favorably if they show that they are keeping animals under good conditions and are also involved in preserving animals? In your opinion, which animals are suited to a life in captivity, and which are not?

Appendix A

Answer Key

Chapter 1

Check Your Progress

1.1: 1. Populations are all of the organisms of a species in a given area, while an ecosystem contains groups of populations (a community) plus the physical environment. 2. Organization, acquisition and use of energy, homeostasis, response to the environment, reproduction and development, and adaptation. 3. Adaptations allow organisms to survive in changing environments; the changes as a result of adaptations represent evolution.
1.2: 1. Domain, Kingdom, Phylum, Class, Order, Family, Genus, Species. 2. Protists are generally unicellular organisms; fungi are multicellular filamentous organisms that absorb food; plants are multicellular organisms that are usually photosynthetic; animals are multicellular organisms that must ingest and process their food. 3. Members of a population that have new adaptive traits reproduce more than other members, and therefore pass on these traits to the next generation in a greater proportion.
1.3: 1. Individuals interact with members of the same species (a population), with other populations (communities), and with the physical environment (ecosystem). 2. By altering the physical environment of the ecosystem such as with pollution, increased urbanization, agriculture, etc. 3. They are more vulnerable, because high biodiversity ecosystems often depend on species with very specific roles that are more vulnerable to changes in the environment.
1.4: 1. Experiments test the contribution of the experimental variable to a given observation. 2. Test groups are exposed to the experimental variables, while control groups are not. 3. Hypotheses are tested by designing experiments that examine the contribution of a single experimental variable to the observation, and by statistically comparing the response of a test group to that of a control group in an experiment.

Testing Yourself

1. c; **2.** The brain thinks but nerve cells do not think; **3.** b; **4.** b; **5.** d; **6.** d; **7.** b; **8.** a; **9.** c; **10.** e; **11.** b; **12.** b; **13.** Energy is brought into an ecosystem for the first time through photosynthesis. The Sun provides energy for photosynthesis. **14.** Excess carbon dioxide emitted alters its level in the atmosphere. This excess carbon dioxide is more readily available to photosynthetic plants and protists, possibly causing them to overpopulate. **15.** Not necessarily, if the new organism does not serve as prey for one species, allowing it to overpopulate, or if it does not prey on or compete with existing species in the ecosystem.

Chapter 2

Check Your Progress

2.1: 1. Atomic number is the number of protons in an atom. Atomic mass is the approximate sum of the masses of the protons and neutrons. 2. Groups indicate the number of electrons in the outer, or valence, shell of an atom. In Group VII , all the atoms including chlorine have seven electrons in the valence shell. Periods indicate the number of shells present in an atom. All atoms in Period III, including chlorine, have 3 shells. 3. Radiation can be used to kill diseased cells, such as those present in cancer. The radiation is used to damage cancer cell DNA, leading to cell death. **2.2:** 1. Ionic and covalent bonds are similar in that both involve electrons, but differ as to whether the electrons are shared or not. Ionic bonds are created when one atom gives up electron(s) and another gains electron(s) so that both atoms have outer shells filled. Covalent bonds are formed when two atoms share electrons to fill their outer shells. 2. Calcium gives away its two outer electrons in order to have a complete outer shell. Calcium then has two more protons than electrons, creating a net charge of +2. 3. By sharing with four hydrogen atoms, carbon acquires the four electrons it needs to fill its outer shell. Hydrogen has only one shell, which is complete with two electrons; therefore, each of four hydrogens can acquire a needed electron by sharing with carbon. **2.3:** 1. Water can absorb a lot of heat energy without large changes in temperature. Because of water's heat-absorbing properties, coastal cities can maintain relatively constant temperatures, even when the Sun's heat energy fluctuates. 2. Much heat energy can be put into water. As water evaporates, it takes heat energy with it, allowing a child playing in a sprinkler to dissipate body heat during a hot summer day. 3. If frozen water were heavier than liquid water, ponds and other bodies of water would freeze from the bottom up. The insulation provided by a layer of floating ice would be lost, and organisms living in aquatic environments would likely freeze to death. Water freezes from the top down because ice is less dense than water; the reason is that hydrogen bonds become more open when water freezes. **2.4:** 1. An acid dissociates in water to release hydrogen ions. A base either takes up hydrogen ions or releases hydroxide ions. 2. Living organisms require relatively narrow pH conditions to function. Both trees and fish die when their environment becomes too acidic. 3. Decreasing the blood's ability to resist large changes in pH would be catastrophic and likely cause biological malfunction or death.

Testing Yourself

1. d; **2.** e; **3.** c; **4.** c; **5.** a; **6.** d; **7.** e; **8.** b; **9.** b; **10.** Red circle is oxygen (partial negative charge). White circles are hydrogen (partial positive charge)**; 11.** c; **12.** a; **13.** a; **14.** e; **15.** b; **16.** d; **17.** a; **18.** c; **19.** b.

Chapter 3

Check Your Progress

3.1: 1. A carbon atom bonds with up to four different elements. Carbon–carbon bonds are stable, so long chains can be built; chains can have branching patterns, and chains can form rings. Isomers are possible. 2. 2-carbon alcohols and 2-carbon carboxylic acids are both soluble in water; however, the acid is more soluble because it easily donates its hydrogen. Both alcohols and acids become less soluble as the number of carbons increases. 3. The degradation, or hydrolysis, of a biomolecule requires water. If no water is present the molecule won't be cut into pieces without some other factor, such as heat.
3.2: 1. Humans have no digestive enzymes capable of breaking the bonds in cellulose. 2. The monomer in cellulose is glucose; in chitin, an amino group is attached to each glucose. Cellulose is found in plant cell walls, while chitin is in the exoskeleton of some animals. **3.3:** 1. In water, oxygen and hydrogen atoms share their electrons unequally in their covalent bonds, resulting in a charge across the bonds, giving the molecule an overall polarity. In lipids, the carbon–carbon covalent bonds tend to share their electrons equally, resulting in no polarity. Because like dissolves like, these physical differences between water and lipids prevent their mixing. 2. A saturated

fatty acid contains no double bonds between carbon atoms, while an unsaturated fatty acid contains one or more double bonds. Saturated fatty acids are flat and tend to stack densely in specific locations in blood vessels, reducing blood flow. Unsaturated fatty acids are kinked, and therefore do not block blood vessels to the same degree as saturated fats. 3. Because like dissolves like, phospholipids, which have hydrophilic and hydrophobic domains, arrange themselves so that their hydrophilic heads are adjacent to water, while the hydrophobic tails point inward toward each other. **3.4:** 1. A polypeptide is composed of a sequence of amino acids that are specified by the sequence of bases within a gene in the DNA. 2. Because like dissolves like, hydrophobic amino acids aggregate away from water in an aqueous environment, whereas hydrophilic amino acids associate with water. 3. Hydrophobic interactions play a major role in protein folding, as do pH, temperature, salt concentration, and other factors. **3.5:** 1. A nucleic acid stores information in the sequences of bases within a gene. Gene sequences specify amino acid sequences, thus assembling the proteins that carry out the functions of life. 2. Phosphate, 5-carbon sugar, and nitrogen-containing base. 3. ATP contains 3 phosphate molecules that are strongly negative and repel each other. The covalent bonds attaching them contain considerable potential energy, which can be captured when the bonds are broken and used to do cellular work.

Testing Yourself

1. c; **2.** e; **3.** e; **4.** b; **5.** b; **6.** c; **7.** d; **8.** d; **9.** c; **10. a.** monomer; **b.** monomer; **c.** dehydration reaction; **d.** H_2O; **e.** monomer; **f.** monomer; **g.** polymer; **11.** c; **12.** d; **13.** d; **14.** a; **15.** a; **16.** b; **17.** b; **18.** d; **19.** b; **20.** d.

Chapter 4

Check Your Progress

4.1: 1. Living organisms are made up of one or more cells, which form the basic unit of life. New cells are produced from old cells. Energy flows within cells. 2. Organisms are composed of cells; both cells and organisms are systems in that they balance input and output and use energy to metabolize. The components of each provide structure and function that is greater than the sum of its parts. 3. The movement of materials into and out of a cell requires a sufficiently large surface area relative to cell volume. Cells that are overly large have an insufficient surface-area-to-volume ratio, thus limiting their overall size. **4.2:** 1. Prokaryotic cells lack a membrane-bounded nucleus, which is present in a eukaryotic cell. 2. Cell envelope:

mesosome, plasma membrane, cell wall, glycocalyx. Cytoplasm: inclusion bodies, nucleoid, ribosomes. Appendages: conjugation pilus, fimbriae, flagellum. **4.3:** 1. Separates various metabolic processes; localizes enzymes, substrates, and products; and allows cells to become specialized. 2. Organelles effectively divide cellular work, so that incompatible processes can occur simultaneously. This division of labor enables the cell to more quickly respond to changing environments. 3. The proportion of a given organelle can change based on cellular function. For example, a muscle cell may have a more extensive endoplasmic reticulum due to its need to regulate ions; a nerve cell has more plasma membrane to help conduct electrical signals over long distances. **4.4:** 1. Cells tightly regulate what enters and exits the nucleus by the use of nuclear pores. 2. Hereditary information encoded in genes located in the nucleus is transcribed into RNA molecules, some of which specify amino acid sequence in proteins. Amino acid sequence is determined by RNA sequence through translation. Polypeptides produced from RNA are then folded into a three-dimensional structure that has biological function. **4.5:** 1. Rough ER contains ribosomes, while smooth ER does not. Rough ER synthesizes proteins and modifies them, while smooth ER synthesizes lipids, among other activities. 2. Membrane-enclosed organelles work together as part of a larger endomembrane system within the cell. Transport vesicles from the ER proceed to the Golgi apparatus, which modifies their contents and repackages them in new vesicles to be delivered to specific locations within the cell based on a molecular address. Incoming food and other particles are packaged inside vesicles and delivered to lysosomes, which help to break down the food for energy or for building cellular structures. 3. Golgi malfunction would prevent materials from reaching their necessary destinations, disrupting cellular function and likely leading to cell death. **4.6:** 1. Both peroxisomes and lysosomes enclose enzymes; a peroxisome is a metabolic assistant to other organelles; a lysosome digests molecules and can break down cell parts and their component molecules. 2. Peroxisomal proteins are generally made in the cytoplasm and imported into the peroxisome, whereas lysosomal proteins are made in the ER and sent through the Golgi apparatus. Lysosomal proteins are made in the cytoplasm and the ER. Lysosomal proteins are sent to the lysosome via a molecular address. **4.7:** 1. Chloroplasts and mitochondria are similar in size to bacteria, also have multiple membranes, replicate via binary fission, and have circular genomes. 2. ATP is produced during photosynthesis and cellular respiration via proton gradients across

membranes. In photosynthesis, ATP provides the energy necessary to produce sugar; in respiration, ATP is the primary product and is subsequently used in many metabolic processes. **4.8:** 1. Microtubules help maintain cellular shape and provide an internal road system used to transport intracellular materials. Intermediate filaments anchor cells to each other and components in the external environment. Actin filaments are used in some forms of cellular movement. 2. Cilia and flagella are both composed of microtubules arranged in a particular pattern and enclosed by the plasma membrane. Cilia are shorter than flagella. ATP is used to produce cellular movement via microtubules. 3. Cellular movement from microtubules is accomplished via motor molecules that use ATP.

Testing Yourself

1. c; **2.** c; **3.** d; **4.** a; **5.** c; **6.** c; **7.** a; **8.** c; **9.** b. **10.** b; **11.** e; **12.** a OR d; **13.** a; **14.** b, mitochondria, because both have double membranes and metabolize energy; c, flagellum, because both require the use of microtubules; d, smooth and rough, because both use membrane-embedded proteins to properly function.

Chapter 5

Check Your Progress

5.1: 1. The plasma membrane is a phospholipid bilayer with cholesterol and embedded proteins. Cholesterol helps maintain membrane fluidity across a range of temperatures. Without cholesterol, membranes would become too fluid at high temperatures and too solid at low temperatures, thus preventing necessary life processes. 2. Proteins are embedded or associated with membranes, creating a mosaic. These proteins influence membrane function. Membranes are considered a fluid mosaic because the phospholipids and membrane proteins can freely move within the membrane. 3. Membrane cores are hydrophobic due to the fatty acid tails of phospholipids. Hydrophobic substances can freely move across the membrane. In contrast, hydrophilic substances require transport mediated by membrane proteins or other mechanisms. **5.2:** 1. Hydrophilic water is able to move across hydrophobic membranes by means of an aquaporin channel protein in membranes. 2. Both move molecules from high to low concentration. Diffusion does not require a membrane or transport proteins, while facilitated transport does. **5.3:** 1. Both require a carrier protein, but active transport also requires energy because unlike facilitated diffusion it moves material against its concentration gradient. 2. Both use vesicles to transport materials across the plasma membrane. Vesicles created as materials enter the cell and reduce membrane surface area, whereas vesicles from the Golgi apparatus increase surface area. The net result of this vesicle traffic is little or no net change in the plasma membrane surface area. **5.4:** 1. The extracellular matrix is composed of polysaccharides and proteins that have a multitude of functions. In addition, the matrix in bone contains mineral salts. 2. A primary cell wall is composed of cellulose and other molecules, such as pectin. Secondary cell walls contain cellulose fibrils and lignin that adds rigidity and strength. 3. Both gap junctions in animals and plasmodesmata in plants allow water and other small molecules to freely pass between adjacent cells.

Testing Yourself

1. **a.** hypertonic—cell shrinks due to loss of water; **b.** hypotonic—central vacuole expands due to gain of water; **2.** b; **3.** b; **4.** b; **5.** c; **6.** c; **7.** e; **8.** e; **9.** b; **10.** b; **11.** See Figure 5.1, page 86; **12.** b; **13.** e; **14.** d; **15.** a; **16.** e.

Chapter 6

Check Your Progress

6.1: 1. Potential energy is stored in the bonds present within the glucose molecule. 2. It takes energy to clean a messy room. The input of energy helps to create the structure associated with a clean room. However, it takes little time and energy for the room to become disorganized and messy again. This is consistent with the second energy law, which states that every energy transformation increases disorder. Entropy is the tendency toward disorder. **6.2:** 1. ATP holds energy but gives it up because it is unstable and the last phosphate group can be easily removed, releasing energy. 2. ATP can donate a phosphate to energize a compound for a reaction. The addition of a high-energy negatively charged phosphate can change the molecule's shape and in that way bring about a structural change that in turn changes its function. **6.3:** 1. They bring reactants together at their active site or position a substrate so it is ready to react. Because enzymes interact very specifically with their reactants, the products produced from enzymes can be regulated, such as is seen in metabolic pathways. 2. Cofactors provide another level of control that cells use to regulate enzyme products. This control enables the cell to maximize its efficiency and ability to survive. **6.4:** 1. Plants fix carbon dioxide from the air to create carbohydrate molecules used for energy and plant structure. Animals consume plants and break these carbohydrates down to derive energy for life processes, and in so

doing produce carbon dioxide as a by-product. This cyclical relationship between plants and animals is essential to life on Earth. 2. Energized electrons are used to create ATP via proton gradients in plants and animals.

Testing Yourself

1. e; **2.** e; **3.** e; **4.** e; **5.** d; **6.** b; **7. a.** active site; **b.** substrates; **c.** product; **d.** enzyme; **e.** enzyme-substrate complex; **f.** enzyme. The shape of an enzyme is important to its activity because it allows an enzyme-substrate complex to form. **8.** a; **9.** a; **10.** c; **11.** b; **12.** c; **13.** c; **14.** c; **15.** e; **16.** c; **17.** e; **18.** c; **19.** e; **20.** See Figure 6.13, page 115.

Chapter 7

Check Your Progress

Plants, algae, and cyanobacteria. 2. Thylakoid membrane absorbs solar energy, and carbohydrate forms in stroma. **7.2:** 1. O_2 is reduced to CH_2O and when the oxygen in water gives its H_2 ($2 H^+ + 2 e^-$), it is oxidized. 2. Enzymes are used to regulate chemical reactions during photosynthesis. **7.3:** 1. Visible light is a small part of the overall electromagnetic spectrum. It ranges from purple to red light. 2. Low energy electrons within chlorophyll in Photosystem II are excited to a higher energy state by sunlight. The high potential energy of these excited electrons is siphoned off during redox reactions in the electron transport chain, creating proton gradients across the thylakoid membrane. These electrons are excited again to a higher energy state by Photosystem I, which harnesses the energy to create NADPH. **7.4:** 1. A 3-carbon G3P molecule would require 3 turns of the Calvin cycle because each turn adds a carbon molecule. RuBP must also be regenerated in order for the cycle to continue. **7.5:** 1. C_4 plants include many grasses, sugarcane, and corn; CAM plants include cacti, stonecrops, orchids, and bromeliads. 2. C_4 plants prevent oxygen from competing with carbon dioxide for an active site on the enzyme rubisco.

Testing Yourself

1. e; **2.** d; **3.** a; **4.** a, b; **5.** c; **6.** a, b, c; **7.** b; **8.** d; **9.** T; **10.** F; **11.** F; **12.** e; **13.** e; **14.** c; **15.** See Figure 7.5, page 123; **f.** thylakoid membranes; **g.** stroma; **16.** a; **17.** e; **18.** e; **19.** c; **20.** d.

Chapter 8

Check Your Progress

8.1: 1. Step-by-step breakdown allows the released energy to be captured and utilized by

the cell. Rapid breakdown would be destructive to the cell. 2. Glycolysis, the preparatory reaction, the citric acid cycle, and the electron transport chain. The prep reaction and the citric acid cycle release CO_2. ETC produces H_2O. **8.2:** 1. During the energy-investment steps, ATP breakdown provides the phosphate groups to activate substrates. During the energy-harvesting steps, NADH and ATP are produced. 2. ADP and phosphate from the cytoplasm are connected together during substrate-level ATP synthesis via enzymes from glycolysis. **8.3:** 1. In the absence of oxygen, cells derive energy through fermentation by continually regenerating NAD^+ so it can be reduced to NADH during glycolysis. **8.4:** 1. Per glucose molecule, the first 2 CO_2 molecules are produced during the preparatory reaction, and the remaining 4 CO_2 molecules are produced during the citric acid cycle. 2. The electron transport chain produces the most ATP during glycolysis breakdown. 3. A dam holds back water, just as the inner membrane holds back hydrogen ions. As water flows over a dam, electricity is produced. As hydrogen ions flow down their concentration gradient through an ATP synthase complex, ATP is produced. **8.5:** 1. Catabolic and anabolic processes are regulated by enzymes, which allow a cell to respond to environmental changes. 2. Both have an inner membrane (thylakoids in chloroplasts; cristae in mitochondria) where complexes form an ETC, and ATP is produced by chemiosmosis. Both have a fluid-filled interior (in the stroma of chloroplasts, NADPH helps reduce CO_2 to a carbohydrate; and in the matrix of mitochondria, NAD helps oxidize glucose products with the release of CO_2).

Testing Yourself

1. b; **2.** c; **3.** a; **4.** c; **5.** c; **6.** c; **7.** a; **8.** b; **9.** e; **10.** c; **11.** a; **12.** c; **13.** b; **14.** b; **15.** c; **16.** a; **17.** c; **18.** a; **19.** b; **20.** b.

Chapter 9

Check Your Progress

9.1: 1. G_1, S, G_2, and M stage. DNA is replicated during S stage, and cell division occurs during M stage. 2. DNA damage, failure to properly replicate the DNA, and failure of chromosomes to attach properly to spindle. 3. Apoptosis controls the overall density of cells by targeting excess cells, or cells with damage, for cell death. **9.2:** 1. Prophase: the nuclear membrane fragments, the nucleus disappears, the chromosomes condense, and the spindle begins to form. Metaphase: the chromosomes align along a central line in the cell. Anaphase: the sister chromatids separate and head to opposite poles. Telophase: the nuclear envelope re-forms, chromosomes decondense; the spindle disassociates. 2. Animal cells furrow and plant cells have a cell plate. Because plant cells have rigid cell walls, they cannot furrow. 3. Because the number of times most cells can divide is controlled, stem cells provide source material for tissues that need to continuously replace cells. **9.3:** 1. Cancer cells lack differentiation, have abnormal nuclei, fail to undergo apoptosis, may form tumors that may undergo angiogenesis, and may also metastasize throughout the body. 2. Malignant tumor cells enter circulation and lodge in other tissues of the body. Benign tumors remain in the tissue in which they form 3. a. Cell commits to cell division even in the absence of proper stimuli. b. Cell fails to stop dividing because the proper stimuli to stop are absent. **9.4:** 1. Binary fission involves inward growth of plasma membrane and cell wall concomitant with the separation of the duplicated chromosome attached to the plasma membrane. Mitosis always involves a mitotic spindle to distribute the daughter chromosomes. 2. Prokaryotes usually have a single, small circular chromosome with a few genes and only a few associated proteins. Eukaryotes have many long, linear chromosomes, which contain many thousands of genes and many more proteins.

Testing Yourself

1. b; **2.** e; **3.** c; **4.** a; **5.** b; **6.** b; **7.** b; **8.** e; **9.** b; **10.** c; **11.** e; **12.** b; **13.** c; **14.** c; **15.** b; **16.** d; **17.** a; **18.** c; **19.** d; **20. a.** chromatid of chromosome; **b.** centriole; **c.** spindle fiber or aster; **d.** nuclear envelope (fragment); early prophase.

Chapter 10

Check Your Progress

10.1: 1. Homologous chromosomes represent two copies of the same kind of chromosome, each containing the same genes for traits in the same order. They are also similar in length and location of the centromere. 2. Homologous chromosomes replicate prior to meiosis I, producing sister chromatids. When they separate each daughter cell receives one pair of sister chromatids, resulting in a reduction from 2n to n chromosomes. Meiosis II splits the sister chromatids, producing n chromosomes in each daughter cell. 3. A bivalent is formed between homologous chromosomes to enable crossing over and strand exchange. This increases the potential genetic variability of the offspring. **10.2:** 1. Independent assortment of chromosomes increases the number of possible combinations of chromosomes in each gamete. Crossing-over shuffles the alleles between homologous

chromosomes to create even more variation. 2. 2^4 or 16 possible combinations. 3. Genetic variability ensures that at least some individuals have traits that may allow a species to survive adverse conditions. **10.3:** 1. Two daughter cells that share the same parent cell from meiosis I are identical unless crossing-over has occurred. 2. Pairs of homologous chromosomes would not split, resulting in cells with incorrect chromosome combinations. Without proper reduction in chromosome number, offspring would have incorrect chromosome combinations and would likely not survive. **10.4:** 1. In metaphase I of meiosis, homologous chromosomes are paired at the metaphase plate with each homologue facing opposite spindle poles. In metaphase II and mitotic metaphase, homologous chromosomes are not paired, and sister chromatids are attached to spindle fibers from opposite spindle poles. 2. Meiosis II resembles mitosis because sister chromatids are separated during both processes. Meiosis II differs from mitosis because the cells are haploid and not diploid. **10.5:** 1. In males, the primary spermatocytes are located within the testes; in females, the primary oocytes are located within the ovaries. 2. Oogenesis produces a single cell, containing the bulk of the cytoplasm and other cellular contents in the one cell that will undergo embryonic development. Spermatogenesis produces four haploid cells, each of which could potentially merge with the haploid egg to create a diploid organism. **10.6:** 1. Nondisjunction in meiosis may cause aneuploidy, an extra or missing chromosome. 2. Sex chromosome aneuploidy is more common because only one of the X chromosomes is active. Any extra X chromosomes become Barr bodies. 3. An inversion involves the reversal of a piece of a chromosome from within, and normally does not cause symptoms. A translocation is swapping of two chromosome fragments from one to the other, and while not usually troublesome, may cause severe problems in offspring if the two chromosomes go into separate cells.

Testing Yourself

1. b; **2.** d; **3.** e; **4.** b; **5.** d; **6.** c; **7.** e; **8.** b; **9.** d; **10.** 24, 12; **11.** spermatogenesis, oogenesis; **12.** fertilization; **13.** diploid, haploid; **14.** b; **15.** b; **16.** a; **17.** d; **18.** a; **19.** a.

Chapter 11

Check Your Progress

11.1: 1. Mendel chose a good model organism, always followed the same well-planned procedure, kept careful records, and analyzed his data mathematically. 2. The garden pea has easily observed traits, a relatively short generation time, each plant

produces many offspring (peas), and cross pollination is only possible by hand. **11.2A:** 1.a. all W; b. 1/2 W, 1/2 w; c. 1/2 T, 1/2 t; d. all T. 2. bb. 3. 3:1, 40. **11.2B:** 1. LG, Lg, lG, lg. 2. 9:3:3:1. **11.2C:** 1. 75% yellow; 25% green. 2. 25%. 3. Tt x tt; **11.2D:** 1. cc, Cc. 2. 25%. 3. woman: Hh; husband: hh. 4. 50%. **11.3A:** 1. A_1A_2. 2. child: ii; mother: $I^A i$; father: $I^A i$, $I^B i$, or i. **11.3B:** 1. Mother $X^B X^b$; father, $X^B Y$; female offspring are $X^B X^b$, and males are $X^b Y$. 2. a. 100%; b. none; c. 100%. 3. $X^b X^b$ mother and $X^B Y$ father. Female offspring will be $X^B X^b$ and have black hair and be carriers; male children will be $X^b Y$ and have brown hair.

Testing Yourself

1. b; **2.** a; **3.** c; **4.** d; **5.** c; **6.** d; **7.** a; **8.** b; **9.** b; **10.** b; **11.** a; **12.** d; **13.** d; **14.** c; **15.** c; **16.** b; **17.** a; **18.** c; **19.** autosomal dominant.

Answers to Figures

11.10. Individual III-1 must be heterozygous since their offspring IV-1 and IV-2 are homozygous recessive (aa).

11.11. Individual III-1 must be heterozygous since their offspring III-3 is homozygous recessive (aa).

Chapter 12

Check Your Progress

12.1: 1. All life on Earth is based on the same four bases in DNA: A, G, C, and T. Because the genetic code is universal, expressing a foreign gene in an organism is possible. 2. DNA is a right-handed double helix with two strands that run in opposite directions. The backbone is composed of alternating sugar-phosphate groups, and the molecule is held together in the center by hydrogen bonds between interacting bases. A always hydrogen-bonds to T, and G to C. **12.2:** 1. (1) The DNA strands are separated by DNA helicase, (2) new nucleotides are positioned by complementary base pairing, and (3) new nucleotides are joined together by DNA polymerase to form a new DNA strand. 2. Prokaryotic DNA replication begins at a single origin of replication and usually proceeds in both directions toward a termination region on the opposite side of the chromosome. Eukaryotic DNA replication begins at multiple origins of replication and continues until the replication forks meet. 3. Telomerase enables eukaryotic chromosomes to fully replicate by using an RNA template in the enzyme to create repeat sequences on the end of linear chromosomes. **12.3:** 1. Information from a gene coded within the DNA is copied into mRNA. mRNA sequence dictates the sequence of amino acids in a protein, which produces the observable traits for an organism. The flow of genetic information is DNA to RNA to protein to trait. 2. mRNA carries information from DNA to direct the synthesis of a protein. rRNA makes up part of the ribosomes that are used to translate messenger RNAs. tRNA transfers amino acids to the ribosome during protein synthesis. 3. Several different codons may specify the same amino acid.

12.4: 1. Transcription reads the template strand in the 3′ to 5′ direction and produces a complementary mRNA strand that is 5′ to 3′. The mRNA has the same orientation and sequence as the gene strand in the DNA and uses uracil instead of thymine. 2. During mRNA processing introns are spliced out and the exons joined together, and a 5′ guanosine cap and a 3′ poly-A tail are added. 3. A pre-mRNA transcript contains noncoding sequences called introns that are spliced out leaving coding sequences, called exons, in the mature mRNA. 4. If a gene strand in the DNA has the sequence 5′ ATGGGCATT 3′, and a template strand sequence of 5′ AATGCCCAT 3′, the mRNA sequence would be 5′ AUGGGCAUU 3′. 5. The ability to create multiple mRNA molecules from a single gene through alternative splicing enables a cell to create a wider variety of proteins whose diversity may positively affect organism survival.

12.5: 1. Transfer RNA delivers amino acids to the ribosome by binding to the appropriate codon on the mRNA being translated. 2. A ribosome consists of a small and large subunit. Each subunit is composed of a mixture of protein and rRNA. Large and small ribosomal subunits work to connect amino acids together in a sequence dictated by the mRNA. 3. Initiation: All components of the translational complex, including the first tRNA carrying methionine, are assembled. Elongation: Amino acids are delivered one by one as tRNA molecules pair with the codons on the mRNA. Termination: A stop codon is reached, a release factor binds to it, and the completed protein is cleaved from the last tRNA as the ribosomal subunits dissociate. **12.6:** 1. Euchromatin may exist in a compact or open configuration. A compact chromatin structure prevents regulatory proteins needed for gene expression from accessing gene control elements. An open configuration allows gene expression to occur.

Testing Yourself

1. c; **2.** a; **3.** c; **4.** b; **5.** d; **6.** e; **7.** b; **8. a.** GGA GGA CUU ACG UUU; **b.** CCU CCU GAA UGC AAA; **c.** glycine-glycine-leucine-threonine-phenylalanine; **9.** d; **10.** a; **11.** a; **12.** a; **13.** c; **14.** d; **15.** d.

Chapter 13

Check Your Progress

13.1: 1. An operon is a group of genes that are regulated in a coordinated manner; a promotor is a regulatory region that controls the initiation of transcription. 2. In a repressible operon, the operon is normally on and is turned off by the action of a repressor. In an inducible operon, the operon is normally off and is turned on by an environmental condition. 3. A gene under positive control is transcribed when it is regulated by a protein that is an activator and not a repressor, whereas one under negative control is not transcribed when it is regulated by a protein that is a repressor. **13.2:** 1. Chromatin, transcriptional, posttranscriptional, translational, and posttranslational. 2. Packing genes into heterochromatin inactivates a gene, whereas it is genetically active when held in loosely packed euchromatin. 3. siRNA molecules participate in posttranscriptional regulation while proteosomes are active in posttranslational regulation.

13.3: 1. Spontaneous: errors in DNA replication and natural chemical changes in the bases in DNA; Induced: organic chemicals and physical mutagens like X-rays and UV radiation. 2. Mutations in these genes disrupt the normal operation of the checkpoints in the cell cycle, allowing cell division to proceed without regulation.

Testing Yourself

1. a; **2.** e; **3.** a; **4.** b; **5.** d; **6.** e; **7.** b; **8.** b; **9.** b; **10.** b; **11.** b; **12.** e; **13.** e; **14.** e; **15. a.** DNA; **b.** regulator gene; **c.** promoter; **d.** operator; **e.** active repressor; **16.** c; **17.** d; **18.** d; **19.** d.

Chapter 14

Check Your Progress

14.1: 1. To create an rDNA molecule, a piece of foreign DNA is cut with restriction enzymes and mixed with a plasmid vector cut with the same restriction enzyme. The DNAs are mixed together and DNA ligase is added to seal the molecule. Then, it can be inserted into bacteria. 2. DNA molecules amplified by PCR can be used to create DNA profiles, or fingerprints, enabling paternity testing and forensic DNA analysis, among other applications. 3. Patterns in DNA fingerprinting can be analyzed to identify the source of a DNA sample. **14.2:** 1. Bacteria: production of medicine and drugs, bioengineering, production of organic chemicals; Animals: gene pharming, studying human disease; Plants: increased food production, production of human medicines. 2. A transgenic animal contains recombinant DNA molecules in addition to its genome, whereas a cloned animal is genetically identical to the one from which it was created, but does not contain rDNA. **14.3:** 1. Liposomes, nasal sprays, and adenoviruses are currently being used to deliver genes to cells for gene therapy. 2. Ex vivo gene therapy is being used to treat SCID and familial hypercholesterolemia. In vivo gene therapy is being used to treat cystic fibrosis. **14.4:** 1. The genome is the sum of all of the genes in a cell whereas the proteome represents the sum of all of the proteins encoded by the genome. The proteome is typically bigger than the genome. 2. A tandem repeat consists of repeated sequences that are one next to the other, whereas transposons are short sequences of DNA that may move within the genome. 3. Microarrays allow scientists to analyze the expression of genes under different environmental conditions. Bioinformatics allows scientists to rapidly analyze experimental data and generate large databases of information.

Testing Yourself

1. c; **2.** c; **3.** e; **4.** d; **5.** e; **6.** c; **7.** e; **8.** a; **9.** c; **10.** a; **11.** b; **12.** d; **13.** e; **14.** d; **15.** e; **16.** a; **17.** d.

Chapter 15

Check Your Progress

15.1: 1. Catastrophism (Cuvier) explains a change in the fossil record by mass extinctions in an area replaced by a new set of species after a catastrophe. 2. Lamarck's inheritance of acquired characteristics is flawed as an explanation of biological diversity because features acquired by an individual during his/her lifetime are not heritable to offspring. Evolution occurs only in traits that are heritable. 3. 1707-1778 Linnaeus (classification); 1731-1802 E. Darwin (first theory of evolution); 1769-1832 Cuvier (catastrophism); 1744-1829 Lamarck (acquired characteristics); 1797-1875 Lyell (uniformitarianism); 1831-1836 voyage of H.M.S *Beagle*; 1859 Darwin publishes *Origin of Species*. **15.2:** 1. Fossils, biogeography, change over time (geology). 2. Individuals have variation that is heritable; organisms compete for resources; differential reproductive success; adaptation to environmental change. 3. Evolution can occur over the span of a human lifetime. One example is artificial selection, which can modify plants and animals through selective breeding. Another are beaks of the Galápagos Islands finches, which were observed to evolve between wet and dry seasons over decades. **15.3:** 1. Biomolecules may change over time as a result of natural selection. Examples are the cytochrome *c* protein in cellular metabolism and the homeobox, or *Hox*, genes that have been shaped by natural selection to orchestrate the development of the body plan in animals. 2. Homologous structures are those that are shared because of common ancestry. Analogous structures are shared because of convergent evolution and do not tell us anything about common ancestry. 3. Transitional fossils represent intermediate evolutionary forms of life in transition from one type to another, or a common ancestor of these types. *Tiktaalik* and *Basilosaurus* are examples of intermediate fossils. 4. (One of the following) a. *Evolution is a theory about how life originated*. Evolution is concerned with how life evolved AFTER the origin of life. b. *There are no transitional fossils*. Not all fossils will ever be found because of the nature of how organisms are preserved and discovered. c. *Evolution proposes that life-forms changed as a result of random events*. New variation arises due to random processes, but natural selection is not a random process; it can only shape pre-existing variation. d. *Evolution is not observable or testable*. Evolution is both observable and testable. Many studies show how traits change in response to environmental pressures. There are examples of evolution over long periods of time, and over short periods of time.

Testing Yourself

1. d; **2.** e; **3.** b; **4.** e; **5.** e; **6.** e; **7.** b, c, d, e; **8.** b, d, e; **9.** c; **10.** d, e; **11.** b; **12.** Life has a history, and it's possible to trace the history of individual organisms. **13.** Two different continents can have similar environments, and therefore unrelated organisms that are similarly adapted. **14.** All vertebrates share a common ancestor that had pharyngeal pouches during development. **15.** Similarities are expected because all species share recent and distant common ancestors. DNA base difference through the occurrence of mutations accounts for the diversity of life.

Chapter 16

Check Your Progress

16.1: 1. a. Random mating, allele frequencies do not change. b. No selection, allele frequencies change. c. No mutation, allele frequencies change. d. No migration, allele frequencies change. e. Large population (no genetic drift), allele frequencies change. 2. AA = p^2 = 0.01, Aa = 2pq = 0.18, aa = q^2 = 0.81. **16.2:** 1. Females produce large gametes and have a large investment in eggs so are choosy about their mates. Males produce many small, inexpensive gametes, and value females as a resource for reproduction, resulting in competition for access to females (mates). 2. Sexual selection is a form of natural selection because traits associated with mating determine whether or not traits are passed on to the next generation. 3. See Figure 16.10 on page 297. **16.3:** 1. Mutation, sexual reproduction, genetic drift. 2. In Africa where malaria is

common, being a heterozygote for the sickle-cell trait is advantageous because it provides some resistance to malaria. Those who are homozygous for normal trait get malaria without natural resistance; those homozygous for the sickle-cell trait die young from sickle-cell disease. Heterozygotes for the cystic fibrosis trait have resistance to typhoid fever. As with sickle-cell trait, heterozygotes are maintained because of stabilizing selection that selects against homozygotes for the cystic fibrosis trait (who have the disease) and homozygous normal trait (who get typhoid fever). 3. The dominant allele (*p*) and the recessive allele (*q*) must be present in the previous generation in order for the heterozygote (*pq*) to appear in the next generation.

Testing Yourself

1. c; **2.** c; **3.** c; **4.** c; **5.** e; **6.** b; **7.** c; **8.** e; **9.** d; **10.** c; **11.** a; **12.** e; **13.** b; **14.** e.

Chapter 17

Check Your Progress

17.1: 1. Pre-zygotic reproductive isolation. 2. (Three of the following) Biological species concept: Individuals of a population cannot interbreed. Phylogenetic species concept: Two populations are on different evolutionary lineages in a phylogeny that are monophyletic. Morphological species concept: A species is defined by a diagnostic trait (or traits). Evolutionary species concept: Relies on identification of certain morphological diagnostic traits that define a different evolutionary pathway. 3. If the frogs cannot recognize each other as mates, they will be reproductively isolated. **17.2:** 1. Show that each of the cats is adapted to a different environment. 2. In a newly discovered African Rift Valley lake, you would expect to see in the fishes the same shape of head and teeth for feeding in similar habitats as those observed in other lakes. Similar forms would evolve independently in this new lake—each of which would match the form of a fish that feeds in the same habitat in a different lake. 3. Allopatric speciation. **17.3:** 1. Punctuated equilibrium model proposes periods of rapid evolution and periods of little evolution (stasis). Cuvier proposed that this pattern in the fossil record was because new groups of organisms moved into an area after a mass extinction (catastrophe). 2. *Hox* genes have a powerful effect on development and offer a mechanism by which evolution could occur rapidly. 3. A change in *Pax6* gene expression shows that changes in the genes that regulate body organization can produce rapid change in an organism, leading to speciation.

Testing Yourself

1. c; **2.** e; **3.** c; **4.** e; **5. a.** species 1; **b.** geographic barrier; **c.** genetic changes; **d.** species 2; **e.** genetic changes; **f.** species 3; **6.** b; **7.** b; **8.** b; **9.** d; **10.** d; **11.** b; **12.** b; **13.** b; **14.** b; **15.** d; **16.** b; **17.** c; **18.** c.

Chapter 18

Check Your Progress

18.1: 1. a. Methane, ammonia, hydrogen, water environment: Recreated by Miller-Urey; b. Reducing atmosphere: Electric spark and chemical reactions. 2. a. Iron-sulfur world hypothesis: Iron-nickel sulfides at thermal vents act as catalysts to join organic molecules. b. Protein-first hypothesis: Amino acids collected in small pools and the heat of the Sun formed protenoids, small polypeptides with catalytic properties. c. RNA-first hypothesis: RNA carried out the processes commonly associated with DNA and proteins before either of these evolved. 3. Protocell: single fatty acid hydrophilic tail; modern cell: double fatty acid hydrophilic tail; Protocell: membrane of a single layer of fatty acids; modern cell: bilayer of phospholipids. **18.2A:** 1. Elements that are radioactive decay at a constant rate of time. The half-life is how long it takes for 1/2 of the number of molecules of an element to decay. If we know how much of the radioactive and decayed isotopes of an element we have left, we can estimate the number of years it took for the element to decay since the organism died. 2. Chemical evolution, evolution of first cells, evolution of eukaryotic cells by endosymbiosis, and first heterotrophic protists before photosynthetic protists. 3. DNA content and double-membrane structure of the mitochondria and chloroplasts. **18.2B:** 1. a. Eukaryote cells arise; b. Multicellular organisms arise. 2. The presence of an exoskeleton. **18.2C:** 1. a. Evolution of flowering plants; b. Reptiles undergo an adaptive radiation; c. Dinosaurs go extinct. 2. Flowering plants, conifers, birds, dinosaurs, placental mammals. **18.3:** 1. The theory of plate tectonics says that the Earth's crust is fragmented into slab-like plates that float on a lower hot mantle layer. Growth of mountains, earthquakes and the layout of the continents are all evidence. 2. Distribution of animals would be similar on continents that were once joined together. Marsupials in South America and Australia are an example. 3. Ordovician: continental drift and cooling of the Earth; Devonian: bolide, or impact of a meteorite with the Earth; Permian: excess carbon dioxide; Triassic: meteorite collision with Earth; Cretaceous: bolide, or impact of an asteroid with the Earth.

Testing Yourself

1. c; **2.** d; **3.** a; **4.** b; **5.** e; **6.** b; **7.** c; **8.** b; **9.** b; **10.** e; **11.** e; **12.** b; **13.** c; **14.** d; **15.** a; **16.** c; **17.** c; **18.** e; **19.** c; **20.** d.

Chapter 19

Check Your Progress

19.1: 1. Domain: Eukarya; Kingdom: Animalia; Phylum: Chordata; Class: Mammalia; Order: Primates; Family: Hominidae; Genus: *Homo*; Species: *Homo sapiens*. 2. Wings in birds and bats are analogous because they have independent evolutionary origins. Thus, birds and bats are not a natural group. 3. Classification is the naming of organisms; taxonomy is the assignment of groups to a taxon; systematic biology is the study of classification and taxonomy, or more generally, the study of biodiversity. **19.2:** 1. Archaea have differences in their rRNA, in their cell wall structure, and in the lipids in their plasma membrane. 2. Molecular data (RNA/DNA sequence data) indicates that fungi are related to animals. 3. Eukarya. **19.3:** 1. Answers may vary. Refer to the material on cladistics (page 356) and Figure 19.7 for examples. 2. Ancestral traits are found in the common ancestor of a lineage and may be present in the descendants. Derived traits are found in the descendants but not in the common ancestor. 3. The phylogeny that requires the fewest number of evolutionary steps is the most parsimonious explanation of evolutionary history, and is thus the best hypothesis.

Testing Yourself

1. e; **2.** e; **3.** d; **4.** a, b, c; **5.** c, d, e; **6.** b, c, d, e; **7.** a; **8.** c; **9.** a; **10.** d; **11.** b; **12.** e; **13.** b.

Chapter 20

Check Your Progress

20.1: 1. All viruses have a nucleic acid and a capsid. 2. Viroids and prions are nonliving because, like viruses, they are noncellular and unable to reproduce without a host. 3. A virus consists of both nucleic acids and proteins, whereas a prion is composed of just protein. 4. If a virus's host survives, many more copies of the virus will be produced and spread to other hosts than if the host dies. **20.2:** 1. Bacteria exist in the air and sterilization kills bacteria. 2. The bacterial nucleoid is not surrounded by a membrane; the eukaryote nucleus has its own membrane 3. Transduction: movement of genetic material from one bacterium to another via a virus; transformation: pick up and incorporate genetic material from the

environment; conjugation: exchange genetic material between bacteria. **20.3:** 1. The peptidoglycan layer is much thicker in Gram-positive cells. In Gram-negative cells this layer is thinner and is located between layers of the plasma membrane. 2. By inhibiting protein synthesis or construction of the cell wall. 3. Endospores permit survival when environmental conditions are harsh. 4. Cyanobacteria are considered responsible for the production of an oxygen-rich atmosphere. **20.4:** 1. Archaea and bacteria differ in their rRNA base sequences, and their plasma membranes and cell walls are biochemically distinct. 2. Methanogens, halophiles, and thermoacidophiles. 3. Archaea and eukaryotes share some of the same ribosomal proteins, initiate transcription in the same way, and have similar tRNA.

Testing Yourself

1. a. attachment; **b.** penetration; **c.** integration; **d.** prophage; **e.** biosynthesis; **f.** maturation; **g.** release; **2.** e; **3.** e; **4.** b; **5.** a; **6.** c; **7.** d; **8.** a; **9.** c; **10.** c; **11.** c; **12.** c; **13.** a; **14.** e; **15.** e; **16.** a; **17.** a; **18.** b; **19.** d.

Chapter 21

Check Your Progress

21.1: 1. Endosymbiosis; mitochondria and chloroplasts were free-living bacteria that were engulfed and incorporated into a eukaryotic protocell. 2. Algae are photoautotrophs; they get their food from photosynthesis; protozoans are heterotrophs and ingest their food from the environment. 3. a. Archaeplastids; b. Opisthokonts. **21.2A:** 1. Haploid stage is the asexual stage of reproduction; diploid is the sexual phase. 2. Accessory pigments allow for the absorption of energy from light of different wavelengths. **21.2B:** 1. Their DNA base sequences are similar, and their ancestor had a flagellum. 2. Brown algae: *Macrocystis, Laminaria, Nereocystis;* Diatoms: *Cyclotella;* Golden brown algae: *Ochromonas*. **21.2C:** 1. Refer to the summary boxes in Fig. 21.15 on page 394. 2. Brown comes from a carotenoid pigment. 3. Aveolates possess small air sacs (alveoli) beneath their plasma membrane; all are unicellular. **21.2D:** 1. Excavates have atypical or absent mitochondria and distinctive flagella and/or deep oral grooves. 2. Parasitic: parabasalids, diplomads, kinetoplastids; free-living: euglenids. 3. Trypanosome: African sleeping sickness and Chagas disease; *Giardia:* giardiasis; *Trichomonas:* vaginitis. **21.2E:** 1. Opisthokonts move using flagella; rhizarians and amoebozoans move using pseudopods. 2. Opisthokonts are multicellular protozoans, animal-like with a flagellum.

Testing Yourself

1. f; **2.** c; **3.** c; **4.** a; **5.** b; **6.** e; **7.** b; **8.** b; **9.** e; **10.** e; **11.** d; **12.** d; **13.** b; **14.** b; **15.** a; **16.** b; **17.** c; **18.** c; **19. a.** sexual reproduction; **b.** gametes pairing; **c.** zygote (2n); **d.** zygospore (2n); **e.** asexual reproduction; **f.** zoospores (n); **g.** nucleus with nucleolus; **h.** chloroplast; **i.** starch granule; **j.** pyrenoid; **k.** flagellum; **l.** eyespot; **m.** gamete formation. See also Figure 21.5, page 388.

Chapter 22

Check Your Progress

22.1: 1. Animals are heterotrophs: they get their nutrition by consuming outside nutrients. Fungi are saprotrophs: they externally digest organic material and absorb nutrients. 2. Plant cell walls are made of cellulose; fungal cell walls are made of chitin. 3. Reproductive structure that can form a new organism without fusing with another reproductive cell. **22.2:** 1. Chitrids are the only fungi to have flagellated cells. 2. Peach leaf curl: *Taphrina;* ergot: *Claviceps;* athletes' foot: *Trichophyton* (tinea); candidiasis: *Candida;* fungal flu: *Histoplasma.* 3. Black mold: *Rhizopus;* ergot: *Claviceps;* athlete's foot: *Trichophyton* (tinea). **22.3:** 1. Lichen has a sac fungus and either a cyanobacterium or green alga. 2. Lichens reproduce asexually by releasing fragments that contain hyphae and an algal cell. In fruticose lichens, the sac fungus reproduces asexually. 3. Fungus enters the cortex of the roots of plants, giving the plants a greater absorptive surface.

Testing Yourself

1. d; **2.** b; **3.** c; **4.** c; **5.** b; **6.** e; **7.** e; **8.** a; **9.** c; **10.** a; **11.** c; **12.** a; **13.** d; **14. a.** spores; **b.** sporangium; **c.** sporangiophore; **d.** stolon; **e.** rhizoid; **15.** a; **16.** e; **17.** e; **18.** d; **19.** e; **20. a.** meiosis; **b.** basidiospores; **c.** dikaryotic mycelium; **d.** button stage of the mushroom (basidiocarp); **e.** stalk; **f.** gill; **g.** cap; **h.** dikaryotic; **i.** diploid; **j.** zygote. See also Figure 22.9, page 412.

Chapter 23

Check Your Progress

23.1: 1. Plentiful light and CO_2. 2. A cellulose cell wall produced in same way; apical cells that produce new tissue; plasmodesmata between cells; transfer of nutrients from haploid cells of previous generation to zygote of new generation. 3. The diploid sporophyte produces haploid spores by meiosis. The haploid gametophyte produces gametes. **23.2:** 1. Bryophytes have a dominant gametophyte generation, produce flagellated sperm that swim to the egg, and can also reproduce asexually. 2. Asexual and sexual reproduction, ability to survive in harsh environments, sporophyte is protected from drying out. 3. The gametophyte portion is most important. The sporophyte is dependent upon the gametophyte. **23.3:** 1. In lycophytes, the dominant sporophyte has vascular tissue, and therefore roots, stems, and leaves. 2. The walls of xylem contains lignin, a strengthening agent. **23.4:** 1. The independent gametophyte generation lacks vascular tissue, and it produces flagellated sperm. 2. In ferns, but not mosses, the sporophyte is dominant and separate from the gametophyte. **23.5:** 1. (1) Water is not required for fertilization because pollen grains (male gametophytes) are windblown, and (2) ovules protect female gametophytes and become seeds that disperse the sporophyte, the generation that has vascular tissue. 2. Conifers: cone bearing and evergreen; cycads: cone bearing, evergreen and wind pollinated; ginkgoes: cone bearing, deciduous; gnetophytes: cone bearing and insect pollinated. 3. The stamen contains the anther and the filament. Pollen forms in the pollen sac of the anther. The carpel contains the stigma, style, and ovary. An ovule in the ovary becomes a seed, and the ovary becomes the fruit. 4. Gymnosperms: cone-bearing, such as cycads, ginkoes, gnetophytes and pine trees. 5. Animal-pollinated flowers are showy in a variety of ways, such as color and fragrance to attract their particular pollinators. Wind-pollinated plants are not very showy.

Testing Yourself

1. e; **2.** a; **3.** b; **4.** c; **5.** b; **6.** b; **7.** e; **8.** c; **9.** c; **10.** e; **11.** d; **12.** b; **13.** a; **14.** b; **15.** b; **16.** e; **17.** c; **18. a.** sporophyte (2n); **b.** meiosis; **c.** gametophyte (n); **d.** fertilization. See also Figure 23.3, page 422.

Chapter 24

Check Your Progress

24.1: 1. Vegetative organs are the leaves (photosynthesis), the stem (support, new growth, transport), and the root (absorb water and minerals). 2. Monocots: embryo with single cotyledon; xylem and phloem in a ring in the root; scattered vascular bundles in the stem; parallel leaf veins; flower parts in multiples of three. Eudicots: embryo with two cotyledons; phloem located between arms of xylem in the root; vascular bundles in a ring in the stem; netted leaf veins; flower parts in multiples of fours or fives. **24.2:** 1. Epidermal tissue: epidermal cells; ground tissue: parenchyma, collenchyma, and sclerenchyma cells; vascular tissue: xylem (vessel elements and tracheids) and phloem (sieve-tube members). 2. Xylem transports water and

minerals usually from roots to leaves. Phloem transports organic compounds throughout the plant. **24.3:** 1. The root apical meristem is located at the tip of the root and is covered by the root cap. 2. Cortex: food storage; endodermis: control of mineral uptake; pericycle: formation of branch roots. **24.4:** 1. A vascular bundle contains xylem and phloem. 2. Vascular bundles are scattered in monocot stems and form a ring in eudicot stems. 3. Primary growth is growth in length and is nonwoody; secondary growth is growth in girth and is woody. 4. Bark is composed of cork, cork cambium, cortex, and phloem. 5. An annual ring is composed of one year's growth of wood—one layer of spring wood followed by one layer of summer wood. **24.5:** 1. Photosynthesis, which produces organic food for a plant, occurs in the mesophyll. 2. The palisade mesophyll contains elongated cells that run photosynthesis; the spongy mesophyll contains irregular cells that increase the surface area for gas exchange. 3. Leaves can be simple with a single blade or compound, which is divided into many leaflets. Pinnate leaves have leaflets occurring in pairs while palmately compound leaves have all the leaflets attached at a single point. Leaves are adapted for environmental conditions.

Testing Yourself

1. c; **2.** b; **3.** c; **4.** c; **5.** b; **6.** b; **7.** b; **8.** c; **9.** c; **10.** b; **11.** d; **12.** e; **13.** d; **14.** d; **15.** d; **16.** c; **17.** c; **18.** a; **19. a.** epidermis; **b.** cortex; **c.** endodermis; **d.** phloem; **e.** xylem. See also Figure 24.8, page 451; **20. a.** upper epidermis; **b.** palisade mesophyll; **c.** leaf vein; **d.** spongy mesophyll; **e.** lower epidermis. See also Figure 24.20, page 459.

Chapter 25

Check Your Progress

25.1: 1. a. Nitrogen and sulfur are needed to form protein. All plant roots take up nitrate (NO_3^-) and sulfate (SO_4^{2-}) from the soil. b. Nitrogen and phosphate (HPO_4^{2-}) are needed to make nucleic acids. Plant roots also take up phosphate from the soil. 2. (1) Helps prevent soil erosion; (2) helps retain moisture; and (3) as the remains decompose, nutrients are returned to the soil. 3. Humus improves soil aeration, soil texture, increases water-holding capacity, decomposes to release nutrients for plant growth, and helps retain positively charged minerals and make them available for plant uptake. **25.2:** 1. The nonpolar tails of phospholipid molecules make the center of the plasma membrane nonpolar. 2. The bacteria convert atmospheric nitrogen to nitrate or ammonium, which can be taken up by plant roots. 3. The fungus

obtains sugars and amino acids from the plant. The plant obtains inorganic nutrients and water from the fungus. **25.3:** 1. Evaporation of water from leaf surfaces causes water to be under tension in stems due to the cohesion of the water molecules. 2. When water molecules are pulled upward during transpiration, their cohesiveness creates a continuous water column. Adhesion allows water molecules to cling to the sides of xylem vessels, so the column of water does not slip down. 3. Sugars enter sieve tubes at sources, creating pressure as water flows in as well. The pressure is relieved at the other end when sugars and water are removed at the sink.

Testing Yourself

1. d; **2.** e; **3.** a; **4.** c; **5.** d; **6.** c; **7.** d; **8.** a; **9.** b; **10.** c; **11.** d; **12.** b; **13.** a; **14.** c; **15.** e; **16.** a; **17.** The diagram shows that air pressure pushing down on mercury in the pan can raise a column of mercury only to 76 cm. When water above the column is transpired, it pulls on the mercury and raises it higher than 76 cm. This suggests that transpiration would be able to raise water to the tops of trees. **18.** e; **19. a.** See Figure 25.13, page 477. **b.** After K^+ enters guard cells, water follows by osmosis and the stoma opens. **20.** There is more solute in bulb 1 than in bulb 2; therefore water enters bulb 1. This creates a positive pressure that causes water, along with solute, to flow toward bulb 2.

Chapter 26

Check Your Progress

26.1: 1. Hormones coordinate the responses of plants to stimuli. 2. You could apply gibberellins to induce growth and cytokinins to increase the number of cells. 3. ABA maintains dormancy and closes stomata. **26.2:** 1. It is adaptive for roots to grow toward water because it enhances their ability to extract water and dissolved minerals from the soil for plant tissues. 2. Positive geotropism is when part of a plant grows downward in response to gravity. Negative geotropism is when a plant grows upward against gravity. 3. Phytochrome is composed of two proteins that contain light-sensitive regions. When triggered by red light phytochrome causes various genes to become active or inactive leading to seed germination, shoot elongation and flowering responses. 4. The plant is responding to a short night, not to the length of the day. 5. Plants have (1) physical and chemical defenses (e.g., secondary metabolites); (2) wound responses (e.g., proteinase inhibitors); (3) hypersensitive responses (e.g., sealing off of infected areas);

and (4) relationships with animals (e.g., acacia with ants).

Testing Yourself

1. c; 2. a; 3. d; 4. e; 5. d; 6. b; 7. e; 8. a; 9. c; 10. c; 11. d; 12. e; 13. b 14. e; 15. d.

Chapter 27

Check Your Progress

27.1: 1. Male gametophytes are produced in the anther of the stamen. The female gametophyte is produced in an ovule within the ovary of the carpel. 2. Each microspore produces a two-celled pollen grain. The generative cell produces two sperm, and the tube cell produces a pollen tube. One of the four megaspores produces a seven-celled female gametophyte, called the embryo sac, within the ovule. 3. In order to accommodate the larger size of the pollinator, natural selection in the flowering plant may lead to an increase in the structural support of the part that the pollinator lands upon. It may also lead to an increase in the size of the flower to accommodate a larger pollinator. **27.2:** 1. The embryo is derived from the zygote; the stored food is derived from the endosperm; and the seed coat is derived from the ovule wall. 2. The ovule is a sporophyte structure produced by the female parent. Therefore, the wall (which becomes seed coat) is 2n. The embryo inside the ovule is the product of fertilization and is, therefore, 2n. 3. Cotyledons are embryonic leaves that are present in seeds. Cotyledons store nutrients derived from endosperm (in eudicots). **27.3:** 1. Dry fruits, with a dull, thin, and dry covering derived from the ovary, are more apt to be windblown. Fleshy fruits, with a juicy covering derived from the ovary and possibly other parts of the flower, are more apt to be eaten by animals. 2. Eudicot seedlings have a hook shape, and monocot seedlings have a sheath to protect the first true leaves. **27.4:** 1. Advantages to asexual reproduction include: (1) the newly formed plant is often supported nutritionally by the parent plant until it is established; (2) if the parent is ideally suited for the environment, the offspring will be as well; and (3) if distance between individuals make cross-pollination unlikely, asexual reproduction is a good alternative. 2. For example, stolons and rhizomes produce new shoots and roots; fruit trees produce suckers; and stem cuttings grow new roots and become a shoot system. 3. Tissue from leaves, meristem, and anthers can become whole plants in tissue culture.

Testing Yourself

1. d; 2. a; 3. b; 4. a; 5. a; 6. a; 7. e; 8. d; 9. b; 10. e; 11. c; 12. a; 13. b; 14. e; 15. a. diploid; b. anther; c. ovule; d. ovary; e. haploid;

f. megaspore; g. male; h. female; i. sperm; j. seed. See also Figure 27.1, page 502.

Chapter 28

Check Your Progress

28.1: 1. Multicellular, usually with specialized tissues, ingest food, diploid life cycle. 2. Animals are descended from an ancestor that resembled a hollow spherical colony of flagellated cells. Individual cells became specialized for reproduction. Two tissue layers arose by invagination. 3. Deuterostomes: blastopore becomes anus, radial cleavage, coelum forms from gut; Protostomes: blastopore becomes mouth, spiral cleavage, coelom forms from mesoderm.
28.2: 1. Sponges are multicellular; no symmetry; no digestive cavity. Cnidarians have true tissues; radial symmetry; have a gastrovascular cavity. 2. Interior of sponges has canals lined with flagellated cells called choanocytes. Flagella produce water current that carries food particles that are filtered out. 3. Polyps have mouths directed upward, medusae are bell-shaped with tentacles around the opening of the bell and mouth downward. 4. Stinging cells called cnidocytes have a fluid-filled capsule called a nematocyst in which a hollow threadlike structure is coiled and is discharged when stimulated. Some trap prey, others contain paralyzing toxins. **28.3:** 1. They all have bilateral symmetry, three tissue layers, and protostome development. They have no body plan, coelom, or any sort of nervous tissue. 2. Annelids and molluscs have a complete digestive tract, a true coelom, and a circulatory system (closed in annelids and open in molluscs). Flatworms have a gastrovascular cavity with only one opening, no coelom, and no circulatory system. 3. Tapeworm, *Taenia*. Host ingests meat with bladder worms; worms attach to intestine and mature; proglottids mature and fill with eggs; eggs leave host in feces; eggs ingested by livestock; worms encysted in muscle of livestock and eaten by host. Blood fluke: *Schistosoma*. Larvae penetrate skin of human, mature in liver; adult worms live and mate in blood vessels of gut; eggs migrate into digestive tract, passed in feces; ciliated larvae hatch in water, enter the snail; larvae emerge from snails, enter skin of humans. 4. Bryozoa, Phoronida, Brachopoda. **28.4:** 1. Roundworms and arthropods are the molting protostomes. They both have a true coelom. 2. Crustaceans breathe by gills and have swimmerets. Insects breathe by tracheae, and they may have wings. 3. The first pair of appendages is the chelicerae (modified fangs), and the second pair is the pedipalps (hold, taste, chew food). **28.5:** 1. The larval stage is bilaterally

symmetrical. 2. The water vascular system functions in locomotion, feeding, gas exchange, and sensory reception.

Testing Yourself

1. d; 2 e; 3. e; 4. e; 5. d; 6. b; 7. a; 8. c; 9. a; 10. a. tapeworm; b. mollusc; c. sponge; d. cnidaria; e. rotifer; f. flatworm; g. arthropod; 11. b; 12. b; 13. a; 14. e; 15. e.

Chapter 29

Check Your Progress

29.1: 1. Humans are chordates, and they have the four chordate characteristics during the embryonic period of their life cycle. Notochord: replaced by vertebral column during development. Dorsal tubular nerve cord becomes the spinal cord. Pharyngeal pouches: the first pair of pouches develops into auditory tubes. Post-anal tail: is present in developing embryo, but lost during development. 2. A sea squirt larva has the four characteristics as a larva, then undergoes metamorphosis to become an adult, which has gill slits but none of the other characteristics. **29.2:** 1. Endoskeleton protects internal organs, provides a place of attachment for muscles, permits rapid, efficient movement. 2. Four legs are useful for locomotion on land where the body is not supported by water. **29.3:** 1. All fishes are aquatic vertebrates and ectothermic. They all live in water, breathe by gills, and have a single circulatory loop (Fig. 29.11a, page 556). 2. Ray-finned bony fishes have fan-shaped fins supported by thin, bony rays. Lobe-finned bony fishes have fleshy fins supported by bones. **29.4:** 1. a. Paired limbs; smooth, nonscaly skin that stays moist; lungs; a three-chambered heart with a double-loop circulatory pathway; sense organs adapted for a land environment; ectothermic; and have aquatic reproduction. b. Lobe-finned fishes and amphibians both have lungs and internal nares that allow them to breathe air. The same bones are present in the front fins of the lobe-finned fishes as in the forelimbs of early amphibians. 2. Usually, amphibians carry out external fertilization in the water. The embryos develop in the eggs until the tadpoles emerge. They then undergo metamorphosis, growing legs and reabsorbing the tail, and become adults. **29.5:** 1. Alligators live in fresh water and have a thick skin, two pairs of legs, powerful jaws, and a long muscular tail that allow them to capture and eat other animals that are in the water or come to the water's edge. Snakes have no limbs and have relatively thin skin. They live close to or in the ground and can escape detection. They use smell (Jacobson's organ) and vibrations to detect prey. Some use venom to subdue prey, which they eat whole because their jaws are distensible. 2. Birds are reptiles: feathers are modified scales; birds have clawed feet and a tail that contains vertebrae. **29.6:** 1. Mammals have hair or fur and mammary glands, endothermy, limbs under body, differentiated teeth, and an enlarged brain. 2. The three groups of mammals are monotremes (have a cloaca and lay eggs), marsupials (young are born immature and finish development in a pouch), and placental (eutherians) mammals (development occurs internally and the fetus is nourished by placenta).

Testing Yourself

1. e; **2.** a; **3.** c; **4.** e; **5.** a; **6.** e; **7.** b; **8.** b; **9.** e; **10.** c; **11.** a; **12.** a; **13. a.** pharyngeal pouches; **b.** dorsal tubular nerve cord; **c.** notochord; **d.** postanal tail; **14.** d; **15.** d.

Chapter 30

Check Your Progress

30.1: 1. Refer to Figure 30.4 on page 573, focusing on the bars on the right of the figure. 2. Both humans and chimpanzees are hominines and they share similar structure of their genomes, plus the general characteristics of all primates. **30.2:** 1. Ardipithecines lived primarily in trees, whereas the australopiths lived both in and out of trees. The brain size of the australopiths was larger, and this group was better adapted for bipedalism. **30.3:** 1. Increasing size of brain cavity, increased height, eventual use of tools and fire. 2. Bipedalism allowed for organisms to move young more easily, increased brain size allowed for higher intellect and thus adaptation to non-forest environments. **30.4:** 1. The replacement model suggests that humans evolved from one group in Africa, and then migrated to other locations. This means that different groups of Cro-Magnon humans could adapt to different locations, eventually forming the major human ethnic groups. 2. Increased brain size and reliance on tool use and a hunter-gatherer lifestyle required development of communication.

Testing Yourself

1. c; **2.** b; **3.** b; **4.** e; **5.** c; **6.** d; **7.** b; **8.** c; **9.** c; **10.** c; **11.** T; **12.** T; **13.** F; **14.** Africa; **15.** erect, small; **16.** Cro-Magnon; **17.** thousands; **18. a.** modern humans; **b.** archaic humans; **c.** *Homo erectus*; **d.** *Homo erectus*. See also Figure 30.10, page 580.

Chapter 31

Check Your Progress

31.1: 1. Squamous epithelium: flat cells that line the blood vessels and air sacs of lungs;

cuboidal epithelium: cube-shaped cells that line the kidney tubules and various glands; columnar epithelium: rectangular cells that line the digestive tract; stratified epithelium: layers of cells that protect various body surfaces; glandular epithelium: modified to secrete products, like the goblet cells of the digestive tract. 2. Fibrous connective tissue has collagen and elastic fibers in a jellylike matrix between fibroblasts; supportive connective tissue has protein fibers in a solid matrix between collagen or bone cells; fluid connective tissue lacks fibers and has a fluid matrix that contains blood cells or lymphatic cells. 3. Skeletal muscle, which is striated with multiple nuclei, causes bones to move when it contracts. Smooth muscle, which is spindle-shaped with a single nucleus, causes the walls of internal organs to constrict. Cardiac muscle, which has branching, striated cells each with a single nucleus, causes the heart to beat. 4. Dendrites conduct signals toward the cell body; the cell body contains most of the cytoplasm and the nucleus; it carries on the usual functions of the cell; the axon conducts nerve impulses. **31.2:** 1. An organ is two or more types of tissues working together to perform a function; an organ system is many organs working to perform a process. 2. The lymphatic and immune systems work together to protect the body from disease (other answers are possible). 3. The dorsal cavity contains the cranial cavity and the vertebral cavity; the ventral cavity contains the thoracic cavity and the abdominopelvic cavity. **31.3:** 1. The skin protects the deeper tissues from pathogens, trauma, and dehydration in all animals. Only birds have feathers, a derivative of skin that are involved in flying. 2. The epidermis is stratified squamous epithelium, and it protects and prevents water loss. The dermis is dense fibrous connective tissue, and it helps regulate body temperature and provides sensory reception. 3. A dark-skinned person in a low sunlight area might develop a deficiency of vitamin D, which is required for normal bone growth. 4. Nails are keratinized cells that grow from the nail root; hair is made of dead epithelial cells; sweat glands are tubules originating from the dermis; oil glands are usually associated with hair follicles. **31.4:** 1. Homeostasis, the dynamic equilibrium of the internal environment, maintains body conditions within a range appropriate for cells to continue living. 2. The circulatory system brings nutrients and removes waste from tissue fluid; the respiratory system carries out gas exchange; the urinary system excretes metabolic wastes and maintains salt-water balance and pH of blood. 3. When conditions go beyond or below a set point, a correction is made to bring conditions back to normality again.

Testing Yourself

1. b; **2.** e; **3.** e; **4.** e; **5.** b; **6.** e; **7.** e; **8.** c; **9. a.** columnar epithelium, lining of intestine (digestive tract), protection and absorption; **b.** cardiac muscle, wall of heart, pumps blood; **c.** compact bone, skeleton, support and protection. **10.** e; **11.** d; **12.** c; **13.** c; **14.** a, c, g; **15.** b, d, e; **16.** b, c, f; **17.** b; **18.** d; **19.** a; **20.** c.

Chapter 32

Check Your Progress

32.1: 1. Circulatory systems carry nutrients and oxygen to cells and to remove their wastes. 2. Blood is always contained within blood vessels, but hemolymph (a mixture of blood and tissue fluid) flows freely in body cavities. 3. With a closed circulatory system, oxygen must diffuse across the capillary wall. **32.2:** 1. Arteries carry blood away from the heart, capillaries exchange their contents with tissue fluid, and veins return blood back to the heart. 2. Veins contain valves, because they are thin-walled and there is insufficient blood pressure in veins to return blood to the heart, so valves plus skeletal muscle contractions are needed. 3. One-circuit pathways are less efficient, because blood supplying the tissues (after leaving the gills) is under low pressure. Two-circuit pathways supply oxygen to tissues more efficiently, which helps land animals meet the increased demands of locomotion on land vs. in water. **32.3:** 1. From the body: venae cavae, right atrium, tricuspid valve, right ventricle, pulmonary semilunar valve, pulmonary trunk and arteries (carrying oxygen-poor blood). From the lungs: pulmonary veins, left atrium, bicuspid valve, left ventricle, aortic semilunar valve, aorta. 2. First the atria contract, then the ventricles contract, and then they both rest. The *lub* sound occurs when the atrioventricular valves close, and the *dub* sound occurs when the semilunar valves close. 3. The wall of the left ventricle is thicker than the wall of the right ventricle, and it generates a greater pressure than the right ventricle. The right ventricle pumps blood into the pulmonary circuit, which takes blood only to the lungs for gas exchange, while the left ventricle pumps blood into the systemic circuit, which takes blood to all the cells of the body. 4. Thromboembolism, stroke, heart attack. **32.4:** 1. Blood contains plasma and formed elements. Plasma transports many substances to and from the capillaries, helps defend against pathogen invasion, helps regulate body temperature, and helps with clotting to prevent excessive blood loss. The formed elements include red blood cells that carry oxygen to tissues and return some carbon dioxide; white blood cells that help protect the body from infections; and platelets that are involved in blood clotting. 2. Platelets accumulate at the site of injury and release a clotting factor that results in the synthesis of thrombin. Thrombin synthesizes fibrin threads that provide a framework for the clot. 3. Any fetal Rh-positive blood cells that enter the circulation of an Rh-negative mother are recognized as foreign antigens, provoking her immune system. An Rh-positive woman does not react to the Rh antigen, because her immune system does not react with "self." 4. Capillary exchange is affected by osmotic pressure (tends to cause water to enter capillaries) and blood pressure (tends to cause water to leave capillaries).

Testing Yourself

1. b; 2. a; 3. d; 4. c; 5. b; 6. b; 7. e; 8. c; 9. e; 10. b; 11. e; 12. a. superior vena cava; b. aorta; c. left pulmonary artery; d. pulmonary trunk; e. left pulmonary veins; f. right pulmonary artery; g. right pulmonary veins; h. semilunar valve; i. left atrium; j. right atrium; k. left atrioventricular (bicuspid) valve; l. right atrioventricular (tricuspid) valve; m. right ventricle; n. chordae tendinae; o. septum; p. left ventricle; q. superior vena cava (see Figure 32.7, page 611).

Chapter 33

Check Your Progress

33.1: 1. Under certain conditions, slime molds develop specialized sentinel cells that engulf pathogens and toxins. 2. PAMPs are highly conserved microbial molecules such as double-stranded viral RNA as well as carbohydrates and proteins found only in bacteria. 3. Immune cells expressing receptors for specific antigens can multiply and differentiate, resulting in immune memory. **33.2:** 1. The lymphatic system consists of the lymphatic vessels, which have the same structure as cardiovascular veins, and the lymphatic organs: red bone marrow, lymph nodes, and spleen. 2. The lymphatic system absorbs fats, returns excess tissue fluid to the bloodstream, produces lymphocytes, and helps defend the body against pathogens. 3. Red bone marrow is a spongy, semisolid red tissue located in certain bones (e.g., ribs, clavicle, vertebral column, heads of femur, and humerus), which produces all the blood cells of the body. The thymus is a soft, bilobed gland located in the thoracic cavity between the trachea and the sternum where T lymphocytes mature. Lymph nodes are small ovoid structures located along lymphatic vessels through which the lymph travels. The spleen is an oval organ with a dull purplish

color that has both immune as well as red blood cell maintenance functions. **33.3:** 1. Physical barriers include the skin, mucus membranes, and ciliated epithelia; chemical barriers include lysozyme, stomach acid, and protective proteins (e.g., complement). 2. Four cardinal signs of inflammation are heat, swelling, redness, and pain. Inflammation generally directs other components of the immune system (molecules and cells) to the inflamed area. 3. Mast cells initiate inflammation; phagocytes (dendritic cells, macrophages, neutrophils) devour pathogens; natural killer cells kill virus-infected cells and cancer cells by cell-to-cell contact. 4. Complement proteins assist other immune defenses by initiating inflammation, enhancing phagocytosis of pathogens, and forming a membrane attack complex. **33.4:** 1. B cells produce antibodies; cytotoxic T cells attack viral-infected or cancer cells, and helper T cells produce cytokines that stimulate the immune response. 2. Antigen complexes can activate the complement system and natural killer cells, or be engulfed by phagocytes. 3. Active immunity is induced in an individual by natural infection, vaccination, or exposure to a toxin; passive immunity is produced by one individual and transferred into someone else, such as maternal antibodies, administration of antibodies to treat diseases, and bone marrow transplants. **33.5:** 1. Most primary immunodeficiencies are due to a genetic defect in a component of the immune system. 2. Autoimmune diseases (e.g., rheumatoid arthritis) are generally treated with drugs that generally suppress the immune system. 3. The transplanting of animal tissues or organs into humans.

Testing Yourself

1. b; 2. e; 3. e; 4. a; 5. b; 6. c; 7. a; 8. b; 9. e; 10. b; 11. d; 12. a; 13. b; 14. e; 15. d.

Chapter 34

Check Your Progress

34.1: 1. Planarians have an incomplete digestive tract, called the gastrovascular cavity; the complete tract of earthworms has a pharynx, crop, gizzard, and intestine. 2. An incomplete tract has only one opening, with parts that cannot become very specialized, because they must serve multiple functions. 3. Carnivores tend to have pointed incisors and enlarged canine teeth to tear off pieces small enough to quickly swallow. The molars are jagged for efficient chewing of meat. Herbivores have reduced canines but sharp even incisors to clip grasses. The large flat molars grind and crush tough grasses. **34.2:** 1. Mouth, pharynx, esophagus, stomach,

duodenum, jejunum, ileum, large intestine. 2. Taste buds enable an animal to discern the difference between nutritious foods, and non-nutritious, potentially dangerous substances that should not be consumed. 3. The stomach mechanically churns food, while acid and pepsin begin protein digestion. The small intestine finishes the digestion of proteins, fats, carbohydrates, and nucleic acids. The villi and microvilli of the intestinal wall greatly enhance the surface area, thereby assisting absorption of the final products of digestion. The large intestine absorbs excess water, and its diameter is larger to permit storage of undigested food prior to defecation. 4. Bile from the liver (stored in the gallbladder) emulsifies fat, while pancreatic amylase, trypsin, and lipase digest carbohydrates, proteins, and lipids. The liver has many other functions, such as the storage of glucose as glycogen. **34.3:** 1. Starch digestion begins in the mouth where salivary amylase digests starch to maltose and pancreatic amylase continues this same process in the small intestine. Maltase and brush-border enzymes digest maltose to glucose, which enters a blood capillary. Protein digestion starts in the stomach where pepsin digests protein to peptides and continues in the small intestine in which trypsin carries out this same process. 2. Carbohydrates are digested to simple sugars (monosaccharides), proteins are digested to amino acids, and fats are digested to glycerol plus fatty acids. **34.4:** 1. Vegetables, if properly chosen, can supply limited calories but all necessary amino acids and vitamins. Much urea results when excess amino acids from proteins are metabolized. The loss of water needed to excrete urea can result in dehydration and loss of calcium ions. 2. A diet high in saturated fats tends to raise LDL cholesterol, which is associated with atherosclerosis. 3. A vitamin is an organic molecule that is required in the diet because it cannot be synthesized.

Testing Yourself

1. a; 2. e; 3. d; 4. b; 5. d; 6. c; 7. e; 8. a; 9. c; 10. c; 11. e; 12. c; 13. d; 14. c; 15. a; 16. b; 17. Test tube 1: no digestion—no enzyme and no HCl; Test tube 2: some digestion—no HCl; Test tube 3: no digestion—no enzyme; Test tube 4: digestion—both enzyme and HCl are present.

Chapter 35

Check Your Progress

35.1: 1. Air has a drying effect, and respiratory surfaces have to be moist. Hydras are aquatic, while earthworms live in moist earth, and salamanders have skin glands that provide this moisture. These animals also have a large surface area compared to their size, or they have many capillaries close to the skin to facilitate gas exchange. 2. When blood containing a low O_2 level flows in an opposite direction as the O_2-rich water passing over the gills, a higher percentage of oxygen is transferred than if both flowed in the same direction (the highest a concurrent mechanism could achieve would be 50% of the O_2 content in the water, because equilibration would occur). 3. Hemolymph distributes some O_2 in the hemocoel, but it is inefficient. Tracheae are air tubes that branch into ever-smaller tracheoles, which deliver oxygen to most cells. Tracheae open at spiracles, and some larger insects have air sacs that can expand and contract. Some aquatic insects have tracheal gills, expansions of the body wall to provide more oxygen-absorbing surface area. **35.2:** 1. During inspiration, the rib cage moves up and out, and the diaphragm contracts and moves down. As the thoracic cavity expands, air flows into the lungs due to decreased air pressure in the lungs. During expiration, the rib cage moves down and the diaphragm relaxes and moves up to its former position. Air flows out as a result of increased pressure in the lungs. 2. The carotid bodies and aortic bodies contain chemoreceptors that send stimulatory messages to the respiratory center if the pH or O_2 levels are too low. 3. In the lungs, oxygen entering pulmonary capillaries combines with hemoglobin (Hb) in red blood cells to form oxyhemoglobin (HbO_2). In the tissues, Hb gives up O_2, while CO_2 enters the blood and the red blood cells. Some CO_2 combines with Hb to form carbaminohemoglobin ($HbCO_2$). Most CO_2 combines with water to form carbonic acid, which dissociates into H^+ and HCO_3^-. The H^+ is absorbed by the globin portions of hemoglobin to form reduced hemoglobin HbH^+. This helps stabilize the pH of the blood. The HCO_3^- is carried in the plasma. **35.3:** 1. Penicillin is an antibiotic that kills bacteria, but most colds are caused by viruses. 2. Narrowing of the airways is seen in bronchitis and asthma; reduced lung expansion is seen in pulmonary fibrosis and emphysema. 3. Smoking causes or contributes to acute and chronic bronchitis, asthma, pulmonary fibrosis, emphysema, and lung cancer (along with many cardiovascular disorders).

Testing Yourself

1. **a.** external respiration; **b.** CO_2; **c.** CO_2; **d.** tissue cells; **e.** internal respiration; **f.** O_2; **g.** O_2; **2.** b; **3.** d; **4.** c; **5.** b; **6.** c; **7.** e; **8.** b; **9.** d; **10.** b; **11.** d; **12.** e; **13. a.** nasal cavity; **b.** nostril; **c.** pharynx; **d.** epiglottis; **e.** glottis;

f. larynx; **g.** trachea; **h.** bronchus; **i.** bronchiole (see also Figure 35.6*a*, page 668).

Chapter 36

Check Your Progress

36.1: 1. Osmoregulation involves the balance between salts and water; metabolic wastes are removed by excretion. 2. Urea is not as toxic as ammonia, and it does not require as much water to excrete; uric acid takes more energy to prepare than urea. 3. Kangaroo rats are active at night, have convoluted nasal passages to capture moisture in exhaled air, fur to prevent water loss from skin, secrete a hypertonic urine, and eliminate very dry feces. **36.2:** 1. The kidneys alone secrete nitrogenous wastes, but share responsibility for regulating blood pressure and water-salt balance. Certain hormones secreted by the kidneys, such as erythropoietin and ADH, have unique functions. 2. In response to low blood pressure, the kidneys secrete renin, which converts angiotensinogen to angiotensin I, which is converted to angiotensin II. Angiotensin II causes blood vessel constriction and stimulates the adrenal glands to release aldosterone, which acts on kidney tubules to increase salt reabsorption. 3. The kidneys maintain blood pH by secreting H^+ ions and reabsorbing bicarbonate ions, as needed.

Testing Yourself

1. d; **2.** a; **3.** c; **4.** b; **5.** e; **6.** b; **7.** d; **8.** c; **9.** c; **10.** d; **11.** c; **12. a.** glomerular capsule; **b.** proximal convoluted tubule; **c.** loop of the nephron; **d.** descending limb; **e.** ascending limb; **f.** distal convoluted tubule; **g.** collecting duct; **h.** renal artery; **i.** afferent arteriole; **j.** glomerulus; **k.** efferent arteriole; **l.** peritubular capillary network; **m.** renal vein (see Figure 36.8, page 685).

Chapter 37

Check Your Progress

37.1: 1. A nerve net is a simple nervous system consisting of interconnected neurons, with no CNS. A ganglion is a cluster of neuron (nerve cell) bodies. In animals with a CNS and a PNS, it is a cluster of neurons located outside the CNS. A centrally located brain controls the ganglia and associated nerves. 2. The hindbrain controls essential functions like breathing, heart functions, and basic motor activity; the midbrain is a relay station connecting the hindbrain with the forebrain; the forebrain, which receives sensory input, includes the hypothalamus (involved with homeostasis) as well as the

cerebrum (involved with higher functions). 3. The more recently evolved parts of the brain are the outer portions, such as the cerebral cortex, and (in mammals) the neocortex. **37.2:** 1. Nerve impulses travel more quickly down myelinated axons due to saltatory conduction ("jumping"). 2. Na^+ moves from the outside of the axon membrane to the inside; K^+ moves from the inside of the axon membrane to the outside. 3. Inhibition of AChE, the enzyme that normally breaks down acetylcholine (ACh), would result in increased activity of nerves that use ACh as a neurotransmitter. **37.3:** 1. Sensory information from internal organs travels via spinal nerves, through the dorsal root ganglia to synapses on spinal cord interneurons whose axons travel in tracts to the brain. These then send motor impulses through tracts, to the ventral root ganglia, and then to the effector organ (smooth muscle in the intestine). 2. The four major lobes of the human brain are the frontal, parietal, temporal, and occipital. 3. Parkinson disease, with symptoms such as tremors, difficult speech, and trouble walking or standing, is associated with a loss of dopamine-producing cells in the basal nuclei of the forebrain (though the inciting cause is unknown); multiple sclerosis is an autoimmune disease that damages the myelin sheaths of neurons in the CNS, resulting in fatigue and in problems with visual and muscular function. **37.4:** 1. A reflex arc can travel from the sensory receptor, synapse on interneurons in the spinal cord, then travel back to the effector (muscle) without being perceived by the brain first. 2. Eating a big lunch mainly stimulates the parasympathetic branch of the autonomic nervous system, diverting blood supply to the digestive tract and away from the muscles. Jogging will engage the sympathetic system, reducing blood flow to the stomach and inhibiting its function. 3. The parasympathetic ("rest and digest") division dominates as you enjoy your meal, but your friend's "surprise" causes a sudden increase in sympathetic ("fight or flight") activity.

Testing Yourself

1. b; **2.** c; **3.** a; **4.** a; **5.** c; **6.** d; **7.** b; **8.** b; **9.** c; **10.** d; **11.** c; **12.** c; **13.** d; **14.** b; **15.** c; **16.** b; **17. a.** central canal; **b.** gray matter; **c.** white matter; **d.** dorsal root; **e.** cell body of sensory neuron in dorsal root ganglion; **f.** spinal nerve; **g.** cell body of motor neuron; **h.** interneuron (see Figure 37.13, page 709).

Chapter 38

Check Your Progress

38.1: 1. Sensory transduction is the conversion of some type of environmental stimulus into a nerve impulse. 2. Some snakes can perceive infrared radiation; bats, dolphins, and whales perceive very high or low frequency sound waves (echolocation); a dog's sense of smell is far more sensitive than a human's. **38.2:** 1. Both are chemical senses that use chemoreceptors to detect molecules in the environment. 2. Sweet, sour, salty, bitter, and umami. 3. Neurons transmit signals from different sensory organs to different areas of the brain, where they are interpreted as different types of information. **38.3:** 1. Rods are for peripheral vision and motion detection; they are well-suited for dim light. Cones are for color perception and fine detail, and are best-suited for bright light. Many rods may excite a single ganglion cell, but much smaller numbers of cones excite individual ganglion cells. 2. Sclera, choroid, retina. Light must pass through the ganglion and bipolar cell layers before reaching the photoreceptor cells. 3. An eyeball that is too long results in nearsightedness; an eyeball that is too short results in farsightedness; an uneven cornea results in astigmatism. **38.4:** 1. a. middle; b. outer; c. inner; d. inner; e. inner; f. outer. 2. Auditory canal, tympanic membrane (eardrum), ossicles (malleus, incus, and stapes), oval window, cochlea. 3. The utricle and saccule are responsible for gravitational equilibrium; the semicircular canals for rotational equilibrium. **38.5:** 1. A person lacking muscle spindles would have trouble walking, sitting, or doing other activities due to a lack of muscle tone. A person lacking nociceptors would be prone to injury due to an absence of warning signs associated with pain. 2. Pain is generally associated with potential harm: i.e., something to be avoided. An animal that quickly adapted to pain would have an increased chance of being injured or killed by a potentially dangerous stimulus.

Testing Yourself

1. b; **2.** c; **3.** c; **4.** e; **5.** d; **6.** c; **7.** c; **8.** b; **9.** d; **10.** a; **11.** b; **12.** c; **13.** a; **14.** d; **15.** b; **16.** d; **17. a.** retina—contains sensory receptors; **b.** choroid—absorbs stray light; **c.** sclera—protects and supports eyeball; **d.** optic nerve—transmits impulses to brain; **e.** fovea centralis—makes acute vision possible; **f.** muscle in ciliary body—holds lens in place, accommodation; **g.** lens—refracts and focuses light rays; **h.** iris—regulates light entrance; **i.** pupil—admits light; **j.** cornea—refracts light rays (see Figure 38.5, page 721).

Chapter 39

Check Your Progress

39.1: 1. Exoskeleton, endoskeleton, exoskeleton, exoskeleton, endoskeleton.

2. The tongue is a muscular hydrostat. 3. Because the muscle layers surrounding the coelom no longer contract, the hydrostatic skeleton cannot provide support for the body. **39.2:** 1. Osteoblasts build bone and osteoclasts break it down. Osteocytes occupy lacunae. 2. Compact bone, which serves mainly to support the body, contains many osteons, in which central canals are surrounded by a hard matrix with lacunae. Spongy bone is lighter, with numerous bars and plates as well as spaces filled with red bone marrow, which produces the blood cells. 3. Axial, axial, appendicular, appendicular, axial, appendicular, axial, appendicular, axial. **39.3:** 1. A pair of muscles that work opposite to one another; for example, if one muscle flexes (bends) the joint the other extends (straightens) it. 2. Myofibrils are tubular contractile units that are divided into sarcomeres. Each sarcomere contains actin (thin filaments) and myosin (thick filaments). 3. Cleavage of ATP allows myosin heads to bind to actin filaments, pulling them toward the center of the sarcomere.

Testing Yourself

1. b; **2.** f; **3.** c; **4.** e; **5.** e; **6.** e; **7.** b; **8.** b; **9.** c; **10.** b; **11.** e; **12.** e; **13.** c; **14.** b; **15. a.** T tubule; **b.** sarcoplasmic reticulum; **c.** myofibril; **d.** Z line; **e.** sarcomere; **f.** sarcolemma of muscle fiber (see Figure 39.13, page 745).

Chapter 40

Check Your Progress

40.1: 1. The nervous system tends to respond rapidly to both external and internal stimuli, while the endocrine system responds more slowly, but often has longer-lasting effects. Both systems use chemicals to communicate with other body systems; the nervous system at synapses, the endocrine system via hormones secreted mainly into the bloodstream. 2. Peptide hormones have receptors in the plasma membrane. Steroid hormones have receptors that are generally in the nucleus, sometimes in the cytoplasm. 3. Since peptide hormones usually bind to receptors on the outside of the cell; they must communicate with the inside of the cell via second messengers. **40.2:** 1. The hypothalamus communicates with the endocrine system via the pituitary gland: two hormones produced by the hypothalamus are stored in the posterior pituitary; several others are produced by the anterior pituitary in response to hypothalamic releasing factors that reach the anterior pituitary via a portal system. 2. ADH conserves body water by causing reabsorption of water by the kidneys; oxytocin causes uterine contractions during

labor and milk letdown during nursing. 3. Thyroid stimulating hormone (TSH) stimulates release of thyroid hormones; adrenocorticotropic hormone (ACTH) stimulates the adrenal glands to produce glucocorticoids, prolactin (PRL) causes breast development and milk production; growth hormone (GH) promotes bone and muscle growth; the gonadotropic hormones FSH and LH stimulate the testes or ovaries to produce gametes and sex hormones; and melanocyte-stimulating hormone (MSH) causes skin color changes in some animals. **40.3:** 1. Angiotensin II causes arterioles to constrict; aldosterone causes reabsorption of Na^+, accompanied by water, in the kidneys. 2. Adrenal cortex, pineal gland, adrenal medulla, kidneys, adipose tissue, pancreas, heart, adrenal cortex, thyroid gland. 3. PTH stimulates osteoclasts and calcitonin inhibits them.

Testing Yourself

1. f; **2.** b; **3.** c; **4.** a; **5.** e; **6.** d; **7.** b; **8.** d; **9.** a; **10.** a; **11.** e; **12.** b; **13.** d; **14.** b; **15.** a; **16.** b; **17.** c; **18.** e; **19.** d; **20.** c.

Chapter 41

Check Your Progress

41.1: 1. Asexual reproduction allows organisms to reproduce rapidly and colonize favorable environments quickly. Sexual reproduction produces offspring with a new combination of genes that may be more adaptive to a changed environment. 2. An oviparous animal lays eggs that hatch outside the body. A viviparous animal gives birth after the offspring have developed within the mother's body. Ovoviviparous animals retain fertilized eggs within a parent's body until they hatch; the parent then gives birth to the young. 3. A shelled egg contains extraembryonic membranes which keep the embryo moist, carry out gas exchange, collect wastes, and provide yolk as food. **41.2:** 1. Seminiferous tubule, epididymis, vas deferens, ejaculatory duct, urethra. 2. Seminal vesicles, prostate gland, and bulbourethral glands. 3. In males, FSH stimulates spermatogenesis and LH stimulates testosterone production. **41.3:** 1. Ovary, oviduct, uterus, cervix, vagina. 2. During the follicular phase, FSH stimulates ovarian follicles to produce primarily estrogen. A surge of LH (and FSH) also triggers ovulation. During the luteal phase, LH stimulates the corpus luteum to produce primarily progesterone. 3. Estrogen secreted by the developing follicle inhibits FSH secretion by the anterior pituitary, ending the follicular phase. Progesterone secreted by the developing corpus luteum inhibits LH secretion by the anterior pituitary, ending the luteal phase. Rising estrogen levels cause the endometrium to thicken (proliferative phase), and progesterone causes uterine glands to mature (secretory phase). If no pregnancy occurs, low levels of estrogen and progesterone initiate menstruation. **41.4:** 1. Male and female condoms and the diaphragm prevent sperm from coming in contact with the egg. 2. Abstinence (100%) and vasectomy (nearly 100%) are the most effective, the birth control pill and condoms are the next most effective, and natural family planning is least effective. 3. In AID, sperm are placed in the vagina or sometimes the uterus. In IVF, conception takes place in laboratory glassware and embryos are transferred to the woman's uterus. In GIFT, eggs and sperm are brought together in laboratory glassware, and placed in the oviducts immediately afterward. In ICSI, one sperm is injected directly into an egg. **41.5:** 1. Antiretroviral drug categories include entry inhibitors (viral attachment to host receptor), reverse transcriptase inhibitors (production of DNA from viral RNA), integrase inhibitors (insertion of viral DNA into host DNA), and protease inhibitors (processing of viral proteins). 2. HPV-induced genital warts can be painful and disfiguring, and some strains cause cancer of the cervix, vagina, vulva, penis, and anus. 3. Chlamydia and gonorrhea are associated with pelvic inflammatory disease and infertility.

Testing Yourself

1. b; **2.** e; **3.** c; **4.** e; **5.** c; **6.** c; **7.** c; **8.** c; **9.** a; **10.** a; **11.** c; **12.** c; **13.** b; **14.** e; **15.** c; **16.** a; **17.** c; **18.** b; **19.** c.

Chapter 42

Check Your Progress

42.1: 1. The fast block is the depolarization of the egg's plasma membrane that occurs upon initial contact with a sperm. The slow block occurs when the secretion of cortical granules converts the zona pellucida into the fertilization membrane. 2. Mesoderm, endoderm, ectoderm, ectoderm, mesoderm, mesoderm, mesoderm, endoderm. 3. Neurula stage. **42.2:** 1. Cytoplasmic segregation is the parceling out of maternal determinants as mitosis occurs. Induction is the influence of one embryonic tissue on the development of another. 2. A morphogen is a transcription factor that is distributed along a concentration gradient in the embryo and helps direct morphogenesis. 3. The homeobox encodes the homeodomain region of the protein product of the gene. The homeodomain is the DNA-binding region of the protein, which is a transcription factor. **42.3:** 1. oviduct.

2. Allantois, yolk sac, and chorion. 3. Structures that begin to develop between the third and fifth weeks include the nervous system, heart, chorionic villi, umbilical cord, and limb buds. **42.3:** 1. The thymus is the site where T cells finish their development; T cells are needed to stimulate other types of immune cells, including B cells that produce antibodies. 2. Menopause is the time when ovarian and uterine cycles cease. 3. Preprogrammed theories suggest aging is partly genetically programmed; single gene mutations influence aging in *C. elegans*. Damage accumulation theories suggest aging is due to an accumulation of cellular damage: e.g., DNA mutations, cross-linking of proteins, or oxidation by free radicals.

Testing Yourself

1. b; **2.** b; **3.** a; **4.** e; **5.** b; **6.** e; **7.** e; **8.** d; **9. a.** chorion: contributes to forming placenta where wastes are exchanged for nutrients and oxygen; **b.** amnion: protects and prevents desiccation; **c.** embryo; **d.** allantois: blood vessels become umbilical blood vessels; **e.** yolk sac: first site of blood cell formation; **f.** chorionic villi: embryonic portion of placenta; **g.** maternal portion of placenta; **h.** umbilical cord: connects developing embryo to the placenta (see also Figure 42.11, page 805); **10.** c; **11.** a; **12.** d; **13.** b; **14.** e; **15.** b; **16.** c; **17.** b; **18.** a; **19.** c; **20.** e.

Chapter 43

Check Your Progress

43.1: 1. Fisher lovebird (carry nesting material in beak) mated to Peach-faced lovebird (carry nesting material in rump feathers) result in offspring with intermediate behavior. Offspring of inland garter snakes (do not eat slugs) and coastal garter snakes (eat slugs) show an intermediate liking for slugs. 2. Gene for egg-laying hormone in *Aplysia* was isolated and its protein product controls egg-laying behavior. The gene *fosB* has been found to control maternal behavior in mice. **43.2:** 1. Associative learning. 2. Just hatched, laughing gull chicks instinctively peck at parents' bill to be fed but their accuracy improves after a few days. 3. Chimpanzees pile up boxes to reach food and ravens use their beaks and feet to bring up food attached to a string. **43.3:** 1. Pheromones are used to mark a territory so other individuals of that species will stay away; honeybees do a waggle dance to guide other bees to a food source; vervet monkeys have calls that make other vervets run away. 2. Chemical (effective all the time, not as fast as auditory); auditory (can be modified but the recipient has to be present when message is sent); visual (need not be

accompanied by chemical or auditory, needs light in order to receive); tactile (permits bonding; recipient must be close). 3. chemical: taste buds and olfactory receptors; auditory: ears; visual: eyes; tactile: touch receptors in skin. **43.4:** 1. One benefit of territoriality is to ensure a source of food. 2. Both an animal's reproductive strategy and sexual selection favors features that increase an animal's chance of leaving offspring. 3. Altruistic behavior is supposed to be selfless but when, for example, an offspring helps its parents raise siblings, the helper may be increasing some of its own genes in the next generation.

Testing Yourself

1. c; **2.** a; **3.** d; **4.** b; **5.** c; **6.** d; **7.** e; **8.** c; **9.** d; **10.** c; **11.** c; **12.** a; **13.** c; **14.** d; **15.** a; **16.** c; **17.** b; **18.** a; **19.** c; **20.** b.

Chapter 44

Check Your Progress

44.1: 1. A population is all the members of one species that inhabit a particular area and a community is all the populations that interact within that area. 2. To develop models that explain and predict the distribution and abundance of organisms. 3. Abiotic means the nonliving aspects of an environment such as rainfall and temperature. **44.2:** 1. Population density is the number of individuals per unit area and population distribution is the pattern of dispersal of individuals across an area of interest. 2. In a type I survivorship curve, most individuals survive well past the midpoint of the life span and death does not come until near the end of the life span. In type II, survivorship decreases at a constant rate throughout the life span. In type III, most individuals die young. 3. In a bell-shaped age pyramid, the pre-reproductive members represent the largest portion of the population. **44.3:** 1. An environment in which the weather, food supply, etc., remains stable favors iteroparity. 2. Exponential growth ceases when the environment cannot support a larger population size; that is, the point at which the size of the population has reached the environment's carrying capacity. **44.4:** 1. As population density increases, competition and predation become more intense. 2. If a flash flood occurs, mice that can stay afloat will survive and reproduce whereas those that quickly sink will not survive and will not reproduce. In this way the ability to stay afloat will be more prevalent in the next generation. **44.5:** 1. A *K*-strategist species: allocate energy to their own growth and survival and to the growth and survival of their limited number of offspring. *r*-strategist species: allocate energy to producing a large number of offspring and little or no energy goes into parental care. 2. Populations may vary between *K* and *r* strategies based upon environmental conditions. **44.6:** 1. Less-developed countries have a high population growth while more-developed countries have a low rate of population growth. 2. The parents don't immediately die after they have had their child which causes the population to increase. 3. Since resources are in limited supply an increase in consumption by the LDC will cause more competition for resources.

Testing Yourself

1. d; **2.** c; **3.** e; **4.** e; **5.** b; **6.** e; **7.** c; **8.** e; **9.** c; **10.** e; **11.** c; **12.** e; **13.** b; **14.** e; **15.** e.

Chapter 45

Check Your Progress

45.1: 1. An organism's habitat is the place where it lives and reproduces. The niche is the role it plays in its community such as whether it is a producer or consumer. 2. The two factors are (1) the predator causes the prey population to decline which leads to a decline in the predator population; later when the prey population recovers so does the predator population; (2) lack of food causes the prey population to decline followed by the predator population; later when food is available to the prey population they both recover. 3. Acacias feed the ants that protect them from herbivores; Clark's nutcrackers feed on the seeds of whitebark pine trees but also disperse the seeds; pollinators take nectar from flowers and carry their pollen to other flowers of the same species. **45.2:** 1. Environmental disturbances, fire, flood, etc., lead to succession. 2. The facilitation model predicts that a community will grow toward becoming a climax community. The inhibition model predicts that colonists will inhibit the growth of a community. **45.3:** 1. A producer of food (photosynthesizer) is at the base of an ecological pyramid. 2. Energy passes from one population to the next, and at each step more is converted to heat until all of the original input has become heat. Therefore energy flows though an ecosystem.

Chemicals pass from one population to the next and then recycle back to the producer populations again. 3. Return of CO_2 to the atmosphere because humans burn fossil fuels and destroy forests that take up CO_2.

Testing Yourself

1. c; **2.** e; **3.** e; **4.** a; **5.** c; **6.** b; **7.** d; **8.** b; **9.** c; **10.** d; **11.** e; **12. a.** producers; **b.** consumers; **c.** inorganic nutrient pool; **d.** decomposers; **13.** a; **14.** e; **15.** c; **16.** d; **17.** c; **18.** b; **19.** c; **20.** d.

Chapter 46

Check Your Progress

46.1: 1. Because the Earth is a sphere, the Sun's rays hit the equator straight on but are angled to reach the poles. 2. The windward side of the mountain receives more rainfall than the other side. Winds blowing over bodies of water collect moisture that they lose when they reach land. **46.2:** 1. A tropical rain forest has a canopy (tops of great variety of tall evergreen hardwood trees) with buttressed trunks at ground level. Long lianas (hanging vines) climb into the canopy. Epiphytes grow on the trees. The understory consists of smaller plants and the forest floor is very sparse. A temperate deciduous forest contains trees (oak, beech, sycamore, and maple) that lose their leaves in the fall. Enough light penetrates the canopy to allow a layer of understory trees. Shrubs, mosses, and ferns grow at ground level. 2. The savanna is an expansive grassland that has a moderate climate. Therefore, the grasses keep producing throughout the year and provide plentiful food for a great variety of and number of herbivores that provide food for carnivores. The tundra is cold much of the year and has a limited growing season; therefore, its productivity is low and it supports only small populations of a few types of herbivores. **46.3:** 1. The cooling and warming of the epilimnion causes the layers of water to change position. 2. Most of the open ocean is the pelagic zone (open waters) divided into the epipelagic zone (contains phytoplankton, zooplankton, many types of fishes and also dolphins and whales); the mesopelagic zone (contains only carnivores adapted to the

absence of light); and the bathypelagic zone (in complete darkness that contains strange-looking fishes and invertebrates). Few vertebrates but many invertebrates (echinoderms, tube worms) exist on the abyssal plain and feed on debris that floats down from above.

Testing Yourself

1. b; **2.** d; **3.** c; **4.** d; **5.** a; **6.** b; **7.** e; **8.** e; **9.** a; **10.** a; **11.** b; **12.** d; **13.** b; **14.** a; **15.** c; **16.** b; **17.** a; **18.** d; **19.** c.

Chapter 47

Check Your Progress

47.1: 1. Many disciplines provide data that support conservation biology. 2. Biodiversity includes the number of species on Earth; genetic diversity (variations in a species); ecosystem diversity (interactions of species); and landscape diversity (interactions of ecosystems). A hotspot is a specific region with a large amount of biodiversity. **47.2:** 1. Direct value is a service that is immediately recognizable, while indirect values may not be as noticeable. 2. Direct values include medicine, food, or commercial products. Indirect values include assisting biogeochemical cycles, waste disposal, providing fresh water, preventing soil erosion, regulating climate, or providing a place for recreation. **47.3:** 1. Habitat loss, exotic species, pollution, overexploitation, disease. 2. Exotic plants displace native plants; predators introduced to kill pests also kill native animals; escaped animals may compete with, prey on, hybridize with, or introduce diseases into native populations. **47.4:** 1. A landscape involves more than one ecosystem and sometimes keystone species move between ecosystems. 2. Begin as soon as possible, mimic natural processes, and strive for sustainable development while providing services to humans.

Testing Yourself

1. e; **2.** b; **3.** e; **4.** e; **5.** e; **6.** b; **7.** e; **8.** e; **9.** c; **10.** c; **11.** e; **12.** e; **13.** e; **14.** b, c; **15. a.** habitat loss; **b.** introduction of exotic species; **c.** pollution; **d.** overexploitation; **e.** disease.

Tree of Life

The tree of life depicted in this appendix is based on the phylogenetic (evolutionary) trees presented in the text. Figure 1.5 showed how the three domains of life—Bacteria, Archaea, and Eukarya—are related. This relationship is also apparent in the tree of life, which combines the individual trees given in the text for eukaryotic protists, plants, fungi, and animals. In combining these trees, we show how all organisms may be related to one another through the evolutionary process.

Prokaryotes

Domains Bacteria and Archaea (Chapter 20) constitute the prokaryotic organisms that are characterized by their simple structure but a complex metabolism. The chromosome of a prokaryote is not bounded by a nuclear envelope, and therefore, these organisms do not have a nucleus. Prokaryotes carry out all the metabolic processes performed by eukaryotes and many others besides. However, they do not have organelles, except for multiple ribosomes.

Domain Bacteria

Bacteria are the most plentiful of all organisms, capable of living in most habitats, and they can carry out many different metabolic processes. Most bacteria are aerobic heterotrophs, but some are photosynthetic, and some are chemosynthetic. Motile forms move by flagella consisting of a single filament. Their cell wall contains peptidoglycan, and they have distinctive RNA sequences.

Domain Archaea

Archaean cell walls lack peptidoglycan, their lipids have a unique branched structure, and their ribosomal RNA sequences are distinctive. Examples are methanogens and the extremophiles.

Domain Eukarya

Eukarya have a complex cell structure with a nucleus and several types of organelles that compartmentalize the cell. Mitochondria that produce ATP and chloroplasts that produce carbohydrates are derived from prokaryotes that took up residence in a larger, nucleated cell. They may be unicellular (the majority of the protists), or multicellular (the plants, fungi, animals). Each multicellular group is characterized by a particular mode of nutrition. Flagella, if present, have a 9 + 2 organization.

Protists

The protists (Chapter 21) represent a group containing those eukaryotes that are not classified as a plant, fungus, or animal. The protists are members of six supergroups whose evolutionary relationships are being actively investigated. A supergroup is a major eukaryotic group, and six supergroups encompass all members of the domain Eukarya, including all protists, plants, fungi, and animals. Examples of protists include amoebas, the brown algae, and the paramecia.

Plants

Plants (Chapter 23) are multicellular photosynthetic eukaryotes that became adapted to living on land. This group includes aquatic green algae called charophytes, which have a haploid life cycle and share certain significant traits with the land plants.

The land plants exhibit an alternation-of-generations life cycle; protect a multicellular sporophyte embryo; produce gametes in gametangia; have apical meristem that produces differentiated tissues and have a waxy cuticle that prevents water loss. Examples include mosses, ferns, conifers, and flowering plants.

Fungi

Fungi (Chapter 22) have multicellular bodies composed of hyphae that absorb nutrients from the environment. They have a haploid life cycle and usually produce nonmotile spores during both asexual and sexual reproduction. Chytrids are aquatic fungi with flagellated spores and gametes. Examples include the mushrooms, cup fungi, and molds.

Animals

Animals (Chapters 28 and 29) are multicellular and have a diploid life cycle. Most have specialized tissues and ingest their food in a digestive cavity. Examples include invertebrate organisms such as sponges, earthworms, molluscs, insects, and vertebrates such as fishes, reptiles, and humans.

Glossary

A

abiogenesis Origin of life from nonliving matter, such as occurred on the early Earth. 329

abiotic synthesis Process of chemical evolution that resulted in the formation of organic molecules (amino acids, monosaccharides, etc.) from inorganic material. 329

abscisic acid (ABA) Plant hormone that causes stomata to close and initiates and maintains dormancy. 488

abscission Dropping of leaves, fruits, or flowers from a land plant. 488

absolute dating (of fossils) Determining the age of a fossil by direct measurement, usually involving radioisotope decay. 334

absorption spectrum For photosynthetic pigments, a graph of how much solar radiation is absorbed versus the wavelength of light. 124

accessory pigment Proteins that assist in the photosynthetic process by transferring energy from the photons to the central chlorophyll molecules. 389

acid Molecules tending to raise the hydrogen ion concentration in a solution and thus to lower its pH numerically. 32

acid deposition The return to Earth in rain or snow of sulfate or nitrate salts of acids produced by commercial and industrial activities. 878

acquired immunodeficiency syndrome (AIDS) Disease caused by the HIV virus that destroys helper T cells and macrophages of the immune system, thus preventing an immune response to pathogens; caused by sexual contact with an infected person, intravenous drug use, and transfusions of contaminated blood (rare). 787

actin One of two major proteins of muscle; makes up thin filaments in myofibrils of muscle fibers. *See also* myosin. 745

actin filament Component of the cytoskeleton; plays a role in the movement of the cell and its organelles; a protein filament in a sarcomere of a muscle, its movement shortens the sarcomere, yielding muscle contraction. 78

action potential Electrochemical changes that take place across the axon membrane; the nerve impulse. 699

active immunity Ability to produce antibodies due to the immune system's response to a microorganism or a vaccine. 637

active site Region of an enzyme where the substrate binds and where the chemical reaction occurs. 110

active transport Use of a plasma membrane carrier protein to move a molecule or ion from a region of lower concentration to one of higher concentration; it opposes equilibrium and requires energy. 95

adaptation Species's modification in structure, function, or behavior that makes a species more suitable to its environment. 278

adaptive immunity Type of immunity that is characterized by the action of lymphocytes to specific antigens. 627

adaptive radiation Rapid evolution of several species from a common ancestor into new ecological or geographical zones. 316

adenine (A) One of four nitrogen-containing bases in nucleotides composing the structure of DNA and RNA. Pairs with uracil (U) and thymine (T). 217

adenosine Portion of ATP and ADP that is composed of the base adenine and the sugar ribose. 54

adhesion junction Junction between cells in which the adjacent plasma membranes do not touch but are held together by intercellular filaments attached to buttonlike thickenings. 99

adipose tissue Connective tissue in which fat is stored. 590

ADP (adenosine diphosphate) Nucleotide with two phosphate groups that can accept another phosphate group and become ATP. 56, 107

adrenal cortex Outer portion of the adrenal gland; secretes mineralocorticoids, such as aldosterone, and glucocorticoids, such as cortisol. 762

adrenal gland Gland that lies atop a kidney; the *adrenal medulla* produces the hormones epinephrine and norepinephrine, and the *adrenal cortex* produces the glucocorticoid and mineralocorticoid hormones. 762

adrenal medulla Inner portion of the adrenal gland; secretes the hormones epinephrine and norepinephrine. 762

adrenocorticotropic hormone (ACTH) Hormone secreted by the anterior lobe of the pituitary gland that stimulates activity in the adrenal cortex. 757

aerobic A chemical process that requires air (oxygen); phase of cellular respiration that requires oxygen. 137

age structure diagram In demographics, a display of the age groups of a population; a growing population has a pyramid-shaped diagram. 842

agglutination Clumping of red blood cells due to a reaction between antigens on red blood cell plasma membranes and antibodies in the plasma. 619

agnathan Fishes that lack jaws; namely, the lampreys and hagfishes. 553

agranular leukocyte Form of white blood cell that lacks spherical vesicles (granules) in the cytoplasm. 620

aldosterone Hormone secreted by the adrenal cortex that regulates the sodium and potassium ion balance of the blood. 690, 763

alkaloid Bitter-tasting nitrogenous compounds that have a basic pH (e.g., caffeine). 497

allantois Extraembryonic membrane that accumulates nitrogenous wastes in the eggs of reptiles, including birds; contributes to the formation of umbilical blood vessels in mammals. 805

allele Alternative form of a gene; alleles occur at the same locus on homologous chromosomes. 196

allele frequency Relative proportion of each allele for a gene in the gene pool of a population. 290

allergy Immune response to substances that usually are not recognized as foreign. 641

allopatric speciation Model that proposes that new species arise due to an interruption of gene flow between populations that are separated geographically. 313

alloploidy Polyploid organism that contains the genomes of two or more different species. 315

allosteric site Site on an allosteric enzyme that binds an effector molecule; binding alters the activity of the enzyme. 112

alpine tundra Tundra near the peak of a mountain. 887

alternation-of-generations Life cycle, typical of land plants, in which a diploid sporophyte alternates with a haploid gametophyte. 176, 422

altruism Social interaction that has the potential to decrease the lifetime reproductive success of the member exhibiting the behavior. 833

alveolates A group of protists that includes unicellular dinoflagellates, apicomplexans, and ciliates; alveoli support plasma membrane. 392

alveolus (pl., alveoli) In humans, terminal, microscopic, grapelike air sac found in lungs. 668

Alzheimer disease Disease of the central nervous system (brain) that is characterized by an accumulation of beta amyloid protein and neurofibrillary tangles in the hippocampus and amygdala. 707

AM fungi (Glomeromycota) Fungi with branching invaginations (arbuscular mycorrhizae or AM) used to invade plant roots. 408

amino acid Organic molecule composed of an amino group and an acid group; covalently bonds to produce peptide molecules. 50

ammonia Nitrogenous end product that takes a limited amount of energy to produce but requires much water to excrete because it is toxic. 681

amnion Extraembryonic membrane of birds, reptiles, and mammals that forms an enclosing, fluid-filled sac. 805

amniote Vertebrate that produces an egg surrounded by four membranes, one of which is the amnion; amniote groups are the reptiles, (including birds), and mammals. 553

amniotic egg Egg that has an amnion, as seen during the development of reptiles, (including birds), and mammals. 558

amoeboid Cell that moves and engulfs debris with pseudopods. 396

amoebozoan Supergroup of eukaryotes that includes amoebas and slime molds and is characterized by lobe-shaped pseudopodia. 396

amphibian Member of vertebrate class Amphibia that includes frogs, toads, and salamanders; they are tied to a watery environment for reproduction. 556

amygdala Part of the limbic system of the brain; associated with emotional experiences. 707

amyotrophic lateral sclerosis (ALS) Neurodegenerative disease affecting the motor neurons in the brain and spinal cord resulting in paralysis and death; also known as Lou Gehrig's disease. 703

anabolic steroid Synthetic steroid that mimics the effect of testosterone. 767

anabolism Chemical reaction in which smaller molecules (monomers) are combined to form larger molecules (polymers); anabolic metabolism. 147

anaerobic A chemical reaction that occurs in the absence of oxygen; an example is the fermentation reactions. 137

analogous, analogous structure Structure that has a similar function in separate lineages but differs in anatomy and ancestry. 284, 317, 357

analogy Similarity of function but not of origin. 357

anaphase Fourth phase of mitosis; chromosomes move toward the poles of the spindle. 160

anaphylactic shock Severe systemic form of anaphylaxis involving bronchiolar constriction, impaired breathing, vasodilation, and a rapid drop in blood pressure with a threat of circulatory failure. 641

anapsid Characteristic of a vertebrate skull in which there is no opening in the skull behind the eye socket (orbit). 558

ancestral traits Traits that are found in a common ancestor and its descendants. 354

androgen Male sex hormone (e.g., testosterone). 767

aneuploidy Condition in which a cell does not contain the correct number, or combinations, of chromosomes. 183

angina pectoris Condition characterized by thoracic pain resulting from occluded coronary arteries; may precede a heart attack. 616

angiogenesis Formation of new blood vessels; rapid angiogenesis is a characteristic of cancer cells. 164

angiosperm Flowering land plant; the seeds are borne within a fruit. 430, 433

angiotensin II Hormone produced from angiotensinogen (a plasma protein) by the kidneys and lungs; raises blood pressure. 690

animals Multicellular, heterotrophic eukaryote that undergoes development to achieve its final form. In general, animals are mobile organisms, characterized by the presence of muscular and nervous tissue. 8

annelid The segmented worms, such as the earthworm and the clam worm. 536

annual ring Layer of wood (secondary xylem) usually produced during one growing season. 456

anterior pituitary Portion of the pituitary gland that is controlled by the hypothalamus and produces six types of hormones, some of which control other endocrine glands. 757

antheridium (pl., antheridia) Sperm-producing structures, as in the moss life cycle. 422

anthropoid Group of primates that includes monkeys, apes, and humans. 572

antibody Protein produced in response to the presence of an antigen; each antibody combines with a specific antigen. 618

antibody-mediated immunity Specific mechanism of defense in which plasma cells derived from B cells produce antibodies that combine with antigens. 634

anticodon Three-base sequence in a transfer RNA molecule base that pairs with a complementary codon in mRNA. 228

antidiuretic hormone (ADH) Hormone secreted by the posterior pituitary that increases the permeability of the collecting ducts in a kidney. 688, 757

antigen Foreign substance, usually a protein or a polysaccharide, that stimulates the immune system to react, such as to produce antibodies. 627

antigen-presenting cell (APC) Cell that displays an antigen to certain cells of the immune system so they can defend the body against that particular antigen. 635

antigen receptor Receptor proteins in the plasma membrane of immune system cells whose shape allows them to combine with a specific antigen. 633

anus Outlet of the digestive tube. 653

aorta In humans, the major systemic artery that takes blood from the heart to the tissues. 614

aortic body Sensory receptor in the aortic arch sensitive to the O_2, CO_2, and H^+ content of the blood. 671

apical Directional term that refers to the tip of a filament or branch of a plant. 421

apical dominance Influence of a terminal bud in suppressing the growth of axillary buds. 485

apical meristem In vascular land plants, masses of cells in the root and shoot that reproduce and elongate as primary growth occurs. 447

apicomplexan Parasitic protozoans, formerly called sporozoans that lack mobility and form spores; now named for a unique collection of organelles. 394

apoptosis Programmed cell death; involves a cascade of specific cellular events leading to death and destruction of the cell. 155, 800

appendicular skeleton Part of the vertebrate skeleton comprising the appendages, shoulder girdle, and hip girdle. 742

appendix (vermiform appendix) In humans, small, tubular appendage that extends outward from the cecum of the large intestine. 653

aquaporin Channel protein through which water can diffuse across a membrane. 91, 688

arboreal Living in trees. 571

archaeans (archaea) Prokaryotic organisms that are members of the domain Archaea. 65, 378

archaeplastid Supergroup of eukaryotes that includes land plants and red and green algae. Developed from endosymbiotic cyanobacteria. 387

archegonium Egg-producing structures, as in the moss life cycle. 422

Arctic tundra Biome that encircles the Earth just south of ice-covered polar seas in the Northern Hemisphere. 888

arteriole Vessel that takes blood from an artery to capillaries. 608

artery Blood vessel that transports blood away from the heart. 608

arthritis Condition characterized by an inflammation of the joints; two common forms are osteoarthritis and rheumatoid arthritis. 743

arthropod Invertebrates, with an exoskeleton and jointed appendages, such as crustaceans and insects. 539

artificial selection Intentional breeding of certain traits, or combinations of traits, over others to produce a desirable outcome. 278

ascus Fingerlike sac in which nuclear fusion, meiosis, and ascospore production occur during sexual reproduction of sac fungi. 409

asexual reproduction Reproduction that requires only one parent and does not involve gametes. 166, 513

associative learning Acquired ability to associate two stimuli or between a stimulus and a response. 824

assortative mating Mating of individuals with similar phenotypes. 295

aster Short, radiating fibers produced by the centrosomes in animal cells. 159

asthma Condition in which bronchioles constrict and cause difficulty in breathing. 673

astigmatism Uneven shape of the cornea or lens of the eye; causes a distortion in the light reaching the retina of the eye. 724

astrocyte Nervous system cell that provides metabolic and structural support to the neurons. 697

asymmetry Lack of any symmetrical relationship in the morphology of an organism. 522

atherosclerosis Form of cardiovascular disease characterized by the accumulation of fatty materials (usually cholesterol) in the arteries. 616

atom Smallest particle of an element that displays the properties of the element. 22

atomic mass Average of atom mass units for all the isotopes of an atom. 23

atomic number Number of protons within the nucleus of an atom. 23

atomic symbol One or two letters that represent the name of an element—e.g., H stands for a hydrogen atom, and Na stands for a sodium atom. 22

ATP (adenosine triphosphate) Nucleotide with three phosphate groups. The breakdown of ATP into ADP + P makes energy available for energy-requiring processes in cells. 54, 107

ATP synthase Complex of proteins in the cristae of mitochondria and thylakoid membrane of chloroplast that produces ATP from the diffusion of hydrogen ions across a membrane. 114, 126

atrial natriuretic hormone (ANH) Hormone secreted by the heart that increases sodium excretion. 690, 763

atrioventricular valve Heart valve located between an atrium and a ventricle. 611

atrium Chamber; particularly an upper chamber of the heart lying above a ventricle. 610

auditory communication Sound that an animal makes for the purpose of sending a message to another individual. 828

auditory tube Also called the eustachian tube; connects the middle ear to the nasopharynx for the equalization of pressure. 727

australopithecine (australopith) One of several species of *Australopithecus*, a genus that contains the first generally recognized humanlike hominins. 577

autoimmune disease Disease that results when the immune system mistakenly attacks the body's own tissues. 642

autonomic system Portion of the peripheral nervous system that regulates internal organs. 708

autoploidy Polyploid organism with multiple chromosome sets all from the same species. 315

autosome Chromosome pairs that are the same between the sexes; in humans, all but the X and Y chromosomes. 201

autotroph Organism that can capture energy and synthesize organic molecules from inorganic nutrients. 120, 870

auxin Plant hormone regulating growth, particularly cell elongation; also called indoleacetic acid (IAA). 485

axial skeleton Part of the vertebrate skeleton forming the vertical support or axis, including the skull, the rib cage, and the vertebral column. 740

axillary bud Bud located in the axil of a leaf. 445

axon Elongated portion of a neuron that conducts nerve impulses, typically from the cell body to the synapse. 697

B

Bacillus A rod-shaped bacterium; also a genus of bacteria, *Bacillus*. 65

bacteriophage Virus that infects bacteria. 367

bacterium (pl., bacteria) Member of the domain Bacteria. 374

bark External part of a tree, containing cork, cork cambium, and phloem. 456

Barr body Dark-staining body in the cell nuclei of female mammals that contains a condensed, inactive X chromosome; named after its discoverer, Murray Barr. 185, 243

basal body A cytoplasmic structure that is located at the base of—and may organize—cilia or flagella. 80

basal nuclei Subcortical nuclei deep within the white matter that serve as relay stations for motor impulses and produce dopamine to help control skeletal muscle activities. 704

base Molecules tending to lower the hydrogen ion concentration in a solution and thus raise the pH numerically. 32

basidium Clublike structure in which nuclear fusion, meiosis, and basidiospore production occur during sexual reproduction of club fungi. 412

basophil White blood cell with a granular cytoplasm; able to be stained with a basic dye. 620

B cell Lymphocyte that matures in the bone marrow and, when stimulated by the presence of a specific antigen, gives rise to antibody-producing plasma cells. 629

B-cell receptor (BCR) Molecule on the surface of a B cell that binds to a specific antigen. 633

behavior Observable, coordinated responses to environmental stimuli. 820

behavioral ecology Study of how natural selection shapes behavior. 830

beneficial nutrient In plants, a molecule or element that is either required or enhances the growth and production of a plant. 465

benign Mass of cells derived from a single mutated cell that has repeatedly undergone cell division but has remained at the site of origin. 163

bicarbonate ion Ion that participates in buffering the blood, and the form in which carbon dioxide is transported in the bloodstream. 672

bilateral symmetry Body plan having two corresponding or complementary halves. 522

bile Secretion of the liver that is temporarily stored and concentrated in the gallbladder before being released into the small intestine, where it emulsifies fat. 652

binary fission Splitting of a parent cell into two daughter cells; serves as an asexual form of reproduction in bacteria. 166, 373

binomial nomenclature Scientific name of an organism, the first part of which designates the genus and the second part of which designates the specific epithet. 8, 349

biocultural evolution Phase of human evolution in which cultural events affect natural selection. 581

biodiversity Total number of species, the variability of their genes, and the communities in which they live. 10, 908

biodiversity hotspot Region of the world that contains unusually large concentrations of species. 909

biogeochemical cycle Circulating pathway of elements such as carbon and nitrogen involving exchange pools, storage areas, and biotic communities. 874

biogeography Study of the geographical distribution of organisms. 275

bioinformatics Area of scientific study that utilizes computer technologies to analyze large sets of data, typically in the study of genomics and proteomics. 265, 908

biological clock Internal mechanism that maintains a biological rhythm in the absence of environmental stimuli. 494

biological species concept The concept that defines species as groups of populations that have the potential to interbreed and that are reproductively isolated from other groups. 310

biology The branch of science that is concerned with the study of life and living organisms. 2

biomagnification The accumulation of pollutants as they move up the food web. 902

biomass The number of organisms multiplied by their weight. 873

biome One of the biosphere's major communities, characterized in particular by certain climatic conditions and particular types of plants. 887

biomolecule Organic molecules such as proteins, nucleic acids, carbohydrates, and fats. 38, 328

biosphere Zone of air, land, and water at the surface of the Earth in which living organisms are found. 9, 839

biotechnology products Commercial or agricultural products that are made with or derived from transgenic organisms. 258

biotic potential Maximum population growth rate under ideal conditions. 841

bird Endothermic reptile that has feathers and wings, is often adapted for flight, and lays hard-shelled eggs. 562

bivalent Homologous chromosomes, each having sister chromatids that are joined by a nucleoprotein lattice during meiosis; also called a tetrad. 173

bivalve Type of mollusc with a shell composed of two valves; includes clams, oysters, and scallops. 534

blade Broad, expanded portion of a land plant leaf that may be single or compound leaflets. 445

blastocoel Fluid-filled cavity of a blastula. 797

blastocyst Early stage of human embryonic development that consists of a hollow, fluid-filled ball of cells. 806

blastopore Opening into the primitive gut formed at gastrulation. 798

blastula Hollow, fluid-filled ball of cells occurring during animal development prior to gastrula formation. 523, 797

blind spot Region of the retina, lacking rods or cones, where the optic nerve leaves the eye. 721

blood Fluid circulated by the heart through a closed system of vessels; type of connective tissue. 591, 606

blood pressure Force of blood pushing against the inside wall of blood vessels. 615

body cavity In vertebrates, defined regions of the body in which organs reside. 596

bog Wet, spongy ground in a low-lying area, usually acidic and low in organic nutrients. 897

bolide Term for a large, crater-forming meteorite that strikes the Earth's surface. 343

bone Connective tissue having protein fibers and a hard matrix of inorganic salts, notably calcium salts. 591

bony fishes Vertebrates belonging to the class of fish called Osteichthyes that have a bony, rather than cartilaginous, skeleton. 554

bottleneck effect Type of genetic drift; occurs when a majority of genotypes are prevented from participating in the production of the next generation as a result of a natural disaster or human interference. 295

brachiopod Lophophorans in the phyla Brachiopoda that are characterized by two shells, one on the top and one on the bottom. 530

brain Ganglionic mass at the anterior end of the nerve cord; in vertebrates, the brain is located in the cranial cavity of the skull. 703

brain stem In mammals; portion of the brain consisting of the medulla oblongata, pons, and midbrain. 704

bronchiole In terrestrial vertebrates, small tube that conducts air from a bronchus to the alveoli. 668

bronchus (pl., bronchi) In terrestrial vertebrates, branch of the trachea that leads to the lungs. 668

brown algae Marine photosynthetic protists with a notable abundance of xanthophyll pigments; this group includes well-known seaweeds of northern rocky shores. 390

bryophyte A nonvascular land plant—including the mosses, liverworts, and hornworts—in which the gametophyte is dominant. 423

bryozoan Lophophorans of the phylum Bryozoa that are characterized as being aquatic and colonial that form colonies called zooids. 53

budding Asexual form of reproduction whereby a new organism develops as an outgrowth of the body of the parent. 406

buffer Substance or group of substances that tend to resist pH changes of a solution, thus stabilizing its relative acidity and basicity. 33

bulbourethral glands Male sex glands that produce pre-ejaculate fluid that neutralizes acid in the urethra. 777

bulk transport Movement of substances, usually large particles, across the plasma membrane using vesicles. 91

C

C$_3$ plant Plant that fixes carbon dioxide via the Calvin cycle; the first stable product of C$_3$ photosynthesis is a 3-carbon compound. 130

C$_4$ plant Plant that fixes carbon dioxide to produce a C$_4$ molecule that releases carbon dioxide to the Calvin cycle. 130

calcitonin Hormone secreted by the thyroid gland that increases the blood calcium level. 761

calorie Amount of heat energy required to raise the temperature of one gram of water 1°C. 29

Calvin cycle reaction Portion of photosynthesis that takes place in the stroma of chloroplasts and can occur in the dark; it uses the products of the light reactions to reduce CO$_2$ to a carbohydrate. 123

calyx The sepals collectively; the outermost flower whorl. 503

CAM Crassulacean-acid metabolism; a form of photosynthesis in succulent plants that separates the light-dependent and Calvin reactions by time. 130

camera-type eye Type of eye found in vertebrates and certain molluscs; a single lens focuses an image on closely packed photoreceptors. 720

camouflage Process of hiding from predators in which an organism's behavior, form, and pattern of coloration allow it to blend into the background and prevent detection. 863

cancer Malignant tumor whose nondifferentiated cells exhibit loss of contact inhibition, uncontrolled growth, and the ability to invade tissue and metastasize. 163

capillary Microscopic blood vessel; gases and other substances are exchanged across the walls of a capillary between blood and tissue fluid. 608

capsid Protective protein containing the genetic material of a virus. 366

capsule A form of glycocalyx that consists of a gelatinous layer; found in blue-green algae and certain bacteria. 65

carbaminohemoglobin Hemoglobin carrying carbon dioxide. 672

carbohydrate Class of organic compounds that typically contain carbon, hydrogen, and oxygen in a 1:2:1 ratio; includes the monosaccharides, disaccharides, and polysaccharides. 41

carbon dioxide fixation Process by which carbon dioxide gas is attached to an organic compound; in photosynthesis, this occurs in the Calvin cycle reactions. 128

carbonic anhydrase Enzyme in red blood cells that speeds the formation of carbonic acid from water and carbon dioxide. 672

carcinogen Environmental agent that causes mutations leading to the development of cancer. 248

cardiac cycle One complete cycle of systole and diastole for all heart chambers. 612

cardiac muscle Striated, involuntary muscle tissue found only in the heart. 593

cardiac output Blood volume pumped by each ventricle per minute (not total output pumped by both ventricles). 612

carnivore Consumer in a food chain that eats other animals. 870

carotenoid An accessory photosynthetic pigment of plants and algae that are often yellow or orange in color; consist of two classes—the xanthophylls and the carotenes. 124

carotid body Structure located at the branching of the carotid arteries; contains chemoreceptors sensitive to the O_2, CO_2, and H^+ content in blood. 671

carpel Ovule-bearing unit that is a part of a pistil. 503

carrier Heterozygous individual who has no apparent abnormality but can pass on an allele for a recessively inherited genetic disorder. 202

carrier protein Protein in the plasma membrane that combines with and transports a molecule or ion across the plasma membrane. 88

carrying capacity (K) Largest number of organisms of a particular species that can be maintained indefinitely by a given environment. 845

cartilage Connective tissue in which the cells lie within lacunae embedded in a flexible, proteinaceous matrix. 590

cartilaginous fish Vertebrates that belong to the class of fish called the Chondrichthyes: possess a cartilaginous, rather than bony, skeleton; includes sharks, rays, and skates. 554

Casparian strip Layer of impermeable lignin and suberin bordering four sides of root endodermal cells; prevents water and solute transport between adjacent cells. 451

catabolism Metabolic process that breaks down large molecules into smaller ones; catabolic metabolism. 147

cataracts Condition where the lens of the eye becomes opaque, preventing the transmission of light to the retina. 724

catastrophism Belief, proposed by Georges Cuvier, that periods of catastrophic extinctions occurred, after which repopulation of surviving species took place, giving the appearance of change through time. 273

cell The smallest unit of life that displays all the properties of life; composed of cytoplasm surrounded by a plasma membrane. 2, 61

cell body Portion of a neuron that contains a nucleus and from which dendrites and an axon extend. 697

cell cycle An ordered sequence of events in eukaryotes that involves cell growth and nuclear division; consists of the stages G_1, S, G_2, and M. 154

cell envelope In a prokaryotic cell, the portion composed of the plasma membrane, the cell wall, and the glycocalyx. 65

cell-mediated immunity Specific mechanism of defense in which T cells destroy antigen-bearing cells. 636

cell plate Structure across a dividing plant cell that signals the location of new plasma membranes and cell walls. 161

cell recognition protein Glycoproteins in the plasma membrane that identify self and help the body defend itself against pathogens. 89

cell suspension culture Small clumps of naked plant cells grown in tissue culture that produce drugs, cosmetics, or agricultural chemicals, among others. 514

cell theory One of the major theories of biology, which states that all organisms are made up of cells; cells are capable of self-reproduction and come only from preexisting cells. 61

cell wall Cellular structure that surrounds a plant, protistan, fungal, or bacterial cell and maintains the cell's shape and rigidity; composed of polysaccharides. 65, 100

cellular differentiation Process and developmental stages by which a cell becomes specialized for a particular function. 800

cellular respiration Metabolic reactions that use the energy from carbohydrate, fatty acid, or amino acid breakdown to produce ATP molecules. 136

cellular response Response to the transduction pathway in which proteins or enzymes change a signal to a format that the cell can understand, resulting in the appropriate response. 484

cellular slime mold Free-living amoeboid cells that feed on bacteria and yeasts by phagocytosis and aggregate to form a plasmodium that produces spores. 397

cellulose Polysaccharide that is the major complex carbohydrate in plant cell walls. 44

centipede Elongated arthropod characterized by having one pair of legs to each body segment; they may have 15 to 173 pairs of legs. 541

central dogma Processes that dictate the flow of information from the DNA to RNA to protein in a cell. 224

central nervous system (CNS) Portion of the nervous system consisting of the brain and spinal cord. 696

central vacuole In a plant cell, a large, fluid-filled sac that stores metabolites. During growth, it enlarges, forcing the primary cell wall to expand and the cell surface-area-to-volume ratio to increase. 75

centriole Cell structure, existing in pairs, that occurs in the centrosome and may help organize a mitotic spindle for chromosome movement during animal cell division. 79, 158

centromere Constriction where sister chromatids of a chromosome are held together. 157

centrosome Central microtubule organizing center of cells. In animal cells, it contains two centrioles. 78, 157

cephalization Having a well-recognized anterior head with a brain and sensory receptors. 522, 694

cephalochordate Small, fishlike invertebrate that is a member of the phylum Chordata. Probably the closest living relative to vertebrates. 550

cephalopod Type of mollusc in which the head is prominent and the foot is modified to form two arms and several tentacles; includes squids, cuttlefish, octopuses, and nautiluses. 536

cerebellum In terrestrial vertebrates, portion of the brain that coordinates skeletal muscles to produce smooth, graceful motions. 704

cerebral cortex Outer layer of cerebral hemispheres; receives sensory information and controls motor activities. 704

cerebral hemisphere Either of the two lobes of the cerebrum in vertebrates. 703

cerebrospinal fluid Fluid found in the ventricles of the brain, in the central canal of the spinal cord, and in association with the meninges. 702

cerebrum Largest part of the brain in mammals. 703

cervix Narrow end of the uterus, which leads into the vagina. 779

channel protein Protein that forms a channel to allow a particular molecule or ion to cross the plasma membrane. 88

chaparral Biome characterized by broad-leafed evergreen shrubs forming dense thickets. 894

chaperone protein Molecule that directs the proper folding of polypeptides. 53

character displacement Tendency for characteristics to be more divergent when similar species belong to the same community than when they are isolated from one another. 860

charophyte Type of living green algae that on the basis of nucleotide sequencing and cellular features is most closely related to land plants. 387, 421

chelicerate Arthropods (e.g., horseshoe crabs, sea spiders, arachnids), that exhibit a pair of pointed appendages used to manipulate food. 543

chemical energy Energy associated with the interaction of atoms in a molecule. 105

chemical signal Molecule that brings about a change in a cell, tissue, organ, or individual when it binds to a specific receptor. 755

chemiosmosis Process by which mitochondria and chloroplasts use the energy of an electron transport chain to create a hydrogen ion gradient that drives ATP formation. 126, 145

chemoautotroph Organism able to synthesize organic molecules by using carbon dioxide as the carbon source and the oxidation of an inorganic substance (such as hydrogen sulfide) as the energy source. 375

chemoheterotroph Organism that is unable to produce its own organic molecules, and therefore requires organic nutrients in its diet. 375

chemoreceptor Sensory receptor that is sensitive to chemical stimulation—for example, receptors for taste and smell. 717

chitin Strong but flexible nitrogenous polysaccharide found in the exoskeleton of arthropods and in the cell walls of fungi. 44, 405

chlorophyll Green photosynthetic pigment of algae and plants that absorbs solar energy; occurs as chlorophyll *a* and chlorophyll *b*. 121

chlorophyte Most abundant and diverse group of green algae, including freshwater, marine, and terrestrial forms that synthesize. Chlorophytes share chemical and anatomical characteristics with land plants. 387

chloroplast Membrane-bounded organelle in algae and plants with chlorophyll-containing membranous thylakoids; where photosynthesis takes place. 76, 121

choanoflagellate Unicellular choanoflagellates have one and colonial forms have many collar cells like those of sponges; choanoflagellates are the protists most closely related to animals. 397

cholesterol A steroid found in the plasma membrane of animal cells and from which other types of steroids are derived. 86

chordate Animals that have a dorsal tubular nerve cord, a notochord, pharyngeal gill pouches, and a postanal tail at some point in their life cycle; includes a few types of invertebrates (e.g., sea squirts and lancelets) and the vertebrates. 356, 550

chorion Extraembryonic membrane functioning for respiratory exchange in birds and reptiles; contributes to placenta formation in mammals. 805

chorionic villus In placental mammals treelike extension of the chorion, projecting into the maternal tissues at the placenta. 809

choroid Vascular, pigmented middle layer of the eyeball. 721

chromalveolate Supergroup of eukaryotes that includes alveolates and stramenopiles. 390

chromatid Following replication, a chromosome consists of a pair of sister chromatids, held together at the centromere; each chromatid is comprised of a single DNA helix. 154

chromatin Network of DNA strands and associated proteins observed within a nucleus of a cell. 70, 157, 241

chromoplast Plastid in land plants responsible for orange, yellow, and red color of plants, including the autumn colors in leaves. 77

chromosome The structure that transmits the genetic material from one generation to the next; composed of condensed chromatin; each species has a particular number of chromosomes that is passed on to the next generation. 70

chyme Thick, semiliquid food material that passes from the stomach to the small intestine. 652

chytrid (Chytridiomycota) Mostly aquatic fungi with flagellated spores that may represent the most ancestral fungal lineage. 406

cilia (sing., cilium) Short, hairlike projections from the plasma membrane, occurring usually in larger numbers. 80

ciliary muscle Within the ciliary body of the vertebrate eye, the ciliary muscle that controls the shape of the lens. 722

ciliate Complex unicellular protist that moves by means of cilia and digests food in food vacuoles. 393

circadian rhythm Biological rhythm with a 24-hour cycle. 494, 768

circulatory system In animals, an organ system that moves substances to and from cells, usually via a heart, blood, and blood vessels. 606, 608

cirrhosis Chronic, irreversible injury to liver tissue; commonly caused by frequent alcohol consumption. 656

citric acid cycle Cycle of reactions in mitochondria that begins with citric acid. This cycle breaks down an acetyl group and produces CO_2, ATP, NADH, and $FADH_2$; also called the Krebs cycle. 137, 143

clade Evolutionary lineage consisting of an ancestral species and all of its descendants, forming a distinct branch on a cladogram. 356

cladistics Method of systematics that uses derived characters to determine monophyletic groups and construct cladograms. 356

cladogram In cladistics, a branching diagram that shows the relationship among species in regard to their shared derived characters. 356

class One of the categories, or taxa, used by taxonomists to group species; the taxon above the order level. 6, 349

classification Process of naming organisms and assigning them to taxonomic groups (taxa). 348

classical conditioning Type of learning whereby an unconditioned stimulus that elicits a specific response is paired with a neutral stimulus so that the response becomes conditioned. 824

cleavage Cell division without cytoplasmic addition or enlargement; occurs during the first stage of animal development. 523, 797

cleavage furrow Indentation in the plasma membrane of animal cells during cell division; formation marks the start of cytokinesis. 160

climate Generalized weather patterns of an area, primarily determined by temperature and average rainfall. 884

climate change Recent changes in the Earth's climate; evidence suggests that this is primarily due to human influence, including the increased release of greenhouse gases. 127, 877, 915

climax community In ecology, community that results when succession has come to an end. 868

clonal selection theory States that the antigen selects which lymphocyte will undergo clonal expansion and produce more lymphocytes bearing the same type of receptor. 633

cloning Production of identical copies. In organisms, the production of organisms with the same genes; in genetic engineering, the

production of many identical copies of a gene. 255

closed circulatory system A type of circulatory system where blood is confined to vessels and is kept separate from the interstitial fluid. 607

clotting Also called coagulation, the response of the body to an injury in the vessels of the circulatory system; involves platelets and clotting proteins. 620

club fungi (Basidiomycota) Fungi that produce spores in club-shaped basidia within a fruiting body; includes mushrooms, shelf fungi and puffballs. 412

cnidarian Invertebrates existing as either a polyp or medusa with two tissue layers and radial symmetry. 528

coacervate droplet An aggregate of colloidal droplets held together by electrostatic forces. 331

coccus A spherical-shaped bacterium. 65

cochlea Spiral-shaped structure of the vertebrate inner ear containing the sensory receptors for hearing. 727

codominance Inheritance pattern in which both alleles of a gene are equally expressed in a heterozygote. 205

codon Three-base sequence in messenger RNA that during translation directs the addition of a particular amino acid into a protein or directs termination of the process. 224

coelom Body cavity of an animal; the method by which the coelom is formed (or lack of formation) is an identifying characteristic in animal classification. 523

coenzyme Nonprotein organic molecule that aids the action of the enzyme to which it is loosely bound. 112

coevolution Mutual evolution in which two species exert selective pressures on the other species. 506, 866

cofactor Nonprotein assistant required by an enzyme in order to function; many cofactors are metal ions, others are coenzymes. 112

cohesion-tension model Explanation for upward transport of water in xylem based upon transpiration-created tension and the cohesive properties of water molecules. 476

cohort Group of individuals having a statistical factor in common, such as year of birth, in a population study. 841

coleoptile Protective sheath that covers the young leaves of a seedling. 485

collagen fiber White fiber in the matrix of connective tissue giving flexibility and strength. 589

collecting duct Duct within the kidney that receives fluid from several nephrons; the reabsorption of water occurs here. 686

collenchyma Plant tissue composed of cells with unevenly thickened walls; supports growth of stems and petioles. 448

colonial flagellate hypothesis Hypothesis that all animals are descended from an ancestor that resembled a hollow colony of flagellated cells, most likely resembling modern choanoflagellates. 521

colony Loose association of cells each remaining independent for most functions. 388

columnar epithelium Type of epithelial tissue with cylindrical cells. 589

comb jelly Invertebrates that resemble jelly fishes and are the largest animals to be propelled by beating cilia. 528

commensalism Symbiotic relationship in which one species is benefited, and the other is neither harmed nor benefited. 375, 865

common ancestor Ancestor common to at least two lines of descent. 354

communication Signal by a sender that influences the behavior of a receiver. 826

community Assemblage of species interacting with one another within the same environment. 9, 839, 858

compact bone Type of bone that contains osteons consisting of concentric layers of matrix and osteocytes in lacunae. 591, 739

comparative genomics Study of genomes through the direct comparison of their genes and DNA sequences from multiple species. 263

competition Results when members of a species attempt to use a resource that is in limited supply. 847

competitive exclusion principle Theory that no two species can occupy the same niche in the same place and at the same time. 860

competitive inhibition Form of enzyme inhibition where the substrate and inhibitor are both able to bind to the enzyme's active site. Only when the substrate is at the active site will product form. 113

complement Collective name for a series of enzymes and activators in the blood, some of which may bind to antibody and may lead to rupture of a foreign cell. 632

complementary base pairing Hydrogen bonding between particular purines and pyrimidines; responsible for the structure of DNA, and some RNA, molecules. 55, 219

complementary DNA (cDNA) DNA that has been synthesized from mRNA by the action of reverse transcriptase. 256

complete digestive tract Digestive tract that has both a mouth and an anus. 647

complex tissue In plants, tissue composed of two or more kinds of cells (e.g., xylem, containing tracheids and vessel elements; phloem, containing sieve-tube members and companion cells). 449

compound Substance having two or more different elements in a fixed ratio. 26

compound eye Type of eye found in arthropods; it is composed of many independent visual units. 720

concentration gradient Gradual change in chemical concentration between two areas of differing concentrations. 89

conclusion Statement made following an experiment as to whether or not the results support the hypothesis. 12

cone Reproductive structure in conifers made up of scales bearing sporangia; pollen cones bear microsporangia, and seed cones bear megasporangia. 430

cone cell Photoreceptor in vertebrate eyes that responds to bright light and makes color vision possible. 721

conidiospore Spore produced by sac and club fungi during asexual reproduction. 409

conifer Member of a group of cone-bearing gymnosperm land plants that includes pine, cedar, and spruce trees. 430

conjugation Transfer of genetic material from one cell to another. 388

conjugation pilus (pl., conjugation pili) In a bacterium, elongated, hollow appendage used to transfer DNA to other cells. 66, 373

conjunctiva Delicate membrane that lines the eyelid protecting the sclera. 721

connective tissue Type of animal tissue that binds structures together, provides support and protection, fills spaces, stores fat, and forms blood cells; adipose tissue, cartilage, bone, and blood are types of connective tissue; living cells in a nonliving matrix. 589

conservation biology Discipline that seeks to understand the effects of human activities on species, communities, and ecosystems and to develop practical approaches to preventing the extinction of species and the destruction of ecosystems. 908

consumer Organism that feeds on another organism in a food chain generally; primary consumers eat plants, and secondary consumers eat animals. 870

continental drift The movement of the Earth's crust by plate tectonics resulting in the movement of continents with respect to one another. 342

contraceptive vaccine Under development, this birth control method immunizes against the hormone HCG, crucial to maintaining implantation of the embryo. 784

control Sample that goes through all the steps of an experiment but does not contain the variable being tested; a standard against which the results of an experiment are checked. 12

convergent evolution Similarity in structure in distantly related groups generally due to similiar selective pressures in like environments. 357

copulation Sexual union between a male and a female. 774

coral reef Coral formations in shallow tropical waters that support an abundance of diversity. 901

corepressor Molecule that binds to a repressor, allowing the repressor to bind to an operator in a repressible operon. 239

cork Outer covering of the bark of trees; made of dead cells that may be sloughed off. 447

cork cambium Lateral meristem that produces cork. 447

cornea Transparent, anterior portion of the outer layer of the eyeball. 721

corolla The petals, collectively; usually the conspicuously colored flower whorl. 503

corpus luteum Follicle that has released an egg and increases its secretion of progesterone. 780

cortex In plants, ground tissue bounded by the epidermis and vascular tissue in stems and roots; in animals, outer layer of an organ, such as the cortex of the kidney or adrenal gland. 451

cortisol Glucocorticoid secreted by the adrenal cortex that responds to stress on a long-term basis; reduces inflammation and promotes protein and fat metabolism. 763

cost-benefit analysis A weighing-out of the costs and benefits (in terms of contributions to reproductive success) of a particular strategy or behavior. 298

cotyledon Seed leaf for embryo of a flowering plant; provides nutrient molecules for the developing plant before photosynthesis begins. 433, 508

countercurrent exchange Fluids flow side-by-side in opposite directions, as in the exchange of fluids in the kidneys. 666

coupled reactions Reactions that occur simultaneously; one is an exergonic reaction that releases energy, and the other is an endergonic reaction that requires an input of energy in order to occur. 108

covalent bond Chemical bond in which atoms share one pair of electrons. 27

cranial nerve Nerve that arises from the brain. 707

crenation In animal cells, shriveling of the cell due to water leaving the cell when the environment is hypertonic. 94

cristae (sing., crista) Short, fingerlike projections formed by the folding of the inner membrane of mitochondria. 77

Cro-Magnon Common name for the first fossils to be designated *Homo sapiens*. 580

crossing-over Exchange of segments between nonsister chromatids of a bivalent during meiosis. 174

crustacean Member of a group of aquatic arthropods that contains, among others, shrimps, crabs, crayfish, and lobsters. 540

cryptic species Species that are very similar in appearance but are considered separate species based on other characteristics, such as behavior or genetics. 307

cuboidal epithelium Type of epithelial tissue with cube-shaped cells. 588

cutaneous receptor Sensory receptors of the dermis that are activated by touch, pain, pressure, and temperature. 730

cuticle Waxy layer covering the epidermis of plants that protects the plant against water loss and disease-causing organisms. 422

cyanobacterium (pl., cyanobacteria) Photosynthetic bacterium that contains chlorophyll and releases oxygen; formerly called a blue-green alga. 66, 377

cyanogenic glycoside Plant compound that contains sugar; produces cyanide. 497

cycad Type of gymnosperm with palmate leaves and massive cones; cycads are most often found in the tropics and subtropics. 432

cyclic adenosine monophosphate (cAMP) ATP-related compound that acts as the second messenger in peptide hormone transduction; it initiates activity of the metabolic machinery. 755

cyclin Protein that cycles in quantity as the cell cycle progresses; combines with and activates the kinases that function to promote the events of the cycle. 155

cyst In protists and invertebrates, resting structure that contains reproductive bodies or embryos. 384, 533

cystic fibrosis (CF) Genetic disease caused by a defect in the *CFTR* gene, which is responsible for the formation of a transmembrane chloride ion transporter; causes the mucus of the body to be viscous. 675

cytochrome Any of several iron-containing protein molecules that are members of the electron transport chain in photosynthesis and cellular respiration. 144

cytokine Type of protein secreted by a T lymphocyte that attacks viruses, virally infected cells, and cancer cells. 633

cytokinesis Division of the cytoplasm following mitosis or meiosis. 155

cytokinin Plant hormone that promotes cell division; often works in combination with auxin during organ development in plant embryos. 487

cytoplasm Region of a cell between the nucleus, or the nucleoid region of a bacterium, and the plasma membrane; contains the organelles of the cell. 65

cytoplasmic segregation Process that parcels out the maternal determinants, which play a role in development, during mitosis. 800

cytosine (C) One of four nitrogen-containing bases in the nucleotides composing the structure of DNA and RNA; pairs with guanine. 217

cytoskeleton Internal framework of the cell, consisting of microtubules, actin filaments, and intermediate filaments. 68

cytotoxic T cell T lymphocyte that attacks and kills antigen-bearing cells. 635

D

data (sing., datum) Facts or information collected through observation and/or experimentation. 12

day-neutral plant Plant whose flowering is not dependent on day length—e.g., tomato and cucumber. 496

deamination Removal of an amino group (—NH$_2$) from an amino acid or other organic compound. 147

deciduous Land plant that sheds its leaves annually. 445

decomposer Organism, usually a bacterium or fungus, that breaks down organic matter into inorganic nutrients that can be recycled in the environment. 871

deductive reasoning The use of general principles to predict specific outcomes. Often uses "if . . . then" statements. 11

dehydration reaction Chemical reaction in which a water molecule is released during the formation of a covalent bond. 40

delayed allergic response Allergic response initiated at the site of the allergen by sensitized T cells, involving macrophages and regulated by cytokines. 642

deletion Change in chromosome structure in which the end of a chromosome breaks off or two simultaneous breaks lead to the loss of an internal segment; often causes abnormalities—e.g., cri du chat syndrome. 187

demographic transition Due to industrialization, a decline in the birthrate following a reduction in the death rate so that the population growth rate is lowered. 851

demography Properties of the rate of growth and the age structure of populations. 840

denatured Loss of a protein's or enzyme's normal shape so that it no longer functions; usually caused by a less than optimal pH and temperature. 53, 111

dendrite Part of a neuron that sends signals toward the cell body. 697

dendritic cell Antigen-presenting cell of the epidermis and mucous membranes. 632

denitrification Conversion of nitrate or nitrite to nitrogen gas by bacteria in soil. 878

dense fibrous connective tissue Type of connective tissue containing many collagen fibers packed together; found in tendons and ligaments, for example. 590

density-dependent factor Biotic factor, such as disease or competition, that affects population size in a direct relationship to the population's density. 847

density-independent factor Abiotic factor, such as fire or flood, that affects population size independent of the population's density. 847

deoxyribose Pentose sugar found in DNA. 42

derived trait Structural, physiological, or behavioral trait that is present in a specific lineage and is not present in the common ancestor for several related lineages. 354

dermis In mammals, thick layer of the skin underlying the epidermis. 598

desert Ecological biome characterized by a limited amount of rainfall; deserts have hot days and cool nights. 896

desmosome(s) Intercellular junctions that connect cytoskeletons of adjacent cells. 99

detritivore Any organism that obtains most of its nutrients from the detritus in an ecosystem. 870

deuterostome Group of coelomate animals in which the second embryonic opening is associated with the mouth; the first embryonic opening, the blastopore, is associated with the anus. 523

development Process of regulated growth and differentiation of cells and tissues. 508, 797

diabetic retinopathy Complication of diabetes that causes the capillaries in the retina to become damaged, potentially causing blindness. 724

diagnostic traits Characteristics that distinguish species from one another. 307

diaphragm In mammals, dome-shaped muscularized sheet separating the thoracic cavity from the abdominal cavity; contraceptive device that prevents sperm from reaching the egg. 669

diapsid Characteristic of a vertebrate skull in which there are two openings in the skull behind the eye socket (orbit). 558

diarrhea Excessively frequent and watery bowel movements. 653

diastole Relaxation period of a heart chamber during the cardiac cycle. 612

diatom Golden-brown alga with a cell wall in two parts, or valves; significant component of phytoplankton. 391

differentiation Specialization in the structure or function of a cell typically caused by the activation of specific genes. 508

diffusion Movement of molecules or ions from a region of higher to lower concentration; it requires no energy and tends to lead to an equal distribution (equilibrium). 91

dihybrid cross Cross between parents that differ in two traits. 198

dikaryotic Having two haploid nuclei that stem from different parent cells; during sexual reproduction, sac and club fungi have dikaryotic cells. 406

dinoflagellate Photosynthetic unicellular protist with two flagella, one whiplash and the other located within a groove between protective cellulose plates; significant part of phytoplankton. 392

dinosaur General term used to describe the large reptiles that existed prior to the start of the Cretaceous period. 559

dioecious Having unisexual flowers or cones, with the male flowers or cones confined to certain land plants and the female flowers or cones of the same species confined to other different plants. 432

diploid (2n) Cell condition in which two of each type of chromosome are present. 157, 172

diplomonad Protist that has modified mitochondria, two equal-sized nuclei, and multiple flagella. 395

directional selection Outcome of natural selection in which an extreme phenotype is favored, usually in a changing environment. 296

disaccharide Sugar that contains two monosaccharide units; e.g., maltose. 42

disruptive selection Outcome of natural selection in which the two extreme phenotypes are favored over the average phenotype, leading to more than one distinct form. 297

distal convoluted tubule Final portion of a nephron that joins with a collecting duct; associated with tubular secretion. 686

diverge Process by which a new evolutionary path begins; on a phylogenetic tree this is indicated by branching lines. 354

DNA (deoxyribonucleic acid) Nucleic acid polymer produced from covalent bonding of nucleotide monomers that contain the sugar deoxyribose; the genetic material of nearly all organisms. 54

DNA ligase Enzyme that links DNA fragments; used during production of recombinant DNA to join foreign DNA to vector DNA. 255

DNA microarray Glass or plastic slide containing thousands of single-stranded DNA fragments arranged in an array (grid); used to detect and measure gene expression; also called gene chips. 263

DNA polymerase During replication, an enzyme that joins the nucleotides complementary to a DNA template. 220

DNA repair enzyme One of several enzymes that restore the original base sequence in an altered DNA strand. 248

DNA replication Synthesis of a new DNA double helix prior to mitosis and meiosis in eukaryotic cells and during prokaryotic fission in prokaryotic cells. 220

domain Largest of the categories, or taxa, used by taxonomists to group species; the three domains are Archaea, Bacteria, and Eukarya. 6, 349

domain Archaea One of the three domains of life; contains prokaryotic cells that often live in extreme habitats and have unique genetic, biochemical, and physiological characteristics; its members are sometimes referred to as *archaea*. 7, 351

domain Bacteria One of the three domains of life; contains prokaryotic cells that differ from archaea because they have their own unique genetic, biochemical, and physiological characteristics. 7, 351

domain Eukarya One of the three domains of life, consisting of organisms with eukaryotic cells; includes protists, fungi, plants, and animals. 7, 351

dominance hierarchy Organization of animals in a group that determines the order in which the animals have access to resources. 298

dominant allele Allele that exerts its phenotypic effect in the heterozygote; it masks the expression of the recessive allele. 196

dormancy In plants, a cessation of growth under conditions that seem appropriate for growth. 487

dorsal root ganglion Mass of sensory neuron cell bodies located in the dorsal root of a spinal nerve. 707

double fertilization In flowering plants, one sperm nucleus unites with the egg nucleus, and a second sperm nucleus unites with the polar nuclei of an embryo sac. 437, 505

double helix Double spiral; describes the three-dimensional shape of DNA. 218

doubling time Number of years it takes for a population to double in size. 851

dryopithecine Tree dwelling primate existing 12–9 MYA; ancestral to apes. 574

duodenum First part of the small intestine, where chyme enters from the stomach. 652

duplication Change in chromosome structure in which a particular segment is present more than once in the same chromosome. 187

E

ecdysozoan Protostome characterized by periodic molting of their exoskeleton. Includes the roundworms and arthropods. 538

echinoderm Invertebrates such as sea stars, sea urchins, and sand dollars; characterized by radial symmetry and a water vascular system. 544

ecological niche Role an organism plays in its community, including its habitat and its interactions with other organisms. 859

ecological pyramid Visual depiction of the biomass, number of organisms, or energy content of various trophic levels in a food web—from the producer to the final consumer populations. 873

ecological release In an ecosystem, the freedom of a species to expand its use of available resources due to an elimination of competition. 316

ecological succession The gradual replacement of communities in an area following a disturbance (secondary succession) or the creation of new soil (primary succession). 868

ecology Study of the interactions of organisms with other organisms and with the physical and chemical environment. 839

ecosystem Biological community together with the associated abiotic environment; characterized by a flow of energy and a cycling of inorganic nutrients. 9, 839, 870

ecosystem diversity Variety of species in a particular locale, dependent on the species interactions. 909

ectoderm Outermost primary tissue layer of an animal embryo; gives rise to the nervous system and the outer layer of the integument. 798

ectotherm Organism having a body temperature that varies according to the environmental temperature. 553

edge effect Phenomenon in which the edges around a landscape patch provide a slightly different habitat than the favorable habitat in the interior of the patch. 919

effector Muscle or gland that receives signals from motor fibers and thereby allows an organism to respond to environmental stimuli. 708

egg Also called an ovum; haploid cell that is usually fertilized by a sperm to form a diploid zygote. 779

elastic cartilage Type of cartilage composed of elastic fibers, allowing greater flexibility. 591

elastic fiber Yellow fiber in the matrix of connective tissue, providing flexibility. 589

electrocardiogram (ECG) Recording of the electrical activity associated with the heartbeat. 613

electron Negative subatomic particle, moving about in an energy level around the nucleus of an atom. 22

electronegativity The ability of an atom to attract electrons toward itself in a chemical bond. 27

electron shell The average location, or energy level, of an electron in an atom. Often drawn as concentric circles around the nucleus. 23

electron transport chain (ETC) Process in a cell that involves the passage of electrons along a series of membrane-bound electron carrier molecules from a higher to lower energy level; the energy released is used for the synthesis of ATP. 137, 144

element Substances that cannot be broken down into substances with different properties; composed of only one type atom. 22

El Niño–Southern Oscillation Warming of water in the Eastern Pacific equatorial region such that the Humboldt Current is displaced, with possible negative results such as reduction in marine life. 904

elongation Middle stage of translation in which additional amino acids specified by the mRNA are added to the growing polypeptide. 231

embryo Stage of a multicellular organism that develops from a zygote before it becomes free-living; in seed plants, the embryo is part of the seed. 797

embryo sac Female gametophyte (megagametophyte) of flowering plants. 504

embryonic development In humans, the first two months of development following fertilization during which the major organs are formed. 805

embryonic disk During human development, flattened area during gastrulation from which the embryo arises. 808

embryophyta Bryophytes and vascular plants; both of which produce embryos. 422

emergent property A function or trait that appears as biological complexity increases. 2

emerging viruses Newly identified viruses that are becoming more prominent usually because they cause serious disease. 369

emphysema Disorder of the respiratory system, specifically the lungs, that is characterized by damage to the alveoli, thus reducing the ability to exchange gases with the external environment. 675

endangered species A species that is in peril of immediate extinction throughout all or most of its range (e.g., California condor, snow leopard). 908

endergonic reaction Chemical reaction that requires an input of energy; opposite of exergonic reaction. 107

endocrine gland Ductless organ that secretes hormone(s) into the bloodstream. 589, 753

endocrine system Organ system involved in the coordination of body activities; uses hormones as chemical signals secreted into the bloodstream. 753

endocytosis Process by which substances are moved into the cell from the environment; includes phagocytosis, pinocytosis, and receptor-mediated endocytosis. 97

endoderm Innermost primary tissue layer of an animal embryo that gives rise to the linings of the digestive tract and associated structures. 798

endodermis Internal plant root tissue forming a boundary between the cortex and the vascular cylinder. 451

endomembrane system Cellular system that consists of the nuclear envelope, endoplasmic reticulum, Golgi apparatus, and vesicles. 72

endometrium Mucous membrane lining the interior surface of the uterus. 779

endoplasmic reticulum (ER) System of membranous saccules and channels in the cytoplasm, often with attached ribosomes. 72

endoskeleton Protective internal skeleton, as in vertebrates. 737

endosperm In flowering plants, nutritive storage tissue that is derived from the union of a sperm nucleus and polar nuclei in the embryo sac. 505

endospore Spore formed within a cell; certain bacteria form endospores. 375

endosymbiosis *See* endosymbiotic theory.

endosymbiotic theory Explanation of the evolution of eukaryotic organelles by phagocytosis of prokaryotes. 67, 335

endotherm Organism in which maintenance of a constant body temperature is independent of the environmental temperature. 563

energy Capacity to do work and bring about change; occurs in a variety of forms. 4, 105

energy of activation Energy that must be added in order for molecules to react with one another. 109

enhancer DNA sequence that acts as a regulatory element to increase the level of transcription when regulatory proteins, such as transcription activators, bind to it. 244

entropy Measure of disorder or randomness in a system. 106

enzymatic protein Protein that catalyzes a specific reaction; may be found in the plasma membrane or the cytoplasm of the cell. 89

enzyme Organic catalyst, usually a protein, that speeds a reaction in cells due to its particular shape. 41, 109

enzyme inhibition Means by which cells regulate enzyme activity; may be competitive or noncompetitive inhibition. 112

eosinophil White blood cell containing cytoplasmic granules that stain with acidic dye. 632

epidermal tissue Exterior tissue, usually one cell thick, of leaves, young stems, roots, and other parts of plants. 447

epidermis In mammals, the outer, protective layer of the skin; in plants, tissue that covers roots, leaves, and stems of nonwoody organisms. 447, 451, 598

epididymis Location of sperm maturation in an adult human; located in the testis. 775

epigenetic inheritance An inheritance pattern in which a nuclear gene has been modified but the changed expression of the gene is not permanent over many generations; the transmission of genetic information by means that are not based on the coding sequences of a gene. 241

epiglottis Structure that covers the glottis, the air-tract opening, during the process of swallowing. 668

epinephrine Hormone secreted by the adrenal medulla in times of stress; adrenaline. 762

epiphyte Plant that takes its nourishment from the air because its placement in other plants gives it an aerial position. 428, 892

epithelial tissue Tissue that lines hollow organs and covers surfaces. 588

erythropoietin (EPO) Hormone produced by the kidneys that speeds red blood cell formation. 688

esophagus Muscular tube for moving swallowed food from the pharynx to the stomach. 651

essential nutrient In plants, substance required for normal growth, development, or reproduction; in humans, a nutrient that cannot be produced in sufficient quantities by the body and must be obtained from the diet. 465

estrogen Female sex hormone that helps maintain sexual organs and secondary sex characteristics. 779

estuary Portion of the ocean located where a river enters and fresh water mixes with salt water. 900

ethylene Plant hormone that causes ripening of fruit and is also involved in abscission. 488

etiolate Changes to a plant, such as yellowing of leaves and increase in shoot length, that occur when it is grown in darkness. 495

euchromatin Chromatin with a lower level of compaction and therefore accessible for transcription. 234

eudicot (Eudicotyledone) Flowering plant group; members have two embryonic leaves (cotyledons), net-veined leaves, vascular bundles in a ring, flower parts in fours or fives and their multiples, and other characteristics. 433, 446

euglenid Flagellated and flexible freshwater unicellular protist that usually contains chloroplasts and has a semirigid cell wall. 395

eukaryotic cell (eukaryote) Type of cell that has a membrane-bounded nucleus and membranous organelles; found in organisms within the domain Eukarya. 7, 65

euploidy Condition in which a cell contains the correct number, and combinations, of chromosomes. 183

eutrophication Enrichment of water by inorganic nutrients used by phytoplankton. Often, overenrichment caused by human activities leads to excessive bacterial growth and oxygen depletion. 877, 898

evergreen Land plant that sheds leaves over a long period, so some leaves are always present. 445

evolution Genetic change in a species over time resulting in the development of genetic and phenotypic differences that are the basis of natural selection; descent of organisms from a common ancestor. 5, 272

evolutionary species concept Every species has its own evolutionary history, which is partly documented in the fossil record. 307

excavate Supergroup of eukaryotes that includes euglenids, kinetoplastids, parabasalids, and diplomonads. 395

excretion Elimination of metabolic wastes by an organism at exchange boundaries such as the plasma membrane of unicellular organisms and excretory tubules of multicellular animals. 681

exergonic reaction Chemical reaction that releases energy; opposite of endergonic reaction. 107

exocrine gland Gland that secretes its product to an epithelial surface directly or through ducts. 589, 651

exocytosis Process in which an intracellular vesicle fuses with the plasma membrane so that the vesicle's contents are released outside the cell. 95

exon Segment of mRNA containing the protein-coding portion of a gene that remains within the mRNA after splicing has occurred. 226

exophthalmos Condition associated with an enlargement of the thyroid gland accompanied by an abnormal protrusion of the eyes. 761

exoskeleton Protective external skeleton, as in arthropods. 736

exotic species Nonnative species that migrate or are introduced by humans into a new ecosystem; also called alien species. 913

experiment A test of a hypothesis that examines the influence of a single variable. Often involves both control and test groups. 11

experimental design Methodology by which an experiment will seek to support the hypothesis. 11

experimental variable Factor of the experiment being tested. 12

expiration Act of expelling air from the lungs; exhalation. 656

exponential growth Growth, particularly of a population, in which the increase occurs in the same manner as compound interest. 844

extant Species, or other levels of taxa, that are still living. 272

external respiration Exchange of oxygen and carbon dioxide between alveoli of the lungs and blood. 664

extinct; extinction Total disappearance of a species or higher group. 10, 338

extracellular matrix (ECM) Nonliving substance secreted by some animal cells; is composed of protein and polysaccharides. 87

extraembryonic membrane Membrane that is not a part of the embryo but is necessary to the continued existence and health of the embryo. 774, 805

ex vivo gene therapy Gene therapy in which cells are removed from an organism, and DNA is injected to correct a genetic defect; the cells are returned to the organism to treat a disease or disorder. 256

F

facilitated transport Passive transfer of a substance into or out of a cell along a concentration gradient by a process that requires a protein carrier. 94

facultative anaerobe Prokaryote that is able to grow in either the presence or the absence of gaseous oxygen. 374

FAD Flavin adenine dinucleotide; a coenzyme of oxidation-reduction that becomes $FADH_2$ as oxidation of substrates occurs in the mitochondria during cellular respiration, FAD then delivers electrons to the electron transport chain. 136

fall overturn Mixing process that occurs in fall in stratified lakes, whereby oxygen-rich top waters mix with nutrient-rich bottom waters. 898

family One of the categories, or taxa, used by taxonomists to group species; the taxon located above the genus level. 6, 349

family pedigree Chart of genetic relationship of family individuals across generations. 204

farsighted (hyperopic) Condition in which an individual cannot focus on objects closely; caused by the focusing of the image behind the retina of the eye. 724

fat Organic molecule that contains glycerol and three fatty acids; energy storage molecule. 46

fatty acid Molecule that contains a hydrocarbon chain and ends with an acid group. 46

fermentation Anaerobic breakdown of glucose that results in a gain of two ATP and end products such as alcohol and lactate; occurs in the cytoplasm of cells. 137, 140

fern Member of a group of land plants that have large fronds; in the sexual life cycle, the independent gametophyte produces flagellated sperm, and the vascular sporophyte produces windblown spores. 428

fertilization Fusion of sperm and egg nuclei, producing a zygote that develops into a new individual. 175, 796

fibroblast Cell found in loose connective tissue that synthesizes collagen and elastic fibers in the matrix. 590

fibrocartilage Cartilage with a matrix of strong collagenous fibers. 591

fibrous protein A protein that has only a secondary structure; generally insoluble; includes collagens, elastins, and keratins. 51

fibrous root system In most monocots, a mass of similarly sized roots that cling to the soil. 452

filament End-to-end chains of cells that form as cell division occurs in only one plane; in plants, the elongated stalk of a stamen. 388

fimbria (pl., fimbriae) Small, bristlelike fiber on the surface of a bacterial cell, which attaches bacteria to a surface; also fingerlike extension from the oviduct near the ovary. 66, 372

fin In fishes and other aquatic animals, membranous, winglike, or paddlelike process used to propel, balance, or guide the body. 553

first messenger Chemical signal such as a peptide hormone that binds to a plasma membrane receptor protein and alters the metabolism of a cell because a second messenger is activated. 755

fishes Aquatic, gill-breathing vertebrate that usually has fins and skin covered with scales; fishes were among the earliest vertebrates that evolved. 553

fitness Ability of an organism to reproduce and pass its genes to the next fertile generation; measured against the ability of other organisms to reproduce in the same environment. 297

five-kingdom system System of classification that contains the kingdoms Monera, Protista, Plantae, Animalia, and Fungi. 351

fixed action pattern (FAP) Innate behavior pattern that is stereotyped, spontaneous, independent of immediate control, genetically encoded, and independent of individual learning. 822

flagellum (pl., flagella) Long, slender extension used for locomotion by some bacteria, protozoans, and sperm. 66, 80, 372

flagship species Species that evoke a strong emotional response in humans; charismatic, cute, regal (e.g., lions, tigers, dolphins, pandas). 918

flatworm Invertebrates such as planarians and tapeworms with extremely thin bodies; a three-branched gastrovascular cavity and a ladder type nervous system. 531

flower Reproductive organ of a flowering plant, consisting of several kinds of modified leaves arranged in concentric rings and attached to a modified stem called the receptacle. 434, 502

fluid-mosaic model Model for the plasma membrane based on the changing location and pattern of protein molecules in a fluid phospholipid bilayer. 87

follicle Structure in the ovary of animals that contains an oocyte; site of oocyte production. 780

follicular phase First half of the ovarian cycle, during which the follicle matures and much estrogen (and some progesterone) is produced. 780

food chain The order in which one population feeds on another in an ecosystem, thereby showing the flow of energy from a detritivore (detrital food chain) or a producer (grazing food chain) to the final consumer. 873

food web In ecosystems, a complex pattern of interlocking and crisscrossing food chains. 873

foraminiferan A protist bearing a calcium carbonate test with many openings through which pseudopods extend. 398

formed elements Portion of the blood that consists of erythrocytes, leukocytes, and platelets (thrombocytes). 618

formula A group of symbols and numbers used to express the composition of a compound. 26

fossil Any past evidence of an organism that has been preserved in the Earth's crust. 280, 333

founder effect Cause of genetic drift due to colonization by a limited number of individuals who, by chance, have different genotype and allele frequencies than the parent population. 295

fovea centralis Region of the retina consisting of densely packed cones; responsible for the greatest visual acuity. 721

frameshift mutation Insertion or deletion of at least one base so that the reading frame of the corresponding mRNA changes. 248

free energy Energy in a system that is capable of performing work. 107

frond Leaf of a fern, palm, or cycad. 428

fruit Flowering plant structure consisting of one or more ripened ovaries that usually contain seeds. 437, 511

fruiting body Spore-producing and spore-disseminating structure found in sac and club fungi. 409

functional genomics Study of gene function at the genome level. It involves the study of many genes simultaneously and the use of DNA microarrays. 263

functional group Specific cluster of atoms attached to the carbon skeleton of organic molecules that enters into reactions and behaves in a predictable way. 39

fungus (pl., fungi) Eukaryotic saprotrophic decomposer; the body is made up of filaments called hyphae that form a mass called a mycelium. 8, 404

G

gallbladder Organ attached to the liver that serves to store and concentrate bile. 656

gametangia Cell or multicellular structure in which gametes are formed. 408

gamete Haploid sex cell; e.g., egg or sperm. 172, 785

gametogenesis Development of the male and female sex gametes. 180

gametophyte Haploid generation of the alternation of generations life cycle of a plant; produces gametes that unite to form a diploid zygote. 180, 422, 504

ganglion (pl., ganglia) Collection or bundle of neuron cell bodies usually outside the central nervous system. 531, 694

gap junction Junction between cells formed by the joining of two adjacent plasma membranes; it lends strength and allows ions, sugars, and small molecules to pass between cells. 100

gastropod Mollusc with a broad, flat foot for crawling (e.g., snails and slugs). 535

gastrovascular cavity Blind digestive cavity in animals that have a sac body plan. 528

gastrula Stage of animal development during which the germ layers form, at least in part, by invagination. 798

gastrulation Formation of a gastrula from a blastula; characterized by an invagination to form cell layers of a caplike structure. 798

gel electrophoresis Process that separates molecules, such as proteins and DNA, based on their size and electrical charge by passing them through a matrix. 257

gene Unit of heredity existing as alleles on the chromosomes; in diploid organisms, typically two alleles are inherited—one from each parent. 5, 70

gene cloning DNA cloning to produce many identical copies of the same gene. 255

gene flow Sharing of genes between two populations through interbreeding. 294

gene mutation Altered gene whose sequence of bases differs from the original sequence. 247

gene pharming Production of pharmaceuticals using transgenic organisms, usually agricultural animals. 258

gene pool Total of the alleles of all the individuals in a population. 290

gene therapy Correction of a detrimental mutation by the insertion of DNA sequences into the genome of a cell. 255, 260

genetically modified organisms (GMO) Organism whose genetic material has been altered or enhanced using DNA technology. 258

genetic code Universal code that has existed for eons and allows for conversion of DNA and RNA's chemical code to a sequence of amino acids in a protein. Each codon consists of three bases that stand for one of the 20 amino acids found in proteins or directs the termination of translation. 224

genetic diversity Variety among members of a population. 908

genetic drift Mechanism of evolution due to random changes in the allelic frequencies of a population; more likely to occur in small populations or when only a few individuals of a large population reproduce. 294

genetic profile An individual's genome, including any possible mutations. 263

genetic recombination Process in which chromosomes are broken and rejoined to form novel combinations; in this way offspring receive alleles in combinations different from their parents. 175

genomics Area of study that examines the genome of a species or group of species. 261

genotype Genes of an organism for a particular trait or traits; often designated by letters—for example, *BB* or *Aa*. 196

genus One of the categories, or taxa, used by taxonomists to group species; contains those species that are most closely related through evolution. 6, 349

geologic timescale History of the Earth based on the fossil record and divided into eras, periods, and epochs. 334

germ cell During zygote development, cells that are set aside from the somatic cells and that will eventually undergo meiosis to produce gametes. 773

germinate Beginning of growth of a seed, spore, or zygote, especially after a period of dormancy. 512

germ layer Primary tissue layer of a vertebrate embryo—namely, ectoderm, mesoderm, or endoderm. 522, 798

gibberellin Plant hormone promoting increased stem growth; also involved in flowering and seed germination. 486

gills Respiratory organ in most aquatic animals; in fish, an outward extension of the pharynx. 550, 664

ginkgo Member of phylum Ginkgophyte; maidenhair tree. 432

girdling Removing a strip of bark from around a tree. 478

gland Epithelial cell or group of epithelial cells that are specialized to secrete a substance. 589

glaucoma Condition in which the fluid in the eye (aqueous humor) accumulates, increasing pressure in the eye and damaging nerve fibers. 724

global warming Predicted increase in the Earth's temperature due to human activities that promote the greenhouse effect. 877

globular protein Most of the proteins in the body; soluble in water or salt solution; includes albumins, globulins, histones. 52

glomerular capsule Cuplike structure that is the initial portion of a nephron. 685

glomerular filtration Movement of small molecules from the glomerulus into the glomerular capsule due to the action of blood pressure. 686

glomerulus Capillary network within the glomerular capsule of a nephron. 686

glottis Opening for airflow in the larynx. 668

glucagon Hormone produced by the pancreas that stimulates the liver to break down glycogen, thus raising blood glucose levels. 765

glucocorticoid Type of hormone secreted by the adrenal cortex that influences carbohydrate, fat, and protein metabolism; *See also* cortisol. 763

glucose Six-carbon monosaccharide; used as an energy source during cellular respiration and as a monomer of the structural polysaccharides. 42

glycerol Three-carbon carbohydrate with three hydroxyl groups attached; a component of fats and oils. 46

glycocalyx Gel-like coating outside the cell wall of a bacterium. If compact, it is called a capsule; if diffuse, it is called a slime layer. 65

glycogen Storage polysaccharide found in animals; composed of glucose molecules joined in a linear fashion but having numerous branches. 43

glycolipid Lipid in plasma membranes that contains an attached carbohydrate chain; assembled in the Golgi apparatus. 88

glycolysis Anaerobic breakdown of glucose that results in a gain of two ATP and the production of pyruvate; occurs in the cytoplasm of cells. 137, 138

glycoprotein Protein in plasma membranes that has an attached carbohydrate chain; assembled in the Golgi apparatus. 88

gnathostome Term used to describe any vertebrates with jaws. 552

gnetophyte Member of one of the four phyla of gymnosperms; Gnetophyta has only three living genera, which differ greatly from one another—e.g., *Welwitschia* and *Ephedra*. 432

golden brown algae Unicellular organism that contains pigments, including chlorophyll *a* and *c* and carotenoids, that produce its color. 391

Golgi apparatus Organelle consisting of sacs and vesicles that processes, packages, and distributes molecules about or from the cell. 72

gonad Organ that produces gametes; the ovary produces eggs, and the testis produces sperm. 773

gonadotropic hormone Substance secreted by the anterior pituitary that regulates the activity of the ovaries and testes; principally, follicle-stimulating hormone (FSH) and luteinizing hormone (LH). 757

granular leukocyte Form of white blood cell that contains spherical vesicles (granules) in its cytoplasm. 620

granum (pl., grana) Stack of chlorophyll-containing thylakoids in a chloroplast. 76, 121

grassland Biome characterized by rainfall greater than 25 cm/yr, grazing animals, and warm summers; includes the prairie of the U.S. midwest and the African savanna. 894

gravitational equilibrium Maintenance of balance when the head and body are motionless. 728

gravitropism Growth response of roots and stems of plants to the Earth's gravity; roots demonstrate positive gravitropism, and stems demonstrate negative gravitropism. 491

gray matter Nonmyelinated axons and cell bodies in the central nervous system. 702

green algae Members of a diverse group of photosynthetic protists; contain chlorophylls *a* and *b* and have other biochemical characteristics like those of plants. 387

greenhouse effect Reradiation of solar heat toward the Earth, caused by an atmosphere that allows the Sun's rays to pass through but traps the heat in the same manner as the glass of a greenhouse. 877

greenhouse gases Gases in the atmosphere such as carbon dioxide, methane, water vapor, ozone, and nitrous oxide that are involved in the greenhouse effect. 876

ground tissue Tissue that constitutes most of the body of a plant; consists of parenchyma, collenchyma, and sclerenchyma cells that function in storage, basic metabolism, and support. 447

growth factor A hormone or chemical, secreted by one cell, that may stimulate or inhibit growth of another cell or cells. 155

growth hormone (GH) Substance secreted by the anterior pituitary; controls size of an individual by promoting cell division, protein synthesis, and bone growth. 758

guanine (G) One of four nitrogen-containing bases in nucleotides composing the structure of DNA and RNA; pairs with cytosine. 217

guard cell One of two cells that surround a leaf stoma; changes in the turgor pressure of these cells cause the stoma to open or close. 477

guttation Liberation of water droplets from the edges and tips of leaves. 475

gymnosperm Type of woody seed plant in which the seeds are not enclosed by fruit and are usually borne in cones, such as those of the conifers. 430

H

habitat Place where an organism lives and is able to survive and reproduce. 839, 859

hair follicle Tubelike depression in the skin in which a hair develops. 599

halophile Type of archaean that lives in extremely salty habitats. 379

haploid (n) Cell condition in which only one of each type of chromosome is present. 157, 172

Hardy-Weinberg principle (equilibrium) Mathematical law stating that the gene frequencies in a population remain stable if evolution does not occur due to nonrandom mating, selection, migration, and genetic drift. 290,291

heart Muscular organ whose contraction causes blood to circulate in the body of an animal. 610

heart attack Damage to the myocardium due to blocked circulation in the coronary arteries; myocardial infarction. 616

heat Type of kinetic energy associated with the random motion of molecules. 105

helper T cell Secretes lymphokines, which stimulate all kinds of immune cells. 635

heme Iron-containing group found in hemoglobin. 672

hemizygous Possessing only one allele for a gene in a diploid organism; males are hemizygous for genes on the X chromosome. 209

hemocoel Residual coelom found in arthropods, which is filled with hemolymph. 534

hemoglobin (Hb) Iron-containing respiratory pigment occurring in vertebrate red blood cells and in the blood plasma of some invertebrates. 49, 618, 672

hemolymph Circulatory fluid that is a mixture of blood and interstitial fluid; seen in animals that have an open circulatory system, such as molluscs and arthropods. 606

hepatitis Inflammation of the liver. Viral hepatitis occurs in several forms. 654

herbaceous stem Nonwoody stem; herbaceous plants tend to die back to ground level at the end of the growing season. 454

herbivore Primary consumer in a grazing food chain; a plant eater. 870

hermaphroditic Type of animal that has both male and female sex organs. 531, 773

heterochromatin Highly compacted chromatin that is not accessible for transcription. 234

heterosporous Seed plant that produces two types of spores—microspores and megaspores. A plant that produces only one type of spore is *homosporous*. 426

heterotrophy Organism that cannot synthesize needed organic compounds from inorganic substances and therefore must take in organic food. 120, 870

heterozygote advantage Situation in which individuals heterozygous for a trait have a selective advantage over those who are homozygous dominant or recessive; an example is sickle-cell disease. 302

heterozygous Possessing unlike alleles for a particular trait. 196

hexose Any monosaccharide that contains six carbons; examples are glucose and galactose. 42

hippocampus Region of the central nervous system associated with learning and memory; part of the limbic system. 705

histamine Substance, produced by basophils in blood and mast cells in connective tissue, that causes capillaries to dilate. 631

histone A group of proteins involved in forming the nucleosome structure of eukaryote chromatin. 157, 233

homeobox 180-nucleotide sequence located in all homeotic genes. 804

homeodomain Conserved DNA-binding region of transcription factors encoded by the homeobox of homeotic genes. 804

homeostasis Maintenance of normal internal conditions in a cell or an organism by means of self-regulating mechanisms. 4, 599

homeothermic Ability to regulate the internal body temperature around an optimum value. 599

homeotic genes Genes that control the overall body plan by controlling the fate of groups of cells during development. 803

hominid Taxon that includes humans, chimpanzees, gorillas, and orangutans. 572

hominin Taxon that includes humans and species very closely related to humans plus chimpanzees. 572

hominine Taxon that includes humans, chimpanzees, and gorillas. 572

hominoid Taxon that includes the hominids plus the gibbons. 572

homologous chromosome Member of a pair of chromosomes that are alike and come together in synapsis during prophase of the first meiotic division; a *homologue*. 172

homologous gene Gene that codes for the same protein, even if the base sequence may be different. 265

homologous, homologous structure A structure that is similar in different types of organisms because these organisms descended from a common ancestor. 283, 317, 357

homologue Member of a homologous pair of chromosomes. 172

homology Similarity of parts or organs of different organisms caused by evolutionary derivation from a corresponding part or organ in a remote ancestor, and usually having a similar embryonic origin. 357

homosporous A plant that produces only one type of asexual spore. 426

homozygous Possessing two identical alleles for a particular trait. 196

hormone Chemical messenger produced in one part of the body that controls the activity of other parts. 484, 753

hornwort A bryophyte of the phylum Anthocerophyta with a thin gametophyte and tiny sporophyte that resembles a broom handle. 424

horsetail A seedless vascular plant having only one genus (*Equisetum*) in existence today;

characterized by rhizomes, scalelike leaves, strobili, and tough, rigid stems. 427

host Organism that provides nourishment and/or shelter for a parasite. 865

human chorionic gonadotropin (HCG) Gonadotropic hormone produced by the chorion that functions to maintain the uterine lining. 782, 806

Human Genome Project (HGP) Initiative to determine the complete sequence of the human genome and to analyze this information. 261

human immunodeficiency virus (HIV) Virus responsible for the disease AIDS. 637, 787

humus Decomposing organic matter in the soil. 467

hunter-gatherer A hominin that hunted animals and gathered plants for food. 580

hyaline cartilage Cartilage whose cells lie in lacunae separated by a white translucent matrix containing very fine collagen fibers. 591

hybridization Interbreeding between two different species; typically prevented by prezygotic isolation mechanisms. 310

hydrogen bond Weak bond that arises between a slightly positive hydrogen atom of one molecule and a slightly negative atom of another molecule or between parts of the same molecule. 28

hydrogen ion (H^+) Hydrogen atom that has lost its electron and therefore bears a positive charge. 32

hydrolysis reaction Splitting of a chemical bond by the addition of water, with the H^+ going to one molecule and the OH^- going to the other. 41

hydrophilic Type of molecule, often polar, that interacts with water by dissolving in water and/or by forming hydrogen bonds with water molecules. 40

hydrophobic Type of molecule, that is typically nonpolar, and therefore does not interact easily with water. 40

hydroponics Technique for growing plants by suspending them with their roots in a nutrient solution. 465

hydrostatic skeleton Fluid-filled body compartment that provides support for muscle contraction resulting in movement; seen in cnidarians, flatworms, roundworms, and segmented worms. 528, 736

hydrothermal vent Hot springs in the seafloor along ocean ridges where heated sea water and sulfate react to produce hydrogen sulfide; here, chemosynthetic bacteria support a community of varied organisms. 902

hydroxide ion (OH^-) One of two ions that results when a water molecule dissociates; it has gained an electron and therefore bears a negative charge. 32

hypersensitive response (HR) Plants respond to pathogens by selectively killing plant cells to block the spread of the pathogen. 498

hyperthyroidism Caused by the over-secretion of hormones from the thyroid gland; symptoms include hyperactivity, nervousness, and insomnia. 761

hypertonic solution Higher solute concentration (less water) than the cytoplasm of a cell; causes cell to lose water by osmosis. 94

hypha Filament of the vegetative body of a fungus. 405

hypertension Form of cardiovascular disease characterized by blood pressure over 140/95 (over 45 years of age) or 130/90 (under 45 years of age). 616

hypothalamic-inhibiting hormone One of many hormones produced by the hypothalamus that inhibits the secretion of an anterior pituitary hormone. 757

hypothalamic-releasing hormone One of many hormones produced by the hypothalamus that stimulates the secretion of an anterior pituitary hormone. 757

hypothalamus In vertebrates, part of the brain that helps regulate the internal environment of the body—for example, heart rate, body temperature, and water balance. 704, 757

hypothesis Supposition established by reasoning after consideration of available evidence; it can be tested by obtaining more data, often by experimentation. 11

hypothyroidism Caused by the under-secretion of hormones from the thyroid gland; symptoms include weight gain, lethargic behavior, and depression. 761

hypotonic solution Solution that contains a lower solute (more water) concentration than the cytoplasm of a cell; causes cell to gain water by osmosis. 93

I

immediate allergic response Allergic response that occurs within seconds of contact with an allergen; caused by the attachment of the allergen to IgE antibodies. 641

immune system System associated with protection against pathogens, toxins, and some cancerous cells; in humans this is an organ system. 627

immunity Ability of the body to protect itself from foreign substances and cells, including disease-causing agents. 630

immunization Strategy for achieving immunity to the effects of specific disease-causing agents. 639

immunoglobulin (Ig) Globular plasma protein that functions as an antibody. 634

implantation In placental mammals, the embedding of an embryo at the blastocyst stage into the endometrium of the uterus. 806

imprinting Learning to make a particular response to only one type of animal or object. 823

inbreeding Mating between closely related individuals; influences the genotype ratios of the gene pool. 295

inclusive fitness Fitness that results from personal reproduction and from helping nondescendant relatives reproduce. 834

incomplete digestive tract Digestive tract that has a single opening, usually called a mouth. 647

incomplete dominance Inheritance pattern in which an offspring has an intermediate phenotype, as when a red-flowered plant and a white-flowered plant produce pink-flowered offspring. 205

incomplete penetrance Dominant alleles that are either not always, or partially expressed. 206

independent assortment Alleles of unlinked genes segregate independently of each other during meiosis so that the gametes could contain all possible combinations of alleles. 175

index fossil Deposits found in certain layers of strata; similar fossils can be found in the same strata around the world. 334

induced fit model Change in the shape of an enzyme's active site that enhances the fit between the active site and its substrate(s). 110

induced mutation Mutation that is caused by an outside influence, such as organic chemicals or ionizing radiation. 247

inducer Molecule that brings about activity of an operon by joining with a repressor and preventing it from binding to the operator. 240

induction Ability of a chemical or a tissue to influence the development of another tissue. 800

inductive reasoning Using specific observations and the process of logic and reasoning to arrive at general scientific principles. 11

infertility Inability to have as many children as desired. 784

inflammatory response Tissue response to injury that is characterized by redness, swelling, pain, and heat. 631

ingroup In a cladistic study of evolutionary relationships among organisms, the group that is being analyzed. 356

inheritance of acquired characteristics Lamarckian belief that characteristics acquired during the lifetime of an organism can be passed on to offspring. 273

initiation First stage of translation in which the translational machinery binds an mRNA and assembles. 230

innate immunity An immune response that does not require a previous exposure to the pathogen. 627

inner ear Portion of the ear consisting of a vestibule, semicircular canals, and the cochlea where equilibrium is maintained and sound is transmitted. 727

inorganic chemistry Branch of science that studies the chemical reactions and properties of all of the elements, except hydrogen and carbon. 38

insect Type of arthropod. The head has antennae, compound eyes, and simple eyes; the thorax has three pairs of legs and often wings; and the abdomen has internal organs. 541

insight learning Ability to apply prior learning to a new situation without trial-and-error activity. 825

inspiration Act of taking air into the lungs; inhalation. 669

insulin Hormone released by the pancreas that serves to lower blood glucose levels by stimulating the uptake of glucose by cells, especially muscle and liver cells. 765

integration Summing up of excitatory and inhibitory signals by a neuron or by some part of the brain. 701

interferon Antiviral agent produced by an infected cell that blocks the infection of another cell. 633

intergenic sequence Region of DNA that lies between genes on a chromosome. 262

interkinesis Period of time between meiosis I and meiosis II during which no DNA replication takes place. 176

intermediate filament Ropelike assemblies of fibrous polypeptides in the cytoskeleton that provide support and strength to cells; so called because they are intermediate in size between actin filaments and microtubules. 78

internal respiration Exchange of oxygen and carbon dioxide between blood and tissue fluid. 664

interneuron Neuron located within the central nervous system that conveys messages between parts of the central nervous system. 698

internode In vascular plants, the region of a stem between two successive nodes. 445

interphase Stages of the cell cycle (G$_1$, S, G$_2$) during which growth and DNA synthesis occur when the nucleus is not actively dividing. 154

interspersed repeat Repeated DNA sequence that is spread across several regions of a chromosome or across multiple chromosomes. 262

intertidal zone Region along a coastline where the tide recedes and returns. 900

intron Intervening sequence found between exons in mRNA; removed by RNA processing before translation. 226

inversion Change in chromosome structure in which a segment of a chromosome is turned around 180°; this reversed sequence of genes can lead to altered gene activity and abnormalities. 187

invertebrate Animal without a vertebral column or backbone. 521

ion Charged particle that carries a negative or positive charge. 26

ionic bond Chemical bond in which ions are attracted to one another by opposite charges. 26

iris Muscular ring that surrounds the pupil and regulates the passage of light through this opening. 721

iron-sulfur world Hypothesis that ocean thermal vents provided all of the materials needed for abiotic synthesis of the first molecules. 329

island biogeography model Proposes that the biodiversity on an island is dependent on its distance from the mainland, with islands located a greater distance having a lower level of diversity. 859

isomer Molecules with the same molecular formula but a different structure, and therefore a different shape. 40

isotonic solution Solution that is equal in solute concentration to that of the cytoplasm of a cell; causes cell to neither lose nor gain water by osmosis. 93

isotope Atoms of the same element having the same atomic number but a different mass number due to a variation in the number of neutrons. 24

iteroparity Repeated production of offspring at intervals throughout the life cycle of an organism. 843

J

jaundice Yellowish tint to the skin caused by an abnormal amount of bilirubin (bile pigment) in the blood, indicating liver malfunction. 654

jawless fishes Type of fishes that lack jaws (agnathan); includes hagfishes and lampreys. 553

joint Articulation between two bones of a skeleton. 742

junction protein(s) Proteins in the cell membrane that assist in cell-to-cell communication. 89

K

karyotype Chromosomes arranged by pairs according to their size, shape, and general appearance in mitotic metaphase. 184

keystone species Species whose activities significantly affect community structure. 918

kidneys Paired organs of the vertebrate urinary system that regulate the chemical composition of the blood and produce a waste product called urine. 684

kinetic energy Energy associated with motion. 105

kinetochore An assembly of proteins that attaches to the centromere of a chromosome during mitosis. 157

kinetoplastid Unicellular, flagellate protist characterized by the presence in their single mitochondrion of a kinetoplast (a structure containing a large mass of DNA). 396

kingdom One of the categories, or taxa, used by taxonomists to group species; the taxon above phylum. 6, 349

kin selection Indirect selection; adaptation to the environment due to the reproductive success of an individual's relatives. 834

K-**selection** Favorable life-history strategy under stable environmental conditions characterized by the production of a few offspring with much attention given to offspring survival. 849

L

lactation Secretion of milk by mammary glands, usually for the nourishment of an infant. 782

lacteal Lymphatic vessel in an intestinal villus; aids in the absorption of fats. 653

lacuna Small pit or hollow cavity, as in bone or cartilage, where a cell or cells are located. 590

lake Body of fresh water, often classified by nutrient status, such as oligotrophic (nutrient-poor) or eutrophic (nutrient-rich). 898

landscape A number of interacting ecosystems. 909

landscape diversity Variety of habitat elements within an ecosystem (e.g., plains, mountains, and rivers). 909

large intestine In vertebrates, portion of the digestive tract that follows the small intestine; in humans, consists of the cecum, colon, rectum, and anal canal. 653

larynx Cartilaginous organ located between the pharynx and the trachea; in humans, contains the vocal cords; sometimes called the voice box. 668

last universal common ancestor (LUCA) The first living organism on the planet, from which all life evolved. 328

lateral line Canal system containing sensory receptors that allow fishes and amphibians to detect water currents and pressure waves from nearby objects. 726

law Universal principle that describes the basic functions of the natural world. 12

law of independent assortment Mendelian principle that explains how combinations of traits appear in gametes; *see also* independent assortment. 198

law of segregation Mendelian principle that explains how, in a diploid organism, alleles separate during the formation of the gametes. 196

laws of thermodynamics Two laws explaining energy and its relationships and exchanges. The first, also called the "law of conservation," says that energy cannot be created or destroyed but can only be changed from one form to another; the second says that energy cannot be changed from one form to another without a loss of usable energy. 105

leaf Lateral appendage of a stem, highly variable in structure, often containing cells that carry out photosynthesis. 445

leaf vein Vascular tissue within a leaf. 450

learning Relatively permanent change in an animal's behavior that results from practice and experience. 823

lens Transparent, disclike structure found in the vertebrate eye behind the iris; brings objects into focus on the retina. 721

leptin Hormone produced by adipose tissue that acts on the hypothalamus to signal satiety (fullness). 768

less-developed country (LDC) Country that is becoming industrialized; typically, population growth is expanding rapidly, and the majority of people live in poverty. 851

leucoplasts Plastid, generally colorless, that synthesizes and stores starch and oils. 77

leukocyte Another name for a white blood cell (WBC). 620

lichen Symbiotic relationship between certain fungi and either cyanobacteria or algae, in which the fungi possibly provide inorganic food or water and the algae or cyanobacteria provide organic food. 377, 414

life cycle Recurring pattern of genetically programmed events by which individuals grow, develop, maintain themselves, and reproduce. 180

ligament Tough cord or band of dense fibrous tissue that binds bone to bone at a joint. 590, 742

light reaction Portion of photosynthesis that captures solar energy and takes place in thylakoid membranes of chloroplasts; it produces ATP and NADPH. 122

lignin Chemical that hardens the cell walls of land plants. 426, 449

limbic system In humans, functional association of various brain centers, including the amygdala and hippocampus; governs learning and memory and various emotions such as pleasure, fear, and happiness. 705

limiting factor Resource or environmental condition that restricts the abundance and distribution of an organism. 840

lineage Line of descent represented by a branch in a phylogenetic tree. 354

lipase Fat-digesting enzyme secreted by the pancreas. 657

lipid Class of organic compounds that tends to be soluble in nonpolar solvents; includes fats and oils. 45

liposome Droplet of phospholipid molecules formed in a liquid environment. 331

liver Large, dark red internal organ that produces urea and bile, detoxifies the blood, stores glycogen, and produces the plasma proteins, among other functions. 654

liverwort Bryophyte with a lobed or leafy gametophyte and a sporophyte composed of a stalk and capsule. 424

lobe-finned fishes Type of fishes with limblike fins; also called the sarcopterygians. 555

locus Physical location of a trait (or gene) on a chromosome. 196

logistic growth Population increase that results in an S-shaped curve; growth is slow at first, steepens, and then levels off due to environmental resistance. 844

long-day plant Plant that flowers when day length is longer than a critical length; e.g., wheat, barley, clover, and spinach. 496

loop of the nephron Portion of a nephron between the proximal and distal convoluted tubules; functions in water reabsorption. 686

loose fibrous connective tissue Tissue composed mainly of fibroblasts widely separated by a matrix containing collagen and elastic fibers. 590

lophophoran A general term to describe several groups of lophotrochozoans that have a feeding structure called a lophophore. 530

lophotrochozoa Main group of protostomes; widely diverse. Includes the flatworms, rotifers, annelids, and molluscs. 530

lumen Cavity inside any tubular structure, such as the lumen of the digestive tract. 651

lung cancer Uncontrolled cell growth that affects any component of the respiratory system. 675

lungs Internal respiratory organ containing moist surfaces for gas exchange. 665

lungfishes Type of lobe-finned fishes that utilize lungs in addition to gills for gas exchange. 555

luteal phase Second half of the ovarian cycle, during which the corpus luteum develops and much progesterone (and some estrogen) is produced. 781

lycophyte Club mosses, among the first vascular plants to evolve and to have leaves. The leaves of the lycophytes are microphylls. 426

lymph Fluid, derived from tissue fluid, that is carried in lymphatic vessels. 592, 622, 629

lymphatic capillary Smallest vessels of the lymphatic system; closed-ended; responsible for the uptake of fluids from the surrounding tissues. 629

lymphatic system Organ system consisting of lymphatic vessels and lymphatic organs; transports lymph and lipids, and aids the immune system. 628

lymphatic vessel Vessel that carries lymph. 628

lymph node Mass of lymphatic tissue located along the course of a lymphatic vessel. 629

lymphocyte Specialized white blood cell that functions in specific defense; occurs in two forms—T lymphocytes and B lymphocytes. 620

lymphoid (lymphatic) organ Organ other than a lymphatic vessel that is part of the lymphatic system; the lymphatic organs are the lymph nodes, tonsils, spleen, thymus gland, and bone marrow. 629

lysogenic cell Cell that contains a prophage (virus incorporated into DNA), which is replicated when the cell divides. 368

lysogenic cycle Bacteriophage life cycle in which the virus incorporates its DNA into that of a bacterium; occurs preliminary to the lytic cycle. 368

lysosome Membrane-bounded vesicle that contains hydrolytic enzymes for digesting macromolecules and bacteria; used to recycle worn-out cellular organelles. 73

lytic cycle Bacteriophage life cycle in which the virus takes over the operation of the bacterium immediately upon entering it and subsequently destroys the bacterium. 368

M

macroevolution Large-scale evolutionary change, such as the formation of new species. 307

macronutrient Essential element needed in large amounts for plant growth, such as nitrogen, calcium, or sulfur. 465

macrophage In vertebrates, large phagocytic cell derived from a monocyte that ingests microbes and debris. 632

macular degeneration Condition in which the capillaries supplying the retina of the eye become damaged resulting in reduced vision and blindness. 724

malignant The power to threaten life; cancerous. 163

maltase Enzyme produced in small intestine that breaks down maltose to two glucose molecules. 656

mammal Endothermic vertebrate characterized especially by the presence of hair and mammary glands. 564

mantle In molluscs, an extension of the body wall that covers the visceral mass and may secrete a shell. 534

marsh Soft wetland, that is treeless. 897

marsupial Member of a group of mammals bearing immature young nursed in a marsupium, or pouch—for example, kangaroo and opossum. 564

mass extinction Episode of large-scale extinction in which large numbers of species disappear in a few million years or less. 338

mass number Mass of an atom equal to the number of protons plus the number of neutrons within the nucleus. 23

mast cell Connective tissue cell that releases histamine in allergic reactions. 631

maternal determinant One of many substances present in the egg that influences the course of development. 800

matrix Unstructured semifluid substance that fills the space between cells in connective tissues or inside organelles. 77

matter Anything that takes up space and has mass. 22

mechanical energy A type of kinetic energy associated with the position, or motion (such as walking or running) of an object. 105

mechanoreceptor Sensory receptor that responds to mechanical stimuli, such as pressure, sound waves, or gravity. 717

medulla oblongata In vertebrates, part of the brain stem that is continuous with the spinal cord; controls heartbeat, blood pressure, breathing, and other vital functions. 705

medusa Among cnidarians, bell-shaped body form that is directed downward and contains much mesoglea. 528

megafauna Large animals, such as humans, bears, and deer. Often defined as those over 100 pounds (44 kg) in adult size. 341

megaphyll Large leaf with several to many veins. 427

megaspore One of the two types of spores produced by seed plants; develops into a female gametophyte (embryo sac). 426, 502

meiosis Type of nuclear division that reduces the chromosome number from 2n to n; daughter cells receive the haploid number of chromosomes in varied combinations; also called reduction division. 172

melanocyte Specialized cell in the epidermis that produces melanin, the pigment responsible for skin color. 598

melanocyte-stimulating hormone (MSH) Substance that causes melanocytes to secrete melanin in most vertebrates. 757

melatonin Hormone, secreted by the pineal gland, that is involved in biorhythms. 768

membrane-first hypothesis Proposes that the plasma membrane was the first component of the early cells to evolve. 331

memory Capacity of the brain to store and retrieve information about past sensations and perceptions; essential to learning. 707

memory B cell Forms during a primary immune response but enters a resting phase until a secondary immune response occurs. 634

memory T cell T cell that differentiated during an initial infection and responds rapidly during subsequent exposure to the same antigen. 636

meninges Protective membranous coverings around the central nervous system. 702

meningitis A condition that refers to inflammation of the brain or spinal cord meninges (membranes). 702

menopause Termination of the ovarian and uterine cycles in older women. 782, 813

menstruation Periodic shedding of tissue and blood from the inner lining of the uterus in primates. 781

meristem Undifferentiated embryonic tissue in the active growth regions of plants. 447

mesoderm Middle primary tissue layer of an animal embryo that gives rise to muscle, several internal organs, and connective tissue layers. 798

mesoglea Transparent jellylike substance located between the endoderm and ectoderm of some sponges and cnidarians. 528

mesophyll Inner, thickest layer of a leaf consisting of palisade and spongy mesophyll; the site of most of photosynthesis. 459

mesosome In a bacterium, plasma membrane that folds into the cytoplasm and increases surface area. 65

messenger RNA (mRNA) Type of RNA formed from a DNA template and bearing coded information for the amino acid sequence of a polypeptide. 223

metabolic pathway Series of linked reactions, beginning with a particular reactant and terminating with an end product. 109

metabolic pool Metabolites that are the products of and/or the substrates for key reactions in cells, allowing one type of molecule to be changed into another type, such as carbohydrates converted to fats. 147

metabolism The sum of the chemical reactions that occur in a cell. 4, 107

metamorphosis Change in shape and form that some animals, such as insects, undergo during development. 521, 540

metaphase Third phase of mitosis; chromosomes are aligned at the metaphase plate. 159

metaphase plate A disk formed during metaphase in which all of a cell's chromosomes lie in a single plane at right angles to the spindle fibers. 159

metapopulation Population subdivided into several small and isolated populations due to habitat fragmentation. 919

metastasis Spread of cancer from the place of origin throughout the body; caused by the ability of cancer cells to migrate and invade tissues. 164

methanogen Type of archaean that lives in oxygen-free habitats, such as swamps, and releases methane gas. 378

MHC (major histocompatibility complex) protein Protein marker that is a part of cell-surface markers anchored in the plasma membrane, which the immune system uses to identify "self." 635

micelle Single layer of fatty acids (or phospholipids) that orientate themselves in an aqueous environment. 331

microevolution Change in gene frequencies between populations of a species over time. 290

microglia Supportive cells of the nervous system that help remove bacteria and debris, thus supporting the activity of the neurons. 697

micronutrient Essential element needed in small amounts for plant growth, such as boron, copper, and zinc. 465

microphyll Small leaf with one vein. 426

microRNA (miRNA) Short sequences of RNA, usually less than 22 nucleotides, that are involved in posttranscriptional regulation of gene expression. These molecules either inhibit, or reduce, the expression of specific genes. 246

microsphere Formed from proteinoids exposed to water; has properties similar to those of today's cells. 330

microspore One of the two types of spores produced by seed plants; develops into a male gametophyte (pollen grain). 426, 502

microtubule Small, cylindrical organelle composed of tubulin protein around an empty central core; present in the cytoplasm, centrioles, cilia, and flagella. 78

midbrain In mammals, the part of the brain located below the thalamus and above the pons. 704

middle ear Portion of the ear consisting of the tympanic membrane, the oval and round windows, and the ossicles, where sound is amplified. 727

migration Regular back-and-forth movement of animals between two geographic areas at particular times of the year. 825

millipede More-or-less cylindrical arthropod characterized by having two pairs of short legs on most of its body segments; may have 13 to almost 200 pairs of legs. 541

mimicry Superficial resemblance of two or more species; a survival mechanism that avoids predation by appearing to be noxious. 864

mineral Naturally occurring inorganic substance containing two or more elements; certain minerals are needed in the diet. 465

mineralocorticoid Hormones secreted by the adrenal cortex that regulate salt and water balance, leading to increases in blood volume and blood pressure. 763

mitochondria (sing., mitochondrion) Membrane-bounded organelle in which ATP molecules are produced during the process of cellular respiration. 76, 142

mitosis The stage of cellular reproduction in which nuclear division occurs; process in which a parent nucleus produces two daughter nuclei, each having the same number and kinds of chromosomes as the parent nucleus. 155

mitotic spindle A complex of microtubules and associated proteins that assist in separating the chromatids during cell division. 155

mixotrophic Organism that can use autotrophic and heterotrophic means of gaining nutrients. 384

model Simulation of a process that aids conceptual understanding until the process can be studied firsthand; a hypothesis that describes how a particular process could possibly be carried out. 12

mold Various fungi whose body consists of a mass of hyphae (filaments) that grow on and receive nourishment from organic matter such as human food and clothing. 410

mole The molecular weight of a molecule expressed in grams; contains 6.023×10^{23} molecules. 107

molecular clock Idea that the rate at which mutational changes accumulate in certain genes is constant over time and is not involved in adaptation to the environment. 359

molecule Union of two or more atoms of the same element; also, the smallest part of a compound that retains the properties of the compound. 26

mollusc Invertebrates including squids, clams, snails, and chitons; characterized by a visceral mass, a mantle, and a foot. 534

monoclonal antibody One of many antibodies produced by a clone of hybridoma cells that all bind to the same antigen. 635

monocot (Monocotyledone) Flowering plant group; members have one embryonic leaf (cotyledon), parallel-veined leaves, scattered vascular bundles, flower parts in threes or multiples of three, and other characteristics. 433, 446

monocyte Type of agranular leukocyte that functions as a phagocyte, particularly after it becomes a macrophage, which is also an antigen-presenting cell. 620

monoecious Having male flowers or cones and female flowers or cones on a single plant. 430

monogamous Breeding pair of organisms that reproduce only with each other through their lifetime. 831

monohybrid cross Cross between parents that differ in only one trait. 195

monomer Small molecule that is a subunit of a polymer—e.g., glucose is a monomer of starch. 40

monophyletic Group of species including the most recent common ancestor and all its descendants. 308, 384

monosaccharide Simple sugar; a carbohydrate that cannot be broken down by hydrolysis—e.g., glucose; also, any monomer of the polysaccharides. 41

monosomy Chromosome condition in which a diploid cell has one less chromosome than normal; designated as 2n-1. 183

monotreme Egg-laying mammal—e.g., duckbill platypus or spiny anteater. 564

monsoon Climate in India and southern Asia caused by wet ocean winds that blow onshore for almost half the year. 885

montane coniferous forest Coniferous forest of a mountain. 887

more-developed country (MDC) Country that is industrialized; typically, population growth is low, and the people enjoy a good standard of living overall. 851

morphogenesis Emergence of shape in tissues, organs, or entire embryo during development. 800

morphological species concept Definition of a species that defines species by specific diagnostic traits. 307

morphology Physical characteristics that contribute to the appearance of an organism. 307

morula Spherical mass of cells resulting from cleavage during animal development prior to the blastula stage. 797

mosaic evolution Concept that human characteristics did not evolve at the same rate; for example, some body parts are more humanlike than others in early hominins. 577

moss Bryophyte that is typically found in moist habitats. 424

motor molecule Protein that moves along either actin filaments or microtubules and translocates organelles. 78

motor (efferent) neuron Nerve cell that conducts nerve impulses away from the central nervous system and innervates effectors (muscle and glands). 697

mouth In humans, organ of the digestive tract where food is chewed and mixed with saliva. 650

mRNA transcript mRNA molecule formed during transcription that has a sequence of bases complementary to a gene. 226

mucosa Epithelial membrane containing cells that secrete mucus; found in the inner cell layers of the digestive (first layer) and respiratory tracts. 651

multicellular Organism composed of many cells; usually has organized tissues, organs, and organ systems. 2

multiple alleles Inheritance pattern in which there are more than two alleles for a particular trait; each individual has only two of all possible alleles. 205

multiple sclerosis Disease of the central nervous system characterized by the breakdown of myelin in the neurons; considered to be an autoimmune disease. 705

muscularis Smooth muscle layer found in the digestive tract. 651

muscular (contractile) tissue Type of animal tissue composed of fibers that shorten and lengthen to produce movements. 592

mutagen Chemical or physical agent that increases the chance of mutation. 248

mutualism Symbiotic relationship in which both species benefit in terms of growth and reproduction. 375, 866

mycelium Tangled mass of hyphal filaments composing the vegetative body of a fungus. 405

mycorrhizae (sing., mycorrhiza) Mutualistic relationship between fungal hyphae and roots of vascular plants. 414, 472

myelin sheath White, fatty material—derived from the membrane of neurolemmocytes—that forms a covering for nerve fibers. 697

myofibril Specific muscle cell organelle containing a linear arrangement of sarcomeres, which shorten to produce muscle contraction. 745

myosin Muscle protein making up the thick filaments in a sarcomere; it pulls actin to shorten the sarcomere, yielding muscle contraction. 745

N

NAD⁺ (nicotinamide adenine dinucleotide) Coenzyme in oxidation-reduction reactions that accepts electrons and hydrogen ions to become NADH + H⁺ as oxidation of substrates occurs. During cellular respiration, NADH carries electrons to the electron transport chain in mitochondria. 114, 136

NADP⁺ (nicotinamide adenine dinucleotide phosphate) Coenzyme in oxidation-reduction reactions that accepts electrons and hydrogen ions to become NADPH + H⁺. During photosynthesis, NADPH participates in the reduction of carbon dioxide to a carbohydrate. 113

nail Flattened epithelial tissue from the stratum lucidum of the skin; located on the tips of fingers and toes. 598

natural killer (NK) cell Lymphocyte that causes an infected or cancerous cell to burst. 632

natural group In systematics, groups of organisms that possess a shared evolutionary history. 348

natural selection Mechanism of evolutionary change caused by environmental selection of organisms most fit to reproduce; results in adaptation to the environment. 8, 277

navigate To steer or manage a course by adjusting one's bearings and following the result of the adjustment. 825

Neandertal Hominin with a sturdy build that lived during the last Ice Age in Europe and the Middle East; hunted large game and left evidence of being culturally advanced. 580

nearsighted (myopic) Condition in which an individual cannot focus on objects at a distance; caused by the focusing of the image in front of the retina of the eye. 724

negative feedback Mechanism of homeostatic response by which the output of a system suppresses or inhibits activity of the system. 600, 757

nematocyst In cnidarians, a capsule that contains a threadlike fiber, the release of which aids in the capture of prey. 528

nephridium (pl., nephridia) Segmentally arranged, paired excretory tubules of many invertebrates, as in the earthworm. 536

nephron Microscopic kidney unit that regulates blood composition by glomerular filtration, tubular reabsorption, and tubular secretion. 685

nerve Bundle of long axons outside the central nervous system. 593, 707

nerve fiber Axon; conducts nerve impulses away from the cell. Axons are classified as either myelinated or unmyelinated based on the presence or absence of a myelin sheath. 697

nerve net Diffuse, noncentralized arrangement of nerve cells in cnidarians. 529, 694

nervous tissue Tissue that contains nerve cells (neurons), which conduct impulses, and neuroglia, which support, protect, and provide nutrients to neurons. 593

neural plate Region of the dorsal surface of the chordate embryo that marks the future location of the neural tube. 799

neural tube Tube formed by closure of the neural groove during development. In vertebrates, the neural tube develops into the spinal cord and brain. 799

neurodegenerative disease Disease, usually caused by a prion, virus, or bacterium, that damages or impairs the function of nervous tissue. 371

neuroglia Nonconducting nerve cells that are intimately associated with neurons and function in a supportive capacity. 593, 697

neuromuscular junction Region where an axon bulb approaches a muscle fiber; contains a presynaptic membrane, a synaptic cleft, and a postsynaptic membrane. 747

neuron Nerve cell that characteristically has three parts: dendrites, cell body, and an axon. 593, 697

neurotransmitter Chemical stored at the ends of axons that is responsible for transmission across a synapse. 700

neutron Neutral subatomic particle, located in the nucleus and assigned one atomic mass unit. 22

neutrophil Granular leukocyte that is the most abundant of the white blood cells; first to respond to infection. 631

nitrification Process by which nitrogen in ammonia and organic compounds is oxidized to nitrites and nitrates by soil bacteria. 878

N₂ (nitrogen) fixation Process whereby free atmospheric nitrogen is converted into compounds, such as ammonium and nitrates, usually by bacteria. 878

node In plants, the place where one or more leaves attach to a stem. 421, 445

nodes of Ranvier Gaps in the myelin sheath around a nerve fiber. 697

noncompetitive inhibition Form of enzyme inhibition where the inhibitor binds to an enzyme at a location other than the active site; while at this site, the enzyme shape changes, the inhibitor is unable to bind to its substrate, and no product forms. 112

noncyclic pathway Light-dependent photosynthetic pathway that is used to generate ATP and NADPH; because the pathway is noncyclic, the electrons must be replaced by the splitting of water (photolysis). 124

nondisjunction Failure of the homologous chromosomes or sister chromatids to separate during either mitosis or meiosis; produces cells with abnormal chromosome numbers. 183

nomenclature In systematics, the process of assigning names to taxonomic groups; usually determined by governing organizations. 350

nonpolar covalent bond Bond in which the sharing of electrons between atoms is fairly equal. 27

nonrandom mating Mating among individuals on the basis of their phenotypic similarities or differences, rather than mating on a random basis. 295

nonseptate Lacking cell walls; some fungal species have hyphae that are nonseptate. 405

nonvascular plants Bryophytes, such as mosses and liverworts, that have no vascular tissue and either occur in moist locations or have special adaptations for living in dry locations. 423

norepinephrine Neurotransmitter of the postganglionic fibers in the sympathetic division of the autonomic system; also, a hormone produced by the adrenal medulla. 762

notochord Cartilage-like supportive dorsal rod in all chordates at some time in their life cycle; replaced by vertebrae in vertebrates. 550, 799

nuclear envelope Double membrane that surrounds the nucleus in eukaryotic cells and is connected to the endoplasmic reticulum; has pores that allow substances to pass between the nucleus and the cytoplasm. 70

nucleariid Protist that may be related to fungi although nucleariids lack the same type of cell wall and have threadlike pseudopods. 398

nuclear envelope Name for the phospholipid double membrane that separates the contents of the nucleus from the cytoplasm. 71

nuclear pore Opening in the nuclear envelope that permits the passage of proteins into the nucleus and ribosomal subunits out of the nucleus. 71

nucleic acid Polymer of nucleotides; both DNA and RNA are nucleic acids. 54

nucleoid Region of prokaryotic cells where DNA is located; it is not bounded by a nuclear envelope. 65, 166, 372

nucleolus Dark-staining, spherical body in the nucleus that produces ribosomal subunits. 70

nucleoplasm Semifluid medium of the nucleus containing chromatin. 70

nucleosome In the nucleus of a eukaryotic cell, a unit composed of DNA wound around a core of eight histone proteins, giving the appearance of a string of beads. 233

nucleotide Monomer of DNA and RNA consisting of a 5-carbon sugar bonded to a nitrogenous base and a phosphate group. 54

nucleus Membrane-bounded organelle within a eukaryotic cell that contains chromosomes and controls the structure and function of the cell. 64

O

obligate anaerobe Prokaryote unable to grow in the presence of free oxygen. 374

observation Initial step in the scientific method that often involves the recording of data from an experiment or natural event. 11

octet rule The observation that an atom is most stable when its outer shell is complete and contains eight electrons; an exception is hydrogen which requires only two electrons in its outer shell to have a completed shell. 25

oil Triglyceride, usually of plant origin, that is composed of glycerol and three fatty acids and is liquid in consistency due to many unsaturated bonds in the hydrocarbon chains of the fatty acids. 46

oil gland Gland of the skin, associated with a hair follicle, that secretes sebum; sebaceous gland. 599

olfactory cell Modified neuron that is a sensory receptor for the sense of smell. 719

oligodendrocyte Type of glial cell that forms myelin sheaths around neurons in the CNS. 697

omnivore Organism in a food chain that feeds on both plants and animals. 870

oncogene Cancer-causing gene formed by a mutation in a proto-oncogene; code for proteins that stimulate the cell cycle and inhibit apoptosis. 164

oocyte Immature egg that is undergoing meiosis; upon completion of meiosis, the oocyte becomes an egg. 779

oogenesis Production of eggs in females by the process of meiosis and maturation. 180

open circulatory system Arrangement of internal transport in which blood bathes the organs directly, and there is no distinction between blood and interstitial fluid. 606

operant conditioning Learning that results from rewarding or reinforcing a particular behavior. 824

operator In an operon, the sequence of DNA that serves as a binding site for a repressor, and thereby regulates the expression of structural genes. 239

operon Group of structural and regulating genes that function as a single unit. 238

opisthokont Supergroup of eukaryotes that choanoflagellates animals, nucleariids and fungi. 397

opposable thumb Fingers arranged in such a way that the thumb can touch the ventral surface of the fingertips of all four fingers. 571

optimal foraging model Analysis of behavior as a compromise of feeding costs versus feeding benefits. 831

order One of the categories, or taxa, used by taxonomists to group species; the taxon located above the family level. 6, 349

organ Combination of two or more different tissues performing a common function. 444, 596

organelle Small, membranous structures in the cytoplasm having a specific structure and function. 67

organic chemistry Branch of science that deals with organic molecules including those that are unique to living things. 38

organic molecule Molecule that always contains carbon and hydrogen, and often contains oxygen as well; organic molecules are associated with living things. 38

organ of Corti Structure in the vertebrate inner ear that contains auditory receptors (also called spiral organ). 727

organ system Group of related organs working together; examples are the digestive and endocrine systems. 596

orientation In birds, the ability to know present location by tracking stimuli in the environment. 825

osmoregulation Regulation of the salt water balance to maintain a normal balance within internal fluids. 681

osmosis Diffusion of water through a selectively permeable membrane. 92

osmotic pressure Measure of the tendency of water to move across a selectively permeable membrane; visible as an increase in liquid on the side of the membrane with higher solute concentration. 93

ossicle One of the small bones of the vertebrate middle ear—malleus, incus, and stapes. 727

osteoblast Bone-forming cell. 738

osteoclast Cell that is responsible for bone resorption. 738

osteocyte Mature bone cell located within the lacunae of bone. 738

osteoporosis Condition characterized by a loss of bone density; associated with levels of sex hormones and diet. 738

ostracoderm Earliest vertebrate fossils of the Cambrian and Devonian periods; these fishes were small, jawless, and finless. 553

otolith Calcium carbonate granule associated with sensory receptors for detecting movement of the head; in vertebrates, located in the utricle and saccule. 728

outer ear Portion of the ear consisting of the pinna and the auditory canal. 726

outgroup In a cladistic study of evolutionary relationships among organisms, a group that has a known relationship to, but is not a member of, the taxa being analyzed. 356

ovarian cycle Monthly changes occurring in the ovary that determine the level of sex hormones in the blood. 780

ovary In flowering plants, the enlarged, ovule-bearing portion of the carpel that develops into a fruit; female gonad in animals that produces an egg and female sex hormones. 434, 503, 773, 779

overexploitation When the number of individuals taken from a wild population is so great that the population becomes severely reduced in numbers. 916

oviparous Type of reproduction in which development occurs in an egg, laid by mother, in reptiles. 774

ovoviviparous Animals that produce eggs that develop internally and hatch at around the same time as they are released to the environment; mostly aquatic. 774

ovulation Bursting of a follicle when a secondary oocyte is released from the ovary; if fertilization occurs, the secondary oocyte becomes an egg. 780

ovule In seed plants, a structure that contains the female gametophyte and has the potential to develop into a seed. 430

oxidation Loss of one or more electrons from an atom or molecule; in biological systems, generally the loss of hydrogen atoms. 113

oxidation-reduction reaction A paired set of chemical reactions in which one molecule gives up electrons (oxidized) while another molecule accepts electrons (reduced); commonly called a redox reaction. 113

oxygen debt Amount of oxygen required to oxidize lactic acid produced anaerobically during strenuous muscle activity. 747

oxyhemoglobin Compound formed when oxygen combines with hemoglobin. 672

oxytocin Hormone released by the posterior pituitary that causes contraction of the uterus and milk letdown. 757

ozone shield Accumulation of O_3, formed from oxygen in the upper atmosphere; a filtering layer that protects the Earth from ultraviolet radiation. 335

P

p53 The protein produced from a tumor suppressor gene that (1) attempts to repair DNA damage or (2) stops the cell cycle, or (3) initiates apoptosis. 155

pacemaker Cells of the sinoatrial node of the heart; electrical device designed to mimic the normal electrical patterns of the heart. 613

paleontology Study of fossils that results in knowledge about the history of life. 272, 333

palisade mesophyll Layer of tissue in a plant leaf containing elongated cells with many chloroplasts. 459

pancreas Internal organ that produces digestive enzymes and the hormones insulin and glucagon. 654, 765

pancreatic amylase Enzyme that digests starch to maltose. 656

pancreatic islet Masses of cells that constitute the endocrine portion of the pancreas. 765

panoramic vision Vision characterized by having a wide field of vision; found in animals with eyes to the side. 721

parabasalid Unicellular protist that lacks mitochondria; possesses flagella in clusters near the anterior of the cell. 395

parasite Species that is dependent on a host species for survival, usually to the detriment of the host species. 865

parasitism Symbiotic relationship in which one species (the *parasite*) benefits in terms of growth and reproduction to the detriment of the other species (the *host*). 375, 865

parasympathetic division Division of the autonomic system that is active under normal conditions; uses acetylcholine as a neurotransmitter. 713

parathyroid gland Gland embedded in the posterior surface of the thyroid gland; it produces parathyroid hormone. 761

parathyroid hormone (PTH) Hormone secreted by the four parathyroid glands that increases the blood calcium level and decreases the phosphate level. 761

parenchyma Plant tissue composed of the least-specialized of all plant cells; found in all organs of a plant. 448

Parkinson disease (PD) Progressive deterioration of the central nervous system due to a deficiency in the neurotransmitter dopamine. 704

parsimony In systematics, the simplest solution in the analysis of evolutionary relationships. 356

partial pressure Pressure exerted by each gas in a mixture of gases. 671

parthenogenesis Development of an egg cell into a whole organism without fertilization. 773

passive immunity Protection against infection acquired by transfer of antibodies to a susceptible individual. 639

pathogen Disease-causing agent such as viruses, parasitic bacteria, fungi, and animals. 375, 592

pattern formation Positioning of cells during development that determines the final shape of an organism. 800

pectoral girdle Portion of the vertebrate skeleton that provides support and attachment for the upper (fore) limbs; consists of the scapula and clavicle on each side of the body. 742

peduncle Flower stalk; expands into the receptacle. 434

pelagic zone Open portion of the ocean. 901

pelvic girdle Portion of the vertebrate skeleton to which the lower (hind) limbs are attached; consists of the coxal bones. 742

penis Male copulatory organ; in humans, the male organ of sexual intercourse. 777

pentose Five-carbon monosaccharide. Examples are deoxyribose found in DNA and ribose found in RNA. 42

pepsin Enzyme secreted by gastric glands that digests proteins to peptides. 656

peptidase Intestinal enzyme that breaks down short chains of amino acids to individual amino acids that are absorbed across the intestinal wall. 657

peptide Two or more amino acids joined together by covalent bonding. 50

peptide bond Type of covalent bond that joins two amino acids. 50

peptide hormone Type of hormone that is a protein, a peptide, or derived from an amino acid. 755

peptidoglycan Polysaccharide that contains short chains of amino acids; found in bacterial cell walls. 44, 374

perennial Flowering plant that lives more than one growing season because the underground parts regrow each season. 444

pericycle Layer of cells surrounding the vascular tissue of roots; produces branch roots. 451

periderm Protective tissue that replaces epidermis; includes cork, cork cambium. 447

peripheral nervous system (PNS) Nerves and ganglia that lie outside the central nervous system. 696

peristalsis Wavelike contractions that propel substances along a tubular structure such as the esophagus. 651

permafrost Permanently frozen ground, usually occurring in the tundra, a biome of Arctic regions. 888

peroxisome Enzyme-filled vesicle in which fatty acids and amino acids are metabolized to hydrogen peroxide that is broken down to harmless products. 75

petal A flower part that occurs just inside the sepals; often conspicuously colored to attract pollinators. 434, 503

petiole The part of a plant leaf that connects the blade to the stem. 445

phagocytosis Process by which cells engulf large substances, forming an intracellular vacuole. 97, 396

pharyngitis Inflammation of the pharynx; often caused by viruses or bacteria. 673

pharynx In vertebrates, common passageway for both food intake and air movement; located between the mouth and the esophagus. 668

phenomenon Observable natural event or fact. 11

phenotype Visible expression of a genotype—e.g., brown eyes or attached earlobes. 197

pheromone Chemical messenger that works at a distance and alters the behavior of another member of the same species. 755, 826

phloem Vascular tissue that conducts organic solutes in plants; contains sieve-tube members and companion cells. 426, 449

phoronids Lophophorans of the phylum Phoronida that are characterized by a long protective tube formed of chitin. 530

phospholipid Molecule that forms the bilayer of the cell's membranes; has a polar, hydrophilic head bonded to two nonpolar, hydrophobic tails. 46

photoautotroph Organism able to synthesize organic molecules by using carbon dioxide as the carbon source and sunlight as the energy source. 375

photoperiod (photoperiodism) Relative lengths of daylight and darkness that affect the physiology and behavior of an organism. 494, 495

photoreceptor Sensory receptor that responds to light stimuli. 717, 720

photorespiration Series of reactions that occurs in plants when carbon dioxide levels are depleted but oxygen continues to accumulate, and the enzyme RuBP carboxylase fixes oxygen instead of carbon dioxide. 130

photosynthesis Process, usually occurring within chloroplasts, that uses solar energy to reduce carbon dioxide to carbohydrate. 4, 120

photosystem Photosynthetic unit where solar energy is absorbed and high-energy electrons are generated; contains a pigment complex and an electron acceptor; occurs as PS (photosystem) I and PS II. 124

phototropism Growth response of plant stems to light; stems demonstrate positive phototropism. 491

pH scale Measurement scale for hydrogen ion concentration. Based on the formula $-\log[\text{H}+]$. 32

phylogenetic species concept Definition of a species that is determined by analysis of a phylogenetic tree to determine a common ancestor. 308

phylogenetic tree Diagram that indicates common ancestors and lines of descent among a group of organisms. 348

phylogeny Evolutionary history of a group of organisms. 348

phylum One of the categories, or taxa, used by taxonomists to group species; the taxon located above the class level. 6, 349

phytochrome Photoreversible plant pigment that is involved in photoperiodism and other responses of plants, such as etiolation. 495

phytoplankton Part of plankton containing organisms that photosynthesize, releasing oxygen to the atmosphere and serving as food producers in aquatic ecosystems. 899

phytoremediation The use of plants to restore a natural area to its original condition. 470

pineal gland Gland—either at the skin surface (fish, amphibians) or in the third ventricle of the brain (mammals)—that produces melatonin. 704, 768

pinocytosis Process by which vesicle formation brings macromolecules into the cell. 98

pioneer species Early colonizer of barren or disturbed habitats that usually has rapid growth and a high dispersal rate. 868

pit Any depression or opening; usually in reference to the small openings in the cell walls of xylem cells that function in providing a continuum between adjacent xylem cells. 449

pith Parenchyma tissue in the center of some stems and roots. 452

pituitary gland Small gland that lies just inferior to the hypothalamus; consists of the anterior and posterior pituitary, both of which produce hormones. 757

placenta Organ formed during the development of placental mammals from the chorion and the uterine wall; allows the embryo, and then the fetus, to acquire nutrients and rid itself of wastes; produces hormones that regulate pregnancy. 564, 774, 809

placental mammal Also called the eutherians; species that rely on internal development whereby the fetus exchanges nutrients and wastes with its mother via a placenta. 564

placoderm First jawed vertebrates; heavily armored fishes of the Devonian period. 553

plankton Freshwater and marine organisms that are suspended on or near the surface of the water; includes phytoplankton and zooplankton. 384

plants Multicellular, photosynthetic, eukaryotes that increasingly became adapted to live on land. 8, 420

plasma In vertebrates, the liquid portion of blood; contains nutrients, wastes, salts, and proteins. 618

plasma cell Mature B cell that mass-produces antibodies. 634

plasma membrane Membrane surrounding the cytoplasm that consists of a phospholipid bilayer with embedded proteins; functions to regulate the entrance and exit of molecules from cell. 65

plasmid Extrachromosomal ring of accessory DNA in the cytoplasm of prokaryotes. 65, 255, 372

plasmodesmata In plants, cytoplasmic connections in the cell wall that connect two adjacent cells. 100

plasmodial slime mold Free-living mass of cytoplasm that moves by pseudopods on a forest floor or in a field, feeding on decaying plant material by phagocytosis; reproduces by spore formation. 396

plasmolysis Contraction of the cell contents due to the loss of water. 94

plastid Organelles of plants and algae that are bounded by a double membrane and contain internal membranes and/or vesicles (i.e., chloroplasts, chromoplasts, leucoplasts). 77

plate tectonics Concept that the Earth's crust is divided into a number of fairly rigid plates whose movements account for continental drift. 343

platelet Component of blood that is necessary to blood clotting. 592, 620

pleiotropy Inheritance pattern in which one gene affects many phenotypic characteristics of the individual. 206

pneumonia Condition of the respiratory system characterized by the filling of the bronchi and alveoli with fluid; caused by a viral, fungal, or bacterial pathogen. 674

poikilothermic Body temperature that varies depending on environmental conditions; informally termed "cold-blooded." 599

point mutation Change of only one base in the sequence of bases in a gene. 248

polar body Nonfunctional product of oogenesis produced by the unequal division of cytoplasm in females during meiosis; in humans three of the four cells produced by meiosis are polar bodies. 181

polar covalent bond Bond in which the sharing of electrons between atoms is unequal. 27

pollen grain In seed plants, structure that is derived from a microspore and develops into a male gametophyte. 430, 504

pollen tube In seed plants, a tube that forms when a pollen grain lands on the stigma and germinates. The tube grows, passing between the cells of the stigma and the style to reach the egg inside an ovule, where fertilization occurs. 430

pollination In gymnosperms, the transfer of pollen from pollen cone to seed cone; in angiosperms, the transfer of pollen from anther to stigma. 430, 505

pollution Any environmental change that adversely affects the lives and health of living things. 915

polyandrous Practice of female animals having several male mates; found in the New World monkeys where the males help in rearing the offspring. 831

polygamous Practice of males having several female mates. 831

polygenic inheritance Pattern of inheritance in which a trait is controlled by several allelic pairs. 207

polygenic trait Traits that are under the control of multiple genes as opposed to monogenic (single-gene) traits. 207, 296

polymer Macromolecule consisting of covalently bonded monomers; for example, a polypeptide is a polymer of monomers called amino acids. 40

polymerase chain reaction (PCR) Technique that uses the enzyme DNA polymerase to produce millions of copies of a particular piece of DNA. 256

polyp Among cnidarians, body form that is directed upward and contains much mesoglea; in anatomy: small, abnormal growth that arises from the epithelial lining. 528, 654

polypeptide Polymer of many amino acids linked by peptide bonds. 50

polyploidy Having a chromosome number that is a multiple greater than twice that of the monoploid number. 315

polyribosome String of ribosomes simultaneously translating regions of the same mRNA strand during protein synthesis. 71, 230

polysaccharide Polymer made from carbohydrate monomers; the polysaccharides starch and glycogen are polymers of glucose monomers. 41

pons Portion of the brain stem above the medulla oblongata and below the midbrain; assists the medulla oblongata in regulating the breathing rate. 704

population Group of organisms of the same species occupying a certain area and sharing a common gene pool. 9, 290, 839

population density The number of individuals per unit area or volume living in a particular habitat. 840

population distribution The pattern of dispersal of individuals living within a certain area. 840

population genetics The study of gene frequencies and their changes within a population. 290

portal system Pathway of blood flow that begins and ends in capillaries, such as the portal system located between the small intestine and liver. 614

positive feedback Mechanism of homeostatic response in which the output of the system intensifies and increases the activity of the system. 601, 757

posterior pituitary Portion of the pituitary gland that stores and secretes oxytocin and antidiuretic hormone produced by the hypothalamus. 757

posttranscriptional control Gene expression following transcription that regulates the way mRNA transcripts are processed. 244

posttranslational control Alternation of gene expression by changing a protein's activity after it is translated. 247

postzygotic isolating mechanism Anatomical or physiological difference between two species that prevents successful reproduction after mating has taken place. 312

potential energy Stored energy in a potentially usable form, as a result of location or spatial arrangement. 105

predation Interaction in which one organism (the predator) uses another (the prey) as a food source. 860

predator Organism that practices predation. 860

prediction Step of the scientific process that follows the formulation of a hypothesis and assists in creating the experimental design. 11

preparatory (prep) reaction Reaction that oxidizes pyruvate with the release of carbon dioxide; results in acetyl CoA and connects glycolysis to the citric acid cycle. 137, 142

pressure-flow model Explanation for phloem transport; osmotic pressure following active transport of sugar into phloem produces a flow of sap from a source to a sink. 478

prey Organism that provides nourishment for a predator. 860

prezygotic isolating mechanism Anatomical, physiological, or behavioral difference between two species that prevents the possibility of mating. 310

primary lymphoid organ Location in the lymphatic system where lymphocytes develop and mature; e.g., bone marrow and thymus. 629

primary root Original root that grows straight down and remains the dominant root of the plant; contrasts with fibrous root system. 452

primate Member of the order Primates; includes prosimians, monkeys, apes, and hominins, all of whom have adaptations for living in trees. 571

primordial soup hypothesis Another name for the hypothesis of abiogenesis proposed by Alexander Oparin and J.B.S. Haldane that the first cells evolved in the oceans from present in the early atmosphere. 329

principle Theory that is generally accepted by an overwhelming number of scientists; also called a law. 12

prion Infectious particle consisting of protein only and no nucleic acid. 53, 369

producer Photosynthetic organism at the start of a grazing food chain that makes its own food—e.g., green plants on land and algae in water. 870

product Substance that forms as a result of a reaction. 107

progesterone Female sex hormone that helps maintain sexual organs and secondary sex characteristics. 779

proglottid Segment of a tapeworm that contains both male and female sex organs and becomes a bag of eggs. 533

prokaryote Organism that lacks the membrane-bounded nucleus and the membranous organelles typical of eukaryotes. 7, 371

prokaryotic cell Cells that generally lack a membrane-bounded nucleus and organelles; the cell type within the domains Bacteria and Archaea. 65

prolactin (PRL) Hormone secreted by the anterior pituitary that stimulates the production of milk from the mammary glands. 757

prometaphase Second phase of mitosis; chromosomes are condensed but not fully aligned at the metaphase plate. 159

promoter In an operon, a sequence of DNA where RNA polymerase binds prior to transcription. 238

prophase First phase of mitosis; characterized by the condensation of the chromatin; chromosomes are visible, but scattered in the nucleus. 158

proprioceptor Class of mechanoreceptors responsible for maintaining the body's equilibrium and posture; involved in reflex actions. 730

prosimian Group of primates that includes lemurs and tarsiers, and may resemble the first primates to have evolved. 575

prostaglandin Hormone that has various and powerful local effects. 768

prostate gland Gland in male humans that secretes an alkaline, cloudy, fluid that increases the motility of sperm. 777

proteasome Cellular structure containing proteases that is involved in the destruction of tagged proteins; used by cells for posttranslational control of gene expression. 247

protease Enzyme that breaks the peptide bonds between amino acids in proteins, polypeptides, and peptides. 247

protein Polymer of amino acids; often consisting of one or more polypeptides and having a complex three-dimensional shape. 49

protein-first hypothesis In chemical evolution, the proposal that protein originated before other macromolecules and made possible the formation of protocells. 330

proteinoid Abiotically polymerized amino acids that, when exposed to water, become microspheres having cellular characteristics. 330

proteome Sum of the expressed proteins in a cell. 265

proteomics Study of the complete collection of proteins that a cell or organism expresses. 232, 265

protists The group of eukaryotic organisms that are not a plant, fungus, or animal. Protists are generally a microscopic complex single cell; they evolved before other types of eukaryotes in the history of Earth. 7, 384

protobiont (protocell) In biological evolution, a possible cell forerunner that became a cell once it acquired genes. 330

proton Positive subatomic particle located in the nucleus and assigned one atomic mass unit. 22

proto-oncogene Gene that promotes the cell cycle and prevents apoptosis; may become an oncogene through mutation. 164

protostome Group of coelomate animals in which the first embryonic opening (the blastopore) is associated with the mouth. 523

protozoan Heterotrophic, unicellular protist that moves by flagella, cilia, or pseudopodia. 374

proximal convoluted tubule Portion of a nephron following the glomerular capsule where tubular reabsorption of filtrate occurs. 686

pseudocoelom Body cavity lying between the digestive tract and body wall that is incompletely lined by mesoderm. 538

pseudopod Cytoplasmic extension of amoeboid protists; used for locomotion and engulfing food. 78, 396

pteridophyte Ferns and their allies (horsetail and whisk ferns). 427

pulmonary circuit Circulatory pathway between the lungs and the heart. 609

pulmonary fibrosis Respiratory condition characterized by the buildup of connective tissue in the lungs; typically caused by inhalation of coal dust, silica, or asbestos. 675

pulmonary tuberculosis Respiratory infection caused by the bacterium *Mycobacterium tuberculosis*. 674

pulse Vibration felt in arterial walls due to expansion of the aorta following ventricle contraction. 613

Punnett square Visual representation developed by Reginald Punnett that is used to calculate the expected results of simple genetic crosses. 200

pupil Opening in the center of the iris of the vertebrate eye. 721

R

radial symmetry Body plan in which similar parts are arranged around a central axis, like spokes of a wheel. 522

radiolarian Protist that has a glassy silicon test, usually with a radial arrangement of spines; pseudopods are external to the test. 398

rain shadow Leeward side (side sheltered from the wind) of a mountainous barrier, which receives much less precipitation than the windward side. 885

rate of natural increase (r) Growth rate dependent on the number of individuals that are born each year and the number of individuals that die each year. 841

ray-finned bony fishes Group of bony fishes with fins supported by parallel bony rays connected by webs of thin tissue. 554

RB The protein of a tumor suppressor gene; interprets growth signals and nutrient availability before allowing the cell cycle to proceed. 155

reactant Substance that participates in a reaction. 107

receptacle Area where a flower attaches to a floral stalk. 434, 484

receptor Type of membrane protein that binds to specific molecules in the environment, providing a mechanism for the cell to sense and adjust to its surroundings. 474

receptor-mediated endocytosis Selective uptake of molecules into a cell by vacuole formation after they bind to specific receptor proteins in the plasma membrane. 98

receptor protein Proteins located in the plasma membrane or within the cell; bind to a substance that alters some metabolic aspect of the cell. 89

recessive allele Allele that exerts its phenotypic effect only in the homozygote; its expression is masked by a dominant allele. 196

reciprocal altruism The trading of helpful or cooperative acts, such as helping at the nest, by individuals—the animal that was helped will repay the debt at some later time. 834

recombinant DNA (rDNA) DNA that contains genes from more than one source. 255

red algae Marine photosynthetic protists with a notable abundance of phycobilin pigments; includes coralline algae of coral reefs. 389

red blood cell Erythrocyte; contains hemoglobin and carries oxygen from the lungs or gills to the tissues in vertebrates. 591, 618

red bone marrow Vascularized, modified connective tissue that is sometimes found in the cavities of spongy bone; site of blood cell formation. 740

radiocarbon dating Process of radiometric dating the measures the decay of ^{14}C to ^{14}N. 334

red tide A population bloom of dinoflagellates that causes coastal waters to turn red. Releases a toxin that can lead to paralytic shellfish poisoning. 392

redox reaction A paired set of chemical reactions in which one molecule gives up electrons (oxidized) while another molecule accepts electrons (reduced); also called an oxidation-reduction reaction. 113

reduction Gain of electrons by an atom or molecule with a concurrent storage of energy; in biological systems, the electrons are accompanied by hydrogen ions. 113

reflex action Automatic, involuntary response of an organism to a stimulus. 702

refractory period Time following an action potential when a neuron is unable to conduct another nerve impulse. 700

regulator gene Gene that controls the expression of another gene or genes; in an operon, regulator genes code for repressor proteins. 238

reinforcement Connection between natural selection and reproductive isolation that occurs when two closely related species come back into contact after a period of isolation. 314

relative dating (of fossils) Determining the age of fossils by noting their sequential relationships in strata; *absolute dating* relies on radioactive dating techniques to assign an actual date. 334

renin Enzyme released by the kidneys that leads to the secretion of aldosterone and a rise in blood pressure. 690, 763

repetitive DNA element Sequence of DNA on a chromosome that is repeated several times. 262

replacement reproduction Population in which each person is replaced by only one child. 852

replication fork In eukaryotic DNA replication, the location where the two parental DNA strands separate. 222

repressor In an operon, protein molecule that binds to an operator, preventing transcription of structural genes. 238

reproduce To produce a new individual of the same kind. 5

reproductive cloning Used to create an organism that is genetically identical to the original individual. 161

reproductive isolation Model by which new species arise when gene flow is disrupted between two populations, genetic changes accumulate, and the populations are subsequently unable to mate and produce viable offspring. 310

reproductively isolated Descriptive term that indicates that a population is incapable of interbreeding with another population. 294

reptile Terrestrial vertebrate with internal fertilization, scaly skin, and an egg with a leathery shell; includes snakes, lizards, turtles, crocodiles, and birds. 558

resource Abiotic and biotic components of an environment that support or are needed by living organisms. 840

resource partitioning Mechanism that increases the number of niches by apportioning the supply of a resource such as food or living space between species. 860

respiration Sequence of events that results in gas exchange between the cells of the body and the environment. 674

respiratory center Group of nerve cells in the medulla oblongata that send out nerve impulses on a rhythmic basis, resulting in involuntary inspiration on an ongoing basis. 670

responding variable Result or change that occurs when an experimental variable is utilized in an experiment. 14

resting potential Membrane potential of an inactive neuron. 698

restriction enzyme Bacterial enzyme that stops viral reproduction by cleaving viral DNA; used to cut DNA at specific points during production of recombinant DNA. 255

reticular activating system (RAS) Area of the brain that contains the reticular formation; acts as a relay for information to and from the peripheral nervous system and higher processing centers of the brain. 705

reticular fiber Very thin collagen fiber in the matrix of connective tissue, highly branched and forming delicate supporting networks. 589

retina Innermost layer of the vertebrate eyeball containing the photoreceptors—rod cells and cone cells. 721

retinal detachment Condition characterized by the separation of the retina from the choroid layer of the eye. 724

retrovirus RNA virus containing the enzyme reverse transcriptase that carries out RNA/DNA transcription. 368

reverse transcriptase Viral enzyme found in retroviruses that is capable of converting their RNA genome into a DNA copy. 368

rhizarian Supergroup of eukaryotes that includes foraminiferans and radiolarians. 398

rhizoid Rootlike hair that anchors a plant and absorbs minerals and water from the soil. 424

rhizome Rootlike underground stem. 426, 458, 513

rhodopsin Light-absorbing molecule in rod cells and cone cells that contains a pigment and the protein opsin. 722

ribose Pentose sugar found in RNA. 42

ribosomal RNA (rRNA) Structural form of RNA found in the ribosomes. 223

ribosome Site of protein synthesis in a cell; composed of proteins and ribosomal RNA (rRNA). 66, 71

ribozyme RNA molecule that functions as an enzyme that can catalyze chemical reactions. 109, 227

RNA (ribonucleic acid) Nucleic acid produced from covalent bonding of nucleotide monomers that contain the sugar ribose; occurs in many forms, including: messenger RNA, ribosomal RNA, and transfer RNA. 54

RNA-first hypothesis In chemical evolution, the proposal that RNA originated before other macromolecules and allowed the formation of the first cell(s). 330

RNA interference Cellular process that utilizes miRNA and siRNA molecules to reduce, or inhibit, the expression of specific genes. 246

RNA polymerase During transcription, an enzyme that creates an mRNA transcript by joining nucleotides complementary to a DNA template. 225

rod cell Photoreceptor in vertebrate eyes that responds to dim light. 721

root apical meristem Meristem tissue located under the root cap; the site of the majority of cell division in the root. 450

root cap Protective cover of the root tip, whose cells are constantly replaced as they are ground off when the root pushes through rough soil particles. 450

root hair Extension of a root epidermal cell that collectively increases the surface area for the absorption of water and minerals. 447

root nodule Structure on plant root that contains nitrogen-fixing bacteria. 452, 471

root pressure Osmotic pressure caused by active movement of mineral into root cells; serves to elevate water in xylem for a short distance. 475

root system Includes the main root and any and all of its lateral (side) branches. 444

rotational equilibrium Maintenance of balance when the head and body are suddenly moved or rotated. 728

rotifer Microscopic invertebrates characterized by ciliated corona that when beating looks like a rotating wheel. 533

rough ER (endoplasmic reticulum) Membranous system of tubules, vesicles, and sacs in cells; has attached ribosomes. 72

roundworm Invertebrates with nonsegmented cylindrical body covered by a cuticle that molts; some forms are free-living in water and soil, and many are parasitic. 538

r-selection Favorable life history strategy under certain environmental conditions; characterized by a high reproductive rate with little or no attention given to offspring survival. 849

RuBP carboxylase An enzyme that starts the Calvin cycle reactions by catalyzing attachment of the carbon atom from CO_2 to RuBP. 128

rumen The first chamber in the digestive tract of a ruminant mammal; microorganisms here break down complex carbohydrates. 649

S

saccule Saclike cavity in the vestibule of the vertebrate inner ear; contains sensory receptors for gravitational equilibrium. 728

sac fungi (Ascomycota) Fungi that produce spores in fingerlike sacs called asci within a fruiting body; includes morels, truffles, yeasts, and molds. 408

salivary amylase In humans, enzyme in saliva that digests starch to maltose. 651, 656

salivary gland In humans, gland associated with the mouth that secretes saliva. 651

salt Solid substances formed by ionic bonds that usually dissociate into individual ions in water. 27

saltatory conduction Movement of nerve impulses from one node to another along a myelinated axon. 699

saprotroph Organism that secretes digestive enzymes and absorbs the resulting nutrients back across the plasma membrane. 375, 404

sarcolemma Plasma membrane of a muscle fiber; also forms the tubules of the T system involved in muscular contraction. 744

sarcomere One of many units, arranged linearly within a myofibril, whose contraction produces muscle contraction. 745

sarcoplasmic reticulum Smooth endoplasmic reticulum of skeletal muscle cells; surrounds the myofibrils and stores calcium ions. 744

saturated fatty acid Fatty acid molecule that lacks double bonds between the carbons of its hydrocarbon chain. The chain bears the maximum number of hydrogens possible. 46

savanna Terrestrial biome that is a grassland in Africa, characterized by few trees and a severe dry season. 895

Schwann cell Cell that surrounds a fiber of a peripheral nerve and forms the myelin sheath. 697

scientific method Process by which scientists formulate a hypothesis, gather data by observation and experimentation, and come to a conclusion. 11

scientific theory Concept, or a collection of concepts, widely supported by a broad range of observations, experiments, and data. 12

sclera White, fibrous, outer layer of the eyeball. 721

sclerenchyma Plant tissue composed of cells with heavily lignified cell walls; functions in support. 449

scolex Tapeworm head region; contains hooks and suckers for attachment to host. 533

sea star An echinoderm with noticeable 5-pointed radial symmetry; found along rocky coasts where they feed on bivalves. 544

secondary lymphoid organ Location in the lymphatic system where lymphocytes are activated by antigens; example is the lymph nodes. 629

secondary metabolite Molecule not directly involved in growth, development, or reproduction of an organism; in plants, these molecules, which include nicotine, caffeine, tannins, and menthols, can discourage herbivores. 496

secondary oocyte In oogenesis, the functional product of meiosis I; becomes the egg. 181

second messenger Chemical signal such as cyclic AMP that causes the cell to respond to the first messenger—a hormone bound to plasma membrane receptor protein. 755

secretion Release of a substance by exocytosis from a cell. 73

sediment Particulate material (sand, clay, etc.) that is carried by streams and rivers and deposited in areas of slow water movement. 333

sedimentation Process by which particulate material accumulates and forms a stratum. 333

seed Mature ovule that contains an embryo, with stored food enclosed in a protective coat. 430, 502

seed plant Vascular plants that disperse seeds; the gymnosperms and angiosperms. 430

seedless vascular plant Collective name for club mosses (lycophytes) and ferns (pteridophytes) Characterized by windblown spores. 426

segmentation Repetition of body units as seen in the earthworm. 536

selectively permeable Property of the plasma membrane that allows some substances to pass, but prohibits the movement of others. 89

semelparity Condition of having a single reproductive effort in a lifetime. 843

semen (seminal fluid) Thick, whitish fluid consisting of sperm and secretions from several glands of the male reproductive tract. 777

semicircular canal One of three half-circle-shaped canals of the vertebrate inner ear; contains sensory receptors for rotational equilibrium. 727

semiconservative replication Process of DNA replication that results in two double helix molecules, each having one parental and one new strand. 220

semilunar valve Valve resembling a half moon located between the ventricles and their attached vessels. 611

seminal vesicles Glands in male humans that secrete a viscous fluid that provides nutrition to the sperm cells. 777

seminiferous tubule Long, coiled structure contained within chambers of the testis where sperm are produced. 776

senescence Sum of the processes involving aging, decline, and eventual death of a plant or plant part. 487

sensory (afferent) neuron Nerve cell that transmits nerve impulses to the central nervous system after a sensory receptor has been stimulated. 697

sensory receptor Structure that receives either external or internal environmental stimuli and is a part of a sensory neuron or transmits signals to a sensory neuron. 717

sensory transduction Process by which a sensory receptor converts an input to a nerve impulse. 717

sepal Outermost, leaflike covering of the flower; usually green in color. 434, 503

septate Having cell walls; some fungal species have hyphae that are septate. 405

septum Partition or wall that divides two areas; the septum in the heart separates the right half from the left half. 405, 610

serosa Outer embryonic membrane of birds and reptiles; chorion. 651

seta (pl., setae) A needlelike, chitinous bristle in annelids, arthropods, and others. 536

severe combined immunodeficiency (SCID) Immune disease characterized by the impairment, or lack of, T or B cells in the body. 641

sexual dimorphism Species that have distinct differences between the sexes resulting in male and female forms. 297

sexual reproduction Reproduction involving meiosis, gamete formation, and fertilization; produces offspring with chromosomes inherited from each parent with a unique combination of genes. 172

sexual selection Changes in males and females, often due to male competition and female selectivity, leading to increased fitness. 297, 831

shoot apical meristem Group of actively dividing embryonic cells at the tips of plant shoots. 453

shoot system Aboveground portion of a plant consisting of the stem, leaves, and flowers. 444

short-day plant Plant that flowers when day length is shorter than a critical length—e.g., cocklebur, poinsettia, and chrysanthemum. 495

short tandem repeat (STR) profiling Procedure of analyzing DNA in which PCR and gel electrophoresis are used to create a banding pattern; these are usually unique for each individual; process used in DNA barcoding. 257

shrubland Arid terrestrial biome characterized by shrubs and tending to occur along coasts that have dry summers and receive most of their rainfall in the winter. 894

sieve-tube member Member that joins with others in the phloem tissue of plants as a means of transport for nutrient sap. 450

sign stimulus The environmental trigger that causes a fixed action pattern or unchanging behavioral response. 822

signal Molecule that stimulates or inhibits an event in the cell. 155

signal peptide Sequence of amino acids that binds with a signal recognition particle (SRP), causing a ribosome to bind to the endoplasmic reticulum (ER). 71

signal transduction Process that occurs within a cell when a molecular signal (protein, hormone, etc.) initiates a response within the interior of the cell. 484

sink In the pressure-flow model of phloem transport, the location (roots) from which sugar is constantly being removed. Sugar will flow to the roots from the source. 479

sink population Population that is found in an unfavorable area where at best the birthrate equals the death rate; sink populations receive new members from source populations. 919

sister chromatid One of two genetically identical chromosomal units that are the result of DNA replication and are attached to each other at the centromere. 154

skeletal muscle Striated, voluntary muscle tissue that comprises skeletal muscles; also called striated muscle. 592

skin Outer covering of the body; can be called the integumentary system because it contains organs such as sense organs. 597

sliding filament model An explanation for muscle contraction based on the movement of actin filaments in relation to myosin filaments. 745

small interfering RNAs (siRNA) Short sequences of RNA, typically less than 25 nucleotides, that are involved in posttranscriptional control of gene expression through a process called RNA interference. 246

small intestine In vertebrates, the portion of the digestive tract that precedes the large intestine; in humans, consists of the duodenum, jejunum, and ileum. 652

smooth (visceral) muscle Nonstriated, involuntary muscles found in the walls of internal organs. 592

smooth ER (endoplasmic reticulum) Membranous system of tubules, vesicles, and sacs in eukaryotic cells; site of lipid synthesis; lacks attached ribosomes. 72

society Group in which members of species are organized in a cooperative manner, extending beyond sexual and parental behavior. 826

sodium-potassium pump Carrier protein in the plasma membrane that moves sodium ions out of and potassium ions into cells; important in the function of nerve and muscle cells in animals. 95

soil Accumulation of inorganic rock material and organic matter that is capable of supporting the growth of vegetation. 467

soil erosion Movement of topsoil to a new location due to the action of wind or running water. 468

soil horizon Major layer of soil visible in vertical profile; for example, topsoil is the A horizon. 468

soil profile Vertical section of soil from the ground surface to the unaltered rock below. 468

solute Substance that is dissolved in a solvent, forming a solution. 30, 91

solution Fluid (the solvent) that contains a dissolved solid (the solute). 30, 91

solvent Liquid portion of a solution that serves to dissolve a solute. 91

somatic cell Body cell; excludes cells that undergo meiosis and become sperm or eggs. 155

somatic system Portion of the peripheral nervous system containing motor neurons that control skeletal muscles. 708

source In the pressure-flow model of phloem transport, the location (leaves) of sugar production. Sugar will flow from the leaves to the sink. 479

source population Population that can provide members to other populations of the species because it lives in a favorable area, and the birthrate is most likely higher than the death rate. 919

speciation Origin of new species due to the evolutionary process of descent with modification. 307, 313

species Group of similarly constructed organisms capable of interbreeding and producing fertile offspring; organisms that share a common gene pool; the taxon at the lowest level of classification. 6, 349

species concepts Models that describe the process by which new species arise. 307

species diversity Variety of species that make up a community. 858

species richness Number of species in a community. 858

specific epithet In the binomial system of taxonomy, the second part of an organism's name; it may be descriptive. 349

sperm Male gamete having a haploid number of chromosomes and the ability to fertilize an egg, the female gamete. 777

spermatogenesis Production of sperm in males by the process of meiosis and maturation. 180

spicule Skeletal structure of sponges composed of calcium carbonate or silicate. 527

spinal cord In vertebrates, the nerve cord that is continuous with the base of the brain and housed within the vertebral column. 702

spinal nerve Nerve that arises from the spinal cord. 707

spirillum (pl., spirilla) Long, rod-shaped bacterium that is twisted into a rigid spiral; if the spiral is flexible rather than rigid, it is called a spirochete. 65

spirochete Long, rod-shaped bacterium that is twisted into a flexible spiral; if the spiral is rigid rather than flexible, it is called a spirillum. 65

spleen Large, glandular organ located in the upper left region of the abdomen; stores and filters blood. 629

sponge Invertebrates that are pore-bearing filter feeders whose inner body wall is lined by collar cells that resemble a unicellular choanoflagellate. 527

spongy bone Type of bone that has an irregular, meshlike arrangement of thin plates of bone. 591, 740

spongy mesophyll Layer of tissue in a plant leaf containing loosely packed cells, increasing the amount of surface area for gas exchange. 459

spontaneous mutation Mutation that arises as a result of anomalies in normal biological processes, such as mistakes made during DNA replication. 247

sporangium (pl., sporangia) Structure that produces spores. 422

spore Asexual reproductive or resting cell capable of developing into a new organism

without fusion with another cell, in contrast to a gamete. 176, 406, 422

sporophyll Modified leaf that bears a sporangium or many sporangia. 426

sporophyte Diploid generation of the alternation-of-generations life cycle of a plant; produces haploid spores that develop into the haploid generation. 180, 422

spring overturn Mixing process that occurs in spring in stratified lakes whereby oxygen-rich top waters mix with nutrient-rich bottom waters. 899

squamous epithelium Type of epithelial tissue that contains flat cells. 588

stabilizing selection Outcome of natural selection in which extreme phenotypes are eliminated and the average phenotype is conserved. 296

standard deviation A statistical analysis of data from an observation or experiment; measures how much the data varies. 12

stamen In flowering plants, the portion of the flower that consists of a filament and an anther containing pollen sacs where pollen is produced. 434, 503

starch Storage polysaccharide found in plants that is composed of glucose molecules joined in a linear fashion with few side chains. 43

statolith Sensors found in root cap cells that cause a plant to demonstrate gravitropism. 491

stem Usually the upright, vertical portion of a plant that transports substances to and from the leaves. 445

stereoscopic vision Vision characterized by depth perception and three-dimensionality. 572, 721

steroid Type of lipid molecule having a complex of four carbon rings—e.g., cholesterol, estrogen, progesterone, and testosterone. 46

steroid hormone Type of hormone that has the same complex of four carbon rings, but each one has different side chains. 755

stigma In flowering plants, portion of the carpel where pollen grains adhere and germinate before fertilization can occur. 434, 503

stolon Stem that grows horizontally along the ground and may give rise to new plants where it contacts the soil—e.g., the runners of a strawberry plant. 456, 513

stomach In vertebrates, muscular sac that mixes food with gastric juices to form chyme, which enters the small intestine. 652

stomata (sing., stoma) Small openings between two guard cells on the underside of leaf epidermis through which gases pass. 121, 422, 447

stramenopile Group of protists that includes water molds, diatoms, and golden brown algae and is characterized by a "hairy" flagellum. 390

strata (sing. stratum) Ancient layer of sedimentary rock; results from slow deposition of silt, volcanic ash, and other materials. 273, 333

striated Having bands; in cardiac and skeletal muscle, alternating light and dark bands produced by the distribution of contractile proteins. 592

strobilus In club mosses, terminal clusters of leaves that bear sporangia. 426

stroke Condition resulting when an arteriole in the brain bursts or becomes blocked by an embolism; cerebrovascular accident. 616, 704

stroma Region within a chloroplast that surrounds the grana; contains enzymes involved in the synthesis of carbohydrates during the Calvin cycle of photosynthesis. 76, 121

stromatolite Domed structure found in shallow seas consisting of cyanobacteria bound to calcium carbonate. 335

structural gene Gene that codes for the amino acid sequence of a peptide or protein. 238

structural genomics Study of the sequence of DNA bases and the amount of genes in organisms. 261

style Elongated, central portion of the carpel between the ovary and stigma. 434, 503

submucosa Tissue layer just under the epithelial lining of the lumen of the digestive tract (second layer). 651

substrate Reactant in an enzyme-controlled reaction. 109

substrate-level ATP synthesis Process in which ATP is formed by transferring a phosphate from a metabolic substrate to ADP. 138

supergroup Systematic term that refers to the major groups of eukaryotes. 384

surface-area-to-volume ratio Ratio of a cell's outside area to its internal volume; the relationship limits the maximum size of a cell. 62

surface tension Force that holds moist membranes together due to the attraction of water molecules through hydrogen bonds. 31

survivorship Probability of newborn individuals of a cohort surviving to particular ages. 841

suture Line of union between two nonarticulating bones, as in the skull. 740

swamp Wet, spongy land that is saturated and sometimes partially or intermittently covered with water. 897

sweat gland Skin gland that secretes a fluid substance for evaporative cooling; sudoriferous gland. 599

swim bladder In fishes, a gas-filled sac whose pressure can be altered to change buoyancy. 554

symbiosis Relationship that occurs when two different species live together in a unique way; it may be beneficial, neutral, or detrimental to one or both species. 865

symbiotic relationship *See also* symbiosis. 375

symmetry Pattern of similarity in an object. 522

sympathetic division Division of the autonomic system that is active when an organism is under stress; uses norepinephrine as a neurotransmitter. 709

sympatric speciation Origin of new species in populations that overlap geographically. 314

synapse Junction between neurons consisting of the presynaptic (axon) membrane, the synaptic cleft, and the postsynaptic (usually dendrite) membrane. 700

synapsid Characteristic of a vertebrate skull in which there is a single opening in the skull behind the eye socket (orbit). 558

synapsis Pairing of homologous chromosomes during meiosis I. 173

synaptic cleft Small gap between presynaptic and postsynaptic cells of a synapse. 700

synaptonemal complex Protein structure that forms between the homologous chromosomes of prophase I of meiosis; promotes the process of crossing-over. 173

synovial joint Freely moving joint in which two bones are separated by a cavity. 742

systematics Study of the diversity of life for the purpose of understanding the evolutionary relationships between species. 6, 348

systemic circuit Circulatory pathway of blood flow between the tissues and the heart. 609

systemin In plants, an 18-amino-acid peptide that is produced by damaged or injured leaves that leads to the wound response. 497

systole Contraction period of the heart during the cardiac cycle. 612

T

tactile communication Communication through touch; for example, when a chick pecks its mother for food, chimpanzees groom each other, and honeybees "dance." 829

taiga Terrestrial biome that is a coniferous forest extending in a broad belt across northern Eurasia and North America. 890

tandem repeat Repetitive DNA sequence in which the repeats occur one after another in the same region of a chromosome. 262

taproot Main axis of a root that penetrates deeply and is used by certain plants (such as carrots) for food storage. 452

taste bud Structure in the vertebrate mouth containing sensory receptors for taste; in humans, most taste buds are on the tongue. 718

taxon (pl., taxa) Group of organisms that fills a particular classification category. 348

taxonomist Scientist that investigates the identification and naming of new organisms. 307, 348

taxonomy Branch of biology concerned with identifying, describing, and naming organisms. 6, 348

T cell Lymphocyte that matures in the thymus and exists in four varieties, one of which kills antigen-bearing cells outright. 629

T-cell receptor (TCR) Molecule on the surface of a T cell that can bind to a specific antigen fragment in combination with an MHC molecule. 635

telomere Tip of the end of a chromosome that shortens with each cell division and may thereby regulate the number of times a cell can divide. 164, 221

telophase Final phase of mitosis; daughter cells are located at each pole. 160

temperate deciduous forest Forest found south of the taiga; characterized by deciduous trees such as oak, beech, and maple, moderate climate, relatively high rainfall, stratified plant growth, and plentiful ground life. 891

temperate grassland Grasslands characterized by very cold winters and dry, hot summers; examples are the North American prairies and Russian steppes. 894

temperate rain forest Coniferous forest—e.g., that running along the west coast of Canada and the United States—characterized by plentiful rainfall and rich soil. 890

template Parental strand of DNA that serves as a guide for the complementary daughter strand produced during DNA replication. 220

tendon Strap of fibrous connective tissue that connects skeletal muscle to bone. 590, 744

terminal bud Bud that develops at the apex of a shoot. 453

termination End of translation that occurs when a ribosome reaches a stop codon on the mRNA that it is translating, causing release of the completed protein. 231

territoriality Marking and/or defending a particular area against invasion by another species member; area often used for the purpose of feeding, mating, and caring for young. 299, 830

territory Area occupied and defended exclusively by an animal or group of animals. 299, 830

test Loose-fitting shell of a foraminiferan or a radiolarian; made of calcium carbonate or silicon, respectively. 398

testcross Cross between an individual with a dominant phenotype and an individual with a recessive phenotype to determine whether the dominant individual is homozygous or heterozygous. 200

testes Male gonads that produce sperm and the male sex hormones. 773, 775

testosterone Male sex hormone that helps maintain sexual organs and secondary sex characteristics. 778

tetany Severe spasm caused by involuntary contraction of the skeletal muscles due to a calcium imbalance. 744

tetrapod Four-footed vertebrate; includes amphibians, reptiles, birds, and mammals. 552

thalamus In vertebrates, the portion of the diencephalon that passes on selected sensory information to the cerebrum. 704

therapeutic cloning Used to create mature cells of various cell types. Facilitates study of specialization of cells and provide cells and tissue to treat human illnesses. 161

thermoacidophile Type of archaean that lives in hot, acidic, aquatic habitats, such as hot springs or near hydrothermal vents. 379

thermoreceptor Sensory receptor that detects heat. 717

thigmotropism In plants, unequal growth due to contact with solid objects, as the coiling of tendrils around a pole. 491

threatened species Species that is likely to become an endangered species in the foreseeable future (e.g., bald eagle, gray wolf, Louisiana black bear). 908

thylakoid Flattened sac within a granum of a chloroplast; membrane contains chlorophyll; location where the light reactions of photosynthesis occur. 66, 76, 121

thymine (T) One of four nitrogen-containing bases in nucleotides composing the structure of DNA; pairs with adenine. 217

thymus gland Lymphoid organ involved in the development and functioning of the immune system; T lymphocytes mature in the thymus gland. 629,768

thyroid gland Large gland in the neck that produces several important hormones, including thyroxine, triiodothyronine, and calcitonin. 762

thyroid-stimulating hormone (TSH) Substance produced by the anterior pituitary that causes the thyroid to secrete thyroxine and triiodothyronine. 760

thyroxine (T_4) Hormone secreted from the thyroid gland that promotes growth and development; in general, it increases the metabolic rate in cells. 760

tight junction Junction between cells when adjacent plasma membrane proteins join to form an impermeable barrier. 99

tissue Group of similar cells combined to perform a common function. 588

tissue culture Process of growing tissue artificially, usually in a liquid medium in laboratory glassware. 513

tissue fluid Fluid that surrounds the body's cells; consists of dissolved substances that leave the blood capillaries by filtration and diffusion. 591, 621

tone Continuous, partial contraction of muscle. 744

tonicity The solute concentration (osmolarity) of a solution compared to that of a cell. If the solution is isotonic to the cell, there is no net movement of water; if the solution is hypotonic, the cell gains water; and if the solution is hypertonic, the cell loses water. 93

topography Surface features of the Earth. 885

totipotent Cell that has the full genetic potential of the organism, including the potential to develop into a complete organism. 514, 800

toxin Poisonous substance produced by living cells or organisms. Toxins are often proteins that are capable of causing disease on contact with or absorption by body tissues. 376

trachea (pl., tracheae) In insects, air tubes located between the spiracles and the tracheoles. In tetrapod vertebrates, air tube (windpipe) that runs between the larynx and the bronchi. 542, 664, 668

tracheid In vascular plants, type of cell in xylem that has tapered ends and pits through which water and minerals flow. 449

tract Bundle of myelinated axons in the central nervous system. 703

trait A characteristic of an organism; may be based on the physiology, morphology, or the genetics of the organism. 348

transcription First stage of gene expression; process whereby a DNA strand serves as a template for the formation of mRNA. 223

transcription activator Protein that participates in the initiation of transcription by binding to the enhancer regulatory regions. 244

transcriptional control Control of gene expression by the use of transcription factors, and other proteins, that regulate either the initiation of transcription or the rate at which it occurs. 244

transcription factor In eukaryotes, protein required for the initiation of transcription by RNA polymerase. 244

transduction Exchange of DNA between bacteria by means of a bacteriophage. 373

transduction pathway Series of proteins or enzymes that change a signal to one understood by the cell. 484

trans-fats Unsaturated fatty acid chains in which the configuration of the carbon-carbon double bonds is such that the hydrogen atoms are across from each other, as opposed to being on the same side (cis). 658

transfer rate Amount of a substance that moves from one component of the environment to another within a specified period of time. 875

transfer RNA (tRNA) Type of RNA that transfers a particular amino acid to a ribosome during protein synthesis; at one end, it binds to the amino acid, and at the other end it has an anticodon that binds to an mRNA codon. 223

transformation Taking up of extraneous genetic material from the environment by bacteria. 373

transgenic organism An organism whose genome has been altered by the insertion of genes from another species. 255

transitional fossil Fossil that bears a resemblance to two groups that in the present day are classified separately. 280

translation During gene expression, the process whereby ribosomes use the sequence of codons in mRNA to produce a polypeptide with a particular sequence of amino acids. 224

translational control Gene expression regulated by influencing the interaction of the mRNA transcripts with the ribosome. 246

translocation Movement of a chromosomal segment from one chromosome to another nonhomologous chromosome, leading to abnormalities—e.g., Down syndrome. 187, 231

transpiration Plant's loss of water to the atmosphere, mainly through evaporation at leaf stomata. 476

transposon DNA sequence capable of randomly moving from one site to another in the genome. 262

trichocyst Found in ciliates; contains long, barbed threads useful for defense and capturing prey. 393

trichomes In plants, specialized outgrowths of the epidermis (e.g., root hairs). 447

triglyceride Neutral fat composed of glycerol and three fatty acids; typically involved in energy storage. 46

triplet code During gene expression, each sequence of three nucleotide bases stands for a particular amino acid. 224

trisomy Chromosome condition in which a diploid cell has one more chromosome than normal; designated as 2n + 1. 183

trochozoan Type of protostome that produces a trochophore larva; also has two bands of cilia around its middle. 530

trophic level Feeding level of one or more populations in a food web. 873

trophoblast Outer membrane surrounding the embryo in mammals; when thickened by a layer of mesoderm, it becomes the chorion, an extraembryonic membrane. 806

tropical rain forest Biome near the equator in South America, Africa, and the Indo-Malay regions; characterized by warm weather, plentiful rainfall, a diversity of species, and mainly tree-living animal life. 892

tropism In plants, a growth response toward or away from a directional stimulus. 490

true coelom Body cavity completely lined with mesoderm; found in certain protostomes and all deuterostomes. 523

trypsin Protein-digesting enzyme secreted by the pancreas. 656

tubular reabsorption Movement of primarily nutrient molecules and water from the contents of the nephron into blood at the proximal convoluted tubule. 686

tubular secretion Movement of certain molecules from blood into the distal convoluted tubule of a nephron so that they are added to urine. 686

tumor Cells derived from a single mutated cell that has repeatedly undergone cell division; benign tumors remain at the site of origin, while malignant tumors metastasize. 164

tumor suppressor gene Gene that codes for a protein that ordinarily suppresses the cell cycle; inactivity due to a mutation can lead to a tumor. 164

turgor movement In plant cells, pressure of the cell contents against the cell wall when the central vacuole is full. 493

turgor pressure Pressure of the cell contents against the cell wall; in plant cells, determined by the water content of the vacuole; provides internal support. 93

tympanic membrane Membranous region that receives air vibrations in an auditory organ; in humans, the eardrum. 727

U

umbilical cord Cord connecting the fetus to the placenta through which blood vessels pass. 809

unicellular An organism comprised of a single cell, as in the bacteria. 2

uniformitarianism Belief, supported by James Hutton, that geological forces act at a continuous, uniform rate. 274

unsaturated fatty acid Fatty acid molecule that contains double bonds between some carbons of its hydrocarbon chain; thus contains fewer hydrogens than a saturated hydrocarbon chain. 46

upwelling Upward movement of deep, nutrient-rich water along coasts; it replaces surface waters that move away from shore when the direction of prevailing wind shifts. 904

uracil (U) Pyrimidine base that occurs in RNA, replacing thymine. 223

urea Main nitrogenous waste of terrestrial amphibians and most mammals. 681

ureter Tubular structure conducting urine from the kidney to the urinary bladder. 684

urethra Tubular structure that receives urine from the bladder and carries it to the outside of the body. 684

uric acid Main nitrogenous waste of insects, reptiles, and birds. 681

urinary bladder Organ where urine is stored. 684

urine Liquid waste product made by the nephrons of the vertebrate kidney through the processes of glomerular filtration, tubular reabsorption, and tubular secretion. 682

urochordate Group of aquatic invertebrate chordates that consists of the tunicates (sea squirts). 551

uterine cycle Cycle that runs concurrently with the ovarian cycle; it prepares the uterus to receive a developing zygote. 781

uterus In mammals, expanded portion of the female reproductive tract through which eggs pass to the environment or in which an embryo develops and is nourished before birth. 779

utricle Cavity in the vestibule of the vertebrate inner ear; contains sensory receptors for gravitational equilibrium. 728

V

vacuole Membrane-bounded sac, larger than a vesicle; usually functions in storage and can contain a variety of substances. In plants, the central vacuole fills much of the interior of the cell. 75

vagina Component of the female reproductive system that serves as the birth canal; receives the penis during copulation. 779

valence shell The outer electron shell of an atom. Contains the valence electrons, which determine the chemical reactivity of the atom. 25

vas deferens Also called the ductus deferens; storage location for mature sperm before they pass into the ejaculatory duct. 775

vascular bundle In plants, primary phloem and primary xylem enclosed by a bundle sheath. 450

vascular cambium In plants, lateral meristem that produces secondary phloem and secondary xylem. 454

vascular cylinder In eudicots, the tissues in the middle of a root, consisting of the pericycle and vascular tissues. 450

vascular plant Plant that has xylem and phloem. 426

vascular tissue Transport tissue in plants, consisting of xylem and phloem. 423, 447

vector In genetic engineering, a means to transfer foreign genetic material into a cell—e.g., a plasmid. 66, 255, 394

vein Blood vessel that arises from venules and transports blood toward the heart. 608

vena cava Large systemic vein that returns blood to the right atrium of the heart in tetrapods; either the superior or inferior vena cava. 614

ventilation Process of moving air into and out of the lungs; breathing. 664

ventricle Cavity in an organ, such as a lower chamber of the heart or the ventricles of the brain. 611, 702

venule Vessel that takes blood from capillaries to a vein. 608

vertebral column Portion of the vertebrate endoskeleton that houses the spinal cord; consists of many vertebrae separated by intervertebral disks. 741

vertebrate Chordate in which the notochord is replaced by a vertebral column. 520

vertigo Equilibrium disorder that is often associated with problems in the receptors of the semicircular canals in the ear. 730

vesicle Small, membrane-bounded sac that stores substances within a cell. 67, 331

vessel element Cell that joins with others to form a major conducting tube found in xylem. 449

vestibule Space or cavity at the entrance to a canal, such as the cavity that lies between the semicircular canals and the cochlea. 727

vestigial structure Remnant of a structure that was functional in some ancestor but is no longer functional in the organism in question. 272

villus Small, fingerlike projection of the inner small intestinal wall. 652

viroid Infectious strand of RNA devoid of a capsid and much smaller than a virus. 369

virus Noncellular parasitic agent consisting of an outer capsid and an inner core of nucleic acid. 364

visual accommodation Ability of the eye to focus at different distances by changing the curvature of the lens. 722

visual communication Form of communication between animals using their bodies, includes various forms of display. 828

vitamin Organic nutrient that is required in small amounts for metabolic functions. Vitamins are often part of coenzymes. 112

viviparous Animal that gives birth after partial development of offspring within mother. 774

vocal cord In humans, fold of tissue within the larynx; creates vocal sounds when it vibrates. 668

W

water column In plants, water molecules joined together in xylem from the leaves to the roots. 476

water (hydrologic) cycle Interdependent and continuous circulation of water from the ocean, to the atmosphere, to the land, and back to the ocean. 875

water mold Filamentous organisms having cell walls made of cellulose; typically decomposers of dead freshwater organisms, but some are parasites of aquatic or terrestrial organisms. 391

water potential Potential energy of water; a measure of the capability to release or take up water relative to another substance. 473

water vascular system Series of canals that takes water to the tube feet of an echinoderm, allowing them to expand. 544

wax Sticky, solid, water-repellent lipid consisting of many long-chain fatty acids usually linked to long-chain alcohols. 48

wetland Area that is covered by water at some point in the year. (*See also* bog, marsh, or swamp.) 897

whisk fern Common name for seedless vascular plant that consists only of stems and has no leaves, or roots. 428

white blood cell Leukocyte, of which there are several types, each having a specific function in protecting the body from invasion by foreign substances and organisms. 620

white matter Myelinated axons in the central nervous system. 703

whorl Cluster of branches, or other plant structures, that occurs in a circular pattern. 421

wobble hypothesis Ability of the tRNAs to recognize more than one codon; the codons differ in their third nucleotide. 229

wood Secondary xylem that builds up year after year in woody plants and becomes the annual rings. 456

X

X-linked Allele that is located on an X chromosome; not all X-linked genes code for sexual characteristics. 208

xylem Vascular tissue that transports water and mineral solutes upward through the plant body; it contains vessel elements and tracheids. 426, 449

Y

yeast Unicellular fungus that has a single nucleus and reproduces asexually by budding or fission, or sexually through spore formation. 408

yolk Dense nutrient material in the egg of a bird or reptile. 774, 797

yolk sac One of the extraembryonic membranes that, in shelled vertebrates, contains yolk for the nourishment of the embryo, and in placental mammals is the first site for blood cell formation. 805

Z

zero population growth No growth in population size. 852

zooflagellate Nonphotosynthetic protist that moves by flagella; typically zooflagellates enter into symbiotic relationships, and some are parasitic. 395

zooplankton Part of plankton containing protozoans and other types of microscopic animals. 899

zoospore Spore that is motile by means of one or more flagella. 407

zygospore Thick-walled resting cell formed during sexual reproduction of zygospore fungi. 408

zygospore fungi (Zygomycota) Fungi such as black bread mold that reproduces by forming windblown spores in sporangia; sexual reproduction involves a thick-walled zygospore. 407

zygote Diploid cell formed by the union of two gametes; the product of fertilization. 172, 310

Credits

PHOTOGRAPHS

DESIGN ELEMENTS Part opener(wolf): Corbis RF/Alamy; p. xv (crab): © Brand X Pictures/PunchStock RF; p. xvii (butterfly): © Wally Eberhart/Getty Images; p. xix (bird): © Brand X Pictures/PunchStock RF.

CHAPTER 1 Opener: © Bob Gibbons/Alamy; 1.1(bacteria): © Dr. Dennis Kunkel/Phototake; 1.1(paramecium): © M. Abbey/Visuals Unlimited; 1.1(morel): © Corbis RF; 1.1(sunflower): © Photodisc Green/Getty RF; 1.1(octopus): © Erica S. Leeds; 1.3a: © Purestock/SuperStock RF; 1.3b: © Photodisc Blue/Getty RF; 1.3c: © Charles Bush Photography; 1.3d: © Michael Abby/Visuals Unlimited; 1.3e: © Pat Pendarvis; 1.3f: Courtesy National Park Service; 1.4: © Photodisc/Getty RF; 1.6: © Ralph Robinson/Visuals Unlimited; 1.7: © A.B. Dowsett/SPL/Photo Researchers, Inc.; 1.8(protist): © Michael Abby/Visuals Unlimited; 1.8(plant): © Pat Pendarvis; 1.8(fungi): © Tinke Hamming/Ingram Publishing RF; 1.8(animal): © Corbis RF; 1.11a: © Getty RF; 1.11b: © Dr. Phillip Dustan; 1.12: Courtesy Leica Microsystems Inc.; 1A(left): © Corbis RF; 1A(right): © JupiterImages/BananaStock/Alamy RF; 1.13: © Dr. Jeremy Burgess/Photo Researchers, Inc.; 1.14(all): Courtesy Jim Bidlack; 1.15: © Erica S. Leeds.

CHAPTER 2 Opener: © Peter Weimann/Animals Animals; 2.1: © Gunter Ziesler/Peter Arnold/Photolibrary; 2.4a: © Biomed Commun./Custom Medical Stock Photo; 2.4b(left): © Mazzlota et al./Photo Researchers, Inc; 2.4b(right): Courtesy National Institutes of Health; 2.5a(both): © Tony Freeman/PhotoEdit; 2.5b: © Geoff Tompkinson/SPL/Photo Researchers, Inc.; 2.7b(crystals): © Evelyn Jo Johnson; 2.7b(shaker): © Evelyn Jo Johnson; 2.10b: © Grant Taylor/Stone/Getty Images.

CHAPTER 3 Opener: Courtesy Sylvia S. Mader; 3.1b: © Getty RF; 3.1c: © Corbis RF; 3.1d: © Brand X Pictures/PunchStock RF; 3.1e: © Ingram Publishing/Alamy RF; 3.1f: © JewelryStock/Alamy RF; 3.1g: © Ingram Publishing/SuperStock RF; 3.3: © The McGraw Hill Companies, Inc. John Thoeming, photographer; 3.5a: © Brand X Pictures/PunchStock RF; 3.5b: © Ingram Publishing/Alamy RF; 3.5c: © H. Pol/CNRI/SPL/Photo Researchers, Inc.; 3.6a: © Steve Bloom/Taxi/Getty; 3.8a: © Jeremy Burgess/SPL/Photo Researchers, Inc.; 3.8b: © Don W. Fawcett/Photo Researchers, Inc.; 3.9: © Science VU; 3.12: © Ernest A. Janes/Bruce Coleman/Photoshot; 3.13a: © Das Fotoarchiv/Peter Arnold/Photolibrary; 3.13b: © Martha Cooper/Peter Arnold/Photolibrary; p. 49(woman running): © Duomo/Corbis; 3.17a: © Gregory Pace/Corbis; 3.17b: © Ronald Siemoneit/Corbis Sygma; 3.17c: © Kjell Sandved/Visuals Unlimited; 3.20a: © Photodisk Red/Getty Images; 3.21c: © Jennifer Loomis/Animals Animals.

CHAPTER 4 Opener: © Oliver Meckes/Nicole Ottawa/Photo Researchers, Inc.; 4.1a: © Geoff Bryant/Photo Researchers, Inc.; 4.1b: Courtesy Ray F. Evert/University of Wisconsin Madison; 4.1c: © Barbara J. Miller/Biological Photo Service; 4.1d: Courtesy O. Sabatakou and E. Xylouri-Frangiadaki; 4Aa: © Robert Brons/Biological Photo Service; 4Ab: © M. Schliwa/Visuals Unlimited; 4Ac: © Kessel/Shih/Peter Arnold/Photolibrary; 4B(bright-field): © Ed Reschke; 4B(bright-field stained): © Biophoto Associates/Photo Researchers, Inc.; 4B(differential, phase contrast, dark-field): © David M. Phillips/Visuals Unlimited; 4.4: © Howard Sochurek/The Medical File/Peter Arnold/Photolibrary; 4.6: © Dr. Dennis Kunkel/Visuals Unlimited; 4.7: © Newcomb/Wergin/Biological Photo Service; 4.8(top right): Courtesy E.G. Pollock; 4.8(bottom left): Courtesy Ron Milligan/Scripps Research Institute; 4.10: © R. Bolender & D. Fawcett/Visuals Unlimited; 4.11: Courtesy Charles Flickinger, from Journal of Cell Biology 49:221-226, 1971, Fig. 1 page 224; 4.12a: Courtesy Daniel S. Friend; 4.12b: Courtesy Robert D. Terry/University of California, San Diego School of Medicine; 4.14: © S.E. Frederick & E.H. Newcomb/Biolog-ical Photo Service; 4.15: © Newcomb/Wergin/Biological Photo Service; 4.16a: Courtesy Herbert W. Israel, Cornell University; 4.17a: Courtesy Dr. Keith Porter; 4.18a(actin): © M. Schliwa/Visuals Unlimited; 4.18a(Chara): © The McGraw-Hill Companies, Inc. Dennis Strete and Darrell Vodopich, photographers; 4.18b(intermediate): © K.G. Murti/Visuals Unlimited; 4.18b(peacock): © Vol. 86/Corbis RF; 4.18c(microtubules): © K.G. Murti/Visuals Unlimited; 4.18c(chameleon): © Photodisc/Vol. 6/Getty RF; 4.19(one centrosome): Courtesy Kent McDonald, University of Colorado Boulder; 4.19(two centrosomes): This image originally appeared in: McGill M, Highfield DP, Monahan TM, Brinkley BR. Effects of nucleic acid specific dyes on centrioles of mammalian cells. J Ultrastruct Res. 1976; 57:43-53. The image was created by Manley McGill in 1976 while he was a member of the William Brinkley laboratory at The University of Texas Medical Branch, Galveston. It has been made available by William Brinkley (Baylor University) for the memory of his former student.; 4.20(sperm): © David M. Phillips/Photo Researchers, Inc.; 4.20(flagellum, basal body): © William L. Dentler/Biological Photo Service.

CHAPTER 5 Opener: © Professors P. Motta & T. Naguro/Science Photo Library/Photo Researchers, Inc.; 5Aa(human egg): © Anatomical Travelogue/Photo Researchers, Inc.; 5Aa(embryo): © Neil Harding/Stone/Getty Images; 5Aa(baby): © Photodisc Collection/Getty RF; 5.12a: © Eric Grave/Phototake; 5.12b: © Don W. Fawcett/Photo Researchers, Inc.; 5.12c(both): Courtesy Mark Bretscher; 5.14a: From Douglas E. Kelly, J. Cell Biol. 28 (1966): 51. Reproduced by copyright permission of The Rockefeller University Press; 5.14b: © David M. Phillips/Visuals Unlimited; 5.14c: Courtesy Camillo Peracchia, M.D.; 5.15: © E.H. Newcomb/Biological Photo Service.

CHAPTER 6 Opener: © PhotoAlto/PunchStock RF; 6.8b: © James Watt/Visuals Unlimited; 6.8c: © Creatas/PunchStock RF; 6.9: © G.K. & Vikki Hart/The Image Bank/Getty Images; 6A: © AP Photo/Chikumo Chiaki.

CHAPTER 7 Opener: © David Muench/Corbis; 7.1(moss): © Steven P. Lynch; 7.1(trees): © Digital Vision/PunchStock RF; 7.1(Euglena): © T.E. Adams/Visuals Unlimited; 7.1(sunflower): © Corbis RF; 7.1(kelp): © Chuck Davis/Stone/Getty Images; 7.1(cyanobacteria): © Sherman Thomas/Visuals Unlimited; 7.1(diatoms): © Ed Reschke/Peter Arnold/Photolibrary; 7.2: © Dr. George Chapman/Visuals Unlimited; 7.3: © Nigel Cattlin/Photo Researchers, Inc.; 7.4: Courtesy Lawrence Berkeley National Lab/Roy Kaltschmidt, LBL Photographer; 7.10: © Herman Eisenbeiss/Photo Researchers, Inc.; 7.11a: © Brand X Pictures/PunchStock RF; 7.11b: Courtesy USDA/Doug Wilson, photographer; 7.12: © PhotoLink/Getty RF.

CHAPTER 8 Opener: © Daniel H. Bailey/Age RF; 8.1: © E. & P. Bauer/zefa/Corbis; 8A(bread, wine, cheese): © The McGraw Hill Companies, Inc./John Thoeming, photographer; 8A(yogurt; pickles, vinegar): © The McGraw Hill Companies, Inc. Bruce M. Johnson, photographer; 8.6: © Dr. Donald Fawcett and Dr. Porter/Visuals Unlimited; 8.10: © C Squared Studios/Getty RF.

CHAPTER 9 Opener: © SPL/Photo Researchers, Inc.; 9.2: Courtesy Douglas R. Green/LaJolla Institute for Allergy and Immunology; 9.3a: © Andrew Syred/Photo Researchers, Inc.; 9.4 Animal cell(early prophase, prophase, metaphase, anaphase, telophase): © Ed Reschke; 9.4 Animal cell(prometaphase): © Michael Abbey/Photo Researchers, Inc.; 9.4 Plant cell(early prophase, prometaphase): © Ed Reschke; 9.4 Plant cell(prophase, metaphase, anaphase): © R. Calentine/Visuals Unlimited; 9.4 Plant cell(telophase): © Jack M. Bostrack/Visuals Unlimited; 9.5(top): © Thomas Deerinck/Visuals Unlimited; 9.5(bottom): © Steve Gschmeissner/SPL/Getty RF; 9.6: © B.A. Palevitz and E.H. Newcomb/BPS/Tom Stack & Associates; 9.8d: © Biophoto Associates/Photo Researchers, Inc.; 9.9: © Dennis Kunkel Microscopy, Inc./Visuals Unlimited.

CHAPTER 10 Opener: © Barcroft Media; 10.1a: © L. Willatt/Photo Researchers, Inc.; 10.3a: Courtesy Dr. D. Von Wettstein; 10.5(all): © Ed Reschke; 10.10a: © Jose Carrilo/PhotoEdit; 10.10b: © CNRI/SPL/Photo Researchers, Inc.; 10.11a(girl): Courtesy UNC Medical Illustration and Photography; 10.11b(boy): Courtesy Stefan D. Schwarz, http://klinefeltersyndrome.org; 10.11a, b(karyotypes): © CNRI/SPL/Photo Researchers, Inc.; 10.13b: Courtesy The Williams Syndrome Association; 10.14b: © Fred, Herbert, and Hendrik van Dijk. "Images of Memorable Cases, 50 Years at the Bedside: Case 133."

CHAPTER 11 Opener: © Felicia Martinez Photography/Photedit; 11.1: © Ned M. Seidler/National Geographic Image Collection; 11.12: Courtesy Division of Medical Toxicology, University of Virginia; 11.13: © Pat Pendarvis; 11.15(man): © AP/Wide World Photos; 11.15(tissue): © Ed Reschke; p. 206(sickle cell): © Phototake, Inc./Alamy; 11.19(left, right): Courtesy Dr. Rabi Tawil, Director, Neuromuscular Pathology Laboratory, University of Rochester Medical Center; 11.19(center): Courtesy Muscular Dystrophy Association.

CHAPTER 12 Openers (hibiscus): © Rosemary Calvert/PunchStock RF; (leopard): © James Martin/Stone/Getty Images; (crab): © Tui DeRoy/Bruce Coleman/Photoshot; (protozoa): © A.M. Siegelman/Visuals Unlimited; 12.2(bacteria): © Martin Shields/Photo Researchers, Inc.; 12.2(jellyfish): © David Wrobel/Visuals Unlimited; 12.2(pigs): Courtesy Shinn-Chih Wu, Ph.D., Dept. of Animal Science and Technology, National Taiwan University, Taipei, Taiwan; 12.2(mouse): © Dr. Charles Mazel/Visuals Unlimited/Corbis; 12.2(plant): Courtesy of The Samuel Roberts Noble Foundation, Ardmore, Oklahoma; 12.4a: © Photo Researchers, Inc.; 12.4c: © Science Source/Photo Researchers, Inc.; 12.5a(DNA model): © Photodisk Red/Getty RF; 12.5d: © A. Barrington Brown/Photo Researchers; 12.12a: © Oscar L. Miller/Photo Researchers, Inc.; 12.15d: Courtesy Alexander Rich; 12.20a: © Ada L. Olins and Donald E. Olins/Biological Photo Service; 12.20b: Courtesy Dr. Jerome Rattner, Cell Biology and Anatomy, University of Calgary; 12.20c: Courtesy of Ulrich Laemmli and J.R. Paulson, Dept. of Molecular Biology, University of Geneva, Switzerland; 12.20d, e: © Peter Engelhardt/Department of Pathology and Virology, Haartman Institute; Centre of Excellence in Computational Complex Systems Research, Biomedical Engineering and Computational Science, Faculty of Information and Natural Sciences, Helsinki University of Technology, Helsinki, Finland.

CHAPTER 13 Opener: © Francois Paquet-Durand/Photo Researchers, Inc.; 13.5a: © Dennis Kunkel Microscopy, Inc./Visuals Unlimited; 13.6: © Chanan Photo 2004; 13A: © Fitzpatrick Color Atlas & Synopsis of Clinical Dermatology 5/e. The McGraw-Hill Companies, Inc.; 13.12b, c: © Stan Flegler/Visuals Unlimited.

CHAPTER 14 Opener: © Zacharias Pereira da Mata/Shutterstock; 14.5: © U.S. Coast Guard photo by Petty Officer 3rd Class Patrick Kelley; 14A: © Deco/Alamy RF; 14.1(human): © Image Source/JupiterImages RF; 14.1(plant): Courtesy USDA/Peggy Greb, photographer; 14.1(mouse): © Redmond Durrell/Alamy RF; 14.1(fruit fly): © Herman Eisenbeiss/Photo Researchers, Inc.; 14.1(roundworm): © CMSP/J.L. Carson/Getty Images; 14.1(yeast): © G. Wanner/Getty Images; 14.10: Courtesy of Dr. Michael Thompson.

CHAPTER 15 Opener: © Tyler Keillor, University of Chicago; 15.1a(Darwin): © Carolina Biological/Visuals Unlimited; 15.1c(rhea): © Wolfgang Kaehler/Corbis; 15.1d(desert): © Luiz C. Marigo/Peter Arnold/Photolibrary; 15.1e(strata): © Gary J. James/Biological Photo Service; 15.1f(waterfall): © Charles Benes/Index Stock Imagery/Photolibrary; 15.1g(iguana): © Galen Rowell/Corbis; 15.4(Lepus): © WILDLIFE/Peter Arnold/Photolibrary; 15.4(Dolichotis): © Juan & Carmecita Munoz/Photo Researchers, Inc.; 15.5a: © Kevin Schafer/Corbis; 15.5b: © Michael Dick/Animals Animals; 15.6: © Lisette

© David Sieren/Visuals Unlimited; 24.14(left): © Ed Reschke; 24.14(right): Courtesy Ray F. Evert/University of Wisconsin Madison; 24.15(top): © CABISCO/Phototake; 24.15(bottom): © Kingsley Stern; 24.17(circular cross section): © Ed Reschke/Peter Arnold/Photolibrary; 24.18a: © Ardea London Limited; 24.19a: © The McGraw-Hill Companies Inc./Evelyn Jo Johnson, photographer; 24.19b: © Science Pictures Limited/Photo Researchers, Inc.; 24.19c: © The McGraw Hill Companies, Inc./Carlyn Iverson, photographer; 24.19d: © The McGraw Hill Companies, Inc. Carlyn Iverson, photographer; 24B(flooring): © Alamy RF; 24B(shoots): © Getty RF; 24B(bamboo grove): © Michele Westmorland/Getty Images; 24.20: © Jeremy Burgess/SPL/Photo Researchers, Inc.; 24.22a: © Patti Murray Animals Animals; 24.22b: © Gerald & Buff Corsi/Visuals Unlimited; 24.22c: © P. Goetgheluck/Peter Arnold/Photolibrary.

CHAPTER 25 Openers (left): © Kit R. Roane/age fotostock; (right): © The Nug/Alamy; 25.2a(all): Courtesy Mary E. Doohan; 25.5a: © CABISCO/Phototake; 25A: © Yann Arthus-Bertrand/Corbis; 25.6(top): © Dwight Kuhn; 25.6(circle): © E.H. Newcomb & S.R. Tardon/Biological Photo Service; 25.7(left): © Runk Schoenberger/Grant Heilman; 25.7(circle): © Dana Richter/Visuals Unlimited; 25.8a: © Kevin Schafer/Corbis; 25.8b(sundew plant): © Barry Rice/Visuals Unlimited; 25.8b(sundew leaf): © Dr. Jeremy Burgess/Photo Researchers, Inc.; 25C(both): © The McGraw Hill Companies, Inc./Ken Cavanagh, photographer; 25.1(all): Courtesy Wilfred A. Cote, from H.A. Core, W.A. Cote, and A.C. Day, Wood: Structure and Identification 2/e; 25.11: © Ed Reschke/Peter Arnold/Photolibrary; 25.13(both): © Jeremy Burgess/SPL/Photo Researchers, Inc.; 25.14a: © M. H. Zimmermann, Courtesy Dr. P. B. Tomlinson, Harvard University; 25.14b: © Steven P. Lynch.

CHAPTER 26 Opener: Courtesy USDA/photo by Bruce Fritz; 26.4a: © Robert E. Lyons/Visuals Unlimited; 26.4b: © Sylvan Whittwer/Visuals Unlimited; 26.5a–d: Courtesy Alan Darvill and Stefan Eberhard, Complex Carbohydrate Research Center, University of Georgia; 26.6: © John Solden/Visuals Unlimited; 26.7: Courtesy Dr. Donald R. McCarty, University of Florida; 26.9(both), 26.11a: © Kingsley Stern; 26.11b: Courtesy Malcolm Wilkins, Glascow University; 26.11c: Micrographs courtesy of Randy Moore; 26.13: © John D. Cunningham/Visuals Unlimited; 26A: Courtesy Elliot Meyerowitz/California Institute of Technology; 26.14(both): © John Kaprielian/Photo Researchers, Inc.; 26.15a(both): © Tom McHugh/Photo Researchers, Inc.; 26.15b(left): © BIOS A. Thais/Peter Arnold/Photolibrary; 26.15b(right): © BIOS Pierre Huguet/Peter Arnold/Photolibrary; 26.17(both): © Nigel Cattlin/Visuals Unlimited; 26.19(bug): Courtesy USDA/Agricultural Research Service, photo by Scott Bauer; 26.19(fungus): © Kingsley Stern; 26.19(caterpillar): © The McGraw Hill Companies, Inc. Ken Cavanagh, photographer; 26.19(butterfly): © Dwight Kuhn.

CHAPTER 27 Opener: © Corbis RF; 27.3a: © Farley Bridges; 27.3b: © Pat Pendarvis; 27.4a: © Radius Images/Getty RF; 27.4b: © Garden World Images/age fotostock; 27.5(pollen grain): Courtesy Graham Kent; 27.5(embryo sac): © Ed Reschke; 27.6a: © George Bernard/Animals Animals; 27.6b: © Simko/Visuals Unlimited; 27.6c: © Dwight Kuhn; 27Aa: © Steven P. Lynch; 27Ab: © Robert Maier/Animals Animals; 27Ba: © Anthony Mercieca/Photo Researchers, Inc.; 27Bb: © Merlin D. Tuttle/Bat Conservation International; 27.7(proembryo, globular, heart): Courtesy Dr. Chun-Ming Liu; 27.7(torpedo): © Biology Media/Photo Researchers, Inc.; 27.7(mature embryo): © Jack Bostrack/Visuals Unlimited; 27.8a(bean): © Dwight Kuhn; 27.8b(corn): Courtesy Ray F. Evert/University of Wisconsin Madison; 27.9a, b: © Kingsley Stern; 27.9c: © Dr. James Richardson/Visuals Unlimited; 27.9d: © James Mauseth; 27.9e: Courtesy Robert A. Schlising; 27.9f: © Ingram Publishing/Alamy RF; 27.10a: © Marie Read/Animals Animals; 27.10b: © Scott Camazine/Photo Researchers, Inc.; 27.11a(bean): © Ed Reschke; 27.11b(corn): © James Mauseth; 27.12: © G.I. Bernard/Animals Animals; 27.13a(all): Courtesy Prof. Dr. Hans-Ulrich Koop, from Plant Cell Reports, 17:601-604; 27.14: © Kingsley Stern.

CHAPTER 28 Opener: © James H. Robinson/Photo Researchers, Inc.; 28.1(all top row, zygote to embryo): © Cabisco/Phototake; 28.1(adult frog and all bottom row): © Dwight Kuhn; 28A(phase I): © Christiane Nusslein-Volhard, Development, Supplement 1, 1991, reproduced with permission, website: http://dev.biologists.org/;

28A(phase II, all): Courtesy Jim Langeland, Steve Paddock, and Sean Carroll/University of Wisconsin, Madison; 28B(chicken): © Photodisc/Getty RF; 28B(mouse): © Alamy RF; 28B(python): © IT Stock/PunchStock RF; 28.6a: © Andrew J. Martinez/Photo Researchers, Inc.; 28.7a: © Jeff Rotman; 28.7b: © J. McCollugh/Visuals Unlimited; 28.8a: © Azure Computer & Photo Services/Animals Animals; 28.8b: © Ron Taylor/Bruce Coleman/Photoshot; 28.8c: © Image courtesy of Islands in the Sea 2002, NOAA/OER; 28.8d: © Amos Nachoum/Corbis; 28.9: © CABISCO/Visuals Unlimited; 28.10a: © Robert Brons/Biological Photo Service; 28.11: © Diane R. Nelson; 28.12e: © Tom E. Adams/Peter Arnold/Photolibrary; 28.13a: © SPL/Photo Researchers, Inc.; 28.14(proglottid): © John D. Cunningham/Visuals Unlimited; 28.14(scolex): © James Webb/Phototake; 28.16b: © Kjell Sandved/Butterfly Alphabet; 28.17a: Courtesy Larry S. Roberts; 28.17b: © Fred Whitehead/Animals Animals; 28.18a: © M. Gibbs/OSF/Animals Animals; 28.18b: © Farley Bridges; 28.18c: © Douglas Faulkner/Photo Researchers, Inc.; 28.18d: © Georgette Douwma/Photo Researchers, Inc.; 28.19c: © Roger K. Burnard/Biological Photo Service; 28.20b: © James H. Carmichael; 28.20c: © St. Bartholomews Hospital/SPL/Photo Researchers, Inc.; 28.21a: © Lauritz Jensen/Visuals Unlimited; 28.21b: © James Solliday/Biological Photo Service; 28.21c: © Vanessa Vick/The New York Times/Redux; 28.22c: © OSF/London Scientific Films/Animals Animals; 28.23a: © Michael Lustbader/Photo Researchers, Inc.; 28.23b: © Bruce Robinson/Corbis; 28.23c: © Kjell Sandved/Butterfly Alphabet; 28.25a: © Larry Miller/Photo Researchers, Inc.; 28.25b: © David Aubrey/Corbis; 28.26(mealybug): © Farley Bridges; 28.26(beetle): © Wolfgang Kaehler/Corbis; 28.26(leafhopper): © Farley Bridges; 28.26(louse): © Darlyne A. Murawski/Peter Arnold/Photolibrary; 28.26(wasp): © Johnathan Smith/LatitudeStock; 28.26(dragonfly): © Farley Bridges; 28.28a: © Jana R. Jirak/Visuals Unlimited; 28.28b: © Tom McHugh/Photo Researchers, Inc.; 28.28c: © Ken Lucas; 28.29b : © Randy Morse, GoldenStateImages.com; 28.29c: © Alex Kerstitch/Visuals Unlimited; 28.29d: © Randy Morse/Animals Animals.

CHAPTER 29 Opener: © 2003 Monty Sloan/Wolf Photography; 29.2(bottom): © Heather Angel/Natural Visions; 29.3: © Corbis RF; 29.6: © Heather Angel/Natural Visions; 29.8a: © James Watt/Animals Animals; 29.8b: © Fred Bavendam/Minden Pictures; 29.9b: © Hal Beral/Visuals Unlimited; 29.9c: © Jane Burton/Bruce Coleman/Photoshot; 29.9d: © Photos by Team Hymas/Getty RF; 29.9e: © Franco Banfi/SeaPics.com; 29.10: © Peter Scoones/SPL/Photo Researchers, Inc.; 29.13a: © Suzanne L. Collins & Joseph T. Collins/Photo Researchers, Inc.; 29.13b: © Joe McDonald/Visuals Unlimited; 29.13c: © Juan Manuel Renjifo/Animals Animals; 29Aa: © MedioImages/SuperStock RF; 29Ab: © Allan Friedlander/SuperStock; 29Ac: © Account Phototake/Phototake; 29.16a: © H. Hall/OSF/Animals Animals; 29.16b: © Joe McDonald/Visuals Unlimited; 29.16c: © Joel Sartorie/National Geographic/Getty Images; 29.16d: © Nathan W. Cohen/Visuals Unlimited; 29.16e: © Martin Harvey/Gallo Images/Corbis; 29.18a: © Thomas Kitchin/Tom Stack & Associates; 29.18b: © Joel McDonald/Corbis; 29.18c: © IT Stock/PunchStock RF; 29.18d: © Kirtley Perkins/Visuals Unlimited; 29.20a: © D. Parer & E. Parer-Cook/Ardea; 29.20b: © Fritz Prenzel/Animals Animals; 29.20c: © Leonard Lee Rue/Photo Researchers, Inc.; 29.2(whale): © Mike Bacon; 29.2(deer): © Stephen J. Krasemann/Photo Researchers, Inc.; 29.2(horse): © Juniors Bildarchiv/Alamy RF; 29.2(lioness): © John Downer/Getty Images; 29.2(pangolin): © Nigel G. Dennis/Photo Researchers, Inc.; 29.2(bat): © Corbis RF; 29.2(hedgehog): © 1996 PhotoDisc, Inc./Getty RF; 29.2(mole): © Digital Vision/Getty RF; 29.2(squirrel): © Nature Picture Library/Alamy RF; 29.2(rabbit): © Rubberball/Getty RF; 29.2(flying lemur): © Getty RF; 29.2(tree shrew): © Correia Patrice/Photolibrary; 29.2(monkey): © Gerald Lacz/Animals Animals; 29.2(armadillo): © Photodisc/Getty RF; 29.2(tenrec): © Martin Harvey/Gallo Images/Getty Images; 29.2(elephant shrew): © Oxford Scientific/Photolibrary/Getty Images; 29.2(aardvark): © National Geographic/Getty RF; 29.2(manatee): © Keith Ramos/USFWS; 29.2(hyrax): © PhotoLink/Getty RF; 29.2(elephant): © Purestock RF.

CHAPTER 30 Opener: © Frank Vinken/Max Planck Institute for Evolutionary Anthropology, Leipzig, Germany; 30.1(tarsier): © Doug Wechsler; 30.1(monkey): © Paul Souders/Corbis; 30.1(baboon): © St. Meyers/Okapia/Photo Researchers, Inc.; 30.1(orangutan): © Tim

Davis/Photo Researchers, Inc.; 30.1(chimpanzee): © Martin Harvey/Peter Arnold/Photolibrary; 30.1(humans): © Comstock Images/JupiterImages RF; 30.5: © National Museums of Kenya; 30.6(S. tchadensis): © Prof. Michel Brunet; 30.6(A. afarensis): © Friedrich Saurer/Alamy; 30.6(A. boisei): © Science VU/NMK/Visuals Unlimited; 30.6(H. habilis): © Herve Conge/ISM/Phototake; 30.6(H. sapiens): © 2007 Educational Images Ltd./Custom Medical Stock Photo; 30.8a: © Dan Dreyfus and Associates; 30.8b: © John Reader/Photo Researchers, Inc.; 30.9: © National Museums of Kenya; 30.11: Transp. #608 Courtesy Dept. of Library Services, American Museum of Natural History; 30.12a: © PhotoDisc/Getty RF; 30.12b: © Sylvia S. Mader; 30.12c: © B & C Alexander/Photo Researchers, Inc.

CHAPTER 31 Opener: © Science Photo Library/Photo Researchers, Inc.; 31.1(all): © Ed Reschke; 31.3a, b, d, e: © Ed Reschke; 31.3c: © The McGraw-Hill Companies, Inc. Dennis Strete, Photographer; 31.5a, c: © Ed Reschke; 31.5b: © The McGraw-Hill Companies, Inc. Dennis Strete, Photographer; 31.6b: © Ed Reschke; 31A(both): © Courtesy Justin Rosenberg; 31.9a: © John D. Cunningham/Visuals Unlimited; 31.9b: © Ken Greer/Visuals Unlimited; 31.9c: © James Stevenson/SPL/Photo Researchers, Inc.

CHAPTER 32 Opener: © AF archive/Alamy RF; 32.1a: © CABISCO/Visuals Unlimited; 32.1b: © Lester V. Bergman/Corbis; 32.1c: © Randy Morse, GoldenStateImages.com; 32.6b: © SIU/Visuals Unlimited; 32.7b: © Dr. Don W. Fawcett/Visuals Unlimited; 32.9b: © Biophoto Associates/Photo Researchers, Inc.; 32.9b, c: © Ed Reschke; 32.9d: © David Joel/MacNeal Hospital/Getty Images; 32A: © Biophoto Associates/Photo Researchers, Inc.; 32.15, 32.16: © J. C. Revy/Phototake; 32.17: © Eye of Science/Photo Researchers, Inc.; 32B: © Andrew J. Martinez/Photo Researchers, Inc.

CHAPTER 33 Opener: © Courtesy Baylor College of Medicine Photo Archives; 33.1a: © Stephen Durr; 33.1b: © Dr. Owen Gilbert, Rice University; 33.3a: © R. Calentine/Visuals Unlimited; 33.3b, d: © Ed Reschke/Peter Arnold/Photolibrary; 33.3c: © Fred E. Hossler/Visuals Unlimited; 33.6: © Dennis Kunkel/Phototake; 33.12b: © Steve Gschmeissner/Photo Researchers, Inc.; p. 638(patient): © A. Ramey/PhotoEdit; p. 638(shingles): © CDC; p. 638(candidiasis): © Everett S. Beneke/Visuals Unlimited; p. 638(pneumonia): © Dr. Dennis Kunkel/Visuals Unlimited; 33.13: © Michael Newman/PhotoEdit; 33.14: © Digital Vision/Getty RF; 33.15(girl): © Damien Lovegrove/SPL/Photo Researchers, Inc.; 33.15(allergens): © David Scharf/SPL/Photo Researchers, Inc.; 33.16: © Southern Illinois University/Photo Researchers, Inc.; 33.17: © Dr. Ken Greer/Visuals Unlimited.

CHAPTER 34 Opener: © Goodshoot/PunchStock RF; 34.9b: © Ed Reschke/Peter Arnold/Photolibrary; 34.10(villi): © Manfred Kage/Peter Arnold/Photolibrary; 34.10(microvilli): This photo was published in Medical Cell Biology, Charles Flickinger, photo by Susumu Ito, Copyright Elsevier, 1979; 34.14: © Amiard/photocuisine/Corbis; 34.15: © Ryan McVay/Getty RF.

CHAPTER 35 Opener: © Timothy A. Clary/AFP/Getty Images; 35.4a(fish): © Dr. Jeffrey Isaacson, Nebraska Wesleyan University; 35.4c(gills): © David M. Phillips/Photo Researchers, Inc.; 35.5, 35.6b: © Ed Reschke; 35.13: © Andrew Syred/Photo Researchers, Inc.; 35.14: © Dr. P. Marazzi/Photo Researchers, Inc.; 35.16a: © Matt Meadows/Peter Arnold/Photolibrary; 35.16b: © SIU/Visuals Unlimited; 35.16c: © Biophoto Associates/Photo Researchers, Inc.; 35A: Courtesy The Wyss Institute, Harvard University.

CHAPTER 36 Opener: © Georgette Douwma/Photo Researchers, Inc.; 36.4: © Bob Calhoun/Bruce Coleman/Photoshot; 36.5: © Eric Hosking/Photo Researchers, Inc.; 36.6a: © James Cavallini/Photo Researchers, Inc.; 36.8b: © Science Photo Library/Getty RF; 36.8c, d: © Ed Reschke/Peter Arnold/Photolibrary; 36.9b: © Joseph F. Gennaro, Jr./Photo Researchers, Inc.; 36A: © AFP/Getty Images.

CHAPTER 37 Opener: © Time & Life Pictures/Getty Images; 37.4a: © M.B. Bunge/Biological Photo Service; 37.4c: © Manfred Kage/Peter Arnold/Photolibrary; 37.7a: Courtesy Dr. E.R. Lewis, University of California Berkeley; 37.8: © Colin Chumbley/Science Source/Photo Researchers, Inc.; 37.12c: © Karl E. Deckart/Phototake; 37B: © Science VU/Visuals Unlimited.

LINE ART & TEXT

CHAPTER 2 Biological Systems: The Interconnectedness of Water, Plants, and People: Textual data from G. Tyler Miller, Living in the Environment, 1983, Wadsworth Publishing Company, Belmont, CA; and Lester R. Brown, State of the World, 1992, W.W. Norton & Company, Inc. New York, NY, p. 29. Graphical data from EPA, 2010.

CHAPTER 17 17.12: Reprinted by permission from Macmillan Publishers Ltd on behalf of Cancer Research UK: RC Albertson, TD Kocher (2006) Genetic and developmental basis of cichlid trophic diversity. Heredity vol. 97 (3) pp. 211-221.

CHAPTER 25 Nature of Science: Plants Can Clean Up Toxic Messess: From Joe Bower, National Wildlife Magazine, June/July 2000, Vol. 38, No. 4, Reprinted with permission of the author.

CHAPTER 43 43.2: Data from S.J. Arnold, "The Microevolution of Feeding Behavior" in Foraging Behavior: Ecology, Ethological, and Psychology Approaches, edited A. Kamil and T. Sargent, 1980, Garland Publishing Company, New York, NY. Evolution: Sexual Selection in Male Bowerbirds: Courtesy of Gail Patricelli, University of Maryland.

CHAPTER 44 44.4b: Data from W.K. Purves, et al., Life: The Science of Biology, 4/e, Sinaeur & Associates. 44.4d: Data from A.K. Hegazy, 1990, "Population Ecology & Implications for Conservation of Cleome Droserifolia: A Threatened Xerophyte, "Journal of Arid Environments, 19:269-82. 44.8: From Raymond Pearl, The Biology of Population Growth. Copyright 1925 The McGraw-Hill Companies. All Rights Reserved. 44.9: Data from Charles J. Krebs, Ecology, 3/e, 1984, Harper & Row; after Scheffer, 1951. 44.16: United Nations Population Division, 2002.

CHAPTER 45 45.6: Data from D.A. MacLulich, Fluctuations in the Numbers of the Varying Hare (Lepus americanus), University of Toronto Press, Toronto, 1937, reprinted 1974.

CHAPTER 46 Nature of Science: Wildlife Conservation and DNA: From T. Friend, "DNA Fingerprinting: Power Tool," National Wildlife Magazine, October/ November 1995, Vol. 33, No. 6. Reprinted with permissioin of the author.

CHAPTER 47 47.2: Redrawn from "Shrimp Stocking, Salmon Collapse, and Eagle Displacement" by C.N. Spencer, B.R. McClelland and J.A. Stanford, Bioscience, 41(1):14-21. Copyright © 1991 American Institute of Biological Sciences. 47.8a: Data from David M. Gates, Climate Change and Its Biological Consequences, 1993, Sinauer & Associates, Inc., Sunderland, MA.

Index

Note: This text contains a substantial number of supporting graphics. To ease index use, regular page numbers indicate *both* discussion and figure(s) on the same page; page numbers with *f* indicate additional figures on a different page; *t* indicates a table

A

A. *See* Adenine (A)
A band, 745
A horizon soil, 468
ABA (abscisic acid), 477, 488, 489*t*
Abalone, 534
ABC Islands, brown bears of, 889
Abdomen
  crustacean, 541*f*
  insect, 542, 543*f*
Abdominal cavity organs, 596
Abiogenesis, 329
Abiotic agents, of natural selection, 8
Abiotic synthesis, 328*f*, 329
ABO blood types, 205, 619
Abortion, 783–84
Aboveground vertical stems, 457*f*, 458
Abscisic acid (ABA), 477, 488, 489*t*
Abscission, 488, 489*f*, 489*t*
Absolute dating of fossils, 334
Absorption spectrum, 124
Abstinence, 783
Abulocetus natans, 281
Abyssal plain, 902
Acacia tree, 498, 866, 895
Accessory organs, digestive tract, 654–55
Accessory pigments, red algae, 389
Accessory structures, skin, 598–99
Accidental transport of alien species, 914
Accommodation, visual, 722
Acetaminophen, 246
Acetic acid bacteria, 141
Acetobacter aceti, 141
Acetyl CoA, 142–43, 147
Acetylcholine (ACh), 700, 708, 713, 747
Acetylcholinesterase (AChE), 701, 748
Acetylene, 39
ACh (acetylcholine), 700, 708, 713, 747
AChE (acetylcholinesterase), 701, 748
Achromatopsia (color blindness), 209, 300–301, 723
Acid deposition, 878, 915
Acid rain, 33, 467, 878
Acid reflux, 651
Acid-base balance, 690
Acidosis, 33
Acids, chemistry of, 32–34
Acinonyx jubatus, 895*f*
Acne, 599
Acquired characteristics, inheritance of, 273–74
Acquired immunity. *See* Adaptive immunity
Acquired immunodeficiency syndrome. *See* AIDS
Acrocephalus, 867*f*
Acromegaly, 759
Acrosome, 775*f*, 776*f*, 777, 796–97
Acrylamide, 248
ACTH (adrenocorticotropic hormone), 754*f*, 757, 758*f*, 764, 810
Actin, 49, 108, 592, 745
Actin filaments
  cell structure and function, 68*f*–69*f*
  cytoskeleton, 78, 79*f*
  in extracellular matrix, 99*f*
  in muscle contraction, 745–46, 747*t*, 748–49
Actinopterygii, 554, 555*f*
Action potentials, 698*f*, 699–700, 744
Active immunity, 637–39
Active site, of enzyme, 110
Active transport, 95–98
  carrier proteins and energy needed, 95, 96*f*

defined, 89*t*, 95
endocytosis, 97–98
exocytosis, 95, 96*f*
phagocytosis, 97–98
plasma membrane, 91
Acute bronchitis, 673, 674*f*
Acute phase proteins, 631
AD (Alzheimer disease), 53, 184, 701, 707
Adam's apple, 668, 778
Adaptation
  behavioral, 830–34
  defined, 5, 278
  to diet, digestive tracts, 648–49
  evolutionary theory, 278
  Lamarck and, 273
  photosynthesis, 131
  plants, 420
Adaptive immunity, 633–39
  active vs. passive, 637–39
  antibody-mediated, 633–35
  cell-mediated, 633, 635–37
  defined, 630
  evolution of, 627–28
  generally, 633–34
Adaptive radiation mode of speciation, 316–17
Addiction to drugs, 710–11
Addison disease, 764
Adductor longus muscle, 744*f*
Adenine (A)
  complimentary base pairing, 55
  DNA structure, 55*f*, 217–20, 223, 223*t*
  molecular structure of, 217*f*
  mRNA codons, 224*f*
  as nucleotide, 54*f*
  RNA structure, 220, 223*t*
Adenosine, 55, 755. *See also* Ribose
Adenosine deaminase deficiency, gene therapy for, 260
Adenosine diphosphate (ADP), 56, 107, 748
Adenosine triphosphate. *See* ATP
Adenovirus, 364*f*
ADH (antidiuretic hormone), 688, 754*f*, 757, 758*f*
Adhesion, 30, 476
Adhesion junctions, 98, 99*f*, 588, 593
Adiantum pedatum, 428*f*
Adipocytes, 590
Adipose tissue
  aging process, 811
  blood glucose regulation, 765
  functions of, 590
  leptin produced by, 768
  skin, 597*f*
  subcutaneous layer, 598
ADP (adenosine diphosphate), 56, 107, 748
Adrenal cortex, 754*f*, 756, 758*f*, 762–64
Adrenal glands, 754*f*, 758*f*, 762–64
Adrenal medulla, 754*f*, 755, 762–63
Adrenaline, 613, 754*f*, 755–56, 762
Adrenocorticotropic hormone (ACTH), 754*f*, 757, 758*f*, 764, 810
Adrenoleukodystrophy (ALD), 75, 210
Adult stem cells. *See* Stem cells
Adventitious roots, 452, 457*f*
AEDs (automatic external defibrillators), 614
Aequorea victoria, 216*f*
Aerial roots, 461*f*
Aerial stems, 428
Aerobic bacteria, 335
Aerobic reactions, in cellular respiration, 137
Aerotropism, 491
AF-2 (food additive), 248
Afferent (sensory) neurons, 697–98, 717
Aflatoxin, 248
Africa
  convergent evolution Rift Valley, 317
  evolutionary hypotheses, 579
  savanna, 895
African sleeping sickness, 396, 398–99

Afrocoricida, 566*t*
Agapornis, 820
Agar, 389
Agaricus bisporus, 406*t*
Age distribution, 842–43, 852–53
Age of Amphibians, 339
Age of Cycads, 340
Age of Fishes, 339
Age spots, 811
Agent Orange, 485
Agglutination, 619
Aggregate fruits, 510*f*, 511, 511*t*
Aging process, 811–14
  cardiovascular systems, 811–12
  digestive systems, 812
  endocrine systems, 813
  excretory systems, 812
  hypotheses about, 813–14
  immune systems, 812
  integumentary systems, 811
  musculoskeletal systems, 737, 738, 812–13
  nervous systems, 812
  organ systems, 811–13
  reproductive systems, 813
  respiratory systems, 812
  sensory systems, 722, 724, 728, 812
Agnathans (jawless fish), 339, 526*t*, 552, 553
Agranular leukocytes, 620
Agriculture
  alien species introduced by, 914
  biodiversity, 910–11
  evolution of, 581
  livestock as tapeworm host, 533
  pollution from, 14–15, 877, 878, 915
  swidden (slash-and-burn), 893
AID (artificial insemination), 785
AIDS (acquired immunodeficiency syndrome). *See also* HIV
  electron micrograph of, 289*f*
  epidemiology of, 787
  microevolution, 289
  opportunistic infections in, 626, 638, 674, 787
  retrovirus, 368
  stages and symptoms of, 787
  treatment of, 788
  virus, 364
Air
  movements of, 884–85, 902
  nutritional function of soil, 467
  pollution of, 33, 414, 878
  temperature of, 902
Air bladder, brown algae, 390*f*
Air sacs, 667, 670*f*
Alagille syndrome, 188
Albumin, 618
Alces americanus, 890*f*
Alcohol
  abuse, 710
  ADH inhibition by, 757
  alcoholic fermentation, 140
  cardiovascular disease, 617
  cirrhosis of liver, 656
  in functional groups, 39*t*
  during pregnancy, 807
ALD (adrenoleukodystrophy), 75, 210
Aldosterone, 690, 763
Alexandrium catanella, 392–93
Alexis (son of Tzar Nicolas I of Russia), 210
Algae
  blue-green. *See* Cyanobacteria
  brown, 385*t*, 386*f*, 390, 900
  classification of, 354
  colonial, 2, 385*t*, 388
  in coral reefs, 901
  as decomposers in soil, 468
  filamentous, 388
  in food chain, 383
  golden brown, 385*t*, 386*f*, 390, 391
  green. *See* Green algae
  multicellular, 388, 389, 390
  photosynthesis by, 76

protist diversity, 385*t*
  red, 385*t*, 386*f*, 389
  size variety of, 384
  sperm production in, 422
Algae blooms, 392–93
Algin, 390
Ali, Muhammad, 693
Alien species, 838, 861, 909, 913–15
Alkaloids, 497
Alkalosis, 33
Allantois, 805, 808*f*, 809
Alleles. *See also* Gene(s)
  defined, 172, 196
  dominant, 290
  frequencies, and microevolution, 290–95, 292*t*
  in homologous chromosomes, 196*f*
  multiple, 205
Allelic traits, multiple, 205
Allen's rule, 583
Allergy(ies), 641–42, 642*t*
Alligators, 558*f*, 561–62, 918
Allopatric speciation mode of speciation, 313–14
Alloploidy, 315–16
Allosteric site, 112
Alouatta pigra, 893*f*
α-helix, 51, 52*f*
ALS (amyotrophic lateral sclerosis), 703
Alternate leaves, 460
Alternation of generations, 176, 388, 407, 422
Alternative splicing, 237
  mRNA, 227, 244–46
Altitude, and biomes, 887
Altman, Sidney, 330
Altruism, 833–34
Alu sequence, 262
Alvarez, Luis, 343
Alvarez, Walter, 343
Alveolates, 385*t*, 392–94
Alveoli (sing., alveolus)
  mammary, 782, 783*f*
  pulmonary, 668
Alyces obstetricans, 848*f*
Alzheimer disease (AD), 53, 184, 701, 707
AM fungi, 404*f*, 406*t*, 408
Amanita phalloides, 411
Amborella trichopoda, 433
Ambulocetus natans, 281*f*, 310*f*
Ambystoma tigrinum, 557*f*
Amebic dysentery, 396
Amebocytes, 622
Amenorrhea, 782
American Cancer Society, 675
American Dietetic Association, 658, 659
American goldfinch, 774*f*
American Heart Association, 659
Ames test, 248
Amine group, polarity of, 27
Amino acids. *See also* Adenine (A); Cytosine (C); Guanine (G); Thymine (T); *specific amino acid*
  cellular respiration, 147
  codons for, 224
  essential, 658–59
  with ionized R groups, 51*f*
  metabolism of, 681
  protein digestion, 657
  as protein monomer, 50
  sequencing, and phylogeny, 358
  synthesis of, 129
  and tRNA, 223, 228–29
Amino functional groups, 39*t*
Aminoacyl-tRNA synthetases, 229
Ammonia
  as atmospheric gas, 329
  as buffer, 690
  in nitrogenous waste, 681
  photosynthesis vs. cellular respiration, 148
  water as solvent for, 30

C

G

M